The College Blue Book®

34th Edition

Distance Learning Programs

MACMILLAN REFERENCE USA

An imprint of Thomson Gale, a part of The Thomson Corporation

THOMSON
GALE

Detroit • New York • San Francisco • New Haven, Conn. • Waterville, Maine • London

The College Blue Book, 34th Edition
Volume 6

Project Editors
Bohdan Romaniuk, Verne Thompson

Editorial
Jessica Boguslawski, Kim Hunt-Lowrance, Amanda Sams, Kristy Swartout

Editorial Support Services
Wayne Fong

Imaging and Multimedia
Randy Bassett, Lezlie Light, Mike Logusz, Dan Newell

Rights and Acquisitions
Dean Dauphinais

Composition and Electronic Prepress
Gary Leach, Evi Seoud

Manufacturing
Rhonda Dover

Product Manager
Jennifer F. Bernardelli

For more information, contact
Thomson Gale
27500 Drake Rd.
Farmington Hills, MI 48331-3535
Or you can visit our Internet site at
http://www.gale.com

ISBN-13:
978-0-02-866006-6 (set)
978-0-02-866012-7 (vol. 6)

ISBN-10:
0-02-866006-4 (set)
0-02-866012-9 (vol. 6)

ISSN 1556-0570

This book is also available as an e-book
ISBN 13: 978-0-02-866084-4 (set) ISBN 10: 0-02-866084-6 (set)
Contact your Thomson Gale sales representative for ordering information.

Printed in the United States of America
10 9 8 7 6 5 4 3 2 1

The College Blue Book®

34th Edition

Distance Learning Programs

TABLE OF CONTENTS

HOW TO USE THIS GUIDE

INSTITUTION PROFILES AND SPECIAL MESSAGES

Here, in alphabetical order, you'll find nearly 900 institutions offering postsecondary education at a distance. Each profile covers such items as accreditation information, availability of financial aid, degrees and awards offered, course subject areas offered outside of degree programs, and the person or office to contact for program information. In addition, there are **Special Messages** from institutions about new programs or special events.

For each institution, specific degrees and award programs are listed, followed by a list of subjects for which individual courses (undergraduate, graduate, and non-credit) are offered.

INSTITUTIONAL INFORMATION

The sections here describe overall characteristics of an institution and its distance learning offerings, featuring key facts and figures about the institutions, including:

- institution Web site,
- background information on the institution,
- the type of accreditation held by the institution,
- when distance learning courses were first offered at the institution,
- the number of students enrolled in distance learning courses in fall 2005,
- the availability of financial aid,
- services available to distance learners, and
- the person or office to contact for more information about the institution's distance learning courses.

DEGREES AND AWARDS

This part of the profile lists each program leading to a degree or certificate that can be completed entirely at a distance. Programs are grouped by the level of award: associate degrees, baccalaureate degrees, graduate degrees, undergraduate certificates, and graduate certificates.

COURSE SUBJECT AREAS OFFERED OUTSIDE OF DEGREE PROGRAMS

Listed here are the general subject areas in which the institution offers courses at a distance. Subjects are divided into those offered for undergraduate credit and for graduate credit and those that are non-credit. Note that this is not a listing of course titles; you will need to contact the institution for a detailed list of courses offered.

IN-DEPTH DESCRIPTIONS OF DISTANCE LEARNING PROGRAMS

Additional details on distance learning offerings are provided by participating institutions and consortia. Each two-page entry provides details on delivery media, programs of study, special programs, credit options, faculty, students, admission, tuition and fees, financial aid, and applying.

An institution's absence from this section does not constitute an editorial decision on the part of Peterson's. Rather, this section is an open forum for institutions to expand upon information provided in the **Institution Profiles and Special Messages** section of the book. The descriptions are arranged alphabetically by institution name.

IN-DEPTH DESCRIPTIONS OF DISTANCE LEARNING CONSORTIA

The organizations listed in this section represent consortia of institutions offering distance learning programs. Each consortium has been formed so that an expanded set of distance learning options can be offered beyond the resources available through any single member institution. These consortia do not have a central application process and/or do not directly award credits and degrees. Applications are processed, and credits and conferred degrees are awarded, through one of the member institutions. Further, consortia generally are not directly granted accreditations; rather, credits and degrees reflect the accreditation of the awarding institution. The reader should obtain specific information directly from the consortium.

APPENDIX

The **Appendix** lists resources that can give you more information on subjects presented in previous sections of this guide.

GLOSSARY

With the **Glossary**, you'll be able to learn all the pertinent terms from A to Z.

INDEXES

If you are interested in locating a certificate or degree program in a specific field of study, refer to the index of **Institutions Offering Degree and Certificate Programs.** Here you'll find institutions offering everything from accounting to theological and ministerial studies.

If it is individual courses you're looking for, the index of **Non-Degree-Related Course Subject Areas** will guide you to institutions offering credit and noncredit courses at either the undergraduate or graduate level.

The **Geographical Listing of Distance Learning Programs** lets you find programs that are offered by institutions that are located near you. Keep in mind that most institutions' offerings are available nationally, and sometimes internationally. See individual listings for details.

DATA COLLECTION PROCEDURES

The information provided in these profiles was collected during the summer of 2006 by way of a survey posted online for colleges and universities. With minor exceptions, all data included in this edition have been submitted by officials at the schools themselves. For a few schools that failed to respond to Thomson Peterson's Web-based survey in time to meet the deadline, information was drawn from their Web sites. In addition, many of the institutions that submitted data were contacted directly by the Peterson's research staff to verify unusual figures, resolve discrepancies, and obtain additional data. All usable information received in time for publication has been included. The omission of any particular item from an index or profile listing signifies that the item is either not applicable to that institution or that data were not available. Although Peterson's has every reason to believe that the information presented in this guide is accurate, students should check with each college or university to verify such figures as tuition and fees, which may have changed since the publication of this guide.

CRITERIA FOR INCLUSION IN THIS BOOK

In the research for this guide, the following definition of distance learning was used: a planned teaching/learning experience in which teacher and students are separated by physical distance and use any of a wide spectrum of media. This definition is based on the one developed by the University of Wisconsin Extension.

The College Blue Book: Distance Learning Programs profiles nearly 900 institutions of higher education currently offering courses or entire programs at a distance. To be included, all U.S. institutions must have full accreditation or candidate-for-accreditation (preaccreditation) status granted by an institutional or specialized accrediting body recognized by the U.S. Department of Education or the Council for Higher Education Accreditation. The six U.S. regional accrediting associations are: the New England Association of Schools and Colleges, Middle States Association of Colleges and Schools, North Central Association of Colleges and Schools, Northwest Commission on Colleges and Universities, Southern Association of Colleges and Schools, and Western Association of Schools and Colleges. Approval by state educational agencies is conferred separately on some distance education courses. Canadian institutions must be chartered and authorized to grant degrees by the provincial government, be affiliated with a chartered institution, or be accredited by a recognized U.S. accrediting body.

WHAT IS DISTANCE LEARNING?

One student is a busy professional who needs to update work-related skills by taking a couple of computer applications courses in his spare time. Another student, a working mother, never finished her bachelor's degree and would love to have that diploma and get a better job. A third student attends a local community college, but what he'd really like is a degree offered by a four-year institution halfway across the country—without moving. Another would-be student is employed full-time in a field in which a master's degree, perhaps even a doctorate, would really give her career a boost. What all these diverse people have in common is an already full life. For them, disrupting family and work by commuting to sometimes distant on-campus classes on a rigid schedule is simply not a workable option. Instead, students like these are turning to distance learning in order to pursue their educational goals. For many people, and perhaps you, distance learning is a blessing—it means you can get the education you need, which might otherwise be difficult or impossible to obtain in the traditional manner.

What, exactly, is distance learning (also called distance education)? Broadly defined, distance learning is the delivery of educational programs to students who are off site. In a distance learning course, the instructor is not in the same place as the student; the students may be widely separated by geography and time; and the instructor and students communicate with each other using various means, from the U.S. mail to the Internet. Students that take a distance education course are called distance learners, whether they live 300 miles from the university or right across the street.

Distance learning makes use of many technologies, and courses are structured in many different ways. Adding to the variety of distance learning programs provided by traditional institutions of higher education are programs offered by new types of institutions, many worthy, others known as diploma mills, that help to fuel the growth in distance education. With so many technologies, courses, programs, and institutions involved in distance education, your distance learning options can be confusing at first. However, it's critical that you understand what distance education involves and which institutions offer a solid education *before* you enroll. That way you'll be sure that you spend your effort, time, and money wisely on a reputable education.

In this section, we'll give you an overview of distance learning; in "Is Distance Learning Right for You?", we'll help you determine whether or not distance education is right for you; and then in later sections we'll give you enough background and guidance so you can make an informed choice when selecting a program. We'll also provide suggestions for handling the application process, paying for your education, and making the most of your distance learning experience.

A BRIEF HISTORY OF DISTANCE EDUCATION

In the last five to ten years, distance education has mushroomed, so it's easy to think of it as a completely recent phenomenon. However, today's distance education, based primarily on video and Internet technologies, has its roots in the correspondence courses that arose in the late 1800s. Instructors would send print materials to students by mail, and students would do their assignments and return them by mail. Correspondence courses were asynchronous; that is, the student was not tied to the instructor's timetable. He or she would do the work when it was convenient. Correspondence courses still exist, mostly for single courses, but they have lost ground over the last seventy years to more modern technologies. The first generation of technology that began to supplant correspondence courses was radio in the 1930s, followed by broadcast television in the 1950s and 1960s. Radio and television courses provided one-way communication, and so they were most suitable for delivering information from the faculty to the students. Typically, there was only minimal interaction between instructor and students, and no interaction at all among students. Another constraint on radio and television courses was time. Broadcast courses are synchronous; students had to be listening to the radio or watching television when the course was broadcast, or they would miss the class.

By about 1960, the advent of cable television, audiocassette recorders, and videocassette recorders solved the time problem posed by the earlier broadcast courses. Courses could be broadcast over cable channels several times so students could watch at their convenience. With a VCR or tape recorder, a student could record a lecture or class session when it was broadcast and view or hear it at any time. In fact, recorders made broadcasting unnecessary. The content of a course could be recorded on an audiocassette or videotape and sent to students, who could listen or view it when they had time. Although recording technology provided convenience for students, because courses are asynchronous, it did not solve the major drawback of broadcast courses—the lack of interaction among faculty members and students.

Beginning in the 1980s, the personal computer, two-way audio and videoconferencing, and the Internet greatly expanded the scope of distance education. With these new technologies, much more information could be conveyed from the faculty to students. More important, two-way communication became possible, using interactive video technology or e-mail, newsgroups, bulletin boards, and chat rooms on the Internet. Today, distance education makes use of a wide range of technologies.

INSTRUCTIONAL TECHNOLOGIES IN DISTANCE LEARNING

Today's distance learning courses can be divided into several main categories according to the primary technologies they use to deliver instruction: print-based courses, audio-based courses, video-based courses, and Internet-based courses. The audio, video, and Internet courses all have variations that are synchronous—

classes take place at specific times only—and asynchronous—classes that occur at flexible times that may be more convenient for the student.

PRINT-BASED COURSES

Correspondence courses use print materials as the medium of instruction. Students receive the materials by mail at the start of the course and return completed assignments by mail. Sometimes fax machines are used to speed up the delivery of assignments, and the telephone can be used if communication between instructor and student is necessary. Patti Iversen, who lives in Montana, completed part of her Bachelor of Science in Nursing degree from the University of Mary in North Dakota by correspondence course. "The correspondence courses offered no direct contact with the instructor or other students," she recalls. "I purchased a syllabus and book and was otherwise on my own." In addition to the lack of interaction between instructor and students, correspondence courses have the disadvantage of being slow. The low-tech nature of a print-based course means lots of delay between assignments and feedback. Of course, the low-tech nature of the course is an advantage, too. Students don't have to invest in expensive technology and can do their work anywhere. Even though print materials continue to play a very important role in distance learning, they are now usually supplemented by more modern instructional technologies.

AUDIO-BASED COURSES

Audio-based courses may involve two-way communication, as in audio or phone conferencing; or they may involve one-way communication, including radio broadcast and prerecorded audiotapes sent to students. Fritz J. Messere, associate professor and coordinator of broadcasting at the State University of New York at Oswego, recalls the first time, in 1981, he was involved in teaching a course that used phone conferencing. Once a week, faculty members and students from ten universities as well as representatives from the Federal Communications Commission "met" for a class. "The first three weeks were chaotic," recalls Messere. "We didn't know who was talking." However, they worked out a plan in which a different faculty member moderated the session each week by asking questions. At midsession there was a break, followed by a round-robin discussion, in which each site participated in a predetermined sequence.

According to the National Center for Education Statistics of the U.S. Department of Education, audio-based technologies are not widely used today, with only about 12 percent of institutions of higher learning reporting their use as the primary means of delivering a course. Instead, audio technologies may be used to supplement the main technology used in the course. For example, in an Internet-based distance education course, students and professors may call one another periodically.

VIDEO-BASED COURSES

Video-based technologies include two-way interactive video conferencing, one-way video with two-way audio, one-way live video, and one-way prerecorded videotapes provided to students. Of these, two-way interactive video and prerecorded videotapes are the most popular. Of the institutions of higher learning surveyed by the U.S. Department of Education, 54 percent used two-way interactive video and 47 percent used prerecorded videotapes as the primary mode of instructional delivery in their distance education courses.

Two-Way Interactive Video

A course taught by means of two-way interactive video takes place simultaneously in two or more sites. The instructor is located in the home site with a group of students, and other students are located in satellite sites, often with a facilitator to help out. Each site has TV monitors or large screens on which the instructor and students can be viewed. One student in a biology of horticulture course at the University of Cincinnati described the technology used in her course: "Both [home and satellite] classrooms are set up with cameras and two video screens each, which show what is going on in both classrooms. There is a technical assistant present in each location, one on the main campus to set things up and work with the camera, etc., and another in the remote location to set equipment up and to adjust settings should there be any problems." The course itself was conducted as a lecture: "For the most part, the instructor lectures, with students occasionally asking or answering questions. When any student speaks in class, they press a button on a little apparatus on the desk in front of them, which makes the camera point to them as they speak and allows their voice to be transmitted to the other location." Quizzes and exams are faxed to the satellite site and faxed back or mailed by an assistant when they are completed. Like the best classroom teaching, two-way interactive video works well when the instructor is comfortable with "performing" on camera. "You have to keep students at all sites involved with you by making the lecture as entertaining as possible," says Dr. Larry Anthony, coordinator of the addiction studies bacealaureate program based at the University of Cincinnati. "I've had to adapt my teaching to the medium. For example, instead of using overheads as I might in a regular classroom, I'm more inclined to use a series of PowerPoint slides because they're more entertaining."

Two-way interactive video bridges geographical distances but not time. Students must be in a particular place at a particular time to take the course.

Prerecorded Video

A far less sophisticated, though almost as popular, means of instruction is prerecorded videotape. Each course session is videotaped and mailed to off-site students. To supplement this, the course may have a Web site where notes and assignments are posted, or these may be mailed to the off-site students along with the tapes. If students have any questions, they can call or e-mail the instructor after they view the tape. For many students, the lack of interactivity is made up for by the benefit of "attending" class at their own convenience. Nicole DeRaleau, who is studying for a Master of Engineering degree at Worcester Polytechnic Institute in Massachusetts, says, "Watching the videotaped class is really not very different from sitting in class, except that I can't raise my hand and ask questions." On the other hand, she points out that the asynchronous nature of prerecorded video is an advantage: "I can watch half a class at one sitting, and the other half at a later time. I often work late, and I don't have to worry about missing class."

INTERNET-BASED COURSES

Today many distance learning courses, called online courses or e-learning, are offered over the Internet. In 1997–1998, almost 80

The time and place dimensions of various distance learning instructional technologies.

	Specific place	**Any place**
Any time (asynchronous)		◆ Online courses (newsgroups, bulletin boards, websites, e-mail) ◆ CD ROMs, DVDs ◆ Videotapes ◆ Audiotapes ◆ Correspondence courses
Specific time (synchronous)	◆ Two-way interactive videoconferencing ◆ Two-way interactive audioconferencing ◆ Traditional on-campus classes	◆ Online course (interactive computer conferencing, chat rooms, MUDs, MOOs) ◆ Radio broadcasts ◆ TV broadcasts, satellite, and cable

percent of the institutions of higher education surveyed by the National Center for Education Statistics used the Internet as the primary technology in some of their distance education courses. Some online courses use synchronous, "real-time" instruction based primarily on interactive computer conferencing or chat rooms. However, most Internet-based courses use asynchronous instruction, making use of online course management systems, Web sites, e-mail, electronic mailing lists, newsgroups, bulletin boards, and messaging programs.

In asynchronous online courses, instructors post instructional material and assignments, including text, images, video, audio, and even interactive simulations, on the course Web site. Using messaging systems, newsgroups, or bulletin boards, they can start online discussions by posting a comment or question; students can log on using a password and join the discussion at their convenience. In some courses there may be periodic "real-time" interaction in chat rooms or interactive environments like MUDS (multiple-user dungeons) and MOOs (multiple-object orientations). Feedback and guidance to individual students can be done by e-mail or telephone. Note that most of the interaction in an online course is text-based; instructors and students communicate primarily through the keyboarded word. Joanne Simon, who is earning a Master of Business Administration degree from the University of Phoenix Online, describes the setup of her courses: "We use newsgroup folders—the main classroom, a chat room, a course material folder, an assignment folder, and four study group folders. We post a minimum of three messages per day to the main folder in which that week's readings are discussed. In those messages we encourage other students to share ideas, experiences, and opinions on various topics . . . ." Besides this seminar-style interaction, there are many assignments, according to Simon. "We also submit weekly summaries, one graded group assignment, and two personal assignments weekly." Needless to say, students must have a computer with the appropriate software and Internet access in order to take an Internet-based course. The cost of technology aside, online distance learning programs have considerable advantages, Because the course material stays on line for a period of time, students can log on at their own convenience. "There are time stamps on everything they submit," says Michael S. Ameigh, Assistant Provost for Distance Learning and Information Resources and Associate Professor of Communication Studies at the State University of New York at Oswego. "I can see that students are often working in the middle of the night." This flexibility is one of the main attractions of online courses for students, but it can also be its main disadvantage. "It's a common misperception that online courses can be dropped into and out of," says Claudine SchWeber, Assistant Vice President for Distance Education and Lifelong Learning at the University of Maryland University College. Without class sessions to attend at scheduled times, the impetus to log on and do course work must come from within, which requires a great deal of self-discipline.

To help ensure that students keep up, many instructors structure the learning environment by setting weekly deadlines for reading lectures and completing assignments, requiring group projects, and making participation in online discussions mandatory. "I personally contact students who do not participate," says Fritz Messere, who has been teaching broadcasting and business courses online for several years. "Students must interact with me in order to pass the course." At the University of Phoenix Online, students are required to log on to a course and post messages five days out of seven as one of the requirements for passing. In online courses with participation requirements, the amount of interaction between the faculty and students is far greater than in a large lecture class held on campus. There's no lying low in the back of the classroom in a well-run online course.

MIXING THE TECHNOLOGIES

Many courses use a combination of technologies as well as print materials. For example, at Southwest Texas State University, a course in geography for elementary and high school teachers begins with a videoconference, with the instructor introducing himself or herself and outlining the course requirements. A printed study guide with all assigned readings and activities is distributed to all participants at the first session. Teachers who cannot get to a videoconferencing site are sent a videocassette of the first session along with the study guide. After the first session, the course moves on line. Using chat rooms, threaded discussions, and e-mail, participants do their assignments and group projects and interact on line. Assignments are snail-mailed to the faculty member. Finally, the class concludes with another synchronous videoconference or recorded videotape.

This course may be unusual in that it combines two of the major distance learning technologies, but it is not unusual to find courses that use one of the major technologies and supplement it with another. For example, e-mail is used for individual student-instructor communication in most courses, even if the course is conducted by two-way interactive videotape or prerecorded video.

FUTURE TRENDS

Today, online instruction, two-way interactive video, and one-way prerecorded video are the most popular instructional technologies in distance education. According to the Department of Education's National Center for Education Statistics, colleges and universities are planning to increase their use of Internet-based instruction and two-way interactive video. Prerecorded video is likely to decrease in popularity. The explosive growth in distance learning in the last five years has come primarily from online courses, and that is likely to continue. With better databases and other sources of information continuing to appear on the Internet, ease of access to reliable data will increase. As high bandwidth connections to the Internet start to replace phone connections, the capacity to quickly transmit large amounts of data will increase dramatically. For example, with a high-speed modem and phone connection, it can take several minutes to download a video snippet. Thus, most online courses today use text, images, and perhaps some animation, but they are limited in their video capabilities. Eventually, high bandwidth technologies will make individualized, customized, and live video interactions possible, with lengthy video programming available. Online distance learning is also causing a shift to a more collaborative learning model. "Because of the nature of online resources and communication, the faculty is no longer the one authoritative voice," explains Claudine SchWeber of the University of Maryland University College. An undergraduate there agrees. "Students learn from each other as well as from the instructor and course materials," she commented. "Instructors who are comfortable with online technology . . . create a classroom environment that is interactive, inviting, stimulating, motivating, and lively." Another interesting trend to note is the incorporation of the new instructional technologies in conventional, classroom-based courses. "What we are finding is that our distance technology is having an impact on the way we teach on-campus courses to undergraduate and graduate students," comments McRae C. Banks, head of the department of management and professor of entrepreneurship at Worcester Polytechnic Institute in Massachusetts. "As one example, some faculty members have students take online quizzes before each class period . . . . Before the professor goes into class, he or she knows what areas the students understand and what areas are troubling them. Now more time can be spent where the students are having difficulty." Other professors hold office hours or help sessions in chat rooms when they are at home or out of town at conferences. Still others require students to respond to each class lecture by posting a comment to a discussion group. "For us, the bottom line is finding ways to enhance the educational experience for students," says Banks.

WHAT CAN YOU LEARN VIA DISTANCE EDUCATION?

The short answer is almost anything. You can take a single course in almost any field, or earn a certificate or degree in many fields, by distance education. Next, we'll give you an overview of what's available, and in "What Can You Study via Distance Learning" we'll discuss these programs in more detail.

COURSE OFFERINGS

According to the National Center for Education Statistics, an estimated 54,470 different distance education courses were offered in academic year 1997–1998, the last year for which reliable figures are available. That number has undoubtedly increased considerably since then. As you can see in Figure 1-1, most of these courses were college-level, credit-granting courses at the undergraduate level, and about one quarter were at the graduate/first professional level. Fewer than one tenth were noncredit-granting courses.

According to Figure 1-2, of the courses offered, the greatest number can be found in fields that are part of a general undergraduate education, such as English, humanities, and the social and behavioral sciences; physical and life sciences; and mathematics. However, in the fields of education, engineering, and library and information sciences, more courses are offered at the graduate/first-professional level than at the undergraduate level. According to the Department of Education, there are three likely reasons for this: the emphasis on graduate education in these fields, the suitability of course content for distance education, and the likelihood that groups of students would be located in particular places, such as a school district or engineering firm, to receive broadcast or interactive video courses.

DEGREE AND CERTIFICATE PROGRAMS

Many institutions of higher learning simply offer a smorgasbord of distance education courses that can be taken for credit. An increasing number of institutions, however, have taken distance education to the next step; they have begun to offer undergraduate and graduate certificate and degree programs that can be completed entirely by distance education. For example, a student with an associate's degree from a local community college can go on to earn a baccalaureate degree from a four-year institution by distance learning, without relocating. Or a working professional can earn a master's degree or professional certificate on a part-time basis through distance learning. According to the National Center on Education Statistics, in 1997–1998, there were an estimated 1,230 degree programs available through distance learning. Peterson's *Guide to Distance Learning Programs: 2003* lists about 3,000 degree and certificate programs, so you can see there

Figure 1–1: Distance Education Course Offerings in 1997–1998 (by level)

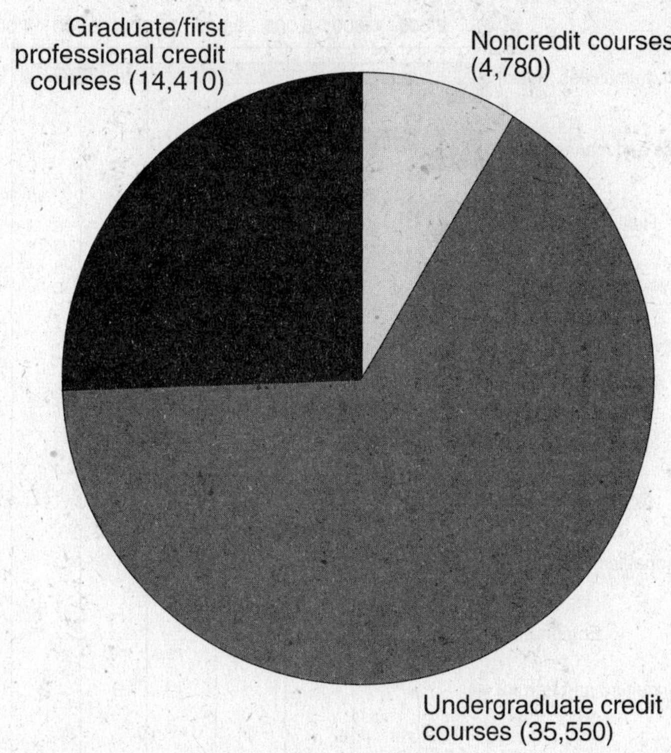

Source: Data from U.S. Department of Education, National Center for Education Statistics, Postsecondary Education Quick Information System, *Survey on Distance Education at Postsecondary Education Institutions*, 1998-1999, p. 19.

has been a phenomenal increase in the last few years. Unlike individual course offerings, degree and certificate programs are more likely to be offered at the graduate and first-professional level than at the undergraduate level, as you can see in Figure 1-3. Most degree and certificate programs are in the fields of liberal/general studies, business and management, health professions, education, and engineering.

WHO OFFERS DISTANCE LEARNING?

The better question might be, "Who doesn't?" With lifelong learning becoming commonplace and communications technologies improving rapidly, the demand for distance education has grown dramatically, and with it the number and variety of providers. The first group of providers consists of the traditional colleges, universities, graduate schools, community colleges, technical schools, and vocational schools. These providers range from schools only their neighbors have heard of to household names like Stanford, Virginia Tech, and the University of California, to name just a few. The challenges posed by distance education have forced colleges and universities to be creative in their approaches. Some schools have formed partnerships with cable companies, public broadcasting services, satellite broadcasters, and online education companies to deliver high-quality distance education. Colleges and universities also partner with corporations to deliver courses and degree programs to employees. For example, the University of Cincinnati's College of Pharmacy offers courses and a master's degree program via distance learning to employees of Procter & Gamble Pharmaceuticals Norwich, New York, location as well as other P&G sites.

Many schools have formed consortia, or collaborative groups, within a state or region or even internationally, which enables students to take courses as needed from all the participating institutions. An example of a consortium is the University of Texas (UT) TeleCampus, which does not confer degrees but supports the participating University of Texas campuses, which do award degrees.

A few colleges and universities are virtual, meaning they don't have a campus. These schools offer most or all of their instruction by means of distance education, providing complete degree programs. The University of Phoenix Online and Walden University are two well-known examples.

Finally, there are many online purveyors of noncredit distance education courses on subjects that range from candlemaking and beauty secrets to C++ programming and Spanish. These courses may be fun and even instructive, but they won't contribute to your formal educational credentials.

We'll discuss the providers of distance education more fully in "Who Offers Distance Education?"

HOW EFFECTIVE IS DISTANCE LEARNING?

There is a great deal of interest in the effectiveness of distance learning. Research into this subject is largely anecdotal and much

Figure 1–2: Distance Education Course Offerings by Field of Study, 1997–1998

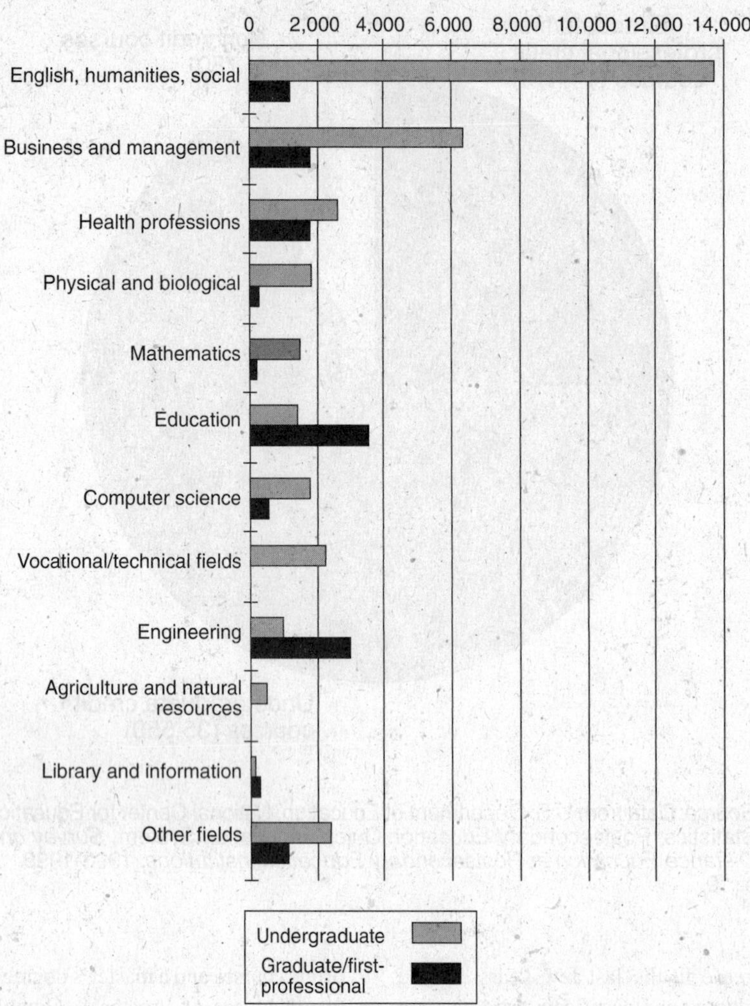

Source: Data from U.S. Department of Education, National Center for Education Statistics, Postsecondary Education Quick Information System, *Survey on Distance Education at Postsecondary Education Institutions*, 1998-1999, p. 25.

of it is out-of-date, given the rapid development of instructional technology in the last few years. However, Thomas L. Russell, in a widely quoted report entitled *The No Significant Difference Phenomenon*, concluded from a review of 355 research studies and summaries published between 1928 and 1999 that the learning outcomes (test scores and course grades) of distance learning and traditional students are similar. In addition, Russell found that distance learners themselves have positive attitudes toward distance education and are generally satisfied with it. There are a number of questions regarding the effectiveness of distance education that have not yet been answered by the research. For example, how do the different learning styles of students relate to the use of particular technologies? How do individual differences among students affect their ability to learn by distance education? Why do more students drop out of distance education courses than drop out of traditional courses? What types of content are most suitable for distance learning? Common sense suggests that distance education is more effective for some people than for others, the different instructional technologies are more effective with different types of learners, and some subjects are more suitable for distance education than other subjects.

Some educators are not fans of distance education, believing that technology, no matter how sophisticated, cannot substitute the face-to-face interactions of a community of teachers and learners. Even proponents of distance learning concede that students who have the time and money for a traditional on-campus education should go for it. "Technology can't provide the intangible experiences of campus life, especially on the undergraduate level," comments Robert V. Steiner, who directs the distance learning project at Columbia University's Teachers College. "However, distance education is extremely helpful for adult learners who need to get their education in a flexible manner."

Barbara Lockee, Virginia Tech's distance learning program developer and an assistant professor of instructional technology, agrees. "Distance education has the increased potential to reach new audiences that haven't had access to higher education," says Lockee. "Because of the changing needs of our work force,

Figure 1–3: Distance Education Degree and Certificate Programs, 1997–1998

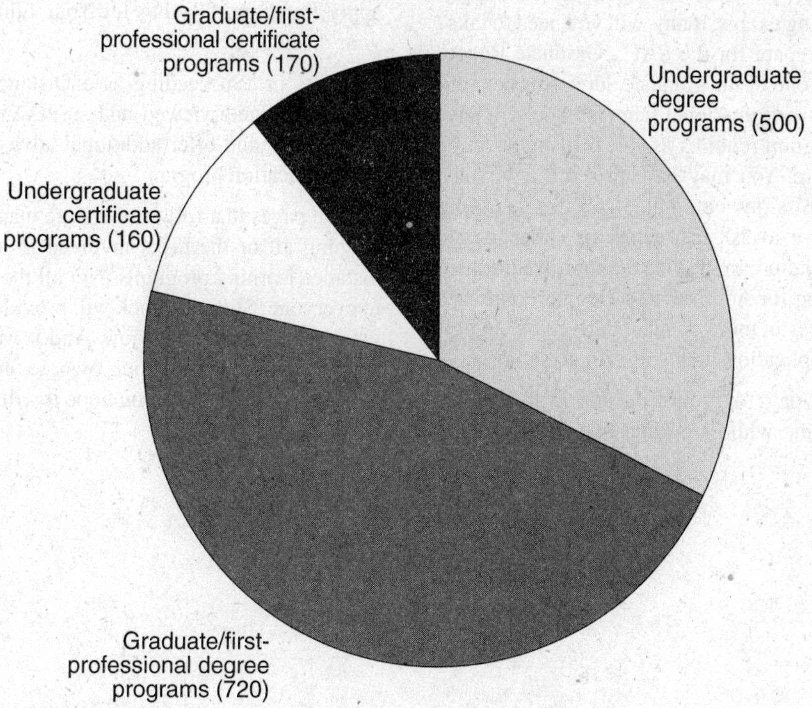

Source: Data from U.S. Department of Education, National Center for Education Statistics, Postsecondary Education Quick Information System, *Survey on Distance Education at Postsecondary Education Institutions*, 1998-1999, p. 34.

people who are employed need on-going, lifelong education. So new higher-ed participants are in their 30s and beyond, and many probably have their undergraduate degree but need skills to be successful in the information age."

Distance education may have benefits beyond accessibility, flexibility, and convenience. For example, when asked to compare the experiences of teaching a course to a single classroom of students and by two-way interactive video, Larry Anthony indicated that the students in the distance learning course had the richer experience. "We were hearing from people in different parts of the country," he explained. "In addiction studies, there are different cultural issues and problems in different places. In terms of diversity, the distance learning class was great." Kevin Ruthen, who earned a Master of Science degree in information resource management from Syracuse University, also thought that distance education had added to the value of his degree: "The students and professors . . . were all different ages, from many professional fields, and from many regions of the world," he recalls. "I learned a tremendous amount and gained many different perspectives due to this diversity as opposed to what would be, in my opinion, a less diverse class environment in an on-campus class."

PURSUING YOUR EDUCATION BY DISTANCE LEARNING

Still interested in distance learning? Then the next question is: What's involved in finding a reputable distance education program and getting in? A lot. The first, and perhaps the most important part of this process, is a combination of introspection and research. You are going to have to assess yourself and what's out there to find a good match. You'll have to answer questions like: What are my professional goals? What are my interests and abilities? Which courses or certificate or degree programs will help me achieve my goals? Am I prepared for higher education in this field? What must I do to improve my qualifications? Do I have the motivation, personal characteristics, and skills that will enable me to learn at a distance? In "Is Distance Learning Right for You?", we will help you assess the advantages and disadvantages of distance learning as well as your strengths and weaknesses; this will enable you to decide whether or not distance education is for you. Then in "What Can You Study via Distance Learning?", we'll describe the different degree and certificate programs that are available, what's involved in transferring credits, and how you may be able to earn credits for prior learning and life experience. In "Who Offers Distance Education?", we'll describe the various types of distance learning providers. We'll give you suggestions on how to find out more about programs and institutions.

Once you've done your research on distance education programs, on what basis should you evaluate them? In addition to finding out the all-important accreditation status of the programs in which you are interested, you'll have to find out what each program is really like and whether it's a good match for you. Will the program help you achieve your educational and professional goals? Is the instructional technology a comfortable match for you? "Selecting a Good Distance Learning Program" discusses these issues and provides a checklist of factors you should consider when you evaluate distance education programs.

Once you've identified the programs to which you will apply, what standardized qualifying exams, if any, will you need to take? What should you do to prepare for the SAT*, Graduate Record Examinations (GRE®), or one of the graduate admissions examinations used by many of the professional schools? You will have to find out what each program requires as part of its application and what the deadlines are. You may have to write a personal statement so that the admissions committee can evaluate your background. You will have to ask instructors or colleagues to write letters of recommendation. In "Taking Standardized Admissions Tests" and "Applying for Admission to Degree Programs" we will describe the process in more detail and give you suggestions on how to prepare applications that will gain you admission.

How are you going to pay for your education? If you are planning to attend part-time while working, that may not be a problem. But for full-time students, financing a distance degree program can be complicated. You will have to figure out how much money you will need, find possible sources of aid, and apply for them. "Paying for Your Education" covers financing your distance education.

Finally, in "Succeeding as a Distance Learner," some of the students we interviewed and surveyed will share more of their experiences and offer additional advice on succeeding in a distance education program.

In the pages that follow, there are many suggestions for accomplishing all of the tasks involved in selecting and applying to distance learning programs. Not all the advice will be applicable to everyone. Still, this book will provide you with an overview of what you will need to know. And it will indicate what you will need to find out on your own to ensure that your distance education does all that you hope it will do.

---

*SAT is a registered trademark of the College Board, which was not involved in the production of, and does not endorse, this book.

GRE® is a registered trademark of Educational Testing Service (ETS). This book is not endorsed or approved by ETS.

IS DISTANCE LEARNING RIGHT FOR YOU?

Distance learning can satisfy a wide range of needs for many people in diverse circumstances, but it's not for everyone. Some students don't have the study skills or self-discipline to succeed as a distance learner. Others are interested in a field of study or a degree that is not offered via distance learning. Still, for most people distance learning has the potential to open up new possibilities in higher education. For many adult students, the advantages of distance learning far outweigh the disadvantages. In this section, we'll discuss the pros and cons of distance learning and help you assess whether or not distance learning is right for you.

THE ADVANTAGES OF DISTANCE LEARNING

Distance learning has many benefits. That's why distance-learning programs meet the needs of so many different people of all ages, genders, professions, and educational backgrounds.

As you read the following list of distance learning benefits, ask yourself if any of them provide a way to overcome an obstacle that is standing in your way when you think about going back to school. Do any of these advantages make continuing your education a real possibility right now, rather than a vague goal for sometime in the future?

Here are the benefits of distance learning in general:

- **Distance learning breaks down time barriers.** In most distance learning programs, you don't have to be at a certain place at a certain time. You can learn when it's convenient for you, so you can fit your education into a busy work and home life. You only take as many courses as you can handle at a time, and sometimes you can start whenever you like instead of at the beginning of a semester.
- **Distance learning breaks down geographical barriers.** Whether you are logging on to a course from your own computer at home or traveling a short distance to a satellite classroom, distance education makes your geographical distance from a college or university irrelevant. Students who live in remote areas, who don't have time to commute to a campus, and who travel a lot on business benefit from this aspect of distance education.
- **Distance learning goes at your own pace.** Distance learning is ideal for students who like to set their own pace and who learn best on their own. As you work through course material, you can spend more time on difficult concepts and less time on easier ones. Although you are likely to have weekly or other periodic deadlines, as long as you make them, you can approach the work at a pace that suits your schedule.
- **Distance learning can save money.** Although the tuition and fees for distance learning courses are usually comparable to those charged for on-campus courses, you can save money on child care, gas, parking, and other commuting costs. In addition, you generally don't have to take time off from work to attend class.
- **Distance learning fits individual needs.** You can often tailor a program to fit your particular educational and professional goals and take courses from various institutions if necessary.
- **Distance learning provides freedom of choice.** Since you are not confined to schools within easy commuting distance, you are able to consider distance learning programs at reputable colleges and universities around the country and the world.
- **Distance learning teaches more than just the course material.** Depending on the type of program you take, distance learning can improve your computer, Internet, reading, writing, and oral communication skills, which benefits you no matter what kind of career you pursue.
- **Distance learning broadens your perspective.** Often, your classmates will be from diverse backgrounds and places. You will interact with a more diverse group of people than you would normally find on most campuses.

Refer to Figure 2-1 for the specific advantages of each of the major distance learning instructional technologies.

THE DISADVANTAGES OF DISTANCE LEARNING

Lest you think that distance learning is the solution to all problems of access to education, it does have its drawbacks. Consider whether or not any of the following general disadvantages would cause you to eliminate distance learning from your education plans. For disadvantages specific to a particular instructional technology, refer to Figure 2-1.

- **Distance learning requires a high degree of discipline and self-motivation.** Dropout rates are higher for distance learning programs than for campus-based programs. No doubt, some dropouts are students who did not realize that distance learning requires as much, if not more, time than a traditional on-campus class. For older distance education students, it's easy for work or family needs to take priority over education. Many distance learners drop out because the distance course is the easiest thing to let go of when things get too hectic.
- **Distance learning can be lonely.** Some people need the face-to-face interaction that a traditional classroom provides. Even though instructors may try to overcome social isolation in distance learning courses, for some students there is simply not enough social contact to keep them enthusiastic and motivated.
- **Distance learning can take longer.** Because distance learning is self-motivated, it's easier to give in to other demands on your time and postpone taking courses, increasing the time it takes to complete a degree program.
- **Distance learning students may get poor student services.** On-campus students have convenient access to the library, academic advisers, job placement services, tutoring, and student centers. Many distance learning programs offer student services

Figure 2-1: Specific Advantages and Disadvantages of the Major Distance Learning Technologies

Distance Learning Technology	Advantages	Disadvantages
Online	▲Course work can be done at any time of day or night. ▲Any computer with Internet access can be used. ▲Courses can easily be taken from more than one school. ▲Computer skills are developed. ▲There are no commuting costs.	▼Lots of self-discipline and motivation are needed. ▼A computer with Internet access is needed—a significant cost. ▼Social interaction is on line only.
Two-way interactive videoconferencing	▲There is access to courses at distant campuses. ▲Social interaction is most similar to that of a traditional classroom. ▲There is no cost to the student for technology.	▼Classes are held at particular times and places.
Videotapes of class sessions	▲Course work can be done at any time of day or night. ▲Any TV and VCR can be used. ▲There are no commuting costs.	▼Lots of self-discipline and motivation are needed. ▼Social interaction is minimal. ▼Distance learners are several days behind on-campus class.

such as online library access and registration, but in most schools the services still can't compare to those available to on-campus students.

- **Distance learning students miss the college experience.** College campuses offer a lot more than classes, with cultural and sports activities, dorm life, faculty-student interaction, and the opportunity to form lifelong friendships. Although this is not an important consideration for most older distance learners, younger students that pursue an undergraduate education may find the on-campus experience too valuable to pass up.
- **A traditional college degree is a better choice to meet some future goals.** Although distance learning is becoming more mainstream and is usually accepted by employers, as long as it is from a reputable institution, it is still regarded by some in the traditional academic community as inferior. Thus, a traditional degree may be more valuable if you are considering applying in the future to the more prestigious graduate and professional programs, including law school and medical school.

ASSESSING YOURSELF

With the advantages and disadvantages of distance learning in mind, you should take some time to honestly answer the following questions. Consider your own goals, circumstances, personality, skills, social support, and comfort with technology to determine whether or not you are a good candidate for distance learning.

GOALS

What are your educational and professional goals?

First you must determine your educational and professional goals. Ask yourself what you would like to be doing in five or ten years, and then determine what courses or degree programs will help you achieve your goals. Do you need a course to update your skills, a certificate to provide professional credentials, or a degree to solidify or advance your professional standing?

For example, when Head Start announced that an associate's degree in early childhood education would soon be a requirement for its teachers, Angela Butcher had a problem. Butcher, who teaches at Jackson-Vinton Community Action Head Start in Ohio, just had a high school diploma. "I was so scared of losing my job. Going to a college campus (the closest is 45 minutes away) after working 8 hours a day and finding a sitter for my two children because my husband works second shift—it was just impossible to even think about doing it. Then my director received a brochure about the distance learning program at the University of Cincinnati and asked if I would like to give college a shot that way." Butcher continues, "I felt this was a true gift to help me to [keep] the profession that is dear to me."

For Butcher, the goal was crystal clear and the means of achieving that goal fell into place quite nicely. However, for any student, it's important to know what you hope to accomplish by undertaking any degree program. "Make sure you have your goals defined," advises Scott Garrod, a Master of Business candidate at Syracuse University. "Then the decision between a distance or traditional [program] will be easy." Keep in mind that in some fields a distance education degree is not as acceptable as it is in others. Although most business employers don't make any distinctions between distance and on-campus degrees, as long as they are from reputable institutions, in academia and some professions employers may not be so accommodating. Be sure you understand what academic credentials will carry weight in the field in which you are interested.

Why are you considering distance education?

Do you have a busy schedule full of commitments to work, family, and community? If so, your top reason for enrolling in a distance education course or program may be the flexibility it offers. The ability to do course work at your own convenience is the key consideration for most distance learners.

"My schedule does not permit consistent attendance in a traditional classroom," comments one 46-year-old undergraduate. "As a consultant, I may be required to spend up to 60 hours at a client site . . . . As a parent, I have many commitments that would take priority over my attending class." She continues, "The online program at the University of Maryland University College offers me maximum flexibility in which to pursue my educational goals without interfering with the rest of my crazy schedule." Another student, Kimberly Foreman, who is studying for a Master of Healthcare Administration from Seton Hall University's online program in New Jersey, investigated several programs. "Traditional on-campus evening classes interfered with work and family obligations. The weekend programs still required that I be at a certain place at a certain time, and this was also inconvenient," she explains. "I wanted flexibility and a program that allowed me to be self-directed but still have interaction with faculty members and classmates." The online program she found at Seton Hall met her needs.

Some students need the flexibility of distance education because their work involves a great deal of travel. "With my job, travel is a requirement . . . sometimes unpredictable travel," says Scott Garrod of Syracuse University. "So a distance learning program that was not classroom-dependent was a great alternative." Another student, Paul Nashawaty, explains, "My profession has me traveling around and moving from place to place." Nashawaty, who is earning a Master of Business Administration from Worcester Polytechnic Institute in Massachusetts, concluded, "It would be very difficult for me to transfer from school to school."

Other students enroll in distance education courses and programs because they live too far from the institutions of higher learning that offer the education they need. These are students for whom the word "distance" in distance learning has a literal meaning. "My husband is a farmer, so my family is not mobile," explains Patti Iversen, a nurse who lives in Montana and is working on a Master of Science in Nursing degree (family nurse practitioner) from Gonzaga University in Spokane, Washington. "I live in a rural community and the closest colleges and universities are 250 to 300 miles from my home. I did not want to leave my family for extended periods of time in order to meet my educational and career objectives." For Iversen, distance learning was the only way to achieve her goals.

"I wanted a degree from a respected and vigorous program but didn't want to move my family or quit my job," says Lara Hollenczer, a marketing manager who lives in Maryland and is pursuing a master's degree in communications management from Syracuse University in New York. Distance learning provided Hollenczer the means to earn the degree she wanted without disrupting her work and family life. So, when you consider taking a course or enrolling in a degree program, ask yourself whether flexibility of time and place is critical for you. If flexibility is one of your top needs, distance learning may be the right choice for you.

PERSONAL ATTITUDES AND SKILLS

Are you prepared to do as much work as you would have to do in a traditional course, and perhaps more?

Many people believe that distance learning is an easier or faster way to earn a degree. This is because in recent years many fraudulent distance-learning schools have sprung up, promising degrees in little or no time for little or no work. These diploma mills have given rise to the false perception that distance learning degrees are somehow easier to earn than degrees earned the traditional way. However, distance learning courses and degree programs offered by reputable schools require just as much time and effort as their on-campus counterparts.

"Some students think that an online course is cybersurfing for credit," says Michael S. Ameigh, Assistant Provost for Distance Learning and Information Resources and Associate Professor of Communication Studies at the State University of New York at Oswego. "But an online course is actually more work than if students took the course in the classroom." That's because online instructors often require a certain amount of participation from students in order to pass the course, whereas most classroom instructors do not demand participation from students beyond completing the assignments and exams. So, at the beginning of each course, Ameigh tries to weed out students who think that online learning is easier than conventional courses. He provides a six-minute "welcome document," a streaming media PowerPoint presentation with narration that gives an overview of what the course covers and what he expects of students. In courses taken by distance learners and on-campus students, instructors make no distinctions between distance learners and traditional students when it comes to the course work that they must do. For example, in Gonzaga University's undergraduate and graduate nursing programs, "Course requirements for students at a distance are identical to those for their on-campus colleagues," according to Dale Ann Abendroth, Assistant Professor of Nursing.

From the student's perspective, a high-quality distance education course is as rigorous as a traditional course. "Certainly the expectations of the instructor and the volume of readings and assignments were as stringent, or even more so, than on-site courses I have taken," comments a high school librarian of her Rutgers University postgraduate course in critical issues for the wired classroom. "Be prepared for a great deal of work. It seems to me that more work is assigned than in a 'regular' class, so students shouldn't perceive distance learning as an easy way out. It isn't!"

Do you have the time-management skills necessary to juggle work, home, and school responsibilities?

As we have seen, a distance learning course or program takes as much time as a traditional one, and sometimes more. So ask yourself, do you have enough time to take a distance learning course or courses? Will you be able to juggle your course work, professional work, family obligations, and community activities to make time for all your responsibilities? "I've seen students register for four or five classes in a semester and try to work full-time," says Patti Wolf, Assistant Academic Director and Assistant Professor of Computer Science at the University of Maryland University College. "Many of these students have underestimated the time required for their online courses and ended up doing poorly." Wolf adds, "You should expect to spend as much time on line (or otherwise preparing for class) as you would in a traditional classroom." Distance learner Patti Iversen advises students to "be realistic about the amount of time that will be needed for study and travel, if required [for programs with residency periods]."

In addition to having enough time to do the course work, students have to be able to plan their time, make a schedule, and stick to it. "The biggest problem I see among my students is an inability to budget their time," says Wolf. "They get to the third week of class and realize that it's Saturday night and they haven't done their homework."

Iversen agrees. "Failure to adequately anticipate and plan for the rigors of independent learning leads to frustration and poor outcomes," she warns. Even though many courses, like Wolf's, are set up in weekly blocks to help students pace themselves, it's still up to the student to make time to log on or watch the videotape and do the assignments.

Do you have the discipline and self-motivation to work regularly if you don't have to show up for class at a given time and place?

When we asked students and faculty members what personal qualities a distance learner needs, most people mentioned discipline and self-motivation as the keys to success. "Success as a distance learner requires more self-discipline and greater ability to learn autonomously than site-based learning," claims distance learner Patti Iversen. M.B.A. candidate Paul Nashawaty echoes her remarks, "You must keep on top of the workload and try not to slack off," he says. "Discipline is my number-one factor for success in this program." A University of Maryland University College undergraduate agrees, "Students [must] have the discipline to complete course work studies and assignments on time and independently without the in-person reminders that come with regularly scheduled class meetings." When you are considering distance education, ask yourself whether or not you have the qualities needed to see it through. According to Denise Petrosino, a certified public accountant working on a master's in organizational management from the University of Phoenix Online, "As long as you are goal-oriented and self-motivated, you can do it."

Do you have the initiative and assertiveness needed to succeed in a distance learning environment?

Initiative and assertiveness are qualities needed for success in distance learning. Students need to take the initiative to ask questions and resolve problems that the instructor may not be able to perceive.

In addition, students in distance learning courses need to be assertive in order to make themselves known to the instructor and to other students. For example, in an online course, a student who never participates in threaded discussions tends to "disappear." "In the online environment, students have to be assertive," says Michael S. Ameigh of the State University of New York at Oswego. "Otherwise we don't know who they are." Similarly, in a prerecorded video course, a student who never contacts the instructor has little presence in the instructor's mind. Of course, initiative and assertiveness are pluses for traditional on-campus students, too. The student who speaks up in class is more likely to have a good learning experience and succeed in a course than the student who sits silently in the back of the room. For many adults, maturity brings assertiveness. "My students are a professional group," says Dale Ann Abendroth, Assistant Professor of Nursing at Gonzaga University. "It's rare that I have a wallflower in a course."

YOUR ACADEMIC AND PROFESSIONAL SKILLS

Do you have sound study skills, including reading, researching, writing papers, and taking exams?

Good study skills are a necessary prerequisite for distance learning. In fact, many institutions that offer distance learning courses and degree programs require that students have taken at least some college-level courses before they enroll in a distance education degree program. For example, some distance education bachelor's programs prefer students with an associate's degree from a community college or a certain minimum number of undergraduate credit hours. In this way, they ensure that students are ready to tackle course work via distance learning without needing much help with basic study skills.

For graduate programs, it is simply assumed that students have the necessary study skills and are ready to undertake graduate-level work. Laurie Noe, a doctoral candidate in management of children and youth programs at Nova Southeastern University, explains, "You are required to produce papers, take tests, conduct research, and formulate and state your opinions just as if you were in a traditional setting."

Do you have good communication skills? Can you present yourself well in writing? Can you speak up on camera?

Good communication skills—reading, writing, listening, and speaking—are necessary to succeed in all types of distance learning courses and programs. However, different distance learning technologies emphasize different communication skills.

"Online students have to be reasonably articulate in the written mode of communication," explains Claudine SchWeber, Assistant Vice President for Distance Education and Lifelong Learning at the University of Maryland University College. That's because virtually all communication in an online course takes place through the written word, therefore you must be comfortable with reading messages and responding in writing.

For some people, this is ideal. "Students who are petrified to talk in class often find it easy to communicate in writing on line. They can make well-reasoned, thought-out responses to the discussion," explains Patti Wolf of the University of Maryland University College. "One of the things that happens on line is that people who talk little in the classroom feel more comfortable and tend to communicate well on line," says Karen Novick, Director of Professional Development Studies at Rutgers University in New Jersey. Robert V. Steiner, who directs the distance learning project at Teachers College, Columbia University, also agrees. "For some students, online learning may provide a more comfortable environment in which to express themselves. Students can reflect on what they want to say before they post a message." On the other hand, some students are simply more visual and more oriented to getting information via television rather than the written word. For them, two-way interactive video is a more comfortable way to communicate. It's easier for these students to speak up and communicate with people they can see and hear rather than to write messages to unseen students and instructors. "Once students get used to being on camera, they react fairly normally," says Larry Anthony, Director of the Addiction Studies

Program at the University of Cincinnati. Of course, students who take courses via video still need written communication skills because most of their assignments and exams are in writing.

If you are pursuing a degree or certificate to improve your professional standing, do you have the background that may be required?

Many graduate-level professional programs require that students have worked in the field for several years before they apply. For example, many programs that offer a Master in Business Administration prefer students who have demonstrated their professional capabilities through several years of work. Graduate-level work in other fields, such as nursing, social work, and education, often requires related work experience. Be sure you have the necessary professional background for the programs you are considering.

SOCIAL FACTORS

Do you have the support of your family and employers?

As you have realized by now, a distance learning course or program can be challenging. Taking such a course or program means that you will be working harder than ever, so having the backing of your family and employer can be very helpful. "It's important to have a good support group behind you," says Barbara Rosenbaum, who is working on a master's degree in communications management from Syracuse University. "My husband, friends, family, and colleagues helped me keep my energy and focus up." Distance learner Patti Iversen agrees. "A local support network is a valuable asset in helping to overcome the occasional slump in motivation that occurs over time."

Are you comfortable with the social interaction that is characteristic of distance learning? Can you overcome or accept the social isolation that often occurs?

The issue of social interaction and isolation is complex because different factors, including instructional technology, personality, and life circumstances, influence how each person reacts to the social element of distance learning.

Instructional technology. As we saw when we discussed communication skills, each distance learning technology draws on particular skills. Similarly, each distance learning technology offers a different type of social interaction. Let's look at each major distance learning technology to get a better idea of how it affects the social elements of distance education.

The technology that offers a social experience most similar to that of the conventional classroom is two-way interactive video. Even though the students may be geographically distant from one another, communication is in real time, people can see one another, and the feeling of social isolation is minimized. Kenneth Wachter, Professor of Demography at the University of California at Berkeley, offered an advanced postgraduate course in mathematical demography via two-way interactive video to students at Berkeley and the University of California at Los Angeles. He was delighted by how the two groups of students were brought together. "The thing that works best is the human back and forth," says Wachter.

Online courses can also offer social interaction, but in a new and, to some, unfamiliar form. "At first it is strange e-mailing someone you don't know. However, you get to know the person via e-mail just as you would talking or writing a letter," explains an undergraduate at the University of Maryland University College. "In the cybercafes that are provided for classmates, we talk about class work, movies, music, time management, and sports. It helps bring the class together socially." Denise Petrosino, who is enrolled in a master's program in organizational management at the University of Phoenix Online, agrees. "If you have a fear of limited interaction with the teacher and students, you can put that aside because I believe that we learn more about our teacher and classmates in the online program than in the live classroom," says Petrosino. "The reason I say this is because you get to read all correspondence between students and teacher."

In courses in which class videotapes are mailed to off-site students, the sense of social isolation is the most pronounced. That's because these courses often do not provide a means for ongoing discussion between off-site students, on-site students, and instructors. "The professors do not know much about the distance students' personalities, or even what they look like," explains Nicole DeRaleau, who lives in Connecticut and is a Master of Engineering student at Worcester Polytechnic Institute in Massachusetts. "Their interaction with us is minimal, and the closest form of personal interaction may be a telephone call, which is almost always initiated by the student." Note that some courses that rely on videotapes for instructional delivery are now moving on line as well, establishing class bulletin boards on which discussions can take place, thus improving the social interaction of the off-site students.

Personality. The second factor that influences how social interaction and social isolation are perceived is an individual's personality—one person's social isolation is another person's cherished privacy. For some people, the type of interaction that characterizes distance learning is not enough to overcome a sense of social isolation. "Eye contact, vocal inflection, body language—all these elements of communication are missing [online]," explains Robert V. Steiner, who directs the distance learning project at Teachers College, Columbia University. "For some people, the sense of isolation can be significant." Joanne Simon, a student at the University of Phoenix Online who actually prefers online classes to traditional classes, admits, "I like to talk, so for me, the social interaction is lacking." Another distance learner thinks that people who are "social butterflies" will find the social interactions of distance learning unfulfilling.

On the other hand, people who are not especially extroverted may find distance learning suits them. They can participate, especially in online courses, without risking too much personal revelation.

Personal circumstances. How important is social interaction? Clearly, there must be enough interaction to facilitate learning. But for many adult students, the lack of social interaction is simply not a problem.

"For the most part, I feel detached from the class itself, and that is okay," says Brigit Dolan, a nurse who lives in Boise, Idaho, and is enrolled in Gonzaga University's Master of Science in Nursing program in Spokane, Washington. In this program, students are required to attend classes three times per semester. The remaining classes are mailed to them on videotape. "I feel okay to share my ideas and experiences when I'm there, but I'm fulfilled enough in other areas of my life that I don't yearn for that much interaction from my school life . . . . I just do my work, communicate with my professors and classmates occasionally, and that's about it." Like Brigit Dolan, most adult students are not looking for the social life and collegiality that are characteristics of the on-campus undergraduate experience. A librarian taking a postgraduate course at Rutgers University explains, "I don't think social interaction is a high priority in the kind of postgrad courses I take; we all have jobs and personal lives, and time is precious." Carla Gentry, a nurse enrolled in a distance learning master's program, agrees. "At my stage in life, I am not going to school for the social benefits."

How well do you work with others?

After the discussion of social interaction and social isolation, you may wonder why working well with others is important in the distance learning environment. The reason is that many instructors try to overcome the potential social isolation of the distance education course by assigning group work, thus forcing people to interact with each other.

Doing a group project in a distance learning class is challenging. The first challenge is to coordinate the activities of a group of people who are extremely busy, geographically distant from one another, and doing their work at different hours of the day and night. The second challenge is to get a group of distance learners to work together. "Since distance learners are so independent and self-motivated, they also like to do things their own way," says Brigit Dolan, who finds group projects the most challenging aspect of distance education. Trust, cooperation, and flexibility are key.

TECHNOLOGY ISSUES

Do you have the technical skills, or the willingness to acquire these skills, that may be required of a distance learning program?

Those of you who see yourselves as technologically challenged may have been dismayed by the discussion in "What Is Distance Learning?" of the technology involved in many distance learning courses. Don't be. Remember that the technology is just a tool, a means to an end, and it can be learned.

In fact, some distance learning technology is not particularly advanced from the user's point of view. For example, in two-way interactive video courses, all you have to do is learn to activate the microphone (some even activate automatically when you speak) and watch the video monitors. For prerecorded video, you just pop the videocassette into the VCR and turn on the TV. Online courses do involve a little more technological savvy. However, consider the experience of one librarian who was taking a traditional on-campus postgraduate course at Rutgers University. "My first online course was thrust upon me," she recalls. The instructor, who developed a serious health problem that prevented her from coming in to class, gave students the option of continuing online. "I, on my own, would never have chosen this mode; I was too computer-illiterate at that time. However, I quickly found that the technical skills required were really not onerous at all and that I could master them easily . . . . If I can succeed—no spring chicken with little technology experience—anyone can." Denise Petrosino agrees. "You do not have to be a technical genius to go to school on line. If you have a computer, can log onto the Web, and know how to use e-mail, you are set."

Do you have or are you willing to gain access to the necessary equipment, which may include a computer, VCR, television, or fax machine?

Most people own a television and VCR, so these are not usually items that a new distance learner needs to purchase. However, investing in the proper computer hardware and software for a distance education program can be costly. Even if you already own a computer with Internet access, you may have to upgrade your hardware or Internet browser or purchase additional software in order to meet the minimum technical requirements of a course.

Can you tolerate dealing with technology problems?

Technology sometimes fails, and distance learners have to learn how to cope when it does. Many schools offer technical support for distance learners, and sometimes problems can be solved quickly. But if your computer system crashes for a week, you'll have to find other alternatives until you can fix the problem. "Students should be comfortable with the technology triad—fax, phone, and computer," says Claudine SchWeber of the University of Maryland University College. "Then if one goes down, they have other channels of communication."

A MINI SELF-ASSESSMENT

If you do an Internet search using the phrase "distance learning self-assessment," you will find dozens of brief quizzes designed to evaluate whether or not distance learning suits your personality, skills, and learning style. Most are posted on the Web sites of colleges and universities that offer distance education courses. For example, the University of Texas at Brownsville's distance learning self-assessment can be found at http://pubs.utb.edu/semester_courses/spring2001/distance_learnself_assessment.htm, and St. Louis Community College offers its self-assessment at http://www.stlcc.cc.mo.us/distance/assessment.

For your convenience, we've provided a brief self-assessment. Although most of the online quizzes focus on Internet-based courses, this assessment is broader. Take it and see how you do!

DISTANCE LEARNING SELF-ASSESSMENT

1. When I think about how I learn, I think:
   (A) I learn best independently. I am self-motivated and like to work at my own pace. I don't need a lot of handholding.
   (B) I like to work independently, but I like to get some feedback once in a while on how I'm doing. I don't need a lot of support, just a little help every once in a while.
   (C) I can work independently, but I want to know where I stand. I like to be in an interactive situation where I get regular feedback on how I am doing.
   (D) I need lots of interaction with my teachers and peers. I like the give and take of the classroom setting. It keeps me engaged in my classes.
2. When I think about learning through different media, such as the Internet or videoconferencing, I think:
   (A) It would be exciting to be able to do my work through a different medium. The idea of sitting in a classroom does nothing for me.

(B) I am open to the idea of trying something different, like an Internet class. I would like to see how it would work for me.
(C) I'm not sure that I would be ready to work that independently. When I think of furthering my education, I see myself in a more traditional setting.
(D) I absolutely want a traditional learning experience. I want to be in a classroom setting and experience all that school has to offer.

3. When I think about interacting with my teachers, I think:
(A) I don't really care whether or not I have any face-to-face contact with my teachers. As long as I'm getting the kind of information I need to be successful in my classes, I can be satisfied as a student.
(B) I don't need a great deal of direct contact with my teachers. I'm a good, independent worker. I do want to be able to ask for help and direction when I need it.
(C) I don't need to be in a situation where I have daily conversations with my teachers, but I do like to know that they are there if I need them. I find a good teacher really helps me get excited about a topic.
(D) I really value my contacts with my teachers. I like to be able to engage in a dialogue in the classroom. A good teacher helps me connect to the subject.

4. When I think about trying to do schoolwork at home, I think:
(A) I have a great setup at home, which is conducive to studying. I like the idea of being able to work in my own "space" and at my own pace.
(B) I can work fairly well at home, I just have to make sure that I don't get too distracted by what is going on around me.
(C) I could work at home, but I really don't see that as an ideal situation. There is too much going on and I would be able to concentrate better in a classroom or library setting.
(D) There is no way I want to learn from home. I want to get out of the house and be in a classroom with other students.

5. When it comes to setting my schedule for learning and studying, I think:
(A) I need as much flexibility as I can get. I've got a lot of other things going on in my life and I'd really like to be able to work at my own pace.
(B) I would like to have some flexibility in scheduling my classes, but I don't want to drag it out either. I want to get through my education as quickly as possible.
(C) I like the idea of having my time fairly structured. If I don't have someone pushing me along, it may take me longer than I want to get through school.
(D) I need to have a structured schedule to keep me on task.

6. When I think about the traditional education experience, I think:
(A) Campus or classroom life doesn't really appeal to me at this stage in my life. I don't need or want the experience, for example, of living in a dorm or sitting in a classroom. I want to find an alternative way of earning my degree or certificate.
(B) I'm not sure if I want to commit to the classroom experience. It may work for me, but I'm willing to look at other ways of earning a degree.
(C) I think I would be happier if I were on a campus somewhere. I think I'd probably regret missing out on the learning experience. I wouldn't rule out the notion of being a commuter, though.
(D) I really want a traditional learning experience where I can get away from home. I'm at a point in my life where that seems to be the logical next step for me.

To evaluate your readiness for distance education, count the number of (A)s, (B)s, (C)s, and (D)s among your responses. If most of your answers were

- (A)—you should carefully investigate distance education as an option for continuing your education.
- (B)—you should investigate whether distance learning programs are suitable for meeting at least part of your educational needs. For example, you may want to complete a significant portion of your academic work through a distance learning program but still allow yourself time for some of your work to be completed in a traditional classroom setting.
- (C)—you're probably better-suited for a traditional campus-based college experience than a distance learning environment. However, some course work through a distance learning program may be a great way to supplement your on-campus course work. You should probably look for a program that will provide you with faculty or mentor feedback on a regular basis.
- (D)—you are clearly suited for a traditional classroom setting where you can have more immediate interaction with your teachers and peers. This is not to say that you may not find distance learning programs useful at some point in the future, but it sounds like you need something more hands-on so you can get immediate feedback in the classroom while enjoying the other benefits of college life.

CONCLUSION

As you have seen in this section, distance learning is not for those who lack motivation or need other people to keep them on task. On the other hand, it is perfectly suited for those who have definite educational and professional goals, are committed to getting an education, are focused and organized, can persevere when things get tough, and need the flexibility that distance education offers.

Finding the time in a busy schedule to successfully complete distance learning courses is a challenge for most adults. It's easy for work and family obligations to take precedence over getting an education. Still, distance learning makes it possible for many adults who cannot regularly attend on-campus classes to get a high-quality education. As one undergraduate distance learner commented, "For working adults (and particularly working parents), distance learning may provide the best means for obtaining an undergraduate or graduate degree from a highly respected university without interfering with life's other commitments."

WHAT CAN YOU STUDY VIA DISTANCE LEARNING?

If you are interested in pursuing your education by distance learning, you are not limited to a few specialized courses or degree programs. Actually, almost every course, certificate, and degree program that you can take on campus is also available in a distance learning format. There are exceptions, of course. Degree programs in subjects that require laboratory work or performance, for example, cannot usually be done completely at a distance. Still, distance education spans a wide range of offerings, from accredited graduate-level degree programs to self-help and hobby courses. Although some programs and courses are limited to residents of certain states or regions, many are available nationwide and internationally.

In this section we will focus on programs and courses offered by institutions of higher education, including technical institutes, community colleges, four-year colleges, and universities. Figure 3-1 shows how higher education is structured in the United States, and how distance learning programs and courses are available at most levels of postsecondary education. The exceptions are some professional degrees, such as doctor of medicine, and postdoctoral study and research. Another partial exception is the law degree (LL.B., J.D.). Although you can acquire a law degree via distance learning, at the time this book was published, no distance learning law program has been accredited by the American Bar Association. Thus, a person with a law degree from an unaccredited distance learning program will not be able to take the bar exam in most states. The accreditation issue is important in many fields besides law, and we will examine it more closely in "Selecting a Good Distance Learning Program." In this section we'll simply give you an overview of the degrees, certificates, and courses that are available via distance learning and guidance on how to find programs and courses of interest to you.

UNDERGRADUATE DEGREE PROGRAMS

Today you can earn an associate or bachelor's degree entirely by distance learning. You may also be able to shorten the time it takes to earn a degree if you transfer college credits from other institutions of higher learning, earn credits through equivalency exams, or present a portfolio of your accomplishments. For adults, earning credits for past academic and other work can cut a year or more off the time it takes to earn an undergraduate degree. So don't be shy about negotiating for credits with the school in which you plan to enroll—the time and money you save may be considerable.

ASSOCIATE DEGREE

The degree conferred by community colleges is the associate degree. Students enrolled full-time can earn an associate degree in two years, but part-time students may take much longer to earn the 60 to 64 credits required. The two most common associate degrees are the Associate of Arts (A.A.) and the Associate of Science (A.S.), although there are many other titles that range from Associate of Business Administration (A.B.A.) to Associate of General Studies (A.G.S.). Distance learning associate degrees are offered in a wide range of fields, including liberal arts, business, computer science, and health professions. Many students who have earned an associate degree go on to apply those credits toward a bachelor's degree.

BACHELOR'S DEGREE

The bachelor's degree is recognized worldwide as the first university degree a student earns. In the United States, the bachelor's degree is conferred by four-year colleges, universities, and technical institutes. Although students enrolled full-time can earn the degree in four years, many actually take up to six years. Part-time students take longer, of course, to earn the 120 to 128 credits required for the bachelor's degree.

In most colleges and universities, the course of study that leads to a bachelor's degree consists of concentrated work in a "major" such as psychology or business and wide-ranging work in a variety of subjects—the liberal arts—to give students a broad foundation of knowledge. However, some bachelor's degree programs focus on intensive study in a particular field without the broad liberal arts background.

The most common bachelor's degrees are the Bachelor of Arts (B.A.) and the Bachelor of Science (B.S.), although there are scores of other titles in use as well. Distance learning bachelor's degrees are offered in many fields, including business, engineering, computer science, economics, English, history, nursing, psychology, and telecommunications. Some colleges and universities offer interdisciplinary degrees, such as environmental studies or arts management, and some permit students to design their own interdisciplinary program.

TRANSFERRING CREDITS

Adult students who have earned some college credits during the course of their career can decrease the time it takes to earn an undergraduate degree by transferring the credits they've earned to a degree program. Many institutions of higher learning will accept transfer credits toward a degree. *Since each school's requirements vary, it's important to check before you enroll.* The school may have rules regarding the maximum number of transfer credits and the types of courses for which credit will be granted. Consult the academic advising office before you register.

EARNING CREDITS BY TAKING EXAMS

It's also possible to earn credit for prior learning if you take examinations to assess your knowledge and skills. For example, if you have worked in the human resources department of a large organization for years, you may know a lot about human resource management. If you take and pass a college-level exam in human resource management, you can earn 3 credits toward your degree—without taking a course or paying tuition. Although some schools

Figure 3–1: The Structure of Higher Education in the U.S.

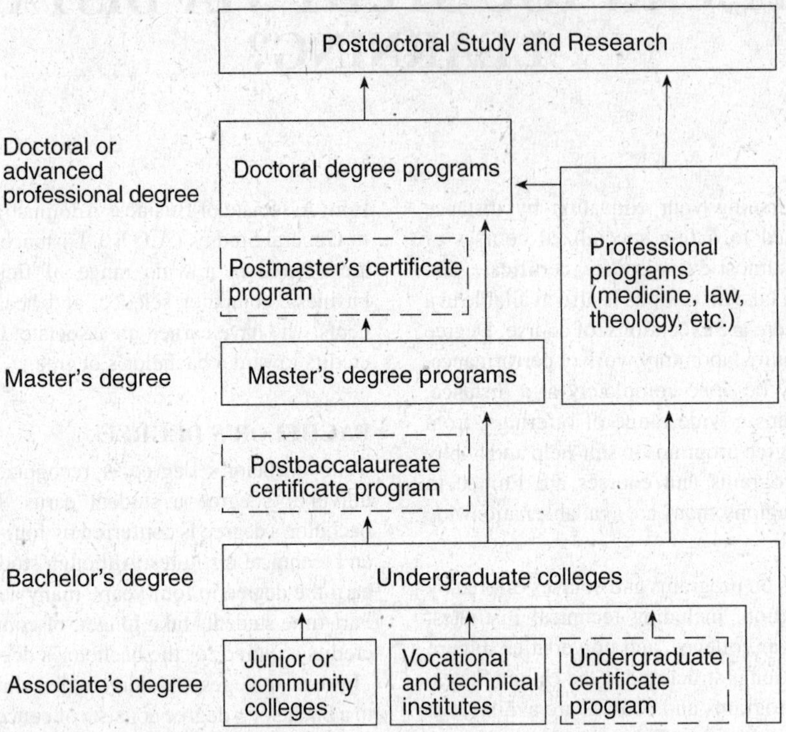

Structure of higher education in the United States. Note that the arrows indicate common pathways of students, but not the only possible pathway. *Source:* Adapted from U.S. Department of Education, National Center for Educational Statistics.

have developed their own equivalency exams, most schools accept the results of examinations taken through national programs.

CLEP Exams. The most well-known of the national equivalency exam programs is the College-Level Examination Program (CLEP), which is administered by the College Entrance Examination Board and recognized by about 2,900 colleges and universities. Most of the CLEP tests are multiple-choice exams, and some are multiple-choice and essay. There are five general exams: social sciences and history, English composition, humanities, college mathematics, and natural sciences. In addition, there are about thirty specific subject area tests, including American government, Spanish, principles of management, and introductory sociology. A good score on an exam is worth between 3 and 12 credits, it depends on the exam and the credits accepted by your school.

Earning credits by scoring well on equivalency exams can save you both time and tuition money. If you'd like more information about the CLEP exams, visit the College Board Web site at www.collegeboard.org/clep, e-mail them at clep@info.collegeboard.org, or call 609-771-7865.

Excelsior College Examinations. The Excelsior College Examination series, formerly the Regents College Examination series, is similar to the CLEP exams. The series consists of about forty subject area equivalency examinations that are 3 or 4 hours long. Subjects include anatomy and physiology, auditing, organizational behavior, and educational psychology; and the exams are recognized by almost 1,000 colleges and universities. For more information, visit the Excelsior College Web site at www.excelsior.edu, e-mail them at testadmn@excelsior.edu, or call 888-647-2388 (toll-free).

DANTES Subject Standardized Tests. Another series of equivalency exams are the DANTES Subject Standardized Tests, or DSSTs. The DSSTs are examinations offered by The Chauncey Group International, a subsidiary of the Educational Testing Service, in trust for the United States Department of Defense as part of the military's Defense Activity for Nontraditional Education Support (DANTES). These tests were originally developed for military personnel but are now available for civilians as well. The tests are similar to the CLEP exams, but there are some subject areas not offered by CLEP, such as geography, criminal justice, marketing, technical writing, and ethics in America.

For more information about the DSSTs, you can check the Chauncey Group Web site at www.chauncey.com/dantes.html, e-mail them at dantes@chauncey.com, or call 609-720-6740. If you are on active duty in the military, you can get further information about the exams from the DANTES Web site at www.voled.doded.mil/dantes/exam or e-mail them at exams@voled.doded.mil.

Graduate Record Examinations Subject Tests. The GRE Subject Tests, administered by the Educational Testing Service (ETS), assess knowledge that would ordinarily be acquired during the course of majoring in a subject as an undergraduate. Although they are usually used as entrance exams for graduate schools, some colleges and universities will award undergraduate credit if you get a good score. The subjects include biochemistry, cell and molecular biology; biology; chemistry; computer science; literature in English; mathematics; physics; and psychology.

For more information about the GRE Subject Tests, visit the GRE Online site at www.gre.org, send an e-mail to gre-info@ets.org, or call 609-771-7670.

EARNING CREDITS FOR LIFE EXPERIENCE

Many undergraduate degree programs, especially those designed for adults, give credit for knowledge and skills you've gained through life experience. Although the knowledge usually comes through paid employment, it can also be acquired through volunteer work, company or military training courses, travel, recreational activities and hobbies, and reading.

There is a catch, of course—you must document the specifics of what you have learned. It's simply not enough to say that you learned about marketing while selling widgets for XYZ Company. Instead, you must demonstrate what you have learned about pricing, promotion, and product mix; for example, showing plans for a marketing campaign. Thus, to earn credit for life experience, you should assemble a file, or portfolio, of information about your work and other accomplishments. The file may include writing samples, awards, taped presentations or performances, copies of speeches, newspaper articles, official job descriptions, military records, works of art, designs, blueprints, films, or photographs. Your portfolio is then evaluated by an institution's faculty. A student can earn as many as 30 credits—one quarter the number needed for a bachelor's degree—as the result of a good portfolio review. For example, through a portfolio evaluation, a senior marketing executive in her forties earned 30 credits, mostly in marketing and communications, toward her distance learning bachelor's degree from University of Maryland University College. For more information about assessment opportunities for adult learners, check the Web site of the Council for Adult and Experiential Learning (CAEL) at www.cael.org or call 312-499-2600.

Credit for Work Training. Since 1974, thousands of employees have been earning college credit for selected educational programs sponsored by businesses, industry, professional associations, labor unions, and government agencies. The American Council on Education's College Credit Recommendation Service evaluates such programs according to established college-level criteria and recommends college credit for those programs that measure up to these standards. You can check their Web site at www.acenet.edu, e-mail them at credit@ace.nche.edu, or call 202-939-9475.

Credit for Military Training. Service in the military, specialized training, and occupational experience have the potential to earn you college credit. Many military programs have already been evaluated in terms of their equivalency to college credit. The institutions that belong to Servicemembers Opportunities Colleges (SOC) have agreed to assess students' prior learning and accept each other's credits in transfer. To find out more, check the SOC Web site at www.soc.aascu.org, e-mail them at socmail@aascu.org, or call 800-368-5622 (toll-free).

GRADUATE DEGREE PROGRAMS

MASTER'S DEGREE

The master's degree is the first academic or professional degree earned after the bachelor's degree. A traditional, full-time master's degree student may take a year or two to earn the required 30 credits. Part-time students usually take longer, it depends on the design of the degree program. In some master's degree programs, students are simply expected to take advanced-level courses and perhaps pass a culminating exam. In others, original research and a thesis are also required. Some distance learning master's degree programs have a brief residency requirement. Students usually earn a Master of Arts (M.A.), a Master of Science (M.S.), or a Master of Business Administration (M.B.A.) degree.

At the time this book was published, distance learning master's degree programs outnumbered other distance learning degree programs by a considerable margin. Most of these degree programs are professional in nature and are designed for working adults with experience in the field. If you are interested in a master's degree in library science, business, or education, you are in luck. These are fields in which there are many distance master's degree programs from which to choose.

However, if you are looking for a distance learning master's degree program in an academic field, such as English language and literature, chemistry, or ethnic and cultural studies, your choices are far more limited. That's because most master's programs in academic fields are campus based. Still, *Peterson's Guide to Distance Learning Programs* lists at least one distance master's degree program in each of these academic subject areas.

Another type of master's degree that is offered via distance learning is the interdisciplinary degree. Some are offered in liberal studies or humanities and are granted for advanced study and a culminating project or thesis. Others combine academic and professional areas of study. Still others are offered in broad subject areas like environmental studies, in which students are expected to design their own course of study based on their particular interests.

In the future, the number of distance academic and interdisciplinary master's degree programs is likely to increase, but far slower than the number of professional degree programs, for which the demand is much greater.

DOCTORAL DEGREE

The doctoral degree, the highest degree awarded, is earned after an advanced course of study that usually culminates in original research and a dissertation, an extended written work. The traditional on-campus doctoral student takes four to ten years to complete the degree, but many distance learning doctoral programs are structured to streamline the process. Thus, some doctoral degrees can be earned in as little as three years. Most distance learning doctoral programs, even those offered by virtual universities like the University of Phoenix Online, have a brief residency requirement. The Doctor of Philosophy (Ph.D.) is the most common doctoral degree; it is awarded in fields that range from philosophy to geology to communication. Other frequently awarded doctoral degrees include the Doctor of Education (Ed.D.), Doctor of Business Administration (D.B.A.), Doctor of Engineering (Eng.D.), and Doctor of Psychology (Psy.D.). There are far fewer distance learning doctoral programs than master's programs. However, you can find programs in a wide range of fields, although the number of programs within each field may be limited. You can earn a distance learning doctoral degree in fields as diverse as business, engineering, computer science, counseling psychology, instructional technology, education, human services, library science, English literature, management, pharmacy, and public policy. As with distance learning master's degrees, distance learning doctoral degrees tend to be professional rather than academic in orientation. Many of these degree programs are designed with the professional working adult in mind.

EARNING GRADUATE-LEVEL CREDIT FOR KNOWLEDGE AND EXPERIENCE

There is disagreement among institutions of higher education about whether or not to award graduate-level credit for knowledge acquired outside academia. At present, many graduate schools do not offer credit to students for knowledge and experience acquired before enrollment in the program, no matter how deep or extensive that knowledge and experience may be. However, other less conservative institutions are more open to granting graduate credit for life experience. Check with the schools and programs in which you are interested to see what their policies are.

CERTIFICATE PROGRAMS

Distance learning certificate programs can train you for a new career or give you a foundation in a new subject even if you've already earned a college degree in an entirely different field. A certificate program usually consists of around six to ten courses, all focused on a single profession or subject, and it can be earned at the undergraduate or graduate level. Some schools now offer a portion of a master's or other degree as a certificate. This allows you to take part of the full degree curriculum and either stop at the certification level or proceed through for the entire degree. If this is an option that interests you, be sure to consider the admissions requirements carefully. If you think you may matriculate through to the entire degree, be sure you understand the admissions requirements for each program because they may differ.

PROFESSIONAL CERTIFICATE PROGRAMS

To give you just a few examples of professional certificate programs offered via distance learning, within the engineering profession there are certificates in computer-integrated manufacturing, systems engineering, and fire-protection engineering. In business, there are distance learning certificate programs in information technology and health services management. In education, distance learning certificates include early reading instruction, children's literature, and English as a second language. In health care, certificates include medical assisting, home health nursing, and health-care administration. In law, distance learning certificates are offered in paralegal/legal assistant studies and legal issues for business professionals.

Professional certificate programs are often designed with the help of professional associations and licensing boards, and thus encompass real-world, practical knowledge. Many are designed to prepare students for professional certification or licensure. At the end of the program, the student sits for an exam and earns a state-recognized certificate from a certifying agency or licensing board. *If this is your goal, you should make sure that the certification program you want to take meets the certifying agency or licensing board's requirements.* That way, you won't waste your time or money completing a program that won't help you meet your ultimate professional goals.

CERTIFICATE PROGRAMS IN ACADEMIC SUBJECTS

Less common, but still available via distance learning, are undergraduate and graduate certificate programs in many academic subjects. At the undergraduate level, you can earn a certificate in areas such as American studies, Chinese language and literature, English composition, creative writing, ethnic and cultural studies, general studies, humanities, and liberal arts and sciences. If you later enroll in an undergraduate degree program, you may be able to apply the credits earned in a certificate program toward your degree.

At the graduate level, you can earn a certificate via distance learning in subjects like biology, English language and literature, geography, physiological psychology, religious studies, and statistics.

INDIVIDUAL COURSES

If you are seeking to update your professional skills, acquire specialized knowledge, earn a few credits toward a degree, or simply take a class for your own pleasure, individual distance learning courses may be for you. Many institutions of higher education venture into distance learning by offering a few classes scattered throughout various departments. As their experience with distance education increases, they begin to offer complete programs of study. Thus, if you are interested in just taking a few courses, you have the widest range of choices. You can find individual courses in subjects that range from accounting to animal sciences and from art history to aviation—and that's just a random sample beginning with the letter *A*.

There are several options that may be open to you when you take an individual course, such as taking the course for credit, taking it without earning credit, or earning Continuing Education Units (CEUs). The option you select depends on your purpose for taking the course.

TAKING A COURSE FOR CREDIT

If you are enrolled in a degree program and need a few credits, taking a distance learning course may help you satisfy your degree requirements. Your own college or university may offer courses via distance learning. In fact, students enrolled in conventional on-campus degree programs sometimes take distance learning courses from their schools when they go home for the summer. For example, Iowa's Drake University offers online summer courses to its students.

If your own institution does not offer suitable distance learning courses, you may be able to take a distance education course from any regionally accredited college or university and get credit for it. You may even be able to save some tuition money if you select a course at a community college or a less expensive four-year college or university. The credits you earn will probably be transferable to the institution in which you are enrolled. *But before you enroll in a course at another college or university, be sure to check with your own school to make sure it will accept the credits.* Many colleges and universities require that you obtain a minimum number of credits from core courses and courses in your major in order to earn their degree. To avoid losing time and money on a course that won't be recognized by your school, it's wise to check with your academic adviser and work out a degree plan before you take courses from other institutions. If you are not currently enrolled in a degree program but think you may be in the future, taking a couple of distance education courses for credit is a good way to see whether or not a distance education degree program is for you. Later you may be able to apply the credits toward your degree.

NONCREDIT COURSES

If learning for the sake of learning or acquiring specific professional knowledge is your goal, taking a distance education course on a noncredit basis may be the way to go. Such courses may help you prepare for a new career or study for professional licensure and certification.

Just as you can audit an on-campus course for a lesser charge than if you were taking the course for credit, you can audit a distance learning course as well. Students who audit a course don't receive a grade, so they are not usually required to turn in assignments or take exams. Still, many do so in order to maximize the learning experience.

CONTINUING EDUCATION UNITS

Distance learning is a good option for working adults whose professions require continuing education, even after they've earned their degree, certificate, or license. Many states mandate continuing education for people in professions such as teaching, nursing, and accounting. For example, New Jersey requires teachers to complete 100 hours of professional development work every five years. Professionals in engineering, business, and computer science may also opt to keep up with developments in their field through distance learning. If you take a distance learning course for professional enhancement, you don't necessarily have to earn regular college credits for it. Instead, you may be able to earn Continuing Education Units. The CEU system is a nationally recognized program that provides a standardized measure for accumulating, transferring, and recognizing participation in continuing education programs. One CEU is defined as 10 contact hours of participation in an organized continuing education experience under responsible sponsorship, capable direction, and qualified instruction. Some institutions will permit you to take courses for continuing education credits rather than for regular credit or no credit. It is still important to take the courses from a properly accredited program, however, so that employers and professional agencies will recognize them.

FINDING PROGRAMS AND COURSES

THE INTERNET

The Internet is an excellent place to start your search for information about distance learning courses and programs. Perhaps the most comprehensive database of distance learning offerings is the one maintained by Peterson's at www.petersons.com/dlearn. Peterson's, an education information provider and publisher of college directories and other education-related material (including this book), provides online access to current information about distance learning programs and courses. You can search the Peterson's distance learning database in a number of ways: by institution, degree program, or field of study. Once you have found courses or programs that match your search criteria, there are links to further information about them. Peterson's distance learning database is especially good for locating degree programs, including undergraduate and graduate certificates, associate degrees, bachelor's degrees, master's degrees, and doctoral degrees.

Another Internet database is the International Distance Learning Course Finder, provided by International Where and How. When you search for a course, you can specify course subject, course name, country, or institution; and you can narrow the search by language of instruction, mode of instructional technology, and type of credit you are seeking. The Course Finder seemed to work well for locating individual courses, but it seemed less efficient when asked to locate degree programs.

If you have particular institutions in mind, you can log on to their Web sites to find out about their distance learning courses and degrees. Some of these sites provide distance learning self-assessments and explanations of course delivery systems as well as academic information about courses and programs.

PRINT DIRECTORIES

Print directories are another excellent source of information about distance education courses and degree programs, although one should adhere to this word of caution about using the print directories: There are many directories still in libraries and bookstores that were published just a year or two ago but that are already quite out of date. So many new distance learning courses and degree programs are being offered each year that you must make sure you consult the most recent directories. Otherwise, you may miss the ideal course or program for you.

WHO OFFERS DISTANCE EDUCATION?

As communication technologies have improved and the need for continuous lifelong learning has increased, the nature of postsecondary education has begun to change. Traditional colleges and universities, which used to be the sole purveyors of higher education, now find themselves competing with a range of unconventional providers, including corporate universities, for-profit virtual universities, and unaffiliated distance learning providers. From the student's point of view, the array of institutions that offer distance learning can be confusing. What difference does it make to you whether you take a distance learning course or program from a traditional college, through a consortium of institutions of higher education, from one of the new virtual universities, or from an unaffiliated online provider?

Whether or not the institution matters depends on your purpose. If you just take a few courses for professional development or for your own pleasure and never plan to seek certification or college credit, then your choice of institution is not critical. You can just choose the distance learning provider that seems to have the courses that best suit your informal needs. However, if you plan to earn college credit, professional certification, or a degree, your choice of provider becomes much more important. You must choose an institution whose courses and degrees are widely recognized and accepted in your field. That may mean sticking to the accredited bricks-and-mortar colleges for distance learning programs, or it may mean enrolling in an innovative degree program from a virtual university only a few years old. In this section, we'll describe some of the institutions and partnerships that offer distance learning in order to acquaint you with the variety of providers that exists. In the next section, we will explain some criteria that you can use to evaluate distance education offerings.

TRADITIONAL COLLEGES AND UNIVERSITIES

The most familiar group of distance education providers consists of the traditional colleges, universities, graduate schools, community colleges, technical schools, and vocational schools. In these institutions, distance education arose as individual administrators and faculty members took the initiative to use new technologies to deliver off-campus instruction to students. As the number of courses grew, many institutions developed whole degree programs as the next step.

Among the traditional colleges and universities, public institutions are more likely to offer distance education courses and degree programs than private institutions. In addition, larger institutions are more likely to have distance learning offerings than smaller institutions.

The greatest advantage that most traditional colleges and universities bring to the distance education field is that they are established, well-known institutions with reputable faculty members and lots of experience in education. In other words, they enter the distance learning market with solid educational credentials. If they fall short, it is likely to be in the areas of instructional and information technology. Because a lot of distance education courses are developed ad hoc, the quality of the instructional technology may vary considerably, even from one course to another within the same school. In addition, traditional colleges and universities may fall short in information technology support for faculty members and students. For example, the Gartner Group, an information technology research organization, recommends that organizations have one information technology staff person for every 50 to 75 users. In contrast, colleges and universities report an average of one technical support person for every 150 to 800 users. Recognizing this shortcoming, many colleges and universities have established policies and procedures to set up instructional technology standards and consistency, and they have increased their technical resources and training efforts to support faculty members and students. In addition, because developing quality distance education courses and programs is time-consuming and expensive, colleges and universities have begun to form partnerships to pool their resources. These partnerships, called consortia, have quickly developed into major players in the world of distance higher education.

CONSORTIA

Distance learning consortia are associations or partnerships of higher education institutions that have agreed to cooperate to provide distance learning courses and resources. Most consortia are designed to provide students with a greater selection of both courses and faculty expertise than is available at a single institution. Some consortia also offer centralized student and faculty support services. Just as there are many variations on the basic on-campus program, there are many distance education consortium models too.

It's important to remember that most distance learning consortia are not degree-granting institutions to which the student applies. Though there are exceptions to this, as in the case of Western Governors University and National Technological University (discussed later in the section), students normally apply directly to at least one school in the consortium as a means of accessing the resources of other member institutions.

Almost without exception, accredited universities in consortia have roughly the same application procedures and admissions requirements for distance degree programs as for traditional campus-based programs. In general, minimum grade point averages, standardized test scores of a certain percentile, and letters of recommendation or intent are required for both bachelor's and master's degree programs. The exception is the competency-based program that waives academic credentials and previous schooling and instead uses workplace experience and learned skill-based assessments to place students. So why do you need to know about consortia if you probably will never apply to one? The answer is that by enrolling in a college or university degree program, you may find yourself in a consortium without even realizing it, especially if you attend a state university.

TYPES OF CONSORTIA

Over the last few years, several types of consortia have emerged as the most successful and most popular distance education models. Among them are statewide consortia of public universities and colleges, statewide consortia of public and private institutions, regional consortia, consortia of peer institutions of higher education, and specialized consortia.

Statewide Consortia of Public Colleges and Universities. On the tightly focused side of the spectrum, a consortium may consist of the campuses of a single state university system. Students access the distance learning offerings of the various state colleges through a portal sometimes referred to as a virtual university.

A good example of a public statewide consortium is the University of Texas TeleCampus collaboration, which consists of fifteen UT campuses (www.telecampus.utsystem.edu). In collaborative degree plans offered via the TeleCampus, you may apply to one school, take courses from several partner institutions, use centralized support services, and receive a fully accredited degree from the "home" campus to which you originally applied. The TeleCampus serves as both a portal to distance education offerings in the Texas system and as a centralized point of service.

Many other states operate or develop consortia of their public colleges and universities, including Connecticut, Illinois, Kansas, Massachusetts, Michigan, New Jersey, New York, Ohio, Oklahoma, Oregon, South Dakota, and Tennessee. All have arrangements in place whereby students can take some transferable credits on line from more than one institution and apply them to a degree at their home institution.

Statewide Consortia of Public and Private Colleges and Universities. Broadening the scope a bit is the statewide consortium that includes both public and private institutions of higher education. Students in the state can use a single Web site to select distance education courses offered by member colleges and universities. If you are enrolled in a degree program at one member institution, you have access to distance learning courses given by other member institutions. Although the consortia members typically work together to maximize the transferability of credits from one college or university to another, it is still usually up to you to ensure that credits earned elsewhere can be applied to your home institution's degree.

For example, Kentucky Commonwealth Virtual University (KCVU) encompasses more than fifty institutions in the state of Kentucky, ranging from universities to technical colleges (www.kcvu.org). Each member institution charges its own tuition rates for in-state and out-of-state students. In addition to maintaining a centralized Internet directory of all distance learning courses offered in Kentucky, KCVU offers exceptional student support services. For example, you can fill out a common form to apply on line to any of the fifty member institutions. Once you are admitted to the KCVU system, you have centralized online access to every library book in the system as well as online access to the full text of 5,000 journals. If you wish to check out a book, it will be sent to the nearest public library, where you can pick it up free of charge. If there is no library nearby, the book will be sent by courier to your home or office. Your academic records will be maintained by each institution at which you take a course, but also by KCVU, which will keep your complete records from all institutions.

Regional Consortia. Regional consortia include institutions of higher education from more than one state. Such consortia may involve public institutions, private institutions, or a mix of both. The Southern Regional Education Board (SREB) launched the Southern Regional Electronic Campus (SREC) in 1998 and now offers more than 3,200 courses from 262 colleges and universities in sixteen states (www.electroniccampus.org). SREC attempts to guarantee a standard of quality in the courses it lists by reviewing them to make sure they are well set up and supported by adequate services. It does not judge curriculum (it leaves that to member institutions) nor does it list courses in their first year of instruction.

From the Electronic Campus Web site, you can identify distance learning programs and courses that are available from all member institutions. For more detailed information, you can search the site by college or university, discipline, level, and state, including course descriptions and how the programs and courses are delivered. You can also connect directly to a particular college or university to learn about registration, enrollment, and cost. To improve its student services, the Electronic Campus has formed a partnership with the University System of Georgia to create a new Web site known as Ways In (www.waysin.org). From that site, due to be operational in 2001–02, students will be able to apply for admission, register for classes, get information about and apply for financial aid, make payments, purchase textbooks, and use new online library services.

The SREC system is administratively decentralized. The acceptance of transfer credits and the use of credits for program requirements are determined by the college or university in which the student is enrolled. Likewise, all institutions set their own levels for in-state and out-of-state tuition, maintain individual student records, and determine policy with respect to access to their own student services. Therefore, if you take three classes from three different institutions you might have to be admitted to all three, pay three different tuition rates, and contact all three institutions for your academic records. A unique model of regional distance education collaboration, consisting of members from nineteen states, is Western Governors University (www.wgu.edu). Unlike most other virtual universities that serve as the hub of a consortium, WGU enrolls its own students and grants its own degrees by assessing students' knowledge through competency-based examinations. WGU does not teach its own courses, but it provides its students with access to courses from member institutions.

Other regional consortia include the National Universities Degree Consortium, a collaboration of ten accredited universities from across the United States (www.nudc.org); and the Canadian Virtual University, which includes seven universities across Canada (www.cvu-uvc.ca). Today, students can even choose to participate in a global consortium like CREAD, the Inter-American network of institutions throughout North, Central, and South America.

Consortia of Peer Institutions of Higher Education. Groups of institutions sometimes form consortia because they have a common orientation or complementary strengths from which students might benefit.

For example, the Jesuit Distance Education Network of the Association of Jesuit Colleges and Universities seeks to expand the array of learning options for students on its twenty-four campuses in nineteen states (www.jesuitnet.com). Administrators hope to develop the JesuitNET system so that a student enrolled at any member institution will be able to take fully transferable online courses at any other member institution. Tuition rates will be set by individual colleges and universities. Through its Web site, JesuitNET promotes these schools' online degree and certificate programs as well as individual courses.

Another, more recent private college and university consortium uses a "team teaching" approach to deliver courses to students on multiple campuses. Thirteen institutions in the Associated Colleges of the South have created a "virtual classics department," (www.sunoikisis.org). In this case, students must all log on at the same time in order to tune in to an online audio broadcast of a lecture. During the lecture students may pose questions and make comments in a live chat room. Classes are "team taught" in the sense that professors from several campuses may take responsibility for course material and all log on together with the students.

Specialized Consortia. Some consortia are formed by institutions that focus on a particular field. For example, National Technological University (NTU) is one of the oldest technology-based consortia (www.ntu.edu). A global university, NTU, arranges for its member colleges and universities across the country to deliver advanced technical education and training, usually to employees of corporate clients. Currently, more than 1,200 courses are available through NTU's participating universities, which provides fourteen master's degree programs. An unusual aspect of the NTU consortium is that the consortium itself, rather than the member institutions, is the degree-granting body.

NTU's focus is on technical education and training that is ready to use in the workforce. Its corporate customers typically have purchased the equipment necessary to receive the courses. Though students who are not employed by an NTU corporate client may take courses, they must pay an extra fee to have tapes or CD-ROMs of courses sent to them. NTU has also partnered with the Public Broadcasting System (PBS) to create the Business and Technology Network, a series of more than seventy-five engineering programs per year delivered directly to organizations via satellite.

PROS AND CONS OF CONSORTIA LEARNING MODELS

One obvious advantage of consortia is the pooling of resources. More university partners translates to more choices in curriculum, and often a shared expense in developing instructional design and technology. Consortia can offer a centralized database or course schedule that allows you to find members' courses easily rather than having to search many institutions' materials and Web sites for what you need. You may also have the chance to choose from among a group of respected faculty members from within the consortia, which allows you to find the teachers with expertise most closely suited to your academic and professional interests. This large sampling of faculty members tends to offer a more diverse worldview in the classroom. And, a consortium can often provide essential student services on a scale not fiscally achievable by a single university. For example, a dozen universities can pool resources for a much broader digital library than any single school could supply on its own.

However, from the student's point of view, consortia can have problems, many of which can be attributed to their relative newness. The most critical of these for students are problems with transferring credits. Other drawbacks may include large class sizes and problems in communication.

Problems with Transferring Credits. One problem that sometimes comes up for students trying to earn an entire degree, or part of a degree, on line is that their home institution may require a minimum number of "home" credits, yet it may not offer enough courses via distance learning for a student to meet that minimum. "I am concerned because [my home campus] offers a limited number of online classes," says Andrea Bessel, who is working toward a bachelor's degree in business administration with a concentration in finance. Bessel, who works full time and prefers the convenience of online to on-campus courses, has been taking classes from several institutions in the State University of New York (SUNY) Learning Network (www.sln.suny.edu). "It is great that other SUNY campuses offer more courses," continues Bessel, "but I am concerned about accumulating too many transfer credits—you are only allowed so many."

In the future, this problem is likely to arise less often for several reasons. First, as distance education degree programs become more common and well known, students are likely to search them out and apply directly to the institution that offers them. In contrast, like many other students, Bessel applied to her local state college campus and only later discovered that taking online courses within the statewide system was much more convenient than traveling to class. Second, individual institutions will continue to add to their distance education offerings, broadening the course choices for their "home" students. And third, some state systems and other consortia may eventually decide to liberalize their rules on transfer credit maximums within the consortium as the demand for distance degrees increases.

Indeed, some consortia have already succeeded in solving credit transfer problems, and others are addressing the challenge of reconciling differing credit transfer policies and logistics. *However, to ensure that any courses you take will successfully transfer from one institution to another (and ultimately toward your degree), you should secure an academic adviser at the start of your program and investigate the transferrability of credits before you register for courses at other institutions within the consortium.* Serving as your own adviser brings the risk that some courses may ultimately not transfer toward your degree.

Large Class Size. Because so many students have access to courses in a consortium, online classes may reach an unmanageable size if limits are not placed on the student-to-teacher ratio. Many schools now adopt a ceiling on the number of students allowed in an online class, with teaching assistants or subsections of the course added for each additional set of students. This is vital to the processing of information and interaction required in the successful online course. Faculty members often find that a class of 25 students is quite manageable, but more may become problematic.

Miscommunication. Communication may be difficult in a consortium. The larger the consortium, the more likely that many universities or university systems are involved, and therefore you may need to communicate with several institutions that have differing policies and procedures. Additional communication snags can arise when you try to move your student records from one campus to the next. Some consortia have spent considerable time, effort, and money to make this tedious and laborious process appear seamless to you as a student. For those that have not, you should be prepared to take a proactive stance in helping to see that your records are successfully moved from one department, college, or university to another.

COMPARING THE SINGLE UNIVERSITY TO THE CONSORTIUM

A student who is looking for a learning community with school pride and a great deal of local loyalty may find the multicampus environment of a consortium less desirable than the collegiality of the single university environment. In today's workplace and economy, however, many students opt for the flexibility and increased curriculum choices of a consortium over an individual school. Many consortia have succeeded in creating a sense of community for learners, and many more are attempting to do so. The high level of dialogue in the online environment can often build friendships, connections, and communities not achieved in a traditional environment. A single university can offer you the chance to immerse yourself in one department (of your major, for example), but a consortium can offer a wider variety of choices in mentors and philosophies. As a student, you should think about which you'd prefer.

VIRTUAL UNIVERSITIES

In recent years, the development of communication technology has led to a new type of institution called a virtual university. It's a school without a campus that delivers instruction and degree programs exclusively via technology and usually for a profit. The University of Phoenix Online, Walden University, the United States Open University, and Jones International University are all examples of virtual universities. Some of these institutions have years of experience in distance learning and have evolved as the technologies have changed. For example, Walden University is more than thirty years old, and the University of Phoenix Online was established in 1989 as an offshoot of the University of Phoenix, which was founded in 1976. Others, like the United States Open University, are newly established with a much shorter track record. What most of these institutions have in common is a focus on education for adults. Their course offerings, degree programs, and student services are all geared toward the busy working adult who needs the flexibility of distance education. For example, courses at the University of Phoenix Online are delivered via the Internet. Students take one 5-week course at a time, which allows them to focus their effort intensively on one subject. Student services can be accessed via the university Web site. "We are customer-service oriented," says Russell Paden, regional executive director of academic affairs at the University of Phoenix Online. "We make things easy and convenient for the student." Virtual universities have a mixed reputation in the world of higher education. Although their degrees are accepted by many employers, they are often looked down upon by traditional academics. A few are regionally accredited, some are too new to be accredited, and some are modern versions of the old diploma mills (see "Selecting a Good Distance Learning Program" for more on accreditation).

From a student's point of view, then, the biggest disadvantage of a virtual university may be its less-than-stellar educational reputation, whether deserved or not. A great advantage of the best of these institutions, however, is that they tend to be sophisticated in terms of instructional technology and design and technical support. To the student, this can mean ease, convenience, and flexibility.

THE NEW ONLINE PROVIDERS

The growth of the distance learning market in higher education, continuing education, and training has attracted investors and educators who are eager to provide courses to adults, primarily via the Internet. There are many of these startup ventures, and they take many forms. A few examples to illustrate:

- UNext.com is working with faculty members from prestigious schools like Columbia and Stanford to develop online business courses for the corporate market. At present, it is piloting courses with groups of employees from large corporations. Eventually it hopes to offer a complete M.B.A. program as well as other degrees through its subsidiary, Cardean University.
- The Global Education Network (GEN) plans to offer distance education courses from some of the top colleges in the United States, including Brown, Wellesley, and Williams.
- Harcourt Higher Education, an online college, a division of Thomson Learning.
- KaplanCollege.com is planning to offer graduate courses for teachers through the John F. Kennedy University.

All of these ventures are so new that it's impossible to guess which will still exist in five years' time. In the next few years, the new online providers will begin to sort themselves out as some models succeed and some fail. If you are taking courses through your employer or for personal reasons, you may find that one of these companies has courses that meet your needs. If, however, you are looking for a degree program, you are better off sticking with well-established institutions of higher education, at least at present.

SELECTING A GOOD DISTANCE LEARNING PROGRAM

As a prospective distance learning student, you should begin to evaluate programs in which you are interested as much as you would any campus-based, traditional program. The first question, of course, is: Does the curriculum meet your educational and professional goals? If it doesn't, there's not much point in looking into that program any further, however flexible and convenient it seems. If the program does seem to meet your educational needs, then the real work of evaluating it must begin.

Distance education students need to be especially concerned about the quality of the programs they are considering for two main reasons. First, there are a lot of diploma mills out there. As we've seen, there has been a proliferation of distance learning degree programs spurred by the Internet. Many are legitimate, but some are not. As one distance bachelor's degree student put it, "Admission to some online programs consists of nothing more than your name, date of birth, and a check." In fact, to demonstrate how easy it is to set up an online "university" that looks authentic, Emir Mohammed created a Web site for Oxford Open University, a fictitious virtual university, complete with a list of imaginary faculty members with degrees from bogus institutions. So if you run across a school that promises you a degree for little time, effort, or money, be cautious. If it sounds too good to be true, it probably is.

The second reason distance learning students must be especially careful about quality is that in many quarters, distance degrees are still considered the poor relations of degrees earned on campus. "One area of confusion for working adult students is the reaction to distance learning from traditional academia," says Russell Paden, regional executive director of academic affairs for the University of Phoenix Online. "Although attitudes are changing, some in the traditional academic world still think their way is the only way." Robert V. Steiner, who directs the distance learning project at Teachers College, Columbia University, agrees. "For better or worse, justly or not," he says, "there continues to be a perception that distance education degree programs are inferior to traditional programs." Fritz J. Messere, associate professor of broadcasting at the State University of New York at Oswego, thinks that in five or six years, that attitude will change. "When we see what the people with distance degrees actually accomplish in the future, our reluctance to acknowledge that these are real degrees and meaningful educational experiences will disappear."

However, in the meantime you need to evaluate each distance education program that looks promising to ensure that its certificate or degree will be of value to you in the future. What can you do to ensure that a distance credential will be recognized in the academic, professional, and/or business communities? What can you do to assess whether or not the program and the university are of high quality? Basically, you must do a lot of research. You must gather information from the program, university, accrediting agencies, professional associations, faculty, current and former students, and colleagues. Only then can you make an informed decision about whether a program is good as well as right for you.

To guide you in this task, this section describes some of the criteria you should keep in mind as you evaluate each distance education program. *Pay particular attention to the sections on reputation and accreditation.* More than any other factors, a school and program's reputation and accreditation status can serve as benchmarks of quality that will affect the value of your degree.

REPUTATION

"Look for a brand name—a recognized university," suggests Fritz J. Messere of SUNY Oswego. For many students, the reputation of the school is the paramount factor in selecting a program. Sonja Cole, a middle-school media specialist who is enrolled in a continuing professional education program at Rutgers University in New Jersey, explains, "I know that Rutgers has an excellent reputation for academic rigor, so I assumed that their online courses would be just as challenging and stimulating." She continues, "The most important factor to me was the reputation of the school, because distance learning programs are not always taken seriously by administrators and business people . . . . If you can say you took distance courses at a very reputable school, they will be more likely to give you credit." Not only should you consider the reputation of a university in general, you should consider the reputation of a distance degree from a university *in your field*. For example, if you plan to earn a bachelor's degree at a distance to prepare for graduate work, find out whether or not graduate programs in your field will accept an undergraduate distance degree, even from a reputable institution.

"If you are in doubt about the validity of a distance degree in your chosen field, ask around," advises Patti Wolf, assistant professor of computer science at University of Maryland University College. When Wolf was looking for a doctoral program for herself, almost all of her colleagues advised her that a distance degree would not be as well accepted in her chosen career as a traditional degree. Another doctoral student, who is earning an Ed.D. from a relatively new virtual university, regrets that "the one thing I didn't do [was] speak to administrators in local universities to review the reputation of the school I finally chose. Even though the program is still exactly what I wanted and the convenience, schedule, and costs meet my needs, the public perception of this program is not wonderful." Carla Gentry, who is earning a distance master's degree in nursing (nurse practitioner) at Gonzaga University in Washington, puts the importance of reputation succinctly: "You wouldn't want to spend all that time and money and then find out that the degree isn't worth anything."

ACCREDITATION

The accreditation status of a college, university, or program can give you an indication of its general quality and reputation. But just what does accreditation mean, and how does it affect distance learners?

WHAT IS ACCREDITATION?

In the United States, authority over postsecondary educational institutions is decentralized. The states, not the federal government, have the authority to regulate educational institutions within their borders, and as a consequence, standards and quality vary considerably for "state-approved" schools. You will find many state-approved schools that are not accredited, and many that are.

In order to ensure a basic level of quality, the practice of accrediting institutions arose. Private, nongovernmental educational agencies with a regional or national scope have adopted standards to evaluate whether or not colleges and universities provide educational programs at basic levels of quality. Institutions that seek accreditation conduct an in-depth self-study to measure their performance against the standards. The accrediting agency then conducts an on-site evaluation and either awards accreditation or preaccreditation status—or denies accreditation. Periodically the agency reevaluates each institution to make sure its continued accreditation is warranted. So accreditation is not a one-shot deal—an institution must maintain high standards or it runs the risk of jeopardizing its accreditation status as a result of one of the periodic evaluations.

Seeking accreditation is entirely voluntary on the part of the institution of higher education. The initial accreditation process takes a long time—as much as five or ten years—and it costs money. You can see that a very new school will not have been in operation long enough to be accredited.

INSTITUTIONAL AND SPECIALIZED ACCREDITATION

There are two basic types of accreditation: institutional accreditation and specialized accreditation. Institutional accreditation is awarded to an institution by one of six regional accrediting agencies and many national accrediting agencies, such as the Distance Education and Training Council. The regional accrediting agencies play the largest role in institutional accreditation (see the Appendix for a list of the regional accrediting agencies). If a college or university is regionally accredited, that means that the institution as a whole has met the accrediting agency's standards. Within the institution, particular programs and departments contribute to the institution's objectives at varying levels of quality. There are several benefits of enrolling in a program at a regionally accredited college or university:

- You are assured of a basic level of quality education and services.
- Any credits you earn are more likely to be transferable to other regionally accredited institutions, although we've seen that each institution makes its own decisions on transfer credits on a case-by-case basis.
- Any certificate or degree you earn is more likely to be recognized by other colleges and universities and by employers as a legitimate credential.
- You may qualify for federal loans and grants because regionally accredited institutions are eligible to participate in Title IV financial aid programs (see "Paying for Your Education" for more on financial aid).

In contrast to institutional accreditation, specialized accreditation usually applies to a single department, program, or school that is part of a larger institution of higher education. The accredited unit may be as big as a college within a university or as small as a curriculum within a field of study. Most specialized accrediting agencies review units within institutions that are regionally accredited, although some also accredit freestanding institutions. There are specialized accrediting agencies in almost fifty fields, including allied health, art and design, Bible college education, business, engineering, law, marriage and family therapy, nursing, psychology, and theology. Specialized accreditation may or may not be a consideration for you when you evaluate distance education programs. That's because the role of specialized accreditation varies considerably depending on the field of study. In some professional fields, you must have a degree or certificate from a program with specialized accreditation in order to take qualifying exams or practice the profession. In other fields, specialized accreditation has little or no effect on your ability to work. Thus, it's especially important that you find out what role accreditation plays in your field since it may affect your professional future as well as the quality of your education.

CHECKING ON A SCHOOL AND ITS ACCREDITORS

Since accreditation is awarded by private organizations, any group can hang out a shingle and proclaim itself an accrediting agency. Some diploma mills, for example, have been known to create their own accrediting agency and then proclaim themselves "accredited." So how can you tell (1) if the school or college in which you are interested is regionally accredited, (2) if the program has the specialized accreditation you need, and (3) if the agencies that have accredited the school and program are legitimate? Of course, you can simply ask the school or program, but since accreditation is so important, it's probably a lot wiser to check elsewhere.

First, check with the regional accrediting agency that covers the state in which the school is located. Then check with any specialized accrediting agency that may assess the particular program in which you are interested.

To find out if an accrediting agency is legitimate and nationally recognized, you can consult the Council for Higher Education Accreditation (CHEA), a private agency that accredits the accreditors (www.chea.org). Or you can check with the U.S. Department of Education. Their Web site has a complete list of institutional and specialized accrediting agencies recognized by the federal government (www.ed.gov/offices/OPE/accreditation/natlagencies.html). This Web site will also tell you whether or not accreditation by a particular agency makes the school eligible to participate in federal financial aid programs. A list of regional and specialized accrediting agencies, with contact information, is also provided in the Appendix.

CHECKING ON CANADIAN INSTITUTIONS OF HIGHER EDUCATION

In Canada, as in the United States, there is no centralized governmental accrediting agency. Instead, the provincial governments evaluate the quality of university programs in each province, with a few nationwide agencies evaluating professional programs. To check on a Canadian university, you can contact the appropriate provincial department of education. To get general information about accreditation in Canada, visit the Web site of the Council of Ministers of Education at www.cmec.ca. Their Web site also has contact information and links to the provincial departments of education.

CHECKING ON AN UNACCREDITED INSTITUTION

As we've seen, seeking accreditation is a voluntary process, and some legitimate schools choose not to undertake it. In addition, the newer virtual universities may not have been around long enough to be accredited. So what can you do to make sure a school is legitimate if it is not accredited?

First, you can call the state agency with jurisdiction over higher education in the state in which the school is located. The agency can at least tell you whether or not the school is operating with a legitimate charter, and it may be able to tell you if any complaints have been lodged or legal action taken against it. Second, you can call the school and ask why it is not accredited and whether the school has plans to seek accreditation. If the school tells you it has applied for accreditation, double-check its status with the agency it names. Third, you can consult with people in your field about the school's reputation and the value of its degree. Remember, in some fields, a degree from an unaccredited school or program will bar you from professional licensure and practice. So keep in mind that enrolling in an unaccredited school or program can be risky. If you can avoid it, do so.

ACCREDITATION ISSUES RELATING TO DISTANCE EDUCATION

In the United States during the 1990s, controversy arose over the accreditation of online programs within traditional universities and the accreditation of completely virtual universities. On the one hand, many felt that online degree programs should be evaluated using the same criteria as other degree programs within institutions of higher education. Others thought that new standards were needed to properly evaluate distance education.

Although this issue has not yet been settled, the six regional accrediting agencies have proposed uniform guidelines for evaluating distance education. The impetus for this move is the fact that many distance education programs cross regional borders; the agencies want to ensure that similar standards are adopted across the country. Among the proposed criteria specific to accrediting distance education are faculty control of course content, technical and program support for both faculty members and students, and evaluation and assessment methods for measuring student learning. However, until these or other guidelines are accepted, distance education programs will continue to be evaluated using the same criteria as on-campus programs.

PROGRAM QUALITY

The reputation of a college or university and its accreditation status can give you a broad idea of its standing in the academic and professional world. If you are pursuing a graduate degree or know your field of interest as an undergraduate, it's important to separate the reputation of the program or department in which you are interested from the reputation of the university to which it belongs. Granted, in many cases, both the program and the university will have similar reputations. But in some cases, you may find a below average program at an excellent university or an above average program at a university with a lesser reputation.

Keep in mind that you should be looking for a high-quality curriculum and good faculty; the fact that the program is taught at a distance should be secondary. "I chose this program because it would have been one of my top three choices if I had decided to pursue a full-time [on-campus] master's program," explains Lara Hollenczer, who is earning a distance master's degree in communications management at Syracuse University. Hollenczer suggests talking to professors and current students to get a better idea of a program in which you are interested.

ACADEMIC QUALITY

One way to assess the quality of a program, as we have seen, is to find out whether or not it is accredited by a specialized agency—if that applies in your field. But there are other ways to assess a program's academic quality. First, look at the curriculum. Does it cover what you need to learn? Is the syllabus up to date? For one master's degree student in nursing (family nurse practitioner studies), the quality of the curriculum was the factor that led her to choose Gonzaga University. "I definitely wanted to know that when I graduated I would have a good education and know what I was doing," she explains.

Next, check some of the program's student data. For example, what percentage of students who enroll actually complete the degree? What percentage of students is employed in a field relating to their studies? What are some of the program's graduates doing today? A program with a high completion rate and successful graduates is preferable to one with a high dropout rate.

FACULTY

Second, check out the faculty members. What are their credentials? What are their areas of expertise? Are they well regarded in their field? If the program is professional in nature, look for faculty members with a blend of academic background and professional experience. If the program is academic, you should find out whether tenure-track professors with Ph.D.'s teach both the on-campus and distance courses or if distance courses are relegated to part-time adjunct faculty members and/or assistants. Finally, evaluate whether or not the faculty is experienced both with the course content and with the instructional medium. If a program looks interesting to you, get in touch with a couple of faculty members to discuss it. You can tell a lot about a program by whether or not the faculty members are willing to take some time to talk to prospective students.

EXPERIENCE WITH ADULT LEARNERS

A third area of concern is the program's experience with adult learners. If you're an adult learner and choose to enroll in a college oriented to young undergraduates, you may find yourself struggling to cope. "My concern would be that in some programs the adult learner is an afterthought," says Claudine SchWeber, assistant vice president for distance education and lifelong learning at University of Maryland University College. "Adults are more critical consumers, and that won't fly these days." Working adult students have different needs than full-time on-campus students, and assessing the degree to which a program takes those needs into account can help you decide whether or not a program is a good match for you.

For Robin Barnes, who is pursuing a distance master's degree in nursing (family nurse practitioner studies) at Gonzaga University, the flexibility of the faculty in dealing with adult students was extremely important. "We were adult learners who had lives and jobs outside of school. If we needed more time for a paper due to work schedules or a family crisis, the instructors were very understanding." Carla Gentry, in the same program, agrees. "The most important factor to me is the flexibility of the program and the staff's willingness to work with my schedule."

INSTRUCTIONAL DESIGN AND TECHNOLOGY

There are several areas that fall under the broad category of instructional design and technology that you should assess for each program you consider.

IS THE INSTRUCTIONAL TECHNOLOGY A GOOD MATCH FOR THE CONTENT?

Your first concern in the area of instructional design and technology should be whether or not the delivery system and the content are a good match. "How can you evaluate whether the technology and content mesh?" asks Robert V. Steiner of Teacher's College, Columbia University. "Online courses are more suitable for knowledge-intensive fields like business and engineering," he points out. "Subjects involving skills development and human interaction are more difficult to convey on line." So, for example, in many behavioral sciences courses that involve clinical components, you need to be able to watch human interaction. In many science courses, you need to be able to do lab work. Such courses are more suited to two-way interactive video or on-campus formats than to the online format.

IS THE INSTRUCTIONAL TECHNOLOGY A GOOD MATCH FOR YOU?

Your second consideration is whether or not the instructional technology is a good match for your skills, personality, and learning style. In "Is Distance Learning Right for You?", we covered the pros and cons of the various technologies and described the skills and temperaments best suited to each.

If you are uncertain about your ability to adapt to a program's instructional technology, there are several things you can do. "If possible, take a tour of the technology being used before you enroll," advises Patti Wolf of University of Maryland University College. Many institutional Web sites offer short demos, previews, or tutorials so you can get an idea of what the instructional technology will be like. For example, if you are interested in a distance program at Penn State, you can take a sample course on its World Campus Web site. If the programs in which you are interested do not offer such amenities, ask previous students how the instructional technology worked and what level of expertise is necessary. If technology is an area of particular concern for you, you might even consider a trial run. "I would recommend taking one course before deciding to apply to a school, to see if the style works for the individual," suggests Nicole DeRaleau, an environmental engineering master's degree candidate at Worcester Polytechnic Institute. "If it doesn't work, then perhaps the credits can be transferred and there is no major loss."

HOW RELIABLE IS THE TECHNOLOGY?

On a related note, because distance students depend on technology, it's important that it be reliable. Not only will you depend on your own computer, VCR, or television, but you will depend on the institution's technology, too. Ask current students what their experiences have been. Does the server often go down? Are there frequent problems with camera equipment or satellite transmissions?

If the program is newly formatted for distance education, be prepared for some technological bugs to be worked out on your watch. If the prospect of participating in a maiden voyage is too anxiety-provoking, look for programs that have been running for at least a year.

Last, find out what technical support is offered to students. The best setup is free technical support accessed via an 800-number 24 hours a day, seven days a week.

HOW DO THE FACULTY AND STUDENTS INTERACT?

You should also investigate how the communication and social issues involved in distance learning are dealt with in the programs in which you are interested. (For a review of these issues, see "Is Distance Learning Right for You?") For example, how do students and faculty members communicate? Will you be expected to log on to an online course at specific times or at your convenience? Will you be expected to participate in online discussions a certain number of times during the course? For example, at the University of Phoenix Online, students are expected to log on and participate five days out of seven. At other schools, participation requirements may be program-wide or set by individual instructors.

Another question to ask is: What is done to overcome the distance learner's social isolation? Some programs do little; others rely on group work to forge a community of learning; and still others use a cohort format, in which a group of students enrolls in a program at the same time and proceeds through it together at the same pace.

Pay particular attention to the faculty-to-student ratio in online courses. If there are more than 25 to 30 students per instructor, you're not likely to get much individual attention.

ADVISING AND OTHER SERVICES

Academic advising is one of the most important student services for distance learners, especially if you are seeking to transfer credits or earn credits through examinations or from life experience to apply to a degree. Check what advising services are offered to distance learners, and see how easy they are to access. "I tested academic advising services," reports a distance learning undergraduate at University of Maryland University College. "That was important to me because I've been out of college for such a long time and I needed some help in selecting courses to complete requirements." Advising is also of particular interest to students in a consortium. If you are interested in a program that is part of a consortium, find out if the consortium offers advising or mentoring to help you navigate among institutions and to guide your overall progress.

Other support services that are important to distance education students are libraries, bookstores, administrative support, record keeping, and technical support (discussed above). Many institutions and consortia offer online and telephone access to these services for distance students. In particular, access to an online library is extremely important, especially if you don't live near a good college or university library. Find out what type of access is offered, what the library's resources are, how materials are delivered, and if training on how to use an online library is offered.

If the program in which you are interested is part of a consortium, be sure you understand how each of these student services is handled. In some cases you will have access only to your home institution's services; in other cases you will have access to the services of all member institutions.

Another thing to watch out for is the extent to which the institution as a whole has kept up with an innovative degree program. For example, at many universities, distance learning courses and programs originate in a couple of departments eager to pursue new ways of educating. However, the university's centralized academic and administrative services may lag behind, leaving distance students to struggle with a system not designed for their needs.

As you investigate a program and its services, keep in mind that the way you are treated as a prospective student can tell you something about what you will encounter once enrolled. "Look at the responsiveness of the institution," advises Robert V. Steiner of Teacher's College, Columbia University, "and ask yourself, 'How client-centered is that program?'"

RESIDENCY REQUIREMENT

Some programs, especially doctoral programs, have a residency requirement for distance learning students. The requirement may be several campus visits during the course of a semester, or a brief on-site meeting at the start of a semester. Some residency periods may last up to a week or two. In addition, you may have to travel to campus to take exams, or you may be able to take them locally with a proctor. Be sure you understand what the on-site requirements of a program are, and whether or not you can fulfill them.

TIME FRAMES

Check to see how much time you have to complete a certificate or degree program, and decide whether or not the time frame meets your needs. Some programs have a generous upper limit on the number of years you may take to complete a degree, which allows you to proceed at your own pace. Other programs may be structured on an accelerated or cohort model, with a timetable and lots of interim deadlines. If that's the case, make sure your own schedule can accommodate this. For example, if a program goes year-round and you are usually at a cabin in the woods without Internet access every summer, the program is not a good match for your lifestyle. In addition, if you are considering an accelerated or cohort degree program, make sure you have the support of your family, who may not get much attention from you during this period.

COST

The cost of a distance education degree or certificate program is often the same for on-campus and distance students. However, there are some things you should look out for:

- If you enroll in a consortium, member institutions may charge tuition at different rates.
- If you enroll in a public university, you will probably be charged out-of-state tuition if you are not a state resident.
- Some institutions charge an extra technology fee to cover the costs associated with distance education.
- If there is a residency period, you should plan on spending money for travel, accommodations, and meals.
- If you enroll in an online program, you need to budget for hardware, software, and Internet access as well as books.
- If you are interested in receiving federal financial aid, you must be enrolled in an institution accredited by one of the regional accrediting agencies or certain of the specialized agencies approved by the U.S. Department of Education (check their Web site at www.ed.gov/offices/OPE/accreditation/natlagencies.html).

YOUR PERSONAL CHECKLIST

This section discusses many factors that you can consider when evaluating a distance education program. Here is a checklist to sum up the criteria you should keep in mind:

- ✓ The institution's reputation
- ✓ Institutional (regional) accreditation
- ✓ Specialized accreditation, if applicable
- ✓ The program's quality: curriculum, faculty, and responsiveness to adult learners
- ✓ A good match between instructional technology and content
- ✓ A good match between instructional technology and your skills, personality, and learning style
- ✓ Interaction among students and faculty members
- ✓ Reliability of technology and good technical support
- ✓ Academic advising services
- ✓ Other support services: library, bookstore, administrative support, and record keeping
- ✓ Residency requirements, if any
- ✓ Time frame for completing certificate or degree
- ✓ Cost

Although we have described many factors, in the end there may be only three or four aspects of a program that really concern you. You may be more interested in a program's reputation than in any other factor. Or accreditation may be the most important issue for you. Perhaps you are concerned about finding a good match between your personality and learning style and the instructional design of a program. That is why the self-assessment you did while reading "Is Distance Learning Right for You?" is so crucial, since you can now focus on what's important to you when you evaluate distance programs.

So remember, keep your own educational, professional, and personal needs in the forefront during the selection process. Choosing a good program not only means choosing a high-quality program; it also means choosing a program that's a good match for you.

TAKING STANDARDIZED ADMISSIONS TESTS

For some people, the prospect of taking one of the standardized admissions tests is enough to make them put aside the idea of earning a degree indefinitely. You may be anxious about taking the SAT, Graduate Record Examinations (GRE), or one of the professional exams, but if you have chosen to apply to a program that requires an admissions test, there is no way of avoiding the experience. Many undergraduate programs require the SAT or American College Testing (ACT) Assessment. Graduate programs often require the GRE or a professional examination, and some require a subject area test and writing assessment as well. Finally, if you are not a native speaker of English, you may need to pass a test of English language proficiency. So unless you've chosen to apply to programs that do not require an examination, you are going to have to take at least one exam—and do well on it.

Note that community colleges and many programs designed specifically for adult learners, including some distance learning programs, do not require a standardized admissions test as part of the application process. Therefore, the first thing you should do is to determine which exam(s), if any, you are expected to take. This information should appear in the packet that accompanies the program's application form. If you do not yet have this material, you should simply call the admissions office or program and ask or check the program's Web site. Once you know which exam you must take, contact the testing service that gives the exam and request registration materials or register on line. Information on contacting the testing services appears in the Appendix.

Before we go into detail about the tests, it might be helpful to discuss how an admissions committee might use your score. The role played by the SAT or ACT Assessment on the undergraduate level is similar to the GRE or GMAT on the graduate level. These tests provide a benchmark. Essentially, your test score is one of the few objective bits of information in your application that can be used to gauge where you fall in the range of applicants. A few programs, especially the top professional programs that receive many more applicants than they can admit, may use the score as a means of reducing the applicant pool. If your score is below their cutoff, they will not even look at the rest of your application. But most programs are much more flexible in the way they evaluate scores. If your score is low, you may still be considered for admission, especially if your grade point average is high, your work experience is relevant, or your application is otherwise strong. Others will index your exam score and your grade point average to arrive at a more balanced number. Some programs offer a conditional admission when a standardized exam score is low. In order to earn an unconditional admission, you may have to retake the exam to boost your score or achieve a certain GPA in the first courses you take.

Basically, you should regard taking a standardized admissions test as an opportunity to improve your application. And that means you must take the test with plenty of time left to meet application deadlines (see "Taking Standardized Admissions Tests" and "Applying for Admission to Degree Programs" for more information on applying). That way, if you take the test early and are disappointed with the results, you will have time to retake it. Note that test registration deadlines precede test dates by about six weeks and that you must also allow a few weeks after the testing date for score reporting.

You must also prepare. Thorough preparation, including taking practice tests, can add points to your score by refreshing your memory and giving you experience with test taking. Preparation is especially important if you have been out of school for a long time. As one student who had been out of school for twenty years put it, "Logarithms?! Geometry rules?!" If this sounds like you, you may need to do a quick recap of high school mathematics to do well on the mathematics portion of the SAT, ACT Assessment, GRE, or GMAT. And you may have forgotten what test taking is like, but if you study and practice it will help you overcome any weaknesses you may have. We'll discuss ways to prepare for the exams later in this section after we describe the various tests.

UNDERGRADUATE ADMISSIONS TESTS

Bachelor's degree programs that require a standardized admissions test will usually accept either the SAT or the ACT Assessment. Some programs will also require SAT Subject Tests in specific subjects.

THE SAT: A TEST OF REASONING

The SAT, which is administered by the Educational Testing Service (ETS) for the College Board, tests your critical reading, writing, and math reasoning skills. These are analytical skills developed over time both in school and at work; the test does not assess your knowledge of specific content areas.

The SAT is a 3-hour-and-45-minute paper test divided into nine sections: three critical reading sections, three math sections, and three writing sections. The 25-minute essay will always be the first section of the test.

Critical Reading Section. The critical reading sections of the SAT test your ability to understand and analyze what you read, see relationships between the parts of a sentence, and understand word meaning in context. In other words, it tests your language skills. The critical reading sections last 25 minutes, and there are three types of questions:

- Reading comprehension questions measure your ability to read, understand, and think analytically about a single reading passage or a pair of passages. Reading passages range from 500 to 800 words.
- Paragraph length critical reading questions are based on paragraphs of about 100 words, followed by questions that are similar to those accompanying the longer reading passages.
- Sentence completion questions assess your ability to understand the meaning of words and to recognize correct grammatical patterns.

Math Sections. The math sections of the SAT assess your ability to solve arithmetic, algebra I, algebra II, and geometry problems. The test does not include trigonometry or calculus. Each section lasts 20 or 25 minutes and has three main types of questions:

- 44 multiple-choice questions with five choices test your ability to solve math problems.
- 10 questions require a student-generated answer.

Writing Sections. The writing sections include multiple-choice questions and a 25-minute essay. The multiple-choice questions assess your ability to improve sentences and paragraphs and to identify grammatical errors. The short essay assesses your ability to organize and express your ideas clearly. The multiple-choice sections last 35 minutes and has three main types of questions:

- Improving sentences
- Improving paragraphs
- Identifying errors

Note that you are permitted to bring, in the College Board's words, "almost any four-function, scientific, or graphing calculator" to use on the math sections. According to the College Board, students who use a calculator do slightly better because they do not make computational errors.

Tips for Taking the SAT I. It pays to familiarize yourself with the test directions and typical question format beforehand so you don't waste precious testing time trying to figure out what to do (see the section below on test preparation). Because the sections appear in a paper booklet, you can do the questions in a section in any order. For that reason, it makes sense to answer the easy questions first and place a check mark beside the hard questions. Later, if you have time, you can return to the hard questions.

The way the SAT I is scored should also influence your approach. First, you are awarded one point for each correct answer. But you lose a fraction of a point for each incorrect answer, except on the student-response questions in the math section. On those questions, you do not lose points for an incorrect answer. If you omit a question, you are not penalized. This means that guessing is only worth it if you can eliminate one or two choices as clearly wrong, improving your odds of picking the correct answer. So if a question and its choices are truly mysterious to you, skip it. The test booklet can be used for computations and notes. Don't make any extra marks on the answer sheet, because it's read by a machine that cannot tell the difference between an answer and a doodle.

THE SAT SUBJECT TESTS

The SAT Subject Tests are 1-hour subject area tests that assess your knowledge of a particular content area taught in high school. The questions are primarily multiple-choice. The subject areas include literature in English, U.S. history, world history, two mathematics tests, biology, chemistry, and physics. There are reading-only language tests in French, German, modern Hebrew, Italian, Latin, and Spanish. Finally, there are reading and listening language tests in Chinese, French, German, Japanese, Korean, Spanish, and English Language Proficiency.

ACT ASSESSMENT

The ACT Assessment, commonly known as the ACT, is an admissions exam consisting of four tests: English, reading, mathematics, and science reasoning. The examination takes about 3½ to 4 hours, and it includes 215 multiple-choice questions with either four or five answer choices, as well as an optional 30-minute essay. Since you are not penalized for an incorrect answer on the ACT, you should answer all the questions even if you have to guess.

Unlike the SAT, the ACT is not an aptitude test. Instead, it is based on the high school English, math, and science curriculum. The questions are directly related to what you learned in high school.

GRADUATE ADMISSIONS TESTS

If you apply to graduate school, you may need to take one of the graduate admissions tests. There are three types of Graduate Record Examinations: the General Test, which is usually referred to as the GRE; the Subject Tests; and the Writing Assessment. Each of these tests has a different purpose, and you may need to take more than one of them. If so, try not to schedule two tests on the same day. The experience may be more arduous than you anticipate. Another general admissions test that is sometimes required instead of the GRE is the Miller Analogies Test. In addition, there are specialized exams required for admission to various professional programs.

THE GENERAL TEST (GRE)

According to ETS, the GRE "measures verbal, quantitative, and analytical reasoning skills that have been developed over a long period of time and are not necessarily related to any field of study." Like the SAT, the GRE is a test designed to assess whether or not you have the aptitude for higher-level study. Even though the GRE may not have subject area relevance, it can indicate that you are capable of doing the difficult reading, synthesizing, and writing demanded of most graduate students.

The test, which is given only on computer, is divided into three separately timed parts, and all the questions are multiple choice: (1) a 30-minute verbal section with 30 questions, (2) a 45-minute quantitative section with 28 questions, and (3) a 60-minute analytical section with 35 questions. The parts may be presented in any order. In addition, an unidentified verbal, quantitative, or analytical section that doesn't count in your score may be included. You won't have any way to tell which of the duplicated sections is the "real" one, so you should complete both carefully. Finally, another section, on which ETS is still doing research, may also appear. This section will be identified as such and will not count toward your score. ETS tells test takers to plan to spend about 4½ hours at the testing site.

Verbal Section. The thirty questions in the verbal section of the GRE test your ability to recognize relationships between words and concepts, analyze sentences, and analyze and evaluate written material. In other words, they test your vocabulary and your reading and thinking skills. There are four main types of questions in this section:

- In sentence completion questions, sentences are presented with missing word(s). You are asked to select the words that best complete the sentences. Answering correctly involves figuring out the meanings of the missing words from their context in the sentence.
- Analogy questions present a pair of words or phrases that are related to one another. Your task is to figure out the relationship

between the two words or phrases. Then you must select the pair of words or phrases whose relationship is most similar to that of the given pair.

- Reading comprehension questions test your ability to understand a reading passage and synthesize information on the basis of what you've read.

The words and reading material on which you are tested in this section come from a wide range of subjects, from daily life to the sciences and humanities.

Quantitative Section. This section of the GRE tests your basic mathematical skills and your understanding of elementary mathematical concepts. You will be tested on your ability to reason quantitatively and solve quantitative problems. There are three main types of questions in this section:

- Quantitative comparison questions require that you determine which of two quantities is the larger, if possible. If such a determination is not possible, then you must so indicate.
- Data analysis questions provide you with a graph or a table on which to base your solution to a problem.
- Problem-solving questions test a variety of mathematical concepts. They may be word problems or symbolic problems.

The quantitative questions test your knowledge of arithmetic and high school algebra, geometry, and data analysis. They do not cover trigonometry or calculus.

Analytical Section. According to ETS, the analytical section of the GRE "tests your ability to understand structured sets of relationships, deduce new information from sets of relationships, analyze and evaluate arguments, identify central issues and hypotheses, draw sound inferences, and identify plausible causal relationships." In other words, can you reason analytically and logically? There are two main types of questions in this section:

- Analytical reasoning questions appear in groups, and they are all based on the same set of conditions or rules. A situation is described and you are told how many people or things you will be manipulating. Then you are asked to manipulate the items according to the conditions. For example, you may be given information about a group of people and then asked to rank them in order of age.
- Logical reasoning questions consist of arguments that you must analyze and evaluate. Each argument has assumptions, facts, and conclusions, and you must answer questions that test your ability to assess these.

The subject matter in the analytical section is drawn from all fields of study as well as everyday life.

Tips for Taking the GRE. The GRE is now given only in computer format, and the test is somewhat different from the old paper-and-pencil test. At the start of each section, you are given questions of moderate difficulty. The computer uses your responses to each question and its knowledge of the test's structure to decide which question to give you next. If your responses continue to be correct, how does the computer reward you? It gives you a harder question. On the other hand, if you answer incorrectly, the next question will typically be easier. In short, the computer uses a cumulative assessment of your performance along with information about the test's design to decide which question you get next.

One result of this format is that you cannot skip a question. The computer needs your answer to a question before it can give you the next one. So you have no choice. You must answer or you get a "no score." In addition, this format means you cannot go back to a previous question to change your answer. The computer has already taken your answer and used it to give you subsequent questions. No backtracking is possible once you've entered and confirmed your answer. What this also means is that each person's test is different. Even if two people start with the same item set in the basic test section, once they differ on an answer, the subsequent portion of the test will branch differently.

According to ETS, even though people take different tests, their scores are comparable. This is because the characteristics of the questions answered correctly and incorrectly, including their difficulty levels, are taken into account in the calculation of the score. In addition, ETS claims that the computer-based test scores are also comparable to the old paper-and-pencil test scores.

One benefit of the computer-based format is that when you finish you can cancel the test results—before seeing them—if you feel you've done poorly. If you do decide to keep the test, then you can see your unofficial scores right away. In addition, official score reporting is relatively fast—ten to fifteen days.

A drawback of the format, besides the fact that you cannot skip around, is that some of the readings, graphs, and questions are too large to appear on the screen in their entirety. You have to scroll up and down to see the whole item. Likewise, referring back to a passage or graph while answering a question means that you must scroll up. In addition, you can't underline sentences in a passage or make marks in the margin as you could on the paper test. To make up for this, ETS provides scratch paper that you can use to make notes and do calculations.

To help test takers accustom themselves to the computerized format, ETS provides a tutorial that you complete before starting on the actual test. The tutorial familiarizes you with the use of a mouse, the conventions of pointing, clicking, and scrolling and the format of the test. If you are familiar with computers, the tutorial will take you less than half an hour. If you are not, you are permitted to spend more time on it. According to ETS, the system is easy to use, even for a person with no previous computer experience. However, if you are not accustomed to computers, you would be far better off if you practice your basic skills before you get to the testing site. Although in theory a mouse is easy to use, novices often have trouble getting the cursor to go where they want it to go. The last thing you want to deal with while taking the GRE is a wild mouse and accidental clicking on the wrong answers. If it's any consolation, no knowledge of the keyboard is required—everything is accomplished by pointing and clicking.

GRE SUBJECT AREA TESTS

The subject area tests are achievement tests, and they test your content knowledge of a particular subject. There are eight subject area tests, and they are given in paper-and-pencil format only. The subjects include biochemistry, cell and molecular biology; biology; chemistry; computer science; literature in English; mathematics; physics; and psychology. The subject area tests assume a level of knowledge consistent with majoring in a subject or at least having an extensive background in it. ETS suggests allowing about 3½ hours at the testing site when taking a subject area test.

Unlike the General Test, which is given many times year round, the subject tests are given only three times a year. Keep in mind that because the tests are paper-based, it takes four to six weeks for your scores to be mailed to your designated institutions. Because the tests are given infrequently and score reporting is slow, be sure you plan ahead carefully so your test results will arrive before your deadlines.

THE WRITING ASSESSMENT

Introduced in 1999 by ETS, the Writing Assessment is a performance-based assessment of critical reasoning skills and analytical writing. It can be taken in computer or paper formats and consists of two parts:

- In the 45-minute "Present Your Perspective on an Issue" task, you must address an issue from any point of view and provide examples and reasons to explain and support your perspective. You are given a choice of two essay topics.
- In the 30-minute "Analyze an Argument" task, you must critique an argument by telling how well reasoned it is. There is no choice of topics in this section.

Scoring of the Writing Assessment is done according to a seven-point scale (0 is the worst; 6 is the best) by college and university faculty members with experience in teaching writing or writing-intensive courses. Each essay is scored independently by two readers. If the two scores are not identical or adjacent, a third reader will be used. The reported score is the average of your two essay scores. If you think the score is unfair, you may request a rescoring.

MILLER ANALOGIES TEST

The Miller Analogies Test (MAT), which is run by Harcourt Assessment, is accepted by over 2,300 graduate school programs. It is a test of mental ability given entirely in the form of analogies. For example, the analogies may tap your knowledge of fine arts, literature, mathematics, natural science, and social science.

On the MAT, you have 50 minutes to solve 100 problems. The test is given on an as-needed basis at more than 600 test centers in the United States.

PROFESSIONAL SCHOOL EXAMS

Professional graduate programs are likely to require you to take the appropriate graduate admissions test. The major tests are the Graduate Management Admissions Test (GMAT), for business school applicants; the Law School Admissions Test (LSAT), for law school applicants; and the Medical College Admissions Test (MCAT), for medical school applicants. However, there are also specialized graduate admissions tests in the fields of dentistry, veterinary science, pharmacy, optometry, and education.

Graduate Management Admissions Test. The test most likely to be taken by prospective distance learning students is the GMAT. It is run by the Graduate Management Admissions Council and administered by ETS. Like the GRE, the GMAT is a computer-based test. It is designed to help schools of business assess applicants' aptitude for graduate level programs in business and management.

The GMAT tests verbal, quantitative, and analytic writing skills:

- In the verbal section, you will be asked to understand and evaluate written English. There are 41 multiple-choice questions of three basic types: reading comprehension, critical reasoning, and sentence correction.
- The quantitative section tests your basic math skills, understanding of elementary mathematical concepts, and ability to solve quantitative problems. There are 37 multiple-choice questions of two basic types: data sufficiency (is there enough information to answer the question?) and problem solving.
- The analytical writing assessment measures your ability to think critically and communicate in writing. There are two essay topics, and you are allowed 30 minutes to respond to each. You must analyze an issue and an argument in this section of the test.

TESTS OF ENGLISH LANGUAGE PROFICIENCY

Regardless of whether you're applying to an undergraduate or graduate program, if your native language is not English, you may be required to take the Test of English as a Foreign Language (TOEFL) or Test of Spoken English (TSE) in order to determine your readiness to take courses in English. Both tests are administered by ETS.

The TOEFL is given in computer-based form throughout most of the world. Like the computer-based GRE, the TOEFL does not require previous computer experience. You are given the opportunity to practice on the computer before the test begins. The TOEFL has four sections—listening, reading, structure, and writing—and it lasts about 4 hours.

The TSE evaluates your ability to speak English. During the test, which takes about a half an hour, you answer questions that are presented in written and recorded form. Your responses are recorded; there is no writing required on this test. The TSE is not given in as many locations as the TOEFL, so you may have to travel a considerable distance to take it.

PREPARING FOR A STANDARDIZED TEST

You can improve your scores and reduce your test anxiety by preparing for the exams you need to take. At the very least, preparation will mean that you are familiar with the test instructions and the types of questions you will be asked. If your computer skills need improvement, adequate preparation will mean that you focus on the questions rather than struggle with the mouse when you take the computer-based tests. For achievement tests such as the subject area tests, you will actually need to study content. There are many ways you can prepare for the tests, but whichever method you choose, start early.

- **Practice by taking old tests.** You can check the Web sites of the various tests to download or request practice tests, or you can buy practice test books at a bookstore. You'll find free sample test questions on many other Web sites, including Peterson's (http://www.petersons.com).
- **Use test-preparation workbooks.** These books give information and test taking strategies, as well as practice items. There are many workbooks on the market, some with CD-ROMs, that will help you prepare for an admissions test. You'll find a long list of titles to choose from in Peterson's online bookstore at http://www.petersons.com.

- **Use test-preparation software.** Test preparation software is becoming more popular as more of the tests shift to computerized format. You can purchase the software in just about any computer software store. You can also take practice tests online at http://www.petersons.com/testprep.
- **Take a test-preparation course.** If you don't trust yourself to stick with a self-study program using practice tests, workbooks, or software, sign up for a review course such as those given by Kaplan. Although the courses are much more expensive than the do-it-yourself approach, they may be worth it if they make you study.
- **If your math is rusty, study math content.** According to the College Board, people who study math boost their scores more than people who focus only on test taking skills.

For a list of test preparation resources, see the Appendix.

REDUCING TEST ANXIETY

The best way to reduce test anxiety is to be thoroughly prepared. If you are well-acquainted with the format, directions, and types of questions you will encounter, you will not need to waste precious testing time puzzling over these aspects of the exam. In addition to thorough preparation, here are some suggestions to reduce the stress of taking the exam.

- Get a good night's rest and don't tank up on caffeinated beverages—they will only make you feel more stressed.
- Make sure you've got all the things you will need, including your admission ticket and proper identification; pencils and erasers if you are taking a paper based test; and a calculator, if one is permitted.
- Dress in layers so you will be prepared for a range of room temperatures.
- Get to the testing site at least a half an hour early. Make sure you know the way and leave yourself plenty of time to get there.
- Pace yourself during the exam. Know how the exam is scored so you can plan your approach.

Last, try to keep things in perspective. Remember, the exam score is just one item on your application. We'll discuss the remaining parts of an application in the next section.

APPLYING FOR ADMISSION TO DEGREE PROGRAMS

Now that you have narrowed your selection of programs and ascertained whether or not you need to take a standardized admissions test, it's time to prepare and assemble your applications. If you have not already done so, request an application and information packet from each program to which you plan to apply, download these items from their Web sites, or review them on line.

When you look over these materials, you will see that there may be a lot of work involved in applying to a degree program. It may take you a few months to register for and take standardized tests and to assemble and submit all the necessary information, especially if you're an international student or you've been out of school for a few years. Because the process can be complicated and time consuming, you should start well ahead of time. Even if you apply to a certificate program or an associate's degree program at a community college, a process that is typically less complicated, you should still make sure to start in time.

DEADLINES

For programs at traditional colleges and universities, application deadlines for fall admission may range from August (one full year prior to your planned enrollment) to late spring or summer for programs with rolling admissions. However, most programs require that you submit your application between January and March of the year in which you wish to start. For certificate programs and at community colleges, the deadlines may be later.

At some of the online universities, students can start their studies at any time of year. For example, at Walden University you can start on the first of any month. At Walden, the deadline for application materials is the first of the month two months prior to the month of enrollment.

Different programs have different deadlines. So be careful when you check the deadlines in the application materials from your various programs. And remember, the deadlines are not suggestions. One student applying to a traditional university who mistook a March deadline for May recalls that "not only would they not consider my application, but they wouldn't refund my application fee, either. I had to reapply the next year and pay again to be considered for their program." So don't be careless about dates—double-check them. Make a checklist like Figure 7-1 to help you keep track of things and stay on top of deadlines.

Application Checklist. Keep track of your applications by inserting a check mark or a completion date in the appropriate column or row. Note that the last four items are financial aid documents, which will be discussed in "Paying for Your Education."

PARTS OF AN APPLICATION

For each program to which you apply, you will have to submit a number of items to make your application complete. For most bachelor's and graduate degree programs, these include:

- Standardized admissions test scores (see "Taking Standardized Admissions Tests")
- An application form
- Your high school, undergraduate, or other transcripts
- Letters of recommendation
- Personal essay(s)

In addition, if you are seeking credit for life experience, an assessment portfolio will be required (see "What Can You Study via Distance Learning?"). A personal interview may be required for some programs, although for most, an interview is optional. A program may require additional items, such as a resume or arts portfolio.

For most associate degree programs at community colleges, the application is much simpler. Typically, it consists of just an application form; you may not even need to submit high school transcripts. For certificate programs, the application may consist of an application form and one or two other items.

Because requirements vary so widely, be sure you read the admissions information thoroughly so you understand what each program expects of you. Since each program may require a slightly different set of items, be sure your checklist reflects this in order to keep track of what you'll need to do.

We'll discuss the main elements of an application below; we'll cover financial aid applications in the next section.

THE APPLICATION FORM

On the application form, you provide basic information such as the program or department to which you are applying; your name, date of birth, social security number, address, and contact information; your citizenship status; your demographic background (usually optional); your current employer and position; your educational background; names of people who are providing references (ask them first!); and admissions test dates. Sometimes the application form also includes a section for applying for financial aid. However, a separate application form for financial aid may be necessary. Be sure you understand what forms you need to submit and to whom if you are applying for aid.

If you use a paper application, you should type the information on the form. If a typewriter is not available, then print your entries neatly. Be sure you do not accidentally omit information, and double-check that there are no spelling errors. "Photocopy the application and fill the copy out," suggests Nicole DeRaleau, a graduate student in engineering at Worcester Polytechnic Institute. "Make sure it is clear and concise, and then copy it onto the actual form."

If you decide to apply on line, don't just sit at the computer and dash off the application. Download the application form, fill it in, then proofread it carefully. Only then should you transmit it, being sure to keep a copy. Note that if you apply to an online degree

Figure 7–1: Application Checklist

Item	Program 1		Program 2		Program 3	
	Date Due/Date Completed		Date Due/Date Completed		Date Due/Date Completed	
Application form						
Test scores requested						
Transcripts requested						
Letters of recommendation solicited						
Letters of recommendation follow up						
Personal essay(s)						
Application fee						
Other items required (specify)						
Application submitted						
Application follow up						
FAFSA						
Other financial aid forms						
Financial aid supporting documents						
Financial aid application follow up						

program and the school does not offer an online application, you should think twice about applying. The lack of an online application is probably indicative of the low level of online student services you can expect once you are enrolled.

Many undergraduate colleges accept a common application form in place of their own. This means that most of the fields you will need to fill in will be the same for all of the schools that accept the common application. You may have to fill out a supplementary form for a college if you use one of these standardized forms. Using a standardized application form lets you concentrate on being organized and writing good essays.

TRANSCRIPTS

As proof of your academic background, you will need to submit official transcripts from each high school (for undergraduate programs), college, and university you have attended, even if you have taken just one course from that institution. To request official transcripts, contact your high school's guidance office or the registrars of your undergraduate college and other institutions you have attended. Be sure to allow two or three months for your request to be processed. It will save time if you call ahead to find out what the fee for each transcript is and what information they need to pull your file and send the transcript to the proper recipient. Then you can enclose a check for that amount with your written request.

Since many schools will send the transcripts directly to the admissions offices of the programs to which you are applying, you may also want to request an unofficial copy of your transcript. You can use this copy for your own reference during the application process.

When you review your transcripts, look for weaknesses that may need explaining, even if they occurred years ago. For example, a low GPA one semester, a very poor grade in a course, or even a below-average overall GPA may hurt your chances of acceptance unless you have a good reason for them. You can explain any shortfalls in your transcripts in your personal essay, cover letter, or addendum to the application.

LETTERS OF RECOMMENDATION

You will probably have to provide letters of recommendation for each program to which you apply. These letters are important, because like the personal essay, they give the members of the admissions committee a more personal view of you than is possible from your grades and test scores. Good letters of recommendation can tremendously increase your chances of admission, and lukewarm letters can harm your application. So it's important to approach the task of choosing and preparing your letter writers in a thoughtful and timely fashion.

In fact, it's a good idea to start asking for references a few months before your application deadline. Professionals and professors are extremely busy people, and the more time that you can give them to work on your recommendation, the better it will reflect who you are. Starting early will also give you an opportunity to follow up with your recommenders well before the application deadlines.

CHOOSING PEOPLE TO WRITE RECOMMENDATIONS

If possible, at least one of your recommendations should be from a teacher or professor, because (1) they are in the best position to judge you as a potential student and (2) members of the admissions committee will consider them peers and so be more inclined to trust their judgment of you.

If you cannot make up the full complement of letters from faculty members or if you are applying to professional programs, you can ask employers or people who know you in a professional capacity to write references for you. In fact, if you are applying to professional programs, having letters of recommendation from those already practicing in the field is a plus.

When you are trying to decide whom to ask for recommendations, keep these criteria in mind. The people you ask should

- have a high opinion of you.
- know you well, preferably in more than one context.
- be familiar with your field.
- be familiar with the programs to which you apply.
- have taught a large number of students (or have managed a large number of employees) so they have a good basis upon which to compare you (favorably!) to your peers.
- be known by the admissions committee as someone whose opinion can be trusted.
- have good writing skills.
- be reliable enough to write and mail the letter on time.

A tall order? Yes. It's likely that no one person you choose will meet all these criteria, but try to find people who come close to this ideal.

APPROACHING YOUR LETTER WRITERS

Once you've decided whom you plan to ask for references, be diplomatic. Don't simply show up in their offices, ask them to write a letter, and give them the letter of recommendation forms. Plan your approach so that you leave the potential recommender, as well as yourself, a graceful "out" in case the recommender reacts less than enthusiastically.

On your first approach, you should remind the person about who you are (if necessary) and then ask if they think they can write you a good letter of recommendation. This gives the person a chance to say no. If the person agrees, but hesitates or seems to be lukewarm, you can thank them for agreeing to help you. Later, you can write them a note saying that you won't need a letter of recommendation after all. On the other hand, if the person seems genuinely pleased to help you, you can then make an appointment to give them the letter of recommendation forms and the other information they will need.

WAIVING YOUR RIGHT TO SEE A LETTER

The letter of recommendation forms in your application packets contain a waiver. If you sign the waiver, you give up your right to see the letter of recommendation. Before you decide whether or not to sign it, discuss the waiver with each person who is writing you a reference. Some people will write you a reference only if you agree to sign the waiver and they can be sure the letter is confidential. This does not necessarily mean they intend to write a negative letter; instead, it means that they think a confidential letter will carry more weight with the admissions committee. In fact, they are right. A confidential letter usually has more validity in the eyes of the admissions committee. From the committee's point of view, an "open" letter may be less than candid because the letter writer knew you were going to read it. So, in general, it's better for you to waive your right to see a letter. If this makes you anxious in regard to a particular recommender, then do not choose that person to write a letter.

HELPING YOUR LETTER WRITERS

Once a faculty member or employer has agreed to write a letter of recommendation for you, he or she wants to write something positive on your behalf. No matter how great you are, this won't be possible if the letter writer cannot remember you and your accomplishments very well.

So when you meet with your letter writers to give them the letter of recommendation forms, use this opportunity to provide them with information about yourself. Bring a resume that highlights your academic, professional, and personal accomplishments. List the course or courses you took with them, the grades you got, and any significant work you did, such as a big research paper or presentation. The resume can be the basis of a conversation you have with the letter writer that amplifies your notable accomplishments.

What should you do if the letter writer asks *you* to draft the letter? Accept gracefully. Then pretend you are the writer, and craft a letter extolling your virtues and accomplishments in detail. Remember, if the letter writer does not like what you've written, he or she is free to change it in the final draft.

You can help your letter writers by filling in as much of the information as you can on the letter of recommendation forms. It's also a nice gesture to provide stamped, addressed envelopes for the letters if they are to be mailed directly to the programs or to you for inclusion in your application. Be sure your letter writers understand what their deadlines are. In other words, do everything you can to expedite the process, especially since you may be approaching people who are already extremely busy.

Last, send thank-you notes to professors and employers who have come through for you with letters of recommendation. Cementing good relationships now can only help you in the future.

IF YOU'VE BEEN OUT OF SCHOOL FOR YEARS

What should you do if you have been out of school for years and have lost touch with your teachers and professors? There are several things you can do to overcome the problems associated with the passage of time.

First, if a teacher or professor is still at your alma mater, you can get in touch by mail or e-mail, remind the person of who you are, describe what you've done since they taught you and what your plans for school are, and include a resume. Tell the instructor what you remember most about the courses you took with him or her. Most people keep their course records for at least a few years and can look up your grades. If you are still near your high school or undergraduate institution, you can make your approach in person. Once you've made this initial approach, you can then call and ask if the person thinks he or she can write a strong recommendation for you.

Another strategy if you've been out of school for a while is to obtain letters of recommendation from faculty members teaching in the programs to which you plan to apply. In order to obtain such a letter, you may have to take a course in the program before you enroll so that the faculty member gets to know you. Members of an admissions committee will hesitate to reject a candidate who has been strongly recommended by one of their colleagues.

Finally, if you are having trouble recruiting teachers and professors to recommend you, call the programs to which you are applying and ask what their policy is for applicants in your situation. Many programs designed for adult learners, especially the professional programs, allow you to use letters from employers. But remember, if you apply to an academic rather than a professional program, letters from employers will not carry as much weight as letters from faculty members.

THE PERSONAL ESSAY

The application to a degree program is not all numbers and outside evaluations. Schools are also interested in finding out about you as an individual and in more intangible qualities, like your ability to write a good essay. Thus, the personal essay is the part of the application in which you can take control and demonstrate who you are and why you deserve to be admitted. Other parts of your application—test scores, grade point average, and transcripts—may reflect your academic ability, but not much else. The letters of recommendation are beyond your control once you've chosen the writers. But a good personal essay can make you stand out. It can show the qualities that will make you an excellent student and professional. In other words, the essay is your showcase and you should make the most of it. Even if you can write superb prose in your sleep, you still need to know *what* to write. In this section, you'll get a step-by-step guide to preparing the personal essay.

REQUIREMENTS VARY

The essays required of applicants vary widely. For some programs, you may just have to explain in one or two paragraphs why you want to go to that school. For others, you may have to write on a more creative topic, such as the person who influenced you the most. Still for others, such as graduate business programs, the application may call for two, three, or even more essays on different topics. Business schools and programs pay a lot of attention to the personal essay because professional experience is an important criterion for admission, and this is best reflected in the essays.

The admissions committee gleans a lot of information from *what* you write. But they can also tell a lot from *how* you write. If your writing is clear and conveys your ideas effectively, you are demonstrating your ability to communicate. If your writing is free of grammatical and spelling errors, you are demonstrating your attention to detail. Good writing skills are essential for a student in any field, so a poorly written essay can hurt an application. A well-written statement, on the other hand, will help your case.

THINK BEFORE YOU WRITE

Do you remember the self-assessment you did in "Is Distance Learning Right for You?" You answered many difficult questions about your goals, interests, strengths, and weaknesses in order to decide if pursuing an education through distance learning was right for you. If you did an honest and thorough job of assessing yourself then, you will have already thought through many of the issues you will now need to address when you write your personal essay.

Things to Think About. Your self-assessment should make it easier for you to get a handle on issues such as:

- your personal and professional goals and their relationship to your education
- how you came to be interested in a particular field and why you think you are well suited for it
- aspects of your life that make you uniquely qualified to pursue study in this field
- experiences or qualities that distinguish you from other applicants
- unusual hardships or obstacles that you've had to overcome
- unusual accomplishments, whether personal, professional, or academic
- professional experiences that have contributed to your personal growth
- how your skills and personal characteristics would contribute to your success in a distance learning degree program

In addition, when you researched and evaluated programs to which you would apply, you learned a lot about the programs that were good matches for you. In your essay, you may also have to address issues like

- what appeals to you about a particular program.
- how your interests and strengths match their needs.

Be Yourself . . . The most common piece of advice from most admissions directors about writing the personal essay is to be yourself. **Remember, you are seeking to be accepted by a program that is a good match for you. If you disguise who you really are in an effort to impress an admissions committee, you are doing yourself—and the school—a disservice. So, be honest. If you demonstrate self-knowledge by presenting your strengths as well as your limitations, your essay will be a true reflection of who you are.**

. . . But Be Diplomatic. Honesty is important, but so is diplomacy. Try not to reveal weaknesses in your personality such as laziness, dishonesty, or selfishness. Don't say you want to enroll in a program just because it's on line or you know you can get in. Even though these things may be true, they are not reasons with which the admissions committee will necessarily be sympathetic. Instead, frame your points in a positive light: you can fulfill the admission requirements because you have the proper prerequisites, and you know of its reputation for quality online teaching.

WRITE A STRONG OPENING

When you write your essay, put yourself in the position of an admissions committee member who may be reading fifty essays a day. By the end of all this reading, this poor individual may be bored to tears and would be pleased by any essay that simply engages his or her interest. How are you going to accomplish this? By writing an opening that grabs the reader's attention.

Describe an Important Experience. Instead of beginning with, "I want to go to school because . . ." try to engage the reader with something significant. For example, was there an experience that led you to make the decision to pursue your education? If so, describe it.

The opening is also the place where you can set forth any unusual experience you have had that contributed significantly to the person you are today. The experience may be growing up poor, being an Olympic athlete, or moving to the United States at the age of fourteen. Whatever the experience is, show how it has formed your character and life and how it relates to the education you want to pursue now.

Be Specific. What if you have not had a defining moment or experience that sparked your interest in further education? Then write an opening that is specific enough to have some real interest. The key is to remember that specific details are usually more interesting than general statements. Use concrete examples of your successes and action verbs to describe events. Be specific and you'll have a better chance of connecting with your readers.

TELL HOW YOUR STORY INTERSECTS WITH THEIRS

If you apply to several programs, you will be tempted to write a boilerplate essay. Resist the temptation. Admissions committees grow adept at picking out the generic personal statements.

Remember that when you were evaluating programs you were looking for a good match for you. The personal essay is the place where you can explain to the admissions committee why you are a good match for that school. The story of your intellectual and professional development and your goals should culminate in your reasons for choosing this particular program. Your reasons should reflect a knowledge of the program.

Use the Brochure or Catalog as a Resource. You can use the knowledge you've gained from researching the program if you don't know it firsthand to explain why you want to enroll in a program. In particular, the program brochure or catalog can be a good resource when you write this section of the essay. It's important to know what a school has to offer before you write the essay. The admissions committee members will be looking for a good fit for their program.

In addition to identifying the tangible characteristics of a program, you can also get a sense of its philosophy and values from the brochure or catalog.

DESCRIBE YOUR GOALS

In most essays, you will have to explain how a degree will help you achieve your goals. Even if you are not exactly sure what you want to do professionally, describe what you might be interested in doing once you receive the degree. Indicating that you have a purpose in obtaining a degree shows that you are focused and motivated and have a real sense of the possibilities.

EXPLAIN SHORTCOMINGS IN YOUR BACKGROUND

There is a difference of opinion on whether or not the personal essay is the place to explain any weaknesses in your academic or professional preparation if you are not directly asked to do so. Some people think that the essay should concentrate on a positive presentation of your qualifications. They feel that an explanation of poor standardized test scores, for example, belongs in an addendum or cover letter. Others think that the essay is the place to address your application's weaknesses.

Perhaps a good rule of thumb is to address any weaknesses or shortcomings that are directly relevant to your proposed studies in the essay. On the other hand, if the weak spot in your application is not directly related to your field of study, you may prefer to address it in an addendum or cover letter. For example, if when you were a college freshman you had a poor GPA, you can explain this separately. Try to put a positive spin on it, too. Explain, for example, how your GPA in your major was much higher, or how your GPA improved as you matured. Essentially, your decision as to where to address your weaknesses will depend on their importance and relevance to your pursuit of a degree.

EDIT YOUR DRAFTS

Follow the Instructions. When you sit down to draft your essay, the first thing you should make sure is that you are *answering the question posed on the application*. Be sure you read the instructions for each program's personal statement carefully. Small differences in wording can affect how you approach writing the essay.

Don't Write Too Much or Too Little. The second thing you should keep in mind as you begin your draft is the length of the essay. Often, the length is specified. What should you do if length is not specified? Write one to two typed pages. An essay that is shorter than one page does not allow room for you to develop your ideas, and an essay that is longer than two pages becomes a chore for the admissions committee to read. Don't play with font size, either, in order to get the statement to come out the right length. Admissions officers don't really want to read eight-point type. Stick with a basic font, such as Times New Roman, and keep the size between 10 and 12 points. If the essay asks for a specific word count, follow it to the letter. If you come in over or under by 10 words or so, don't worry too much about it. But if you're 100 or more words short or long, you'll have some adding or cutting to do.

Finally, when you write your first draft, do not waste space by repeating information that the admissions committee can get from other parts of your application like your transcript or resume. Use the essay to provide new information or to highlight particular accomplishments.

Review the First Draft. Once you have drafted your essay, read the question again. Has your draft answered the question fully? If the essay is incomplete, go back and fill in the missing material. Then ask people for feedback. Although your spouse and friends may be helpful, you may get more valuable suggestions from faculty members or colleagues who know you and who also know what a personal essay should be like. Ask whether you've included things you should leave out or should add things you've forgotten. Is the tone right? Have you achieved the right balance between boasting and being too modest? Are there any problems with organization, clarity, grammar, or spelling?

Prepare the Final Draft. Once you've revised the essay, set it aside for a couple of days. Then proofread it with a fresh eye. If you are satisfied with your final draft, ask someone else to proofread it for you. The final draft should be absolutely free of grammar and spelling errors, so do not rely on grammar or spellcheckers to find all the errors. Once you are done, be sure to keep backup files as well as a hard copy. Although you won't be able to use the whole essay for all your applications, you may be able to use parts of it. If you do work this way, be absolutely sure when you submit the final essays to different programs that you have not made any embarrassing cutting and pasting mistakes.

Finally, if you submit the statement on separate sheets of paper rather than on the application form itself, put your name, social security number, and the question at the top of the essay and type "see attached essay" on the application form.

MAKE IT YOURS

If after reading this section you are still daunted by the prospect of writing your personal statement, just put the whole task aside for a few days. You will find that the ideas and suggestions you've just read will trigger some mental activity and that soon you will have some ideas of your own to jot down.

Remember, also, that it's not necessary to have an exotic background or a dramatic event to recount in order to write a good essay and gain admission to a program. Admissions committees look for diversity—in gender, race, ethnicity, nationality, and socioeconomic status—to name some obvious characteristics. But they are also look for people with diverse life experiences to add richness to their student body. Your background, which may seem perfectly ordinary to you, nevertheless has unique and relevant elements that can be assets to the program you choose. Your task is to identify and build upon these elements to persuade the admissions committee that you should be selected.

INTERVIEWS

Interviews are rarely a requirement of the distance education application process. However, if you think you do well in interviews, you can call each program and ask for an interview. A good interview may be an opportunity to sway the admissions committee in your favor. Human nature being what it is, an excellent half-hour interview may loom larger than years of average grades in the minds of those who evaluate your application.

Most interviewers are interested in the way you approach problems, think, and articulate your ideas, and so they will concentrate on questions that will reveal these aspects of your character and not on questions that test your technical knowledge. They may ask you controversial questions or give you hypothetical problems to solve. Or they may ask about your professional goals, motivation for study, and areas of interest—much the same material that is in a typical personal essay. Remember that interviewers are interested more in how you think than in what you think.

When you prepare for an interview, it would be helpful if you have already written your personal essay, because the thought processes involved in preparing the essay will help you articulate many of the issues that are likely to come up in an interview. It is also helpful to do your homework on the program, so if the opportunity arises for you to ask questions, you can do so intelligently. Last, be sure you are dressed properly. That means dress as if you are going to a professional job interview.

SUBMITTING YOUR APPLICATION

As we mentioned at the beginning of this section, you should submit your completed applications well before they are due. *Be sure to keep a copy of everything.* That way, you won't lose hours of work if the application gets lost. You can either mail the application to the admissions office or file portions of it on line through the programs' Web sites. Remember, however, that some elements of the application, such as the fee and official transcripts, will still need to be mailed in paper form. Note also that most schools that accept online applications simply print them and process them as if they had come in by regular mail.

Try to submit all of your materials at once, which simplifies the task of compiling and tracking your application at the admissions office. If that's impossible, as it is for many students, keep track of missing items and forward them as soon as possible. Remember that if items are missing, your application is likely just to sit in the admissions office.

FOLLOWING UP

It's important that you check up on the status of your applications, especially if you don't receive acknowledgment that an application is complete. Give the admissions office a couple of weeks to process your application, and then call or send an e-mail to find out whether or not it's complete. For some schools, you can check the status of your application on line through their Web sites. Usually the missing items are transcripts or letters of recommendation.

IN SUMMARY

Preparing a thorough, focused, and well-written application is one of the most important tasks you will ever undertake. A good application can gain you admission to a program that can help you achieve your goals. "The application process is just one of those hoops you have to jump through to get where you want to go," advises a distance learning student at Gonzaga University. With your destination in mind, work on your applications as if they are the most important things you can possibly be doing, because they are.

PAYING FOR YOUR EDUCATION

Pursuing a certificate or degree can cost a lot of money, but it is usually money well spent. On average, people with undergraduate and graduate degrees make more money than those who do not have these credentials. Still, the question remains: How are you going to pay for school and support yourself (and perhaps your family) at the same time?

Most adult distance learning students solve the problem of paying for their education by continuing to work full-time and attending school part time. As one student put it, "I work and I pay as I go." Although attending part-time does not cut the total cost of your certificate or degree, it does have the advantage of spreading your costs over a longer period and enables you to pay for your education out of your current income. Note, however, that attending school less than half-time will disqualify you from most forms of financial aid.

In this section, we'll discuss ways to pay for your education, both by looking for low-cost alternatives and by finding financial aid. We'll discuss types and sources of aid, where you can find information about financial aid, and the application process. Finally, we'll describe some of the tax issues that may be relevant to students pursuing higher education.

LOOKING FOR LOW-COST ALTERNATIVES

There are ways you can cut the cost of your education, even before you look for sources of financial aid. These include attending a community college rather than a four-year college and attending a public institution of higher education rather than a private one.

COMMUNITY COLLEGE VERSUS FOUR-YEAR COLLEGE

If you are an undergraduate pursuing a bachelor's degree, you could consider enrolling at a community college for your first two years of study. Most community colleges charge less tuition than four-year colleges do. Toward the end of your second year of study, you can apply to a four-year college as a transfer student and complete your bachelor's degree there.

PUBLIC VERSUS PRIVATE COLLEGE OR UNIVERSITY

Since four-year public colleges and universities get most of their support from government funding, they are less expensive than private colleges and universities. Public colleges and universities usually have two scales for tuition and fees—one for out-of-state residents and a much less expensive scale for state residents.

With so much money at stake, and if moving is an option for you, it is definitely worthwhile to find out how you can establish residency in the state in which you plan to get your degree. You may simply have to reside in the state for a year—your first year of school—in order to be considered a legal resident. But being a resident while a student may not count, and you may have to move to the state a year before you plan to enroll. The legal residency requirements of each state vary, so be sure you have the right information if you decide to pursue this strategy.

TYPES OF FINANCIAL AID

Before we get into a discussion of the various sources of financial aid, it would be helpful to understand some basics. For example, financial aid can be classified in a few ways. First, it can be categorized by type of aid:

- **Grants, scholarships,** and **fellowships** are gifts that do not have to be repaid. These words are used somewhat interchangeably; there is no real difference among them, except that scholarships are usually awarded to undergraduates and fellowships are awarded to graduate students.
- **Loans** are awards that do have to be repaid, with interest, either while you are in school or after you leave school, it depends on the terms of the loan. If you consider loans, note that financial aid counselors recommend that your total student debt payment should not exceed 8 to 15 percent of your projected monthly income after you receive your degree.
- **Work-study awards** are amounts you earn through part-time work in a federal aid program.
- **Reimbursements**, generally from employers, repay you for amounts you've already spent on tuition.

You can also classify financial aid according to the reason the student is awarded the aid:

- **Need-based aid** is financial aid awarded on the basis of your financial need. It may take the form of grants, loans, or work-study.
- **Merit-based aid** is funding awarded on the basis of academic merit, regardless of financial need.

A subset of merit-based aid is student profile-based aid—financial aid to students because of their identities. For example, some scholarships are targeted for veterans, minorities, or women; and others are targeted for people with very specific qualifications that the philanthropist wants to reward, such as an Eagle Scout studying labor relations.

A third way to classify financial aid is by its source. The major sources of aid for students are as follows:

- The **federal government**, by far the largest disburser of financial aid—over $50 billion to more than 8.5 million students each year
- **State governments**, some of which have large financial aid programs
- **Private sources of aid**, which include colleges and universities, employers, foundations, service organizations, national scholarship and fellowship programs, home equity loans, and private loan programs

THE LANGUAGE OF FINANCIAL AID

There's some financial aid jargon that you'll have to master in order to understand need-based financial aid programs. Some terms that you'll see frequently include the following:

- **Enrollment status**—Whether you are enrolled full-time, three-quarter time, half-time, or less than half-time in a degree or certificate program. Your status affects your eligibility for most types of aid.
- **Expected Family Contribution (EFC)**—The amount you and your family are expected to contribute to the cost of your education per academic year. If you are a dependent, *family* means you and your parents; if you are independent, this means you and your spouse, if you are married. The formula was established by the U.S. Congress to help estimate federal aid amounts for eligible students, and it is used by college financial aid offices as well as the U.S. Department of Education.
- **Cost of attendance**—The total cost—tuition, fees, living expenses, books, supplies, and miscellaneous expenses—of attending a particular school for an academic year. Each school estimates its own cost of attendance, and you can find out what it is if you check your admissions information packet or call the financial aid office. Distance learners should make sure that technology costs are included in the school's cost of attendance and in their own budgets. The cost of transportation, hotels, and meals during residency periods, if any, should also be accounted for in the cost of attendance.
- **Financial need**—The amount of money you need to be given or loaned or that you will earn through work-study in order to attend your school. It is calculated by subtracting your Estimated Family Contribution from your cost of attendance:

  Cost of Attendance
  – Expected Family Contribution
  = Financial Need

  Note that your financial need will differ from program to program. That's because the cost of attendance will vary from school to school, but your Expected Family Contribution will remain the same, whether you attend the local community college or an expensive private university.

FEDERAL FINANCIAL AID

As we've mentioned, the U.S. government is the largest player in the financial aid arena, and most of your financial aid is likely to come from this source. The federal government provides need-based aid in the form of grants, work-study programs, and loans. Up-to-date information about federal financial aid programs can be found at the U.S. Department of Education's Web site, www.ed.gov/studentaid, or by calling 800-4-FEDAID (toll-free). Eligibility issues relevant to distance learners and some of the basics of federal aid are discussed below. Note that some of these eligibility criteria may change in the future as distance degrees become more common and financial aid programs are modified to reflect the new realities.

ARE YOU ELIGIBLE FOR FEDERAL FINANCIAL AID?

Your financial need is just one criterion used to determine whether or not you are eligible to receive aid from the federal government. In addition, you must

- have a high school diploma or GED or pass a test approved by the Department of Education.
- be enrolled in a degree or certificate program.
- be enrolled in an eligible institution (see below).
- be a U.S. citizen or eligible noncitizen.
- have a Social Security number.
- register with the Selective Service if required.
- maintain satisfactory academic progress once you are in school.

If you have been convicted under federal or state laws of the sale or possession of illegal drugs, you may not be eligible to participate in federal financial aid programs. Call the Federal Student Aid Information Center at 800-4-FEDAID (toll-free) for further information.

If you are not sure if you qualify as an eligible noncitizen, call the financial aid office of the school you plan to attend.

INSTITUTIONAL ELIGIBILITY: AN ISSUE PERTINENT TO DISTANCE LEARNERS

In order to participate in federal financial aid programs, an institution of higher learning must fulfill the criteria established by Congress for the disbursement of Title IV funds, as federal student aid is officially known. There are many complex regulations that establish institutional eligibility. Of these, several may apply to institutions that offer certificates or degrees at a distance. For example, in order to be eligible to participate in federal financial aid programs, an institution must be accredited by an agency—other than the Distance Education and Training Council (DETC)—recognized by the U.S. Department of Education. The reason that schools accredited only by the DETC are not eligible is that they are classified as "correspondence schools;" and schools that teach primarily by correspondence are ineligible according to the law. In order to qualify to disburse Title IV aid, an institution must teach at least 50.1 percent of its classes in the traditional classroom or must be classified as an independent study institution rather than a correspondence school. Other requirements for participation in federal financial aid programs involve the academic schedule; for example, there must be a thirty-week academic year, a template that doesn't fit some of the new virtual universities.

The Distance Education Demonstration Program. The rules governing federal aid were originally promulgated to prevent fraud and to assure that funds would be provided to students at schools that met certain standards. However, with the growth of distance education, these regulations are increasingly becoming obstacles to provide aid to students at legitimate but innovative institutions. Recognizing this, Congress established the Distance Education Demonstration Program under the direction of the Department of Education. "The purpose of the Distance Education Demonstration Program is to collect data that will provide some understanding of what constitutes quality in distance education," explains Marianne R. Phelps, former special assistant to the assistant secretary for postsecondary education. "Congress needs information in order to become comfortable with the risks involved in funding distance education." Under this program, the department is permitted to waive some of the Title IV regulations, if necessary, for the fifteen participating institutions of higher education. Eventually, the experiences and data generated by the Distance Education Demonstration Program may provide a basis for a review of current rules and regulations.

Determining the Eligibility Status of an Institution or Program. In the meantime, what can you do to make sure that the school and program in which you are interested are eligible to participate in federal financial aid programs? The simple answer, of course, is call them and ask. However, you can also do some double-checking on your own to confirm what the school tells you.

If you plan to enroll in a regionally accredited traditional college or university, you can safely assume that the institution as a whole is eligible to participate in federal aid programs—since distance certificates and degrees are likely to be a very small proportion of its overall offerings (see "Selecting a Good Distance Learning Program" for a discussion of accreditation). However, because institutions have the discretion to exclude specific programs, you should double-check to see if the school disperses federal aid to students enrolled in programs that interest you. Call the financial aid office and ask. If you are not sure of the accreditation status, and therefore the Title IV status, of the school in which you are interested, first check with the school to find out which agencies, if any, have accredited it. Then visit the Department of Education's Web site to check on the accrediting agencies. The department lists the accrediting agencies of which it approves, and in its short description of each agency, it indicates whether or not the institutions it accredits qualify for Title IV funding. You can then call the accrediting agency to make sure it has indeed accredited the school or program in which you are interested.

FEDERAL AID PROGRAMS

Once you've established the eligibility of the institution and program in which you are interested, you may want to check the federal aid programs in which they participate. Not all schools participate in all the available programs.

Among the federal aid programs are Pell Grants, Federal Supplemental Educational Opportunity Grants, work-study, Federal Family Education Loans (FFEL) and William D. Ford Direct Loans (commonly called Stafford loans), and Perkins Loans.

Pell Grants. Pell Grants, which do not have to be repaid, are awarded to undergraduate students on the basis of need, even if they are enrolled less than half time. In some cases, a student enrolled in a postbaccalaureate teacher certification program may be awarded a Pell Grant. There are no Pell Grants for other graduate students.

The maximum amount of the Pell Grant changes each year and depends on annual funding allocations by Congress. The maximum award for the school year 2004–05 was $4,050. The amount of an award depends on a combination of your financial need, your costs to attend school, your enrollment status as a full-time or part-time student, and whether or not you plan to study for a full academic year or less.

If you are awarded a Pell Grant, the money can be applied directly to your school costs or be paid to you directly or some combination of these methods. Your school must inform you on how it will be disbursing your grant. Disbursements must occur at least once per term or a minimum of twice a year.

Federal Supplemental Educational Opportunity Grants. Federal Supplemental Educational Opportunity Grants (FSEOGs) are awards to undergraduates with exceptional financial need, even if they are enrolled less than half time. These grants generally go to Pell Grant recipients with the lowest Estimated Family Contributions. The amount of an FSEOG ranges from $100 to $4,000 per year.

Unlike the Pell Grant program, which provides funds to each eligible student, the FSEOG program is campus-based. This means that the federal government awards each participating institution a certain amount of money, and the school's financial aid office decides how to allocate it. When the school uses up its funding for the year, there are no more FSEOGs awarded. Check with your school to see whether or not it participates in this program.

Federal Work-Study Program. Some colleges and universities participate in the federal work-study program, which provides part-time jobs in public and private nonprofit organizations to both undergraduate and graduate students who demonstrate financial need. The government pays up to 75 percent of your wages, and your employer pays the balance. The value of a work-study job depends on your need, the other elements in your financial aid package, and the amount of money the school has to offer. Not all universities have work-study funds, and some that do have the funds limit their use to undergraduates.

If you receive work-study funds, you may be able to use them in a job that is related to your field. You will have to check with the financial aid office to find out what jobs are available, whether or not you can use the funds in a job you find elsewhere, and what bureaucratic requirements you will have to satisfy.

Stafford Loan Programs (FFEL and Direct Loans). The Federal Family Education Loan (FFEL) program and the William D. Ford Direct Loan Program, commonly called Stafford loans, are two loan programs sponsored by the federal government. Schools generally participate in one of the two programs. The terms and conditions of these loans are similar; the major differences are the source of the funds and some repayment provisions. If you get a FFEL, your funds will come from a bank, credit union, or other participating lender. If you get a Direct Loan, the money comes directly from the federal government.

You are eligible to borrow under these loan programs if you are enrolled at least half time and have financial need remaining after your Estimated Family Contribution, Pell Grant eligibility, and aid from other sources are subtracted from your annual cost of attendance. Depending on your need, you may be eligible for a subsidized loan in which the government pays the interest that accrues while you are enrolled at least half time. If you cannot demonstrate sufficient financial need according to government criteria, you may still be able to borrow, but your Stafford loan will be unsubsidized. This means that interest will accrue on the loan while you are still in school unless you arrange to pay it during this period.

In both types of Stafford loans, repayment of the principal as well as future interest begins six months after you are last enrolled on at least a half-time basis. Undergraduates may borrow a maximum of $6,625 to $10,500 per year. Graduate students may borrow up to $18,500 per year up to a maximum of $138,500, which includes any undergraduate loans you may still have. The interest rate varies annually and is set each July. Right now it is capped at 8.25 percent.

Perkins Loan Program. Another source of federal funds is the Perkins Loan program. The Perkins Loan is available to both undergraduate and graduate students who demonstrate exceptional financial need, whether enrolled full-time or part-time, and it is administered by each individual college or university. In some cases, schools reserve Perkins Loans for undergraduates. If you are an undergraduate eligible for a Perkins Loan, you may be able to borrow up to $4,000 per year with a $20,000 maximum. An eligible graduate student may be able to borrow up to $6,000 per year with a $40,000 maximum including undergraduate and graduate Perkins borrowing.

At present, the interest rate is 5 percent, and no interest accrues while you are enrolled in school at least half-time. You must start repaying the loan nine months after you are last enrolled on a half-time basis. This loan is the best deal offered by the government.

REPAYING YOUR FEDERAL LOANS

After you graduate, leave school, or drop below half-time status, you will have a grace period of either six or nine months before loan payments start. During the grace period, you will be sent information about payment plans and your first payment due date. You can repay the loan over a maximum of 10 years with a $50 minimum monthly payment, with a graduated plan in which the payments start out low and gradually increase, or with a plan that bases your payments on your income level.

You can also consolidate all your outstanding federal loans into one loan. Having one loan to repay will minimize the chances of administrative error and allow you to write one check per month rather than several.

If you have trouble repaying your federal loans, you may qualify for a deferment or forbearance on your loan. During a deferment, payments are suspended, and if the loan is subsidized, interest does not accrue. During forbearance, payments are postponed or reduced. Repayment assistance may be available if you serve in the military.

STATE AID PROGRAMS

Some states offer financial aid to state residents that attend school in-state, some offer aid to state residents that attend school in-state or elsewhere, and some offer aid to students that attend school in their state regardless of their residency status. Some states, like California, New York, Michigan, Oklahoma, and Texas, have large aid programs. Other states may have little or nothing to offer. Contact your state scholarship office directly to find out what's available and whether you are eligible to apply. Telephone numbers are listed in the Appendix.

PRIVATE SOURCES OF FINANCIAL AID

In addition to the federal government, other organizations provide financial aid to students. These include your school, national and local organizations, private lenders, employers, internships, and cooperative education programs.

THE COLLEGE OR UNIVERSITY

Second only to the federal government in the amount of financial aid disbursed yearly are colleges and universities. Many of these institutions award both need-based and merit-based aid to deserving students. To find out more about the types of aid that the school you are interested in disburses, contact the financial aid office.

NATIONAL AND LOCAL ORGANIZATIONS

Foundations, nonprofit organizations, churches, service and fraternal organizations, professional associations, corporations, unions, and many other national and local organizations award grants to students of higher education. Many of these awards go to students who fit a certain profile, but many of them are open to anyone who applies. The drawback of this type of aid is that you have to locate it and apply on your own.

PRIVATE LENDERS

Many students borrow from private lenders, whether through alternative loan programs, home equity loans, or other types of loans.

Alternative Loan Programs. In addition to the federal loan programs, there are many private alternative loan programs designed to help students. Most private loan programs disburse funds based on your creditworthiness rather than your financial need. Some loan programs target all types of students; others are designed specifically for graduate or professional students. In addition, you can use other types of private loans not specifically designed for education to help finance your degree. For more information, check with your bank and your school's financial aid office.

Home Equity Loans. For students who own their own homes, a home equity loan or line of credit can be an attractive financing alternative to private loan programs. Some of these loans are offered at low rates and allow you to defer payment of the principal for years. In addition, if you use the loan to pay for educational expenses, the interest on the loan is tax deductible.

Credit Cards. Whatever you do, do not use your credit cards to borrow money for school on a long-term basis. The interest rates and finance charges will be high, and the balance will grow astronomically. Credit cards are useful to pay tuition and fees if you (1) can pay the balance in full, (2) expect a student loan to come through shortly, (3) expect your employer to reimburse your costs. Otherwise, avoid them.

INTERNSHIPS AND COOPERATIVE EDUCATION PROGRAMS

In addition to the federal work-study program, there are other employment opportunities that may help you finance your education. Internships with organizations outside the university can provide money as well as practical experience in your field. As an intern, you are usually paid by the outside organization, and you may or may not get credit for the work you do. Although they have been common in the professional programs, such as design and business, for years, lately internships have been growing in popularity in academic programs as well.

In cooperative education programs, you usually alternate periods of full-time work in your field with periods of full-time study. You are paid for the work you do, and you may or may not get academic credit for it as well.

Internship and cooperative education programs may be administered in your department or by a separate office, so you will have to ask to find out.

EMPLOYER REIMBURSEMENT

If you work full-time and attend school part-time, you may be reimbursed for part or all of your tuition by your employer. Many employers require that you receive a minimum grade in order to qualify for reimbursement. Keep in mind, however, that your employer will withhold taxes and other deductions when it reimburses you, and you will have to make up the difference.

Check with your employer before you enroll; some employers reimburse tuition only for job-related courses. Others will not reimburse employees for distance learning courses.

Some large corporations that consider job-related certificate and degrees as forms of employee training may underwrite the entire cost of a program. For example, AT&T pays Denise Petrosino's tuition directly to the University of Phoenix Online. "As long as I maintain a B average, I have 100 percent coverage," explains Petrosino, who is earning a master's degree in organizational management.

LOCATING INFORMATION ABOUT FINANCIAL AID

Finding information about financial aid can be a challenge. There is no one central clearinghouse for information about financial aid for undergraduate and graduate study. You are going to have to check a number of different sources to get the full picture on possible sources of aid that is available for you. We'll discuss a few of them here, but for a list of financial aid resources, see the Appendix.

THE GOVERNMENT

The best source of information on federal aid for students is the U.S. government itself. The federal aid programs are administered by the U.S. Department of Education. You can contact them through their Web site, by telephone, or by mail. (See the Appendix for specifics.) Remember, however, that not all colleges and universities participate in each federal program, so if a particular federal aid program interests you, you will have to contact your school's financial aid office to make sure it's available.

If you are a graduate student, you should note that many agencies of the federal government offer fellowships to graduate students in related fields. Contact the agencies that are relevant to your field of study for further information.

For information on state aid, contact your state agency of higher education (see the Appendix).

THE COLLEGE OR UNIVERSITY

At a small college, the financial aid office is usually the source of all financial aid information. However, at a university, there is more than one office involved with student aid, and thus more than one source of information about it. Each university has a different administrative structure, so you will have to figure out the offices you will most likely need to contact. These may include:

- **The financial aid office.** The university-wide financial aid office is generally the best source of information about federal and private loan programs as well as university-based grants and federal work-study assistance. They may also be able to steer you to other sources of information.
- **The college or school's administrative office.** The next place to check is the administrative office of the college or school to which you are applying. For example, you may be applying for a master's degree in special education. This department may be under the jurisdiction of the College of Education. That office may or may not administer grants to the students of the college. Call to find out.
- **The office of the graduate school.** If you are a graduate student, it pays to check this administrative office; it may or may not have funding to award. If it does, the fellowships or grants are likely to be awarded on a university-wide, competitive basis.
- **The specific program or department to which you are applying.** Often a program brochure describes the types of aid that the department awards its students. If you cannot find this information in the materials you have, then call the program and ask. You'll be able to find out about program aid from this source.

It's important to check with all these offices to see what's available. It's also important to be proactive and call the financial aid office as well as other offices to find out your chances of receiving aid.

THE INTERNET

The Internet is an excellent source of information about all types of financial aid. One of the best places to start your Internet search for financial aid is the Financial Aid Information Page at www.finaid.org. This site has a great deal of information about the different types of financial aid and provides links to other relevant sites as well. It provides a good overview of the financial aid situation. In addition, the site offers several calculators that enable you to estimate many useful figures, including your Estimated Family Contribution, projected costs of attendance, and future student loan payments. There are also a number of searchable databases of national scholarships and fellowships on the Internet. One searchable database of financial aid resources can be found on Peterson's Web site (www.petersons.com/resources/finance.html) listing 1.6 million sources of private aid totaling nearly $4 billion. Another scholarship database is FastWeb at www.fastweb.com. On each of these sites, you'll need to answer a questionnaire about your educational background, field of study, and personal characteristics. When you are done, the database is searched to match your data with eligibility requirements of several hundred thousand fellowships and scholarships. You are then given a list of possible fellowships and scholarships to pursue on your own. There is no cost for either of these services.

There are a few things you should beware of when using Internet search services. First, a searchable database is only as good as its index, so you may find yourself getting some odd matches. In addition, most searchable databases of scholarships and fellowships are designed primarily for undergraduates, so the number of potential matches for a graduate student is far fewer than the several hundred thousand sources of aid that a database may contain. Finally, some of these Internet search services charge a fee. Given the amount of free information that's available, both on the Internet and in libraries, it's not necessary to pay for this type of research.

PRINT DIRECTORIES

Although the searchable databases on the Internet are easy to use, it's still a good idea to check print directories of national scholarships, grants, and fellowships. These directories have indexes that make locating potential sources of funds easy. Scholarships, grants, and fellowships are indexed by field of study as well as by type of student. So, for example, you can search for all funding related to the study of Latin America or electrical engineering. Or you can search for funding that is targeted to Hispanic students, disabled students, or adult students. It's a good idea just to browse, too, in case something catches your eye.

There are quite a few directories that you can consult. For undergraduates, Peterson's *Scholarships, Grants, & Prizes 2006* lists many private sources of aid, and Peterson's *College Money Handbook 2006* covers college and university sources of financial aid. For graduate students, the *Annual Register of Grant Support: A Directory of Funding Sources*, published by the National Register Publishing Company, is a comprehensive guide to awards from the government, foundations, and business and professional organizations.

APPLYING FOR FINANCIAL AID

Depending on your personal situation and the requirements of the school, you may have to submit just one or a number of applications for financial aid. If you apply for need-based aid, university merit aid, national scholarships and fellowships, or private loan programs, you will have several application forms to deal with. However many applications you must submit, start the process early.

DEADLINES

"I cannot overemphasize the importance of applying early," says Emerelle McNair, director of scholarships and financial aid at Southern Polytechnic State University in Georgia. "Most awards are made in spring for the following academic year." Be sure you've picked the correct deadlines from your program application information packet. *Students applying for financial aid often have an earlier deadline for the entire application.* If you look for sources of aid outside the program and university, such as national scholarships and fellowships, then it is even more important to start your research early—a full year or more before you plan to enroll.

Remember, it can easily take months to fill out applications and assemble all the supporting data for a financial aid request. You may need to submit income tax forms, untaxed income verification, asset verification, and documents that support any special circumstances you are claiming. For private scholarship applications, you may need to write an essay and provide letters of recommendation. So give yourself plenty of time to submit the initial application. Later, if you are asked to provide additional information or supporting documents, do so as quickly as possible.

THE FAFSA

The Free Application for Federal Student Aid (FAFSA) is the only form you will need to apply for most federal need-based aid programs and state aid programs as well. FAFSA is used by both undergraduate and graduate students. The FAFSA form is issued annually by the Department of Education at the end of each calendar year (see www.fafsa.ed.gov), and it is available both in paper and on line. You use it to report financial data from the previous year in order to be considered for aid in the school year that starts the following fall. It's much easier to fill out the FAFSA if you have already done your federal income tax forms for the year, but since most schools require you to file the FAFSA in January or February, that may be difficult. If your federal income tax return is not done, use estimates so you can file the FAFSA on time. You can amend it later if necessary. Because the FAFSA is designed for undergraduate students who are dependent on their parents, if you are a working adult student you may find you are having difficulty interpreting some of the questions or that the questions do not cover all your circumstances. If there is information about your financial situation that is not elicited by the FAFSA but that you feel is germane to your application, then explain the circumstances in a separate letter to the financial aid office of the schools to which you apply. Suppose, for example, that you have been working full-time for a few years but you are planning to quit your job and attend school full-time. You would complete the FAFSA using the previous year's full-time income figures, but this would not be an accurate reflection of your financial situation during the following school year because your income will drop precipitously. In such a case, you would notify the financial aid office so that it can make a professional judgment as to whether or not your need should be revised upward.

After you submit the FAFSA, you will receive a Student Aid Report (SAR), an acknowledgment that includes a summary of the data you have sent them. Check to make sure the information is accurate and that the schools you have chosen to have the data sent to are correctly listed. If there are errors, make corrections right away. The SAR will also show your Expected Family Contribution, the amount you and your spouse (or parents if you are still a dependent) will be expected to contribute. This information is used by each school to calculate your financial need (cost of attendance minus Expected Family Contribution) and to award need-based aid.

SCHOOL'S FINANCIAL AID APPLICATION FORM OR CSS PROFILE

A school may require that you submit a separate financial aid application in addition to the program application and the FAFSA. If you do not see such a form in the program application packet, call the admissions office to find out whether or not you need to obtain it from another office.

Some schools do not have their own financial aid application form. Instead, they require you to submit a standardized form, the College Scholarship Service's (CSS) Financial Aid PROFILE. This form is similar to the FAFSA, but it is used to award university aid.

THE PROGRAM APPLICATION

For many schools, the program application is the main application for university-based aid. Much of the nonfederal university-based aid for incoming students is determined by the admissions committee's assessment of the merit of program applications. So a strong program application, submitted on time, will improve your chances of getting aid from the program or university. Since you cannot predict which elements of your application will be weighted most heavily by a given admissions committee, do your best on all of them.

NATIONAL AND PRIVATE SCHOLARSHIP AND FELLOWSHIP APPLICATIONS

If you apply for national and/or private scholarships and fellowships, you will have to submit separate applications for each one to the awarding organizations. Follow instructions carefully, making sure you meet all deadlines. Some scholarship applications can be as elaborate as program applications, with letters of recommendation and essays, so allow yourself a lot of time to complete them.

FOLLOWING UP

Just as you do with your program application, follow up with your financial aid applications as well. If you do not receive the SAR, an acknowledgment that your FAFSA form was received, within a few weeks of filing the FAFSA, check on its status. In addition, call the university offices with which you are dealing to make sure everything is proceeding smoothly.

TAX BENEFITS FOR STUDENTS

Whether or not you receive financial aid, there are many recently enacted tax benefits for adults who want to return to school (as well as for parents who send or plan to send their children to college). In effect, these tax cuts make the first two years of college universally available, and they give many more working adults the financial means to go back to school. About 12.9 million students benefit—5.8 million under the HOPE Scholarship tax credit and 7.1 million under the Lifetime Learning tax credit. Countless others benefit from new rules concerning Individual Retirement Accounts (IRAs) and state tuition savings plans as well as from deductions on student loan interest and employer reimbursements for education expenses.

THE HOPE SCHOLARSHIP TAX CREDIT

The HOPE Scholarship tax credit helps make the first two years of college or career school more affordable. Students whose adjusted gross income falls within certain limits receive a 100 percent tax credit for the first $1,000 of tuition and required fees and a 50 percent credit on the second $1,000. This credit is available for tuition and required fees less grants, scholarships, and other tax-free educational assistance. The credit is phased out for joint filers whose adjusted gross income is between $80,000 and $100,000 and for single filers whose adjusted gross income is between $40,000 and $50,000.

The HOPE Scholarship tax credit can be claimed for students who are in their first two years of college or career school and who are enrolled on at least a half-time basis in a degree or certificate program for any portion of the year. The taxpayer can claim a credit for his own tuition expense or for the expenses of his or her spouse or dependent children.

THE LIFETIME LEARNING TAX CREDIT

The Lifetime Learning tax credit is targeted toward adults who want to go back to school, change careers, or take a course or two to upgrade their skills as well as to college juniors, seniors, and graduate and professional degree students. A family may receive a 20 percent tax credit for the first $5,000 of tuition and required fees paid each year through 2002, and for the first $10,000 thereafter.

Just like the HOPE Scholarship tax credit, the Lifetime Learning tax credit is available for tuition and required fees less grants, scholarships, and other tax-free educational assistance. The maximum credit is determined on a per-taxpayer (family) basis, regardless of the number of postsecondary students in the family, and it is phased out at the same income levels as the HOPE Scholarship tax credit. Families can claim the Lifetime Learning tax credit for some members of their family and the HOPE Scholarship tax credit for others who qualify in the same year.

INDIVIDUAL RETIREMENT ACCOUNTS

Since January 1, 1998, taxpayers have been able to withdraw funds from an IRA, without penalty, for their own higher education expenses or those of their spouse, child, or even grandchild. However, you do have to pay income taxes on the amount you withdraw.

In addition, for each child under age 18, families may deposit $500 per year into an education IRA in the child's name. Earnings in the education IRA accumulate tax-free, and no taxes are due upon withdrawal if the money is used to pay for postsecondary tuition and required fees (less grants, scholarships, and other tax-free educational assistance), books, equipment, and eligible room and board expenses. Once the child reaches age 30, his or her education IRA must be closed or transferred to a younger member of the family.

A taxpayer's ability to contribute to an education IRA is phased out when the taxpayer is a joint filer with an adjusted gross income between $150,000 and $160,000, or a single filer with an adjusted gross income between $95,000 and $110,000. There are a few restrictions. For example, a student who receives the tax-free distributions from an education IRA may not, in the same year, benefit from the HOPE Scholarship or Lifetime Learning tax credits.

STATE TUITION PLANS

When a family uses a qualified state-sponsored tuition plan to save for college, no tax is due in connection with the plan until the time of withdrawal. Families can now use these plans to save not only for tuition but also for certain room and board expenses for students who attend college on at least a half-time basis. Tuition and required fees paid with withdrawals from a qualified state tuition plan are eligible for the HOPE Scholarship tax credit and Lifetime Learning tax credit.

TAX-DEDUCTIBLE STUDENT LOAN INTEREST

For many graduates, one of the first financial obligations is to repay their student loans. The new student loan interest deduction reduces the burden of the repayment obligation by allowing students or their families to take a tax deduction for interest paid in the first 60 months of repayment on student loans. The deduction is available even if an individual does not itemize other deductions.

The maximum deduction of $2,000 in 2000 rose to $2,500 in 2001 and beyond. It is phased out for joint filers with adjusted gross income between $60,000 and $75,000, and for single filers with adjusted gross income between $40,000 and $55,000.

TAX-DEDUCTIBLE EMPLOYER REIMBURSEMENTS

If you take undergraduate courses and your employer reimburses you for education-related expenses, you may be able to exclude up to $5,250 of employer-provided education benefits from your income. Reimbursement for graduate and professional courses is not eligible for this exclusion and is counted as taxable income.

COMMUNITY SERVICE LOAN FORGIVENESS

This provision excludes from your income any student loan amounts forgiven by nonprofit, tax-exempt charitable, or educational institutions for borrowers who take community-service jobs that address unmet community needs. For example, a recent graduate who takes a low-paying job in a rural school will not owe any additional income tax if in recognition of this service her college or another charity forgives a loan it made to her to help pay her college costs. This provision applies to loans forgiven after August 5, 1997.

FOR ADDITIONAL INFORMATION

The tax issues relating to higher education are discussed in more detail in Internal Revenue Service Publication 970, *Tax Benefits for Higher Education.* To obtain a copy, visit the Internal Revenue Service Web site at www.irs.gov or call 800-829-3676 (toll-free).

PAYING FOR SCHOOL IS POSSIBLE

You can see that it *is* possible to find the financial aid that will help you pay for school. You will have to be persistent in your search for funds. You may have to spend time working on financial aid research and applications. You may have to borrow money. And once you enter a program, you may have to simplify your lifestyle in order to cut your expenses.

But if you really want to earn a degree or certificate, you can find the financial help that will make it possible. Be realistic about your needs, leave yourself enough time to complete all the paperwork, and do your homework. Now is a good time to look back on all the reasons why you want to continue your education—to remind yourself why it's worth it.

SUCCEEDING AS A DISTANCE LEARNER

Congratulations! You have weathered the selection and application process and you are about to embark on a new phase of your education. As you will soon find out for yourself, taking courses at a distance is not like going to class on campus. Distance learners often have the convenience of setting their own hours and pacing themselves in their studies. As we have seen in previous sections, the instructional technology lends itself to innovative approaches to teaching and learning, including more student participation and collaboration, especially in online courses. You'll find that because you work at a distance you will have more time to reflect about and respond to what you learn as well as to take part in discussions. You may be surprised at the ways in which the community of learning develops in a well-run distance course.

Of course, distance learners face a few challenges unique to the instructional design of distance courses. As a distance learner, you'll be expected to organize your time, work independently as well as collaboratively, take the initiative in your studies, and monitor your own progress, all while mastering the technology and using it as a valuable tool for learning.

So, in addition to the basic study skills you would need to earn any degree—reading, writing, analytical thinking, and test-taking skills—you will need other skills and strategies to succeed at distance learning. In this section we'll give you some suggestions and tips from successful distance learners that will help you become a more effective and successful student yourself.

MASTERING THE TECHNOLOGY

We'll start with technology, because success in distance learning depends first upon reliable technology that you understand how to use. Once you've mastered the technology, it will recede into the background and become something you simply use and even take for granted.

HAVING THE RIGHT EQUIPMENT

Before you start a course, make sure you have the technological tools you will need to participate in discussions and complete assignments. Most programs provide a list of technical requirements ahead of time. If your course is on line, get a list of the hardware and software required, and make sure the computer you plan to use is properly equipped and that you have a reliable Internet service provider. If you take a course via broadcast or videotapes, learn how to use your VCR. If you have to buy equipment, don't skimp on specifications to save a few dollars now. The money you spend now to make sure you have the appropriate hardware and software is money well spent, because you'll find it much easier to get your work done properly if you are not struggling with inadequate machinery.

IMPROVING YOUR TECHNOLOGY SKILLS

If you have the proper equipment but think you may not be up to speed technologically, try to improve your technology skills before courses start. As we discussed in "Selecting a Good Distance Learning Program," many colleges offer online tutorials or sample minicourses that you can take if you feel you need some practice with the technology before you actually take your first course. "I am a computer novice and never realized the extent of the computer's online capabilities until I had to learn about it through trial and error," reports a language arts literacy teacher who took a graduate course on line from Rutgers University. "This was very frustrating." So if you have the opportunity for a sample course or practice session before courses begin, take it.

TIPS FOR SUCCEEDING WITH TECHNOLOGY

To master the technology involved in your distance courses:

- Make sure you have the appropriate hardware and software for your courses, and don't skimp on the specifications if you need to purchase any items.
- Take a tutorial or sample minicourse ahead of time to familiarize yourself with the instructional technology.
- Allow yourself extra time at the beginning of the course to navigate the technology.
- Keep copies of your assignments and back up your computer files.
- Ask for help when you need it. Well-run distance programs have technological support via telephone seven days a week, 24 hours a day.

Remember, the technology involved in distance learning is a tool that anyone can master—it just may take some effort.

LEARNING ABOUT LIBRARY RESOURCES

Once you've got the technology working for you, the next resource you need to familiarize yourself with is the library. Understanding how to use a library is important to any student's success, but it is especially important for distance students who may not be able to get to a good bricks-and-mortar university library to get the materials they need.

TAKING AN ORIENTATION PROGRAM

One of the first things you should check before courses begin is whether or not a library services orientation program designed for distance students is available. If it is, sign up to take the orientation right away. "An early orientation to library resources, particularly interlibrary loans, is needed for those who can't physically access a library," recommends Kurt Krause, a hotel manager who took an online hospitality management course from Virginia Tech. Learning about library services through an orientation program will save you time later on when you actually need to do research for a course.

LEARNING WHAT'S AVAILABLE ON LINE

Although the Internet has revolutionized the way we look for and store information, don't make the mistake of thinking that all the information you will need is available on the Internet. True, many journals, databases, catalogs, and newspapers are instantaneously available on line, and you can access them directly or through the university library if a subscription is needed. However, the material that's available on line is only a fraction of the total resources of a library. Books, for example, are still primarily in print form. Many academic journals provide only abstracts (not full-text articles) on line, and a few are not on line at all. Reference services may be available only face-to-face or by telephone. And reserve collections may or may not be available on line. So one of the first tasks you face is to learn just what you can access on line via the university library or directly on the Internet and what you must access in paper, microform, or other physical media.

PLANNING AHEAD TO GET THE MATERIALS YOU NEED

The reason you will need to know what your research resources are fairly early in the game is that you will have to plan ahead if you need to access nondigitized (paper) information at a distance, especially if the material needs to be secured via interlibrary loan. "Because I did not have physical access to a medical library in my community, I had to organize my data collection for assigned papers early in the semester," explains Patti Iversen. "The biggest handicap was the time delay in ordering and receiving full-text articles. A time lapse of three weeks from time of request to delivery of articles was common." You can see the need to plan ahead under these circumstances.

TIPS FOR SUCCEEDING WITH LIBRARY RESOURCES

In order to be prepared for course work, early in the term or, even better, before the term starts:

- **Take a library orientation if one is available.** If there is no formal distance orientation, call the library and ask for an informal orientation.
- **Check your local public and university libraries.** Find out what resources they have and whether or not you can arrange access.
- **Check each course syllabus very early in the term.** Determine whether you can obtain everything you will need on line or whether you will have to make other arrangements for some items.
- **Use the reference services of your university library.** Ask for help. Reference librarians are there to help you, even if it's by e-mail or over the phone.

MANAGING YOUR TIME

"If you are a student at any college, there is one thing you just don't have enough of....TIME! Everything is about time," says Cena Barber, an undergraduate who has taken online courses toward her degree in political science and history at Drake University in Iowa. For students who have family and work responsibilities as well, lack of time is a particularly acute problem. "With life's challenges, kids, family, job—it's hard to keep your studies a high priority," explains Scott Garrod, who is earning a master's degree in business from Syracuse University. "When your four-year-old wants a story read, do you have to study your accounting? That's an easy choice, but it means making up the accounting at a later time."

GENERAL TIPS FOR MANAGING YOUR TIME

Not having enough time is a common problem. Distance learners can approach this problem in several ways:

- **Be realistic about how many courses you can handle.** If you work and/or have a family, you will have relatively little time to spend on schoolwork. Start out with one or two courses at a time, and then if you feel you can increase your courseload, do so. This is especially important if you take a distance course for the first time and don't know exactly what to expect.
- **Set up a regular time to study, but expect to be interrupted.** If you have a study schedule, you are more likely to get your schoolwork done, but be sure to leave some extra time. Unless you live alone, you'll need time for your family commitments. Young kids, especially, don't much care what you are doing when they need a parent, so if possible try to schedule study time when they are not around.
- **Set up a regular place to study.** Although it may be difficult if you are doing schoolwork at home, try to establish a study area that's yours alone to use. If possible, the area should be quiet and free of distractions. "Since you are doing the work at home you can be easily distracted," explains Andrea Bessel, who is earning a bachelor's degree in business administration from the State University of New York at Oswego. "A lot of times something comes up and I end up setting my homework aside, which is not a good habit to get into." So if necessary, do schoolwork at your local public library or from work if your employer permits it.
- **Set priorities on what you have to do.** Make judgments about what you need to do, and then spend your time on activities that are the most important and must be done first. Get used to the fact that you may have to postpone some tasks.
- **Set deadlines.** Distance learning can be very unstructured, so you probably will have to be your own taskmaster. "I have learned that I have to set deadlines for myself," says Brigit Dolan, who is earning a master's degree from Gonzaga University in Washington, "or I will never get anything done."
- **Don't procrastinate.** "Procrastination is your worst enemy," claims Robin Barnes, who earned a master's degree in nursing (family nurse-practitioner) from Gonzaga University.
- **Use time-management tools to help you schedule your time.** Planners, whether paper or electronic, can help you allocate time and keep track of deadlines. "To do" lists can help you manage your short-term commitments.

MANAGING TIME IN ONLINE COURSES

In addition to the lack of time that all students contend with, online distance learners face unique challenges associated with time, namely, managing the flexibility of the online format and dealing with lag time when communicating with students and faculty members.

MANAGING THE FLEXIBILITY OF ONLINE COURSES

Flexibility is a unique advantage that attracts people to asynchronous courses, especially online courses. But flexibility can have a downside as well. "The best thing about distance learning is the freedom to set one's own hours for study and learning. The worst thing about distance learning is the freedom to set one's own hours for study and learning!" exclaims a middle school language arts literacy teacher taking an online graduate course from Rutgers. "Although it hasn't happened to me, it is easy to put aside work and projects for the course when one is not locked into a regular schedule. I can see how one could easily fall behind through a lack of discipline." So you can see that you'll have to use your time-management skills to take advantage of the flexibility and not let it take advantage of you.

MANAGING THE AMOUNT OF TIME SPENT ON LINE

Not only does the flexibility of online courses mean that you need discipline to log on regularly, but once you are connected you have, in theory, as much time as you want to spend on the course. Cena Barber points out, "There is no time limit as to how long the class lasts. It could be five minutes one day and five hours the next." Unless you are careful, it's easy to spend more time than you really have on an online course, so before you log on, decide how much time you have to spend during that session.

GETTING ACCUSTOMED TO THE PACE

Another difference between online and traditional courses that comes as a surprise to many students is the pace at which discussions proceed. In an online course, there is a time interval between when you post a message and when you get a response—in an asynchronous discussion group—or when you send an e-mail and get a reply. Hours, even days, may elapse between exchanges on a topic, and it can take a while to get used to the slow progress of communication.

The time delay sometimes becomes a problem when students work on a group project with deadlines. "Given the time lag, it took ever so much more time to get anything done if you had to collaborate with anyone," explains a library media specialist taking an online postgraduate course from Rutgers. "When would they open the discussion thread? When would they respond? These were frustrations that I hadn't counted on and found difficult to deal with." To solve these problems, groups working on projects often communicate by telephone or in real-time chat rooms.

TIPS FOR MANAGING TIME IN ONLINE COURSES

Given the asynchronous nature of online courses, you will not be able to completely solve the time problems they pose. However, you can minimize or avoid them to some degree.

- **Set a schedule for logging on.** Even though no one may have given you a daily class schedule, you will benefit if you work one out for yourself. "You should become accustomed to getting on line on a regular basis," advises Vania McBean, a computer studies major at University of Maryland University College. "I log on each day to see what is new."
- **Limit the amount of time you will spend on line at one session.** The limit might be 1 hour, for example. On some days that will be too much time, and on others, too little, but at least you will have a benchmark to aim for.
- **Don't fret about the time delays in asynchronous discussions.** Before you know it, you will have become used to this method of communication and it will no longer seem odd.
- **Use a chat room or the telephone when asynchronous communication becomes too slow.** You can make an appointment to meet in a chat room or have a teleconference if group work needs to be accomplished more efficiently. If e-mailing a fellow student or the instructor takes too long, try telephoning.

MANAGING TIME IN VIDEOTAPED COURSES

Students that take courses in which on-campus lectures are videotaped and mailed to them face a different set of time-management challenges. First, the weekly videotapes may take a considerable amount of time to watch. And second, the taping, duplicating, and delivery time means that distance students lag behind on-campus students in the same course.

SCHEDULING TIME TO WATCH THE VIDEOS

Depending on the course load, students that take videotaped courses may find themselves with 3 to 12 hours or more of videotape to watch each week on top of their assignments. Essentially, the amount of time is the same as it would be if they had to attend classes. Since they don't have to attend classes, inexperienced students may put off watching the videos, thinking they can catch up at a later date. "In the first semester, the learning curve is steep," comments Dale Ann Abendroth, assistant professor of nursing at Gonzaga University. "So I set up my assignments to force students into a pattern of watching the videotapes." If you have a savvy instructor, the assignments will put you on a schedule. If the instructor doesn't take a structured approach, you will need to plan a regular schedule to watch the videos in order to keep up with the course work.

MANAGING THE DELAY BETWEEN DISTANCE AND ON-CAMPUS STUDENTS

In videotaped courses, the distance students are a half-week to a week behind the on-campus students. "It can get a little confusing when reading topics don't correspond with lecture topics because the tapes arrive one week later than the class," explains Carla Gentry, who is earning a Master of Science in Nursing (family nurse practitioner) from Gonzaga University. If the course also has a Web-based component, the distance students have to cope with joining the Web-based discussion group and receiving the readings before the videotaped lectures arrive.

Schools do try to solve this time-delay problem, with mixed success. "Throughout the semester, we have a one-week lag on assignment due dates (in comparison to the students who are actually in class on campus)," explains Nicole DeRaleau, who is earning a master's degree in engineering from Worcester Polytechnic Institute in Massachusetts. "At the end of the semester, however, we have a one-week disadvantage because the whole class has to turn in final assignments, projects, and finals on the same date in order to get grades done on time," says DeRaleau. "This can be *very* stressful." In contrast, at Gonzaga University's nursing program, distance students are permitted to take their final exams in their local communities a few days later than the on-campus students. "These are logistical problems that both the faculty and students become accustomed to solving," explains Abendroth.

TIPS FOR MANAGING TIME IN VIDEOTAPED COURSES

There are a couple of things you can do to manage your time if you take videotaped courses:

- **Set a schedule for watching the videotapes.** Even though you don't have to show up for class, you still need to put in classroom time in front of your own TV. If you're good at multitasking, you can follow Brigit Dolan's lead. "Sometimes I'm able to pick up my house while listening and taking in the information," explains the graduate student.
- **Keep up with your course work.** Since at times you may need to complete assignments or take exams with less lead time than on-campus students have, it's imperative that you keep up with the work on a regular basis. You may face an end-of-term time crunch, so study regularly throughout the course to minimize its effect.

COMMUNICATING WITH FACULTY

When you are a distance learner you can't just raise your hand and ask a question or stay after class to talk with the instructor. Even in two-way interactive video classes, which are more similar to traditional classes than other distance learning formats, there can be difficulties in communicating with an instructor at a remote location. "It can be a little more inconvenient to speak with your instructor if you need to ask about something you wouldn't ask in front of the whole class," reports a horticulture student taking a two-way interactive video course from the University of Cincinnati.

For students in online and videotaped courses, communicating with an instructor can be slow. "Sometimes you do more self-teaching because you cannot just drop into the instructor's office," explains Robin Barnes. "You may have to wait a day or two for an answer to a question. Have patience and be kind to yourself." However, you can use technology to your advantage in communicating with faculty members. E-mail, for example, is an excellent way to contact a faculty member to find out what his or her expectations are, to clarify assignments, or simply to ask a question. You may not get a response immediately, but most faculty members will answer their e-mail within a day or two. In fact, you should make a point of communicating with your instructor in distance courses. "Be sure to communicate regularly with your professor because [the course] can seem pretty far removed if you are not getting feedback every week or so," advises Sonja Cole, a middle school media specialist taking online courses from Rutgers.

TIPS FOR COMMUNICATING WITH FACULTY MEMBERS

To ensure you get the input an instructor can provide and to make yourself known, here are some strategies for communicating with faculty members:

- **Participate in online discussion groups.** Although your instructor may not comment all the time, he or she is following the class's discussions and will get to know you there.
- **Participate in class discussions in two-way interactive video courses.** It's easy to "hide in the back of the class" if you attend a course in a remote location, but you'll get more out of the class if you respond to the instructor and the class discussion.
- **Be assertive in communicating with your instructors.** "You have to take the initiative," advises a distance learning student. "If you do not make sure that you get the best learning opportunity that you can, no one is going to do that for you." Remember, most faculty members are more than happy to help their students.
- **Use e-mail or the telephone.** If you need to communicate with the instructor privately, use e-mail or the telephone. Most faculty members will respond within a day or two.

REACHING OUT TO YOUR FELLOW STUDENTS

Just as you should take the initiative in communicating with your instructors, you should also be proactive in communicating with fellow students. Communicating with your peers has two benefits: it helps you feel connected to the learning community and it enables you to learn from your fellow students. In addition, establishing good communication with fellow students is key to successful collaborative efforts.

MAKING CONNECTIONS WITH THE LEARNING COMMUNITY

"I have made a conscious effort to build relationships with other students and to keep e-mail contact with them," explains Patti Iversen, a graduate student who lives in Montana and takes distance courses from Gonzaga University in Washington. "This allows each of us the opportunity to get feedback and commiserate." Another student, who is earning a bachelor's degree in information systems management from University of Maryland University College, reports, "My experience with fellow classmates in the online classroom has been very positive. I have found that establishing relationships, despite the fact that they are short-lived, has aided me." During periods when your motivation flags, this connection with others in your courses can help energize you and put you back on track.

TAKING ADVANTAGE OF WHAT YOUR PEERS HAVE TO OFFER

Second, your fellow students can be resources for you. Many distance students are adults with considerable life and professional experience, so they can contribute as much as they learn from the interactions in a course. According to Michael Olsen, who teaches distance courses on the hospitality industry at Virginia Tech, students in his courses "are mature, industry-experienced professionals who come extremely well prepared. They are good contributors and they are not afraid to interact." Scott Garrod, who is pursuing a master's degree in business from Syracuse University, likes the broad range of people he meets through his distance courses. "You do not develop deep relationships," he explains, "but in a distance program you meet a wider range of individuals across multiple countries and careers."

Since all this knowledge and experience is within easy reach, you should take advantage of it. "You need to read through the responses that others post on the Web, so that you actually gain something from the forum discussion," explains Beth Grote, a Drake University student who took a course on line. Some students do more than simply participate in class and in online discussion groups—they form study groups of their own. "You just have to make it a point to form an Internet study group," suggests Robin Barnes. "We would try to converse once a week, more often if we were working on a project."

WORKING ON GROUP PROJECTS

Since instructors often assign group projects in distance courses to help forge a community of learners, you will probably find yourself working with others much more frequently than you did in your past on-campus classes. According to several distance students we surveyed, doing group projects well is one of the most challenging aspects of distance learning. Often the logistics of getting a group of busy working adults in different time zones to meet at an appointed time in a chat room or be available for a conference call can be daunting. In some online courses, separate discussion groups are formed so group members can communicate asynchronously. "You need to have lots of patience and dedication," warns Kevin Ruthen, who earned a master's degree in information resource management from Syracuse University. "Interaction in an online environment can often be more time-consuming than an on-campus meeting."

And the problems of interaction are not limited to time factors. In the online environment, it's sometimes difficult for a group to coalesce and assign roles and tasks to its members. "In one of my courses, members tiptoed around each other, no one wanting to seem overbearing and declare themselves the leader, boss, facilitator, whatever. But we really needed one," explains a library media specialist taking online courses from Rutgers. "It took quite a while for a shakedown to occur so that some work could be accomplished." She continues, "Another problem was what to do about members of the team who were unproductive. It's very hard to prod people over the Internet. On the other hand, since you don't have the opportunity for meandering, off-topic conversations that start in onsite classes, things move swiftly, on schedule."

TIPS FOR COMMUNICATING WELL WITH YOUR PEERS

To make the most of your interactions with your fellow students, you can use these suggestions:

- **Participate.** You should participate in discussions, whether they are in class in two-way interactive video courses or are on line. You will get a lot more out of your courses if you take an active part. In addition, you will get to know the other students and they will get to know you.
- **Share your knowledge and experiences.** Don't assume you have nothing to offer. Most adults have plenty of experience and knowledge that can be of value to others.
- **If you need support from other students, ask for it.** Everyone runs into occasional problems in a course, even if the problem is simply feeling overwhelmed by the amount of work you have to do. Communicating with other students can help you solve problems and get back on track, or it can simply make you feel better because you've let off some steam.
- **Use various forms of communication as needed.** Don't feel limited to class time or discussion groups. You can e-mail or call people with whom you'd like to converse in private. Remember, other distance students may feel somewhat disconnected from the group, too, and they will probably welcome an overture from you.
- **Be assertive.** When you work in a group, be assertive about what you can contribute. If the group is not making progress, try to use some of your leadership skills to get things moving.

ENLISTING YOUR FAMILY'S SUPPORT

One of the main benefits of most distance learning courses is that you can take the course from home. But unless you live alone, that means that you are working from a shared space in the presence of your family. Not only do they have to cope with the fact that you have less time for them, but they have to watch you be inaccessible—not an easy task. Therefore you should make sure you enlist the support and cooperation of your family; having their support will make your life—and theirs—much easier.

One distance student has made her education something of a family enterprise. "I work full-time, and I am blessed with a wonderful, supportive husband and the two greatest children one could ever dream of," says LaVonne Johnson, who is earning a master's degree in nursing from Gonzaga University. "We are in this together, everyone helping on some level," she continues. "My husband cooks, cleans, does laundry, and will proof papers if he is the last resort. My thirteen-year-old daughter is a great help around the house and my sixteen-year-old son is always helping with Power Point projects, statistical analyses, and Excel graphs. Needless to say, in return I try really hard not to impact my family any more than they already are, and we get by."

IN CONCLUSION

Distance learning is challenging, but with motivation, self-discipline, and the support of family, coworkers, and fellow students, you can succeed in your courses and earn a certificate or degree if that's your goal. Perhaps the best summation of distance education we encountered from the scores of students we surveyed came from Patti Iversen:

> Distance learning isn't for the faint of heart or those who require considerable reinforcement to remain on task. It is sometimes difficult for others to recognize the challenges of the distance learner, as job, family, and community activities all continue as before. Finding a way to carve out of a busy schedule the time necessary to successfully complete courses that seem relatively invisible is a big challenge. At the same time, there is absolutely no way that I could have hoped to accomplish the goal that I have set for myself except as a distance learner. I am able to stretch and grow, professionally and personally, while continuing to live a lifestyle that I value immensely. It isn't always an easy task—it is often rigorous and sometimes frustrating—but distance learning has opened a gate of opportunity for me that previously was inaccessible.

Distance learning can provide that opportunity for you as well.

APPENDIX

RESOURCES

WHAT IS DISTANCE EDUCATION?

You can find countless sources of information about distance education by doing an Internet search. One Web site that lists links to distance learning resources is dmoz.org/Reference/Education/Distance_Learning. Some other good sources of information include the following:

The Chronicle of Higher Education
1255 23d Street, NW
Washington, DC 20037
Telephone: 202-466-1000
E-mail: circulation@chronicle.com
Web site: http://chronicle.com

Distance Learning in Higher Education. Council for Higher Education Accreditation, CHEA Update No. 3, June 2000. Available at www.chea.org/Commentary/distance-learning-3.cfm.

Russell, Thomas L. *The No Significant Difference Phenomenon.* Available at teleeducation.nb.ca/nosignificantdifference/.

Survey on Distance Education at Postsecondary Education Institutions, 1997–1998. NCES 2000-13, by Laurie Lewis, Kyle Snow, Elizabeth Farris, Douglas Levin. Bernie Green, project officer. U.S. Department of Education, National Center for Education Statistics, Washington, DC, 1999. Available online at http://nces.ed.gov.

U.S. Distance Learning Association
140 Gould Street
Needham, MA 02494-2397
Telephone: 800-275-5162 (toll-free)
Web site: www.usdla.org

IS DISTANCE LEARNING RIGHT FOR YOU?

Sometimes it helps to have some objective help when you are assessing your goals, aptitudes, strengths, and weaknesses:

National Board for Certified Counselors
3 Terrace Way, Suite D
Greensboro, NC 27403-3660
Telephone: 800-398-5389 (toll-free)
E-mail: nbcc@nbcc.org
Web site: www.nbcc.org

WHAT CAN YOU STUDY VIA DISTANCE LEARNING?

Internet Databases

Peterson's: www.petersons.com/distancelearning

Print Directories

Guide to Distance Learning Programs in Canada 2001. Education International, 2001.

Peterson's *MBA Distance Learning Programs 2000.* Princeton, NJ: Peterson's, 1999.

Peterson's *Guide to Distance Learning Programs 2005.* Lawrenceville, NJ: Thomson Peterson's, 2004.

Equivalency Examinations

College Level Examination Program (CLEP)
P.O. Box 6600
Princeton, NJ 08541-6600
Telephone: 609-771-7865
E-mail: clep@info.collegeboard.org
Web site: www.collegeboard.org/clep

CLEP Success. Lawrenceville, NJ: Thomson Peterson's, 2003.
Lieberman, Leo, et al. *CLEP.* Arco, 2002.

DANTES Subject Standardized Tests (DSSTs)
Telephone: 609-720-6740
E-mail: dantes@chauncey.com *or* exams@voled.doded.mil
Web site: www.chauncey.com/dantes *or* www.voled.doded.mil/dantes/exam

Excelsior College Examination Program (formerly Regents College Examinations)
Test Administration Office
Excelsior College
7 Columbia Circle
Albany, NY 12203-5159
Telephone: 888-647–2388 (toll-free)
E-mail: testadmn@excelsior.edu
Web site: www.excelsior.edu/100.htm

GRE Subject Area Tests
GRE-ETS
P.O. Box 6000
Princeton, NJ 08541-6000
Telephone: 609-771-7670
E-mail: gre-info@ets.org
Web site: www.gre.org

Assessment for Life Experience

Council for Adult and Experiential Learning (CAEL)
55 East Monroe Street, Suite 1930
Chicago, IL 60603
Telephone: 312-499-2600
Web site: www.cael.org

Credit for Work Training

American Council on Education
Center for Adult Learning Educational Credentials
One Dupont Circle NW

Washington, DC 20036
Telephone: 202-939-9475
E-mail: credit@ace.nche.edu
Web site: www.acenet.edu

Credit for Military Training
Servicemembers Opportunities Colleges
1307 New York Avenue NW, fifth floor
Washington, DC 20005-4701
Telephone: 800-368-5622 (toll-free)
E-mail: socmail@aascu.org
Web site: www.soc.aascu.org

SELECTING A GOOD DISTANCE LEARNING PROGRAM

The names and contact information of all agencies recognized by the U.S. Department of Education (www.ed.gov/offices/OPE/accreditation/natlagencies.html) and the Council for Higher Education Accreditation (www.chea.org) are listed below.

Institutional Accrediting Agencies—Regional

Middle States Association of Colleges and Schools
Accredits institutions in Delaware, District of Columbia, Maryland, New Jersey, New York, Pennsylvania, Puerto Rico, and the Virgin Islands.
Jean Avnet Morse, Executive Director
Commission on Higher Education
3624 Market Street
Philadelphia, PA 19104-2680
Telephone: 267-284-5000
Fax: 215-662-5501
E-mail: info@msache.org
Web site: www.msache.org

New England Association of Schools and Colleges
Accredits institutions in Connecticut, Maine, Massachusetts, New Hampshire, Rhode Island, and Vermont.
Jacob Ludes III, Executive Director
Commission on Institutions of Higher Education
209 Burlington Road
Bedford, MA 01730-1433
Telephone: 781-271-0022
Fax: 781-271-0950
E-mail: ccook@neasc.org
Web site: www.neasc.org

North Central Association of Colleges and Schools
Accredits institutions in Arizona, Arkansas, Colorado, Illinois, Indiana, Iowa, Kansas, Michigan, Minnesota, Missouri, Nebraska, New Mexico, North Dakota, Ohio, Oklahoma, South Dakota, West Virginia, Wisconsin, and Wyoming.
Steve Crow, Executive Director
The Higher Learning Commission
30 North LaSalle Street, Suite 2400
Chicago, IL 60602-2504
Telephone: 800-621-7440
Fax: 312-263-7462
E-mail: scrow@hlcommission.org
Web site: www.ncahigherlearningcommission.org

Northwest Commission on Colleges and Universities
Accredits institutions in Alaska, Idaho, Montana, Nevada, Oregon, Utah, and Washington.
Sandra E. Elman, Executive Director
Commission on Colleges
8060 165th Avenue, NE, Ste 100
Redmond, WA 98052
Telephone: 425-558-4224
Fax: 425-376-0596
E-mail: selman@nwccu.org
Web site: www.nwccu.org

Southern Association of Colleges and Schools
Accredits institutions in Alabama, Florida, Georgia, Kentucky, Louisiana, Mississippi, North Carolina, South Carolina, Tennessee, Texas, and Virginia.
Belle Wheelan, President
Commission on Colleges
1866 Southern Lane
Decatur, GA 30033-4097
Telephone: 404-679-4500
Fax: 404-679-4528
E-mail: bwheelan@sacscoc.org
Web site: www.sacscoc.org

Western Association of Schools and Colleges
Accredits institutions in California, Guam, and Hawaii.
Ralph A. Wolff, Executive Director
Accrediting Commission for Senior Colleges and Universities
985 Atlantic Avenue, Suite 100
Alameda, CA 94501
Telephone: 510-748-9001
Fax: 510-748-9797
E-mail: rwolff@wascsenior.org
Web site: www.wascweb.org

Institutional Accrediting Agencies—Other

Accrediting Council for Independent Colleges and Schools
Stephen A. Eggland, Executive Director
750 First Street, NE, Suite 980
Washington, DC 20002-4241
Telephone: 202-336-6780
Fax: 202-842-2593
E-mail: steve@acics.org
Web site: www.acics.org

Distance Education and Training Council
Michael P. Lambert, Executive Secretary
1601 Eighteenth Street, NW
Washington, DC 20009-2529
Telephone: 202-234-5100
Fax: 202-332-1386
E-mail: detc@detc.org
Web site: www.detc.org

Specialized Accrediting Agencies

Acupuncture

Dort S. Bigg, Executive Director
Accreditation Commission for Acupuncture and Oriental Medicine
1010 Wayne Avenue, Suite 1270

Silver Spring, MD 20910
Telephone: 301-608-9680
Fax: 301-608-9576
E-mail: ccaom@compuserve.com
Web site: www.ccaom.org

Art and Design

Samuel Hope, Executive Director
National Association of Schools of Art and Design
11250 Roger Bacon Drive, Suite 21
Reston, VA 20190
Telephone: 703-437-0700
Fax: 703-437-6312
E-mail: info@arts-accredit.org
Web site: www.arts-accredit.org

Chiropractic

Paul D. Walker, Executive Director
The Council on Chiropractic Education
8049 North 85th Way
Scottsdale, AZ 85258-4321
Telephone: 480-443-8877
Fax: 480-483-7333
E-mail: cce@cce-usa.org
Web site: www.cce-usa.org

Clinical Laboratory Science

Betty Craft, Chairman
National Accrediting Agency for Clinical Laboratory Sciences
8410 West Bryn Mawr Avenue, Suite 670
Chicago, IL 60631
Telephone: 312-714-8880
Fax: 312-714-8886
E-mail: naaclsinfo@naacls.org
Web site: www.naacls.org

Dance

Samuel Hope, Executive Director
National Association of Schools of Dance
11250 Roger Bacon Drive, Suite 21
Reston, VA 20190
Telephone: 703-437-0700
Fax: 703-437-6312
E-mail: info@arts-accredit.org
Web site: www.arts-accredit.org

Dentistry

Laura M. Neumann, D.D.S., M.P.H., Associate Executive Director, Education
American Dental Association
211 East Chicago Avenue, 18th Floor
Chicago, IL 60611
Telephone: 312-440-2500
Fax: 312-440-2800
E-mail: education@ada.org
Web site: www.ada.org

Education

Arthur Wise, President
National Council for Accreditation of Teacher Education
2010 Massachusetts Avenue, NW
Washington, DC 20036-1023
Telephone: 202-466-7496
Fax: 202-296-6620
E-mail: info@ncate.org
Web site: www.ncate.org

Engineering

George D. Peterson, Executive Director
Accreditation Board for Engineering and Technology, Inc.
111 Market Place, Suite 1050
Baltimore, MD 21202
Telephone: 410-347-7700
Fax: 410-625-2238
E-mail: accreditation@abet.org
Web site: www.abet.org

Environment

National Environmental Health Science and Protection Accreditation Council
720 South Colorado Boulevard, Suite 970-S
Denver, CO 80246-1925
Telephone: 303-756-9090
Fax: 303-691-9490
E-mail: staff@neha.org
Web site: www.neha.org/AccredCouncil.html

Forestry

Michele Harvey, Director, Science and Education
Committee on Education
Society of American Foresters
5400 Grosvenor Lane
Bethesda, MD 20814-2198
Telephone: 301-897-8720 Ext. 119
Fax: 301-897-3690
E-mail: harveym@safnet.org
Web site: www.safnet.org

Health Services Administration

Andrea Barone-Wodjouatt, Executive Director
Accrediting Commission on Education for Health Services Administration
730 11th Street, NW, Fourth Floor
Washington, DC 20001-4510
Telephone: 202-638-5131
Fax: 202-638-3429
E-mail: accredcom@aol.com
Web site: monkey.hmi.missouri.edu/acehsa

Interior Design

Kayem Dunn, Director
Foundation for Interior Design Education Research
60 Monroe Center, NW, Suite 300
Grand Rapids, MI 49503-2920
Telephone: 616-458-0400
Fax: 616-458-0460
E-mail: fider@fider.org
Web site: www.fider.org

Journalism and Mass Communications

Susanne Shaw, Executive Director
Accrediting Council on Education in Journalism and Mass Communications
School of Journalism
Stauffer-Flint Hall
University of Kansas
Lawrence, KS 66045
Telephone: 785-864-3986

Fax: 785-864-5225
E-mail: sshaw@kuhub.cc.ukans.edu
Web site: www.ukans.edu/P5acejmc

Landscape Architecture

Ronald C. Leighton, Accreditation Manager
Landscape Architectural Accreditation Board
American Society of Landscape Architects
636 Eye Street, NW
Washington, DC 20001-3736
Telephone: 202-898-2444
Fax: 202-898-1185
E-mail: rleighton@asla.org
Web site: www.asla.org/asla/

Law

Carl Monk, Executive Vice President and Executive Director
Accreditation Committee
Association of American Law Schools
1201 Connecticut Avenue, NW, Suite 800
Washington, DC 20036-2605
Telephone: 202-296-8851
Fax: 202-296-8869
E-mail: cmonk@aals.org
Web site: www.aals.org

John A. Sebert, Consultant on Legal Education
American Bar Association
750 North Lake Shore Drive
Chicago, IL 60611
Telephone: 312-988-6746
E-mail: legaled@abanet.org
Web site: www.abanet.org/legaled

Library

Mary Taylor, Assistant Director
Committee on Accreditation
American Library Association
50 East Huron Street
Chicago, IL 60611
Telephone: 800-545-2433 (toll-free)
Fax: 312-280-2433
E-mail: mtaylor@ala.org
Web site: www.ala.org/accreditation

Marriage and Family Therapy

Michael Bowers, Executive Director
American Association for Marriage and Family Therapy
1133 15th Street, NW, Suite 300
Washington, DC 20005-2710
Telephone: 202-452-0109
Fax: 202-232-2329
E-mail: COAMFTE@aamft.org
Web site: www.aamft.org

Medical Illustration

William C. Andrea, Chair
Accreditation Review Committee for the Medical Illustrator
St. Luke's Hospital
Instructional Resources
232 South Woods Mill Road
Chesterfield, MO 63017
Telephone: 314-205-6158
Fax: 314-205-6144
E-mail: andrwc@stlo.smhs.com
Web site: www.caahep.org/accreditation/mi/mi-accreditation.htm

Medicine

Liaison Committee on Medical Education
The LCME is administered in even-numbered years, beginning each July 1, by:
David P. Stevens, M.D., Secretary
Association of American Medical Colleges
2450 N Street, NW
Washington, DC 20037
Telephone: 202-828-0596
Fax: 202-828-1125
E-mail: dstevens@aamc.org
Web site: www.aamc.org
The LCME is administered in odd-numbered years, beginning each July 1, by:
Frank Simon, M.D., Secretary
American Medical Association
515 North State Street
Chicago, IL 60610
Telephone: 312-464-4657
Fax: 312-464-5830
E-mail: frank_simon@ama-assn.org
Web site: www.ama-assn.org

Music

Samuel Hope, Executive Director
National Association of Schools of Music
11250 Roger Bacon Drive, Suite 21
Reston, VA 20190
Telephone: 703-437-0700
Fax: 703-437-6312
E-mail: info@arts-accredit.org
Web site: www.arts-accredit.org

Naturopathic Medicine

Robert Lofft, Executive Director
Council on Naturopathic Medical Education
P.O. Box 11426
Eugene, OR 97440-3626
Telephone: 541-484-6028
E-mail: dir@cnme.org
Web site: www.cnme.org

Nurse Anesthesia

Betty J. Horton, Director of Accreditation
Council on Accreditation of Nurse Anesthesia Educational Programs
222 South Prospect Avenue, Suite 304
Park Ridge, IL 60068-4010
Telephone: 847-692-7050
Fax: 847-693-7137
E-mail: cwargin@compuserve.com
Web site: www.aana.com/coa

Nurse Midwifery

Betty Watts Carrington, Chair
Division of Accreditation
American College of Nurse-Midwives
818 Connecticut Avenue, NW, Suite 900
Washington, DC 20006
Telephone: 202-728-9877
Fax: 202-728-9897

E-mail: educatio@acnm.org
Web site: www.midwife.org/educ

Nursing

Geraldene Felton, Executive Director
National League for Nursing
61 Broadway, 33rd Floor
New York, NY 10006
Telephone: 800-669-1656 (toll-free)
Fax: 212-812-0393
E-mail: gfelton@nlnac.org
Web site: www.nln.org

Occupational Therapy

Doris Gordon, Director of Accreditation
American Occupational Therapy Association
4720 Montgomery Lane
P.O. Box 31220
Bethesda, MD 20824-1220
Telephone: 301-652-2682
Fax: 301-652-7711
E-mail: accred@aota.org
Web site: www.aota.org

Optometry

Joyce Urbeck, Administrative Director
Council on Optometric Education
American Optometric Association
243 North Lindbergh Boulevard
St. Louis, MO 63141
Telephone: 314-991-4100
Fax: 314-991-4101
E-mail: coe@theaoa.org
Web site: www.aoanet.org

Osteopathic Medicine

John B. Crosby, Executive Director
Bureau of Professional Education, Council on Predoctoral Education
American Osteopathic Association
142 East Ontario Street
Chicago, IL 60611
Telephone: 800-621-1773 (toll-free)
Fax: 312-202-8200
E-mail: ssweet@aoa-net.org
Web site: www.aoa-net.org

Pastoral Education

Reverend Teresa E. Snorton, Executive Director
Accreditation Commission
Association for Clinical Pastoral Education, Inc.
1549 Clairmont Road, Suite 103
Decatur, GA 30033-4611
Telephone: 404-320-1472
Fax: 404-320-0849
E-mail: teresa@acpe.edu
Web site: www.acpe.edu

Pharmacy

Peter H. Vlasses, Executive Director
American Council on Pharmaceutical Education
311 West Superior Street
Chicago, IL 60610
Telephone: 312-664-3575
Fax: 312-664-4652
E-mail: csinfo@acpe-accredit.org
Web site: www.acpe-accredit.org

Physical Therapy

Mary Jane Harris, Director
Department of Accreditation
American Physical Therapy Association
1111 North Fairfax Street
Alexandria, VA 22314-1488
Telephone: 800-999-2782 (toll-free) *or* 703-684-2782
Fax: 703-684-7343
E-mail: accreditation@apta.org
Web site: www.apta.org

Planning

Beatrice Clupper, Director
American Institute of Certified Planners/Association of Collegiate Schools of Planning
Merle Hay Tower, Suite 302
3800 Merle Hay Road
Des Moines, IA 50310
Telephone: 515-252-0729
Fax: 515-252-7404
E-mail: fi_pab@netins.net
Web site: http://netins.net/web/pab_fi66

Podiatric Medicine

Alan R. Tinkleman, Director
Council on Podiatric Medical Education
American Podiatric Medical Association
9312 Old Georgetown Road
Bethesda, MD 20814-1698
Telephone: 301-571-9200
Fax: 301-530-2752
E-mail: sbsaylor@apma.org
Web site: www.apm.org/cpme

Psychology and Counseling

Susan F. Zlotlow, Director
Committee on Accreditation
American Psychological Association
750 First Street, NE
Washington, DC 20002-4242
Telephone: 202-336-5979
Fax: 202-336-5978
E-mail: apaaccred@apa.org
Web site: www.apa.org/ed/accred.html

Carol L. Bobby, Executive Director
Council for Accreditation of Counseling and Related Educational Programs
American Counseling Association
5999 Stevenson Avenue, Fourth Floor
Alexandria, VA 22304
Telephone: 800-347-6647 Ext. 301 (toll-free)
Fax: 703-823-1581
E-mail: cacrep@aol.com
Web site: www.counseling.org/CACREP

Public Affairs and Administration

Michael A. Brintnall, Executive Director
Commission on Peer Review and Accreditation

National Association of Schools of Public Affairs and Administration
1120 G Street, NW, Suite 730
Washington, DC 20005
Telephone: 202-628-8965
Fax: 202-626-4978
E-mail: naspaa@naspaa.org
Web site: www.naspaa.org

Public Health

Patricia Evans, Executive Director
Council on Education for Public Health
800 I Street, NW, Suite 202
Washington, DC 20001-3710
Telephone: 202-789-1050
Fax: 202-789-1895
E-mail: patevans@ceph.org
Web site: www.ceph.org

Rabbinical and Talmudic Education

Bernard Fryshman, Executive Vice President
Association of Advanced Rabbinical and Talmudic Schools
175 Fifth Avenue, Suite 711
New York, NY 10010
Telephone: 212-477-0950
Fax: 212-533-5335

Rehabilitation Education

Jeanne Patterson, Executive Director
Council on Rehabilitation Education
Commission on Standards and Accreditation
1835 Rohlwing Road, Suite E
Rolling Meadows, IL 60008
Telephone: 847-394-1785
Fax: 847-394-2108
E-mail: patters@polaris.net
Web site: www.core-rehab.org

Social Work

Nancy Randolph, Director
Council on Social Work Education
1725 Duke Street, Suite 500
Alexandria, VA 22314
Telephone: 703-683-8080
Fax: 703-683-8099
E-mail: accred@cswe.org
Web site: www.cswe.org

Speech-Language Pathology and Audiology

Sharon Goldsmith, Director
American Speech-Language-Hearing Association
10801 Rockville Pike
Rockville, MD 20852
Telephone: 301-897-5700
Fax: 301-571-0457
E-mail: accreditation@asha.org
Web site: www.asha.org

Theater

Samuel Hope, Executive Director
National Association of Schools of Theatre
11250 Roger Bacon Drive, Suite 21
Reston, VA 20190
Telephone: 703-437-0700
Fax: 703-437-6312
E-mail: info@arts-accredit.org
Web site: www.arts-accredit.org

Theology

Daniel O. Aleshire, Executive Director
Association of Theological Schools in the United States and Canada
10 Summit Park Drive
Pittsburgh, PA 15275-1103
Telephone: 412-788-6505
Fax: 412-788-6510
E-mail: ats@ats.edu
Web site: www.ats.edu

Veterinary Medicine

Donald G. Simmons, Director of Education and Research Division
American Veterinary Medical Association
1931 North Meacham Road, Suite 100
Schaumburg, IL 60173
Telephone: 847-925-8070
Fax: 847-925-1329
E-mail: dsimmons@avma.org
Web site: www.avma.org

Accreditation in Canada

To get general information about accreditation in Canada, visit the Web site of the Council of Ministers of Education. Their Web site also has contact information and links to the provincial departments of education.

Council of Ministers of Education, Canada
95 St. Clair Avenue West, Suite 1106
Toronto, Ontario
Canada M4V 1N6
Telephone: 416-962-8100
Fax: 416-962-2800
E-mail: cmec@cmec.ca
Web site: www.cmec.ca

Other Resources for Evaluating Programs

Bear, Mariah P., John Bear, and John B. Bear. *Bear's Guide to Earning Degrees Nontraditionally, 13th ed.*

Ten Speed Press, 1999.

Quality on the Line: Benchmarks for Success in Internet-Based Distance Education. Washington, DC: The Institute for Higher Education Policy, March 2000. Available at www.ihep.com/qualityonline.pdf.

TAKING STANDARDIZED ADMISSIONS TESTS

SATs

For information about the SATs, contact the College Board:

SAT Program
The College Board
P.O. Box 6202
Princeton, NJ 08541-6202
Telephone: 609-771-7600
E-mail: sat@info.collegeboard.org
Web site: www.collegeboard.org

The College Board offers free preparation advice and practice tests. The Web site also offers other test-preparation materials, including books, videos, and software, for a charge. Order at www.collegeboard.org or call 609-771-7243:

The Official SAT Study Guide. 889 pp. 2004.

Real SAT Subject Tests. 740 pp. 2005.

Other test-preparation resources:

Carris, Joan. *Panic Plan for the SAT.* Lawrenceville, NJ: Thomson Peterson's, 2004.

Ultimate SAT Toolkit. Lawrenceville, NJ: Thomson Peterson's, 2006.

ACT Assessment

ACT Registration
P.O. Box 414
Iowa City, IA 52243-0414
Telephone: 319-337-1270
Web site: www.act.org/aap

The Web site offers test-preparation strategies, sample questions, and information about other ACT resources.

ACT Inc., *The Real ACT Prep Guide.* Lawrenceville, NJ: Thomson Peterson's, 2004.

GREs

For information about the GREs, contact the Educational Testing Service:

GRE-ETS
PO Box 6000
Princeton, NJ 08541-6000
Telephone: (609) 771-7670
E-mail: gre-info@ets.org
Web site (GRE Online): www.gre.org

The Web site offers a lot of material that can be downloaded: information bulletins, practice tests, descriptions of the subject area tests, and preparation software. Order from ETS at www.gre.org:

GRE Big Book

GRE Powerprep Software. Includes test preparation for both the General Test and the Writing Assessment.

GRE Practicing to Take the General Test

Practice Books for Subject Area Tests

Other resources:

Ultimate GRE Toolkit. Lawrenceville, NJ: Thomson Peterson's, 2004.

MAT

Harcourt Assessment
19500 Bulverde Rd.
San Antonio, TX 78259
Telephone: (800) 211-8378 (toll-free)
Web site: www.milleranalogies.com

Bader, William, and Daniel S. Burt. *Master the Miller Analogies Test.* Lawrenceville, NJ: Thomson Peterson's, 2006.

GMAT

GMAT
Distribution and Receiving Center
225 Phillips Boulevard
Ewing, NJ 08628-7435
Telephone: 609-771-7330
E-mail: gmat@ets.org
Web site (MBA Explorer): www.gmac.com

Ultimate GMAT Toolkit. Lawrenceville, NJ: Thomson Peterson's, 2004.

TOEFL

Information on the TOEFL can be obtained from the Educational Testing Service:

TOEFL
PO Box 6151
Princeton, NJ 08541-6151
Telephone: 609-771-7100
E-mail: toefl@ets.org
Web site: www.toefl.org

Master TOEFL Writing Skills, Master TOEFL Reading Skills, Master TOEFL Vocabulary. Lawrenceville, NJ: Peterson's, 2007.

APPLYING FOR ADMISSION TO DEGREE PROGRAMS

Davidson, Wilma, and Susan McCloskey. *Writing a Winning College Application Essay.* Lawrenceville, NJ: Peterson's, 2002.

Hayden, Thomas C. *Insider's Guide to College Admissions.* Lawrenceville, NJ: Peterson's, 2000.

Stelzer, Richard J. *How to Write a Winning Personal Statement for Graduate and Professional School, 3rd ed.* Princeton, NJ: Peterson's, 1997. Lots of suggestions, both from the author and admissions representatives of graduate and professional schools, along with many sample essays.

PAYING FOR YOUR EDUCATION

General Information

Financial Aid Information Page (www.finaid.org). The best place to start an Internet search for financial aid information.

National Association of Student Financial Aid Administrators (www.nasfaa.org). Lots of essays explain various aspects of financial aid, including educational tax credits.

State Residency

Todd, Daryl F., Jr. *How to Cut Tuition: The Complete Guide to In-State Tuition.* Linwood, NJ: Atlantic Educational Publishing, 1997.

Federal Aid

Federal Student Aid Information Center
P.O. Box 84
Washington, DC 20044-0084
Telephone: 800-4-FED-AID (toll-free) (general information, assistance, and publications)
Web sites:
General information and home page: www.ed.gov/studentaid

For a copy of *Financial Aid: The Student Guide:* www.ed.gov/prog_info/SFA/StudentGuide.

For the FAFSA, go to FAFSA Online: www.fafsa.ed.gov.

For more on the Distance Education Demonstration Program: www.ed.gov/offices/OPE/PPI/DistEd/proginfo.html.

State Agencies of Higher Education

Alabama: 334-242-2274
Alaska: 907-465-6741
Arizona: 602-229-2591
Arkansas: 800-547-8839 (toll-free)
California: 916-526-7590
Colorado: 303-866-2723
Connecticut: 860-947-1855
Delaware: 800-292-7935 (toll-free)
District of Columbia: 202-698-2400
Florida: 888-827-2004 (toll-free)
Georgia: 770-724-9030 or 404-656-5969
Hawaii: 808-956-8213
Idaho: 208-334-2270
Illinois: 800-899-4722 (toll-free)
Indiana: 317-232-2350
Iowa: 515-242-3344
Kansas: 785-296-3517
Kentucky: 800-928-8926 (toll-free)
Louisiana: 800-259-5626 (toll-free)
Maine: 800-228-3734 (toll-free)
Maryland: 410-260-4565
Massachusetts: 617-727-9420
Michigan: 877-323-2287 (toll-free)
Minnesota: 800-657-3866 (toll-free)
Mississippi: 601-432-6997
Missouri: 800-473-6757 (toll-free)
Montana: 800-537-7508 (toll-free)
Nebraska: 402-471-2847
Nevada: 775-687-9228
New Hampshire: 603-271-2555
New Jersey: 800-792-8670 (toll-free)
New Mexico: 800-279-9777 (toll-free)
New York: 800-642-6234 (toll-free)
North Carolina: 800-600-3453 (toll-free)
North Dakota: 701-328-4114
Ohio: 888-833-1133 (toll-free)
Oklahoma: 800-858-1840 (toll-free)
Oregon: 800-452-8807 (toll-free)
Pennsylvania: 800-692-7392 or 7435(toll-free)
Rhode Island: 800-922-9855 (toll-free)
South Carolina: 803-737-2260
South Dakota: 605-773-3134
Tennessee: 800-342-1663 (toll-free)
Texas: 800-242-3062 (toll-free)
Utah: 800-418-8757 (toll-free)
Vermont: 800-642-3177 (toll-free)
Virginia: 804-786-1690
Washington: 360-753-7850
West Virginia: 888-825-5707 (toll-free)
Wisconsin: 608-267-2206
Wyoming: 307-777-7763
Guam: 671-475-0457
Northern Marianas: 670-234-6128
Puerto Rico: 787-724-7100
Republic of Palau: 680-488-2471
Virgin Islands: 340-774-4546

CSS Financial Aid Profile

Contact the College Scholarship Service at www.collegeboard.org or 305-829-9793.

Grants, Fellowships, and Scholarships

AJR Newslink (www.newslink.org). Awards, grants, and scholarships for journalism students.

Annual Register of Grant Support: A Directory of Funding Sources. Wilmette, IL.: National Register Publishing Company.

College Money Handbook 2007. Lawrenceville, NJ: Thomson Peterson's, 2006.

Corporate Foundation Profiles. New York: Foundation Center, 1999 (http://fdncenter.org or 212-620-4230).

FastWeb (http://fastweb.com). Online searchable database of scholarships and fellowships.

Petersons.com. Online searchable database of scholarships and fellowships.

Getting Money for Graduate School. Lawrenceville, NJ: Thomson Peterson's, 2002.

Scholarships, Grants, & Prizes 2007. Lawrenceville, NJ: Thomson Peterson's, 2006.

Cooperative Education

Re, Joseph M. *Earn and Learn.* Octameron Associates, 1997.

Credit Reporting Agencies

It's a good idea to check your credit rating before you apply for any loans. Call first to find out if there is a fee.

Experian
PO Box 9530
Allen, TX 75013
Telephone: 888-397-3742 (toll-free)

Equifax
PO Box 105873
Atlanta, GA 30348
Telephone: 800-685-1111 (toll-free)

CSC Credit Services
Consumer Assistance Center
PO Box 674402
Houston, TX 77267-4402
Telephone: 800-759-5979 (toll-free)

Trans Union Corporation
PO Box 390
Springfield, PA 19064-0390
Telephone: 800-888-4213 (toll-free)

Tax Issues

Educational Expenses, IRS Publication 508.

Tax Benefits for Higher Education. IRS Publication 970.

To get a copy of these publications, visit the Internal Revenue Service Web site at www.irs.ustreas.gov/prod/forms_pubs/pubs or call 800-829-3676 (toll-free).

Women, Minority Students, Disabled Students, and Veterans

Bruce-Young, Doris M., and William C. Young. *Higher Education Money Book for Women and Minorities.* Young Enterprises International, 1997.

Minority and Women's Complete Scholarship Book; plus Scholarships for Religious Affiliations and People with Disabilities. Sourcebooks, 1998.

Olson, Elizabeth A. *Dollars for College (Women).* Garrett Park Press, 1995.

Saludos Web Education Center (www.saludos.com). Internships and scholarships targeted to Hispanic Americans as well as those not considering race or ethnicity.

Schlachter, Gail Ann, and R. David Weber. *Financial Aid for African Americans.* Reference Service Press, 1997.

Schlachter, Gail Ann, and R. David Weber. *Financial Aid for the Disabled and Their Families.* Reference Service Press, 1998.

Schlachter, Gail Ann, and R. David Weber. *Financial Aid for Veterans, Military Personnel, and Their Dependents.* Reference Service Press, 1996.

Schlachter, Gail Ann. *Directory of Financial Aid for Women.* Reference Service Press, 1997.

International Students

Funding for U.S. Study—A Guide for International Students and Professionals and *Financial Resources for International Study.* New York: Institute of International Education (www.iiebooks.org).

SUCCEEDING AS A DISTANCE LEARNER

Bruno, Frank J. *Going Back to School: College Survival Strategies for Adult Students.* New York, Arco, 1998.

GLOSSARY

accreditation—in the United States, the process by which private, nongovernmental educational agencies with regional or national scope certify that colleges and universities provide educational programs at basic levels of quality

ACT Assessment—a standardized undergraduate admissions test that is based on the typical high school curriculum

associate degree—a degree awarded upon the successful completion of a prebaccalaureate-level program, usually consisting of two years of full-time study at the college level

asynchronous—not simultaneous or concurrent; for example, discussion groups in online courses are asynchronous because students can log on and post messages at any time

audioconferencing—electronic meeting in which participants in remote locations can communicate with one another using phones

bachelor's degree—a degree awarded upon the successful completion of about four years of full-time study at the college level

bandwidth—the width of frequencies required to transmit a communications signal without too much distortion; video, animation, and sound require more bandwidth than text

broadband—a high-speed, high-capacity transmission channel carried on coaxial or fiber-optic cable; it has a higher *bandwidth* than telephone lines and so can transmit more data more quickly than telephone lines

broadcast radio and television—radio and television programs sent out over the airwaves; one of the earliest distance learning technologies still used today

browser—a computer program used to view, download, upload, or otherwise access documents (sites) on the World Wide Web

bulletin board—a site on the Internet where people can post messages

cable television—television programming transmitted over optical fiber, coaxial, or twisted pair (telephone) cables

CD-ROM—compact disc, read-only memory; an optical storage technology that allows you to store and play back data

certificate—an educational credential awarded upon completion of a structured curriculum, typically including several courses but lasting for a period of time less than that required for a degree

certification—the awarding of a credential, usually by a professional or industry group, usually after a course of study and the passing of an exam

chat room—a site on the Internet in which people can communicate synchronously by typing messages to one another

CLEP—the College Level Examination Program, administered by the College Board, that tests students' subject knowledge in order to award college-level credit for noncollegiate learning

common application form—a standardized basic admissions application form, available online, that is used by many colleges

consortium—a group of colleges and universities that pool resources to enable students to take courses as needed from all participating institutions

continuing education unit—10 contact hours of participation in an organized continuing education program; a nationwide, standardized measure of continuing education courses

correspondence course—individual or self-guided study by mail from a college or university for which credit is typically granted through written assignments and proctored examinations; also referred to as *independent study*

correspondence school—a school whose primary means of delivering instruction is via *correspondence courses*

cost of attendance—the total cost, including tuition, fees, living expenses, books, supplies, and miscellaneous expenses, of attending a particular school for an academic year

DANTES Subject Standardized Tests—a series of equivalency examinations used primarily by the U.S. Department of Defense but available to civilians as well

distance learning—the delivery of educational programs to students who are off site; also called *distance education*

doctoral degree—the highest degree awarded upon demonstrated mastery of a subject, including the ability to do scholarly research

DVD—digital video disc; an optical storage technology that allows you to store and retrieve audio and video data

e-learning—distance learning via the Internet; sometimes called *online learning*

e-mail—text or other messages sent over the Internet

enrollment status—whether a student is enrolled full-time, three-quarter-time, half-time, or less than half-time in a degree or certificate program

equivalency examination—an examination similar to the final exam of a college-level course; if you pass, you may be awarded college-level credit; for example, the CLEP and DANTES exams

Excelsior College Examinations—a series of equivalency examinations administered by Excelsior College; formerly the Regents College Examinations

Expected Family Contribution (EFC)—the amount a student and his or her family are expected to contribute to the cost of the student's education per academic year

FAFSA—the Free Application for Federal Student Aid; needed to apply for federal aid programs

fax machine—a telecopying device that transmits written or graphic material over telephone lines to produce a hard copy at a remote location

Federal Supplemental Educational Opportunity Grant (FSEOG)—a federal grant awarded to students that demonstrate the greatest financial need

Federal Work-Study Program—provides part-time jobs in public and private nonprofit organizations to both undergraduate and graduate students who demonstrate financial need; the government pays up to 75 percent of the student's wages, and the employer pays the balance

fellowship—monies to be used for a student's education that does not have to be repaid; also called a *grant* or *scholarship*

financial need—the amount of money a student needs to be given or loaned or earn through work-study, in order to attend school for one year, calculated by subtracting Expected Family Contribution (EFC) from cost of attendance

first-professional degree—a degree awarded upon the successful completion of a program of study (for which a bachelor's degree is normally the prerequisite) that prepares a student for a specific profession

GMAT—the Graduate Management Admissions Test, a standardized test used by many graduate programs in business

graduate degree—a degree awarded upon the successful completion of a program of study at the postbaccalaureate level; usually a master's or doctoral degree

grant—monies to be used for a student's education that do not have to be repaid; also called a *scholarship* or *fellowship*

GRE General Test—the Graduate Record Examinations General Test, which tests verbal, quantitative, and analytical skills; usually taken by prospective graduate students

GRE Subject Area Tests—examinations that assess knowledge usually acquired in college-level courses

instructional design—the way course content is organized for the learner; it varies from one distance technology to another

Internet—the global computer network of networks that allows for the transmission of words, images, and sound to anyone with an Internet connection; one of the major instructional delivery systems for distance learning

Internet service provider (ISP)—a company such as AOL or Earthlink that serves as a gateway to the Internet; by subscribing to its service, an individual can connect to the Internet

life experience—a basis for earning college credit, usually demonstrated by means of a portfolio

LSAT—the Law School Admissions Test, taken by law school applicants

master's degree—a degree awarded upon the successful completion of a program of study beyond the baccalaureate level that typically requires one or two years of full-time study

MAT—the Miller Analogies Test, a standardized admissions test used by some graduate programs

MCAT—the Medical College Admissions Test, taken by medical school applicants

merit-based aid—funding awarded on the basis of academic merit, regardless of financial need

modem—MOdulator DEModulator; a device that allows a computer to connect with other computers (and therefore the Internet) over telephone lines; the faster the modem speed, the faster data is transmitted

need-based aid—financial aid awarded on the basis of financial need; it may take the form of grants, loans, or work-study

online course—a course offered primarily over the Internet

online learning—distance learning via the Internet; sometimes called *e-learning*

Pell Grant—a federal grant that is awarded to students on the basis of financial need

Perkins Loan—a loan offered by the federal government to students with exceptional financial need

PowerPoint—a software program that enables the user to prepare slides with text, graphics, and sound; often used by instructors in their class presentations

PROFILE®—the financial aid application service of the College Board is a standardized financial aid application form used by many colleges and universities

SAT—a standardized undergraduate admissions test

SAT Subject Tests—subject area tests that assess high school–level knowledge; used by some schools for undergraduate admissions

satellite television—programming beamed to an orbiting satellite, then retrieved by one or more ground-based satellite dishes

scholarship—monies to be used for a student's education that do not have to be repaid; also called a *grant* or *fellowship*

Stafford Loan—a subsidized or unsubsidized loan that is offered by the federal government

streaming video—high *bandwidth* video data transmission

synchronous—occurring simultaneously, in real time

Title IV funds—federal money disbursed to eligible students through eligible, accredited institutions of higher learning or directly from the government

TOEFL—the Test of English as a Foreign Language, taken by students who are not native speakers of English

two-way interactive video—two-way communication of video and audio signals so that people in remote locations can see and hear one another

videoconferencing—one-way video and two-way audio transmission, or two-way video transmission conducted via satellite; instructors and students can communicate between remote locations

videotaped lecture—recording of an on-campus lecture or class session; usually mailed to distance learners enrolled in the course

virtual university—a college or university that offers most or all of its instruction exclusively via technology and usually for a profit

whiteboard—a program that allows multiple users at their own computers to draw and write comments on the same document

work-study award—an amount a student earns through part-time work as part of the Federal Work-Study Program

Institution Profiles

This section contains factual profiles of institutions, with a focus on their Distance Learning programs. Each profile covers such items as accreditation information, availability of financial aid, degree and certificate programs offered, non-degree-related course topics offered, and whom to contact for program information.

The profile information presented here was collected during the summer of 2006 via an online survey for Distance Learning Programs and is arranged alphabetically.

ABILENE CHRISTIAN UNIVERSITY
Abilene, Texas
Instructional Technology
http://www.acu.edu/distanceeducation

Abilene Christian University was founded in 1906. It is accredited by Southern Association of Colleges and Schools. It first offered distance learning courses in 1996. In fall 2005, there were 350 students enrolled in distance learning courses. Institutionally administered financial aid is available to distance learners.

Services Distance learners have accessibility to academic advising, bookstore, campus computer network, career placement assistance, e-mail services, library services, tutoring.

Contact Dr. Gary R. Tucker, Director of Distance Education, Abilene Christian University, 1600 Campus Court, ACU Box 29144, Abilene, TX 79699-9201. Telephone: 325-674-2950. Fax: 325-674-2717. E-mail: gary.tucker@acu.edu.

DEGREES AND AWARDS

Technical Certificate Applied Studies

MA Conflict Resolution and Reconciliation

MEd Leadership of Learning

COURSE SUBJECT AREAS OFFERED OUTSIDE OF DEGREE PROGRAMS

Undergraduate—biblical studies; business/corporate communications; communication and media; economics; education; English; sociology.

Graduate—biblical studies; education; human development, family studies, and related services.

ACADEMY OF ART UNIVERSITY
San Francisco, California

Academy of Art University was founded in 1929. It is accredited by Accrediting Council for Independent Colleges and Schools. It first offered distance learning courses in 2002. In fall 2005, there were 2,279 students enrolled in distance learning courses. Institutionally administered financial aid is available to distance learners.

Services Distance learners have accessibility to academic advising, bookstore, campus computer network, career placement assistance, e-mail services, tutoring.

Contact Admissions, Academy of Art University, 79 New Montgomery Street, San Francisco, CA 94105. Telephone: 800-544-2787. E-mail: info@academyart.edu.

DEGREES AND AWARDS

AA Advertising; Animation and Visual Effects; Computer Arts/New Media; Fashion; Fine Art; Graphic Design; Illustration; Industrial Design; Interior Architecture and Design; Motion Pictures and Television; Photography

BA Advertising; Animation and Visual Effects; Computer Arts/New Media; Fashion; Fine Art; Graphic Design; Illustration; Industrial Design; Interior Architecture and Design; Motion Pictures and Television; Photography

MFA Advertising; Animation and Visual Effects; Computer Arts/New Media; Fashion; Fine Art; Graphic Design; Illustration; Industrial Design; Interior Architecture and Design; Motion Pictures and Television; Photography

COURSE SUBJECT AREAS OFFERED OUTSIDE OF DEGREE PROGRAMS

Undergraduate—apparel and textiles; design and applied arts; film/video and photographic arts; graphic communications; interior architecture; visual and performing arts.

Graduate—apparel and textiles; design and applied arts; film/video and photographic arts; graphic communications; interior architecture; visual and performing arts.

ACADIA UNIVERSITY
Wolfville, Nova Scotia, Canada
Division of Continuing and Distance Education
http://conted.acadiau.ca

Acadia University was founded in 1838. It is provincially chartered. It first offered distance learning courses in 1968. In fall 2005, there were 1,000 students enrolled in distance learning courses. Institutionally administered financial aid is available to distance learners.

Services Distance learners have accessibility to academic advising, bookstore, campus computer network, e-mail services, library services, tutoring.

Contact Ms. Tara Moorehead, Student Services Representative, Acadia University, Division of Continuing and Distance Education, 38 Crowell Drive, Wolfville, NS B4P 2R6, Canada. Telephone: 800-565-6568. Fax: 902-585-1068. E-mail: continuing.education@acadiau.ca.

DEGREES AND AWARDS

Certificate Business Administration; Computer Science

MEd Curriculum Studies in Learning and Technology

COURSE SUBJECT AREAS OFFERED OUTSIDE OF DEGREE PROGRAMS

Undergraduate—biology; business administration, management and operations; business/commerce; business/corporate communications; business, management, and marketing related; chemistry; computer programming; computer science; economics; education; educational/instructional media design; education related; English; English composition; English language and literature related; experimental psychology; fine and studio art; foods, nutrition, and related services; geological and earth sciences/geosciences; gerontology; health psychology; history; languages (foreign languages related); liberal arts and sciences, general studies and humanities; linguistic, comparative, and related language studies; marketing; microbiological sciences and immunology; multi-/interdisciplinary studies related; nutrition sciences; philosophy; physics; political science and government; psychology; social sciences; sociology; special education.

Graduate—educational assessment, evaluation, and research; educational/instructional media design; education related.

ADAMS STATE COLLEGE
Alamosa, Colorado
Division of Extended Studies
http://exstudies.adams.edu

Adams State College was founded in 1921. It is accredited by North Central Association of Colleges and Schools. It first offered distance learning courses in 1978. In fall 2005, there were 590 students enrolled in distance learning courses. Institutionally administered financial aid is available to distance learners.

Services Distance learners have accessibility to academic advising, bookstore, e-mail services, library services.

Contact Mr. Walter Roybal, Student Advisor, Adams State College, Extended Studies, 208 Edgemont Boulevard, Alamosa, CO 81102. Telephone: 800-548-6679. Fax: 719-587-7974. E-mail: ascexdeg@adams.edu.

DEGREES AND AWARDS

AA General Education requirements

AS General Education requirements

BA Business Administration; Interdisciplinary Studies; Sociology

BS Business Administration

COURSE SUBJECT AREAS OFFERED OUTSIDE OF DEGREE PROGRAMS

Undergraduate—business/commerce; business/corporate communications; business, management, and marketing related; business/managerial economics; criminal justice and corrections; criminology; English composition; English language and literature related; finance and financial management services; history; human resources management; legal studies (non-professional general, undergraduate); legal support services; medieval and Renaissance studies; sociology.

Graduate—biology; education; educational/instructional media design; education (specific subject areas); technology education/industrial arts.
Non-credit—accounting and related services; business/commerce; computer software and media applications; creative writing; data processing; entrepreneurial and small business operations; gerontology; linguistic, comparative, and related language studies; sales, merchandising, and related marketing operations (general); sales, merchandising, and related marketing operations (specialized).

See full description on page 310.

ADIRONDACK COMMUNITY COLLEGE
Queensbury, New York
http://www.sunyacc.edu/

Adirondack Community College was founded in 1960. It is accredited by Middle States Association of Colleges and Schools. It first offered distance learning courses in 1999. In fall 2005, there were 400 students enrolled in distance learning courses. Institutionally administered financial aid is available to distance learners.

Services Distance learners have accessibility to academic advising, bookstore, career placement assistance, e-mail services, library services, tutoring.

Contact Mr. Douglas Gaulin, Distance Learning Advisor, Adirondack Community College, 640 Bay Road, Queensbury, NY 12804. Telephone: 518-743-2253. E-mail: gaulind@sunyacc.edu.

DEGREES AND AWARDS
AAS Business Administration; Marketing
AS Business Administration; Criminal Justice (Police Science)

COURSE SUBJECT AREAS OFFERED OUTSIDE OF DEGREE PROGRAMS
Undergraduate—accounting and related services; business administration, management and operations; business/commerce; business/corporate communications; computer software and media applications; criminal justice and corrections; criminology; developmental and child psychology; economics; English; English composition; fine and studio art; foods, nutrition, and related services; health and physical education/fitness; history; marketing; mathematics; philosophy; psychology; sociology; technical and business writing.

ALASKA PACIFIC UNIVERSITY
Anchorage, Alaska
RANA (Rural Alaska Native Adult) Program
http://rana.alaskapacific.edu

Alaska Pacific University was founded in 1959. It is accredited by Northwest Commission on Colleges and Universities. It first offered distance learning courses in 1999. In fall 2005, there were 46 students enrolled in distance learning courses. Institutionally administered financial aid is available to distance learners.

Services Distance learners have accessibility to academic advising, bookstore, campus computer network, career placement assistance, e-mail services, library services, tutoring.

Contact Ms. Karma Ulvi, Recruitment Counselor, Alaska Pacific University, 4101 University Drive, Anchorage, AK 99508. Telephone: 907-564-8222. Fax: 907-564-8317. E-mail: karma@alaskapacific.edu.

DEGREES AND AWARDS
AA Education (K-8)
BA Business Administration and Management–Nonprofit emphasis; Business Administration and Management; Education (K-8); Health Services Administration; Human Services

ALCORN STATE UNIVERSITY
Alcorn State, Mississippi
Office of Academic Technologies
http://www.blackboard.alcorn.edu

Alcorn State University was founded in 1871. It is accredited by Southern Association of Colleges and Schools. It first offered distance learning courses in 1997. In fall 2005, there were 339 students enrolled in distance learning courses. Institutionally administered financial aid is available to distance learners.

Services Distance learners have accessibility to academic advising, e-mail services, library services.

Contact Mr. Prashant D. Shinde, Director of Academic Technology, Alcorn State University, 1000 ASU Drive, #569, Alcorn State, MS 39096-7500. Telephone: 601-877-6142. Fax: 601-877-6256. E-mail: prashant@alcorn.edu.

DEGREES AND AWARDS
MSN Nursing

COURSE SUBJECT AREAS OFFERED OUTSIDE OF DEGREE PROGRAMS
Undergraduate—curriculum and instruction; education (specific subject areas); nursing.
Graduate—accounting and related services; environmental/environmental health engineering.

ALPENA COMMUNITY COLLEGE
Alpena, Michigan
http://www.alpenacc.edu

Alpena Community College was founded in 1952. It is accredited by North Central Association of Colleges and Schools. It first offered distance learning courses in 1997. In fall 2005, there were 160 students enrolled in distance learning courses. Institutionally administered financial aid is available to distance learners.

Services Distance learners have accessibility to academic advising, bookstore, e-mail services, library services, tutoring.

Contact Mr. Roy Smith, Dean of Instruction, Alpena Community College, 666 Johnson Street, Alpena, MI 49707. Telephone: 989-358-7443. Fax: 989-358-7561. E-mail: smithr@alpenacc.edu.

DEGREES AND AWARDS
Programs offered do not lead to a degree or other formal award.

COURSE SUBJECT AREAS OFFERED OUTSIDE OF DEGREE PROGRAMS
Undergraduate—computer/information technology administration and management; computer systems networking and telecommunications; criminal justice and corrections; electrical and electronic engineering technologies; English composition; fine and studio art; health and medical administrative services; philosophy; political science and government; psychology; sociology.

ALVIN COMMUNITY COLLEGE
Alvin, Texas
Instructional Services
http://www.alvincollege.edu/de

Alvin Community College was founded in 1949. It is accredited by Southern Association of Colleges and Schools. It first offered distance learning courses in 1995. In fall 2005, there were 1,100 students enrolled in distance learning courses. Institutionally administered financial aid is available to distance learners.

Services Distance learners have accessibility to academic advising, bookstore, career placement assistance, library services.

Contact Mrs. Dena L. Faust, Coordinator of Distance Education, Alvin Community College, 3110 Mustang Road, Alvin, TX 77511. Telephone: 281-756-3728. Fax: 281-756-3880. E-mail: dfaust@alvincollege.edu.

DEGREES AND AWARDS
Programs offered do not lead to a degree or other formal award.

COURSE SUBJECT AREAS OFFERED OUTSIDE OF DEGREE PROGRAMS
Undergraduate—American literature (United States and Canadian); anthropology; applied mathematics; biology; business administration, management and operations; business/commerce; business/corporate communications; business operations support and assistant services; computer and information sciences; computer and information sciences and support services related; computer/information technology administration and management; computer programming; computer science; computer software and media applications; creative writing; curriculum and instruction; economics; English; English composition; English language and literature related; geography and cartography; geological and

earth sciences/geosciences; history; liberal arts and sciences, general studies and humanities; mathematics; mathematics and computer science; mathematics and statistics related; psychology; psychology related.
Non-credit—business operations support and assistant services; computer and information sciences; computer and information sciences and support services related.

AMBERTON UNIVERSITY
Garland, Texas
http://www.amberton.edu/

Amberton University was founded in 1971. It is accredited by Southern Association of Colleges and Schools. It first offered distance learning courses in 1992. In fall 2005, there were 800 students enrolled in distance learning courses. Institutionally administered financial aid is available to distance learners.
Services Distance learners have accessibility to academic advising, bookstore, library services.
Contact Dr. Jo Lynn Loyd, Vice President for Strategic Services, Amberton University, 1700 Eastgate Drive, Garland, TX 75041. Telephone: 972-279-6511 Ext. 126. Fax: 972-279-9773. E-mail: jloyd@amberton.edu.

DEGREES AND AWARDS

BA Professional Development
BBA Management
MA Professional Development
MBA Management
MS Human Relations and Business

COURSE SUBJECT AREAS OFFERED OUTSIDE OF DEGREE PROGRAMS

Undergraduate—accounting and related services; business administration, management and operations.
Graduate—business administration, management and operations; counseling psychology.

AMERICAN GRADUATE UNIVERSITY
Covina, California
http://www.agu.edu/

American Graduate University was founded in 1969. It is accredited by Distance Education and Training Council. It first offered distance learning courses in 1975. In fall 2005, there were 800 students enrolled in distance learning courses. Institutionally administered financial aid is available to distance learners.
Services Distance learners have accessibility to academic advising, bookstore, library services.
Contact Ms. Marie J. Sirney, Vice President, Administration and Accreditation, American Graduate University, 733 North Dodsworth Avenue, Covina, CA 91724. Telephone: 626-966-4576. Fax: 626-915-1709. E-mail: mariesirney@agu.edu.

DEGREES AND AWARDS

MA Acquisition Management–Master of Acquisition Management; Contract Management–Master of Contract Management; Project Management–Master of Project Management
MBA Acquisition and Contracting concentration or Project Management concentration

COURSE SUBJECT AREAS OFFERED OUTSIDE OF DEGREE PROGRAMS

Graduate—accounting and related services; business administration, management and operations; business/corporate communications; business/managerial economics.

AMERICAN HEALTH SCIENCES UNIVERSITY
Aurora, Colorado

American Health Sciences University was founded in 1980. It is accredited by Distance Education and Training Council. It first offered distance learning courses in 1980. In fall 2005, there were 203 students enrolled in distance learning courses. Institutionally administered financial aid is available to distance learners.
Services Distance learners have accessibility to academic advising, e-mail services, tutoring.
Contact Terry Curran, Marketing Manager, American Health Sciences University, 1010 South Joliet Street, Suite 107, Aurora, CO 80012. Telephone: 800-530-8079. Fax: 303-367-2577. E-mail: cn@ahsu.edu.

DEGREES AND AWARDS

Diploma Nutrition Science–Master of Nutrition Science; Nutrition Science–Master of Nutrition Science
CCCPE Certified Nutritionist

COURSE SUBJECT AREAS OFFERED OUTSIDE OF DEGREE PROGRAMS

Undergraduate—nutrition sciences.
Non-credit—nutrition sciences.

AMERICAN INTERCONTINENTAL UNIVERSITY ONLINE
Hoffman Estates, Illinois
http://www.aiuonline.edu

American InterContinental University Online was founded in 1970. It is accredited by Southern Association of Colleges and Schools. It first offered distance learning courses in 2001. Institutionally administered financial aid is available to distance learners.
Services Distance learners have accessibility to academic advising, bookstore, career placement assistance, e-mail services, library services.
Contact Debbie Love, Vice President of Admissions, American InterContinental University Online, 5550 Prairie Stone Parkway, Suite 400, Hoffman Estates, IL 60192. Telephone: 877-701-3800. Fax: 866-647-9403. E-mail: info@aiuonline.edu.

DEGREES AND AWARDS

AAB Completion Program; Criminal Justice Administration concentration; Healthcare Administration concentration; Human Resources concentration; Visual Communication concentration
ABA Business concentration; Information Systems concentration
BA Visual Communication–Digital Design concentration (Completion Program); Visual Communication–Web Design concentration (Completion Program)
BBA Accounting and Finance concentration (Completion Program); Healthcare Management concentration (Completion Program); Human Resource Management concentration (Completion Program); International Business concentration (Completion Program); Management concentration (Completion Program); Marketing concentration (Completion Program); Operations Management concentration (Completion Program); Organizational Psychology and Development concentration (Completion Program); Project Management concentration (Completion Program)
BS Criminal Justice (13-month program)
BST Information Technology–Bachelor of Information Technology (BIT)–Computer Systems concentration (Completion Program); Information Technology–Bachelor of Information Technology (BIT)–Network Administration concentration (Completion Program); Information Technology–Bachelor of Information Technology (BIT)–Programming concentration (Completion Program)
MBA Accounting and Finance concentration (10-month program); Healthcare Management concentration (10-month program); Human Resource Management concentration (10-month program); International Business concentration (10-month program); Management concentration (10-month program); Marketing concentration (10-month program); Operations Management concentration (10-month program); Organizational Psychology and Development concentration (10-month program); Project Management concentration (10-month program)
MEd Curriculum and Instruction concentration (10-month program); Educational Assessment and Evaluation concentration (10-month program); Instructional Technology concentration (10-month program); Leadership of Educational Organizations concentration (10-month program)
MIT Internet Security concentration (10-month program)

See full description on page 312.

AMERICAN MILITARY UNIVERSITY
Charles Town, West Virginia
http://www.apus.edu/

American Military University was founded in 1991. It first offered distance learning courses in 1993. In fall 2005, there were 13,000 students enrolled in distance learning courses. Institutionally administered financial aid is available to distance learners.

Services Distance learners have accessibility to academic advising, bookstore, library services, tutoring.

Contact Ms. Terry Grant, Director of Admissions, American Military University, 111 West Congress Street, Charles Town, WV 25414. Telephone: 877-468-6268 Ext. 3720. E-mail: tgrant@apus.edu.

DEGREES AND AWARDS

AA General Studies
BA African and African American Studies; Asian Studies; Child Development; Criminal Justice; Emergency and Disaster Management; English; Family Development; Fire Science Management; History; Homeland Security; Hospitality Management; Interdisciplinary Studies; International Relations; Legal Studies; Management; Marketing; Military History, Military Management, Intelligence Studies; Philosophy; Political Science; Psychology; Religion; Security Management; Sociology; Transportation and Logistics Management
BBA Business Administration
BS Aerospace Studies; Environmental Studies; Information Technology Management; Middle Eastern Studies; Public Health; Sports and Health Sciences
MA Criminal Justice; Emergency and Disaster Management; History; Homeland Security; Humanities; International Peace and Conflict Resolution; Military Studies; National Security Studies; Political Science; Security Management; Sports Management; Strategic Intelligence; Transportation Management
MAM Management
MBA Business Administration
MPA Public Administration
MS Environmental Policy and Management; Space Studies
MS/MPH Public Health

COURSE SUBJECT AREAS OFFERED OUTSIDE OF DEGREE PROGRAMS

Undergraduate—area studies; business administration, management and operations; computer/information technology administration and management; criminal justice and corrections; criminology; English; English composition; health and medical administrative services; history; human development, family studies, and related services; human resources management; international business; international relations and affairs; liberal arts and sciences, general studies and humanities; management information systems; military studies; military technologies; philosophy; philosophy and religious studies related; political science and government; psychology; public administration; public policy analysis.
Graduate—business/commerce; criminal justice and corrections; history; international relations and affairs; military studies; military technologies; public administration and social service professions related.

AMERICAN PUBLIC UNIVERSITY
Charles Town, West Virginia
http://www.apus.edu/

American Public University was founded in 2002. In fall 2005, there were 13,000 students enrolled in distance learning courses. Institutionally administered financial aid is available to distance learners.

Services Distance learners have accessibility to academic advising, bookstore, library services, tutoring.

Contact Ms. Terry Grant, Director of Admissions, American Public University, 111 West Congress Street, Charles Town, WV 25414. Telephone: 877-468-6268 Ext. 3720. E-mail: tgrant@apus.edu.

DEGREES AND AWARDS

AA General Studies
BA African and African American Studies; Asian Studies; Child Development; Criminal Justice; Emergency and Disaster Management; English; Family Development; Fire Science Management; History; Homeland Security; Hospitality Management; Interdisciplinary Studies; International Relations; Legal Studies; Management; Marketing; Military History, Military Management, Intelligence Studies; Philosophy; Political Science; Psychology; Religion; Security Management; Sociology; Transportation and Logistics Management
BBA Business Administration
BS Aerospace Studies; Environmental Studies; Information Technology Management; Middle Eastern Studies; Public Health; Sports and Health Sciences
MA Criminal Justice; Emergency and Disaster Management; History; Homeland Security; Humanities; International Peace and Conflict Resolution; Military Studies; National Security Studies; Political Science; Security Management; Sports Management; Strategic Intelligence; Transportation Management
MAM Management
MBA Business Administration
MPA Public Administration
MS Environmental Policy and Management; Space Studies
MS/MPH Public Health

COURSE SUBJECT AREAS OFFERED OUTSIDE OF DEGREE PROGRAMS

Undergraduate—business administration, management and operations; computer/information technology administration and management; criminal justice and corrections; criminology; English; English composition; health and medical administrative services; history; human development, family studies, and related services; human resources management; international business; international relations and affairs; liberal arts and sciences, general studies and humanities; management information systems; military studies; military technologies; philosophy; philosophy and religious studies related; political science and government; psychology; public administration; public policy analysis.
Graduate—business/commerce; criminal justice and corrections; ethnic, cultural minority, and gender studies; history; international relations and affairs; military studies; military technologies; public administration and social service professions related.

See full description on page 314.

ANDERSON UNIVERSITY
Anderson, Indiana
http://www.anderson.edu/

Anderson University was founded in 1917. It is accredited by North Central Association of Colleges and Schools. It first offered distance learning courses in 1999. In fall 2005, there were 25 students enrolled in distance learning courses. Institutionally administered financial aid is available to distance learners.

Services Distance learners have accessibility to academic advising, bookstore, campus computer network, e-mail services, library services.

Contact Dr. John H. Aukerman, Director of Distance Education, Anderson University, 1100 East 5th Street, Anderson, IN 46012. Telephone: 765-641-4530. Fax: 765-641-3005. E-mail: jhaukerman@anderson.edu.

DEGREES AND AWARDS

MA Christian Ministries

ANDREW JACKSON UNIVERSITY
Birmingham, Alabama
http://www.aju.edu/

Andrew Jackson University was founded in 1994. It is accredited by Distance Education and Training Council. It first offered distance learning courses in 1994. In fall 2005, there were 500 students enrolled in distance learning courses. Institutionally administered financial aid is available to distance learners.

Services Distance learners have accessibility to academic advising.

Contact Ms. Betty J. Howell, Director of Marketing and Enrollment, Andrew Jackson University, 2919 John Hawkins Parkway, Birmingham, AL 35244. Telephone: 205-871-9288 Ext. 108. Fax: 205-871-9294. E-mail: admissions@aju.edu.

DEGREES AND AWARDS

AS Business; Communication; Criminal Justice
BA Communications
BS Business–Entrepreneurship; Business–General Business concentration; Business–Management/Leadership concentration; Business–Sales Management; Business–Sales concentration; Criminal Justice
MBA Entrepreneurship concentration; Finance concentration; Health Services Management concentration; Human Resource Management concentration; Management Concentration; Marketing concentration; Sales Management concentration; Strategic Leadership concentration
MPA Public Administration
MS Criminal Justice

COURSE SUBJECT AREAS OFFERED OUTSIDE OF DEGREE PROGRAMS

Undergraduate—business administration, management and operations; communication and media; criminal justice and corrections; entrepreneurial and small business operations.
Graduate—business administration, management and operations; criminal justice and corrections; entrepreneurial and small business operations; finance and financial management services; human resources management; public administration; sales, merchandising, and related marketing operations (specialized).

ANNE ARUNDEL COMMUNITY COLLEGE
Arnold, Maryland
Distance Learning Center
http://www.aacc.edu/diseduc

Anne Arundel Community College was founded in 1961. It is accredited by Middle States Association of Colleges and Schools. It first offered distance learning courses in 1981. In fall 2005, there were 2,976 students enrolled in distance learning courses. Institutionally administered financial aid is available to distance learners.
Services Distance learners have accessibility to academic advising, bookstore, campus computer network, career placement assistance, e-mail services, library services, tutoring.
Contact Mrs. Patty McCarthy-O'Neill, Distance Learning Center Coordinator, Anne Arundel Community College, Distance Learning Center, 101 College Parkway, Arnold, MD 21012-1895. Telephone: 410-777-2514. Fax: 410-777-2691. E-mail: pmmccarthyoneill@aacc.edu.

DEGREES AND AWARDS

AA General Studies
AAS Business Management
AS Business Administration Transfer

COURSE SUBJECT AREAS OFFERED OUTSIDE OF DEGREE PROGRAMS

Undergraduate—accounting and related services; allied health and medical assisting services; applied mathematics; behavioral sciences; biological and physical sciences; business administration, management and operations; business, management, and marketing related; business/managerial economics; chemistry; communication and media; computer and information sciences; computer science; criminal justice and corrections; developmental and child psychology; economics; English composition; finance and financial management services; geography and cartography; health and physical education/fitness; history; hospitality administration; intercultural/multicultural and diversity studies; legal studies (non-professional general, undergraduate); legal support services; marketing; mathematics and statistics related; philosophy; political science and government; social psychology; social sciences related; sociology; statistics.

ANTIOCH UNIVERSITY MCGREGOR
Yellow Springs, Ohio
http://www.mcgregor.edu

Antioch University McGregor was founded in 1988. It is accredited by North Central Association of Colleges and Schools. It first offered distance learning courses in 1988. In fall 2005, there were 187 students enrolled in distance learning courses. Institutionally administered financial aid is available to distance learners.
Services Distance learners have accessibility to academic advising, bookstore, campus computer network, e-mail services, library services.
Contact Mr. Seth Gordon, Enrollment Services Manager, Antioch University McGregor, 800 Livermore Street, Yellow Springs, OH 45387. Telephone: 937-769-1825. Fax: 937-769-1804. E-mail: admiss@mcgregor.edu.

DEGREES AND AWARDS

MA Community Change and Civic Leadership; Community College Management; Conflict Resolution; Individualized Liberal and Professional Studies (various self-designed topics); Intercultural Conflict Management

COURSE SUBJECT AREAS OFFERED OUTSIDE OF DEGREE PROGRAMS

Undergraduate—business administration, management and operations; education; ethnic, cultural minority, and gender studies; human resources management; human services.

ARIZONA STATE UNIVERSITY
Tempe, Arizona
Distance Learning and Technology
http://www.dlt.asu.edu

Arizona State University was founded in 1885. It is accredited by North Central Association of Colleges and Schools. It first offered distance learning courses in 1955. In fall 2005, there were 9,248 students enrolled in distance learning courses. Institutionally administered financial aid is available to distance learners.
Services Distance learners have accessibility to academic advising, bookstore, campus computer network, career placement assistance, e-mail services, library services, tutoring.
Contact Jennie Fleege, Student Support Specialist, Senior, Arizona State University, PO Box 874001, Tempe, AZ 85287-4001. Telephone: 480-965-3335. Fax: 480-965-3300. E-mail: jennie.fleege@asu.edu.

DEGREES AND AWARDS

Certificate Multi-Media Writing and Technical Communication
Graduate Certificate Statistics–Graduate Certificate in Statistics, Six Sigma Black Belt Program
MEngr Embedded Systems; Engineering–Arizona Tri-University Master of Engineering program; Microelectronics Packaging; Modeling and Simulation; Quality and Reliability; Semiconductor Processing and Manufacturing; Software Engineering; Systems Engineering
MS Environmental Technology Management; Graphic Information Technology
MSE Electrical Engineering; Materials Science and Engineering

COURSE SUBJECT AREAS OFFERED OUTSIDE OF DEGREE PROGRAMS

Undergraduate—accounting and related services; American literature (United States and Canadian); botany/plant biology; chemical engineering; city/urban, community and regional planning; computer science; computer systems networking and telecommunications; curriculum and instruction; dramatic/theater arts and stagecraft; educational/instructional media design; electrical and electronic engineering technologies; English; English composition; ethnic, cultural minority, and gender studies; fine and studio art; geography and cartography; history; housing and human environments; human development, family studies, and related services; journalism; legal studies (non-professional general, undergraduate); liberal arts and sciences, general studies and humanities; linguistic, comparative, and related language studies; marketing; mathematics; medieval and Renaissance studies; peace studies and conflict resolution; plant sciences; public relations, advertising, and applied communication related; sales, merchandising, and related marketing operations (specialized); sociology; special education; technical and business writing.
Graduate—aerospace, aeronautical and astronautical engineering; chemical engineering; curriculum and instruction; environmental/environmental health engineering; fine and studio art; international business; mechanical engineering; medieval and Renaissance studies.

ARIZONA STATE UNIVERSITY AT THE POLYTECHNIC CAMPUS

Mesa, Arizona

Distance Learning and Technology

http://www.dlt.asu.edu

Arizona State University at the Polytechnic Campus was founded in 1995. It is accredited by North Central Association of Colleges and Schools. It first offered distance learning courses in 1997. In fall 2005, there were 100 students enrolled in distance learning courses. Institutionally administered financial aid is available to distance learners.

Services Distance learners have accessibility to academic advising, bookstore, campus computer network, career placement assistance, e-mail services, library services, tutoring.

Contact Jennie Fleege, Student Support Specialist, Senior, Arizona State University at the Polytechnic Campus, PO Box 874001, Tempe, AZ 85287-4001. Telephone: 480-965-3335. Fax: 480-965-3300. E-mail: jennie.fleege@asu.edu.

DEGREES AND AWARDS

Certificate Multi-Media Writing and Technical Communication

MS Environmental Technology Management; Graphic Information Technology

COURSE SUBJECT AREAS OFFERED OUTSIDE OF DEGREE PROGRAMS

Undergraduate—communication and media; dance; English composition; environmental control technologies; fire protection; health and physical education/fitness; history; nutrition sciences; political science and government; sociology.

Graduate—communication and media; environmental control technologies; mechanical engineering.

ARIZONA STATE UNIVERSITY WEST

Phoenix, Arizona

Office of Extended Instruction

http://www.dlt.asu.edu

Arizona State University West was founded in 1984. It is accredited by North Central Association of Colleges and Schools. It first offered distance learning courses in 1995. In fall 2005, there were 191 students enrolled in distance learning courses. Institutionally administered financial aid is available to distance learners.

Services Distance learners have accessibility to academic advising, bookstore, campus computer network, career placement assistance, e-mail services, library services, tutoring.

Contact Jennie Fleege, Student Support Specialist, Senior, Arizona State University West, PO Box 874001, Tempe, AZ 85287-4001. Telephone: 480-965-3335. Fax; 480-965-3300. E-mail: jennie.fleege@asu.edu.

DEGREES AND AWARDS

Programs offered do not lead to a degree or other formal award.

COURSE SUBJECT AREAS OFFERED OUTSIDE OF DEGREE PROGRAMS

Undergraduate—education related; special education.

Graduate—educational/instructional media design; education related; special education.

ARIZONA WESTERN COLLEGE

Yuma, Arizona

http://www.azwestern.edu

Arizona Western College was founded in 1962. It is accredited by North Central Association of Colleges and Schools. It first offered distance learning courses in 1992. In fall 2005, there were 1,100 students enrolled in distance learning courses. Institutionally administered financial aid is available to distance learners.

Services Distance learners have accessibility to academic advising, bookstore, campus computer network, e-mail services, library services.

Contact Bryan Doak, Registrar, Arizona Western College, PO Box 929, Yuma, AZ 85366-0929. Telephone: 928-317-6100. Fax: 928-344-7543. E-mail: bryan.doak@azwestern.edu.

DEGREES AND AWARDS

AD Administration of Justice; Business Administration; Education

COURSE SUBJECT AREAS OFFERED OUTSIDE OF DEGREE PROGRAMS

Undergraduate—accounting and related services; business/commerce; computer and information sciences; criminal justice and corrections; English; fire protection; liberal arts and sciences, general studies and humanities.

ARKANSAS STATE UNIVERSITY–BEEBE

Beebe, Arkansas

http://www.asub.edu

Arkansas State University–Beebe was founded in 1927. It is accredited by North Central Association of Colleges and Schools. It first offered distance learning courses in 1999. In fall 2005, there were 700 students enrolled in distance learning courses. Institutionally administered financial aid is available to distance learners.

Services Distance learners have accessibility to academic advising, bookstore, career placement assistance, e-mail services, library services, tutoring.

Contact Chris Boyett, Director of Distance Learning, Arkansas State University–Beebe, PO Box 1000, Beebe, AR 72012. Telephone: 501-882-4442. Fax: 501-882-4403. E-mail: jcboyett@asub.edu.

DEGREES AND AWARDS

AA Liberal Arts–Associate of Arts in Liberal Arts

COURSE SUBJECT AREAS OFFERED OUTSIDE OF DEGREE PROGRAMS

Undergraduate—accounting and related services; agricultural business and management; biological and physical sciences; biology; business administration, management and operations; business/corporate communications; business, management, and marketing related; chemistry; communication and media; computer and information sciences; computer programming; computer systems networking and telecommunications; creative writing; criminal justice and corrections; data entry/microcomputer applications; developmental and child psychology; economics; English; English composition; geography and cartography; history; mathematics; microbiological sciences and immunology; music; philosophy; physical sciences; political science and government; psychology; visual and performing arts.

ARKANSAS STATE UNIVERSITY–MOUNTAIN HOME

Mountain Home, Arkansas

http://www.asumh.edu

Arkansas State University–Mountain Home is accredited by North Central Association of Colleges and Schools. It first offered distance learning courses in 2000. In fall 2005, there were 164 students enrolled in distance learning courses. Institutionally administered financial aid is available to distance learners.

Services Distance learners have accessibility to academic advising, bookstore, campus computer network, e-mail services, library services, tutoring.

Contact Ms. Rosalyn Blagg, Registrar, Arkansas State University–Mountain Home, 1600 South College Street, Mountain Home, AR 72653. Telephone: 870-508-6104 Ext. 128. Fax: 870-508-6287. E-mail: rblagg@asumh.edu.

DEGREES AND AWARDS

AAS Hearing Healthcare; Opticianry

COURSE SUBJECT AREAS OFFERED OUTSIDE OF DEGREE PROGRAMS

Undergraduate—biology; computer science; dramatic/theater arts and stagecraft; economics; English composition; health professions related; mathematics.

ARKANSAS TECH UNIVERSITY
Russellville, Arkansas
Virtual Learning Center
http://ccc.atu.edu

Arkansas Tech University was founded in 1909. It is accredited by North Central Association of Colleges and Schools. It first offered distance learning courses in 1996. In fall 2005, there were 829 students enrolled in distance learning courses. Institutionally administered financial aid is available to distance learners.

Services Distance learners have accessibility to academic advising, bookstore, campus computer network, career placement assistance, e-mail services, library services.

Contact Admissions Office, Arkansas Tech University, Russellville, AR 72801. Telephone: 479-968-0343. E-mail: tech.enroll@atu.edu.

DEGREES AND AWARDS
AS Early Childhood Education
BS Early Childhood Education; Emergency Administration and Management
MS College Student Personnel

COURSE SUBJECT AREAS OFFERED OUTSIDE OF DEGREE PROGRAMS
Undergraduate—agricultural business and management; biology; business administration, management and operations; computer and information sciences; educational/instructional media design; education related; education (specific levels and methods); education (specific subject areas); electrical, electronics and communications engineering; English language and literature related; health and medical administrative services; history; hospitality administration; journalism; marketing; mathematics; mechanic and repair technologies related; music; nursing; physical sciences; political science and government; psychology; rehabilitation and therapeutic professions; security and protective services related.

Graduate—educational administration and supervision; educational/instructional media design; education related; education (specific subject areas); journalism.

ARLINGTON BAPTIST COLLEGE
Arlington, Texas
Distance Education Department
http://www.abconline.edu/

Arlington Baptist College was founded in 1939. It is accredited by Association for Biblical Higher Education. It first offered distance learning courses in 1994. In fall 2005, there were 27 students enrolled in distance learning courses. Institutionally administered financial aid is available to distance learners.

Services Distance learners have accessibility to academic advising, bookstore.

Contact Janie Taylor, Registrar, Arlington Baptist College, 3001 West Division, Arlington, TX 76012. Telephone: 817-461-8741 Ext. 105. Fax: 817-274-1138. E-mail: jhall@abconline.org.

DEGREES AND AWARDS
Programs offered do not lead to a degree or other formal award.

COURSE SUBJECT AREAS OFFERED OUTSIDE OF DEGREE PROGRAMS
Undergraduate—biblical studies; theological and ministerial studies.
Non-credit—biblical studies; theological and ministerial studies.

ASHEVILLE-BUNCOMBE TECHNICAL COMMUNITY COLLEGE
Asheville, North Carolina
http://www.abtech.edu

Asheville-Buncombe Technical Community College was founded in 1959. It is accredited by Southern Association of Colleges and Schools. It first offered distance learning courses in 1999. In fall 2005, there were 680 students enrolled in distance learning courses. Institutionally administered financial aid is available to distance learners.

Services Distance learners have accessibility to academic advising, bookstore, campus computer network, career placement assistance, e-mail services, library services.

Contact Darlene Wilson, Director of Distance Learning, Asheville-Buncombe Technical Community College, 340 Victoria Road, Asheville, NC 28801. Telephone: 828-254-1921 Ext. 300. Fax: 828-281-9831. E-mail: dcwilson@abtech.edu.

DEGREES AND AWARDS
Programs offered do not lead to a degree or other formal award.

COURSE SUBJECT AREAS OFFERED OUTSIDE OF DEGREE PROGRAMS
Undergraduate—accounting and related services; applied mathematics; biology; business administration, management and operations; computer and information sciences; computer programming; data entry/microcomputer applications; economics; health and physical education/fitness; history; human development, family studies, and related services; linguistic, comparative, and related language studies; mathematics; philosophy and religious studies related; psychology; sociology; speech and rhetoric; statistics.

Non-credit—building/construction finishing, management, and inspection; business administration, management and operations; business/corporate communications; computer programming; computer systems networking and telecommunications; data entry/microcomputer applications; entrepreneurial and small business operations; family and consumer economics; film/video and photographic arts; human development, family studies, and related services; human resources management; linguistic, comparative, and related language studies; marketing; quality control and safety technologies; sales, merchandising, and related marketing operations (specialized).

ASHFORD UNIVERSITY
Clinton, Iowa
http://www.tfu.edu

Ashford University was founded in 1918. It is accredited by North Central Association of Colleges and Schools. It first offered distance learning courses in 2002. In fall 2005, there were 399 students enrolled in distance learning courses. Institutionally administered financial aid is available to distance learners.

Services Distance learners have accessibility to academic advising, bookstore, e-mail services, library services, tutoring.

Contact Mr. Ross Woodard, Vice President of Marketing, Ashford University, 400 North Bluff Boulevard, PO Box 2967, Clinton, IA 52733-2967. Telephone: 858-513-9240 Ext. 2251. Fax: 866-385-6093. E-mail: admissions@ashford.edu.

DEGREES AND AWARDS
AAB Business
BA Organizational Management; Psychology
MA Teach and Learning with Technology
MAT Teaching
MBA Business Administrations

COURSE SUBJECT AREAS OFFERED OUTSIDE OF DEGREE PROGRAMS
Graduate—education related.

ASHWORTH COLLEGE
Norcross, Georgia
http://www.ashworthcollege.edu

Ashworth College is accredited by Distance Education and Training Council. It first offered distance learning courses in 2000. In fall 2005, there were 40,000 students enrolled in distance learning courses. Institutionally administered financial aid is available to distance learners.

Services Distance learners have accessibility to academic advising, e-mail services, library services, tutoring.

Contact John Graves, Dean, Ashworth College, 430 Technology Parkway, Norcross, GA 30092. Fax: 770-729-9389. E-mail: jgraves@pcdi.com.

DEGREES AND AWARDS
AD Accounting; Computer Information Management; Criminal Justice; Early Childhood Education; Health Information Management; Human Resource Management; Management; Paralegal; Psychology

AS Finance
MBA Business Administration
MCJ Criminal Justice

COURSE SUBJECT AREAS OFFERED OUTSIDE OF DEGREE PROGRAMS

Non-credit—accounting and related services; allied health and medical assisting services; animal sciences; business administration, management and operations; carpentry; computer and information sciences; computer programming; culinary arts and related services; English as a second language; entrepreneurial and small business operations; finance and financial management services; heating, air conditioning, ventilation and refrigeration maintenance technology; hospitality administration; human development, family studies, and related services; landscape architecture; marketing; natural resources conservation and research; sales, merchandising, and related marketing operations (specialized); security and protective services related; taxation; teaching assistants/aides.

ASSEMBLIES OF GOD THEOLOGICAL SEMINARY
Springfield, Missouri
Office of Continuing Education
http://www.agts.edu

Assemblies of God Theological Seminary was founded in 1972. It is accredited by North Central Association of Colleges and Schools. It first offered distance learning courses in 1980. In fall 2005, there were 23 students enrolled in distance learning courses. Institutionally administered financial aid is available to distance learners.

Services Distance learners have accessibility to academic advising, bookstore, campus computer network, e-mail services, library services, tutoring.

Contact Dr. Randy C. Walls, Director, Assemblies of God Theological Seminary, 1435 North Glenstone Avenue, Springfield, MO 65802. Telephone: 800-467-2487 Ext. 1045. Fax: 417-268-1009. E-mail: rwalls@agts.edu.

DEGREES AND AWARDS

Programs offered do not lead to a degree or other formal award.

COURSE SUBJECT AREAS OFFERED OUTSIDE OF DEGREE PROGRAMS

Graduate—biblical and other theological languages and literatures; biblical studies; history; missionary studies and missiology; pastoral counseling and specialized ministries; philosophy and religious studies related; religious studies; theological and ministerial studies; theology and religious vocations related.

ATHABASCA UNIVERSITY
Athabasca, Alberta, Canada
http://www.athabascau.ca

Athabasca University was founded in 1970. It is provincially chartered. It first offered distance learning courses in 1972. In fall 2005, there were 32,000 students enrolled in distance learning courses. Institutionally administered financial aid is available to distance learners.

Services Distance learners have accessibility to academic advising, bookstore, campus computer network, e-mail services, library services, tutoring.

Contact Information Centre, Athabasca University, 1 University Drive, Athabasca, AB T9S 3A3, Canada. Telephone: 800-788-9041. Fax: 780-675-6437. E-mail: inquire@athabascau.ca.

DEGREES AND AWARDS

BA Anthropology (3 year); Anthropology (4 year); Canadian Studies (3 year); Canadian Studies (4 year); English (3 year); English (4 year); French (3 year); French (4 year); History (3 year); History (4 year); Human Resources Management/Marketing (3 year); Human Resources Management/Marketing (4 year); Human Resources and Labour Relations; Humanities (3 year); Humanities (4 year); Information Systems (3 year); Information Systems (4 year); Labour Studies (3 year); Labour Studies (4 year); Management Post-Diploma (3 year); Management Post-Diploma (4 year); Political Economy (3 year); Political Economy (4 year); Psychology (3 year); Psychology (4 year); Sociology (3 year); Sociology (4 year); Women's Studies (3 year); Women's Studies (4 year)
BComm Accounting; E-Commerce
BGS Applied Studies; Arts and Science
BN Nursing–Post-LPN; Nursing–Post-RN
BPA Communication Studies; Criminal Justice; Governance, Law, and Management; Human Services
BS Computing and Information Systems–Post-Diploma; Computing and Information Systems; Health Administration Post-Diploma; Health Administration; Human Science–Post-Diploma; Human Science
Certificate Accounting; Accounting, advanced; Administration; Career Development; Computers and Management Information Systems; Computing and Information Systems; Counselling Women; English Language Studies; French Language Proficiency; Health Development Administration; Human Resources and Labour Relations; Labour Studies; Public Administration
Diploma Arts; Inclusive Education
Advanced Graduate Diploma Distance Education (Technology); Management; Nursing–Nursing Practice, advanced; Project Management
MA Integrated Studies
MBA Business Administration; MBA Energy Elective; MBA–Policing Elective; Project Management
MCDCC Counseling
MCH Health Studies–Master of Health Studies
MDE Distance Education
MN Nursing
MSIS Information Systems

COURSE SUBJECT AREAS OFFERED OUTSIDE OF DEGREE PROGRAMS

Undergraduate—accounting and related services; anthropology; astronomy and astrophysics; biological and biomedical sciences related; biological and physical sciences; biology; business administration, management and operations; business/commerce; business/corporate communications; business, management, and marketing related; business/managerial economics; chemistry; communication and journalism related; communication and media; communication disorders sciences and services; communications technology; community health services; community organization and advocacy; community psychology; comparative literature; computer and information sciences; computer and information sciences and support services related; computer/information technology administration and management; computer programming; computer science; computer software and media applications; computer systems analysis; computer systems networking and telecommunications; counseling psychology; creative writing; criminal justice and corrections; criminology; data processing; demography and population; developmental and child psychology; economics; educational assessment, evaluation, and research; English; English as a second language; English composition; environmental control technologies; finance and financial management services; fine and studio art; foods, nutrition, and related services; geography and cartography; geological and earth sciences/geosciences; health and medical administrative services; health/medical preparatory programs; health professions related; history; human development, family studies, and related services; human resources management; human services; industrial and organizational psychology; international relations and affairs; journalism; legal studies (non-professional general, undergraduate); linguistic, comparative, and related language studies; management information systems; marketing; mathematics; mathematics and computer science; mental and social health services and allied professions; music; natural resources conservation and research; natural resources management and policy; nursing; philosophy; philosophy and religious studies related; physical sciences; physiological psychology/psychobiology; plant sciences; political science and government; psychology; psychology related; public administration; public health; public policy analysis; public relations, advertising, and applied communication related; sales, merchandising, and related marketing operations (general); social sciences; sociology; statistics.

Graduate—accounting and related services; agricultural business and management; business administration, management and operations; business/corporate communications; business, management, and marketing related; business/managerial economics; community health services; community organization and advocacy; community psychology; computer and information sciences; computer and information sciences and support services related; computer/information technology administration and management; computer science; computer systems analysis; counseling psychology; curriculum and instruction; developmental and child psychology; economics; educational administration and supervision; educational assessment, evaluation, and research; educational psychology; education related; health/medical preparatory programs; health professions related; history; human development, family studies, and related services; human resources management; human services; industrial and organizational psychology; information science/studies; international business; international relations and affairs; management information systems; management sciences and quantitative methods; marketing; mathematics and computer science; mental and social health services and allied professions; nursing; philosophy; political science and government; psychology; public administration; public administration and social service professions related; public health; public policy analysis; public relations, advertising, and applied communication related; sales, merchandising, and related marketing operations (general); sales, merchandising, and related marketing operations (specialized); social sciences; social sciences related; social work; sociology; special education; taxation.

Non-credit—accounting and related services; anthropology; astronomy and astrophysics; biology; building/construction finishing, management, and inspection; business administration, management and operations; business/commerce; business/corporate communications; business, management, and marketing related; business/managerial economics; business operations support and assistant services; chemistry; city/urban, community and regional planning; clinical psychology; communication and media; communication disorders sciences and services; communications technology; community health services; community organization and advocacy; community psychology; computer and information sciences; computer/information technology administration and management; computer programming; computer science; computer software and media applications; computer systems analysis; counseling psychology; criminal justice and corrections; criminology; data entry/microcomputer applications; data processing; developmental and child psychology; economics; educational administration and supervision; educational assessment, evaluation, and research; educational/instructional media design; educational psychology; education related; English; English as a second/foreign language (teaching); English as a second language; English composition; environmental control technologies; ethnic, cultural minority, and gender studies; finance and financial management services; fine and studio art; foods, nutrition, and related services; geological and earth sciences/geosciences; gerontology; health professions related; history; human development, family studies, and related services; human resources management; human services; industrial and organizational psychology; international business; international relations and affairs; journalism; liberal arts and sciences, general studies and humanities; linguistic, comparative, and related language studies; management information systems; management sciences and quantitative methods; marketing; mathematics; mathematics and computer science; medical basic sciences; mental and social health services and allied professions; music; nursing; philosophy; philosophy and religious studies related; physical sciences; political science and government; psychology; public administration; public administration and social service professions related; public health; public policy analysis; public relations, advertising, and applied communication related; radio, television, and digital communication; sales, merchandising, and related marketing operations (general); sales, merchandising, and related marketing operations (specialized); school psychology; science technologies related; science, technology and society; social and philosophical foundations of education; social psychology; social sciences; social sciences related; social work; sociology; statistics; taxation.

See full description on page 316.

ATHENS TECHNICAL COLLEGE
Athens, Georgia
http://www.athenstech.edu

Athens Technical College was founded in 1958. It is accredited by Southern Association of Colleges and Schools. It first offered distance learning courses in 1995. In fall 2005, there were 700 students enrolled in distance learning courses. Institutionally administered financial aid is available to distance learners.

Services Distance learners have accessibility to academic advising, campus computer network, career placement assistance, e-mail services, library services, tutoring.

Contact Mr. Jason Ritchie, Webmaster, Athens Technical College, 800 US Highway 29 North, Athens, GA 30601-1500. Telephone: 706-355-5134. E-mail: jritchie@athenstech.edu.

DEGREES AND AWARDS
Programs offered do not lead to a degree or other formal award.

COURSE SUBJECT AREAS OFFERED OUTSIDE OF DEGREE PROGRAMS
Undergraduate—accounting and related services; business/commerce; computer and information sciences; economics; electrical/electronics maintenance and repair technology; English composition; legal studies (non-professional general, undergraduate); mathematics; psychology; psychology related; technical and business writing.

Non-credit—accounting and computer science; allied health and medical assisting services; business, management, and marketing related; computer programming; computer software and media applications; creative writing; data entry/microcomputer applications; English language and literature related; family and consumer economics; gerontology; real estate; teaching assistants/aides; technical and business writing.

ATLANTIC SCHOOL OF THEOLOGY
Halifax, Nova Scotia, Canada
http://www.astheology.ns.ca/

Atlantic School of Theology was founded in 1971. It is provincially chartered. It first offered distance learning courses in 1999. In fall 2005, there were 45 students enrolled in distance learning courses. Institutionally administered financial aid is available to distance learners.

Services Distance learners have accessibility to academic advising, bookstore, e-mail services, library services.

Contact Dr. Thomas McIllwraith, Director of Distributed Education, Atlantic School of Theology, 660 Francklyn Street, Halifax, NS B3H 3B5, Canada. Telephone: 902-496-7945. Fax: 902-492-4048. E-mail: tmcillwraith@astheology.ns.ca.

DEGREES AND AWARDS
Programs offered do not lead to a degree or other formal award.

COURSE SUBJECT AREAS OFFERED OUTSIDE OF DEGREE PROGRAMS
Graduate—biblical studies; religious education; religious/sacred music; religious studies; theological and ministerial studies; theology and religious vocations related.

Non-credit—biblical studies; religious education; religious studies; theological and ministerial studies; theology and religious vocations related.

ATLANTIC UNIVERSITY
Virginia Beach, Virginia
http://www.atlanticuniv.edu/

Atlantic University was founded in 1930. It is accredited by Distance Education and Training Council. It first offered distance learning courses in 1985. In fall 2005, there were 159 students enrolled in distance learning courses. Institutionally administered financial aid is available to distance learners.

Services Distance learners have accessibility to academic advising, e-mail services, library services.

Contact Mr. Gregory Deming, Director of Admissions, Atlantic University, 215 67th Street, Virginia Beach, VA 23451. Telephone: 757-631-8101 Ext. 7173. Fax: 757-631-8096. E-mail: admissions@atlanticuniv.edu.

DEGREES AND AWARDS

MA Transpersonal Studies

COURSE SUBJECT AREAS OFFERED OUTSIDE OF DEGREE PROGRAMS

Graduate—alternative and complementary medical support services; alternative and complementary medicine and medical systems; biblical studies; counseling psychology; creative writing; education related; fine and studio art; movement and mind-body therapies; peace studies and conflict resolution; philosophy and religious studies related; psychology related; religious studies; visual and performing arts.

Non-credit—alternative and complementary medical support services; alternative and complementary medicine and medical systems; biblical studies; counseling psychology; creative writing; education related; fine and studio art; movement and mind-body therapies; peace studies and conflict resolution; philosophy and religious studies related; psychology related; religious studies; visual and performing arts.

AUBURN UNIVERSITY
Auburn University, Alabama
Distance Learning/Outreach Technology
http://www.auburn.edu/auonline

Auburn University was founded in 1856. It is accredited by Southern Association of Colleges and Schools. It first offered distance learning courses in 1975. In fall 2005, there were 1,000 students enrolled in distance learning courses. Institutionally administered financial aid is available to distance learners.

Services Distance learners have accessibility to academic advising, bookstore, campus computer network, career placement assistance, e-mail services, library services.

Contact Distance Learning, Auburn University, 305 O.D. Smith Hall, Auburn University, AL 36849. Telephone: 334-844-3103. Fax: 334-844-3118.

DEGREES AND AWARDS

Certificate Dietary Management
EMBA Business Administration; Physicians Executive MBA
MA Early Childhood Intervention
MAE Aerospace Engineering; Foreign Language
MBA Business Administration
MBA/M Acc Accountancy
MBA/MSMIS Management Information Systems
MCE Chemical Engineering; Civil Engineering
MCSE Computer Science and Engineering
MEd Collaborative Teacher and Early Childhood Education; Music; Rehabilitation Counseling
MISE Industrial and Systems Engineering
MME Materials Engineering; Mechanical Engineering
MS Hotel and Restaurant Management
PharmD Pharmacy

COURSE SUBJECT AREAS OFFERED OUTSIDE OF DEGREE PROGRAMS

Undergraduate—agriculture; animal sciences; communication and media; communication disorders sciences and services; computer science; film/video and photographic arts; geography and cartography; health and physical education/fitness; political science and government; speech and rhetoric.

Graduate—accounting and related services; aerospace, aeronautical and astronautical engineering; business administration, management and operations; civil engineering; civil engineering technology; computer science; education; education related; education (specific levels and methods); education (specific subject areas); engineering-related fields; engineering science; foods, nutrition, and related services; pharmacy, pharmaceutical sciences, and administration; special education.

Non-credit—construction management; dietetics and clinical nutrition services; engineering; veterinary biomedical and clinical sciences.

See full description on page 318.

AUBURN UNIVERSITY MONTGOMERY
Montgomery, Alabama
http://www.aum.edu/

Auburn University Montgomery was founded in 1967. It is accredited by Southern Association of Colleges and Schools. It first offered distance learning courses in 1999. In fall 2005, there were 200 students enrolled in distance learning courses. Institutionally administered financial aid is available to distance learners.

Services Distance learners have accessibility to academic advising, bookstore, campus computer network, e-mail services, library services.

Contact Dr. Alan S. Hackel, Dean, Auburn University Montgomery, PO Box 244023, Montgomery, AL 36124-4023. Telephone: 334-244-3338. Fax: 334-244-3865. E-mail: ahackel@mail.aum.edu.

DEGREES AND AWARDS

Programs offered do not lead to a degree or other formal award.

COURSE SUBJECT AREAS OFFERED OUTSIDE OF DEGREE PROGRAMS

Undergraduate—business administration, management and operations; criminal justice and corrections; educational administration and supervision; education related; nursing.

Graduate—business administration, management and operations; criminal justice and corrections; educational administration and supervision; educational assessment, evaluation, and research.

Non-credit—business administration, management and operations; business operations support and assistant services; computer software and media applications; health and medical administrative services.

AUSTIN PEAY STATE UNIVERSITY
Clarksville, Tennessee
http://www.apsu.edu/

Austin Peay State University was founded in 1927. It is accredited by Southern Association of Colleges and Schools. It first offered distance learning courses in 1996. In fall 2005, there were 4,075 students enrolled in distance learning courses. Institutionally administered financial aid is available to distance learners.

Services Distance learners have accessibility to academic advising, bookstore, campus computer network, e-mail services, library services, tutoring.

Contact Dr. Stanley Groppel, Dean of Extended and Distance Education, Austin Peay State University, PO Box 4678, Clarksville, TN 37044. Telephone: 931-221-7816. Fax: 931-221-7748. E-mail: groppels@apsu.edu.

DEGREES AND AWARDS

AS Law Enforcement Administration; Liberal Arts
BPS Regents Online degree program
BS Computer Science–Information Systems; Criminal Justice/Homeland Security; Political Science; Professional Studies
MA Corporate Communication
MS Health Service Administration

COURSE SUBJECT AREAS OFFERED OUTSIDE OF DEGREE PROGRAMS

Undergraduate—astronomy and astrophysics; health and physical education/fitness; mathematics and computer science; psychology; public administration; sociology; speech and rhetoric.

Graduate—communication and journalism related; health and physical education/fitness.

AZUSA PACIFIC UNIVERSITY
Azusa, California
http://online.apu.edu/

Azusa Pacific University was founded in 1899. It is accredited by Western Association of Schools and Colleges. It first offered distance learning courses in 1999. In fall 2005, there were 1,000 students enrolled in distance learning courses. Institutionally administered financial aid is available to distance learners.

Services Distance learners have accessibility to bookstore, e-mail services, library services.

Contact Dr. Bruce Simmerok, Director of Distance Learning and Continuing Education, Azusa Pacific University, 901 East Alosta Avenue, Azusa, CA 91702-7000. Telephone: 626-815-5038. E-mail: bsimmerok@apu.edu.

DEGREES AND AWARDS

Certificate Library Media Teaching
MA Educational Technology
MAE Library Science–School Librarianship

COURSE SUBJECT AREAS OFFERED OUTSIDE OF DEGREE PROGRAMS

Undergraduate—computer science; history; religious studies.
Graduate—computer science; educational administration and supervision; educational assessment, evaluation, and research; educational/instructional media design; education (specific subject areas); nursing; theological and ministerial studies.

BAINBRIDGE COLLEGE
Bainbridge, Georgia
http://www.bainbridge.edu

Bainbridge College was founded in 1972. It is accredited by Southern Association of Colleges and Schools. It first offered distance learning courses in 2000. Institutionally administered financial aid is available to distance learners.

Services Distance learners have accessibility to academic advising, bookstore, career placement assistance, e-mail services, library services, tutoring.

Contact Ms. Connie B. Snyder, Director of Admissions and Records, Bainbridge College, 2500 East Shotwell Street, PO Box 990, Bainbridge, GA 39818-0990. Telephone: 229-248-2504. Fax: 229-248-2623. E-mail: csnyder@bainbridge.edu.

DEGREES AND AWARDS

Programs offered do not lead to a degree or other formal award.

COURSE SUBJECT AREAS OFFERED OUTSIDE OF DEGREE PROGRAMS

Undergraduate—accounting and related services; applied mathematics; business/commerce; business operations support and assistant services; computer and information sciences; liberal arts and sciences, general studies and humanities; speech and rhetoric.
Non-credit—allied health and medical assisting services; business administration, management and operations; communication and media; computer software and media applications; computer systems networking and telecommunications; linguistic, comparative, and related language studies; real estate.

BAKER COLLEGE OF FLINT
Flint, Michigan
Baker College OnLine
http://online.baker.edu

Baker College of Flint was founded in 1911. It is accredited by North Central Association of Colleges and Schools. It first offered distance learning courses in 1994. In fall 2005, there were 15,021 students enrolled in distance learning courses. Institutionally administered financial aid is available to distance learners.

Services Distance learners have accessibility to academic advising, bookstore, campus computer network, career placement assistance, e-mail services, library services, tutoring.

Contact Mr. Chuck J. Gurden, Vice President of Graduate and Online Admissions, Baker College of Flint, 1116 West Bristol Road, Flint, MI 48507. Telephone: 800-469-3165. Fax: 810-766-2051. E-mail: cgurde01@baker.edu.

DEGREES AND AWARDS

ABA Business Administration
BBA Business Administration
MBA Business Administration

COURSE SUBJECT AREAS OFFERED OUTSIDE OF DEGREE PROGRAMS

Undergraduate—business administration, management and operations; computer/information technology administration and management.

See full description on page 320.

BAKKE GRADUATE UNIVERSITY OF MINISTRY
Seattle, Washington

Bakke Graduate University of Ministry was founded in 1990. It is accredited by Transnational Association of Christian Colleges and Schools. It first offered distance learning courses in 1995. In fall 2005, there were 5 students enrolled in distance learning courses. Institutionally administered financial aid is available to distance learners.

Services Distance learners have accessibility to academic advising, e-mail services, library services.

Contact Mrs. Judi Melton, Registrar, Bakke Graduate University of Ministry, 1013 Eighth Avenue, Seattle, WA 98104. Telephone: 206-264-9100 Ext. 14. Fax: 206-264-8828. E-mail: judim@bgu.edu.

DEGREES AND AWARDS

Programs offered do not lead to a degree or other formal award.

COURSE SUBJECT AREAS OFFERED OUTSIDE OF DEGREE PROGRAMS

Graduate—biblical studies; religious studies; theological and ministerial studies; theology and religious vocations related; urban studies/affairs.

BALL STATE UNIVERSITY
Muncie, Indiana
School of Continuing Education and Public Service
http://www.bsu.edu/distance

Ball State University was founded in 1918. It is accredited by North Central Association of Colleges and Schools. It first offered distance learning courses in 1984. In fall 2005, there were 2,700 students enrolled in distance learning courses. Institutionally administered financial aid is available to distance learners.

Services Distance learners have accessibility to academic advising, bookstore, campus computer network, career placement assistance, e-mail services, library services.

Contact Ms. Diane K. Watters, Marketing Manager, Ball State University, School of Extended Education, Carmichael Hall, Room 200, Muncie, IN 47306. Telephone: 765-285-9042. Fax: 765-285-7161. E-mail: dbuck@bsu.edu.

DEGREES AND AWARDS

AA General Program
BGS General Studies
BSN Nursing
MA Career and Technical Education; Physical Education–Coaching specialization; Technology Education
MAE Educational Administration and Supervision; Elementary Education
MBA Business Administration
MSN Nursing

BAPTIST BIBLE COLLEGE OF PENNSYLVANIA
Clarks Summit, Pennsylvania
http://academics.bbc.edu

Baptist Bible College of Pennsylvania was founded in 1932. It is accredited by Association for Biblical Higher Education. It first offered distance learning courses in 1998. In fall 2005, there were 50 students enrolled in distance learning courses. Institutionally administered financial aid is available to distance learners.

Services Distance learners have accessibility to academic advising, bookstore, e-mail services, library services.

Contact Mr. Kai-Chun Cheng, Distance Learning Facilitator, Baptist Bible College of Pennsylvania, 538 Venard Road, Clarks Summit, PA 18411. Telephone: 570-585-9408. Fax: 570-585-4057. E-mail: kccheng @bbc.edu.

DEGREES AND AWARDS
Programs offered do not lead to a degree or other formal award.

COURSE SUBJECT AREAS OFFERED OUTSIDE OF DEGREE PROGRAMS
Graduate—biblical studies; counseling psychology; education; missionary studies and missiology; religious studies; theological and ministerial studies; theology and religious vocations related.

THE BAPTIST COLLEGE OF FLORIDA
Graceville, Florida
Division of Distance Learning
http://www.baptistcollege.edu

The Baptist College of Florida was founded in 1943. It is accredited by Southern Association of Colleges and Schools. It first offered distance learning courses in 1999. In fall 2005, there were 100 students enrolled in distance learning courses. Institutionally administered financial aid is available to distance learners.

Services Distance learners have accessibility to academic advising, bookstore, campus computer network, career placement assistance, e-mail services, library services, tutoring.

Contact David Coggins, Director of Distance Learning, The Baptist College of Florida, 5400 College Drive, Graceville, FL 32440. Telephone: 850-263-3261 Ext. 482. Fax: 850-263-7506. E-mail: jdcoggins @baptistcollege.edu.

DEGREES AND AWARDS
AD Divinity
BS Biblical Studies

COURSE SUBJECT AREAS OFFERED OUTSIDE OF DEGREE PROGRAMS
Undergraduate—biblical studies; counseling psychology; philosophy and religious studies related.

BARCLAY COLLEGE
Haviland, Kansas
Home College Program
http://www.barclaycollege.edu

Barclay College was founded in 1917. It is accredited by Association for Biblical Higher Education. It first offered distance learning courses in 1993. In fall 2005, there were 31 students enrolled in distance learning courses. Institutionally administered financial aid is available to distance learners.

Services Distance learners have accessibility to academic advising, bookstore, e-mail services, library services.

Contact Dr. Glenn Leppert, Registrar, Barclay College, 607 North Kingman, Haviland, KS 67059-0288. Telephone: 620-862-5252 Ext. 46. Fax: 620-862-5242. E-mail: registrar@barclaycollege.edu.

DEGREES AND AWARDS
Programs offered do not lead to a degree or other formal award.

COURSE SUBJECT AREAS OFFERED OUTSIDE OF DEGREE PROGRAMS
Undergraduate—biblical studies; education related; English; English composition; mathematics; missionary studies and missiology; physical sciences; psychology; religious/sacred music; sociology; theological and ministerial studies.

BELLEVUE COMMUNITY COLLEGE
Bellevue, Washington
Telecommunications Program–Distance Learning Department
http://distance-ed.bcc.ctc.edu

Bellevue Community College was founded in 1966. It is accredited by Northwest Commission on Colleges and Universities. It first offered distance learning courses in 1980. In fall 2005, there were 2,700 students enrolled in distance learning courses. Institutionally administered financial aid is available to distance learners.

Services Distance learners have accessibility to academic advising, bookstore, e-mail services, library services.

Contact Liz Anderson, Director of Distance Education, Bellevue Community College, 3000 Landerholm Circle SE, Bellevue, WA 98007-6484. Telephone: 425-564-2438. Fax: 425-564-5564. E-mail: landerso@bcc.ctc.edu.

DEGREES AND AWARDS
AA General Studies
AAS Transfer degree for Business Students; Transfer degree
Certificate of Achievement Business Intelligence Developer
Certificate Bookkeeping–Paraprofessional Accounting program; Business Intelligence Analyst; Business Software Specialist–Business Technology Systems; Introductory C++ Programming

COURSE SUBJECT AREAS OFFERED OUTSIDE OF DEGREE PROGRAMS
Undergraduate—accounting and related services; American literature (United States and Canadian); anthropology; archeology; astronomy and astrophysics; atmospheric sciences and meteorology; biology; botany/plant biology; business administration, management and operations; business/commerce; business/corporate communications; business, management, and marketing related; business operations support and assistant services; chemistry; communication and media; comparative literature; computer and information sciences; computer and information sciences and support services related; computer programming; computer science; computer software and media applications; creative writing; criminology; developmental and child psychology; ecology, evolution, and population biology; economics; education; English; English composition; English language and literature related; English literature (British and Commonwealth); entrepreneurial and small business operations; fire protection; geography and cartography; geological and earth sciences/geosciences; health professions related; history; liberal arts and sciences, general studies and humanities; management information systems; marketing; mathematics; mathematics and statistics related; medieval and Renaissance studies; music; natural sciences; nutrition sciences; philosophy; physical sciences; physical sciences related; plant sciences; political science and government; psychology; psychology related; social psychology; social sciences; social sciences related; sociology; speech and rhetoric.

BELLEVUE UNIVERSITY
Bellevue, Nebraska
Online Programs
http://www.bellevue.edu

Bellevue University was founded in 1965. It is accredited by North Central Association of Colleges and Schools. It first offered distance learning courses in 1996. In fall 2005, there were 3,000 students enrolled in distance learning courses. Institutionally administered financial aid is available to distance learners.

Services Distance learners have accessibility to academic advising, campus computer network, e-mail services, library services.

Contact Roberta Mersch, Online Admissions, Bellevue University, 1000 Galvin Road South, Bellevue, NE 68005. Telephone: 800-756-7920. Fax: 402-293-3730. E-mail: mm@bellevue.edu.

DEGREES AND AWARDS

BA Leadership
BS Business Administration of Technical Studies; Business Information Systems; Correctional Administration and Management; Criminal Justice Administration; E-Business; Global Business Management; Health Care Administration; Internet Systems and Software Technology; Management Information Systems; Management of Human Resources; Management; Marketing Management
BSBA Business Administration
MA Leadership; Management
MBA Business Administration
MS Computer Information Systems; Health Care Administration

COURSE SUBJECT AREAS OFFERED OUTSIDE OF DEGREE PROGRAMS

Undergraduate—American literature (United States and Canadian); biological and physical sciences; business administration, management and operations; business/commerce; business, management, and marketing related; business/managerial economics; communication and media; comparative literature; computer and information sciences; computer and information sciences and support services related; computer/information technology administration and management; computer programming; computer software and media applications; computer systems analysis; computer systems networking and telecommunications; English; English literature (British and Commonwealth); finance and financial management services; fine and studio art; health and medical administrative services; human resources management; human services; management information systems; management sciences and quantitative methods; marketing; sales, merchandising, and related marketing operations (specialized).
Graduate—business administration, management and operations; business/commerce; business/corporate communications; business, management, and marketing related; business/managerial economics; health and medical administrative services; management information systems; management sciences and quantitative methods; sales, merchandising, and related marketing operations (specialized).

See full description on page 322.

BELLINGHAM TECHNICAL COLLEGE
Bellingham, Washington
http://www.btc.ctc.edu/

Bellingham Technical College is accredited by Northwest Commission on Colleges and Universities. It first offered distance learning courses in 2000. In fall 2005, there were 387 students enrolled in distance learning courses. Institutionally administered financial aid is available to distance learners.
Services Distance learners have accessibility to academic advising, bookstore, campus computer network, e-mail services, library services.
Contact Ms. Sharon Carpenter, Dean of Professional and Technical Education, Bellingham Technical College, 3028 Lindbergh Avenue, Bellingham, WA 98225-1599. Telephone: 360-752-8331. Fax: 360-752-7131. E-mail: scarpent@btc.ctc.edu.

DEGREES AND AWARDS

AAS Operations Management

COURSE SUBJECT AREAS OFFERED OUTSIDE OF DEGREE PROGRAMS

Undergraduate—accounting and related services; business administration, management and operations; business/commerce; business/corporate communications; computer and information sciences and support services related; computer science; computer systems networking and telecommunications; human resources management; medical basic sciences.
Non-credit—accounting and related services; computer and information sciences; computer engineering; computer/information technology administration and management; computer software and media applications; health/medical preparatory programs; manufacturing engineering.

BELMONT TECHNICAL COLLEGE
St. Clairsville, Ohio
http://www.belmont.cc.oh.us/

Belmont Technical College was founded in 1971. It is accredited by North Central Association of Colleges and Schools. It first offered distance learning courses in 1999. Institutionally administered financial aid is available to distance learners.
Services Distance learners have accessibility to academic advising, bookstore, career placement assistance, library services, tutoring.
Contact Catherine L. Bennett, Associate Dean of Learning, Information Services and Technology, Belmont Technical College, 120 Fox Shannon Place, St. Clairsville, OH 43950. Telephone: 740-695-9500 Ext. 1088. Fax: 740-695-2247. E-mail: cbennett@btc.edu.

DEGREES AND AWARDS

AAS Information Technology–Information Services Library Paraprofessional

COURSE SUBJECT AREAS OFFERED OUTSIDE OF DEGREE PROGRAMS

Undergraduate—accounting and computer science; computer software and media applications.

BENEDICT COLLEGE
Columbia, South Carolina
http://www.benedict.edu

Benedict College was founded in 1870. It is accredited by Southern Association of Colleges and Schools. Institutionally administered financial aid is available to distance learners.
Contact Mr. Gary Knight, Vice President of Institutional Effectiveness, Benedict College, 1600 Harden Street, Columbia, SC 29204. Telephone: 803-253-5275. Fax: 803-252-5215. E-mail: knightg@benedict.edu.

DEGREES AND AWARDS

Programs offered do not lead to a degree or other formal award.

BERGEN COMMUNITY COLLEGE
Paramus, New Jersey
Center for Distance Learning
http://www.bergen.edu/

Bergen Community College was founded in 1965. It is accredited by Middle States Association of Colleges and Schools. It first offered distance learning courses in 1974. In fall 2005, there were 1,680 students enrolled in distance learning courses. Institutionally administered financial aid is available to distance learners.
Services Distance learners have accessibility to academic advising, bookstore, e-mail services, library services, tutoring.
Contact Ms. Kathy Morley, Distance Learning Supervisor, Bergen Community College, 400 Paramus Road, Paramus, NJ 07652. Telephone: 201-612-5288. Fax: 201-612-8225. E-mail: kmorley@bergen.edu.

DEGREES AND AWARDS

Programs offered do not lead to a degree or other formal award.

COURSE SUBJECT AREAS OFFERED OUTSIDE OF DEGREE PROGRAMS

Undergraduate—accounting and related services; American literature (United States and Canadian); anthropology; business administration, management and operations; computer programming; computer science; criminal justice and corrections; developmental and child psychology; dramatic/theater arts and stagecraft; education; educational psychology; English composition; finance and financial management services; foods, nutrition, and related services; geological and earth sciences/geosciences; history; journalism; philosophy; philosophy and religious studies related; political science and government; psychology; religious studies; social psychology; social sciences; sociology; speech and rhetoric; visual and performing arts.

BERKELEY COLLEGE
West Paterson, New Jersey
http://www.berkeleycollege.edu/

Berkeley College was founded in 1931. It is accredited by Middle States Association of Colleges and Schools. It first offered distance learning courses in 2001. In fall 2005, there were 384 students enrolled in distance learning courses. Institutionally administered financial aid is available to distance learners.

Services Distance learners have accessibility to academic advising, bookstore, campus computer network, career placement assistance, e-mail services, library services, tutoring.

Contact Ms. Susan Mandra, Director, Online Admissions, Berkeley College, 44 Rifle Camp Road, West Paterson, NJ 07424. Telephone: 973-278-5400 Ext. 1213. Fax: 973-278-2431. E-mail: srm@berkeleycollege.edu.

DEGREES AND AWARDS

AAS Business Administration; Health Services Administration; International Business; Justice Studies–Criminal Justice
BS Business Administration; Management

COURSE SUBJECT AREAS OFFERED OUTSIDE OF DEGREE PROGRAMS

Undergraduate—accounting and related services; American literature (United States and Canadian); area, ethnic, cultural, and gender studies related; business administration, management and operations; business/commerce; business, management, and marketing related; business/managerial economics; communication and media; computer software and media applications; criminal justice and corrections; criminology; data entry/microcomputer applications; economics; English composition; English language and literature related; entrepreneurial and small business operations; ethnic, cultural minority, and gender studies; finance and financial management services; health and medical administrative services; history; human resources management; industrial and organizational psychology; intercultural/multicultural and diversity studies; international business; legal studies (non-professional general, undergraduate); liberal arts and sciences, general studies and humanities; management sciences and quantitative methods; marketing; mathematics and statistics related; multi-/interdisciplinary studies related; philosophy; philosophy and religious studies related; political science and government; psychology; public relations, advertising, and applied communication related; sales, merchandising, and related marketing operations (general); sales, merchandising, and related marketing operations (specialized); social sciences related; sociology; statistics.

BERKELEY COLLEGE-NEW YORK CITY CAMPUS
New York, New York
http://www.berkeleycollege.edu/

Berkeley College-New York City Campus was founded in 1936. It is accredited by Middle States Association of Colleges and Schools. It first offered distance learning courses in 1998. In fall 2005, there were 338 students enrolled in distance learning courses. Institutionally administered financial aid is available to distance learners.

Services Distance learners have accessibility to academic advising, bookstore, campus computer network, career placement assistance, e-mail services, library services, tutoring.

Contact Ms. Susan Mandra, Director, Online Admissions, Berkeley College-New York City Campus, 3 East 43rd Street, New York, NY 10017. Telephone: 800-446-5400. Fax: 212-818-1079. E-mail: srm@berkeleycollege.edu.

DEGREES AND AWARDS

BBA Business, general

COURSE SUBJECT AREAS OFFERED OUTSIDE OF DEGREE PROGRAMS

Undergraduate—accounting and related services; American literature (United States and Canadian); area, ethnic, cultural, and gender studies related; business administration, management and operations; business/commerce; business, management, and marketing related; business/managerial economics; communication and media; computer software and media applications; criminology; data entry/microcomputer applications; economics; English composition; English language and literature related; entrepreneurial and small business operations; ethnic, cultural minority, and gender studies; finance and financial management services; history; human resources management; industrial and organizational psychology; intercultural/multicultural and diversity studies; international business; legal studies (non-professional general, undergraduate); liberal arts and sciences, general studies and humanities; management sciences and quantitative methods; marketing; mathematics and statistics related; multi-/interdisciplinary studies related; philosophy; philosophy and religious studies related; political science and government; psychology; public relations, advertising, and applied communication related; sales, merchandising, and related marketing operations (general); sales, merchandising, and related marketing operations (specialized); social sciences related; sociology; statistics.

BERKELEY COLLEGE-WESTCHESTER CAMPUS
White Plains, New York
http://www.berkeleycollege.edu/

Berkeley College-Westchester Campus was founded in 1945. It is accredited by Middle States Association of Colleges and Schools. It first offered distance learning courses in 1998. In fall 2005, there were 108 students enrolled in distance learning courses. Institutionally administered financial aid is available to distance learners.

Services Distance learners have accessibility to academic advising, bookstore, campus computer network, career placement assistance, e-mail services, library services, tutoring.

Contact Ms. Susan Mandra, Director, Online Admissions, Berkeley College-Westchester Campus, 44 Rifle Camp Road, West Paterson, NJ 07424. Telephone: 973-278-5400 Ext. 1213. Fax: 973-278-2431. E-mail: srm@berkeleycollege.edu.

DEGREES AND AWARDS

BBA Business, general

COURSE SUBJECT AREAS OFFERED OUTSIDE OF DEGREE PROGRAMS

Undergraduate—accounting and related services; American literature (United States and Canadian); area, ethnic, cultural, and gender studies related; business administration, management and operations; business/commerce; business, management, and marketing related; business/managerial economics; communication and media; computer software and media applications; criminology; data entry/microcomputer applications; economics; English composition; English language and literature related; entrepreneurial and small business operations; ethnic, cultural minority, and gender studies; finance and financial management services; history; human resources management; industrial and organizational psychology; intercultural/multicultural and diversity studies; international business; legal studies (non-professional general, undergraduate); liberal arts and sciences, general studies and humanities; management sciences and quantitative methods; marketing; mathematics and statistics related; multi-/interdisciplinary studies related; philosophy; philosophy and religious studies related; political science and government; psychology; public relations, advertising, and applied communication related; sales, merchandising, and related marketing operations (general); sales, merchandising, and related marketing operations (specialized); social sciences related; sociology; statistics.

BERKLEE COLLEGE OF MUSIC
Boston, Massachusetts
Berkleemusic
http://www.berklee.edu/

Berklee College of Music was founded in 1945. It is accredited by New England Association of Schools and Colleges. It first offered distance learning courses in 2002. In fall 2005, there were 1,200 students enrolled in distance learning courses. Institutionally administered financial aid is available to distance learners.

Services Distance learners have accessibility to academic advising, bookstore.

Contact Dorothy Lannon, Continuing Education Registrar, Berklee College of Music, 1140 Boylston Street, MS-855, Boston, MA 02215. Telephone: 617-747-2146. Fax: 617-747-2149. E-mail: registrar@berkleemusic.com.

DEGREES AND AWARDS

Programs offered do not lead to a degree or other formal award.

COURSE SUBJECT AREAS OFFERED OUTSIDE OF DEGREE PROGRAMS

Undergraduate—business/commerce; music; visual and performing arts.
Non-credit—business/commerce; music; visual and performing arts.

BETHANY UNIVERSITY
Scotts Valley, California
External Degree Program
http://bethany.edu/edp/

Bethany University was founded in 1919. It is accredited by Western Association of Schools and Colleges. It first offered distance learning courses in 1992. In fall 2005, there were 120 students enrolled in distance learning courses. Institutionally administered financial aid is available to distance learners.

Services Distance learners have accessibility to academic advising, bookstore, campus computer network, e-mail services, library services, tutoring.

Contact eBethany, School of Distributed Learning, Bethany University, 800 Bethany Drive, Scotts Valley, CA 95066. Telephone: 800-843-9410. Fax: 831-430-0953. E-mail: appl@fc.bethany.edu.

DEGREES AND AWARDS

AA Early Child Development; General Studies
BA Addiction Studies; Applied Professional Studies; Biblical and Theological Studies; Church Leadership; Early Child Development; General Ministries; Psychology
Certificate Addiction Counseling (CPAC)

COURSE SUBJECT AREAS OFFERED OUTSIDE OF DEGREE PROGRAMS

Undergraduate—anthropology; applied mathematics; archeology; area, ethnic, cultural, and gender studies related; biblical and other theological languages and literatures; biblical studies; bilingual, multilingual, and multicultural education; biological and biomedical sciences related; biological and physical sciences; biology; clinical psychology; communication and media; communications technology; community psychology; counseling psychology; demography and population; developmental and child psychology; English; English composition; ethnic, cultural minority, and gender studies; fine and studio art; geography and cartography; history; human development, family studies, and related services; languages (classics and classical); languages (Modern Greek); liberal arts and sciences, general studies and humanities; linguistic, comparative, and related language studies; missionary studies and missiology; pastoral counseling and specialized ministries; philosophy and religious studies related; physical sciences; political science and government; psychology; religious education; religious studies; social psychology; social sciences; social sciences related; sociology; statistics; theological and ministerial studies.

BIG SANDY COMMUNITY AND TECHNICAL COLLEGE
Prestonsburg, Kentucky
http://www.bigsandy.kctcs.edu/

Big Sandy Community and Technical College was founded in 1964. It is accredited by Council on Occupational Education. It first offered distance learning courses in 1995. In fall 2005, there were 1,800 students enrolled in distance learning courses. Institutionally administered financial aid is available to distance learners.

Services Distance learners have accessibility to academic advising, bookstore, e-mail services, library services, tutoring.

Contact Ms. Della F. Pack, Coordinator of Academic Programs, Big Sandy Community and Technical College, One Bert T. Combs Drive, Prestonsburg, KY 41653. Telephone: 606-886-3863 Ext. 67343. E-mail: della.pack@kctcs.edu.

DEGREES AND AWARDS

AA Arts; Arts; Business (Transfer Framework)–AA to BS
AAS Applied Science

COURSE SUBJECT AREAS OFFERED OUTSIDE OF DEGREE PROGRAMS

Undergraduate—accounting and related services; biological and physical sciences; business/commerce; business, management, and marketing related; business operations support and assistant services; computer and information sciences; computer/information technology administration and management; criminal justice and corrections; economics; English; history; hospitality administration; human services; mathematics; political science and government; psychology; social sciences related; sociology; statistics.

BISMARCK STATE COLLEGE
Bismarck, North Dakota
http://www.bismarckstate.edu

Bismarck State College was founded in 1939. It is accredited by North Central Association of Colleges and Schools. It first offered distance learning courses in 1991. In fall 2005, there were 1,200 students enrolled in distance learning courses. Institutionally administered financial aid is available to distance learners.

Services Distance learners have accessibility to academic advising, bookstore, career placement assistance, e-mail services, library services, tutoring.

Contact Lane Huber, Director of Distance Education, Bismarck State College, PO Box 5587, Bismarck, ND 58506-5587. Telephone: 701-224-5714. Fax: 701-224-5719. E-mail: lane.huber@bsc.nodak.edu.

DEGREES AND AWARDS

AA Criminal Justice
AAS Criminal Justice; Electric Power Technology; Electric Transmission System Technology; Human Services; Nuclear Power Technology; Power Plant Technology; Process Plant Technology; Web Page Development and Design
Certificate of Completion Electric Power Technology; Electric Transmission System Technology; Information Processing Specialist; Power Plant Technology; Process Plant Technology

COURSE SUBJECT AREAS OFFERED OUTSIDE OF DEGREE PROGRAMS

Undergraduate—accounting and computer science; accounting and related services; area, ethnic, cultural, and gender studies related; biology; business/commerce; communication and journalism related; computer science; computer software and media applications; criminal justice and corrections; criminology; English; English composition; history; human services; information science/studies; mathematics; nuclear and industrial radiologic technologies; philosophy; philosophy and religious studies related; physical sciences related; psychology; sales, merchandising, and related marketing operations (general); social sciences; sociology; technical and business writing.
Non-credit—electrical and electronic engineering technologies; heavy/industrial equipment maintenance technologies; industrial production technologies; nuclear and industrial radiologic technologies; nuclear engineering; plant sciences.

BLACKHAWK TECHNICAL COLLEGE
Janesville, Wisconsin
http://www.blackhawk.edu

Blackhawk Technical College was founded in 1968. It is accredited by North Central Association of Colleges and Schools. It first offered distance learning courses in 2000. In fall 2005, there were 269 students enrolled in distance learning courses. Institutionally administered financial aid is available to distance learners.

Services Distance learners have accessibility to academic advising, bookstore, career placement assistance, e-mail services, library services.

Contact Ms. Linda Brown, High School Community Relations Specialist, Blackhawk Technical College, PO Box 5009, Janesville, WI 53547. Telephone: 608-757-7670. E-mail: lbrown@blackhawk.edu.

DEGREES AND AWARDS

AS Accounting

COURSE SUBJECT AREAS OFFERED OUTSIDE OF DEGREE PROGRAMS

Undergraduate—accounting and related services; allied health and medical assisting services; business administration, management and operations; business, management, and marketing related; business operations support and assistant services; computer and information sciences and support services related; computer programming; computer systems networking and telecommunications; criminal justice and corrections; culinary arts and related services; dental support services and allied professions; education (specific levels and methods); electromechanical and instrumentation and maintenance technologies; fire protection; health and medical administrative services; heating, air conditioning, ventilation and refrigeration maintenance technology; legal support services; marketing; mechanical engineering related technologies; nursing.

Non-credit—apparel and textiles; business operations support and assistant services; computer software and media applications; crafts, folk art and artisanry; creative writing; criminal justice and corrections; drafting/design engineering technologies; English as a second language; film/video and photographic arts; fire protection; foods, nutrition, and related services; human development, family studies, and related services; languages (foreign languages related); leatherworking and upholstery; real estate; sales, merchandising, and related marketing operations (specialized); woodworking.

BLACK HILLS STATE UNIVERSITY
Spearfish, South Dakota
Extended Services and Instructional Technology
http://www.bhsu.edu/academics/distlrn/

Black Hills State University was founded in 1883. It is accredited by North Central Association of Colleges and Schools. It first offered distance learning courses in 1994. In fall 2005, there were 685 students enrolled in distance learning courses. Institutionally administered financial aid is available to distance learners.

Services Distance learners have accessibility to academic advising, bookstore, campus computer network, career placement assistance, e-mail services, library services.

Contact Sheila R. Aaker, Extended Services Coordinator, Black Hills State University, Extended Services, 1200 University Street, Unit 9508, Spearfish, SD 57799-9508. Telephone: 605-642-6258. Fax: 605-642-6031. E-mail: sheilaaaker@bhsu.edu.

DEGREES AND AWARDS

AA General Studies

Advanced Graduate Diploma Curriculum and Instruction

COURSE SUBJECT AREAS OFFERED OUTSIDE OF DEGREE PROGRAMS

Undergraduate—accounting and computer science; biblical and other theological languages and literatures; business administration, management and operations; business/commerce; business, management, and marketing related; developmental and child psychology; economics; educational psychology; education related; English; English composition; finance and financial management services; fine and studio art; geography and cartography; human resources management; international business; languages (foreign languages related); library science related; marketing; mathematics; psychology; psychology related; social sciences; sociology; technical and business writing.

Graduate—developmental and child psychology; education; educational assessment, evaluation, and research; educational/instructional media design; education related; hospitality administration.

BLINN COLLEGE
Brenham, Texas
Distance Education Center
http://www.blinn.edu/disted/

Blinn College was founded in 1883. It is accredited by Southern Association of Colleges and Schools. It first offered distance learning courses in 1996. In fall 2005, there were 1,750 students enrolled in distance learning courses. Institutionally administered financial aid is available to distance learners.

Services Distance learners have accessibility to academic advising, bookstore, campus computer network, career placement assistance, e-mail services, library services, tutoring.

Contact Sheri Pappas, Dean of Distance Education, Blinn College, Distance Education, PO Box 6030, Bryan, TX 77805. Telephone: 979-209-7298. Fax: 979-209-7462. E-mail: support@blinn.edu.

DEGREES AND AWARDS

Programs offered do not lead to a degree or other formal award.

COURSE SUBJECT AREAS OFFERED OUTSIDE OF DEGREE PROGRAMS

Undergraduate—accounting and related services; anthropology; biology; business administration, management and operations; computer and information sciences; computer programming; criminal justice and corrections; criminology; economics; English; English composition; fine and studio art; geography and cartography; geological and earth sciences/geosciences; history; legal studies (non-professional general, undergraduate); management information systems; mathematics and statistics related; nursing; philosophy; political science and government; psychology; sociology; speech and rhetoric.

BLOOMFIELD COLLEGE
Bloomfield, New Jersey
http://www.bloomfield.edu/

Bloomfield College was founded in 1868. It is accredited by Middle States Association of Colleges and Schools. It first offered distance learning courses in 1997. In fall 2005, there were 204 students enrolled in distance learning courses. Institutionally administered financial aid is available to distance learners.

Services Distance learners have accessibility to campus computer network, e-mail services, library services.

Contact Dr. Marion Terenzio, Vice President for Academic Affairs, Bloomfield College, 467 Franklin Street, Bloomfield, NJ 07003. Telephone: 973-748-9000. Fax: 973-743-3998. E-mail: marion_terenzio@bloomfield.edu.

DEGREES AND AWARDS

Programs offered do not lead to a degree or other formal award.

COURSE SUBJECT AREAS OFFERED OUTSIDE OF DEGREE PROGRAMS

Undergraduate—business administration, management and operations; computer/information technology administration and management; English; nursing; political science and government; psychology.

Non-credit—computer systems networking and telecommunications.

BLOOMSBURG UNIVERSITY OF PENNSYLVANIA
Bloomsburg, Pennsylvania
School of Graduate Studies
http://www.bloomu.edu

Bloomsburg University of Pennsylvania was founded in 1839. It is accredited by Middle States Association of Colleges and Schools. It first offered distance learning courses in 1983. In fall 2005, there were 125 students enrolled in distance learning courses. Institutionally administered financial aid is available to distance learners.

Services Distance learners have accessibility to academic advising, bookstore, campus computer network, career placement assistance, e-mail services, library services.

Contact Dr. James Matta, Dean, Bloomsburg University of Pennsylvania, 400 East 2nd Street, Bloomsburg, PA 17815-1301. Telephone: 570-389-4015. Fax: 570-389-3054. E-mail: jmatta@bloomu.edu.

DEGREES AND AWARDS
MS Instructional Technology Education Specialist; Radiologist Assistant

COURSE SUBJECT AREAS OFFERED OUTSIDE OF DEGREE PROGRAMS
Undergraduate—business, management, and marketing related; nursing.
Graduate—business, management, and marketing related; curriculum and instruction; educational/instructional media design.

BLUE RIDGE COMMUNITY COLLEGE
Flat Rock, North Carolina
http://www.blueridge.edu

Blue Ridge Community College was founded in 1969. It is accredited by Southern Association of Colleges and Schools. It first offered distance learning courses in 1998. In fall 2005, there were 890 students enrolled in distance learning courses. Institutionally administered financial aid is available to distance learners.
Services Distance learners have accessibility to academic advising, bookstore, career placement assistance, e-mail services, library services.
Contact Ms. Alice F. Crisp, Director for Instructional Technology and Distance Learning Support, Blue Ridge Community College, 180 West Campus Drive, Flat Rock, NC 28731. Telephone: 828-694-1890. Fax: 828-694-1690. E-mail: alicec@blueridge.edu.

DEGREES AND AWARDS
AAS Marketing and Retailing

COURSE SUBJECT AREAS OFFERED OUTSIDE OF DEGREE PROGRAMS
Undergraduate—American Sign Language (ASL); business administration, management and operations; business, management, and marketing related; business operations support and assistant services; computer and information sciences; computer/information technology administration and management; computer programming; computer software and media applications; computer systems networking and telecommunications; criminal justice and corrections; education; education (specific levels and methods); education (specific subject areas); English; English composition; entrepreneurial and small business operations; human development, family studies, and related services; marketing; mathematics and statistics related; sales, merchandising, and related marketing operations (general); special education; teaching assistants/aides.
Non-credit—accounting and computer science; business/commerce; business, management, and marketing related; communication and media; community health services; computer and information sciences; computer/information technology administration and management; computer programming; computer software and media applications; computer systems networking and telecommunications; creative writing; criminal justice and corrections; education related; film/video and photographic arts; health and medical administrative services; languages (foreign languages related); legal support services; marketing; sales, merchandising, and related marketing operations (specialized); technical and business writing.

BOISE STATE UNIVERSITY
Boise, Idaho
Division of Extended Studies
http://www.boisestate.edu/distance

Boise State University was founded in 1932. It is accredited by Northwest Commission on Colleges and Universities. It first offered distance learning courses in 1980. In fall 2005, there were 3,373 students enrolled in distance learning courses. Institutionally administered financial aid is available to distance learners.
Services Distance learners have accessibility to academic advising, bookstore, career placement assistance, e-mail services, library services, tutoring.
Contact Joann Swanson, Coordinator, Distance Education, Boise State University, 1910 University Drive, Boise, ID 83725-1120. Telephone: 208-426-5622. Fax: 208-426-3467. E-mail: joannswanson@boisestate.edu.

DEGREES AND AWARDS
MS Instructional and Performance Technology
MSE Educational Technology

COURSE SUBJECT AREAS OFFERED OUTSIDE OF DEGREE PROGRAMS
Undergraduate—accounting and related services; anthropology; behavioral sciences; biological and physical sciences; business, management, and marketing related; chemistry; criminal justice and corrections; curriculum and instruction; dramatic/theater arts and stagecraft; economics; education; educational/instructional media design; electrical and electronic engineering technologies; English composition; geological and earth sciences/geosciences; health and medical administrative services; history; human resources management; languages (Romance languages); mathematics; music; nursing; philosophy; physics; psychology; social work; sociology; technical and business writing.
Graduate—educational/instructional media design; education related; health and medical administrative services; human resources management.

BOISE STATE UNIVERSITY
Boise, Idaho
Department in Educational Technology
http://education.boisestate.edu/edtech2

Boise State University was founded in 1932. It is accredited by Northwest Commission on Colleges and Universities. It first offered distance learning courses in 1999. In fall 2005, there were 220 students enrolled in distance learning courses. Institutionally administered financial aid is available to distance learners.
Services Distance learners have accessibility to academic advising, bookstore, career placement assistance, e-mail services, library services, tutoring.
Contact Jerry Foster, Admissions Counselor and Academic Advisor, Boise State University, Department of Educational Technology, E-304, 1910 University Drive, MS-1747, Boise, ID 83725-1747. Telephone: 208-426-1966. Fax: 208-426-1451. E-mail: edtech@boisestate.edu.

DEGREES AND AWARDS
Graduate Certificate School Technology Coordination; Teaching–Online Teaching; Technology Integration
MEd Educational Technology
MS Educational Technology
MSE Educational Technology emphasis

COURSE SUBJECT AREAS OFFERED OUTSIDE OF DEGREE PROGRAMS
Graduate—computer software and media applications; educational/instructional media design; education related; education (specific subject areas).

BOISE STATE UNIVERSITY
Boise, Idaho
Program in Instructional and Performance Technology
http://ipt.boisestate.edu

Boise State University was founded in 1932. It is accredited by Northwest Commission on Colleges and Universities. It first offered distance learning courses in 1989. In fall 2005, there were 155 students enrolled in distance learning courses. Institutionally administered financial aid is available to distance learners.
Services Distance learners have accessibility to academic advising, bookstore, campus computer network, career placement assistance, e-mail services, library services, tutoring.
Contact Ms. Jo Ann Fenner, Associate Program Developer, Boise State University, Instructional and Performance Technology, 1910 University Drive, ET-327, Boise, ID 83725-2070. Telephone: 208-424-5135. Fax: 208-426-1970. E-mail: bsuipt@boisestate.edu.

DEGREES AND AWARDS

MS Instructional and Performance Technology

COURSE SUBJECT AREAS OFFERED OUTSIDE OF DEGREE PROGRAMS

Graduate—computer software and media applications; curriculum and instruction; educational assessment, evaluation, and research; educational/instructional media design; human resources management.

BOSTON ARCHITECTURAL COLLEGE
Boston, Massachusetts
http://www.the-bac.edu/

Boston Architectural College was founded in 1889. It is accredited by New England Association of Schools and Colleges. It first offered distance learning courses in 2000. In fall 2005, there were 60 students enrolled in distance learning courses. Institutionally administered financial aid is available to distance learners.

Services Distance learners have accessibility to academic advising, e-mail services, library services.

Contact Ms. Maia Brindley-Nilsson, Director of Continuing Education, Boston Architectural College, 320 Newbury Street, Boston , MA 02115. Telephone: 617-585-0101. Fax: 617-585-0121. E-mail: ce@the-bac.edu.

DEGREES AND AWARDS

Programs offered do not lead to a degree or other formal award.

COURSE SUBJECT AREAS OFFERED OUTSIDE OF DEGREE PROGRAMS

Undergraduate—architectural engineering; architectural engineering technology; architectural technology; architecture; architecture related; ecology, evolution, and population biology; environmental design; heating, air conditioning, ventilation and refrigeration maintenance technology; interior architecture.

Graduate—architectural engineering; architectural engineering technology; architectural technology; architecture; architecture related; ecology, evolution, and population biology; environmental design; heating, air conditioning, ventilation and refrigeration maintenance technology; interior architecture.

Non-credit—architectural engineering; architectural engineering technology; architectural technology; architecture; architecture related; ecology, evolution, and population biology; environmental design; heating, air conditioning, ventilatión and refrigeration maintenance technology; interior architecture.

BOSTON UNIVERSITY
Boston, Massachusetts
Boston University Online
http://www.bu.edu/disted

Boston University was founded in 1839. It is accredited by New England Association of Schools and Colleges. It first offered distance learning courses in 2001. In fall 2005, there were 3,500 students enrolled in distance learning courses. Institutionally administered financial aid is available to distance learners.

Services Distance learners have accessibility to academic advising, bookstore, campus computer network, career placement assistance, e-mail services, library services.

Contact Susan Kryczka, Director of Distance Education, Boston University, Office of Distance Education, 1010 Commonwealth Avenue, Boston, MA 02215. Telephone: 617-358-1960. Fax: 617-358-1961. E-mail: kryczka@bu.edu.

DEGREES AND AWARDS

BLS Degree Completion and Bachelor's Degree Completion program
Graduate Certificate Clinical Investigation; Instructional Technology
MCJ Criminal Justice
MSCS Computer Information Systems–Master of Science in Computer Information Systems
MSHRM Human Resource Management
MSM Insurance Management–Master of Science in Insurance Management
DPT Physical Therapy

COURSE SUBJECT AREAS OFFERED OUTSIDE OF DEGREE PROGRAMS

Graduate—curriculum and instruction; educational/instructional media design.
Non-credit—finance and financial management services.

BOSTON UNIVERSITY
Boston, Massachusetts
Metropolitan College (Continuing Education)
http://www.bu.edu/disted

Boston University was founded in 1839. It is accredited by New England Association of Schools and Colleges. It first offered distance learning courses in 2002. In fall 2005, there were 2,500 students enrolled in distance learning courses. Institutionally administered financial aid is available to distance learners.

Services Distance learners have accessibility to academic advising, bookstore, campus computer network, career placement assistance, e-mail services, library services.

Contact Ms. Nancy Coleman, Assistant Director, Boston University, 1010 Commonwealth Avenue, 2nd Floor, Boston, MA 02215. Telephone: 617-358-1977. Fax: 617-358-1961. E-mail: online@bu.edu.

DEGREES AND AWARDS

BLS Degree Completion–Executive Undergraduate Degree completion
Graduate Certificate Clinical Investigation; Instructional Technology
MCJ Criminal Justice
MSCS Computer Science

BOSTON UNIVERSITY
Boston, Massachusetts
Department of Manufacturing Engineering
http://www.bu.edu/mfg/dlp

Boston University was founded in 1839. It is accredited by New England Association of Schools and Colleges. It first offered distance learning courses in 1989. In fall 2005, there were 20 students enrolled in distance learning courses. Institutionally administered financial aid is available to distance learners.

Services Distance learners have accessibility to academic advising, bookstore, campus computer network, e-mail services, library services, tutoring.

Contact Ms. Sarah Cowen, Distance Learning Administrator, Boston University, Department of Manufacturing Engineering, 15 St. Mary's Street, Brookline, MA 02446. Telephone: 617-353-2943. Fax: 617-353-5548. E-mail: scowen@bu.edu.

DEGREES AND AWARDS

MS Manufacturing Engineering

COURSE SUBJECT AREAS OFFERED OUTSIDE OF DEGREE PROGRAMS

Graduate—electrical, electronics and communications engineering; engineering design; industrial production technologies; management information systems; manufacturing engineering; materials engineering; mechanical engineering related technologies; operations research; systems engineering.

See full description on page 324.

BOWLING GREEN STATE UNIVERSITY
Bowling Green, Ohio
http://ideal.bgsu.edu

Bowling Green State University was founded in 1910. It is accredited by North Central Association of Colleges and Schools. It first offered distance learning courses in 1998. In fall 2005, there were 1,100 students enrolled in distance learning courses. Institutionally administered financial aid is available to distance learners.

Services Distance learners have accessibility to academic advising, bookstore, campus computer network, career placement assistance, e-mail services, library services, tutoring.

Contact Connie Molnar, Director of Distance Learning, Bowling Green State University, 14 College Park, CEE/IDEAL, Bowling Green, OH 43403. Telephone: 419-372-8181. Fax: 419-372-8667. E-mail: cmolnar@bgnet.bgsu.edu.

DEGREES AND AWARDS

BLS Liberal Studies–Bachelor of Liberal Studies Online Degree program
BS Technological Education, advanced
BSN Nursing–RN-to-BSN Completion
Graduate Certificate Food and Nutrition; Gifted Education Endorsement; International Scientific and Technical Communication; Ohio Reading Endorsement Program; Quality Systems
MEd Assistive Technology specialization
PhD Technology Management

COURSE SUBJECT AREAS OFFERED OUTSIDE OF DEGREE PROGRAMS

Undergraduate—American literature (United States and Canadian); applied mathematics; business/commerce; business, management, and marketing related; communication and media; computer and information sciences; computer science; computer software and media applications; computer systems networking and telecommunications; creative writing; educational administration and supervision; educational/instructional media design; English; English composition; English literature (British and Commonwealth); environmental control technologies; environmental/environmental health engineering; ethnic, cultural minority, and gender studies; foods, nutrition, and related services; geography and cartography; geological and earth sciences/geosciences; health and medical administrative services; history; human development, family studies, and related services; information science/studies; international/global studies; liberal arts and sciences, general studies and humanities; library science related; mathematics; music; nursing; philosophy; philosophy and religious studies related; political science and government; psychology; public health; social work; sociology; technical and business writing; technology education/industrial arts.
Graduate—American literature (United States and Canadian); building/construction finishing, management, and inspection; computer software and media applications; construction engineering technology; creative writing; educational assessment, evaluation, and research; English; English literature (British and Commonwealth); foods, nutrition, and related services; gerontology; languages (Romance languages); mathematics; psychology; special education; speech and rhetoric; technical and business writing; technology education/industrial arts.
Non-credit—business/commerce; computer and information sciences and support services related; computer software and media applications; construction trades related; health professions related.

BRADLEY UNIVERSITY
Peoria, Illinois
Division of Continuing Education and Professional Development
http://www.bradley.edu/continue

Bradley University was founded in 1897. It is accredited by North Central Association of Colleges and Schools. It first offered distance learning courses in 1985. In fall 2005, there were 170 students enrolled in distance learning courses. Institutionally administered financial aid is available to distance learners.
Services Distance learners have accessibility to academic advising, bookstore, campus computer network, e-mail services, library services.
Contact Andy Kindler, Associate Registrar, Bradley University, 1501 West Bradley Avenue, Peoria, IL 61625. Telephone: 309-677-3106. Fax: 309-677-2715. E-mail: akindler@bradley.edu.

DEGREES AND AWARDS

Programs offered do not lead to a degree or other formal award.

COURSE SUBJECT AREAS OFFERED OUTSIDE OF DEGREE PROGRAMS

Undergraduate—business, management, and marketing related; communication and media; computer and information sciences; education; English; family and consumer sciences/human sciences; international business; nursing; psychology; sociology; theological and ministerial studies.
Graduate—education; electrical and electronic engineering technologies; nursing; political science and government.

BRAMSON ORT COLLEGE
Forest Hills, New York

Bramson ORT College was founded in 1977. It is accredited by New York State Board of Regents. It first offered distance learning courses in 1999. In fall 2005, there were 80 students enrolled in distance learning courses. Institutionally administered financial aid is available to distance learners.
Services Distance learners have accessibility to academic advising, campus computer network, career placement assistance, e-mail services, library services, tutoring.
Contact Mr. Yefim Baskin, Academic Coordinator, Bramson ORT College, 69-30 Austin Street, Forest Hills, NY 11375. Telephone: 718-261-5800 Ext. 126. Fax: 718-459-6565. E-mail: ybaskin@bramsonort.edu.

DEGREES AND AWARDS

AAS Business Management

COURSE SUBJECT AREAS OFFERED OUTSIDE OF DEGREE PROGRAMS

Undergraduate—accounting and computer science; business administration, management and operations.
Non-credit—accounting and computer science.

BRAZOSPORT COLLEGE
Lake Jackson, Texas
http://www.brazosport.edu/

Brazosport College was founded in 1968. It is accredited by Southern Association of Colleges and Schools. It first offered distance learning courses in 1997. In fall 2005, there were 600 students enrolled in distance learning courses. Institutionally administered financial aid is available to distance learners.
Services Distance learners have accessibility to academic advising, bookstore, e-mail services, library services.
Contact Mr. Terry Comingore, Director, Learning Assistance and Instructional Media, Brazosport College, 500 College Drive, Lake Jackson, TX 77566. Telephone: 979-230-3318. Fax: 979-230-3443. E-mail: terry.comingore@brazosport.edu.

DEGREES AND AWARDS

Programs offered do not lead to a degree or other formal award.

COURSE SUBJECT AREAS OFFERED OUTSIDE OF DEGREE PROGRAMS

Undergraduate—accounting and related services; chemistry; computer and information sciences; economics; English composition; fine and studio art; history; mathematics; nutrition sciences; political science and government; psychology.

BRENAU UNIVERSITY
Gainesville, Georgia
Department of Distance Learning
http://online.brenau.edu

Brenau University was founded in 1878. It is accredited by Southern Association of Colleges and Schools. It first offered distance learning courses in 1998. In fall 2005, there were 338 students enrolled in distance learning courses. Institutionally administered financial aid is available to distance learners.
Services Distance learners have accessibility to academic advising, bookstore, career placement assistance, e-mail services, library services, tutoring.
Contact Dr. Heather Snow Gibbons, Director of the Online College, Brenau University, 500 Washington Street, SE, Gainesville, GA 30501. Telephone: 770-718-5327. Fax: 770-718-5329. E-mail: hgibbons@brenau.edu.

DEGREES AND AWARDS

BA Criminal Justice
BBA Management; Marketing
BS Criminal Justice
BSN Nursing–RN to BSN
MBA Accounting; Healthcare Management; Leadership Development; Management Studies, advanced
MEd Early Childhood Education; Middle Grades Education

COURSE SUBJECT AREAS OFFERED OUTSIDE OF DEGREE PROGRAMS

Undergraduate—accounting and related services; allied health and medical assisting services; American literature (United States and Canadian); anthropology; astronomy and astrophysics; business administration, management and operations; business/commerce; business/corporate communications; business, management, and marketing related; business/managerial economics; communication and media; community health services; computer and information sciences; criminal justice and corrections; criminology; curriculum and instruction; design and applied arts; developmental and child psychology; economics; education; educational administration and supervision; educational assessment, evaluation, and research; educational/instructional media design; educational psychology; education related; education (specific levels and methods); education (specific subject areas); English; English composition; English language and literature related; geography and cartography; health/medical preparatory programs; health professions related; history; human development, family studies, and related services; human resources management; information science/studies; international business; journalism; legal studies (non-professional general, undergraduate); liberal arts and sciences, general studies and humanities; linguistic, comparative, and related language studies; management information systems; management sciences and quantitative methods; marketing; mathematics; mathematics and statistics related; museum studies; music; nursing; peace studies and conflict resolution; pharmacology and toxicology; philosophy; political science and government; psychology; psychology related; public administration; public administration and social service professions related; public relations, advertising, and applied communication related; sales, merchandising, and related marketing operations (specialized); social and philosophical foundations of education; social sciences; sociology; special education; statistics; taxation; technical and business writing; visual and performing arts related.
Graduate—accounting and related services; allied health diagnostic, intervention, and treatment professions; business administration, management and operations; business/commerce; business/corporate communications; business, management, and marketing related; business/managerial economics; computer and information sciences; economics; education; educational administration and supervision; educational assessment, evaluation, and research; educational psychology; education related; finance and financial management services; health and medical administrative services; health professions related; international business; management information systems; management sciences and quantitative methods; marketing; nursing; rehabilitation and therapeutic professions; sales, merchandising, and related marketing operations (general); sales, merchandising, and related marketing operations (specialized); taxation.

See full description on page 326.

BRIAR CLIFF UNIVERSITY
Sioux City, Iowa
http://www.briarcliff.edu/

Briar Cliff University was founded in 1930. It is accredited by North Central Association of Colleges and Schools. It first offered distance learning courses in 1994. In fall 2005, there were 70 students enrolled in distance learning courses. Institutionally administered financial aid is available to distance learners.
Services Distance learners have accessibility to academic advising, bookstore, campus computer network, career placement assistance, e-mail services, library services.
Contact Ms. Sharisue Wilcoxon, Vice President of Enrollment Management, Briar Cliff University, 3303 Rebecca Street, Sioux City, IA 51104-2100. Telephone: 712-279-5200. Fax: 712-279-5410. E-mail: sharisue.wilcoxon@briarcliff.edu.

DEGREES AND AWARDS

BA the Arts; the Arts; the Arts; the Arts
Graduate Certificate Human Resources Management
MAE Education

BRIDGEWATER STATE COLLEGE
Bridgewater, Massachusetts
Distance Learning and Technology Programs
http://www.bridgew.edu/distance

Bridgewater State College was founded in 1840. It is accredited by New England Association of Schools and Colleges. It first offered distance learning courses in 1996. In fall 2005, there were 700 students enrolled in distance learning courses. Institutionally administered financial aid is available to distance learners.
Services Distance learners have accessibility to bookstore, campus computer network, e-mail services, library services.
Contact Dr. Mary W. Fuller, Director of Continuing and Distance Education, Bridgewater State College, John Joseph Moakley Center for Technological Applications, Burrill Avenue, Bridgewater, MA 02325. Telephone: 508-531-6145. Fax: 508-531-6121. E-mail: mfuller@bridgew.edu.

DEGREES AND AWARDS

Programs offered do not lead to a degree or other formal award.

COURSE SUBJECT AREAS OFFERED OUTSIDE OF DEGREE PROGRAMS

Undergraduate—anthropology; business/corporate communications; business/managerial economics; communication and media; communication disorders sciences and services; computer/information technology administration and management; criminology; curriculum and instruction; education; educational administration and supervision; educational assessment, evaluation, and research; English composition; entrepreneurial and small business operations; ethnic, cultural minority, and gender studies; geography and cartography; geological and earth sciences/geosciences; history; music; political science and government; psychology; sociology; special education; technical and business writing.
Graduate—communication and media; economics; educational administration and supervision; linguistic, comparative, and related language studies; psychology; special education.
Non-credit—accounting and related services; allied health and medical assisting services; business administration, management and operations; business/commerce; business, management, and marketing related; business/managerial economics; business operations support and assistant services; communication and media; computer systems analysis; creative writing; finance and financial management services; health and medical administrative services; information science/studies; sales, merchandising, and related marketing operations (specialized).

BRIERCREST DISTANCE LEARNING
Caronport, Saskatchewan, Canada
http://www.briercrest.ca/bdl/

Briercrest Distance Learning was founded in 1980. It is provincially chartered. It first offered distance learning courses in 1981. In fall 2005, there were 800 students enrolled in distance learning courses. Institutionally administered financial aid is available to distance learners.
Services Distance learners have accessibility to academic advising, bookstore, career placement assistance, library services, tutoring.
Contact Kevin Weeks, Enrollment Coordinator, Briercrest Distance Learning, 510 College Drive, Caronport, SK S0H 0S0, Canada. Telephone: 800-667-5199. Fax: 800-667-2329. E-mail: distanceinfo@briercrest.ca.

DEGREES AND AWARDS

AA Christian Studies
BA Christian Studies
Certificate Bible

COURSE SUBJECT AREAS OFFERED OUTSIDE OF DEGREE PROGRAMS

Undergraduate—biblical studies; business administration, management and operations; counseling psychology; English; English as a second/foreign language (teaching); history; missionary studies and missiology; religious education; religious studies; theological and ministerial studies; theology and religious vocations related.

Graduate—biblical and other theological languages and literatures; biblical studies; history; religious education; religious studies; theological and ministerial studies; theology and religious vocations related.

Non-credit—biblical studies; history; religious studies.

BRIGHAM YOUNG UNIVERSITY
Provo, Utah
Independent Study
http://elearn.byu.edu

Brigham Young University was founded in 1875. It is accredited by Northwest Commission on Colleges and Universities. It first offered distance learning courses in 1961. In fall 2005, there were 100,000 students enrolled in distance learning courses. Institutionally administered financial aid is available to distance learners.

Services Distance learners have accessibility to academic advising, bookstore, e-mail services, library services, tutoring.

Contact Rachel Andersen, Coordinator, Brigham Young University, 206 Harman Building, PO Box 21514, Provo, UT 84602-1514. Telephone: 800-914-8931. Fax: 801-422-0102. E-mail: indstudy@byu.edu.

DEGREES AND AWARDS

Programs offered do not lead to a degree or other formal award.

COURSE SUBJECT AREAS OFFERED OUTSIDE OF DEGREE PROGRAMS

Undergraduate—accounting and related services; American literature (United States and Canadian); anthropology; astronomy and astrophysics; biological and biomedical sciences related; biology; botany/plant biology; business administration, management and operations; business/corporate communications; business, management, and marketing related; chemical engineering; chemistry; civil engineering; communication and media; communication disorders sciences and services; curriculum and instruction; dance; developmental and child psychology; dramatic/theater arts and stagecraft; economics; education; educational administration and supervision; educational psychology; education related; English composition; film/video and photographic arts; fine and studio art; food science and technology; geography and cartography; geological and earth sciences/geosciences; health and physical education/fitness; history; information science/studies; languages (Germanic); languages (Middle/Near Eastern and Semitic); languages (Romance languages); liberal arts and sciences, general studies and humanities; marketing; mathematics and statistics related; microbiological sciences and immunology; music; nursing; philosophy; philosophy and religious studies related; physical sciences; physics; political science and government; psychology; religious education; religious studies; social work; sociology; special education; speech and rhetoric; statistics; technology education/industrial arts; visual and performing arts; zoology/animal biology.

Graduate—education.

Non-credit—computer and information sciences; computer software and media applications; creative writing; English language and literature related; history; human development, family studies, and related services; religious studies.

BROCK UNIVERSITY
St. Catharines, Ontario, Canada
Centre for Adult Studies and Distance Learning, Faculty of Education
http://adult.ed.brocku.ca

Brock University was founded in 1964. It is provincially chartered. It first offered distance learning courses in 1993. In fall 2005, there were 500 students enrolled in distance learning courses. Institutionally administered financial aid is available to distance learners.

Services Distance learners have accessibility to academic advising, bookstore, campus computer network, career placement assistance, e-mail services, library services, tutoring.

Contact Sandra Plavinskis, Coordinator of B.Ed. in Adult Education Degree and Certificate Programs, Brock University, Centre for Adult Education and Community Outreach, Faculty of Education, St. Catharines, ON L2S 3A1, Canada. Telephone: 905-688-5550 Ext. 4308. Fax: 905-984-4842. E-mail: adulted@brocku.ca.

DEGREES AND AWARDS

BEd Adult Education (BEd in Adult Education)
Certificate Adult Education

COURSE SUBJECT AREAS OFFERED OUTSIDE OF DEGREE PROGRAMS

Undergraduate—education; education related.

BROOME COMMUNITY COLLEGE
Binghamton, New York
http://www.sunybroome.edu/

Broome Community College was founded in 1946. It is accredited by Middle States Association of Colleges and Schools. It first offered distance learning courses in 1998. In fall 2005, there were 966 students enrolled in distance learning courses. Institutionally administered financial aid is available to distance learners.

Services Distance learners have accessibility to academic advising, bookstore, campus computer network, career placement assistance, e-mail services, library services, tutoring.

Contact Martin J. Guzzi, Registrar, Broome Community College, PO Box 1017, Binghamton, NY 13902. Telephone: 607-778-5527. Fax: 607-778-5294. E-mail: guzzi_m@sunybroome.edu.

DEGREES AND AWARDS

Programs offered do not lead to a degree or other formal award.

COURSE SUBJECT AREAS OFFERED OUTSIDE OF DEGREE PROGRAMS

Undergraduate—accounting and related services; astronomy and astrophysics; business/commerce; chemistry; computer/information technology administration and management; computer science; computer software and media applications; English composition; geological and earth sciences/geosciences; health and medical administrative services; history; human services; international business; mathematics; pharmacy, pharmaceutical sciences, and administration; physical sciences; physics; political science and government; psychology; sales, merchandising, and related marketing operations (general); social work; statistics.

Non-credit—accounting and related services; business administration, management and operations; computer and information sciences; computer programming; computer software and media applications; data entry/microcomputer applications.

BRYANT AND STRATTON ONLINE
Lackawanna, New York
http://www.bryantstratton.edu

Bryant and Stratton Online is accredited by Middle States Association of Colleges and Schools. It first offered distance learning courses in 1997. In fall 2005, there were 577 students enrolled in distance learning courses. Institutionally administered financial aid is available to distance learners.

Services Distance learners have accessibility to academic advising, bookstore, e-mail services, library services, tutoring.

Contact Admissions, Bryant and Stratton Online, Sterling Park, 200 Redtail, Orchard Park, NY 14127. Telephone: 716-677-8800 Ext. 241. Fax: 716-677-8899. E-mail: online@bryantstratton.edu.

DEGREES AND AWARDS

AD Accounting; Business Online; Information Technology Online

COURSE SUBJECT AREAS OFFERED OUTSIDE OF DEGREE PROGRAMS

Undergraduate—accounting and related services; business administration, management and operations; business/commerce; business/corporate communications; computer/information technology administration and management; computer programming; computer software and media applications; computer systems networking and telecommunications.

BUENA VISTA UNIVERSITY
Storm Lake, Iowa
Master of Education
http://www.bvu.edu/

Buena Vista University was founded in 1891. It is accredited by North Central Association of Colleges and Schools. It first offered distance learning courses in 2004. In fall 2005, there were 150 students enrolled in distance learning courses. Institutionally administered financial aid is available to distance learners.

Services Distance learners have accessibility to academic advising, bookstore, campus computer network, career placement assistance, e-mail services, library services, tutoring.

Contact BVU Online, Buena Vista University, 610 West 4th Street, Storm Lake, IA 50588. Telephone: 712-749-1880. Fax: 712-749-1241.

DEGREES AND AWARDS

MAE Education

MEd Curriculum and Instruction–Effective Teaching and Instructional Leadership emphasis; Curriculum and Instruction–Teaching English as a Second Language emphasis

COURSE SUBJECT AREAS OFFERED OUTSIDE OF DEGREE PROGRAMS

Undergraduate—accounting and related services; business administration, management and operations; business/commerce; business/corporate communications; business, management, and marketing related; business/managerial economics; communication and journalism related; communication and media; criminal justice and corrections; curriculum and instruction; education; English; English composition; finance and financial management services; marketing; political science and government; psychology.

Graduate—curriculum and instruction; education; English as a second/foreign language (teaching).

See full description on page 328.

BUFFALO STATE COLLEGE, STATE UNIVERSITY OF NEW YORK
Buffalo, New York
http://www.buffalostate.edu/offices/elearning

Buffalo State College, State University of New York was founded in 1867. It is accredited by Middle States Association of Colleges and Schools. It first offered distance learning courses in 1998. In fall 2005, there were 224 students enrolled in distance learning courses. Institutionally administered financial aid is available to distance learners.

Services Distance learners have accessibility to academic advising, bookstore, campus computer network, career placement assistance, e-mail services, library services, tutoring.

Contact Melaine Kenyon, Associate Director for Instructional Technology, Buffalo State College, State University of New York, 1300 Elmwood Avenue, BC 103, Buffalo, NY 14222. Telephone: 716-878-3877. Fax: 716-878-3131. E-mail: kenyonmc@buffalostate.edu.

DEGREES AND AWARDS

CAGS Adult Education; Creativity, Change Leadership, and Creative Problem Solving; Human Resource Development

MS Adult Education; Creative Studies

COURSE SUBJECT AREAS OFFERED OUTSIDE OF DEGREE PROGRAMS

Undergraduate—computer science.

Graduate—education related.

BURLINGTON COUNTY COLLEGE
Pemberton, New Jersey
Distance Learning Office
http://www.bcc.edu/

Burlington County College was founded in 1966. It is accredited by Middle States Association of Colleges and Schools. It first offered distance learning courses in 1978. In fall 2005, there were 1,544 students enrolled in distance learning courses. Institutionally administered financial aid is available to distance learners.

Services Distance learners have accessibility to academic advising, bookstore, campus computer network, e-mail services, library services, tutoring.

Contact Kathleen Devone, Coordinator of Distance Learning, Burlington County College, 601 Pemberton-Browns Mills Road, Pemberton, NJ 08068. Telephone: 609-894-9311 Ext. 1790. Fax: 609-894-4189. E-mail: kdevone@bcc.edu.

DEGREES AND AWARDS

AA Liberal Arts and Sciences

AS Business Management

COURSE SUBJECT AREAS OFFERED OUTSIDE OF DEGREE PROGRAMS

Undergraduate—anthropology; biology; developmental and child psychology; ecology, evolution, and population biology; English composition; film/video and photographic arts; fine and studio art; history; languages (Romance languages); marketing; sociology; statistics.

BUTLER COMMUNITY COLLEGE
El Dorado, Kansas
http://www.butlercc.edu/

Butler Community College was founded in 1927. It is accredited by North Central Association of Colleges and Schools. It first offered distance learning courses in 1998. In fall 2005, there were 1,500 students enrolled in distance learning courses. Institutionally administered financial aid is available to distance learners.

Services Distance learners have accessibility to academic advising, bookstore, e-mail services, library services.

Contact Ms. Meg McGranaghan, Director, Instructional Technology, Butler Community College, 901 South Haverhill Road, El Dorado, KS 67042. Telephone: 316-322-3345. Fax: 316-322-3315. E-mail: megmcg@butlercc.edu.

DEGREES AND AWARDS

Programs offered do not lead to a degree or other formal award.

COURSE SUBJECT AREAS OFFERED OUTSIDE OF DEGREE PROGRAMS

Undergraduate—accounting and related services; allied health and medical assisting services; applied mathematics; astronomy and astrophysics; behavioral sciences; business, management, and marketing related; chemistry; computer programming; criminal justice and corrections; criminology; data entry/microcomputer applications; developmental and child psychology; drafting/design engineering technologies; economics; English composition; fine and studio art; gerontology; health and physical education/fitness; health professions related; history; human development, family studies, and related services; human resources management; marketing; mathematics; mathematics and statistics related; music; nursing; nutrition sciences; philosophy; philosophy and religious studies related; physical sciences; physical sciences related; physics; political science and government; psychology; social sciences; social sciences related; sociology; speech and rhetoric.

BUTLER COUNTY COMMUNITY COLLEGE
Butler, Pennsylvania
http://www.bc3.edu/distlearn

Butler County Community College was founded in 1965. It is accredited by Middle States Association of Colleges and Schools. It first offered distance learning courses in 1998. In fall 2005, there were 600 students enrolled in distance learning courses. Institutionally administered financial aid is available to distance learners.

Services Distance learners have accessibility to academic advising, bookstore, career placement assistance, e-mail services, library services, tutoring.

Contact Deborah Ayers, Assistant Dean of Distance Education, Butler County Community College, PO Box 1203, Butler, PA 16003. Telephone: 888-826-2829 Ext. 8279. E-mail: deborah.ayers@bc3.edu.

DEGREES AND AWARDS

AA General Studies

COURSE SUBJECT AREAS OFFERED OUTSIDE OF DEGREE PROGRAMS

Undergraduate—accounting and related services; allied health and medical assisting services; applied mathematics; biology; business administration, management and operations; business, management, and marketing related; chemistry; communication and media; computer programming; computer science; creative writing; criminology; data entry/microcomputer applications; economics; education; educational psychology; English composition; finance and financial management services; fire protection; foods, nutrition, and related services; health and physical education/fitness; history; human resources management; marketing; mathematics; music; philosophy; philosophy and religious studies related; political science and government; psychology; sociology; technical and business writing.

CALDWELL COLLEGE
Caldwell, New Jersey
Center for Continuing Education
http://www.caldwell.edu/adult-admissions/index.html

Caldwell College was founded in 1939. It is accredited by Middle States Association of Colleges and Schools. It first offered distance learning courses in 1979. In fall 2005, there were 800 students enrolled in distance learning courses. Institutionally administered financial aid is available to distance learners.

Services Distance learners have accessibility to academic advising, bookstore, campus computer network, career placement assistance, e-mail services, library services, tutoring.

Contact Ms. Peg Johnston, External Degree Coordinator, Caldwell College, 9 Ryerson Avenue, Caldwell, NJ 07006. Telephone: 973-618-3215. Fax: 973-618-3690. E-mail: pjohnsto@caldwell.edu.

DEGREES AND AWARDS

BA Criminal Justice; English; Foreign Language; History; Multidisciplinary Studies/Humanities; Multidisciplinary Studies/Social Science/Fire Science; Multidisciplinary Studies/Social Science/Pharmacy Management; Multidisciplinary Studies/Social Sciences; Political Science; Psychology; Sociology; Theology

BS Accounting; Business; Computer Information Systems; Financial Economics; International Business; Management; Marketing

COURSE SUBJECT AREAS OFFERED OUTSIDE OF DEGREE PROGRAMS

Undergraduate—accounting and related services; biology; business administration, management and operations; chemistry; communication and journalism related; computer and information sciences and support services related; criminal justice and corrections; economics; education; education (specific levels and methods); fine and studio art; information science/studies; mathematics and computer science; music; political science and government; psychology; religious studies; sociology.

CALDWELL COMMUNITY COLLEGE AND TECHNICAL INSTITUTE
Hudson, North Carolina
http://www.cccti.edu

Caldwell Community College and Technical Institute was founded in 1964. It is accredited by Southern Association of Colleges and Schools. It first offered distance learning courses in 1989. In fall 2005, there were 1,200 students enrolled in distance learning courses. Institutionally administered financial aid is available to distance learners.

Services Distance learners have accessibility to academic advising, bookstore, career placement assistance, library services, tutoring.

Contact Jennifer S. Sime, Director, Distance Learning, Caldwell Community College and Technical Institute, 2855 Hickory Boulevard, Hudson, NC 28638-2397. Telephone: 828-726-2707. Fax: 828-759-4632. E-mail: jsime@cccti.edu.

DEGREES AND AWARDS

AA College Transfer

AAS Emergency Preparedness Technology

COURSE SUBJECT AREAS OFFERED OUTSIDE OF DEGREE PROGRAMS

Undergraduate—accounting and related services; biological and biomedical sciences related; biological and physical sciences; biology; business administration, management and operations; business/commerce; business/corporate communications; business operations support and assistant services; communication and media; computer and information sciences; educational psychology; English; English composition; fine and studio art; fire protection; history; human development, family studies, and related services; liberal arts and sciences, general studies and humanities; marketing; mathematics; music; physical sciences; psychology; social sciences; sociology; technical and business writing.

Non-credit—accounting and related services; business administration, management and operations; business/corporate communications; business/managerial economics; business operations support and assistant services; computer and information sciences and support services related; computer/information technology administration and management; computer software and media applications; creative writing; criminal justice and corrections; finance and financial management services; health/medical preparatory programs; linguistic, comparative, and related language studies; peace studies and conflict resolution; sales, merchandising, and related marketing operations (specialized); technical and business writing.

CALIFORNIA COLLEGE FOR HEALTH SCIENCES
Salt Lake City, Utah
http://www.cchs.edu/

California College for Health Sciences was founded in 1978. It is accredited by Accrediting Commission of Career Schools and Colleges of Technology. It first offered distance learning courses in 1978. In fall 2005, there were 1,000 students enrolled in distance learning courses. Institutionally administered financial aid is available to distance learners.

Services Distance learners have accessibility to academic advising, bookstore, campus computer network, e-mail services, tutoring.

Contact Justin Spencer, Director of Educational Alliances, California College for Health Sciences, 5295 South Commerce Drive, Suite G-50, Salt Lake City, UT 84107. Telephone: 800-481-9440. Fax: 801-263-0345. E-mail: jspencer@cchs.edu.

DEGREES AND AWARDS

AS Allied Health; Business Accounting; Business Finance; Business Marketing; Business in General Business; Business; Early Childhood Education; Respiratory Therapy

BS Business Accounting; Business Finance; Business Management; Business Marketing; Business, general; Health Services Management; Respiratory Care

MBA Health Care

MS Health Care Administration; Health Services Community Health; Health Services Wellness Promotion; Nursing Administration; Nursing Community Health; Nursing Gerontology; Nursing Wellness; Nursing; Public Health

COURSE SUBJECT AREAS OFFERED OUTSIDE OF DEGREE PROGRAMS

Non-credit—business administration, management and operations; community health services; gerontology; health psychology.

CALIFORNIA INSTITUTE OF INTEGRAL STUDIES
San Francisco, California
Transformative Studies
http://www.ciis.edu

California Institute of Integral Studies was founded in 1968. It is accredited by Western Association of Schools and Colleges. It first offered distance learning courses in 1993. In fall 2005, there were 135 students enrolled in distance learning courses. Institutionally administered financial aid is available to distance learners.

Services Distance learners have accessibility to academic advising, bookstore, campus computer network, library services.

Contact Ms. Allyson Werner, Admissions Counselor for the School of Consciousness and Transformation, California Institute of Integral Studies, 1453 Mission Street, San Francisco, CA 94103. Telephone: 415-575-6155. Fax: 415-575-1268. E-mail: awerner@ciis.edu.

DEGREES AND AWARDS
MA Transformative Leadership
PhD Transformative Studies

COURSE SUBJECT AREAS OFFERED OUTSIDE OF DEGREE PROGRAMS
Graduate—area studies; ecology, evolution, and population biology; ethnic, cultural minority, and gender studies; philosophy and religious studies related; religious studies; sociology.

Non-credit—area studies; ecology, evolution, and population biology; ethnic, cultural minority, and gender studies; philosophy and religious studies related; religious studies; sociology.

See full description on page 330.

CALIFORNIA NATIONAL UNIVERSITY FOR ADVANCED STUDIES
Northridge, California
http://www.cnuas.edu/

California National University for Advanced Studies was founded in 1993. It is accredited by Distance Education and Training Council. It first offered distance learning courses in 1993. In fall 2005, there were 450 students enrolled in distance learning courses. Institutionally administered financial aid is available to distance learners.

Services Distance learners have accessibility to academic advising, bookstore, campus computer network, e-mail services.

Contact Dr. Lolly Horn, CEO and Vice President for Academic Affairs, California National University for Advanced Studies, 8550 Balboa Boulevard, Suite 210, Northridge, CA 91325. Telephone: 800-782-2422. Fax: 818-830-2418. E-mail: lhorn@mail.cnuas.edu.

DEGREES AND AWARDS
BS Business Administration; Computer Science; Engineering; Quality Assurance Science
Certificate Human Resource Management Practice
MBA Business Administration
MEM Engineering Management
MHRM Human Resources
MS Engineering

COURSE SUBJECT AREAS OFFERED OUTSIDE OF DEGREE PROGRAMS
Undergraduate—accounting and related services; business administration, management and operations; business/corporate communications; business/managerial economics; computer and information sciences; economics; electrical and electronic engineering technologies; engineering; environmental/environmental health engineering; finance and financial management services; human resources management; international business; management information systems; marketing; mechanical engineering; quality control and safety technologies.

Graduate—accounting and related services; business administration, management and operations; computer and information sciences; computer engineering; electrical and electronic engineering technologies; engineering; environmental/environmental health engineering; human resources management; management information systems; marketing; mechanical engineering.

CALIFORNIA STATE UNIVERSITY, CHICO
Chico, California
Center for Regional and Continuing Education
http://rce.csuchico.edu/online

California State University, Chico was founded in 1887. It is accredited by Western Association of Schools and Colleges. It first offered distance learning courses in 1975. In fall 2005, there were 850 students enrolled in distance learning courses. Institutionally administered financial aid is available to distance learners.

Services Distance learners have accessibility to academic advising, bookstore, campus computer network, e-mail services, library services, tutoring.

Contact Mr. Jeffrey S. Layne, Program Director, California State University, Chico, Chico, CA 95929-0250. Telephone: 530-898-6105. Fax: 530-898-4020. E-mail: jlayne@csuchico.edu.

DEGREES AND AWARDS
BA Liberal Studies; Social Science
BS Computer Science
BSN Nursing
MS Computer Science

COURSE SUBJECT AREAS OFFERED OUTSIDE OF DEGREE PROGRAMS
Undergraduate—agriculture; area, ethnic, cultural, and gender studies related; behavioral sciences; community health services; curriculum and instruction; dance; education; ethnic, cultural minority, and gender studies; health and medical administrative services; history; human development, family studies, and related services; legal professions and studies related; legal studies (non-professional general, undergraduate); liberal arts and sciences, general studies and humanities; nursing; psychology; social sciences; sociology.

Graduate—computer science.

CALIFORNIA STATE UNIVERSITY, DOMINGUEZ HILLS
Carson, California
Distance Learning
http://dominguezonline.csudh.edu

California State University, Dominguez Hills was founded in 1960. It is accredited by Western Association of Schools and Colleges. It first offered distance learning courses in 1974. In fall 2005, there were 4,000 students enrolled in distance learning courses. Institutionally administered financial aid is available to distance learners.

Services Distance learners have accessibility to academic advising, bookstore, campus computer network, e-mail services, library services, tutoring.

Contact Registration Department, California State University, Dominguez Hills, College of Extended and International Education, 1000 East Victoria Street, Carson, CA 90747. Telephone: 877-GO-HILLS. Fax: 310-516-3971. E-mail: eereg@csudh.edu.

DEGREES AND AWARDS
BS Applied Studies; Nursing Completion program; Quality Assurance
Certificate of Completion Quality Assurance
Certificate Assistive Technology; Community College Teaching; Production and Inventory Control; Purchasing
MA Humanities; Negotiation, Conflict Resolution and Peacebuilding
MS Nursing; Quality Assurance

COURSE SUBJECT AREAS OFFERED OUTSIDE OF DEGREE PROGRAMS
Undergraduate—education; educational administration and supervision; education related; nursing; quality control and safety technologies.

Graduate—business/commerce; liberal arts and sciences, general studies and humanities; nursing; peace studies and conflict resolution; public administration; quality control and safety technologies.

Non-credit—accounting and related services; business/corporate communications; business, management, and marketing related; computer and information sciences; computer/information technology administration and management; education; finance and financial management services; health and medical administrative services; human resources management; music; sales, merchandising, and related marketing operations (general); sales, merchandising, and related marketing operations (specialized).

See full description on page 332.

CALIFORNIA STATE UNIVERSITY, EAST BAY
Hayward, California
Division of Continuing and International Education
http://www.online.csuhayward.edu

California State University, East Bay was founded in 1957. It is accredited by Western Association of Schools and Colleges. It first offered distance learning courses in 1998. In fall 2005, there were 200 students enrolled in distance learning courses. Institutionally administered financial aid is available to distance learners.

Services Distance learners have accessibility to academic advising, bookstore, campus computer network, e-mail services, library services.

Contact Dr. Nan Chico, Graduate Coordinator, M.S.Ed (Option Online Teaching and Learning), California State University, East Bay, College of Education and Allied Studies, Interdisciplinary Education, Hayward, CA 94542. Telephone: 510-885-4384. Fax: 510-885-4498. E-mail: nan.chico@csueastbay.edu.

DEGREES AND AWARDS
Certificate Teaching and Learning–Online Teaching and Learning

MSE Teaching and Learning–Option in Online Teaching and Learning

COURSE SUBJECT AREAS OFFERED OUTSIDE OF DEGREE PROGRAMS
Undergraduate—biomedical/medical engineering; computer software and media applications; fine and studio art; sales, merchandising, and related marketing operations (specialized).

Graduate—biomathematics and bioinformatics; education related.

CALIFORNIA STATE UNIVERSITY, NORTHRIDGE
Northridge, California
Distance Learning
http://www.csun.edu/exl/distance.htm

California State University, Northridge was founded in 1958. It is accredited by Western Association of Schools and Colleges. It first offered distance learning courses in 1998. In fall 2005, there were 350 students enrolled in distance learning courses. Institutionally administered financial aid is available to distance learners.

Services Distance learners have accessibility to academic advising, bookstore, campus computer network, career placement assistance, e-mail services, library services.

Contact Karena Senchack, Distance Learning Program Manager, California State University, Northridge, College of Extended Learning, 18111 Nordhoff Street, Mail Code 8401, Northridge, CA 91330-8401. Telephone: 818-677-6405. Fax: 818-677-6408. E-mail: karena.senchack@csun.edu.

DEGREES AND AWARDS
CCCPE Communication Disorders and Science–CEUs in Communication Disorders and Science

MAE Educational Administration

MS Communication Disorders and Sciences

MSE Engineering Management

COURSE SUBJECT AREAS OFFERED OUTSIDE OF DEGREE PROGRAMS
Non-credit—communication disorders sciences and services.

CALIFORNIA STATE UNIVERSITY, SAN BERNARDINO
San Bernardino, California
http://www.csusb.edu/

California State University, San Bernardino was founded in 1965. It is accredited by Western Association of Schools and Colleges. It first offered distance learning courses in 1988. In fall 2005, there were 7,000 students enrolled in distance learning courses. Institutionally administered financial aid is available to distance learners.

Services Distance learners have accessibility to academic advising, bookstore, e-mail services, library services.

Contact Dr. James Michael Monaghan, EdD, Director, California State University, San Bernardino, 5500 University Parkway, San Bernardino, CA 92407. Telephone: 909-537-7439. Fax: 909-537-7637. E-mail: monaghan@csusb.edu.

DEGREES AND AWARDS
BSN Nursing–Online RN to BSN program

COURSE SUBJECT AREAS OFFERED OUTSIDE OF DEGREE PROGRAMS
Undergraduate—accounting and computer science; accounting and related services; Air Force J.R.O.T.C/R.O.T.C; allied health and medical assisting services; American literature (United States and Canadian); area, ethnic, cultural, and gender studies related; astronomy and astrophysics; bilingual, multilingual, and multicultural education; business administration, management and operations; business, management, and marketing related; clinical child psychology; cognitive psychology and psycholinguistics; communication and journalism related; communication and media; communications technology; community health services; criminal justice and corrections; economics; education; educational/instructional media design; education related; education (specific subject areas); English; ethnic, cultural minority, and gender studies; finance and financial management services; languages (foreign languages related); liberal arts and sciences, general studies and humanities; mathematics; multi-/interdisciplinary studies related; nursing; political science and government; psychology; social work; visual and performing arts.

Graduate—allied health diagnostic, intervention, and treatment professions; communication and media; communications technology; criminal justice and corrections; education; educational/instructional media design; education (specific subject areas); public administration.

Non-credit—education related.

CALIFORNIA STATE UNIVERSITY, SAN MARCOS
San Marcos, California
Extended Studies
http://www.csusm.edu/es

California State University, San Marcos was founded in 1990. It is accredited by Western Association of Schools and Colleges. It first offered distance learning courses in 1997. In fall 2005, there were 100 students enrolled in distance learning courses. Institutionally administered financial aid is available to distance learners.

Services Distance learners have accessibility to bookstore, library services.

Contact Ms. Anna Dubois, Director of Community Programs, California State University, San Marcos, 333 South Twin Oaks Valley Road, San Marcos, CA 92096. Telephone: 760-750-4003. Fax: 760-750-3138. E-mail: adubois@csusm.edu.

DEGREES AND AWARDS
Programs offered do not lead to a degree or other formal award.

COURSE SUBJECT AREAS OFFERED OUTSIDE OF DEGREE PROGRAMS
Undergraduate—accounting and computer science; allied health and medical assisting services; applied mathematics; business administration, management and operations; business operations support and assistant services; computer and information sciences and support services related; computer programming; education (specific subject areas); mathematics; social work.

Graduate—education related; education (specific subject areas).

Non-credit—accounting and computer science; business/commerce; communication and journalism related; community health services; comparative literature; computer and information sciences; dramatic/theater arts and stagecraft; English as a second language; family and consumer economics; fine and studio art; health/medical preparatory programs; health services/allied health/health sciences; languages (foreign languages related); mathematics; nursing; philosophy; psychology related; work and family studies.

CALIFORNIA UNIVERSITY OF PENNSYLVANIA
California, Pennsylvania
http://www.cup.edu/graduate

California University of Pennsylvania was founded in 1852. It is accredited by Middle States Association of Colleges and Schools. It first offered distance learning courses in 2004. In fall 2005, there were 750 students enrolled in distance learning courses. Institutionally administered financial aid is available to distance learners.

Services Distance learners have accessibility to academic advising, bookstore, campus computer network, career placement assistance, e-mail services, library services.

Contact Ms. Millie Rodriguez, Director, Office of Web Based Programs, California University of Pennsylvania, School of Graduate Studies and Research, 250 University Avenue, California, PA 15419. Telephone: 724-938-5958. Fax: 724-938-4270. E-mail: rodriguez@cup.edu.

DEGREES AND AWARDS

BS Science and Technology Legal Studies Option; Sport Management Studies–Wellness and Fitness Track
Certification Administrative Principals program; Superintendent's Letter of Eligibility
MA Tourism Planning and Development
MAT Secondary Education, advanced studies
MEd Administrative Principal program
MS Exercise Science and Health Promotion–Performance Enhancement and Injury Prevention; Exercise Science and Health Promotion–Sports Psychology; Exercise Science and Health Promotion–Wellness and Fitness; Exercise Science and Health Promotion-Rehabilitation Sciences; Legal Studies–Homeland Security; Legal Studies–Law and Public Policy; Sport Management Studies

COURSE SUBJECT AREAS OFFERED OUTSIDE OF DEGREE PROGRAMS

Undergraduate—applied mathematics; business administration, management and operations; criminal justice and corrections; dramatic/theater arts and stagecraft; education; geological and earth sciences/geosciences; health and physical education/fitness; industrial production technologies; music; philosophy; philosophy and religious studies related; psychology; sociology; technology education/industrial arts.

Graduate—criminal justice and corrections; educational administration and supervision; health and physical education/fitness; health professions related; legal research and advanced professional studies; public administration.

CAMPBELLSVILLE UNIVERSITY
Campbellsville, Kentucky
http://www.campbellsville.edu/

Campbellsville University was founded in 1906. It is accredited by Southern Association of Colleges and Schools. It first offered distance learning courses in 1999. In fall 2005, there were 255 students enrolled in distance learning courses. Institutionally administered financial aid is available to distance learners.

Services Distance learners have accessibility to academic advising, bookstore, campus computer network, career placement assistance, e-mail services, library services.

Contact Ms. Karla Deaton, Coordinator of Academic Outreach, Campbellsville University, 1 University Drive, Campbellsville, KY 42718-2799. Telephone: 270-789-5078. Fax: 270-789-5550. E-mail: krdeaton@campbellsville.edu.

DEGREES AND AWARDS

MSE Special Education

COURSE SUBJECT AREAS OFFERED OUTSIDE OF DEGREE PROGRAMS

Undergraduate—religious studies; social work.

Graduate—educational administration and supervision; religious studies; social work.

CAMPBELL UNIVERSITY
Buies Creek, North Carolina
http://www.campbell.edu

Campbell University was founded in 1887. It is accredited by Southern Association of Colleges and Schools. It first offered distance learning courses in 2000. In fall 2005, there were 630 students enrolled in distance learning courses. Institutionally administered financial aid is available to distance learners.

Services Distance learners have accessibility to bookstore, campus computer network, e-mail services, library services.

Contact Mr. Frank Signorile, Jr., Director, Distance Education, Campbell University, PO Box 264, Buies Creek, NC 27506. Telephone: 910-814-4739. Fax: 910-814-4736. E-mail: signorile@campbell.edu.

DEGREES AND AWARDS

Programs offered do not lead to a degree or other formal award.

COURSE SUBJECT AREAS OFFERED OUTSIDE OF DEGREE PROGRAMS

Undergraduate—accounting and related services; American literature (United States and Canadian); biblical studies; business administration, management and operations; business/corporate communications; English composition; fine and studio art; geography and cartography; history; mathematics and computer science; political science and government; psychology; sociology; statistics.

CAPE BRETON UNIVERSITY
Sydney, Nova Scotia, Canada
http://www.uccb.ca/distance

Cape Breton University was founded in 1974. It is provincially chartered. It first offered distance learning courses in 1997. In fall 2005, there were 572 students enrolled in distance learning courses. Institutionally administered financial aid is available to distance learners.

Services Distance learners have accessibility to academic advising, bookstore, career placement assistance, e-mail services, library services.

Contact Jennifer Pino, Coordinator of Distance Education, Cape Breton University, PO Box 5300, Sydney, NS B1P 6L2, Canada. Telephone: 902-563-1806. Fax: 902-539-9451. E-mail: distance_ed@capebretonu.ca.

DEGREES AND AWARDS

BA Community Studies
BES Environmental Science
BHS Public Health–Bachelor of Technology in Public Health
BST Manufacturing
Certificate Public Administration
MBE Education Counseling; Education Technology

COURSE SUBJECT AREAS OFFERED OUTSIDE OF DEGREE PROGRAMS

Undergraduate—accounting and related services; creative writing; developmental and child psychology; environmental/environmental health engineering; international business; marketing; social psychology; statistics.

Graduate—education.

Non-credit—business, management, and marketing related; computer/information technology administration and management; computer programming; computer software and media applications.

CAPE COD COMMUNITY COLLEGE
West Barnstable, Massachusetts
Distance and Learning Technology
http://learning.capecod.mass.edu

Cape Cod Community College was founded in 1961. It is accredited by New England Association of Schools and Colleges. It first offered distance learning courses in 1993. In fall 2005, there were 500 students enrolled in distance learning courses. Institutionally administered financial aid is available to distance learners.

Services Distance learners have accessibility to academic advising, bookstore, campus computer network, career placement assistance, e-mail services, library services, tutoring.

Contact Greg Masterson, Director of Distance Learning, Cape Cod Community College, 2240 Iyanough Road, West Barnstable, MA 02668. Telephone: 508-375-4040 Ext. 4345. Fax: 508-375-4041. E-mail: gmasters@capecod.edu.

DEGREES AND AWARDS

Programs offered do not lead to a degree or other formal award.

COURSE SUBJECT AREAS OFFERED OUTSIDE OF DEGREE PROGRAMS

Undergraduate—business administration, management and operations; computer software and media applications; developmental and child psychology; economics; English composition; fine and studio art; history; marketing; mathematics; natural sciences; nursing; psychology; psychology related; social sciences; sociology.

Non-credit—dental support services and allied professions.

CAPE FEAR COMMUNITY COLLEGE
Wilmington, North Carolina
http://cfcc.edu

Cape Fear Community College was founded in 1959. It is accredited by Southern Association of Colleges and Schools. It first offered distance learning courses in 1988. In fall 2005, there were 1,472 students enrolled in distance learning courses. Institutionally administered financial aid is available to distance learners.

Services Distance learners have accessibility to academic advising, bookstore, campus computer network, career placement assistance, e-mail services, library services, tutoring.

Contact Dr. Larolyn Zylicz, Chair, Distance Learning Department, Cape Fear Community College, 411 North Front Street, Wilmington, NC 28401. Telephone: 910-362-7245. Fax: 910-362-7152. E-mail: lzylicz@cfcc.edu.

DEGREES AND AWARDS

AA General Studies; General Studies

COURSE SUBJECT AREAS OFFERED OUTSIDE OF DEGREE PROGRAMS

Undergraduate—accounting and computer science; accounting and related services; American literature (United States and Canadian); business administration, management and operations; business/commerce; chemistry; communication and media; computer science; computer software and media applications; creative writing; criminology; economics; education; English composition; fine and studio art; health and physical education/fitness; history; legal professions and studies related; legal studies (non-professional general, undergraduate); marketing; mathematics; mathematics and statistics related; music; natural sciences; philosophy; psychology; religious studies; sales, merchandising, and related marketing operations (general); social sciences; sociology; statistics; technical and business writing.

Non-credit—business/commerce.

CAPELLA UNIVERSITY
Minneapolis, Minnesota
http://www.capellauniversity.edu/

Capella University was founded in 1993. It is accredited by North Central Association of Colleges and Schools. It first offered distance learning courses in 1993. In fall 2005, there were 15,000 students enrolled in distance learning courses. Institutionally administered financial aid is available to distance learners.

Services Distance learners have accessibility to academic advising, bookstore, career placement assistance, library services.

Contact Enrollment Services, Capella University, 225 South Sixth St, 9th Floor, Minneapolis, MN 55402. Telephone: 888-227-2736 Ext. 8. Fax: 612-977-5060. E-mail: info@capella.edu.

DEGREES AND AWARDS

BS Business/Accounting; Business/Business Administration; Business/Finance; Business/Human Resource Management; Business/Management and Leadership; Business/Marketing; Information Technology/General; Information Technology/Graphics and Multimedia; Information Technology/Information Assurance and Security; Information Technology/Network Technology; Information Technology/Project Management; Information Technology/Web Application Development

MBA Accounting; Business, general; Finance; Health Care Management; Information Technology Management; Marketing; Project Management

MS Human Services/Counseling Studies; Human Services/Criminal Justice; Human Services/General Human Services; Human Services/Health Care Administration; Human Services/Management of Nonprofit Agencies; Human Services/Marital, Couple, and Family Counseling/Therapy (CACREP Accredited); Human Services/Mental Health Counseling; Human Services/Social and Community Services; Information Technology/General Information Technology; Information Technology/Information Security; Information Technology/Network Architecture and Design; Information Technology/Project Management; Information Technology/System Design and Programming; Organization and Management/General; Organization and Management/Human Resource Management; Organization and Management/Information Technology Management; Organization and Management/Leadership; Psychology/Clinical Psychology; Psychology/Counseling Psychology; Psychology/Educational Psychology; Psychology/General Psychology; Psychology/Industrial-Organizational Psychology; Psychology/School Psychology; Psychology/Sport Psychology

MSE Curriculum and Instruction (for Licensed K-12 Teachers); Enrollment Management; Instructional Design for Online Learning; K-12 Studies in Education (For Licensed K-12 Teachers); Leadership in Educational Administration (For Licensed K-12 Teachers); Leadership in Higher Education; Postsecondary and Adult Education; Professional Studies in Education; Reading and Literacy (For Licensed K-12 Teachers); Training and Performance Improvement

PhD Education/Curriculum and Instruction; Education/Instructional Design for Online Learning; Education/K-12 Studies in Education; Education/Leadership for Higher Education; Education/Leadership in Educational Administration; Education/Postsecondary and Adult Education; Education/Professional Studies in Education; Education/Training and Performance Improvement; Human Services/Counseling Studies; Human Services/Criminal Justice; Human Services/General Human Services; Human Services/Health Care Administration; Human Services/Management of Nonprofit Agencies; Human Services/Social and Community Services; Organization and Management/General Business; Organization and Management/Human Resource Management; Organization and Management/Information Technology Management; Organization and Management/Leadership; Psychology/Educational Psychology; Psychology/General Psychology; Psychology/Industrial-Organizational Psychology

COURSE SUBJECT AREAS OFFERED OUTSIDE OF DEGREE PROGRAMS

Undergraduate—business administration, management and operations; business/commerce; business/corporate communications; business, management, and marketing related; computer/information technology administration and management; computer software and media applications; computer systems networking and telecommunications; human resources management; marketing; sales, merchandising, and related marketing operations (general).

Graduate—business administration, management and operations; business/corporate communications; business, management, and marketing related; clinical psychology; computer/information technology administration and management; computer systems networking and telecommunications; counseling psychology; criminal justice and corrections; education; educational administration and supervision; educational/instructional media design; educational psychology; human resources management; human services; industrial and organizational psychology;

international business; marketing; psychology; sales, merchandising, and related marketing operations (general); school psychology.

See full description on page 334.

CAPITOL COLLEGE
Laurel, Maryland
http://www.capitol-college.edu/academicprograms/graduateprograms/index.shtml

Capitol College was founded in 1964. It is accredited by Middle States Association of Colleges and Schools. It first offered distance learning courses in 1998. In fall 2005, there were 400 students enrolled in distance learning courses. Institutionally administered financial aid is available to distance learners.

Services Distance learners have accessibility to academic advising, bookstore, career placement assistance, e-mail services, library services.

Contact Mr. Darnell Edwards, Director of Admissions, Capitol College, Office of Admissions, 11301 Springfield Road, Laurel, MD 20708. Telephone: 301-369-2800 Ext. 3033. Fax: 301-953-3876. E-mail: gradprograms@capitol-college.edu.

DEGREES AND AWARDS

MBA Business Administration

MS Computer Science; Electrical Engineering; Information Assurance; Information and Telecommunication Systems Management; Internet Engineering; Network Security

COURSE SUBJECT AREAS OFFERED OUTSIDE OF DEGREE PROGRAMS

Graduate—computer and information sciences; computer and information sciences and support services related; computer engineering technologies; computer/information technology administration and management; computer science; computer software and media applications; computer systems networking and telecommunications; engineering; information science/studies; management information systems; management sciences and quantitative methods; systems engineering; systems science and theory.

CARDINAL STRITCH UNIVERSITY
Milwaukee, Wisconsin
College of Education
http://www.stritch.edu/

Cardinal Stritch University was founded in 1937. It is accredited by North Central Association of Colleges and Schools. It first offered distance learning courses in 1995. Institutionally administered financial aid is available to distance learners.

Services Distance learners have accessibility to bookstore, campus computer network, career placement assistance, e-mail services, library services.

Contact Judy Wendorf, Director of University Outreach–Professional Development, Cardinal Stritch University, 6801 North Yates Road, Milwaukee, WI 53217-3985. Telephone: 414-410-4428. E-mail: jawendorf@stritch.edu.

DEGREES AND AWARDS

Programs offered do not lead to a degree or other formal award.

COURSE SUBJECT AREAS OFFERED OUTSIDE OF DEGREE PROGRAMS

Graduate—education.

Non-credit—business administration, management and operations; computer software and media applications; creative writing; family and consumer sciences/human sciences business services.

CARL ALBERT STATE COLLEGE
Poteau, Oklahoma
http://www.carlalbert.edu

Carl Albert State College was founded in 1934. It is accredited by North Central Association of Colleges and Schools. It first offered distance learning courses in 1996. In fall 2005, there were 200 students enrolled in distance learning courses. Institutionally administered financial aid is available to distance learners.

Services Distance learners have accessibility to academic advising, bookstore, library services.

Contact Ms. Kathy A. Harrell, Dean of Instruction, Carl Albert State College, 1507 South McKenna, Poteau, OK 74953. Telephone: 918-647-1230. Fax: 918-647-1201. E-mail: kharrell@carlalbert.edu.

DEGREES AND AWARDS

Programs offered do not lead to a degree or other formal award.

COURSE SUBJECT AREAS OFFERED OUTSIDE OF DEGREE PROGRAMS

Undergraduate—accounting and related services; biological and physical sciences; business administration, management and operations; computer and information sciences; computer systems networking and telecommunications; data entry/microcomputer applications; English composition; health and physical education/fitness; history; mathematics; political science and government; psychology.

CARLOW UNIVERSITY
Pittsburgh, Pennsylvania
http://www.carlow.edu/

Carlow University was founded in 1929. It is accredited by Middle States Association of Colleges and Schools. It first offered distance learning courses in 1995. In fall 2005, there were 1,499 students enrolled in distance learning courses. Institutionally administered financial aid is available to distance learners.

Services Distance learners have accessibility to academic advising, bookstore, campus computer network, career placement assistance, e-mail services, library services, tutoring.

Contact Nola Coulson, Coordinator, Instructional Technology, Carlow University, 3333 Fifth Avenue, Pittsburgh, PA 15213. Telephone: 412-578-6338. Fax: 412-578-6595. E-mail: coulsonna@carlow.edu.

DEGREES AND AWARDS

Programs offered do not lead to a degree or other formal award.

COURSE SUBJECT AREAS OFFERED OUTSIDE OF DEGREE PROGRAMS

Undergraduate—accounting and computer science; business, management, and marketing related; chemistry; computer science; education; English; information science/studies; mathematics; nursing; philosophy; political science and government; psychology; social psychology; social work; sociology; special education.

Graduate—business, management, and marketing related; counseling psychology; education; nursing; special education.

CARL SANDBURG COLLEGE
Galesburg, Illinois
http://www.sandburg.edu

Carl Sandburg College was founded in 1967. It is accredited by North Central Association of Colleges and Schools. It first offered distance learning courses in 1986. In fall 2005, there were 500 students enrolled in distance learning courses. Institutionally administered financial aid is available to distance learners.

Services Distance learners have accessibility to bookstore, campus computer network, e-mail services, library services.

Contact Carol Kreider, Director of Admissions, Carl Sandburg College, 2400 Tom L. Wilson Boulevard, Galesburg, IL 61401. Telephone: 309-341-5234. Fax: 309-344-3291. E-mail: ckreider@sandburgl.edu.

DEGREES AND AWARDS

Programs offered do not lead to a degree or other formal award.

COURSE SUBJECT AREAS OFFERED OUTSIDE OF DEGREE PROGRAMS

Undergraduate—accounting and related services; cell biology and anatomical sciences; computer software and media applications; English; English composition; fine and studio art; geography and cartography; health services/allied health/health sciences; music; psychology; sociology.

CARROLL COLLEGE
Waukesha, Wisconsin
http://www.cc.edu/

Carroll College was founded in 1846. It is accredited by North Central Association of Colleges and Schools. It first offered distance learning courses in 1995. In fall 2005, there were 293 students enrolled in distance learning courses. Institutionally administered financial aid is available to distance learners.

Services Distance learners have accessibility to academic advising, bookstore, campus computer network, career placement assistance, e-mail services, library services, tutoring.

Contact Ms. Tina Wood, Director of Admissions, Carroll College, 100 North East Avenue, Waukesha, WI 53186. Telephone: 262-524-7518. Fax: 262-650-4851. E-mail: twood@cc.edu.

DEGREES AND AWARDS
Programs offered do not lead to a degree or other formal award.

COURSE SUBJECT AREAS OFFERED OUTSIDE OF DEGREE PROGRAMS
Undergraduate—business, management, and marketing related; computer science; English; finance and financial management services; history.

Graduate—computer science; computer software and media applications.

CASPER COLLEGE
Casper, Wyoming
http://www.caspercollege.edu/

Casper College was founded in 1945. It is accredited by North Central Association of Colleges and Schools. It first offered distance learning courses in 1986. In fall 2005, there were 1,000 students enrolled in distance learning courses. Institutionally administered financial aid is available to distance learners.

Services Distance learners have accessibility to academic advising, bookstore, career placement assistance, e-mail services, library services, tutoring.

Contact Paul J. Marquard, Director of Distance Education, Casper College, 125 College Drive, Casper, WY 82601-4699. Telephone: 307-268-2250. Fax: 307-268-2224. E-mail: marquard@caspercollege.edu.

DEGREES AND AWARDS
AS Early Childhood Education; Education

COURSE SUBJECT AREAS OFFERED OUTSIDE OF DEGREE PROGRAMS
Undergraduate—accounting and related services; anthropology; astronomy and astrophysics; biological and biomedical sciences related; biological and physical sciences; biology; business administration, management and operations; business/commerce; business, management, and marketing related; chemistry; computer and information sciences; computer programming; computer science; computer software and media applications; creative writing; economics; education; educational psychology; education related; engineering; engineering science; English composition; fine and studio art; geography and cartography; mathematics; music; psychology; sociology; special education; statistics; teaching assistants/aides; zoology/animal biology.

THE CATHOLIC DISTANCE UNIVERSITY
Hamilton, Virginia
http://www.cdu.edu/

The Catholic Distance University was founded in 1983. It is accredited by Distance Education and Training Council. It first offered distance learning courses in 1983. In fall 2005, there were 950 students enrolled in distance learning courses. Institutionally administered financial aid is available to distance learners.

Services Distance learners have accessibility to academic advising, bookstore, e-mail services, library services.

Contact Dr. Carolann Cirbee, PhD, Dean of Students, The Catholic Distance University, 120 East Colonial Highway, Hamilton, VA 20158. Telephone: 540-338-2700 Ext. 718. Fax: 540-338-4788. E-mail: ccirbee@cdu.edu.

DEGREES AND AWARDS
BA Theology — degree completion program
Certification Catechist Certificate, advanced
Diploma Apostolic Catechetical Diploma
MA Theology

COURSE SUBJECT AREAS OFFERED OUTSIDE OF DEGREE PROGRAMS
Undergraduate—religious education; religious studies; theology and religious vocations related.

Graduate—religious education; religious studies; theology and religious vocations related.

Non-credit—religious education; religious studies; theological and ministerial studies; theology and religious vocations related.

CAYUGA COUNTY COMMUNITY COLLEGE
Auburn, New York
http://www.cayuga-cc.edu/

Cayuga County Community College was founded in 1953. It is accredited by Middle States Association of Colleges and Schools. It first offered distance learning courses in 1998. In fall 2005, there were 600 students enrolled in distance learning courses. Institutionally administered financial aid is available to distance learners.

Services Distance learners have accessibility to academic advising, bookstore, career placement assistance, e-mail services, library services, tutoring.

Contact Ed Kowalski, Director of Online Programs, Cayuga County Community College, 197 Franklin Street, Auburn, NY 13021. Telephone: 315-255-1743. Fax: 315-255-2117. E-mail: kowalskie@cayuga-cc.edu.

DEGREES AND AWARDS
AA Liberal Arts and Humanities
AAS Business Administration; Criminal Justice–Police
AS Business Administration; Liberal Arts and Sciences/Mathematics and Sciences

COURSE SUBJECT AREAS OFFERED OUTSIDE OF DEGREE PROGRAMS
Undergraduate—accounting and related services; anthropology; biological and physical sciences; biology; business administration, management and operations; business/commerce; computer science; computer systems networking and telecommunications; economics; English; health and physical education/fitness; history; mathematics; political science and government; psychology; social psychology; social sciences; social sciences related; statistics.

CECIL COMMUNITY COLLEGE
North East, Maryland
http://www.cecilcc.edu

Cecil Community College was founded in 1968. It is accredited by Middle States Association of Colleges and Schools. It first offered distance learning courses in 1999. In fall 2005, there were 205 students enrolled in distance learning courses. Institutionally administered financial aid is available to distance learners.

Services Distance learners have accessibility to bookstore, campus computer network, e-mail services.

Contact Carrie S. Ray-Murray, Operations Technician, Cecil Community College, One Seahawk Drive, North East, MD 21901. Telephone: 410-287-6060 Ext. 552. Fax: 410-287-1001. E-mail: cray@cecilcc.edu.

DEGREES AND AWARDS
Programs offered do not lead to a degree or other formal award.

COURSE SUBJECT AREAS OFFERED OUTSIDE OF DEGREE PROGRAMS

Undergraduate—astronomy and astrophysics; business/commerce; chemistry; mathematics; physics; psychology; sociology.

CEDARVILLE UNIVERSITY
Cedarville, Ohio
http://www.cedarville.edu/

Cedarville University was founded in 1887. It is accredited by North Central Association of Colleges and Schools. It first offered distance learning courses in 1999. In fall 2005, there were 250 students enrolled in distance learning courses. Institutionally administered financial aid is available to distance learners.

Services Distance learners have accessibility to academic advising, bookstore, campus computer network, career placement assistance, e-mail services, library services.

Contact Chuck Allport, Assistant to the Academic Vice President, Cedarville University, 251 North Main Street, Cedarville, OH 45314. Telephone: 937-766-7681. Fax: 937-766-3217. E-mail: chuckallport@cedarville.edu.

DEGREES AND AWARDS

Programs offered do not lead to a degree or other formal award.

COURSE SUBJECT AREAS OFFERED OUTSIDE OF DEGREE PROGRAMS

Undergraduate—anthropology; biology; business/corporate communications; English; history; mathematics; social sciences; sociology; soil sciences; special education.

CENTRAL CAROLINA COMMUNITY COLLEGE
Sanford, North Carolina
http://www.cccc.edu

Central Carolina Community College was founded in 1962. It is accredited by Southern Association of Colleges and Schools. It first offered distance learning courses in 1997. In fall 2005, there were 1,300 students enrolled in distance learning courses. Institutionally administered financial aid is available to distance learners.

Services Distance learners have accessibility to academic advising, bookstore, campus computer network, career placement assistance, e-mail services, library services, tutoring.

Contact Mrs. Lara Manton, Distance Education Counselor, Central Carolina Community College, 1105 Kelly Drive, Sanford, NC 27330. Telephone: 919-718-7511. Fax: 919-718-7380. E-mail: lmanton@cccc.edu.

DEGREES AND AWARDS

AA General Studies

Certificate Bioprocess Manufacturing Technology

Diploma Applied Science–Associate in Applied Science

COURSE SUBJECT AREAS OFFERED OUTSIDE OF DEGREE PROGRAMS

Undergraduate—accounting and related services; agriculture; American literature (United States and Canadian); biblical studies; biological and physical sciences; biomedical/medical engineering; biotechnology; business/commerce; business operations support and assistant services; computer programming; computer science; criminal justice and corrections; economics; education; electrical and electronic engineering technologies; English; health and physical education/fitness; history; journalism; languages (foreign languages related); library science related; marketing; mathematics; sociology.

Non-credit—clinical/medical laboratory science and allied professions; computer and information sciences; criminal justice and corrections; English as a second language; management information systems.

CENTRAL LAKES COLLEGE
Brainerd, Minnesota
http://www.clc.cc.mn.us/

Central Lakes College was founded in 1938. It is accredited by North Central Association of Colleges and Schools. It first offered distance learning courses in 1998. In fall 2005, there were 300 students enrolled in distance learning courses. Institutionally administered financial aid is available to distance learners.

Services Distance learners have accessibility to academic advising, bookstore, e-mail services, library services, tutoring.

Contact Rebecca Best, Associate Vice President, Central Lakes College, 501 West College Drive, Brainerd, MN 56401. Telephone: 218-855-8143. Fax: 218-855-8141. E-mail: rbest@clcmn.edu.

DEGREES AND AWARDS

Programs offered do not lead to a degree or other formal award.

COURSE SUBJECT AREAS OFFERED OUTSIDE OF DEGREE PROGRAMS

Undergraduate—American Sign Language (ASL); biology; business/commerce; business operations support and assistant services; chemistry; computer and information sciences; computer software and media applications; criminal justice and corrections; English composition; history; languages (Romance languages); marketing; mathematics; music; nursing; philosophy; political science and government; psychology; speech and rhetoric; visual and performing arts.

CENTRAL MICHIGAN UNIVERSITY
Mount Pleasant, Michigan
Distance/Distributed Learning
http://DDLcampus.cmich.edu

Central Michigan University was founded in 1892. It is accredited by North Central Association of Colleges and Schools. It first offered distance learning courses in 1971. In fall 2005, there were 8,000 students enrolled in distance learning courses. Institutionally administered financial aid is available to distance learners.

Services Distance learners have accessibility to academic advising, bookstore, campus computer network, career placement assistance, e-mail services, library services, tutoring.

Contact Ms. Marnie Roestel, Coordinator of Recruitment Services, Central Michigan University, 802 Industrial Drive, Mount Pleasant , MI 48858. Telephone: 800-950-1144 Ext. 3937. E-mail: roest1m@cmich.edu.

DEGREES AND AWARDS

BS Administration–Building Code Administration; Administration–Organizational Administration; Community Development, Community Services major; Community Development, Health Sciences major; Community Development, Public Administration major

MAE Education

MS Administration–General Administration concentration; Administration–Health Services Administration concentration; Administration–Human Resource Administration; Administration–Information Resource Management concentration; Administration–Leadership concentration; Administration–Public Administration concentration; Nutrition and Dietetics

DH Sc Healthcare Administration

COURSE SUBJECT AREAS OFFERED OUTSIDE OF DEGREE PROGRAMS

Undergraduate—accounting and computer science; allied health and medical assisting services; architecture related; behavioral sciences; building/construction finishing, management, and inspection; business administration, management and operations; business/commerce; business/corporate communications; business, management, and marketing related; business/managerial economics; business operations support and assistant services; community health services; community organization and advocacy; construction management; construction trades; economics; family and consumer sciences/human sciences; family and consumer sciences/human sciences related; health and medical administrative services; health and physical education/fitness; health professions related; health services/allied health/health sciences; human development, family studies, and related services; human resources management; human services; industrial and organizational psychology; marketing; multi-/interdisciplinary studies related; political science and government; psychology; psychology related; public administration; public administration and social service professions related; public policy analysis; work and family studies.

Graduate—accounting and computer science; behavioral sciences; business administration, management and operations; business/commerce; business/corporate communications; business, management, and marketing related; business/managerial economics; communication and journalism related; communications technology; computer and information sciences; computer and information sciences and support services related; computer systems analysis; curriculum and instruction; dietetics and clinical nutrition services; economics; education (specific levels and methods); education (specific subject areas); entrepreneurial and small business operations; finance and financial management services; food science and technology; foods, nutrition, and related services; health and medical administrative services; health professions related; hospitality administration; human resources management; management information systems; management sciences and quantitative methods; marketing; multi-/interdisciplinary studies related; nutrition sciences; political science and government; public administration; public administration and social service professions related; public policy analysis; public relations, advertising, and applied communication related; sales, merchandising, and related marketing operations (general).

See full description on page 336.

CENTRAL MISSOURI STATE UNIVERSITY
Warrensburg, Missouri
Department of Nursing
http://www.cmsu.edu/extcamp

Central Missouri State University was founded in 1871. It is accredited by North Central Association of Colleges and Schools. It first offered distance learning courses in 1993. In fall 2005, there were 1,100 students enrolled in distance learning courses. Institutionally administered financial aid is available to distance learners.

Services Distance learners have accessibility to academic advising, bookstore, campus computer network, career placement assistance, e-mail services, library services, tutoring.

Contact Ms. Barbra Carder, Assistant Director for Distance Learning, Central Missouri State University, Office of Extended Campus, 410 Humphreys, Warrensburg, MO 64093. Telephone: 800-729-2678 Ext. 22. Fax: 660-543-8480. E-mail: bcarder@cmsu1.cmsu.edu.

DEGREES AND AWARDS

BSN Nursing

MSN Nursing–Rural Family Nursing

COURSE SUBJECT AREAS OFFERED OUTSIDE OF DEGREE PROGRAMS

Undergraduate—computer science; criminal justice and corrections; curriculum and instruction; educational assessment, evaluation, and research; educational psychology; education (specific subject areas); foods, nutrition, and related services; library science; technology education/industrial arts.

Graduate—criminal justice and corrections; curriculum and instruction; educational assessment, evaluation, and research; educational psychology; library science; nursing; special education; technology education/industrial arts.

Non-credit—accounting and related services; computer programming; computer software and media applications; computer systems networking and telecommunications; entrepreneurial and small business operations.

See full description on page 342.

CENTRAL MISSOURI STATE UNIVERSITY
Warrensburg, Missouri
Department of Criminal Justice
http://www.cmsu.edu/extcamp

Central Missouri State University was founded in 1871. It is accredited by North Central Association of Colleges and Schools. It first offered distance learning courses in 1993. In fall 2005, there were 1,100 students enrolled in distance learning courses. Institutionally administered financial aid is available to distance learners.

Services Distance learners have accessibility to academic advising, bookstore, campus computer network, career placement assistance, e-mail services, library services, tutoring.

Contact Ms. Barbra Carder, Assistant Director for Distance Learning, Central Missouri State University, Office of Extended Campus, 410 Humphreys, Warrensburg, MO 64093. Telephone: 800-729-2678 Ext. 22. Fax: 660-543-8480. E-mail: bcarder@cmsu1.cmsu.edu.

DEGREES AND AWARDS

MS Criminal Justice

COURSE SUBJECT AREAS OFFERED OUTSIDE OF DEGREE PROGRAMS

Undergraduate—computer science; criminal justice and corrections; curriculum and instruction; educational assessment, evaluation, and research; educational psychology; education (specific subject areas); foods, nutrition, and related services; library science; technology education/industrial arts.

Graduate—criminal justice and corrections; curriculum and instruction; educational assessment, evaluation, and research; educational psychology; library science; nursing; special education; technology education/industrial arts.

Non-credit—accounting and related services; computer programming; computer software and media applications; computer systems networking and telecommunications; entrepreneurial and small business operations.

See full description on page 338.

CENTRAL MISSOURI STATE UNIVERSITY
Warrensburg, Missouri
School of Technology
http://www.cmsu.edu/extcamp

Central Missouri State University was founded in 1871. It is accredited by North Central Association of Colleges and Schools. It first offered distance learning courses in 1993. In fall 2005, there were 1,100 students enrolled in distance learning courses. Institutionally administered financial aid is available to distance learners.

Services Distance learners have accessibility to academic advising, bookstore, campus computer network, career placement assistance, e-mail services, library services, tutoring.

Contact Ms. Barbra Carder, Assistant Director for Distance Learning, Central Missouri State University, Office of Extended Campus, 410 Humphreys, Warrensburg, MO 64093. Telephone: 800-729-2678 Ext. 22. Fax: 660-543-8480. E-mail: bcarder@cmsu1.cmsu.edu.

DEGREES AND AWARDS

MS Industrial Management

PhD Technology Management

COURSE SUBJECT AREAS OFFERED OUTSIDE OF DEGREE PROGRAMS

Undergraduate—computer science; criminal justice and corrections; curriculum and instruction; educational assessment, evaluation, and research; educational psychology; education (specific subject areas); foods, nutrition, and related services; library science; technology education/industrial arts.

Graduate—criminal justice and corrections; curriculum and instruction; educational assessment, evaluation, and research; educational psychology; library science; nursing; special education; technology education/industrial arts.

Non-credit—accounting and related services; computer programming; computer software and media applications; computer systems networking and telecommunications; entrepreneurial and small business operations.

See full description on page 340.

CENTRAL NEW MEXICO COMMUNITY COLLEGE
Albuquerque, New Mexico
http://planet.tvi.edu/distancelearn

Central New Mexico Community College was founded in 1965. It is accredited by North Central Association of Colleges and Schools. It first offered distance learning courses in 1997. In fall 2005, there were 1,686 students enrolled in distance learning courses. Institutionally administered financial aid is available to distance learners.

Services Distance learners have accessibility to academic advising, bookstore, campus computer network, e-mail services, library services, tutoring.

Contact Mr. Brian Ditmer, Distance Learning Specialist, Central New Mexico Community College, Distance Learning Office, 525 Buena Vista SE, Albuquerque, NM 87106. Telephone: 505-224-3318. Fax: 505-224-3321. E-mail: bditmer@cnm.edu.

DEGREES AND AWARDS
AAS Business Administration; Office Administration

COURSE SUBJECT AREAS OFFERED OUTSIDE OF DEGREE PROGRAMS
Undergraduate—accounting and related services; biology; building/construction finishing, management, and inspection; business administration, management and operations; business/commerce; business, management, and marketing related; business/managerial economics; business operations support and assistant services; clinical/medical laboratory science and allied professions; communication and media; computer and information sciences; computer programming; creative writing; criminal justice and corrections; culinary arts and related services; data processing; economics; English; English composition; entrepreneurial and small business operations; fire protection; foods, nutrition, and related services; information science/studies; international business; legal studies (non-professional general, undergraduate); mathematics; microbiological sciences and immunology; nursing; philosophy; psychology; real estate; sales, merchandising, and related marketing operations (general); sociology; speech and rhetoric.

CENTRAL OREGON COMMUNITY COLLEGE
Bend, Oregon
Open Campus Distance Learning Program
http://www.cocc.edu/opencampus

Central Oregon Community College was founded in 1949. It is accredited by Northwest Commission on Colleges and Universities. It first offered distance learning courses in 1996. In fall 2005, there were 379 students enrolled in distance learning courses. Institutionally administered financial aid is available to distance learners.

Services Distance learners have accessibility to academic advising, bookstore, campus computer network, e-mail services, library services, tutoring.

Contact Barbara Klett, Instructional Technology Coordinator, Central Oregon Community College, 2600 Northwest College Way, Bend, OR 97701. Telephone: 541-383-7785. E-mail: bklett@cocc.edu.

DEGREES AND AWARDS
Programs offered do not lead to a degree or other formal award.

COURSE SUBJECT AREAS OFFERED OUTSIDE OF DEGREE PROGRAMS
Undergraduate—biological and physical sciences; business administration, management and operations; chemistry; communication and media; computer and information sciences; criminal justice and corrections; developmental and child psychology; foods, nutrition, and related services; geography and cartography; history; information science/studies; liberal arts and sciences, general studies and humanities; mathematics; psychology.

CENTRAL PIEDMONT COMMUNITY COLLEGE
Charlotte, North Carolina
Distance Learning Services
http://www.cpcc.edu/

Central Piedmont Community College was founded in 1963. It is accredited by Southern Association of Colleges and Schools. It first offered distance learning courses in 1977. In fall 2005, there were 5,205 students enrolled in distance learning courses. Institutionally administered financial aid is available to distance learners.

Services Distance learners have accessibility to academic advising, campus computer network, e-mail services, tutoring.

Contact Ms. Erin Reed, Instructional Developer, Central Piedmont Community College, PO Box 35009, Charlotte, NC 28235. Telephone: 704-330-6051. Fax: 704-330-6945. E-mail: erin.reed@cpcc.edu.

DEGREES AND AWARDS
AA College Transfer Degree

COURSE SUBJECT AREAS OFFERED OUTSIDE OF DEGREE PROGRAMS
Undergraduate—accounting and computer science; accounting and related services; American Sign Language (ASL); anthropology; architectural technology; biology; botany/plant biology; carpentry; chemistry; community health services; computer programming; computer science; criminal justice and corrections; developmental and child psychology; English composition; geography and cartography; legal studies (non-professional general, undergraduate); mathematics and statistics related; sociology; statistics.

Non-credit—accounting and computer science; culinary arts and related services; dietetics and clinical nutrition services; management information systems.

CENTRAL TEXAS COLLEGE
Killeen, Texas
Distance Education and Educational Technology
http://online.ctcd.edu

Central Texas College was founded in 1967. It is accredited by Southern Association of Colleges and Schools. It first offered distance learning courses in 1972. In fall 2005, there were 18,000 students enrolled in distance learning courses. Institutionally administered financial aid is available to distance learners.

Services Distance learners have accessibility to academic advising, bookstore, career placement assistance, library services, tutoring.

Contact Coordinator, Distance Learning Recruiting and Retention, Central Texas College, PO Box 1800, Killeen, TX 76540. Telephone: 254-526-1656. Fax: 254-526-1481. E-mail: ctc.info@ctcd.edu.

DEGREES AND AWARDS
AAS Applied Technology; At-Risk Youth specialization; Business Management; Chemical Dependency Specialization; Computer Science–Information Technology; Criminal Justice; Hospitality Management; Social Work
AGS General Studies
ASAST Applied Science

COURSE SUBJECT AREAS OFFERED OUTSIDE OF DEGREE PROGRAMS
Undergraduate—accounting and related services; anthropology; applied mathematics; area, ethnic, cultural, and gender studies related; biblical studies; business administration, management and operations; business/corporate communications; business, management, and marketing related; business operations support and assistant services; communication and media; community psychology; computer and information sciences; computer and information sciences and support services related; computer programming; computer science; computer software and media applications; computer systems analysis; computer systems networking and telecommunications; counseling psychology; criminal justice and

corrections; criminology; culinary arts and related services; developmental and child psychology; economics; English; English composition; entrepreneurial and small business operations; ethnic, cultural minority, and gender studies; fine and studio art; fire protection; foods, nutrition, and related services; health and physical education/fitness; history; hospitality administration; human resources management; legal studies (non-professional general, undergraduate); management information systems; marketing; mathematics; mathematics and statistics related; mental and social health services and allied professions; military studies; multi-/interdisciplinary studies related; nursing; philosophy; philosophy and religious studies related; political science and government; psychology; psychology related; real estate; religious studies; sales, merchandising, and related marketing operations (specialized); social sciences; social sciences related; sociology; statistics; technical and business writing.

CENTRAL VIRGINIA COMMUNITY COLLEGE
Lynchburg, Virginia
Learning Resources
http://www.cvcc.vccs.edu

Central Virginia Community College was founded in 1966. It is accredited by Southern Association of Colleges and Schools. It first offered distance learning courses in 1984. In fall 2005, there were 1,253 students enrolled in distance learning courses. Institutionally administered financial aid is available to distance learners.

Services Distance learners have accessibility to academic advising, bookstore, campus computer network, e-mail services, library services, tutoring.

Contact Susan S. Beasley, Distance Education Coordinator, Central Virginia Community College, 3506 Wards Road, Lynchburg, VA 24502. Telephone: 434-832-7742. Fax: 434-832-7746. E-mail: beasleys@cvcc.vccs.edu.

DEGREES AND AWARDS
AAS Medical Laboratory Technology

COURSE SUBJECT AREAS OFFERED OUTSIDE OF DEGREE PROGRAMS
Undergraduate—accounting and related services; applied mathematics; astronomy and astrophysics; biology; business operations support and assistant services; chemistry; computer and information sciences; economics; education related; English; English composition; health professions related; history; information science/studies; library science related; marketing; music; philosophy; political science and government; psychology; religious studies; sociology; speech and rhetoric; technical and business writing; visual and performing arts related.

CENTRAL WASHINGTON UNIVERSITY
Ellensburg, Washington
Center for Learning Technologies
http://www.cwu.edu/~media/

Central Washington University was founded in 1891. It is accredited by Northwest Commission on Colleges and Universities. It first offered distance learning courses in 1996. In fall 2005, there were 1,133 students enrolled in distance learning courses. Institutionally administered financial aid is available to distance learners.

Services Distance learners have accessibility to academic advising, bookstore, campus computer network, e-mail services, library services.

Contact Tracy Terrell, Registrar, Central Washington University, Mitchell Hall, 400 East University Way, Ellensburg, WA 98926-7465. Telephone: 509-963-3076. Fax: 509-963-3022. E-mail: terrell@cwu.edu.

DEGREES AND AWARDS
MS Physical Education, Health, and Leisure Studies

COURSE SUBJECT AREAS OFFERED OUTSIDE OF DEGREE PROGRAMS
Undergraduate—accounting and related services; business/commerce; computer/information technology administration and management; criminal justice and corrections; history; philosophy and religious studies related; psychology.

Graduate—accounting and related services; business administration, management and operations; education; health and physical education/fitness.

Non-credit—education.

CENTRAL WYOMING COLLEGE
Riverton, Wyoming
Distance Education and Extended Studies
http://www.cwc.edu

Central Wyoming College was founded in 1966. It is accredited by North Central Association of Colleges and Schools. It first offered distance learning courses in 1983. In fall 2005, there were 783 students enrolled in distance learning courses. Institutionally administered financial aid is available to distance learners.

Services Distance learners have accessibility to academic advising, bookstore, campus computer network, e-mail services, library services.

Contact Mrs. Tami Shultz, Admissions Officer, Central Wyoming College, 2660 Peck Avenue, Riverton, WY 82501. Telephone: 307-855-2231. Fax: 307-855-2093. E-mail: admit@cwc.edu.

DEGREES AND AWARDS
Programs offered do not lead to a degree or other formal award.

COURSE SUBJECT AREAS OFFERED OUTSIDE OF DEGREE PROGRAMS
Undergraduate—accounting and related services; anthropology; area, ethnic, cultural, and gender studies related; biology; chemistry; communication and media; computer and information sciences; computer science; criminal justice and corrections; economics; education (specific subject areas); English composition; fine and studio art; geography and cartography; health and physical education/fitness; history; human development, family studies, and related services; human services; languages (American Indian/Native American); library science; mathematics; music; nursing; political science and government; psychology; religious studies; social sciences; sociology; zoology/animal biology.

Non-credit—allied health and medical assisting services; allied health diagnostic, intervention, and treatment professions; business/commerce; communication and media; computer and information sciences; computer software and media applications; dance; data entry/microcomputer applications; design and applied arts; electrical and power transmission installation; ethnic, cultural minority, and gender studies; finance and financial management services; health and physical education/fitness; history; human development, family studies, and related services; linguistic, comparative, and related language studies; management information systems; mental and social health services and allied professions; music; precision metal working; psychology.

CHADRON STATE COLLEGE
Chadron, Nebraska
Extended Campus Programs
http://www.csc.edu

Chadron State College was founded in 1911. It is accredited by North Central Association of Colleges and Schools. It first offered distance learning courses in 1991. In fall 2005, there were 700 students enrolled in distance learning courses. Institutionally administered financial aid is available to distance learners.

Services Distance learners have accessibility to academic advising, bookstore, campus computer network, career placement assistance, e-mail services, library services, tutoring.

Contact Ms. Jodi Banzhaf, Distance Learning Coordinator, Chadron State College, 1000 Main Street, Chadron, NE 69337. Telephone: 308-432-6432. Fax: 308-432-6473. E-mail: jbanzhaf@csc.edu.

DEGREES AND AWARDS
BA Business Administration/Management Information Systems; Business Administration/Management; Business Administration/Marketing; Business, general; Library Information Management; Psychology
BS Math
MAE Math
MBA Business Administration
MEd Educational Technology; Math

COURSE SUBJECT AREAS OFFERED OUTSIDE OF DEGREE PROGRAMS

Undergraduate—accounting and computer science; accounting and related services; applied mathematics; biological and physical sciences; business administration, management and operations; business/commerce; business/corporate communications; business, management, and marketing related; business/managerial economics; computer and information sciences; criminology; developmental and child psychology; economics; education; educational administration and supervision; educational assessment, evaluation, and research; educational/instructional media design; educational psychology; education related; education (specific levels and methods); education (specific subject areas); English composition; English literature (British and Commonwealth); family and consumer sciences/human sciences; family and consumer sciences/human sciences related; geography and cartography; history; housing and human environments; human development, family studies, and related services; human resources management; human services; industrial and organizational psychology; information science/studies; legal professions and studies related; legal studies (non-professional general, undergraduate); liberal arts and sciences, general studies and humanities; library science; library science related; management information systems; management sciences and quantitative methods; marketing; mathematics; mathematics and computer science; mathematics and statistics related; philosophy; philosophy and religious studies related; physical sciences; physical sciences related; physiological psychology/psychobiology; psychology; psychology related; real estate; sales, merchandising, and related marketing operations (general); sales, merchandising, and related marketing operations (specialized); social sciences; social sciences related; social work; sociology; special education; statistics; technical and business writing.

Graduate—accounting and computer science; accounting and related services; business administration, management and operations; business/commerce; business, management, and marketing related; business/managerial economics; counseling psychology; curriculum and instruction; economics; education; educational administration and supervision; educational assessment, evaluation, and research; educational/instructional media design; educational psychology; education related; education (specific levels and methods); education (specific subject areas); English; history; human resources management; industrial and organizational psychology; management information systems; management sciences and quantitative methods; marketing; mathematics; mathematics and computer science; mathematics and statistics related; psychology; psychology related; sales, merchandising, and related marketing operations (general); sales, merchandising, and related marketing operations (specialized); school psychology; special education; statistics; technology education/industrial arts.

CHAMPLAIN COLLEGE
Burlington, Vermont
Continuing Education Division
http://www.champlain.edu/coce

Champlain College was founded in 1878. It is accredited by New England Association of Schools and Colleges. It first offered distance learning courses in 1993. In fall 2005, there were 800 students enrolled in distance learning courses. Institutionally administered financial aid is available to distance learners.

Services Distance learners have accessibility to academic advising, bookstore, career placement assistance, e-mail services, library services, tutoring.

Contact Bridget Baldwin, Enrollment Counselor, Champlain College, Center for OnLine and Continuing Education, 163 South Willard Street, Burlington, VT 05401. Telephone: 800-545-3459. Fax: 802-865-6447. E-mail: coce@champlain.edu.

DEGREES AND AWARDS

AS Accounting; Business; Software Development; Web Site Development and Management

BS Accounting; Business; Computer Information Systems; Computer and Digital Forensics; Professional Studies; Software Engineering; Web Site Development and Management

Certificate Accounting; Accounting, advanced; Business; Computer and Digital Forensics; Financial Accounting; Foundations of Network Design; Global Logistics and Finance; Human Resource Management; Information Security; International Business Development; Java Development; Managerial Accounting; Managing through Information Technology; Software Development; Web Production; Web Programming; Web Site Development and Management

MBA Business Administration

MS Managing Innovation and Information Technology

COURSE SUBJECT AREAS OFFERED OUTSIDE OF DEGREE PROGRAMS

Undergraduate—accounting and related services; business administration, management and operations; business/commerce; business/corporate communications; chemistry; communication and journalism related; communication and media; computer and information sciences; computer and information sciences and support services related; computer/information technology administration and management; computer programming; computer software and media applications; computer systems networking and telecommunications; creative writing; economics; English; English composition; entrepreneurial and small business operations; finance and financial management services; geography and cartography; history; human resources management; international business; liberal arts and sciences, general studies and humanities; mathematics; mathematics and computer science; physical sciences; psychology; public relations, advertising, and applied communication related; sociology.

Graduate—business/commerce; business, management, and marketing related; business/managerial economics; information science/studies.

See full description on page 344.

CHARTER OAK STATE COLLEGE
New Britain, Connecticut
http://www.charteroak.edu/

Charter Oak State College was founded in 1973. It is accredited by New England Association of Schools and Colleges. It first offered distance learning courses in 1992. In fall 2005, there were 700 students enrolled in distance learning courses. Institutionally administered financial aid is available to distance learners.

Services Distance learners have accessibility to academic advising, bookstore, career placement assistance, e-mail services, library services, tutoring.

Contact Peggy Intravia, Associate, Academic Affairs, Charter Oak State College, 55 Paul J. Manafort Drive, New Britain, CT 06053-2150. Telephone: 860-832-3837. Fax: 860-832-3999. E-mail: mintravia@charteroak.edu.

DEGREES AND AWARDS

AA General Studies

AS General Studies

BA General Studies

BS General Studies

Diploma General Studies

COURSE SUBJECT AREAS OFFERED OUTSIDE OF DEGREE PROGRAMS

Undergraduate—accounting and related services; biology/biotechnology laboratory technician; business, management, and marketing related; cognitive psychology and psycholinguistics; communication and journalism related; computer and information sciences; criminology; educational administration and supervision; educational/instructional media design; English language and literature related; finance and financial management services; foods, nutrition, and related services; forensic psychology; genetics; geological and earth sciences/geosciences; health services/allied health/health sciences; management information systems; marketing; mathematics and statistics related; philosophy and religious studies related; psychology; psychology related; public administration and social service professions related; social sciences related; statistics.

Non-credit—nursing; pharmacy, pharmaceutical sciences, and administration.

See full description on page 346.

CHATHAM COLLEGE
Pittsburgh, Pennsylvania
Chatham College was founded in 1869. It is accredited by Middle States Association of Colleges and Schools. It first offered distance learning courses in 2005.

Services Distance learners have accessibility to academic advising, bookstore, campus computer network, career placement assistance, e-mail services, library services.

Contact Jenna Godfrey, Program Coordinator, Enrollment Services, Chatham College, The School of Continuing Education, Woodland Road, Pittsburgh, PA 15232. Telephone: 412-365-1148. Fax: 412-365-1720. E-mail: sce@chatham.edu.

DEGREES AND AWARDS
BSN Nursing–RN-BSN–-RN to Bachelor of Science in Nursing
MEd Health
MHS Health Sciences–Master of Health Sciences
MSE Education; Education
OTD Professional Doctor of Occupational Therapy

CHATTANOOGA STATE TECHNICAL COMMUNITY COLLEGE
Chattanooga, Tennessee
Distance Learning Program
http://www.chattanoogastate.edu/cde/
Chattanooga State Technical Community College was founded in 1965. It is accredited by Southern Association of Colleges and Schools. It first offered distance learning courses in 1985. In fall 2005, there were 1,500 students enrolled in distance learning courses. Institutionally administered financial aid is available to distance learners.

Services Distance learners have accessibility to academic advising, bookstore, campus computer network, career placement assistance, e-mail services, library services, tutoring.

Contact Tim Dills, Assistant Director, Center for Distributed Education, Chattanooga State Technical Community College, 4501 Amnicola Highway, Chattanooga, TN 37406-1097. Telephone: 423-697-2592. Fax: 423-697-4479. E-mail: tim.dills@chattanoogastate.edu.

DEGREES AND AWARDS
Programs offered do not lead to a degree or other formal award.

COURSE SUBJECT AREAS OFFERED OUTSIDE OF DEGREE PROGRAMS
Undergraduate—accounting and computer science; accounting and related services; allied health and medical assisting services; American literature (United States and Canadian); American Sign Language (ASL); behavioral sciences; biblical studies; biology; building/construction finishing, management, and inspection; business administration, management and operations; business/commerce; business, management, and marketing related; chemistry; communication and media; computer and information sciences; computer science; dental support services and allied professions; developmental and child psychology; economics; education; educational psychology; English; English composition; English literature (British and Commonwealth); finance and financial management services; fire protection; geography and cartography; health and medical administrative services; health/medical preparatory programs; health professions related; history; liberal arts and sciences, general studies and humanities; marketing; mathematics; mathematics and statistics related; music; philosophy; philosophy and religious studies related; physics; political science and government; psychology; religious studies; sociology; speech and rhetoric; statistics; technical and business writing.

CHESAPEAKE COLLEGE
Wye Mills, Maryland
http://www.chesapeake.edu/distance
Chesapeake College was founded in 1965. It is accredited by Middle States Association of Colleges and Schools. It first offered distance learning courses in 1994. In fall 2005, there were 895 students enrolled in distance learning courses. Institutionally administered financial aid is available to distance learners.

Services Distance learners have accessibility to academic advising, bookstore, campus computer network, e-mail services, library services, tutoring.

Contact Mary Celeste Alexander, Director, Chesapeake College, 1000 College Circle, Wye Mills, MD 21679. Telephone: 410-822-5400 Ext. 263. Fax: 410-827-5875. E-mail: mcalexander@chesapeake.edu.

DEGREES AND AWARDS
Programs offered do not lead to a degree or other formal award.

COURSE SUBJECT AREAS OFFERED OUTSIDE OF DEGREE PROGRAMS
Undergraduate—accounting and computer science; allied health and medical assisting services; American literature (United States and Canadian); behavioral sciences; biological and physical sciences; business, management, and marketing related; communication and media; computer and information sciences and support services related; criminal justice and corrections; education; English; English as a second language; liberal arts and sciences, general studies and humanities; mathematics and computer science; nursing.

CINCINNATI STATE TECHNICAL AND COMMUNITY COLLEGE
Cincinnati, Ohio
http://www.cincinnatistate.edu
Cincinnati State Technical and Community College was founded in 1966. It is accredited by North Central Association of Colleges and Schools. It first offered distance learning courses in 1994. In fall 2005, there were 916 students enrolled in distance learning courses. Institutionally administered financial aid is available to distance learners.

Services Distance learners have accessibility to academic advising, bookstore, campus computer network, e-mail services, library services.

Contact Ms. Gaby Boeckermann, Director of Admissions, Cincinnati State Technical and Community College, 3520 Central Parkway, Cincinnati, OH 45223. Telephone: 513-569-1550. E-mail: gaby.boeckermann@cincinnatistate.edu.

DEGREES AND AWARDS
Programs offered do not lead to a degree or other formal award.

COURSE SUBJECT AREAS OFFERED OUTSIDE OF DEGREE PROGRAMS
Undergraduate—accounting and related services; allied health and medical assisting services; applied horticulture/horticultural business services; business administration, management and operations; business/commerce; business operations support and assistant services; civil engineering technology; computer and information sciences; computer/information technology administration and management; computer software and media applications; computer systems networking and telecommunications; data processing; engineering technologies related; health and medical administrative services; health professions related; information science/studies; management information systems; mechanical engineering related technologies.

CITRUS COLLEGE
Glendora, California
Distance Education
http://www.citruscollege.com
Citrus College was founded in 1915. It is accredited by Western Association of Schools and Colleges. It first offered distance learning courses in 1996. In fall 2005, there were 2,000 students enrolled in distance learning courses. Institutionally administered financial aid is available to distance learners.

Services Distance learners have accessibility to academic advising, bookstore, campus computer network, e-mail services, library services, tutoring.

Contact Ms. Lari Kirby, Distance Education Supervisor, Citrus College, 1000 West Foothill Boulevard, Glendora, CA 91741-1899. Telephone: 626-914-8569. E-mail: online@citruscollege.edu.

DEGREES AND AWARDS
AA Liberal Arts

COURSE SUBJECT AREAS OFFERED OUTSIDE OF DEGREE PROGRAMS
Undergraduate—anthropology; biological and physical sciences; business/commerce; communication and media; computer and information sciences; economics; English composition; history; journalism; liberal arts and sciences, general studies and humanities; mathematics; philosophy; psychology; sociology.

CITY COLLEGE OF SAN FRANCISCO
San Francisco, California
Telecourses
http://www.ccsf.edu/
City College of San Francisco was founded in 1935. It is accredited by Western Association of Schools and Colleges. It first offered distance learning courses in 1988. In fall 2005, there were 1,100 students enrolled in distance learning courses. Institutionally administered financial aid is available to distance learners.
Services Distance learners have accessibility to academic advising, bookstore, career placement assistance, e-mail services.
Contact Don Suyeyasu, Program Developer, City College of San Francisco, Continuing Education, Laguna and Marina Boulevard, Building B, San Francisco, CA 94123. Telephone: 415-561-1860. E-mail: dsuyeyas@ccsf.edu.

DEGREES AND AWARDS
Programs offered do not lead to a degree or other formal award.

COURSE SUBJECT AREAS OFFERED OUTSIDE OF DEGREE PROGRAMS
Undergraduate—anthropology; dramatic/theater arts and stagecraft; ecology, evolution, and population biology; film/video and photographic arts; fine and studio art; languages (Romance languages); social psychology.

CITY UNIVERSITY
Bellevue, Washington
Distance Learning Option
http://www.cityu.edu
City University was founded in 1973. It is accredited by Northwest Commission on Colleges and Universities. It first offered distance learning courses in 1985. In fall 2005, there were 600 students enrolled in distance learning courses. Institutionally administered financial aid is available to distance learners.
Services Distance learners have accessibility to academic advising, bookstore, e-mail services, library services, tutoring.
Contact Office of Admissions, City University, 11900 NE First Street, Bellevue, WA 98005. Telephone: 800-422-4898. Fax: 425-709-5361. E-mail: info@cityu.edu.

DEGREES AND AWARDS
AS General Studies
BA Psychology–Applied Psychology
BS Accounting; Business Administration (Information Systems/Technology emphasis); Business Administration (Marketing emphasis); Business Administration (Project Management emphasis); Business Administration–E-Commerce emphasis (Bulgaria); Business Administration–General Management emphasis; Business Administration–Human Resource emphasis; Business Administration–Individualized Study emphasis; Computer Systems (Networking/Telecommunications emphasis); Computer Systems (Programming in C++ emphasis); Computer Systems (Web Design emphasis); Computer Systems–Database Technology emphasis; Computer Systems–Individualized Study emphasis; Computer Systems–Information Technology Security emphasis; Computer Systems–Web Languages emphasis; General Studies
Certificate Accounting; Marketing; Networking/Telecommunications; Programming in C++; Project Management; Web Design; Web Languages
Graduate Certificate Computer Programming–C++ Programming; Financial Management; General Management; Information Systems; Marketing; Personal Financial Planning; Project Management; Technology Management; Web Development; Web Programming in E-Commerce
MA Management–General Management emphasis
MBA Personal Financial Planning
MS Computer Systems–C++ Programming emphasis; Computer Systems–Individualized Study emphasis; Computer Systems–Technology Management emphasis; Computer Systems–Web Development emphasis; Computer Systems–Web Programming in E-Commerce emphasis; Project Management
See full description on page 348.

CLACKAMAS COMMUNITY COLLEGE
Oregon City, Oregon
Learning Resources
http://dl.clackamas.edu
Clackamas Community College was founded in 1966. It is accredited by Northwest Commission on Colleges and Universities. It first offered distance learning courses in 1997. In fall 2005, there were 1,722 students enrolled in distance learning courses. Institutionally administered financial aid is available to distance learners.
Services Distance learners have accessibility to academic advising, bookstore, campus computer network, career placement assistance, e-mail services, library services, tutoring.
Contact Steffen Moller, Director of Distance Learning, Clackamas Community College, 19600 South Molalla Avenue, Oregon City, OR 97045. Telephone: 503-657-6958 Ext. 2768. E-mail: steffenm@clackamas.edu.

DEGREES AND AWARDS
Programs offered do not lead to a degree or other formal award.

COURSE SUBJECT AREAS OFFERED OUTSIDE OF DEGREE PROGRAMS
Undergraduate—accounting and computer science; accounting and related services; allied health and medical assisting services; astronomy and astrophysics; biology; building/construction finishing, management, and inspection; business administration, management and operations; business, management, and marketing related; chemistry; computer science; criminal justice and corrections; education; English composition; English literature (British and Commonwealth); environmental/environmental health engineering; human development, family studies, and related services; legal professions and studies related; mathematics; music; physics; speech and rhetoric; technical and business writing.

CLARION UNIVERSITY OF PENNSYLVANIA
Clarion, Pennsylvania
Extended Studies and Distance Learning Department
http://www.clarion.edu/academic/distance/index.shtml
Clarion University of Pennsylvania was founded in 1867. It is accredited by Middle States Association of Colleges and Schools. It first offered distance learning courses in 1996. In fall 2005, there were 775 students enrolled in distance learning courses. Institutionally administered financial aid is available to distance learners.
Services Distance learners have accessibility to academic advising, bookstore, campus computer network, e-mail services, library services.
Contact Ms. Lynne M. Lander Fleisher, Associate Director, Clarion University of Pennsylvania, Office of Extended Programs, 840 Wood Street, Clarion, PA 16214. Telephone: 814-393-2778. Fax: 814-393-2779. E-mail: lfleisher@clarion.edu.

DEGREES AND AWARDS
AA Arts and Sciences
AD Early Childhood Education
BSN Nursing
MA Rehabilitative Science
MBA Business Administration; Business Administration
MLS Library Science
MSN Nursing–Family Nurse Practitioner

COURSE SUBJECT AREAS OFFERED OUTSIDE OF DEGREE PROGRAMS

Undergraduate—atmospheric sciences and meteorology; biology; chemistry; communication and media; computer science; economics; education related; English composition; health and physical education/fitness; languages (foreign languages related); legal professions and studies related; library science; music; nursing; philosophy; psychology; real estate; visual and performing arts related.

Graduate—business administration, management and operations; education; library science; nursing; rehabilitation and therapeutic professions.

Non-credit—real estate.

CLARK COLLEGE
Vancouver, Washington
http://www.clark.edu/

Clark College was founded in 1933. It is accredited by Northwest Commission on Colleges and Universities. It first offered distance learning courses in 1982. In fall 2005, there were 1,800 students enrolled in distance learning courses. Institutionally administered financial aid is available to distance learners.

Services Distance learners have accessibility to academic advising, bookstore, campus computer network, career placement assistance, e-mail services, library services, tutoring.

Contact Chastity R. Clark, Administrative Assistant, Clark College, 1800 East McLoughlin Boulevard, Vancouver, WA 98663. Telephone: 360-992-2654. Fax: 360-992-2895. E-mail: distance@clark.edu.

DEGREES AND AWARDS

Programs offered do not lead to a degree or other formal award.

COURSE SUBJECT AREAS OFFERED OUTSIDE OF DEGREE PROGRAMS

Undergraduate—accounting and computer science; accounting and related services; behavioral sciences; bioethics/medical ethics; business administration, management and operations; business, management, and marketing related; business/managerial economics; chemistry; computer software and media applications; computer systems networking and telecommunications; economics; education related; electrical and electronic engineering technologies; English; English composition; entrepreneurial and small business operations; finance and financial management services; foods, nutrition, and related services; health and physical education/fitness; human development, family studies, and related services; liberal arts and sciences, general studies and humanities; mathematics; mathematics and statistics related; music; psychology; psychology related; statistics; wildlife and wildlands science and management.

CLARKSON COLLEGE
Omaha, Nebraska
Office of Distance Education
http://www.clarksoncollege.edu

Clarkson College was founded in 1888. It is accredited by North Central Association of Colleges and Schools. It first offered distance learning courses in 1986. In fall 2005, there were 426 students enrolled in distance learning courses. Institutionally administered financial aid is available to distance learners.

Services Distance learners have accessibility to academic advising, bookstore, campus computer network, career placement assistance, e-mail services, library services, tutoring.

Contact Admissions, Clarkson College, 101 South 42nd Street, Omaha, NE 68131. Telephone: 800-647-5500. Fax: 402-552-6057. E-mail: admiss@clarksoncollege.edu.

DEGREES AND AWARDS

AD Health Information Management

BS Health Care Business–Health Information Management major; Health Care Business–Informatics major; Health Care Business–Management major; Medical Imaging

BSN Nursing–RN to BSN

Certificate Health Information Management–Foundations; Health Information Management–HIM; PACS Administrator; PACS Manager

MS Health Care Business Leadership

MSN Adult Nurse Practitioner; Family Nurse Practitioner; Nursing Education; Nursing Health Care Leadership

CLARK STATE COMMUNITY COLLEGE
Springfield, Ohio
Alternative Methods of Instructional Delivery
http://www.clarkstate.edu/

Clark State Community College was founded in 1962. It is accredited by North Central Association of Colleges and Schools. It first offered distance learning courses in 1996. In fall 2005, there were 2,000 students enrolled in distance learning courses. Institutionally administered financial aid is available to distance learners.

Services Distance learners have accessibility to academic advising, bookstore, campus computer network, career placement assistance, library services, tutoring.

Contact Amy Sues, Coordinator of Advising, Clark State Community College, PO Box 570, Springfield, OH 45501-0570. Telephone: 937-328-3867. Fax: 937-328-3853. E-mail: suesa@clarkstate.edu.

DEGREES AND AWARDS

AAS Medical Laboratory Technology; Nursing–Registered Nursing; Physical Therapist Assistant

COURSE SUBJECT AREAS OFFERED OUTSIDE OF DEGREE PROGRAMS

Undergraduate—accounting and computer science; agricultural business and management; allied health and medical assisting services; applied horticulture/horticultural business services; behavioral sciences; biological and biomedical sciences related; biological and physical sciences; biology; biology/biotechnology laboratory technician; business administration, management and operations; business/commerce; business, management, and marketing related; cell biology and anatomical sciences; chemistry; communication and media; computer and information sciences and support services related; computer software and media applications; creative writing; English; English composition; geological and earth sciences/geosciences; health professions related; history; nursing; psychology; psychology related; sociology; technical and business writing.

CLATSOP COMMUNITY COLLEGE
Astoria, Oregon
http://www.clatsopcc.edu

Clatsop Community College was founded in 1958. It is accredited by Northwest Commission on Colleges and Universities. It first offered distance learning courses in 1986. In fall 2005, there were 130 students enrolled in distance learning courses. Institutionally administered financial aid is available to distance learners.

Services Distance learners have accessibility to bookstore, e-mail services, library services.

Contact Kirsten Horning, Online Education Coordinator, Clatsop Community College, 1680 Lexington, Astoria, OR 97103. Telephone: 503-338-2341. Fax: 503-338-2387. E-mail: khorning@clatsopcc.edu.

DEGREES AND AWARDS

Programs offered do not lead to a degree or other formal award.

COURSE SUBJECT AREAS OFFERED OUTSIDE OF DEGREE PROGRAMS

Undergraduate—accounting and related services; anthropology; business administration, management and operations; business/commerce; computer and information sciences; creative writing; criminology; developmental and child psychology; English; English composition; foods, nutrition, and related services; health and physical education/fitness; history; human development, family studies, and related services; mathematics; political science and government; psychology; sociology; statistics.

CLEAR CREEK BAPTIST BIBLE COLLEGE
Pineville, Kentucky
http://www.ccbbc.edu/OnlineClasses/default.asp

Clear Creek Baptist Bible College was founded in 1926. It is accredited by Association for Biblical Higher Education. It first offered distance learning courses in 2002. In fall 2005, there were 50 students enrolled in distance learning courses. Institutionally administered financial aid is available to distance learners.

Services Distance learners have accessibility to academic advising, bookstore, career placement assistance, e-mail services, library services.

Contact Rev. Billy Howell, Director of Admissions, Clear Creek Baptist Bible College, 300 Clear Creek Road, Pineville, KY 40977. Telephone: 606-337-3196 Ext. 103. Fax: 606-337-2372. E-mail: bhowell@ccbbc.edu.

DEGREES AND AWARDS
Programs offered do not lead to a degree or other formal award.

COURSE SUBJECT AREAS OFFERED OUTSIDE OF DEGREE PROGRAMS
Undergraduate—biblical studies; theological and ministerial studies; theology and religious vocations related.

CLEMSON UNIVERSITY
Clemson, South Carolina
Distance Education, Educational Technology Services
http://www.ets.clemson.edu/

Clemson University was founded in 1889. It is accredited by Southern Association of Colleges and Schools. It first offered distance learning courses in 1988. In fall 2005, there were 1,750 students enrolled in distance learning courses. Institutionally administered financial aid is available to distance learners.

Services Distance learners have accessibility to academic advising, bookstore, campus computer network, career placement assistance, e-mail services, library services.

Contact Carla Rathbone, Director, ETS and Distance Education, Clemson University, 445 Brackett Hall, PO Box 342803, Clemson, SC 29634-2803. Telephone: 864-656-4322. Fax: 864-656-0750. E-mail: bone@clemson.edu.

DEGREES AND AWARDS
BS Nursing
MCSM Construction Science and Management
MEngr Electrical Engineering
MS Human Resource Development; Nursing; Youth Development
PhD Educational Leadership

COURSE SUBJECT AREAS OFFERED OUTSIDE OF DEGREE PROGRAMS
Undergraduate—astronomy and astrophysics; business/commerce; communication and media; construction management; economics; electrical and electronic engineering technologies; English composition; marketing; mathematics; music; nutrition sciences; parks, recreation and leisure; physics; sociology.

Graduate—agriculture; animal sciences; business administration, management and operations; communication and media; construction management; electrical and electronic engineering technologies; English; history; human resources management; nutrition sciences; statistics.

Non-credit—accounting and related services; allied health and medical assisting services; building/construction finishing, management, and inspection; business/commerce; business, management, and marketing related; business operations support and assistant services; communication and media; computer and information sciences; computer programming; computer software and media applications; computer systems networking and telecommunications; construction engineering technology; creative writing; data entry/microcomputer applications; data processing; English composition; languages (Romance languages); legal professions and studies related; mathematics; publishing; teaching assistants/aides; technical and business writing.

CLEVELAND COMMUNITY COLLEGE
Shelby, North Carolina
Distance Learning Program
http://www.cleveland.cc.nc.us

Cleveland Community College was founded in 1965. It is accredited by Southern Association of Colleges and Schools. It first offered distance learning courses in 1999. In fall 2005, there were 500 students enrolled in distance learning courses. Institutionally administered financial aid is available to distance learners.

Services Distance learners have accessibility to library services.

Contact Jody Ledford, Distance Learning Coordinator, Cleveland Community College, 137 South Post Road, Shelby, NC 28152. Telephone: 704-484-4000. Fax: 704-484-4036. E-mail: ledford@cleveland.cc.nc.us.

DEGREES AND AWARDS
Programs offered do not lead to a degree or other formal award.

COURSE SUBJECT AREAS OFFERED OUTSIDE OF DEGREE PROGRAMS
Undergraduate—accounting and computer science; allied health and medical assisting services; American Sign Language (ASL); biology; biology/biotechnology laboratory technician; business administration, management and operations; business/managerial economics; carpentry; chemistry; computer/information technology administration and management; computer programming; computer software and media applications; economics; education; fire protection; heating, air conditioning, ventilation and refrigeration maintenance technology; human development, family studies, and related services; insurance; psychology; teaching assistants/aides.

Non-credit—fire protection.

CLEVELAND INSTITUTE OF ELECTRONICS
Cleveland, Ohio
http://www.cie-wc.edu/WorldCollege/Main.html

Cleveland Institute of Electronics was founded in 1934. It is accredited by Distance Education and Training Council. It first offered distance learning courses in 1941.

Services Distance learners have accessibility to academic advising, bookstore, library services, tutoring.

Contact Guidance Counselor, Cleveland Institute of Electronics, 1766 East 17th Street, Cleveland, OH 44114. Telephone: 216-781-9400. Fax: 216-781-0331. E-mail: instruct@cie-wc.edu.

DEGREES AND AWARDS
AAS Computer Information Technology and Systems Management; Electronic Engineering Technology
Diploma Broadcast Engineering; Computer Programming; Computer Science–A+ Certification and Computer Technology; Electronics Engineering; Electronics Technology and Advanced Troubleshooting; Electronics Technology with Digital Microprocessor Lab; Electronics Technology with FCC License Preparation; Electronics Technology with Laboratory; Industrial Electronics with PLC Technology; Network+ Certification and Computer Technology; Wireless and Electronic Communications
Specialized diploma Introduction to Home Automation Installation

COURSE SUBJECT AREAS OFFERED OUTSIDE OF DEGREE PROGRAMS
Undergraduate—communication and media; computer engineering; electrical and electronic engineering technologies; engineering; social sciences related.

Non-credit—accounting and computer science; building/construction finishing, management, and inspection; business administration, management and operations; business/commerce; business/corporate communications; carpentry; computer/information technology administration and management; computer programming; computer science; computer software and media applications; construction engineering; construction trades; counseling psychology; crafts, folk art and artisanry; creative writing; data entry/microcomputer applications; drafting/design engineering technologies; electrical and power transmission installation; electrical/electronics maintenance and repair technology; engineering design; engineering/industrial management; film/video and photographic arts; marketing; mathematics; mathematics and computer science; mechanical engineering related technologies; mechanic and repair technologies related; mechanics and repair; woodworking.

CLEVELAND INSTITUTE OF MUSIC
Cleveland, Ohio

Cleveland Institute of Music was founded in 1920. It is accredited by North Central Association of Colleges and Schools. It first offered distance learning courses in 1997. In fall 2005, there were 10,000 students enrolled in distance learning courses. Institutionally administered financial aid is available to distance learners.

Contact Mr. Adam Phillips, Manager of Distance Learning Programs, Cleveland Institute of Music, 11021 East Boulevard, Cleveland, OH 44106. Telephone: 216-707-4516. E-mail: axp99@cwru.edu.

DEGREES AND AWARDS

Programs offered do not lead to a degree or other formal award.

COURSE SUBJECT AREAS OFFERED OUTSIDE OF DEGREE PROGRAMS

Undergraduate—music.
Graduate—music.
Non-credit—music.

CLEVELAND STATE COMMUNITY COLLEGE
Cleveland, Tennessee
Instructional Computer Technology Center of Emphasis
http://www.clscc.cc.tn.us

Cleveland State Community College was founded in 1967. It is accredited by Southern Association of Colleges and Schools. It first offered distance learning courses in 1998. In fall 2005, there were 800 students enrolled in distance learning courses. Institutionally administered financial aid is available to distance learners.

Services Distance learners have accessibility to academic advising, bookstore, campus computer network, career placement assistance, e-mail services, library services, tutoring.

Contact Dr. Spencer Culbreth, Vice President of Academic Affairs, Cleveland State Community College, 3535 Adkisson Drive, Cleveland, TN 37312. Telephone: 423-472-4171 Ext. 381. E-mail: sculbreth@clevelandstatecc.edu.

DEGREES AND AWARDS

Programs offered do not lead to a degree or other formal award.

COURSE SUBJECT AREAS OFFERED OUTSIDE OF DEGREE PROGRAMS

Undergraduate—accounting and related services; biological and physical sciences; business/commerce; computer and information sciences; data entry/microcomputer applications; education; English composition; history; mathematics; music; pharmacology and toxicology; psychology; religious studies; sociology; speech and rhetoric.

CLEVELAND STATE UNIVERSITY
Cleveland, Ohio
Off-Campus Academic Programs
http://www.csuohio.edu/offcampus

Cleveland State University was founded in 1964. It is accredited by North Central Association of Colleges and Schools. It first offered distance learning courses in 1994. In fall 2005, there were 1,353 students enrolled in distance learning courses. Institutionally administered financial aid is available to distance learners.

Services Distance learners have accessibility to academic advising, bookstore, campus computer network, career placement assistance, e-mail services, library services, tutoring.

Contact Mr. Fred G. Mehalik, Coordinator of Extended and Off-Campus Programs, Cleveland State University, West Center, 2121 Euclid Avenue, Cleveland, OH 44114-2214. Telephone: 216-687-4863. Fax: 216-875-9650. E-mail: f.mehalik@csuohio.edu.

DEGREES AND AWARDS

Certificate Bioethics
Endorsement Computer/Technology
Graduate Certificate Adult Learning and Development; Bioethics; Research Administration
MEd Adult Learning and Development; Educational Technology
MS Health Science
MSW Social Work

COURSE SUBJECT AREAS OFFERED OUTSIDE OF DEGREE PROGRAMS

Undergraduate—accounting and computer science; accounting and related services; area, ethnic, cultural, and gender studies related; bioethics/medical ethics; biological and biomedical sciences related; biology; chemistry; city/urban, community and regional planning; civil engineering; communication and journalism related; communication and media; computer and information sciences; computer engineering; computer programming; computer science; computer software and media applications; education; electrical and electronic engineering technologies; engineering; engineering-related fields; engineering technology; English; geography and cartography; geological and earth sciences/geosciences; history; linguistic, comparative, and related language studies; nursing; pharmacy, pharmaceutical sciences, and administration; philosophy; public administration; public administration and social service professions related; social work; special education; urban studies/affairs.

Graduate—accounting and related services; area, ethnic, cultural, and gender studies related; bioethics/medical ethics; chemical engineering; city/urban, community and regional planning; civil engineering; computer engineering; crafts, folk art and artisanry; curriculum and instruction; education; educational assessment, evaluation, and research; education related; education (specific levels and methods); education (specific subject areas); electrical, electronics and communications engineering; engineering; engineering/industrial management; engineering related; engineering-related fields; engineering-related technologies; environmental/environmental health engineering; health and medical administrative services; health/medical preparatory programs; health professions related; health services/allied health/health sciences; industrial engineering; linguistic, comparative, and related language studies; manufacturing engineering; mechanical engineering; mechanical engineering related technologies; nursing; philosophy; philosophy and religious studies related; public administration; public administration and social service professions related; social work; special education; student counseling and personnel services; technology education/industrial arts; urban studies/affairs.

Non-credit—accounting and related services; business administration, management and operations; business/commerce; business/corporate communications; computer software and media applications; computer systems networking and telecommunications; data entry/microcomputer applications; education related; entrepreneurial and small business operations; family and consumer economics; film/video and photographic arts; foods, nutrition, and related services; health and physical education/fitness; health professions related; human development, family studies, and related services; journalism; languages (foreign languages related); legal support services; management information systems; public health; sales, merchandising, and related marketing operations (specialized); technology education/industrial arts.

CLINTON COMMUNITY COLLEGE
Plattsburgh, New York
http://clinton.edu

Clinton Community College was founded in 1969. It is accredited by Middle States Association of Colleges and Schools. It first offered distance learning courses in 2000. In fall 2005, there were 300 students enrolled in distance learning courses. Institutionally administered financial aid is available to distance learners.

Services Distance learners have accessibility to academic advising, bookstore, campus computer network, career placement assistance, e-mail services, library services, tutoring.

Contact Prof. Vicky Sloan, Distance Learning Coordinator, Clinton Community College, 136 Clinton Point Drive, Plattsburgh, NY 12901. Telephone: 518-562-4281. E-mail: vicky.sloan@clinton.edu.

DEGREES AND AWARDS

AA Liberal Arts/Humanities and Social Science

AS Business Administration and Liberal Arts; Humanities and Social Science

COURSE SUBJECT AREAS OFFERED OUTSIDE OF DEGREE PROGRAMS

Undergraduate—accounting and related services; applied mathematics; biological and physical sciences; business administration, management and operations; business/corporate communications; clinical/medical laboratory science and allied professions; computer and information sciences; computer programming; criminal justice and corrections; economics; English; English composition; history; liberal arts and sciences, general studies and humanities; music; psychology; sociology; statistics.

CLOVIS COMMUNITY COLLEGE

Clovis, New Mexico

http://www.clovis.edu/

Clovis Community College was founded in 1990. It is accredited by North Central Association of Colleges and Schools. It first offered distance learning courses in 1990. In fall 2005, there were 700 students enrolled in distance learning courses. Institutionally administered financial aid is available to distance learners.

Services Distance learners have accessibility to academic advising, bookstore, e-mail services, library services, tutoring.

Contact Ms. Susan M. Veronikas, Educational Technologist, Clovis Community College, 417 Schepps Boulevard, Clovis, NM 88101. Telephone: 505-769-4903. Fax: 505-769-4190. E-mail: susan.veronikas@clovis.edu.

DEGREES AND AWARDS

AAS Criminal Justice

COURSE SUBJECT AREAS OFFERED OUTSIDE OF DEGREE PROGRAMS

Undergraduate—biblical studies; biology; business administration, management and operations; communication and media; computer and information sciences; criminal justice and corrections; developmental and child psychology; economics; English composition; fine and studio art; history; languages (Romance languages); mathematics; mathematics and statistics related; sociology.

COCONINO COMMUNITY COLLEGE

Flagstaff, Arizona

http://www.coconino.edu/extended/online.html

Coconino Community College was founded in 1991. It is accredited by North Central Association of Colleges and Schools. It first offered distance learning courses in 1999. In fall 2005, there were 800 students enrolled in distance learning courses. Institutionally administered financial aid is available to distance learners.

Services Distance learners have accessibility to academic advising, bookstore, career placement assistance, library services, tutoring.

Contact Mr. Rick McDonald, Director, Online and Media Services, Coconino Community College, 2800 South Lone Tree Road, Flagstaff, AZ 86001. Telephone: 928-226-4278. E-mail: rick.mcdonald@coconino.edu.

DEGREES AND AWARDS

AA Elementary Education

AAB Business (ABus)

COURSE SUBJECT AREAS OFFERED OUTSIDE OF DEGREE PROGRAMS

Undergraduate—business/commerce; communication and media; computer and information sciences; criminal justice and corrections; education; English composition; geography and cartography; health professions related; history; mathematics; philosophy; psychology; psychology related; social sciences; sociology.

Non-credit—computer software and media applications; creative writing; English composition; linguistic, comparative, and related language studies; music.

COFFEYVILLE COMMUNITY COLLEGE

Coffeyville, Kansas

Coffeyville Community College was founded in 1923. It is accredited by North Central Association of Colleges and Schools. It first offered distance learning courses in 1987. In fall 2005, there were 450 students enrolled in distance learning courses. Institutionally administered financial aid is available to distance learners.

Services Distance learners have accessibility to academic advising, bookstore, e-mail services, library services.

Contact Mr. Bill Strecker, Dean of Technology, Coffeyville Community College, 400 West 11th Street, Coffeyville, KS 67337. Telephone: 620-251-7700 Ext. 2078. Fax: 620-252-7098. E-mail: bills@coffeyville.edu.

DEGREES AND AWARDS

Programs offered do not lead to a degree or other formal award.

COURSE SUBJECT AREAS OFFERED OUTSIDE OF DEGREE PROGRAMS

Undergraduate—agricultural and domestic animal services; biological and physical sciences; business, management, and marketing related; chemistry; computer software and media applications; computer systems networking and telecommunications; English composition; history; mathematics; music; political science and government; psychology; sociology; speech and rhetoric; visual and performing arts.

COGSWELL POLYTECHNICAL COLLEGE

Sunnyvale, California

http://www.cogswell.edu/

Cogswell Polytechnical College was founded in 1887. It is accredited by Western Association of Schools and Colleges. It first offered distance learning courses in 1981. In fall 2005, there were 87 students enrolled in distance learning courses. Institutionally administered financial aid is available to distance learners.

Services Distance learners have accessibility to academic advising, e-mail services, library services.

Contact Ms. Milla Zlatanov, Data Manager, Cogswell Polytechnical College, 1175 Bordeaux Drive, Sunnyvale, CA 94089. Telephone: 408-541-0100 Ext. 133. Fax: 408-747-0764. E-mail: mzlatanov@cogswell.edu.

DEGREES AND AWARDS

BS Fire Science

COLEMAN COLLEGE

La Mesa, California

http://www.coleman.edu

Coleman College was founded in 1963. It is accredited by Accrediting Council for Independent Colleges and Schools. It first offered distance learning courses in 2001. In fall 2005, there were 250 students enrolled in distance learning courses. Institutionally administered financial aid is available to distance learners.

Services Distance learners have accessibility to academic advising, bookstore, career placement assistance, e-mail services, library services.

Contact Karen Hynes, Registrar, Coleman College, 8888 Balboa Avenue, San Diego, CA 92123. Telephone: 858-499-0202 Ext.. E-mail: khynes@coleman.edu.

DEGREES AND AWARDS

MS Business Technology Management–Master of Science in Business Technology Management

COURSE SUBJECT AREAS OFFERED OUTSIDE OF DEGREE PROGRAMS

Undergraduate—accounting and related services; business administration, management and operations; computer and information sciences; computer/information technology administration and management; computer programming; creative writing; English composition; history; human resources management; marketing; mathematics; philosophy; physical sciences; psychology; statistics; technical and business writing.

Graduate—business administration, management and operations; business/commerce; business/corporate communications; marketing.

COLLEGE OF DUPAGE
Glen Ellyn, Illinois
Alternative Learning Division
http://www.cod.edu/cil

College of DuPage was founded in 1967. It is accredited by North Central Association of Colleges and Schools. It first offered distance learning courses in 1980. In fall 2005, there were 6,000 students enrolled in distance learning courses. Institutionally administered financial aid is available to distance learners.

Services Distance learners have accessibility to academic advising, bookstore, campus computer network, e-mail services, library services, tutoring.

Contact Ron Schiesz, Counselor, Alternative Learning Program, College of DuPage, Center for Independent Learning, 425 Fawell Street, Glen Ellyn, IL 60137-6599. Telephone: 630-942-3326 Ext. 3326. Fax: 630-942-3764. E-mail: schiesz@cdnet.cod.edu.

DEGREES AND AWARDS
Programs offered do not lead to a degree or other formal award.

COURSE SUBJECT AREAS OFFERED OUTSIDE OF DEGREE PROGRAMS
Undergraduate—accounting and related services; anthropology; biology; business administration, management and operations; chemistry; communication and media; computer programming; computer software and media applications; computer systems networking and telecommunications; criminal justice and corrections; developmental and child psychology; economics; English as a second language; English composition; history; human services; journalism; languages (Romance languages); liberal arts and sciences, general studies and humanities; library assistant; library science; mathematics; music; philosophy and religious studies related; physics; psychology; religious studies; sales, merchandising, and related marketing operations (general); social psychology; social sciences; social sciences related; sociology.

COLLEGE OF EMMANUEL AND ST. CHAD
Saskatoon, Saskatchewan, Canada

College of Emmanuel and St. Chad was founded in 1879. It is provincially chartered. It first offered distance learning courses in 1995. In fall 2005, there were 5 students enrolled in distance learning courses. Institutionally administered financial aid is available to distance learners.

Services Distance learners have accessibility to academic advising, bookstore, campus computer network, library services.

Contact Ms. Colleen Walker, Registrar, College of Emmanuel and St. Chad, 114 Seminary Crescent, Saskatoon, SK S7N 0X3, Canada. Telephone: 306-975-1558. Fax: 306-934-2683. E-mail: colleen.walker@usask.ca.

DEGREES AND AWARDS
Programs offered do not lead to a degree or other formal award.

COURSE SUBJECT AREAS OFFERED OUTSIDE OF DEGREE PROGRAMS
Graduate—biblical and other theological languages and literatures; biblical studies; theological and ministerial studies; theology and religious vocations related.

THE COLLEGE OF ST. SCHOLASTICA
Duluth, Minnesota
Graduate Studies
http://grad.css.edu

The College of St. Scholastica was founded in 1912. It is accredited by North Central Association of Colleges and Schools. It first offered distance learning courses in 1986. In fall 2005, there were 331 students enrolled in distance learning courses. Institutionally administered financial aid is available to distance learners.

Services Distance learners have accessibility to academic advising, bookstore, campus computer network, career placement assistance, e-mail services, library services, tutoring.

Contact Tonya J. Roth, Graduate Recruitment Counselor, The College of St. Scholastica, 1200 Kenwood Avenue, Duluth, MN 55811. Telephone: 218-723-6285, Fax: 218-733-2275. E-mail: gradstudies@css.edu.

DEGREES AND AWARDS
BA Health Information Management Degree completion; Nursing–RN to BA completion
Certificate Computer Information Systems; Graduate Teaching Licensure; Healthcare Informatics
MA Computer Information Systems; Health Information Management
MEd Curriculum and Instruction; Educational Media and Technology; Graduate Teaching Licensure

COURSE SUBJECT AREAS OFFERED OUTSIDE OF DEGREE PROGRAMS
Undergraduate—biology; computer and information sciences; economics; gerontology; health and medical administrative services; music; nursing; psychology.

Graduate—biology; curriculum and instruction; health and medical administrative services; library science related; music; nursing.

COLLEGE OF SAN MATEO
San Mateo, California
http://www.collegeofsanmateo.edu

College of San Mateo was founded in 1922. It is accredited by Western Association of Schools and Colleges. It first offered distance learning courses in 1977. In fall 2005, there were 1,000 students enrolled in distance learning courses. Institutionally administered financial aid is available to distance learners.

Services Distance learners have accessibility to academic advising, bookstore, campus computer network, career placement assistance, e-mail services, library services, tutoring.

Contact Betty Fleming, Distance Learning Coordinator, College of San Mateo, 1700 West Hillsdale Boulevard, San Mateo, CA 94402-3784. Telephone: 650-524-6933. Fax: 650-574-6345. E-mail: fleming@smccd.edu.

DEGREES AND AWARDS
Programs offered do not lead to a degree or other formal award.

COURSE SUBJECT AREAS OFFERED OUTSIDE OF DEGREE PROGRAMS
Undergraduate—accounting and related services; anthropology; astronomy and astrophysics; business/commerce; business/corporate communications; chemistry; computer programming; English composition; film/video and photographic arts; health and physical education/fitness; languages (Romance languages); legal studies (non-professional general, undergraduate); marketing; mathematics; philosophy; political science and government; psychology; sociology.

COLLEGE OF SANTA FE
Santa Fe, New Mexico
http://www.csf.edu

College of Santa Fe was founded in 1947. It is accredited by North Central Association of Colleges and Schools.

Contact J. Taylor Gantt, College of Santa Fe, 1600 St. Michael's Drive, Santa Fe, NM 87505. Telephone: 505-473-6138. Fax: 505-473-6129. E-mail: tgantt@csf.edu.

DEGREES AND AWARDS
Programs offered do not lead to a degree or other formal award.

COLLEGE OF SOUTHERN MARYLAND
La Plata, Maryland
Distance Learning Department
http://www.csmd.edu

College of Southern Maryland was founded in 1958. It is accredited by Middle States Association of Colleges and Schools. It first offered distance learning courses in 1980. In fall 2005, there were 1,817 students enrolled in distance learning courses. Institutionally administered financial aid is available to distance learners.

Services Distance learners have accessibility to academic advising, bookstore, campus computer network, career placement assistance, e-mail services, library services, tutoring.

Contact Paul Toscano, Distance Learning Coordinator, College of Southern Maryland, 8730 Mitchell Road, PO Box 910, La Plata, MD 20646-0910. Telephone: 301-934-7615. Fax: 301-934-7699. E-mail: pault@csmd.edu.

DEGREES AND AWARDS

AA Arts and Sciences–Applied Science and Technology; Arts and Sciences–Arts and Humanities; Arts and Sciences–Social Sciences; Arts and Sciences; General Studies

AAS Computer Programming; Information Services Technology–Web Developer; Information Services Technology; Management Development

AS Business Administration–Technical Management; Business Administration

Certificate Accounting, advanced; Accounting, basic; Computer Skills for Managers; General Studies; Information Services Technology; Management Development–Marketing; Management Development; Web Developer

COURSE SUBJECT AREAS OFFERED OUTSIDE OF DEGREE PROGRAMS

Undergraduate—accounting and related services; astronomy and astrophysics; biology; business/commerce; business/corporate communications; communication and media; computer systems analysis; computer systems networking and telecommunications; creative writing; criminal justice and corrections; economics; educational psychology; education related; English composition; fine and studio art; geography and cartography; health and physical education/fitness; history; human development, family studies, and related services; human resources management; information science/studies; international business; languages (Romance languages); legal studies (non-professional general, undergraduate); marketing; mathematics; mathematics and statistics related; philosophy; philosophy and religious studies related; physics; political science and government; psychology; sociology; statistics; technical and business writing.

Non-credit—computer/information technology administration and management; education; health professions related; nursing.

COLLEGE OF STATEN ISLAND OF THE CITY UNIVERSITY OF NEW YORK
Staten Island, New York
http://www.csi.cuny.edu/

College of Staten Island of the City University of New York was founded in 1955. It is accredited by Middle States Association of Colleges and Schools. It first offered distance learning courses in 2001. In fall 2005, there were 75 students enrolled in distance learning courses. Institutionally administered financial aid is available to distance learners.

Services Distance learners have accessibility to bookstore, career placement assistance, library services.

Contact Geraldine Johnson, Registrar, College of Staten Island of the City University of New York, Continuing Education and Professional Development, 2800 Victory Boulevard, 2A-201, Staten Island, NY 10314. Telephone: 718-982-2182. Fax: 718-982-2038. E-mail: johnsong@mail.csi.cuny.edu.

DEGREES AND AWARDS

Programs offered do not lead to a degree or other formal award.

COURSE SUBJECT AREAS OFFERED OUTSIDE OF DEGREE PROGRAMS

Non-credit—accounting and related services; applied mathematics; business/commerce; business operations support and assistant services; communication and media; computer/information technology administration and management; computer programming; construction engineering technology; film/video and photographic arts; health aides/attendants/orderlies; human development, family studies, and related services; linguistic, comparative, and related language studies; technical and business writing.

COLLEGE OF THE ALBEMARLE
Elizabeth City, North Carolina
Distance Education
http://www.albemarle.edu

College of The Albemarle was founded in 1960. It is accredited by Southern Association of Colleges and Schools. It first offered distance learning courses in 1993. In fall 2005, there were 1,000 students enrolled in distance learning courses. Institutionally administered financial aid is available to distance learners.

Services Distance learners have accessibility to academic advising, bookstore, career placement assistance, e-mail services, library services, tutoring.

Contact Jerry Oliver, Distance Education Coordinator, College of The Albemarle, PO Box 2327, Elizabeth City, NC 27906-2327. Telephone: 252-335-0821 Ext. 2313. Fax: 252-337-6710. E-mail: joliver@albemarle.edu.

DEGREES AND AWARDS

AAS Business Administration; Criminal Justice

COURSE SUBJECT AREAS OFFERED OUTSIDE OF DEGREE PROGRAMS

Undergraduate—accounting and related services; biology; business administration, management and operations; business/commerce; business/corporate communications; computer and information sciences; computer science; economics; education related; electrical and electronic engineering technologies; English composition; English literature (British and Commonwealth); fine and studio art; health and physical education/fitness; history; human development, family studies, and related services; legal studies (non-professional general, undergraduate); marketing; mathematics and statistics related; psychology; sociology.

Non-credit—accounting and related services; business administration, management and operations; business/commerce; business/corporate communications; business, management, and marketing related; business operations support and assistant services; communication and media; computer and information sciences; computer engineering; computer/information technology administration and management; computer programming; computer science; computer software and media applications; computer systems networking and telecommunications; data entry/microcomputer applications; data processing; educational administration and supervision; English; English composition; gerontology; human services; information science/studies; management information systems; mental and social health services and allied professions; public administration; public administration and social service professions related; sales, merchandising, and related marketing operations (specialized); technical and business writing.

COLLEGE OF THE HUMANITIES AND SCIENCES, HARRISON MIDDLETON UNIVERSITY
Tempe, Arizona

College of the Humanities and Sciences, Harrison Middleton University was founded in 1998. It is accredited by Distance Education and Training Council. It first offered distance learning courses in 2000. In fall 2005, there were 500 students enrolled in distance learning courses. Institutionally administered financial aid is available to distance learners.

Services Distance learners have accessibility to academic advising, e-mail services, tutoring.

Contact Kathleen Mirabile, Vice President, Director of Education, College of the Humanities and Sciences, Harrison Middleton University, 1105 East Broadway Road, Tempe, AZ 85282. Telephone: 877-248-6724. E-mail: kmirabile@chumsci.edu.

DEGREES AND AWARDS

AA Humanities
BA Humanities
MA Imaginative Literature; Jurisprudence; Natural Science; Philosophy and Religion; Social Science
MAE Education

COURSE SUBJECT AREAS OFFERED OUTSIDE OF DEGREE PROGRAMS

Undergraduate—American literature (United States and Canadian); biology; English as a second language; English composition; English

literature (British and Commonwealth); history; languages (foreign languages related); languages (Romance languages); mathematics; philosophy; social sciences.
Graduate—education related; English language and literature related; mathematics; social sciences related.

COLLEGE OF THE SISKIYOUS
Weed, California
Distance Learning
http://www.siskiyous.edu/distancelearning/

College of the Siskiyous was founded in 1957. It is accredited by Western Association of Schools and Colleges. It first offered distance learning courses in 1975. In fall 2005, there were 550 students enrolled in distance learning courses. Institutionally administered financial aid is available to distance learners.
Services Distance learners have accessibility to academic advising, career placement assistance, e-mail services, library services, tutoring.
Contact Nancy Shepard, Telecommunications Specialist, College of the Siskiyous, 800 College Avenue, Weed, CA 96094. Telephone: 530-938-5520. E-mail: shepard@siskiyous.edu.

DEGREES AND AWARDS
Programs offered do not lead to a degree or other formal award.

COURSE SUBJECT AREAS OFFERED OUTSIDE OF DEGREE PROGRAMS
Undergraduate—accounting and related services; business/commerce; business/corporate communications; computer science; English composition; English language and literature related; English literature (British and Commonwealth); family and consumer economics; health and physical education/fitness; history; liberal arts and sciences, general studies and humanities; mathematics; nursing; political science and government; psychology; social sciences; student counseling and personnel services; teaching assistants/aides.
Non-credit—creative writing.

COLLEGE OF THE SOUTHWEST
Hobbs, New Mexico
http://www.csw.edu/

College of the Southwest was founded in 1962. It is accredited by North Central Association of Colleges and Schools. It first offered distance learning courses in 1994. In fall 2005, there were 300 students enrolled in distance learning courses. Institutionally administered financial aid is available to distance learners.
Services Distance learners have accessibility to academic advising, bookstore, campus computer network, e-mail services, library services, tutoring.
Contact Renee M. Stark, Registrar, College of the Southwest, 6610 Lovington Highway, Hobbs, NM 88240. Telephone: 505-392-6561 Ext. 1008. Fax: 505-392-6006. E-mail: rstark@csw.edu.

DEGREES AND AWARDS
BS Criminal Justice
MSE Educational Administration and Counseling; Educational Diagnostician

COURSE SUBJECT AREAS OFFERED OUTSIDE OF DEGREE PROGRAMS
Undergraduate—accounting and related services; biology; business administration, management and operations; computer science; creative writing; criminal justice and corrections; developmental and child psychology; economics; education; English as a second language; English composition; history; industrial and organizational psychology; marketing; psychology; religious studies; social psychology; sociology.
Graduate—counseling psychology; curriculum and instruction; educational administration and supervision; educational assessment, evaluation, and research.

COLORADO CHRISTIAN UNIVERSITY
Lakewood, Colorado
Academic Technologies Group
http://www.ccuonline.org

Colorado Christian University was founded in 1914. It is accredited by North Central Association of Colleges and Schools. It first offered distance learning courses in 1999. In fall 2005, there were 608 students enrolled in distance learning courses. Institutionally administered financial aid is available to distance learners.
Services Distance learners have accessibility to academic advising, bookstore, campus computer network, e-mail services, library services.
Contact Mr. Jonathan Hodges, Manager, Online Support and Training, Colorado Christian University, 8787 West Alameda Avenue, Lakewood, CO 80226. Telephone: 303-963-3305. Fax: 303-963-3301. E-mail: jhodges@ccu.edu.

DEGREES AND AWARDS
AA Arts (General)
BS Organizational Management in Christian Leadership; Organizational Management in Human Resources
BSBA Business Administration
Certificate Biblical Studies; Project Management
MBA Business Administration

COURSE SUBJECT AREAS OFFERED OUTSIDE OF DEGREE PROGRAMS
Undergraduate—accounting and related services; biblical and other theological languages and literatures; computer and information sciences; computer software and media applications; education (specific subject areas); ethnic, cultural minority, and gender studies; history; marketing; philosophy and religious studies related; physiological psychology/psychobiology; technology education/industrial arts.
Graduate—business administration, management and operations; educational assessment, evaluation, and research; finance and financial management services; marketing.

COLORADO MOUNTAIN COLLEGE DISTRICT SYSTEM
Glenwood Springs, Colorado
Educational Technology
http://www.coloradomtn.edu/distlearn/

Colorado Mountain College District System first offered distance learning courses in 1985. In fall 2005, there were 800 students enrolled in distance learning courses. Institutionally administered financial aid is available to distance learners.
Services Distance learners have accessibility to bookstore, library services.
Contact Mr. Daryl D. Yarrow, Division Director for Distance Learning, Colorado Mountain College District System, 831 Grand Avenue, Glenwood Springs, CO 81601. Telephone: 800-621-8559 Ext. 8336. Fax: 970-947-8307. E-mail: distance@coloradomtn.edu.

DEGREES AND AWARDS
Programs offered do not lead to a degree or other formal award.

COURSE SUBJECT AREAS OFFERED OUTSIDE OF DEGREE PROGRAMS
Undergraduate—accounting and related services; anthropology; astronomy and astrophysics; biology; business/commerce; business/corporate communications; chemistry; computer science; computer software and media applications; developmental and child psychology; economics; education related; English composition; fine and studio art; geography and cartography; health professions related; history; hospitality administration; languages (foreign languages related); library science related; mathematics and statistics related; philosophy; physics; psychology; social psychology; sociology; statistics.

COLORADO STATE UNIVERSITY
Fort Collins, Colorado
Division of Continuing Education
http://www.learn.colostate.edu

Colorado State University was founded in 1870. It is accredited by North Central Association of Colleges and Schools. It first offered distance learning courses in 1967. In fall 2005, there were 1,168 students enrolled in distance learning courses. Institutionally administered financial aid is available to distance learners.

Services Distance learners have accessibility to academic advising, bookstore, library services.

Contact Debi Colbert, Director of Distance Degrees, Colorado State University, 1040 Campus Delivery, Fort Collins, CO 80523-1040. Telephone: 970-491-5288. Fax: 970-491-7885. E-mail: dcolbert@learn.colostate.edu.

DEGREES AND AWARDS
BA Liberal Arts
BS Human Development and Family Studies
Certificate of Completion Veterinary Medicine Online
Certificate Apparel and Merchandising; Apparel and Merchandising; Applied Statistics and Data Analysis; Business; Child Care Administration Training; Community-Based Development; Ergonomics (Basic and Advanced); Fire and Emergency Services Administration (FESA); Information Science and Technology; Natural Resources and the Environment; Postsecondary Teaching; Seed Analysis Training; Six Sigma eBlack Belt (20 weeks); Six Sigma eGreen Belt (12 weeks); Statistical Theory and Method
EMBA Business Administration
MAg Agricultural Education
MBA Business Administration
MCS Computer Science
ME Civil Engineering; Electrical and Computer Engineering (Telecommunications); Mechanical Engineering (Engineering Management program); Mechanical Engineering (Ind Engg and Operations Res program); Mechanical Engineering (Materials Engineering)
MEd Education and Human Resource Studies (Adult Education and Training–AET); Education and Human Resource Studies (Organizational Performance and Change-OPC); Education and Human Resource Studies (Organizational Performance and Change-OPC)
MS Apparel and Merchandising; Mechanical Engineering (Engineering Management program); Mechanical Engineering (Ind Engg and Operations Res program); Mechanical Engineering (Materials Engineering); Rangeland Ecosystem Science; Statistics
MSW Social Work
PhD Mechanical Engineering (Ind Engg and Operations Res program)

COURSE SUBJECT AREAS OFFERED OUTSIDE OF DEGREE PROGRAMS
Undergraduate—accounting and computer science; agricultural production; agriculture; animal sciences; anthropology; biology; business/commerce; computer science; construction management; design and applied arts; developmental and child psychology; economics; education; engineering; engineering technologies related; English; English composition; ethnic, cultural minority, and gender studies; finance and financial management services; fine and studio art; fishing and fisheries sciences and management; foods, nutrition, and related services; geography and cartography; health and physical education/fitness; landscape architecture; marketing; mathematics; music; natural resources conservation and research; plant sciences; psychology; social sciences; sociology; speech and rhetoric; statistics; wildlife and wildlands science and management.
Graduate—agriculture; business administration, management and operations; civil engineering; computer science; drafting/design engineering technologies; education; education related; fishing and fisheries sciences and management; human resources management; human services; mathematics; mechanical engineering; natural resources management and policy; social work; statistics; wildlife and wildlands science and management.
Non-credit—accounting and computer science; animal sciences; business, management, and marketing related; community health services; community organization and advocacy; community psychology; education; health and physical education/fitness; information science/studies; legal support services; management sciences and quantitative methods; veterinary biomedical and clinical sciences.

See full description on page 350.

COLORADO STATE UNIVERSITY
Fort Collins, Colorado
College of Business
http://www.csumba.com

Colorado State University was founded in 1870. It is accredited by North Central Association of Colleges and Schools. It first offered distance learning courses in 1968. In fall 2005, there were 400 students enrolled in distance learning courses. Institutionally administered financial aid is available to distance learners.

Services Distance learners have accessibility to academic advising, bookstore, campus computer network, career placement assistance, e-mail services, library services.

Contact Ms. Rachel Stoll, Graduate Admissions Coordinator, Colorado State University, College of Business, 1270 Campus Delivery, 164 Rockwell Hall, Fort Collins, CO 80523-1270. Telephone: 800-491-4622 Ext. 1. Fax: 970-491-3481. E-mail: rachel.stoll@colostate.edu.

DEGREES AND AWARDS
MBA Business Administration–Distance MBA program; Distance MBA Program

See full description on page 352.

COLORADO STATE UNIVERSITY-PUEBLO
Pueblo, Colorado
Division of Continuing Education
http://coned.colostate-pueblo.edu

Colorado State University-Pueblo was founded in 1933. It is accredited by North Central Association of Colleges and Schools. It first offered distance learning courses in 1970. In fall 2005, there were 1,500 students enrolled in distance learning courses. Institutionally administered financial aid is available to distance learners.

Services Distance learners have accessibility to academic advising, bookstore, library services.

Contact Ms. Angela Healy, Program Manager, Colorado State University-Pueblo, 2200 Bonforte Boulevard, Pueblo, CO 81001-4901. Telephone: 800-388-6154. Fax: 719-549-2438. E-mail: coned@colostate-pueblo.edu.

DEGREES AND AWARDS
BS Social Sciences; Sociology; Sociology/Criminology
Certificate Paralegal Studies

COURSE SUBJECT AREAS OFFERED OUTSIDE OF DEGREE PROGRAMS
Undergraduate—anthropology; biology; business/commerce; chemistry; economics; education; English; English composition; geography and cartography; geological and earth sciences/geosciences; history; liberal arts and sciences, general studies and humanities; marketing; mathematics; nursing; political science and government; psychology; sociology.
Graduate—education.
Non-credit—business administration, management and operations; business operations support and assistant services; computer software and media applications; data entry/microcomputer applications; entrepreneurial and small business operations; health and medical administrative services; management information systems; sales, merchandising, and related marketing operations (specialized).

COLORADO TECHNICAL UNIVERSITY
Colorado Springs, Colorado
http://www.ctuonline.edu

Colorado Technical University was founded in 1965. It is accredited by North Central Association of Colleges and Schools. It first offered distance learning courses in 2003. Institutionally administered financial aid is available to distance learners.

Services Distance learners have accessibility to academic advising, bookstore, campus computer network, career placement assistance, e-mail services, library services.

Contact Admissions Department, Colorado Technical University, 4435 North Chestnut Street, Suite E, Colorado Springs, CO 80907. Telephone: 800-416-8904. E-mail: info@ctuonline.edu.

DEGREES AND AWARDS

BS Accounting–BSAcc; Criminal Justice (BSCJ)

BSBA Finance concentration; Health Care Management concentration; Human Resource Management concentration; Information Technology concentration; International Business; Management concentration; Marketing concentration; Project Management concentration

EMBA Business Administration–Executive Master of Business Administration

MBA Accounting; Finance; Health Care Management concentration; Human Resource Management concentration; Marketing

MSM Business Management concentration; Information Systems Security concentration; Information Technology Management concentration; Project Management concentration

COURSE SUBJECT AREAS OFFERED OUTSIDE OF DEGREE PROGRAMS

Undergraduate—accounting and computer science; accounting and related services; business administration, management and operations; business/commerce; business, management, and marketing related; computer and information sciences; computer/information technology administration and management; computer science; criminal justice and corrections; criminology; finance and financial management services; health and medical administrative services; human resources management; legal professions and studies related; management sciences and quantitative methods; marketing; sales, merchandising, and related marketing operations (general); systems engineering.

Graduate—business administration, management and operations; business/commerce; business, management, and marketing related; computer/information technology administration and management; health and medical administrative services; human resources management; management sciences and quantitative methods; systems engineering.

See full description on page 354.

COLUMBIA BASIN COLLEGE
Pasco, Washington
http://www.columbiabasin.edu/distance/

Columbia Basin College was founded in 1955. It is accredited by Northwest Commission on Colleges and Universities. It first offered distance learning courses in 1985. In fall 2005, there were 3,000 students enrolled in distance learning courses. Institutionally administered financial aid is available to distance learners.

Services Distance learners have accessibility to academic advising, bookstore, campus computer network, career placement assistance, e-mail services, library services, tutoring.

Contact Dr. Deborah R. Meadows, Dean for Business/IT, Social Science/Foreign Language, and eLearning, Columbia Basin College, 2600 North 20th Avenue, Pasco, WA 99301. Telephone: 509-547-0511 Ext. 2373. Fax: 509-546-0401. E-mail: dmeadows@columbiabasin.edu.

DEGREES AND AWARDS

AAS Business, Humanities, Social Sciences

COURSE SUBJECT AREAS OFFERED OUTSIDE OF DEGREE PROGRAMS

Undergraduate—accounting and related services; anthropology; behavioral sciences; business administration, management and operations; business/commerce; business operations support and assistant services; communication and media; computer and information sciences and support services related; computer programming; computer science; computer software and media applications; counseling psychology; economics; English; English composition; ethnic, cultural minority, and gender studies; fine and studio art; geography and cartography; health and physical education/fitness; history; mathematics; mathematics and statistics related; political science and government; psychology; sociology; technical and business writing.

COLUMBIA COLLEGE
Columbia, Missouri
http://www.ccis.edu/online

Columbia College was founded in 1851. It is accredited by North Central Association of Colleges and Schools. It first offered distance learning courses in 2000. In fall 2005, there were 6,200 students enrolled in distance learning courses. Institutionally administered financial aid is available to distance learners.

Services Distance learners have accessibility to academic advising, bookstore, campus computer network, career placement assistance, e-mail services, library services.

Contact Ms. Marilyn Whitehead, Assistant Director for Online Campus, Columbia College, 1001 Rogers Street, Attention: Online Campus, Columbia, MO 65216. Telephone: 573-875-7459. Fax: 573-875-7445. E-mail: mawhitehead@ccis.edu.

DEGREES AND AWARDS

AA General Studies

AGS General Studies

AS Business Administration; Criminal Justice; Environmental Studies; Fire Science Administration; Human Services

BA American Studies; American Studies; Business Administration; Criminal Justice; General Studies; History; Interdisciplinary Studies; Psychology; Sociology

BS Business Administration

COURSE SUBJECT AREAS OFFERED OUTSIDE OF DEGREE PROGRAMS

Undergraduate—accounting and related services; American literature (United States and Canadian); anthropology; area, ethnic, cultural, and gender studies related; astronomy and astrophysics; behavioral sciences; biological and biomedical sciences related; business administration, management and operations; business/commerce; business, management, and marketing related; chemistry; computer and information sciences; criminal justice and corrections; curriculum and instruction; education; English literature (British and Commonwealth); entrepreneurial and small business operations; history; mathematics; mathematics and computer science; multi-/interdisciplinary studies related; philosophy and religious studies related; political science and government; psychology; sales, merchandising, and related marketing operations (general); social sciences related; social work; sociology.

Graduate—business administration, management and operations; business, management, and marketing related; business/managerial economics.

COLUMBIA-GREENE COMMUNITY COLLEGE
Hudson, New York
Educational Technology Center
http://www.sunycgcc.edu/

Columbia-Greene Community College was founded in 1969. It is accredited by Middle States Association of Colleges and Schools. It first offered distance learning courses in 1995. In fall 2005, there were 104 students enrolled in distance learning courses. Institutionally administered financial aid is available to distance learners.

Services Distance learners have accessibility to campus computer network, e-mail services.

Contact Ms. Patrice Jenkins, Assistant Dean, Columbia-Greene Community College, Room 110, 4400 Route 23, Hudson, NY 12534. Telephone: 518-828-4181 Ext. 3350. Fax: 518-828-8543. E-mail: jenkins@sunycgcc.edu.

DEGREES AND AWARDS

Programs offered do not lead to a degree or other formal award.

COURSE SUBJECT AREAS OFFERED OUTSIDE OF DEGREE PROGRAMS

Undergraduate—business administration, management and operations; computer programming; developmental and child psychology; English composition; psychology; sociology.

COLUMBIA INTERNATIONAL UNIVERSITY
Columbia, South Carolina
Distance Education Center
http://www.ciuextension.com

Columbia International University was founded in 1923. It is accredited by Association for Biblical Higher Education. It first offered distance learning courses in 1978. In fall 2005, there were 900 students enrolled in distance learning courses. Institutionally administered financial aid is available to distance learners.

Services Distance learners have accessibility to academic advising, bookstore, campus computer network, career placement assistance, e-mail services, library services.

Contact Mrs. Alisa Fulton, Director of Customer Service, Columbia International University, PO Box 3122, Columbia, SC 29230-3122. Telephone: 800-777-2227 Ext. 3710. Fax: 803-754-9119. E-mail: distance@ciu.edu.

DEGREES AND AWARDS

Programs offered do not lead to a degree or other formal award.

COURSE SUBJECT AREAS OFFERED OUTSIDE OF DEGREE PROGRAMS

Undergraduate—biblical studies; missionary studies and missiology; religious studies; theological and ministerial studies; theology and religious vocations related.

Graduate—anthropology; biblical and other theological languages and literatures; biblical studies; curriculum and instruction; education; educational administration and supervision; education related; history; languages (classics and classical); linguistic, comparative, and related language studies; missionary studies and missiology; religious studies; theological and ministerial studies; theology and religious vocations related.

Non-credit—anthropology; biblical studies; education; educational psychology; missionary studies and missiology; religious studies; theological and ministerial studies; theology and religious vocations related.

COLUMBIA UNIVERSITY
New York, New York
Columbia Video Network
http://www.cvn.columbia.edu

Columbia University was founded in 1754. It is accredited by Middle States Association of Colleges and Schools. It first offered distance learning courses in 1986. In fall 2005, there were 470 students enrolled in distance learning courses. Institutionally administered financial aid is available to distance learners.

Services Distance learners have accessibility to academic advising, campus computer network, career placement assistance, e-mail services, library services.

Contact Online Recruiter, Columbia University, 530 Mudd Building, MC 4719, 500 West 120th Street, New York, NY 10027. Telephone: 212-854-6447. Fax: 212-854-2325. E-mail: info@cvn.columbia.edu.

DEGREES AND AWARDS

Certificate of Achievement Business and Technology; Civil Engineering; Financial Engineering; Industrial Engineering; Information Systems; Intelligent Systems; Manufacturing Engineering; Materials Science and Engineering; Mathematics–Applied Mathematics; Multimedia Networking; Nanotechnology; Networking and Systems; New Media Engineering; Operations Research; Telecommunications; Wireless and Mobile Communications

MS Biomedical Engineering; Chemical Engineering; Civil Engineering–Construction Engineering and Management; Civil Engineering; Computer Science; Earth and Environmental Engineering; Engineering and Management Systems; Finance–Methods in Finance; Materials Science and Engineering; Mathematics–Applied Mathematics

MSEE Electrical Engineering

MSME Mechanical Engineering

PMC Computer Science; Electrical Engineering; Industrial Engineering and Operations Research; Mechanical Engineering

COURSE SUBJECT AREAS OFFERED OUTSIDE OF DEGREE PROGRAMS

Undergraduate—computer science; electrical and electronic engineering technologies; materials science.

Graduate—applied mathematics; biomedical/medical engineering; chemical engineering; civil engineering; computer science; electrical, electronics and communications engineering; engineering/industrial management; environmental/environmental health engineering; finance and financial management services; materials science; mechanical engineering.

Non-credit—applied mathematics; business/commerce; chemical engineering; civil engineering; computer science; engineering; engineering/industrial management; environmental/environmental health engineering; finance and financial management services; mechanical engineering.

COLUMBUS STATE COMMUNITY COLLEGE
Columbus, Ohio
Global Campus
http://www.cscc.edu

Columbus State Community College was founded in 1963. It is accredited by North Central Association of Colleges and Schools. It first offered distance learning courses in 1980. In fall 2005, there were 8,000 students enrolled in distance learning courses. Institutionally administered financial aid is available to distance learners.

Services Distance learners have accessibility to academic advising, bookstore, campus computer network, career placement assistance, e-mail services, library services, tutoring.

Contact Tom Erney, Dean of Instructional Services, Columbus State Community College, Box 1609, Columbus, OH 43216-1609. Telephone: 614-287-2532. Fax: 614-287-5123. E-mail: terney@cscc.edu.

DEGREES AND AWARDS

AA General Studies

AAS Business Management; Marketing

CCCPE E-Commerce; Geographic Information Systems

COURSE SUBJECT AREAS OFFERED OUTSIDE OF DEGREE PROGRAMS

Undergraduate—accounting and related services; allied health and medical assisting services; allied health diagnostic, intervention, and treatment professions; American literature (United States and Canadian); anthropology; biological and biomedical sciences related; business administration, management and operations; business/corporate communications; chemistry; communication and journalism related; comparative literature; computer and information sciences; computer programming; computer software and media applications; construction management; counseling psychology; creative writing; culinary arts and related services; developmental and child psychology; drafting/design engineering technologies; dramatic/theater arts and stagecraft; economics; engineering mechanics; engineering technologies related; English; English composition; English language and literature related; English literature (British and Commonwealth); environmental control technologies; ethnic, cultural minority, and gender studies; finance and financial management services; foods, nutrition, and related services; geography and cartography; graphic communications; health and medical administrative services; health and physical education/fitness; health professions related; history; hospitality administration; human resources management; languages (Romance languages); legal studies (non-professional general, undergraduate); legal support services; marketing; mathematics; mechanical engineering related technologies; mental and social health services and allied professions; natural sciences; nursing; nutrition sciences; philosophy; philosophy and religious studies related; political science and government; psychology; public relations, advertising, and applied communication related; quality control and safety technologies; sales, merchandising, and related marketing operations (general); science technologies related; social sciences related; sociology; speech and rhetoric; technical and business writing; vehicle maintenance and repair technologies; visual and performing arts related.

COLUMBUS STATE UNIVERSITY
Columbus, Georgia
Instructional Technology Services
http://www.colstate.edu

Columbus State University was founded in 1958. It is accredited by Southern Association of Colleges and Schools. It first offered distance learning courses in 1991. In fall 2005, there were 862 students enrolled in distance learning courses. Institutionally administered financial aid is available to distance learners.

Services Distance learners have accessibility to academic advising, bookstore, career placement assistance, e-mail services, library services.

Contact Sandra K. Stratford, Instructional Technology Services Coordinator, Columbus State University, 4225 University Avenue, Columbus, GA 31907. Telephone: 706-568-2043. Fax: 706-568-2459. E-mail: stratford_sandra@colstate.edu.

DEGREES AND AWARDS

MS Computer Science–Applied Computer Science

COURSE SUBJECT AREAS OFFERED OUTSIDE OF DEGREE PROGRAMS

Undergraduate—computer science; education.

Graduate—computer programming; education (specific subject areas); psychology.

THE COMMUNITY COLLEGE OF BALTIMORE COUNTY
Baltimore, Maryland
Office of Distance/Extended Learning
http://www.ccbcmd.edu/distance/index.html

The Community College of Baltimore County was founded in 1957. It is accredited by Middle States Association of Colleges and Schools. It first offered distance learning courses in 1997. In fall 2005, there were 2,700 students enrolled in distance learning courses. Institutionally administered financial aid is available to distance learners.

Services Distance learners have accessibility to academic advising, bookstore, campus computer network, e-mail services, library services, tutoring.

Contact Tinnie A. Ward, Senior Director of Distance Learning, The Community College of Baltimore County, 7201 Rossville Boulevard, Baltimore, MD 21237. Telephone: 410-780-6504. Fax: 410-780-6144. E-mail: tward@ccbcmd.edu.

DEGREES AND AWARDS

AA Business Administration

AAS E-Business Management; E-Business Management; E-Business Technology; E-Business Technology; Information Technology, general

AGS General Studies

COURSE SUBJECT AREAS OFFERED OUTSIDE OF DEGREE PROGRAMS

Undergraduate—accounting and related services; applied mathematics; astronomy and astrophysics; biology; business administration, management and operations; business/commerce; business/corporate communications; business operations support and assistant services; cell biology and anatomical sciences; communication and media; computer and information sciences; computer/information technology administration and management; computer programming; computer science; computer systems analysis; computer systems networking and telecommunications; criminal justice and corrections; criminology; data processing; economics; English composition; entrepreneurial and small business operations; geography and cartography; history; human resources management; legal studies (non-professional general, undergraduate); marketing; mathematics; parks, recreation and leisure; parks, recreation, and leisure related; physical sciences; political science and government; psychology; sociology; statistics; technical and business writing.

Non-credit—computer and information sciences; computer and information sciences and support services related; computer programming; computer software and media applications.

COMMUNITY COLLEGE OF BEAVER COUNTY
Monaca, Pennsylvania
http://www.ccbc.cc.pa.us/

Community College of Beaver County was founded in 1966. It is accredited by Middle States Association of Colleges and Schools. It first offered distance learning courses in 1998. In fall 2005, there were 500 students enrolled in distance learning courses. Institutionally administered financial aid is available to distance learners.

Services Distance learners have accessibility to academic advising, bookstore, campus computer network, e-mail services, library services, tutoring.

Contact Registrar, Community College of Beaver County, One Campus Drive, Registrar's Office, Building 1, Monaca, PA 15061-2588. Telephone: 724-775-8561 Ext. 253. Fax: 724-775-4687. E-mail: dan.slater@ccbc.edu.

DEGREES AND AWARDS

Programs offered do not lead to a degree or other formal award.

COURSE SUBJECT AREAS OFFERED OUTSIDE OF DEGREE PROGRAMS

Undergraduate—accounting and computer science; air transportation; American literature (United States and Canadian); behavioral sciences; business administration, management and operations; business, management, and marketing related; business/managerial economics; cognitive psychology and psycholinguistics; computer and information sciences; computer programming; computer science; computer software and media applications; criminal justice and corrections; developmental and child psychology; economics; education; English; English composition; English literature (British and Commonwealth); fine and studio art; history; liberal arts and sciences, general studies and humanities; mathematics; nursing; nutrition sciences; philosophy; psychology; psychology related; social psychology; social sciences; social sciences related; sociology; statistics; technical and business writing.

Non-credit—accounting and computer science; business administration, management and operations; business/commerce; business/corporate communications; business, management, and marketing related; business/managerial economics; business operations support and assistant services; computer and information sciences; computer science; computer software and media applications; entrepreneurial and small business operations; graphic communications.

COMMUNITY COLLEGE OF DENVER
Denver, Colorado
Distance Learning
http://www.ccd.edu/OnlineLearning/index.html

Community College of Denver was founded in 1970. It is accredited by North Central Association of Colleges and Schools. It first offered distance learning courses in 1986. In fall 2005, there were 2,000 students enrolled in distance learning courses. Institutionally administered financial aid is available to distance learners.

Services Distance learners have accessibility to academic advising, bookstore, e-mail services, library services, tutoring.

Contact Jeanne Stroh, Director for Online Learning, Community College of Denver, Campus Box 204, PO Box 173363, Denver, CO 80217-3363. Telephone: 303-352-3302. Fax: 303-556-2171. E-mail: jeanne.stroh@ccd.edu.

DEGREES AND AWARDS

AA Business Administration; Economics; English/Literature emphasis; History emphasis; Humanities/Philosophy emphasis; Psychology emphasis; Sociology emphasis

AAS Business Administration–Management emphasis; Business Generalist emphasis; Management emphasis, General Management; Marketing emphasis

AGS Elementary Education; Generalist

AS Generalist

Certificate Business Administration; Business Administration, Entrepreneurship; Business Administration, International Business; Early Childhood Education, Group/Leader/Child Development Associate–Infant/Toddler; Early Childhood Education, Group/Leader/Child Development Associate–Preschool; Teacher Education, Paraeducator

Diploma Business Administration

COURSE SUBJECT AREAS OFFERED OUTSIDE OF DEGREE PROGRAMS

Undergraduate—accounting and related services; anthropology; astronomy and astrophysics; biology; business administration, management and operations; business/corporate communications; business, management, and marketing related; chemistry; comparative literature; computer/information technology administration and management; computer software and media applications; creative writing; economics; education (specific levels and methods); education (specific subject areas); English; English composition; entrepreneurial and small business operations; fine and studio art; geography and cartography; geological and earth sciences/geosciences; health/medical preparatory programs; history; human development, family studies, and related services; liberal arts and sciences, general studies and humanities; mathematics; microbiological sciences and immunology; nursing; philosophy; philosophy and religious studies related; physics; political science and government; psychology; religious studies; sales, merchandising, and related marketing operations (general); sociology; speech and rhetoric; teaching assistants/aides; technical and business writing.

COMMUNITY COLLEGE OF SOUTHERN NEVADA
North Las Vegas, Nevada
http://www.ccsn.nevada.edu/

Community College of Southern Nevada was founded in 1971. It is accredited by Northwest Commission on Colleges and Universities. It first offered distance learning courses in 1997. In fall 2005, there were 8,500 students enrolled in distance learning courses. Institutionally administered financial aid is available to distance learners.

Services Distance learners have accessibility to academic advising, bookstore, campus computer network, e-mail services, library services, tutoring.

Contact Haunani Taylor, Distance Education Specialist, Community College of Southern Nevada, 6375 West Charleston Boulevard, WM3, Las Vegas, NV 89146. Telephone: 702-651-5619. E-mail: haunani_taylor@ccsn.nevada.edu.

DEGREES AND AWARDS

AA Elementary Education emphasis; English emphasis; Psychology emphasis; Secondary Education emphasis; Social Science emphasis; Special Education emphasis; the Arts

AAS Accounting emphasis; Computing and Information Technology

ABA Business

AGS General Studies

COURSE SUBJECT AREAS OFFERED OUTSIDE OF DEGREE PROGRAMS

Undergraduate—accounting and computer science; allied health and medical assisting services; allied health diagnostic, intervention, and treatment professions; American literature (United States and Canadian); animal sciences; anthropology; astronomy and astrophysics; atmospheric sciences and meteorology; behavioral sciences; biology; business, management, and marketing related; communication and journalism related; communications technology; computer programming; computer software and media applications; criminal justice and corrections; dental support services and allied professions; developmental and child psychology; education; English; English language and literature related; fire protection; health services/allied health/health sciences; history; languages (foreign languages related); liberal arts and sciences, general studies and humanities; mathematics; nursing; ophthalmic and optometric support services and allied professions; philosophy; physical sciences; political science and government; social sciences; technical and business writing; veterinary biomedical and clinical sciences; visual and performing arts.

CONCORDIA COLLEGE
Bronxville, New York
CUENET (Concordia University Education Network)
http://www.concordia-ny.edu

Concordia College was founded in 1881. It is accredited by Middle States Association of Colleges and Schools. It first offered distance learning courses in 1995. In fall 2005, there were 15 students enrolled in distance learning courses. Institutionally administered financial aid is available to distance learners.

Contact Prof. Sherry Fraser, Academic Dean, Concordia College, 171 White Plains Road, Bronxville, NY 10708. Telephone: 914-337-9300 Ext. 2211. Fax: 914-395-4500. E-mail: sjf@concordia-ny.edu.

DEGREES AND AWARDS

Programs offered do not lead to a degree or other formal award.

COURSE SUBJECT AREAS OFFERED OUTSIDE OF DEGREE PROGRAMS

Undergraduate—biblical studies; education; religious studies.

CONCORDIA UNIVERSITY
Irvine, California
School of Education
http://www.cui.edu

Concordia University was founded in 1972. It is accredited by Western Association of Schools and Colleges. It first offered distance learning courses in 2003. In fall 2005, there were 35 students enrolled in distance learning courses. Institutionally administered financial aid is available to distance learners.

Services Distance learners have accessibility to academic advising, bookstore, library services.

Contact Ms. Jill Gredvig, Administrative Assistant, MA Education Online and Non-Tradition, School of Education, Concordia University, 1530 Concordia West, Irvine, CA 92612-3299. Telephone: 949-854-8002 Ext. 1487. Fax: 949-854-6878. E-mail: jill.gredvig@cui.edu.

DEGREES AND AWARDS

MAE Education

CONCORDIA UNIVERSITY, ST. PAUL
St. Paul, Minnesota

Concordia University, St. Paul was founded in 1893. It is accredited by North Central Association of Colleges and Schools. It first offered distance learning courses in 1998. In fall 2005, there were 650 students enrolled in distance learning courses. Institutionally administered financial aid is available to distance learners.

Services Distance learners have accessibility to academic advising, bookstore, campus computer network, e-mail services, library services, tutoring.

Contact Mr. Scott Morrell, Vice President for Admission and Marketing, Concordia University, St. Paul, 275 Syndicate Street North, Saint Paul, MN 55104-5494. Telephone: 800-333-4705. Fax: 651-603-6320. E-mail: morrell@csp.edu.

DEGREES AND AWARDS

AA General Studies program

BA Child Development; Criminal Justice; Family Life Education; Information and Technology Management; Marketing Management; Organizational Management–Human Resources; Organizational Managment and Communications

MA Christian Outreach; Human Services–Criminal Justice Leadership; Human Services–Family Life Education; Organizational Management–Human Resources; Organizational Management

MAE Differentiated Learning; Early Childhood

COURSE SUBJECT AREAS OFFERED OUTSIDE OF DEGREE PROGRAMS

Undergraduate—business/commerce; developmental and child psychology; education; human development, family studies, and related services; sociology.

Graduate—business/commerce; developmental and child psychology; education; human development, family studies, and related services; sociology.
Non-credit—business/commerce; communication and media; fine and studio art; mathematics and computer science; social sciences.

CONCORDIA UNIVERSITY WISCONSIN
Mequon, Wisconsin
Continuing Education Division
http://www.cuw.edu

Concordia University Wisconsin was founded in 1881. It is accredited by North Central Association of Colleges and Schools. It first offered distance learning courses in 1994. In fall 2005, there were 500 students enrolled in distance learning courses. Institutionally administered financial aid is available to distance learners.
Services Distance learners have accessibility to academic advising, bookstore, campus computer network, career placement assistance, e-mail services, library services, tutoring.
Contact Sarah Weaver Pecor, Director, Concordia University Wisconsin, 12800 North Lake Shore Drive, Mequon, WI 53097. Telephone: 262-243-4257. Fax: 262-243-4459. E-mail: sarah.weaver@cuw.edu.

DEGREES AND AWARDS
MBA Business Administration
MS Curriculum and Instruction; Education Administration; Education Counseling; Reading
MSN Nursing

COURSE SUBJECT AREAS OFFERED OUTSIDE OF DEGREE PROGRAMS
Undergraduate—accounting and related services; business, management, and marketing related; computer science; economics; finance and financial management services; history; management sciences and quantitative methods; marketing; nursing.
Graduate—business administration, management and operations; curriculum and instruction; educational administration and supervision; educational psychology; education related; nursing.

CONNECTICUT STATE UNIVERSITY SYSTEM
Hartford, Connecticut
OnlineCSU
http://www.onlinecsu.net

Connecticut State University System is accredited by New England Association of Schools and Colleges. It first offered distance learning courses in 1998. In fall 2005, there were 1,000 students enrolled in distance learning courses. Institutionally administered financial aid is available to distance learners.
Services Distance learners have accessibility to academic advising, bookstore, career placement assistance, e-mail services, library services, tutoring.
Contact Ms. Rebecca L. Putt, Marketing and Planning Manager, Connecticut State University System, 39 Woodland Street, Hartford, CT 06105-2337. Telephone: 860-493-0039. E-mail: puttr@so.ct.edu.

DEGREES AND AWARDS
BSN Nursing–RN to BSN Bachelor's completion program
Certificate Education–Sixth Year in Educational Foundations
MLS Library Science
MS Data Mining; Educational Technology

COURSE SUBJECT AREAS OFFERED OUTSIDE OF DEGREE PROGRAMS
Undergraduate—accounting and related services; anthropology; area studies; communication and media; computer science; criminal justice and corrections; curriculum and instruction; economics; education (specific levels and methods); English composition; geography and cartography; information science/studies; management information systems; marketing; mechanical engineering; nursing; philosophy; sociology; statistics.
Graduate—accounting and related services; anthropology; area studies; computer systems networking and telecommunications; curriculum and instruction; educational/instructional media design; education (specific levels and methods); English composition; management information systems; marketing; mechanical engineering; social work; sociology; statistics.
Non-credit—statistics.
See full description on page 356.

CONTRA COSTA COLLEGE
San Pablo, California
http://www.contracosta.cc.ca.us

Contra Costa College was founded in 1948. It is accredited by Western Association of Schools and Colleges. It first offered distance learning courses in 1990. In fall 2005, there were 700 students enrolled in distance learning courses. Institutionally administered financial aid is available to distance learners.
Services Distance learners have accessibility to academic advising, bookstore, campus computer network, career placement assistance, library services, tutoring.
Contact Dean Lynda A. Lawrence, Senior Dean of Instruction, Contra Costa College, 2600 Mission Bell Drive, San Pablo, CA 94806. Telephone: 510-235-7800 Ext. 4597. Fax: 510-236-6768. E-mail: lschweid @contracosta.cc.ca.us.

DEGREES AND AWARDS
Programs offered do not lead to a degree or other formal award.

COURSE SUBJECT AREAS OFFERED OUTSIDE OF DEGREE PROGRAMS
Undergraduate—accounting and related services; anthropology; behavioral sciences; business, management, and marketing related; chemistry; cognitive psychology and psycholinguistics; computer and information sciences; criminal justice and corrections; culinary arts and related services; dramatic/theater arts and stagecraft; education; health and physical education/fitness; library science related; nursing; philosophy; physical sciences; political science and government; sociology; speech and rhetoric.

COPIAH-LINCOLN COMMUNITY COLLEGE
Wesson, Mississippi
http://www.colin.edu/distancelearning

Copiah-Lincoln Community College was founded in 1928. It is accredited by Southern Association of Colleges and Schools. It first offered distance learning courses in 1995. In fall 2005, there were 650 students enrolled in distance learning courses. Institutionally administered financial aid is available to distance learners.
Services Distance learners have accessibility to academic advising, bookstore, campus computer network, career placement assistance, e-mail services, library services, tutoring.
Contact Laura E. Lofton, Director of Distance Learning, Copiah-Lincoln Community College, PO Box 649, Wesson, MS 39191. Telephone: 601-643-8619. Fax: 601-643-8612. E-mail: laura.lofton@colin.edu.

DEGREES AND AWARDS
AA General Studies

COURSE SUBJECT AREAS OFFERED OUTSIDE OF DEGREE PROGRAMS
Undergraduate—biology; business/commerce; business/corporate communications; computer/information technology administration and management; computer science; English composition; health and physical education/fitness; mathematics and statistics related; social sciences related.

CORBAN COLLEGE
Salem, Oregon
Management and Communication Online Program/Family Studies Online Program
http://www.wbc.edu

Corban College was founded in 1935. It is accredited by Northwest Commission on Colleges and Universities. It first offered distance learning courses in 1994. In fall 2005, there were 130 students enrolled in distance learning courses. Institutionally administered financial aid is available to distance learners.

Services Distance learners have accessibility to academic advising, bookstore, campus computer network, e-mail services, library services, tutoring.

Contact Ms. Nancy L. Martyn, Dean of Adult Studies, Corban College, Adult Studies, 5000 Deer Park Drive, SE, Salem, OR 97301. Telephone: 503-375-7590. Fax: 503-375-7583. E-mail: nmartyn@corban.edu.

DEGREES AND AWARDS

BS Business, Management, and Communication; Psychology/Family Studies

COURSE SUBJECT AREAS OFFERED OUTSIDE OF DEGREE PROGRAMS

Undergraduate—biblical studies; business administration, management and operations; counseling psychology; history; human development, family studies, and related services; marketing; physical sciences; psychology related; religious studies; theological and ministerial studies.

See full description on page 358.

CORNING COMMUNITY COLLEGE
Corning, New York
Open Learning Program
http://corning-cc.edu/distancelearning

Corning Community College was founded in 1956. It is accredited by Middle States Association of Colleges and Schools. It first offered distance learning courses in 1996. In fall 2005, there were 396 students enrolled in distance learning courses. Institutionally administered financial aid is available to distance learners.

Services Distance learners have accessibility to academic advising, bookstore, campus computer network, career placement assistance, e-mail services, library services, tutoring.

Contact Barry Garrison, Executive Assistant to the President, Corning Community College, 1 Academic Drive, Corning, NY 14830. Telephone: 607-962-9527. Fax: 607-962-9485. E-mail: garrisbb@coning-cc.edu.

DEGREES AND AWARDS

Programs offered do not lead to a degree or other formal award.

COURSE SUBJECT AREAS OFFERED OUTSIDE OF DEGREE PROGRAMS

Undergraduate—accounting and related services; applied mathematics; business administration, management and operations; business/managerial economics; business operations support and assistant services; chemistry; computer programming; computer systems networking and telecommunications; economics; education; English composition; health and physical education/fitness; history; human services; mathematics; nutrition sciences; philosophy; psychology; social psychology; sociology.

COSUMNES RIVER COLLEGE
Sacramento, California
Media Resources Center
http://crc.losrios.edu

Cosumnes River College was founded in 1970. It is accredited by Western Association of Schools and Colleges. It first offered distance learning courses in 1992. In fall 2005, there were 1,400 students enrolled in distance learning courses. Institutionally administered financial aid is available to distance learners.

Services Distance learners have accessibility to academic advising, bookstore, campus computer network, career placement assistance, e-mail services, library services.

Contact Prof. Grĕgory Beyrer, Distance Education Coordinator, Cosumnes River College, 8401 Center Parkway, Sacramento, CA 95823-5799. E-mail: beyrerg@crc.losrios.edu.

DEGREES AND AWARDS

Programs offered do not lead to a degree or other formal award.

COURSE SUBJECT AREAS OFFERED OUTSIDE OF DEGREE PROGRAMS

Undergraduate—accounting and related services; allied health and medical assisting services; American literature (United States and Canadian); anthropology; business/commerce; computer and information sciences; economics; English composition; environmental control technologies; family and consumer economics; fine and studio art; foods, nutrition, and related services; geological and earth sciences/geosciences; marketing; mathematics; physics; psychology related.

COUNTY COLLEGE OF MORRIS
Randolph, New Jersey
Professional Programs and Distance Education
http://www.ccm.edu

County College of Morris was founded in 1966. It is accredited by Middle States Association of Colleges and Schools. It first offered distance learning courses in 1979. In fall 2005, there were 1,400 students enrolled in distance learning courses. Institutionally administered financial aid is available to distance learners.

Services Distance learners have accessibility to academic advising, bookstore, campus computer network, e-mail services, library services.

Contact Ms. Sheri Ventura, Coordinator of Distance Learning Services, County College of Morris, 214 Center Grove Road, Randolph, NJ 07869-2086. Telephone: 973-328-5184. Fax: 973-328-5082. E-mail: sventura@ccm.edu.

DEGREES AND AWARDS

AA Humanities
AS Business Administration

COURSE SUBJECT AREAS OFFERED OUTSIDE OF DEGREE PROGRAMS

Undergraduate—applied horticulture/horticultural business services; applied mathematics; biological and biomedical sciences related; biology; business/commerce; computer science; creative writing; economics; English composition; health and physical education/fitness; history; mathematics; psychology; sociology.

COVENANT THEOLOGICAL SEMINARY
St. Louis, Missouri
External Studies Office
http://access.covenantseminary.edu

Covenant Theological Seminary was founded in 1956. It is accredited by North Central Association of Colleges and Schools. It first offered distance learning courses in 1989. In fall 2005, there were 150 students enrolled in distance learning courses. Institutionally administered financial aid is available to distance learners.

Services Distance learners have accessibility to academic advising, bookstore, campus computer network, e-mail services, library services, tutoring.

Contact Rev. Brad Anderson, Director of Admissions, Covenant Theological Seminary, 12330 Conway Road, St. Louis, MO 63141. Telephone: 800-264-8064. Fax: 314-434-4819. E-mail: admissions@covenantseminary.edu.

DEGREES AND AWARDS

Graduate Certificate Theology
MA Theology

COURSE SUBJECT AREAS OFFERED OUTSIDE OF DEGREE PROGRAMS

Graduate—biblical studies; missionary studies and missiology; philosophy and religious studies related; religious studies; theological and ministerial studies; theology and religious vocations related.

Non-credit—biblical studies; missionary studies and missiology; philosophy and religious studies related; religious studies; theological and ministerial studies; theology and religious vocations related.

COWLEY COUNTY COMMUNITY COLLEGE AND AREA VOCATIONAL–TECHNICAL SCHOOL

Arkansas City, Kansas

http://www.cowleycollege.com

Cowley County Community College and Area Vocational–Technical School was founded in 1922. It is accredited by North Central Association of Colleges and Schools. It first offered distance learning courses in 1992. In fall 2005, there were 2,000 students enrolled in distance learning courses. Institutionally administered financial aid is available to distance learners.

Services Distance learners have accessibility to academic advising, bookstore, library services, tutoring.

Contact LeArta R. Watkins, Director of Distance Learning, Cowley County Community College and Area Vocational–Technical School, 125 South Second Street, Arkansas City, KS 67005. Telephone: 800-593-2222 Ext. 5366. Fax: 620-441-5377. E-mail: watkins@cowleycollege.com.

DEGREES AND AWARDS

Programs offered do not lead to a degree or other formal award.

COURSE SUBJECT AREAS OFFERED OUTSIDE OF DEGREE PROGRAMS

Undergraduate—agricultural and domestic animal services; allied health and medical assisting services; American literature (United States and Canadian); animal sciences; astronomy and astrophysics; behavioral sciences; biological and physical sciences; biology; business/commerce; business/corporate communications; chemistry; computer software and media applications; creative writing; developmental and child psychology; education; education related; English; English composition; health and physical education/fitness; health professions related; history; mathematics; mathematics and computer science; mathematics and statistics related; natural sciences; nutrition sciences; pharmacology and toxicology; philosophy; political science and government; psychology; religious studies; social sciences; sociology; speech and rhetoric; statistics.

Non-credit—computer and information sciences.

CRAFTON HILLS COLLEGE

Yucaipa, California

Distance Education Office

http://www.craftonhills.edu

Crafton Hills College was founded in 1972. It is accredited by Western Association of Schools and Colleges. It first offered distance learning courses in 1980. In fall 2005, there were 737 students enrolled in distance learning courses. Institutionally administered financial aid is available to distance learners.

Services Distance learners have accessibility to academic advising, bookstore, campus computer network, e-mail services, library services.

Contact Mr. Chuck Dean, Computer Technician, Crafton Hills College, 441 West 8th Street, San Bernardino, CA 92401. Telephone: 909-384-4318. Fax: 909-885-3035. E-mail: cdean@sbccd.cc.ca.us.

DEGREES AND AWARDS

Programs offered do not lead to a degree or other formal award.

COURSE SUBJECT AREAS OFFERED OUTSIDE OF DEGREE PROGRAMS

Undergraduate—anthropology; astronomy and astrophysics; biology; business administration, management and operations; developmental and child psychology; economics; geography and cartography; geological and earth sciences/geosciences; health and physical education/fitness; history; human development, family studies, and related services; philosophy and religious studies related; political science and government; real estate; religious studies; social psychology; sociology.

CREIGHTON UNIVERSITY

Omaha, Nebraska

School of Pharmacy and Health Professions

http://spahp.creighton.edu

Creighton University was founded in 1878. It is accredited by North Central Association of Colleges and Schools. It first offered distance learning courses in 1995. In fall 2005, there were 427 students enrolled in distance learning courses. Institutionally administered financial aid is available to distance learners.

Services Distance learners have accessibility to academic advising, bookstore, campus computer network, career placement assistance, e-mail services, library services.

Contact Ms. Marie E. Bensman, Executive Director of Admission, Creighton University, School of Pharmacy and Health Professions, Criss Science Building III, 2500 California Plaza, Omaha, NE 68178. Telephone: 800-325-2830 Ext. 1. Fax: 402-280-5739. E-mail: mbensman@creighton.edu.

DEGREES AND AWARDS

DPT Physical Therapy
OTD Occupational Therapy–Post-Professional Occupational Therapy Program
PharmD Pharmacy

COURSE SUBJECT AREAS OFFERED OUTSIDE OF DEGREE PROGRAMS

Graduate—health and medical administrative services; health professions related; pharmacy, pharmaceutical sciences, and administration.

CROWN COLLEGE

St. Bonifacius, Minnesota

Crown College Online

http://www.crownonline.org

Crown College was founded in 1916. It is accredited by Association for Biblical Higher Education. It first offered distance learning courses in 2000. In fall 2005, there were 200 students enrolled in distance learning courses. Institutionally administered financial aid is available to distance learners.

Services Distance learners have accessibility to academic advising, bookstore, campus computer network, career placement assistance, e-mail services, library services, tutoring.

Contact Dr. Gordon McAlister, Dean of Online Learning, Crown College, 8700 College View Drive, St. Bonifacius, MN 55375. Telephone: 952-446-4153. Fax: 952-446-4149. E-mail: cconline@crown.edu.

DEGREES AND AWARDS

AS Christian Ministries
BS Christian Ministry
MA Educational Leadership; Intercultural Studies; Ministry Leadership; Organizational Leadership

COURSE SUBJECT AREAS OFFERED OUTSIDE OF DEGREE PROGRAMS

Undergraduate—missionary studies and missiology; pastoral counseling and specialized ministries; philosophy and religious studies related; religious education; religious studies.

Graduate—biblical studies; business administration, management and operations; business/managerial economics; business operations support and assistant services; education; educational administration and supervision; education related; missionary studies and missiology; philosophy and religious studies related; theological and ministerial studies.

CULVER-STOCKTON COLLEGE

Canton, Missouri

http://www.culver.edu/

Culver-Stockton College was founded in 1853. It is accredited by North Central Association of Colleges and Schools. It first offered distance learning courses in 2002. In fall 2005, there were 61 students enrolled in distance learning courses. Institutionally administered financial aid is available to distance learners.

Services Distance learners have accessibility to academic advising, bookstore, campus computer network, career placement assistance, e-mail services, library services, tutoring.

Contact Dr. R. Joseph Dieker, Dean of Academic Affairs, Culver-Stockton College, One College Hill, Canton, MO 63435. Telephone: 573-288-6325. Fax: 573-288-6616. E-mail: jdieker@culver.edu.

DEGREES AND AWARDS

BS Business Administration

COURSE SUBJECT AREAS OFFERED OUTSIDE OF DEGREE PROGRAMS

Undergraduate—astronomy and astrophysics; biology; business administration, management and operations; computer and information sciences; management information systems; nursing.

CUMBERLAND COUNTY COLLEGE
Vineland, New Jersey
Multimedia and Distance Learning Services
http://www.cccnj.edu

Cumberland County College was founded in 1963. It is accredited by Middle States Association of Colleges and Schools. It first offered distance learning courses in 1990. In fall 2005, there were 150 students enrolled in distance learning courses. Institutionally administered financial aid is available to distance learners.

Services Distance learners have accessibility to academic advising, bookstore, campus computer network, career placement assistance, e-mail services, library services, tutoring.

Contact Michael R. Farinelli, Senior Manager, Multimedia Support Services, Cumberland County College, College Drive, PO Box 1500, Vineland, NJ 08362-0517. Telephone: 856-691-8600 Ext. 303. Fax: 856-691-9489. E-mail: mfarinelli@cccnj.edu.

DEGREES AND AWARDS

Programs offered do not lead to a degree or other formal award.

COURSE SUBJECT AREAS OFFERED OUTSIDE OF DEGREE PROGRAMS

Undergraduate—anthropology; business administration, management and operations; clinical child psychology; economics; English composition; history; languages (foreign languages related); psychology; sociology; speech and rhetoric.

DAEMEN COLLEGE
Amherst, New York
http://distance.daemen.edu

Daemen College was founded in 1947. It is accredited by Middle States Association of Colleges and Schools. It first offered distance learning courses in 1999. In fall 2005, there were 1,200 students enrolled in distance learning courses. Institutionally administered financial aid is available to distance learners.

Services Distance learners have accessibility to academic advising, bookstore, campus computer network, e-mail services, library services.

Contact Ms. Cheryl Littlejohn, Distance Learning Coordinator, Daemen College, 4380 Main Street, BC211A, Amherst, NY 14226. Telephone: 716-839 8532. Fax: 716-839 8261. E-mail: clittlej@daemen.edu.

DEGREES AND AWARDS

Programs offered do not lead to a degree or other formal award.

COURSE SUBJECT AREAS OFFERED OUTSIDE OF DEGREE PROGRAMS

Undergraduate—business/commerce; education; English composition; entrepreneurial and small business operations; health and medical administrative services; health/medical preparatory programs; health professions related; linguistic, comparative, and related language studies; nursing.
Graduate—medical clinical sciences/graduate medical studies; nursing.

DAKOTA COUNTY TECHNICAL COLLEGE
Rosemount, Minnesota
http://www.dctc.edu

Dakota County Technical College was founded in 1970. It is accredited by North Central Association of Colleges and Schools. It first offered distance learning courses in 1999. In fall 2005, there were 850 students enrolled in distance learning courses. Institutionally administered financial aid is available to distance learners.

Services Distance learners have accessibility to academic advising, bookstore, career placement assistance, e-mail services, library services, tutoring.

Contact Patrick Lair, Admissions Coordinator, Dakota County Technical College, 1300 145th Street East, County Road 42, Rosemount, MN 55068. Telephone: 651-423-8301. Fax: 651-423-8775. E-mail: patrick.lair@dctc.edu.

DEGREES AND AWARDS

Certificate Human Resource Development; Marketing Communications Specialist; Meeting and Event Management; Quality Improvement; Sales Specialist; Supervisory Leadership

COURSE SUBJECT AREAS OFFERED OUTSIDE OF DEGREE PROGRAMS

Undergraduate—allied health and medical assisting services; architectural technology; architecture; area, ethnic, cultural, and gender studies related; bilingual, multilingual, and multicultural education; biological and biomedical sciences related; biological and physical sciences; biology; business administration, management and operations; business/commerce; business/corporate communications; business, management, and marketing related; comparative literature; computer/information technology administration and management; computer programming; computer software and media applications; computer systems networking and telecommunications; creative writing; design and applied arts; developmental and child psychology; economics; education related; engineering technologies related; English; English composition; entrepreneurial and small business operations; family psychology; health and medical administrative services; health and physical education/fitness; health professions related; health psychology; health services/allied health/health sciences; history; human development, family studies, and related services; human resources management; intercultural/multicultural and diversity studies; international business; liberal arts and sciences, general studies and humanities; manufacturing engineering; marketing; mathematics; mathematics and statistics related; natural sciences; psychology; public relations, advertising, and applied communication related; sales, merchandising, and related marketing operations (general); sales, merchandising, and related marketing operations (specialized); social psychology; social sciences; social sciences related; sociology; technical and business writing.
Non-credit—business administration, management and operations; health professions related; manufacturing engineering.

DAKOTA STATE UNIVERSITY
Madison, South Dakota
E-Education Services
http://www.departments.dsu.edu/disted/

Dakota State University was founded in 1881. It is accredited by North Central Association of Colleges and Schools. It first offered distance learning courses in 1990. In fall 2005, there were 631 students enrolled in distance learning courses. Institutionally administered financial aid is available to distance learners.

Services Distance learners have accessibility to academic advising, bookstore, campus computer network, career placement assistance, e-mail services, library services, tutoring.

Contact Dr. Deb Gearhart, Director of E-Education Services, Dakota State University, 820 North Washington Avenue, Madison, SD 57042-1799. Telephone: 800-641-4309. Fax: 605-256-5095. E-mail: dsuinfo@dsu.edu.

DEGREES AND AWARDS

AS Health Information Technology
BS Health Information Administration Degree Completion program

MS Educational Technology; Information Assurance and Computer Security
MSIS Information Systems

COURSE SUBJECT AREAS OFFERED OUTSIDE OF DEGREE PROGRAMS

Undergraduate—accounting and related services; communications technology; computer and information sciences; computer and information sciences and support services related; computer programming; computer science; computer systems analysis; education related; English; English composition; fine and studio art; health and medical administrative services; human resources management; information science/studies; mathematics; music; psychology; sociology; speech and rhetoric.
Graduate—computer and information sciences; computer and information sciences and support services related; educational/instructional media design; education related; information science/studies.

DALLAS BAPTIST UNIVERSITY
Dallas, Texas
Dallas Baptist University Online (DBU Online)
http://online.dbu.edu

Dallas Baptist University was founded in 1965. It is accredited by Southern Association of Colleges and Schools. It first offered distance learning courses in 1998. In fall 2005, there were 1,153 students enrolled in distance learning courses. Institutionally administered financial aid is available to distance learners.
Services Distance learners have accessibility to academic advising, bookstore, campus computer network, career placement assistance, e-mail services, library services, tutoring.
Contact Ms. Billie Joy Upshaw, Online Student Coordinator, Dallas Baptist University, Online Education, 3000 Mountain Creek Parkway, Dallas, TX 75211-9299. Telephone: 800-460-8188. Fax: 214-333-5373. E-mail: online@dbu.edu.

DEGREES AND AWARDS

BA Biblical Studies; Christian Ministries; Psychology; Sociology
BBA Management Information Systems; Management
BS Business Administration; Management Information Systems; Management
Certificate E-Business
MACE Christian Education
MAM Human Resource Management; Management, general
MBA E-Business; Finance; International Business; Management Information Systems; Management; Marketing
MEd Educational Leadership; Higher Education

COURSE SUBJECT AREAS OFFERED OUTSIDE OF DEGREE PROGRAMS

Undergraduate—accounting and related services; American literature (United States and Canadian); atmospheric sciences and meteorology; biblical studies; biological and physical sciences; biology; business administration, management and operations; communication and media; computer and information sciences; criminal justice and corrections; criminology; economics; education; English; finance and financial management services; fine and studio art; geological and earth sciences/geosciences; health and physical education/fitness; history; liberal arts and sciences, general studies and humanities; management information systems; marketing; mathematics; mathematics and statistics related; missionary studies and missiology; natural sciences; philosophy; political science and government; psychology; religious studies; social psychology; sociology; speech and rhetoric; statistics; theological and ministerial studies.
Graduate—accounting and related services; business administration, management and operations; computer/information technology administration and management; criminal justice and corrections; curriculum and instruction; economics; educational administration and supervision; educational assessment, evaluation, and research; education related; entrepreneurial and small business operations; finance and financial management services; human resources management; information science/studies; international business; management sciences and quantitative methods; marketing; religious education; religious studies; sales, merchandising, and related marketing operations (general).

DALLAS COUNTY COMMUNITY COLLEGE DISTRICT
Dallas, Texas
Dallas TeleCollege
http://www.telecollege.dcccd.edu

Dallas County Community College District is accredited by Southern Association of Colleges and Schools. It first offered distance learning courses in 1972. In fall 2005, there were 12,000 students enrolled in distance learning courses. Institutionally administered financial aid is available to distance learners.
Services Distance learners have accessibility to academic advising, bookstore, campus computer network, e-mail services, library services, tutoring.
Contact Mrs. Angela Auzenne, Public Information Director, Dallas County Community College District, 9596 Walnut Street, Dallas, TX 75243-2112. Telephone: 972-669-6657. Fax: 972-669-6409. E-mail: aauzenne@dcccd.edu.

DEGREES AND AWARDS

AA Liberal Arts and General Studies
AS Business; General Studies

COURSE SUBJECT AREAS OFFERED OUTSIDE OF DEGREE PROGRAMS

Undergraduate—accounting and related services; anthropology; astronomy and astrophysics; biology; business operations support and assistant services; computer and information sciences; computer and information sciences and support services related; computer engineering; computer/information technology administration and management; computer programming; computer science; computer software and media applications; computer systems analysis; computer systems networking and telecommunications; creative writing; data entry/microcomputer applications; data processing; developmental and child psychology; drafting/design engineering technologies; economics; education; education related; English as a second language; English composition; health and medical administrative services; health professions related; history; human development, family studies, and related services; human resources management; journalism; liberal arts and sciences, general studies and humanities; marketing; mathematics; mathematics and computer science; mathematics and statistics related; music; philosophy; philosophy and religious studies related; physical sciences; physical sciences related; psychology; real estate; social sciences; social sciences related; sociology; speech and rhetoric.

DANVILLE COMMUNITY COLLEGE
Danville, Virginia
Learning Resource Center
http://www.dcc.vccs.edu

Danville Community College was founded in 1967. It is accredited by Southern Association of Colleges and Schools. It first offered distance learning courses in 1990. In fall 2005, there were 500 students enrolled in distance learning courses. Institutionally administered financial aid is available to distance learners.
Services Distance learners have accessibility to academic advising, bookstore, career placement assistance, e-mail services, library services, tutoring.
Contact Dr. Chris Ezell, Vice President of Instruction and Student Services, Danville Community College, 1008 South Main Street, Danville, VA 24541. Telephone: 434-797-8410. Fax: 434-797-8415. E-mail: cezell@dcc.vccs.edu.

DEGREES AND AWARDS

Programs offered do not lead to a degree or other formal award.

COURSE SUBJECT AREAS OFFERED OUTSIDE OF DEGREE PROGRAMS

Undergraduate—accounting and related services; allied health and medical assisting services; allied health diagnostic, intervention, and treatment professions; behavioral sciences; biological and biomedical sciences related; biology; business administration, management and operations; business/commerce; business, management, and marketing related; business operations support and assistant services; communication and media; community health services; computer programming; computer science; computer software and media applications; criminal justice and corrections; criminology; dental support services and allied professions; dentistry and oral sciences (advanced/graduate); design and applied arts; developmental and child psychology; drafting/design engineering technologies; educational/instructional media design; education (specific levels and methods); English; English composition; English language and literature related; English literature (British and Commonwealth); foods, nutrition, and related services; geography and cartography; graphic communications; health and physical education/fitness; health professions related; human development, family studies, and related services; marketing; mathematics; mathematics and computer science; music; natural sciences; nursing; nutrition sciences; psychology; social psychology; sociology; theological and ministerial studies.

DARTON COLLEGE
Albany, Georgia
Office of Distance Learning
http://www.darton.edu

Darton College was founded in 1965. It is accredited by Southern Association of Colleges and Schools. It first offered distance learning courses in 1993. In fall 2005, there were 1,386 students enrolled in distance learning courses. Institutionally administered financial aid is available to distance learners.

Services Distance learners have accessibility to academic advising, bookstore, campus computer network, career placement assistance, e-mail services, library services, tutoring.

Contact Ms. Tarrah N. Mirus, Technology Coordinator, Darton College, 2400 Gillionville Road, Albany, GA 31707. Telephone: 229-317-6838. Fax: 229-317-6682. E-mail: tarrah.mirus@darton.edu.

DEGREES AND AWARDS

AA Art; English; Foreign Language; History; History; Journalism and Mass Communication; Music; Philosophy; Speech; Theater
AAS Accounting; Business Computer Specialist option; Governmental Services; Histologic Technology; Management; Management; Office Administration (Administrative Support)
AS Anthropology; Biological Science; Business Administration; Business Education; Computer Information Systems; Criminal Justice; Dentistry–Pre-Dentistry; Diagnostic Medical Sonography; Economics; Forensic Science; General Studies; Health Information Management; Health Information Technology; Health and Physical Education (Exercise Science); Health and Physical Education (Recreation); Health and Physical Education (Sports Management); Health and Physical Education (Teacher Ed option); Law–Pre-Law; Medical Laboratory Technology; Medical Technology; Nuclear Medicine Technology; Nursing; Occupational Therapy; Office Administration (Secretarial Science); Optometry–Pre-Optometry; Pharmacy–Pre-Pharmacy; Physical Therapy Assistant; Physical Therapy; Political Science; Pre-Medicine; Pre-Physician's Assistant; Psychology; Respiratory Therapy; Social Work; Sociology; Teacher Education (Early Childhood); Teacher Education (Middle Grades); Teacher Education (Secondary Education); Teacher Education (Special Education); Teacher Education (Trade and Industrial Education); Trade and Industrial Education; Veterinary Science–Pre-Veterinary Science
Certificate Histology; Medical Coding

COURSE SUBJECT AREAS OFFERED OUTSIDE OF DEGREE PROGRAMS

Undergraduate—accounting and computer science; accounting and related services; allied health and medical assisting services; allied health diagnostic, intervention, and treatment professions; American literature (United States and Canadian); applied mathematics; biological and biomedical sciences related; business administration, management and operations; business/commerce; cell biology and anatomical sciences; clinical/medical laboratory science and allied professions; communication and media; computer software and media applications; computer systems networking and telecommunications; criminal justice and corrections; economics; education; education related; education (specific levels and methods); education (specific subject areas); English; English composition; English literature (British and Commonwealth); finance and financial management services; health and medical administrative services; health and physical education/fitness; health/medical preparatory programs; health professions related; health services/allied health/health sciences; history; languages (East Asian); languages (foreign languages related); languages (Germanic); languages (Romance languages); liberal arts and sciences, general studies and humanities; linguistic, comparative, and related language studies; mathematics; mathematics and computer science; mathematics and statistics related; music; philosophy; philosophy and religious studies related; physical sciences; physiology, pathology and related sciences; political science and government; psychology; social work; sociology; speech and rhetoric; statistics.

Non-credit—business administration, management and operations; business/corporate communications; business, management, and marketing related; computer software and media applications; creative writing; finance and financial management services; real estate; sales, merchandising, and related marketing operations (specialized); technical and business writing.

DAVENPORT UNIVERSITY ONLINE
Grand Rapids, Michigan
http://www.davenport.edu

Davenport University Online is accredited by North Central Association of Colleges and Schools. It first offered distance learning courses in 1999. In fall 2005, there were 5,500 students enrolled in distance learning courses. Institutionally administered financial aid is available to distance learners.

Services Distance learners have accessibility to academic advising, bookstore, career placement assistance, e-mail services, library services, tutoring.

Contact Jeff Wiggerman, Admissions Representative, Davenport University Online, 415 East Fulton Street, Grand Rapids, MI 49503. Telephone: 800-203-5323. Fax: 800-811-2658. E-mail: duonline@davenport.edu.

DEGREES AND AWARDS

AAS Health Information Technology; Information and Computer Security
ABA Accounting; Administrative Office Technology–Executive Office Administration specialty; Management; Marketing
BAA Business–Applied Business; Public Safety and Security Management
BBA Accounting Information Management–Internal Auditing specialty; Accounting Information Management–Management Accounting specialty; Accounting–Internal Auditing specialty; Business Professional Studies; Computer Information Systems–Database Management Specialty (BAS); Health Services Administration; Human Resource Management; Information and Computer Security; Integrative Professional Studies; Management–Financial Management specialty; Management–Governance and Leadership specialty; Management–Manufacturing specialty; Marketing–Advertising/Promotion specialty; Marketing–Business to Business specialty; Marketing–Marketing Management specialty; Service Management and Marketing
BST Biometric Security
Certificate Forensic Accounting; Human Resources Management; Information and Computer Security
Diploma Medical Billing; Medical Coding
MBA Accounting specialty; Health Care Management specialty; Human Resource Management specialty; Strategic Management Specialty

DAVIS COLLEGE
Johnson City, New York

Davis College was founded in 1900. It is accredited by Association for Biblical Higher Education. It first offered distance learning courses in 2004. In fall 2005, there were 2 students enrolled in distance learning courses. Institutionally administered financial aid is available to distance learners.

Services Distance learners have accessibility to academic advising, bookstore, e-mail services, library services, tutoring.

Contact Mr. Spencer Key, Academic Dean, Davis College, 400 Riverside Drive, Johnson City, NY 13790. Telephone: 607-729-1581 Ext. 405. Fax: 607-729-2962. E-mail: skey@davisny.edu.

DEGREES AND AWARDS

Programs offered do not lead to a degree or other formal award.

COURSE SUBJECT AREAS OFFERED OUTSIDE OF DEGREE PROGRAMS

Undergraduate—biblical studies; biological and physical sciences; business, management, and marketing related; English; English language and literature related; mathematics; multi-/interdisciplinary studies related; philosophy and religious studies related; work and family studies.

DAWSON COMMUNITY COLLEGE
Glendive, Montana
Continuing and Extension Education Department
http://www.dawson.edu

Dawson Community College was founded in 1940. It is accredited by Northwest Commission on Colleges and Universities. It first offered distance learning courses in 1990. In fall 2005, there were 59 students enrolled in distance learning courses. Institutionally administered financial aid is available to distance learners.

Services Distance learners have accessibility to academic advising, bookstore, career placement assistance, library services.

Contact Jolene Myers, Director of Admissions, Dawson Community College, 300 College Drive, Glendive, MT 59330. Telephone: 406-377-9410. Fax: 406-377-8132. E-mail: myers@dawson.edu.

DEGREES AND AWARDS

AA General Studies

AAS Business Management; Human Services

COURSE SUBJECT AREAS OFFERED OUTSIDE OF DEGREE PROGRAMS

Undergraduate—agricultural business and management; agriculture; American literature (United States and Canadian); anthropology; biology; business administration, management and operations; communication and media; computer software and media applications; creative writing; criminal justice and corrections; developmental and child psychology; English composition; fine and studio art; human services; psychology; sociology.

DAYMAR COLLEGE
Owensboro, Kentucky
http://online.daymarcollege.edu

Daymar College was founded in 1963. It is accredited by Accrediting Council for Independent Colleges and Schools. It first offered distance learning courses in 1999. In fall 2005, there were 36 students enrolled in distance learning courses. Institutionally administered financial aid is available to distance learners.

Services Distance learners have accessibility to academic advising, campus computer network, career placement assistance.

Contact Jim Weber, Director of eLearning, Daymar College, 5030 Back Square Drive, Owensboro, KY 42301. Telephone: 270-926-1188. Fax: 270-686-8912. E-mail: jweber@daymarcollege.edu.

DEGREES AND AWARDS

Programs offered do not lead to a degree or other formal award.

COURSE SUBJECT AREAS OFFERED OUTSIDE OF DEGREE PROGRAMS

Undergraduate—accounting and computer science; accounting and related services; business administration, management and operations; business operations support and assistant services; computer software and media applications; medical basic sciences.

DE ANZA COLLEGE
Cupertino, California
Distance Learning Center
http://distance.deanza.fhda.edu

De Anza College was founded in 1967. It is accredited by Western Association of Schools and Colleges. It first offered distance learning courses in 1974. In fall 2005, there were 3,293 students enrolled in distance learning courses. Institutionally administered financial aid is available to distance learners.

Services Distance learners have accessibility to academic advising, bookstore, e-mail services, library services, tutoring.

Contact Ann Leever, Instructional Associate, De Anza College, 21250 Stevens Creek Boulevard, Cupertino, CA 95014. Telephone: 408-864-8969. Fax: 408-864-8245. E-mail: information@dadistance.fhda.edu.

DEGREES AND AWARDS

Programs offered do not lead to a degree or other formal award.

COURSE SUBJECT AREAS OFFERED OUTSIDE OF DEGREE PROGRAMS

Undergraduate—accounting and related services; allied health and medical assisting services; anthropology; area studies; biology; business administration, management and operations; computer programming; computer software and media applications; computer systems networking and telecommunications; data entry/microcomputer applications; developmental and child psychology; economics; English composition; environmental control technologies; ethnic, cultural minority, and gender studies; graphic communications; history; human development, family studies, and related services; journalism; legal studies (nonprofessional general, undergraduate); marketing; mathematics and statistics related; music; philosophy and religious studies related; political science and government; psychology; real estate; social psychology; sociology; statistics; visual and performing arts.

DEFIANCE COLLEGE
Defiance, Ohio
Design for Leadership
http://www.defiance.edu/pages/design_leadership.html

Defiance College was founded in 1850. It is accredited by North Central Association of Colleges and Schools. It first offered distance learning courses in 1971. In fall 2005, there were 35 students enrolled in distance learning courses. Institutionally administered financial aid is available to distance learners.

Services Distance learners have accessibility to academic advising, bookstore, campus computer network, career placement assistance, e-mail services, library services, tutoring.

Contact Dr. Marian R. Plant, Coordinator, Design for Leadership, Defiance College, 701 North Clinton Street, Defiance, OH 43512. Telephone: 419-783-2465. Fax: 419-784-0426. E-mail: design@defiance.edu.

DEGREES AND AWARDS

AA Religious Education

BA Religious Education

Certificate African American Ministry Leadership module; Church Education; Youth Ministry Leadership Module

COURSE SUBJECT AREAS OFFERED OUTSIDE OF DEGREE PROGRAMS

Undergraduate—biblical studies; religious education.

DELTA COLLEGE
University Center, Michigan
Distance Learning Office and Telelearning
http://www.delta.edu/distancelearning

Delta College was founded in 1961. It is accredited by North Central Association of Colleges and Schools. It first offered distance learning courses in 1982. In fall 2005, there were 1,500 students enrolled in distance learning courses. Institutionally administered financial aid is available to distance learners.

Services Distance learners have accessibility to academic advising, bookstore, campus computer network, career placement assistance, e-mail services, library services, tutoring.

Contact Ms. Jane M. Knochel, eLearning Coordinator, Delta College, 1961 Delta Road, University Center, MI 48710. Telephone: 989-686-9088. E-mail: janeknochel@delta.edu.

DEGREES AND AWARDS

Programs offered do not lead to a degree or other formal award.

COURSE SUBJECT AREAS OFFERED OUTSIDE OF DEGREE PROGRAMS

Undergraduate—accounting and computer science; American literature (United States and Canadian); biology; biology/biotechnology laboratory technician; business/corporate communications; computer and information sciences; computer programming; computer software and media applications; criminal justice and corrections; developmental and child psychology; economics; engineering/industrial management; English; English composition; film/video and photographic arts; fine and studio art; health and physical education/fitness; history; industrial production technologies; languages (Romance languages); legal studies (non-professional general, undergraduate); marketing; materials engineering; mathematics; mathematics and statistics related; metallurgical engineering; microbiological sciences and immunology; philosophy; political science and government; psychology; sociology; speech and rhetoric; statistics; technical and business writing; visual and performing arts.

DENVER SEMINARY
Denver, Colorado
http://www.denverseminary.edu

Denver Seminary was founded in 1950. It is accredited by North Central Association of Colleges and Schools. It first offered distance learning courses in 1988. In fall 2005, there were 100 students enrolled in distance learning courses. Institutionally administered financial aid is available to distance learners.

Services Distance learners have accessibility to academic advising, bookstore, career placement assistance, library services.

Contact Ms. Venita Doughty, Director of Educational Technology, Denver Seminary, 6399 South Santa Fe Drive, Littleton, CO 80120. Telephone: 303-762-6933. Fax: 303-761-8060. E-mail: venita.doughty@denverseminary.edu.

DEGREES AND AWARDS

Programs offered do not lead to a degree or other formal award.

COURSE SUBJECT AREAS OFFERED OUTSIDE OF DEGREE PROGRAMS

Graduate—biblical and other theological languages and literatures; biblical studies; history; philosophy and religious studies related; religious education; religious studies; theological and ministerial studies.

DEPAUL UNIVERSITY
Chicago, Illinois
School of Computer Science, Telecommunications, and Information Systems
http://www.cti.depaul.edu/admissions

DePaul University was founded in 1898. It is accredited by North Central Association of Colleges and Schools. It first offered distance learning courses in 1995. In fall 2005, there were 900 students enrolled in distance learning courses. Institutionally administered financial aid is available to distance learners.

Services Distance learners have accessibility to academic advising, bookstore, campus computer network, career placement assistance, e-mail services, library services, tutoring.

Contact Maureen Garvey, Director of Admissions, DePaul University, DePaul CTI, 243 South Wabash Avenue, Chicago, IL 60604. Telephone: 312-362-8714. Fax: 312-362-6116. E-mail: ctiadmissions@cti.depaul.edu.

DEGREES AND AWARDS

MA Information Technology
MS Computer Science; Computer, Information, and Network Security; E-Commerce Technology; Information Systems; Instructional Technology Systems; Software Engineering; Telecommunication Systems

COURSE SUBJECT AREAS OFFERED OUTSIDE OF DEGREE PROGRAMS

Undergraduate—computer and information sciences; computer programming; computer science; computer systems networking and telecommunications.

Graduate—cognitive science; communications technology; computer and information sciences; computer and information sciences and support services related; computer/information technology administration and management; computer programming; computer science; computer software and media applications; computer systems analysis; computer systems networking and telecommunications; educational/instructional media design; information science/studies; systems engineering.

See full description on page 362.

DEPAUL UNIVERSITY
Chicago, Illinois
School for New Learning
http://www.snlonline.net

DePaul University was founded in 1898. It is accredited by North Central Association of Colleges and Schools. It first offered distance learning courses in 1996. In fall 2005, there were 838 students enrolled in distance learning courses. Institutionally administered financial aid is available to distance learners.

Services Distance learners have accessibility to academic advising, bookstore, campus computer network, career placement assistance, e-mail services, library services.

Contact School for New Learning Advising Center, DePaul University, School for New Learning, 25 East Jackson Boulevard, LC 200, Chicago, IL 60604. Telephone: 866-765-3678. Fax: 312-362-5053. E-mail: snladvising@snlonline.net.

DEGREES AND AWARDS

BA Individually designed focus area

COURSE SUBJECT AREAS OFFERED OUTSIDE OF DEGREE PROGRAMS

Undergraduate—liberal arts and sciences, general studies and humanities.

See full description on page 360.

DES MOINES AREA COMMUNITY COLLEGE
Ankeny, Iowa
Distance Learning/Continuing Education
http://www.dmacc.edu/online

Des Moines Area Community College was founded in 1966. It is accredited by North Central Association of Colleges and Schools. It first offered distance learning courses in 1970. In fall 2005, there were 2,500 students enrolled in distance learning courses. Institutionally administered financial aid is available to distance learners.

Services Distance learners have accessibility to academic advising, bookstore, career placement assistance, e-mail services, library services, tutoring.

Contact Pat Thieben, Director of Distance Learning, Des Moines Area Community College, 2006 South Ankeny Boulevard, Ankeny, IA 50023. Telephone: 515-965-7086. Fax: 515-965-6002. E-mail: pathieben@dmacc.edu.

DEGREES AND AWARDS

AAS Business Administration
Certification Management

COURSE SUBJECT AREAS OFFERED OUTSIDE OF DEGREE PROGRAMS

Undergraduate—accounting and computer science; accounting and related services; American literature (United States and Canadian); anthropology; applied mathematics; behavioral sciences; biblical and other theological languages and literatures; biological and physical sciences; biology; business administration, management and operations; business/commerce; business/corporate communications; business, management, and marketing related; business/managerial economics; business operations support and assistant services; chemistry; communication and media; comparative literature; computer and information sciences; computer and information sciences and support services related; computer programming; computer science; creative writing; criminal justice and corrections; criminology; data entry/microcomputer applications; data processing; developmental and child psychology; ecology, evolution, and

population biology; economics; educational psychology; education related; English; English composition; English language and literature related; English literature (British and Commonwealth); entrepreneurial and small business operations; finance and financial management services; fire protection; foods, nutrition, and related services; funeral service and mortuary science; geography and cartography; gerontology; health and medical administrative services; history; hospitality administration; human development, family studies, and related services; human resources management; human services; international business; international/global studies; journalism; library science related; management information systems; management sciences and quantitative methods; marketing; mathematics; mathematics and statistics related; music; natural sciences; nursing; personality psychology; philosophy; philosophy and religious studies related; physical sciences; psychology; psychology related; religious education; religious studies; sales, merchandising, and related marketing operations (specialized); social psychology; social sciences; social sciences related; sociology; statistics; technical and business writing.
Non-credit—computer software and media applications.

DEVRY UNIVERSITY ONLINE
Oakbrook Terrace, Illinois
http://www.devry.edu/online

DeVry University Online was founded in 2000. It is accredited by North Central Association of Colleges and Schools. In fall 2005, there were 6,569 students enrolled in distance learning courses. Institutionally administered financial aid is available to distance learners.
Services Distance learners have accessibility to academic advising, bookstore, career placement assistance, library services.
Contact Diane Stegmeyer, DeVry University Online, 1200 East Diehl Road, Naperville, IL 60563. Telephone: 877-496-9050. Fax: 630-382-2939. E-mail: dstegmeyer@devry.com.

DEGREES AND AWARDS
AAS Accounting Technology; Health Information Technology; Network Systems Administration
BS Business Administration; Computer Information Systems; Game and Simulation Programming; Information Technology; Network and Communications Management; Technical Management
MAFM Accounting and Financial Management
MBA Business Administration
MHRM Human Resource Management
MISM Information Systems Management
MPA Public Administration
MPM Project Management
MTM Network and Communications Management

COURSE SUBJECT AREAS OFFERED OUTSIDE OF DEGREE PROGRAMS
Undergraduate—accounting and related services; area, ethnic, cultural, and gender studies related; biological and biomedical sciences related; business/commerce; communication and media; computer and information sciences; creative writing; economics; English composition; legal studies (non-professional general, undergraduate); liberal arts and sciences, general studies and humanities; marketing; mathematics; taxation; technical and business writing.
Graduate—accounting and related services; business/commerce; communication and media; communications technology; computer and information sciences; computer systems networking and telecommunications; economics; entrepreneurial and small business operations; finance and financial management services; health professions related; human resources management; marketing; mathematics; public administration; taxation.

See full description on page 364.

DODGE CITY COMMUNITY COLLEGE
Dodge City, Kansas

Dodge City Community College was founded in 1935. It is accredited by North Central Association of Colleges and Schools. In fall 2005, there were 1,500 students enrolled in distance learning courses. Institutionally administered financial aid is available to distance learners.
Services Distance learners have accessibility to academic advising.
Contact Stephanie Lanning, Registrar, Dodge City Community College, 2501 North 14th, Dodge City, KS 67801. Telephone: 620-227-9409. E-mail: slg@dc3.edu.

DEGREES AND AWARDS
Programs offered do not lead to a degree or other formal award.

COURSE SUBJECT AREAS OFFERED OUTSIDE OF DEGREE PROGRAMS
Undergraduate—biology; economics; English; languages (foreign languages related); mathematics; music; psychology; sociology; speech and rhetoric.

DRAKE UNIVERSITY
Des Moines, Iowa
Distance Learning Program
http://www.onlinelearning.drake.edu/summer/

Drake University was founded in 1881. It is accredited by North Central Association of Colleges and Schools. It first offered distance learning courses in 1997. In fall 2005, there were 10,000 students enrolled in distance learning courses. Institutionally administered financial aid is available to distance learners.
Services Distance learners have accessibility to academic advising, bookstore, campus computer network, e-mail services, library services.
Contact Ms. Sandra K. Smeltzer, Assistant to the Provost, Drake University, Office of the Provost, 25th and University, Des Moines, IA 50311. Telephone: 515-271-4985. Fax: 515-271-2954. E-mail: sandra.smeltzer@drake.edu.

DEGREES AND AWARDS
Programs offered do not lead to a degree or other formal award.

COURSE SUBJECT AREAS OFFERED OUTSIDE OF DEGREE PROGRAMS
Undergraduate—accounting and related services; biochemistry, biophysics and molecular biology; business administration, management and operations; business/commerce; business/managerial economics; communication and journalism related; communication and media; computer and information sciences; creative writing; economics; education; education related; English; fine and studio art; health professions related; history; human resources management; information science/studies; international relations and affairs; journalism; legal research and advanced professional studies; liberal arts and sciences, general studies and humanities; management information systems; management sciences and quantitative methods; marketing; mathematics and computer science; peace studies and conflict resolution; pharmacy, pharmaceutical sciences, and administration; political science and government; psychology; psychology related; public relations, advertising, and applied communication related; social sciences related; special education; visual and performing arts related.
Graduate—accounting and computer science; business administration, management and operations; business/commerce; economics; education; finance and financial management services; health professions related; health services/allied health/health sciences; history; human resources management; information science/studies; insurance; journalism; music; peace studies and conflict resolution; pharmacy, pharmaceutical sciences, and administration; political science and government; psychology; public administration; public administration and social service professions related; public health; public relations, advertising, and applied communication related; rehabilitation and therapeutic professions.

DREW UNIVERSITY
Madison, New Jersey

Drew University was founded in 1867. It is accredited by Middle States Association of Colleges and Schools. It first offered distance learning courses in 1998. In fall 2005, there were 60 students enrolled in distance learning courses. Institutionally administered financial aid is available to distance learners.
Services Distance learners have accessibility to academic advising, bookstore, campus computer network, e-mail services, library services.

Contact Dr. Carl Savage, Associate Director, Doctor of Ministry Program, Drew University, 36 Madison Avenue, Madison, NJ 07940. Telephone: 973-408-3586. Fax: 973-408-3178. E-mail: csavage@drew.edu.

DEGREES AND AWARDS

Programs offered do not lead to a degree or other formal award.

COURSE SUBJECT AREAS OFFERED OUTSIDE OF DEGREE PROGRAMS

Graduate—theological and ministerial studies.
Non-credit—theological and ministerial studies.

DREXEL UNIVERSITY
Philadelphia, Pennsylvania
E-Learning
http://www.drexel.com

Drexel University was founded in 1891. It is accredited by Middle States Association of Colleges and Schools. It first offered distance learning courses in 1997. In fall 2005, there were 1,500 students enrolled in distance learning courses. Institutionally administered financial aid is available to distance learners.

Services Distance learners have accessibility to academic advising, bookstore, career placement assistance, e-mail services, library services, tutoring.

Contact Drexel eLearning, Drexel University, One Drexel Plaza, 3001 Market Street, Suite 300, Philadelphia, PA 19104. Telephone: 866-440-1949. Fax: 215-895-0525. E-mail: info@drexel.com.

DEGREES AND AWARDS

BS Business Administration; Communications and Applied Technology; Computing Technology; Education; General Studies–Finance specialization; General Studies–Management specialization; Psychology
BSN Nursing–RN to BSN
Certificate Applied Retail Management; Clinical Trials; Education–Graduate Intern Teaching Certificate; Education–Post-Bachelor's Teaching Certificate; Epidemiology and Biostatistics; Healthcare Informatics; Instructional Technology Specialist; Nursing Education; Nursing–Leadership and Management; Principal's Certification; Teaching English as a Second Language (TESL); Toxicology and Industrial Hygiene
Graduate Certificate Engineering Management
MBA Business Administration
MHS Physicians Assistant Studies
MS Clinical Research Organization and Management; Computer Science; Educational Administration–Collaborative Leadership; Electrical Engineering; Engineering Management; Global and International Education; Higher Education; Information Systems; Library and Information Science; Science of Instruction; Software Engineering
MSN Clinical Trials; Leadership and Management; Nursing Education; Nursing–Acute Care Nurse Practitioner; Nursing–Adult Psychiatric Mental Health Nurse Practitioner; Nursing–Completion Program for Nurse Practitioners

COURSE SUBJECT AREAS OFFERED OUTSIDE OF DEGREE PROGRAMS

Undergraduate—business administration, management and operations; business/commerce; business, management, and marketing related; communications technologies and support services related; computer and information sciences; computer science; finance and financial management services; health professions related; health services/allied health/health sciences; marketing; nursing; psychology; sales, merchandising, and related marketing operations (general).

Graduate—business administration, management and operations; business/commerce; business/corporate communications; business, management, and marketing related; clinical/medical laboratory science and allied professions; computer and information sciences; computer and information sciences and support services related; computer engineering; computer engineering technologies; computer science; curriculum and instruction; education; educational administration and supervision; educational assessment, evaluation, and research; educational/instructional media design; education related; education (specific levels and methods); education (specific subject areas); electrical and electronic engineering technologies; electrical, electronics and communications engineering; engineering; engineering related; engineering-related fields; engineering science; engineering technology; English as a second/foreign language (teaching); English as a second language; entrepreneurial and small business operations; finance and financial management services; health professions related; information science/studies; international and comparative education; international/global studies; library science; library science related; management information systems; marketing; nursing; public health; sales, merchandising, and related marketing operations (general); sales, merchandising, and related marketing operations (specialized); science technologies related; teaching assistants/aides.

See full description on page 366.

DREXEL UNIVERSITY
Philadelphia, Pennsylvania
LeBow College of Business
http://mbaonline.lebow.drexel.edu

Drexel University was founded in 1891. It is accredited by Middle States Association of Colleges and Schools. It first offered distance learning courses in 1998. In fall 2005, there were 335 students enrolled in distance learning courses. Institutionally administered financial aid is available to distance learners.

Services Distance learners have accessibility to academic advising, bookstore, campus computer network, career placement assistance, e-mail services, library services.

Contact Mr. Robert Palachick, LeBow Graduate Admissions, Drexel University, LeBow College of Business, 207 Matheson Hall, 3141 Chestnut Street, Philadelphia, PA 19104. Telephone: 215-895-0975. Fax: 215-895-1012. E-mail: mba@drexel.edu.

DEGREES AND AWARDS

MBA Business; Pharmaceutical Management

COURSE SUBJECT AREAS OFFERED OUTSIDE OF DEGREE PROGRAMS

Undergraduate—accounting and related services; business administration, management and operations; business/commerce; business/corporate communications; business/managerial economics; management sciences and quantitative methods; marketing; sales, merchandising, and related marketing operations (general); taxation.

Graduate—accounting and related services; business administration, management and operations; business, management, and marketing related; business/managerial economics; computer/information technology administration and management; management sciences and quantitative methods; marketing; sales, merchandising, and related marketing operations (general).

DRURY UNIVERSITY
Springfield, Missouri
http://www.drury.edu/

Drury University was founded in 1873. It is accredited by North Central Association of Colleges and Schools. It first offered distance learning courses in 1999. In fall 2005, there were 928 students enrolled in distance learning courses. Institutionally administered financial aid is available to distance learners.

Services Distance learners have accessibility to academic advising, bookstore, campus computer network, e-mail services, library services.

Contact Dr. John Gary Rader, Director for Online Education, Drury University, 900 North Benton Avenue, Springfield, MO 65802. Telephone: 417-873-7406. E-mail: grader@drury.edu.

DEGREES AND AWARDS

AS Criminal Justice; English; Environmental Studies Management; General Studies; History; Psychology
BGS General Studies
MEd Instructional Math; Instructional Technology

COURSE SUBJECT AREAS OFFERED OUTSIDE OF DEGREE PROGRAMS

Undergraduate—accounting and related services; behavioral sciences; biology; business, management, and marketing related; chemistry; com-

munication and media; computer and information sciences; criminology; English; geography and cartography; history; legal studies (non-professional general, undergraduate); liberal arts and sciences, general studies and humanities; management information systems; marketing; mathematics; music; natural resources and conservation related; philosophy and religious studies related; physical sciences; political science and government; psychology; religious studies; social sciences; sociology.
Graduate—communication and media; criminology; education.
Non-credit—criminal justice and corrections.

DUKE UNIVERSITY
Durham, North Carolina
Nicholas School of the Environment and Earth Sciences
http://www.nicholas.duke.edu/del

Duke University was founded in 1838. It is accredited by Southern Association of Colleges and Schools. Institutionally administered financial aid is available to distance learners.
Services Distance learners have accessibility to academic advising, bookstore, campus computer network, career placement assistance, e-mail services, library services.
Contact Sara Ashenburg, Director, Duke Environmental Leadership Program, Duke University, Nicholas School of the Environment and Earth Sciences, Box 90328, Durham, NC 27708-0328. Telephone: 919-613-8082. Fax: 919-613-9002. E-mail: del@env.duke.edu.

DEGREES AND AWARDS
MEM Duke Environmental Leadership Master of Environmental Management

DUQUESNE UNIVERSITY
Pittsburgh, Pennsylvania
Center for Distance Learning
http://www.distancelearning.duq.edu

Duquesne University was founded in 1878. It is accredited by Middle States Association of Colleges and Schools. It first offered distance learning courses in 1996. In fall 2005, there were 2,085 students enrolled in distance learning courses. Institutionally administered financial aid is available to distance learners.
Services Distance learners have accessibility to academic advising, bookstore, campus computer network, career placement assistance, e-mail services, library services, tutoring.
Contact Ruth Newberry, Director, Educational Technology, Duquesne University, Rockwell Hall, 600 Forbes Avenue, Pittsburgh, PA 15282. Telephone: 412-396-1813. Fax: 412-396-5144. E-mail: virtualcampus@duq.edu.

DEGREES AND AWARDS
BS Degree Completion; Humane Leadership
BSN Nursing–RN to BSN/MSN
Certificate Nursing–Post-BSN
Graduate Certificate Nursing–Post-Master's; Organizational Leadership in Animal Advocacy
MA Leadership and Liberal Studies
MEM Environmental Science and Management
MS Community Leadership; Leadership and Business Ethics; Leadership and Information Technology–Masters of Leadership and Information Technology; Music Education–Masters in Music Education; Sports Leadership
MSN Nursing
EdD Instructional Technology
PhD Nursing

COURSE SUBJECT AREAS OFFERED OUTSIDE OF DEGREE PROGRAMS
Undergraduate—accounting and computer science; business administration, management and operations; business, management, and marketing related; communication and media; computer and information sciences; fine and studio art; philosophy; philosophy and religious studies related; theological and ministerial studies; theology and religious vocations related.
Graduate—accounting and computer science; business administration, management and operations; communication and media; community health services; community organization and advocacy; computer and information sciences and support services related; computer/information technology administration and management; computer software and media applications; curriculum and instruction; education; educational/instructional media design; management information systems; music; nursing; pastoral counseling and specialized ministries; philosophy and religious studies related; public administration; public policy analysis; technology education/industrial arts.
Non-credit—animal sciences; computer and information sciences; legal support services.

D'YOUVILLE COLLEGE
Buffalo, New York
Distance Learning
http://ddl.dyc.edu

D'Youville College was founded in 1908. It is accredited by Middle States Association of Colleges and Schools. It first offered distance learning courses in 1996. In fall 2005, there were 1,500 students enrolled in distance learning courses. Institutionally administered financial aid is available to distance learners.
Services Distance learners have accessibility to academic advising, bookstore, campus computer network, e-mail services, library services.
Contact Dr. John T. Murphy, Director of Instructional Support Services and Distance Education, D'Youville College, 320 Porter Avenue, Buffalo, NY 14201. Telephone: 716-829-8147. Fax: 716-829-7760. E-mail: murphyj@dyc.edu.

DEGREES AND AWARDS
Programs offered do not lead to a degree or other formal award.

COURSE SUBJECT AREAS OFFERED OUTSIDE OF DEGREE PROGRAMS
Undergraduate—American literature (United States and Canadian); biological and physical sciences; business administration, management and operations; business, management, and marketing related; clinical/medical laboratory science and allied professions; comparative literature; computer and information sciences; computer/information technology administration and management; economics; education; education (specific subject areas); English literature (British and Commonwealth); health professions related; history; human resources management; international business; natural sciences; physics; political science and government; social sciences; special education; statistics.
Graduate—biological and biomedical sciences related; biological and physical sciences; business/commerce; business/managerial economics; cognitive science; creative writing; education; health and medical administrative services; information science/studies; international business; medical clinical sciences/graduate medical studies; nursing; nutrition sciences; social and philosophical foundations of education; special education; statistics.

EARLHAM SCHOOL OF RELIGION
Richmond, Indiana
http://esr.earlham.edu

Earlham School of Religion was founded in 1960. It first offered distance learning courses in 2001. In fall 2005, there were 41 students enrolled in distance learning courses. Institutionally administered financial aid is available to distance learners.
Services Distance learners have accessibility to academic advising, bookstore, campus computer network, e-mail services, library services.
Contact Ms. Susan G. Axtell, Director of Recruitment and Admissions, Earlham School of Religion, 228 College Avenue, Richmond, IN 47374. Telephone: 800-432-1377. Fax: 765-983-1688. E-mail: axtelsu@earlham.edu.

DEGREES AND AWARDS
MA ESR Access
MDiv ESR Access

COURSE SUBJECT AREAS OFFERED OUTSIDE OF DEGREE PROGRAMS

Graduate—biblical and other theological languages and literatures; biblical studies; creative writing; pastoral counseling and specialized ministries; peace studies and conflict resolution; religious studies; theological and ministerial studies; theology and religious vocations related.

EAST ARKANSAS COMMUNITY COLLEGE
Forrest City, Arkansas
http://www.eacc.edu

East Arkansas Community College was founded in 1974. It is accredited by North Central Association of Colleges and Schools. It first offered distance learning courses in 2000. In fall 2005, there were 119 students enrolled in distance learning courses. Institutionally administered financial aid is available to distance learners.

Services Distance learners have accessibility to academic advising, bookstore, career placement assistance, e-mail services, library services, tutoring.

Contact Jeffrey Watson, EdD, Director of Administrative Services, East Arkansas Community College, 1700 Newcastle Road, Forrest City, AR 72335. Telephone: 870-699-4480 Ext. 201. Fax: 870-633-7222. E-mail: jwatson@eacc.edu.

DEGREES AND AWARDS

Programs offered do not lead to a degree or other formal award.

COURSE SUBJECT AREAS OFFERED OUTSIDE OF DEGREE PROGRAMS

Undergraduate—business/managerial economics; education (specific levels and methods); English composition; English literature (British and Commonwealth); environmental/environmental health engineering; geography and cartography; health and physical education/fitness; health services/allied health/health sciences; history; legal professions and studies related; mathematics; mathematics and statistics related.

EAST CAROLINA UNIVERSITY
Greenville, North Carolina
Division of Continuing Studies
http://www.options.ecu.edu

East Carolina University was founded in 1907. It is accredited by Southern Association of Colleges and Schools. It first offered distance learning courses in 1947. In fall 2005, there were 4,822 students enrolled in distance learning courses. Institutionally administered financial aid is available to distance learners.

Services Distance learners have accessibility to academic advising, bookstore, campus computer network, e-mail services, library services.

Contact Carolyn Dunn, Marketing Coordinator, East Carolina University, Self Help Center, 404-E, Greenville, NC 27858. Telephone: 800-398-9275. E-mail: dunnca@ecu.edu.

DEGREES AND AWARDS

BS Communication/Public Relations/Journalism concentration; Education–Birth-Kindergarten Education; Health Information Management; Health Services Management; Hospitality Management; Hospitality Management; Industrial Technology; Information Technologies
BSBA Business Administration
BSN Nursing–RN to BSN
Graduate Certificate Assistive Technology; Communication–Professional Communication; Computer Network Professional; Distance Learning; Information Assurance; Multicultural Literature; Performance Improvement; Security Studies; Virtual Reality in Education and Training; Website Developer
MA English–Professional and Technical Communication concentration; Health Education; Psychology, general
MAE Art Education; Business Education; Health/Teacher Education; Science Teacher Education; Special Education
MBA Business Administration
MCM Construction Management
MLS Library Science
MS Criminal Justice; Instructional Technology; Nutrition and Dietetics; Occupational Safety; Speech Language and Auditory Pathology; Technology Systems–Computer Networking Management; Technology Systems–Digital Communications; Technology Systems–Distribution and Logistics; Technology Systems–Information Security; Technology Systems–Manufacturing; Technology Systems–Performance Improvement; Vocational Education–Information Technologies
MSE Instructional Technology; Music Education
MSN Clinical Nurse Specialist; Nurse Midwifery; Nursing Education; Nursing Leadership; Nursing–Family Nurse Practitioner

COURSE SUBJECT AREAS OFFERED OUTSIDE OF DEGREE PROGRAMS

Undergraduate—bilingual, multilingual, and multicultural education; biology; business administration, management and operations; business/commerce; business/corporate communications; business, management, and marketing related; business operations support and assistant services; chemistry; communication and journalism related; communication and media; computer and information sciences; computer and information sciences and support services related; computer/information technology administration and management; curriculum and instruction; data entry/microcomputer applications; data processing; education; educational assessment, evaluation, and research; educational psychology; education (specific subject areas); engineering technology; hospitality administration; human development, family studies, and related services; industrial production technologies; information science/studies; journalism; management information systems; manufacturing engineering; nursing; philosophy; philosophy and religious studies related; sales, merchandising, and related marketing operations (specialized); technology education/industrial arts.

Graduate—accounting and related services; building/construction finishing, management, and inspection; business administration, management and operations; business/commerce; business, management, and marketing related; communication disorders sciences and services; computer and information sciences; computer/information technology administration and management; computer science; computer software and media applications; computer systems networking and telecommunications; construction management; criminal justice and corrections; criminology; data processing; education; educational assessment, evaluation, and research; educational/instructional media design; educational psychology; engineering technologies related; English; fine and studio art; foods, nutrition, and related services; industrial production technologies; library science; nursing; nutrition sciences; psychology; psychology related; quality control and safety technologies; rehabilitation and therapeutic professions; special education; technical and business writing; technology education/industrial arts.

See full description on page 368.

EAST CENTRAL COMMUNITY COLLEGE
Decatur, Mississippi
Adult and Continuing Education
http://www.eccc.cc.ms.us/

East Central Community College was founded in 1928. It is accredited by Southern Association of Colleges and Schools. It first offered distance learning courses in 2000. In fall 2005, there were 450 students enrolled in distance learning courses. Institutionally administered financial aid is available to distance learners.

Services Distance learners have accessibility to academic advising, bookstore, campus computer network, e-mail services, library services, tutoring.

Contact Dr. Chris C. Jenkins, Distance Learning Coordinator, East Central Community College, PO Box 129, Decatur, MS 39327. Telephone: 601-635-2111 Ext. 322. Fax: 601-635-4011. E-mail: cjenkins@eccc.edu.

DEGREES AND AWARDS

Programs offered do not lead to a degree or other formal award.

COURSE SUBJECT AREAS OFFERED OUTSIDE OF DEGREE PROGRAMS

Undergraduate—accounting and computer science; allied health and medical assisting services; American literature (United States and

Canadian); biblical studies; biological and physical sciences; business administration, management and operations; chemistry; computer and information sciences; developmental and child psychology; economics; education; English; English composition; history; mathematics; music; nursing; physical sciences; psychology; sociology.

EASTERN MENNONITE UNIVERSITY
Harrisonburg, Virginia
Eastern Mennonite Seminary
http://www.emu.edu/seminary

Eastern Mennonite University was founded in 1917. It is accredited by Southern Association of Colleges and Schools. It first offered distance learning courses in 1997. In fall 2005, there were 24 students enrolled in distance learning courses. Institutionally administered financial aid is available to distance learners.

Services Distance learners have accessibility to academic advising, bookstore, campus computer network, career placement assistance, e-mail services, library services.

Contact Don Yoder, Director of Admissions, Seminary and Graduate Programs, Eastern Mennonite University, 1200 Park Road, Harrisonburg, VA 22802-2462. Telephone: 540-432-4257. Fax: 540-432-4444. E-mail: semadmiss@emu.edu.

DEGREES AND AWARDS

Programs offered do not lead to a degree or other formal award.

COURSE SUBJECT AREAS OFFERED OUTSIDE OF DEGREE PROGRAMS

Graduate—biblical studies; pastoral counseling and specialized ministries; peace studies and conflict resolution; philosophy; philosophy and religious studies related; religious studies; theological and ministerial studies.

EASTERN MICHIGAN UNIVERSITY
Ypsilanti, Michigan
Distance Education
http://www.ce.emich.edu

Eastern Michigan University was founded in 1849. It is accredited by North Central Association of Colleges and Schools. It first offered distance learning courses in 1997. In fall 2005, there were 3,375 students enrolled in distance learning courses. Institutionally administered financial aid is available to distance learners.

Services Distance learners have accessibility to academic advising, bookstore, campus computer network, career placement assistance, e-mail services, library services, tutoring.

Contact Jody Cebina, Assistant Director, Distance Education, Eastern Michigan University, Continuing Education, 101 Boone Hall, Ypsilanti, MI 48197. Telephone: 734-487-1081. Fax: 734-487-6695. E-mail: distance.education@emich.edu.

DEGREES AND AWARDS

BS Dietetics; Technology Management (degree completion)
Graduate Certificate Educational Media and Technology; Geographic Information Systems; Human Resource Management
MS Educational Media and Technology; Engineering; Human Nutrition; Integrated Marketing Communications; Quality

COURSE SUBJECT AREAS OFFERED OUTSIDE OF DEGREE PROGRAMS

Undergraduate—applied mathematics; Army J.R.O.T.C/R.O.T.C; biological and physical sciences; biology; biotechnology; business administration, management and operations; business/commerce; business/corporate communications; business, management, and marketing related; cell biology and anatomical sciences; chemistry; communication and journalism related; communication and media; computer systems networking and telecommunications; dietetics and clinical nutrition services; dramatic/theater arts and stagecraft; education; educational administration and supervision; educational assessment, evaluation, and research; education (specific subject areas); English; English composition; entrepreneurial and small business operations; ethnic, cultural minority, and gender studies; finance and financial management services; fine and studio art; food science and technology; foods, nutrition, and related services; genetics; geography and cartography; history; hospitality administration; human resources management; legal professions and studies related; legal research and advanced professional studies; legal studies (non-professional general, undergraduate); legal support services; liberal arts and sciences, general studies and humanities; marketing; mathematics; military studies; nursing; nutrition sciences; philosophy; philosophy and religious studies related; political science and government; psychology; sales, merchandising, and related marketing operations (general); sales, merchandising, and related marketing operations (specialized); social sciences; sociology; special education; technology education/industrial arts.

Graduate—accounting and computer science; accounting and related services; biomathematics and bioinformatics; business administration, management and operations; business/commerce; business/corporate communications; business, management, and marketing related; computer software and media applications; dietetics and clinical nutrition services; education; educational administration and supervision; educational assessment, evaluation, and research; educational/instructional media design; educational psychology; education related; education (specific levels and methods); education (specific subject areas); engineering; engineering/industrial management; engineering related; engineering science; engineering technologies related; ethnic, cultural minority, and gender studies; food science and technology; foods, nutrition, and related services; geography and cartography; geological and earth sciences/geosciences; human resources management; languages (Germanic); legal research and advanced professional studies; marketing; mathematics; mathematics and statistics related; nursing; psychology related; quality control and safety technologies; sales, merchandising, and related marketing operations (general); school psychology; statistics; technology education/industrial arts.

Non-credit—accounting and related services; education; education related; human resources management.

See full description on page 370.

EASTERN NEW MEXICO UNIVERSITY
Portales, New Mexico
Extended Learning
http://www.enmu.edu/academics/learning

Eastern New Mexico University was founded in 1934. It is accredited by North Central Association of Colleges and Schools. It first offered distance learning courses in 1998. In fall 2005, there were 700 students enrolled in distance learning courses. Institutionally administered financial aid is available to distance learners.

Services Distance learners have accessibility to academic advising, bookstore, campus computer network, career placement assistance, e-mail services, library services, tutoring.

Contact Ms. Alta Elder, Outreach Coordinator, Eastern New Mexico University, Station # 9, 1500 South Avenue K, Portales, NM 88130. Telephone: 505-562-4110. Fax: 505-562-2691. E-mail: alta.elder@enmu.edu.

DEGREES AND AWARDS

BBA Business Administration
BEd Education
BSN Nursing
BUS University Studies
MA English; **MED** Masters of Education
MBA Business Administration
MS Communicative Disorders
MSE Special Education

COURSE SUBJECT AREAS OFFERED OUTSIDE OF DEGREE PROGRAMS

Undergraduate—accounting and related services; biblical studies; business/commerce; computer and information sciences; computer software and media applications; education; English composition; history; psychology; sociology.

Graduate—accounting and related services; business/commerce; education related; history; sociology.

EASTERN OKLAHOMA STATE COLLEGE
Wilburton, Oklahoma
http://www.eosc.edu

Eastern Oklahoma State College was founded in 1908. It is accredited by North Central Association of Colleges and Schools. It first offered distance learning courses in 1994. In fall 2005, there were 569 students enrolled in distance learning courses. Institutionally administered financial aid is available to distance learners.

Services Distance learners have accessibility to academic advising, campus computer network, career placement assistance, e-mail services, library services, tutoring.

Contact MaryEdith Butler, Assistant Vice President, IR, Eastern Oklahoma State College, 1301 West Main Street, Wilburton, OK 74578. Telephone: 918-465-1779. Fax: 918-465-0112. E-mail: mebutler@eosc.edu.

DEGREES AND AWARDS
Programs offered do not lead to a degree or other formal award.

COURSE SUBJECT AREAS OFFERED OUTSIDE OF DEGREE PROGRAMS
Undergraduate—business administration, management and operations; computer software and media applications; criminal justice and corrections; English composition; family and consumer economics; geography and cartography; history; mathematics and statistics related; nursing; political science and government; psychology; social psychology.

EASTERN OREGON UNIVERSITY
La Grande, Oregon
Division of Distance Education
http://www.eou.edu/dde/

Eastern Oregon University was founded in 1929. It is accredited by Northwest Commission on Colleges and Universities. It first offered distance learning courses in 1978. In fall 2005, there were 1,800 students enrolled in distance learning courses. Institutionally administered financial aid is available to distance learners.

Services Distance learners have accessibility to academic advising, bookstore, campus computer network, career placement assistance, e-mail services, library services, tutoring.

Contact Melanie Rowley, Inquiry Coordinator, Eastern Oregon University, Division of Distance Education, One University Boulevard, La Grande, OR 97850-2899. Telephone: 800-544-2195. Fax: 541-962-3627. E-mail: dde@eou.edu.

DEGREES AND AWARDS
BA Philosophy, Politics, and Economics; Physical Activity and Health; Psychology
BS Business Administration; Business and Economics; Fire Services Administration; Liberal Studies; Physical Activity and Health; Psychology

COURSE SUBJECT AREAS OFFERED OUTSIDE OF DEGREE PROGRAMS
Undergraduate—accounting and related services; agricultural business and management; anthropology; biology; botany/plant biology; business/commerce; chemistry; computer science; criminology; dramatic/theater arts and stagecraft; economics; English; geography and cartography; health and physical education/fitness; music; philosophy; physics; political science and government; psychology.

EASTERN WEST VIRGINIA COMMUNITY AND TECHNICAL COLLEGE
Moorefield, West Virginia

Eastern West Virginia Community and Technical College was founded in 1999. It is accredited by North Central Association of Colleges and Schools. It first offered distance learning courses in 2001. In fall 2005, there were 150 students enrolled in distance learning courses. Institutionally administered financial aid is available to distance learners.

Services Distance learners have accessibility to academic advising; bookstore, library services, tutoring.

Contact Monica See, Academic Services Program Coordinator, Eastern West Virginia Community and Technical College, 1929 State Road 55, Moorefield, WV 26836. Telephone: 304-434-8000. Fax: 304-434-7000. E-mail: msee1@eastern.wvnet.edu.

DEGREES AND AWARDS
Programs offered do not lead to a degree or other formal award.

COURSE SUBJECT AREAS OFFERED OUTSIDE OF DEGREE PROGRAMS
Undergraduate—accounting and computer science; business, management, and marketing related; business operations support and assistant services; computer and information sciences; economics; English; history; music; political science and government; psychology; sociology.

EASTERN WYOMING COLLEGE
Torrington, Wyoming
Outreach
http://ewc.wy.edu

Eastern Wyoming College was founded in 1948. It is accredited by North Central Association of Colleges and Schools. It first offered distance learning courses in 1990. In fall 2005, there were 250 students enrolled in distance learning courses. Institutionally administered financial aid is available to distance learners.

Services Distance learners have accessibility to academic advising, bookstore, library services, tutoring.

Contact Dee Ludwig, Associate Dean of Instruction, Eastern Wyoming College, 3200 West C Street, Torrington, WY 82240. Telephone: 307-532-8221. Fax: 307-532-8222. E-mail: dludwig@ewc.wy.edu.

DEGREES AND AWARDS
AA Criminal Justice; Interdisciplinary Studies
AAS Business Administration
AS Interdisciplinary Studies

COURSE SUBJECT AREAS OFFERED OUTSIDE OF DEGREE PROGRAMS
Undergraduate—accounting and related services; biology; business administration, management and operations; business/commerce; computer and information sciences; computer software and media applications; criminal justice and corrections; economics; English; English composition; geological and earth sciences/geosciences; health and physical education/fitness; physiological psychology/psychobiology; political science and government; sociology; zoology/animal biology.

EAST GEORGIA COLLEGE
Swainsboro, Georgia
http://www.ega.peachnet.edu/

East Georgia College was founded in 1973. It is accredited by Southern Association of Colleges and Schools. It first offered distance learning courses in 1997. In fall 2005, there were 148 students enrolled in distance learning courses. Institutionally administered financial aid is available to distance learners.

Contact Mrs. Mary Smith, Director, Continuing Education, East Georgia College, 131 College Circle, Swainsboro, GA 30401. Telephone: 478-289-2108. Fax: 478-289-2057. E-mail: mcsmith@ega.edu.

DEGREES AND AWARDS
Programs offered do not lead to a degree or other formal award.

COURSE SUBJECT AREAS OFFERED OUTSIDE OF DEGREE PROGRAMS
Non-credit—health and medical administrative services.

EAST LOS ANGELES COLLEGE
Monterey Park, California
http://www.elac.edu

East Los Angeles College was founded in 1945. It is accredited by Western Association of Schools and Colleges. It first offered distance learning courses in 1998. In fall 2005, there were 1,400 students enrolled in distance learning courses. Institutionally administered financial aid is available to distance learners.

Services Distance learners have accessibility to academic advising, bookstore, e-mail services, library services.

Contact Ms. Kerrin McMahan, Distance Education Coordinator, East Los Angeles College, 1301 Avenida Cesar Chavez, Monterey Park, CA 91754. Telephone: 323-265-8774. E-mail: mcmahakm@elac.edu.

DEGREES AND AWARDS

Programs offered do not lead to a degree or other formal award.

COURSE SUBJECT AREAS OFFERED OUTSIDE OF DEGREE PROGRAMS

Undergraduate—accounting and related services; business operations support and assistant services; computer and information sciences; family and consumer economics; fine and studio art; foods, nutrition, and related services; health and physical education/fitness; history; liberal arts and sciences, general studies and humanities; management information systems; mathematics; philosophy; psychology; speech and rhetoric; visual and performing arts.

EAST TENNESSEE STATE UNIVERSITY
Johnson City, Tennessee
Office of Distance Education
http://online.etsu.edu

East Tennessee State University was founded in 1911. It is accredited by Southern Association of Colleges and Schools. It first offered distance learning courses in 1990. In fall 2005, there were 3,900 students enrolled in distance learning courses. Institutionally administered financial aid is available to distance learners.

Services Distance learners have accessibility to academic advising, bookstore, campus computer network, career placement assistance, e-mail services, library services, tutoring.

Contact Pat Westington, Internet Program Support Coordinator, East Tennessee State University, Box 70427, Johnson City, TN 37614-0427. Telephone: 423-439-7058. Fax: 423-439-8564. E-mail: westingt@etsu.edu.

DEGREES AND AWARDS

BGS General Studies–Bachelor of General Studies

BS Allied Health Leadership–BS completion program; Applied Science–Bachelor of Applied Science; Dental Hygiene–BS completion program

MA Liberal Studies

COURSE SUBJECT AREAS OFFERED OUTSIDE OF DEGREE PROGRAMS

Undergraduate—accounting and related services; communications technology; comparative literature; criminal justice and corrections; curriculum and instruction; developmental and child psychology; education; educational psychology; education related; English; English composition; geography and cartography; history; psychology; sales, merchandising, and related marketing operations (general); special education; statistics; technical and business writing.

Graduate—education; educational assessment, evaluation, and research; educational/instructional media design; education related; marketing; sales, merchandising, and related marketing operations (general).

Non-credit—allied health and medical assisting services; alternative and complementary medical support services; behavioral sciences; business administration, management and operations; business, management, and marketing related; communication and journalism related; computer and information sciences; computer and information sciences and support services related; computer programming; computer software and media applications; computer systems analysis; computer systems networking and telecommunications; creative writing; culinary arts and related services; entrepreneurial and small business operations; legal support services; liberal arts and sciences, general studies and humanities; marketing; sales, merchandising, and related marketing operations (general).

EDGECOMBE COMMUNITY COLLEGE
Tarboro, North Carolina
http://www.edgecombe.edu

Edgecombe Community College was founded in 1968. It is accredited by Southern Association of Colleges and Schools. It first offered distance learning courses in 1991. In fall 2005, there were 234 students enrolled in distance learning courses. Institutionally administered financial aid is available to distance learners.

Services Distance learners have accessibility to academic advising, bookstore, campus computer network, career placement assistance, e-mail services, library services, tutoring.

Contact Mr. Richard Greene, Distance Learning Coordinator, Edgecombe Community College, 225 Tarboro Street, Rocky Mount, NC 27801. Telephone: 252-823-5166 Ext. 340. Fax: 252-985-2212. E-mail: greener@edgecombe.edu.

DEGREES AND AWARDS

AAS Health Information Technology

COURSE SUBJECT AREAS OFFERED OUTSIDE OF DEGREE PROGRAMS

Undergraduate—accounting and related services; business administration, management and operations; business/commerce; business/corporate communications; business, management, and marketing related; computer and information sciences; computer and information sciences and support services related; computer/information technology administration and management; computer programming; computer software and media applications; computer systems analysis; computer systems networking and telecommunications; data entry/microcomputer applications; education (specific subject areas); English composition; ethnic, cultural minority, and gender studies; health and medical administrative services; health/medical preparatory programs; history; human development, family studies, and related services; management information systems; psychology; sociology; technical and business writing.

Non-credit—accounting and related services; area, ethnic, cultural, and gender studies related; business administration, management and operations; business/commerce; business/corporate communications; business, management, and marketing related; business/managerial economics; business operations support and assistant services; communication and media; community health services; computer and information sciences; computer and information sciences and support services related; computer/information technology administration and management; computer programming; computer science; computer software and media applications; data entry/microcomputer applications; English; English as a second language; health and medical administrative services; management information systems; sales, merchandising, and related marketing operations (specialized).

EDISON STATE COMMUNITY COLLEGE
Piqua, Ohio
http://www.edisonohio.edu/

Edison State Community College was founded in 1973. It is accredited by North Central Association of Colleges and Schools. It first offered distance learning courses in 1987. In fall 2005, there were 500 students enrolled in distance learning courses. Institutionally administered financial aid is available to distance learners.

Services Distance learners have accessibility to academic advising, bookstore, career placement assistance, library services, tutoring.

Contact Ann Marie Miller, Webmaster and Learning Systems Coordinator, Edison State Community College, 1973 Edison Drive, Piqua, OH 45356. Telephone: 937-778-7882. E-mail: amiller@edisonohio.edu.

DEGREES AND AWARDS

AAB Medical Office Assistant

COURSE SUBJECT AREAS OFFERED OUTSIDE OF DEGREE PROGRAMS

Undergraduate—accounting and related services; anthropology; biology; business administration, management and operations; business/commerce; business/corporate communications; business operations support and assistant services; cell biology and anatomical sciences; chemistry; computer and information sciences; computer engineering; computer/

information technology administration and management; computer programming; computer science; computer software and media applications; computer systems analysis; computer systems networking and telecommunications; design and applied arts; dramatic/theater arts and stagecraft; ecology, evolution, and population biology; economics; engineering design; engineering/industrial management; English composition; fine and studio art; human development, family studies, and related services; human resources management; industrial production technologies; management information systems; marketing; mathematics; mathematics and computer science; nursing; philosophy; philosophy and religious studies related; physics; public relations, advertising, and applied communication related; sociology; statistics.

Non-credit—accounting and related services; business administration, management and operations; business/commerce; business operations support and assistant services; computer and information sciences; computer/information technology administration and management; computer software and media applications; human resources management.

EDMONDS COMMUNITY COLLEGE
Lynnwood, Washington
Continuing Education
http://online.edcc.edu

Edmonds Community College was founded in 1967. It is accredited by Northwest Commission on Colleges and Universities. It first offered distance learning courses in 1995. In fall 2005, there were 2,500 students enrolled in distance learning courses. Institutionally administered financial aid is available to distance learners.

Services Distance learners have accessibility to academic advising, bookstore, campus computer network, career placement assistance, library services, tutoring.

Contact Tina Torres, Distance Learning Program Assistant, Edmonds Community College, 20000 68th Avenue West, Lynnwood, WA 98036-5999. Telephone: 425-640-1098. Fax: 425-640-1704. E-mail: ttorres@edcc.edu.

DEGREES AND AWARDS

AA Business Administration; Business Education; Business Information Technology; Business Management; Family Support Studies/Human Development; Social Sciences

Certificate Computer Game Development

COURSE SUBJECT AREAS OFFERED OUTSIDE OF DEGREE PROGRAMS

Undergraduate—accounting and related services; business administration, management and operations; computer programming; developmental and child psychology; English; mathematics.

ELGIN COMMUNITY COLLEGE
Elgin, Illinois
http://www.elgin.edu

Elgin Community College was founded in 1949. It is accredited by North Central Association of Colleges and Schools. It first offered distance learning courses in 1980. In fall 2005, there were 1,500 students enrolled in distance learning courses. Institutionally administered financial aid is available to distance learners.

Services Distance learners have accessibility to academic advising, bookstore, e-mail services, library services, tutoring.

Contact Billie B. Barnett, Distance Learning Operations Coordinator, Elgin Community College, 1700 Spartan Drive, Elgin, IL 60123. Telephone: 847-214-7945. Fax: 847-608-5479. E-mail: bbarnett@elgin.edu.

DEGREES AND AWARDS

Programs offered do not lead to a degree or other formal award.

COURSE SUBJECT AREAS OFFERED OUTSIDE OF DEGREE PROGRAMS

Undergraduate—accounting and related services; allied health and medical assisting services; anthropology; business, management, and marketing related; computer and information sciences; computer/information technology administration and management; education related; English; English composition; legal studies (non-professional general, undergraduate); liberal arts and sciences, general studies and humanities; marketing; mathematics; music; psychology.

ELIZABETHTOWN COLLEGE
Elizabethtown, Pennsylvania
Center for Continuing Education and Distance Learning
http://www.etown.edu/cce

Elizabethtown College was founded in 1899. It is accredited by Middle States Association of Colleges and Schools. It first offered distance learning courses in 2001. In fall 2005, there were 130 students enrolled in distance learning courses. Institutionally administered financial aid is available to distance learners.

Services Distance learners have accessibility to academic advising, bookstore, campus computer network, e-mail services, library services.

Contact Dr. John Kokolus, Dean of Continuing Education and Distance Learning, Elizabethtown College, 1 Alpha Drive, Elizabethtown, PA 17022. Telephone: 717-361-1291. Fax: 717-361-1466. E-mail: kokolusj@etown.edu.

DEGREES AND AWARDS

Programs offered do not lead to a degree or other formal award.

COURSE SUBJECT AREAS OFFERED OUTSIDE OF DEGREE PROGRAMS

Undergraduate—accounting and computer science; accounting and related services; American literature (United States and Canadian); area, ethnic, cultural, and gender studies related; business administration, management and operations; business/commerce; business/corporate communications; communication and journalism related; communication and media; English; history; human resources management; medieval and Renaissance studies.

EMBRY-RIDDLE AERONAUTICAL UNIVERSITY
Daytona Beach, Florida
Distance Learning
http://www.erau.edu/db/degrees/ma-mbaaonline.html

Embry-Riddle Aeronautical University was founded in 1926. It is accredited by Southern Association of Colleges and Schools. It first offered distance learning courses in 2003. In fall 2005, there were 81 students enrolled in distance learning courses. Institutionally administered financial aid is available to distance learners.

Services Distance learners have accessibility to academic advising, bookstore, career placement assistance, e-mail services, library services.

Contact Mr. Tom Shea, Director of International and Graduate Admissions, Embry-Riddle Aeronautical University, 600 South Clyde Morris Boulevard, Daytona Beach, FL 32114. Telephone: 386-226-7178. Fax: 386-226-7070. E-mail: graduate.admissions@erau.edu.

DEGREES AND AWARDS

MBA Business Administration in Aviation

COURSE SUBJECT AREAS OFFERED OUTSIDE OF DEGREE PROGRAMS

Undergraduate—aerospace, aeronautical and astronautical engineering; business administration, management and operations; business/managerial economics; English composition; finance and financial management services; legal studies (non-professional general, undergraduate); management sciences and quantitative methods; marketing; mathematics and statistics related; statistics.

Graduate—business administration, management and operations; management information systems; management sciences and quantitative methods.

Non-credit—air transportation.

EMBRY-RIDDLE AERONAUTICAL UNIVERSITY, EXTENDED CAMPUS
Daytona Beach, Florida
Distance Learning Enrollment Office
http://www.erau.edu/ec/dleo/index.html

Embry-Riddle Aeronautical University, Extended Campus was founded in 1970. It is accredited by Southern Association of Colleges and Schools. It first offered distance learning courses in 1983. In fall 2005, there were 1,899 students enrolled in distance learning courses. Institutionally administered financial aid is available to distance learners.

Services Distance learners have accessibility to academic advising, bookstore, career placement assistance, library services.

Contact Mr. David Weagle, Recruitment Advisor, Embry-Riddle Aeronautical University, Extended Campus, 600 South Clyde Morris Boulevard, Daytona Beach, FL 32114-3900. Telephone: 386-226-6363. Fax: 386-226-7627. E-mail: dleo.student.recruiter@erau.edu.

DEGREES AND AWARDS

AS Aircraft Maintenance Technology; Professional Aeronautics; Technical Management
BS Aviation Maintenance Management; Professional Aeronautics; Technical Management
MAS Aeronautical Science
MS Management

COURSE SUBJECT AREAS OFFERED OUTSIDE OF DEGREE PROGRAMS

Undergraduate—applied mathematics; business/commerce; computer science; economics; English; legal studies (non-professional general, undergraduate); social sciences; statistics; technical and business writing.
Graduate—air transportation; business administration, management and operations; business/commerce; psychology.
Non-credit—air transportation.

See full description on page 372.

EMORY UNIVERSITY
Atlanta, Georgia
Rollins School of Public Health
http://www.sph.emory.edu/CMPH

Emory University was founded in 1836. It is accredited by Southern Association of Colleges and Schools. It first offered distance learning courses in 1997. In fall 2005, there were 140 students enrolled in distance learning courses. Institutionally administered financial aid is available to distance learners.

Services Distance learners have accessibility to academic advising, bookstore, campus computer network, career placement assistance, e-mail services, library services.

Contact Ms. Robie Freeman-Burks, Assistant Director of Academic Programs, Emory University, 1518 Clifton Road-RSPH, Office 148, Atlanta, GA 30322. Telephone: 404-727-8739. Fax: 404-727-3996. E-mail: rfreem2@sph.emory.edu.

DEGREES AND AWARDS

MPH Public Health–Career Master of Public Health program

COURSE SUBJECT AREAS OFFERED OUTSIDE OF DEGREE PROGRAMS

Graduate—public health.

ENDICOTT COLLEGE
Beverly, Massachusetts
http://www.endicott.edu/

Endicott College was founded in 1939. It is accredited by New England Association of Schools and Colleges. It first offered distance learning courses in 2000. In fall 2005, there were 150 students enrolled in distance learning courses. Institutionally administered financial aid is available to distance learners.

Services Distance learners have accessibility to academic advising, bookstore, campus computer network, career placement assistance, e-mail services, library services.

Contact Paul Squarcia, Vice President and Dean of School of Graduate and Professional Studies, Endicott College, 376 Hale Street, Beverly, MA 01915. Telephone: 978-232-2084. Fax: 978-232-3000. E-mail: psquarci@endicott.edu.

DEGREES AND AWARDS

Programs offered do not lead to a degree or other formal award.

COURSE SUBJECT AREAS OFFERED OUTSIDE OF DEGREE PROGRAMS

Undergraduate—business/commerce; education.
Graduate—business/commerce; education.
Non-credit—business/commerce.

ERIE COMMUNITY COLLEGE
Buffalo, New York
http://www.ecc.edu/

Erie Community College was founded in 1971. It is accredited by Middle States Association of Colleges and Schools. It first offered distance learning courses in 1992. In fall 2005, there were 2,489 students enrolled in distance learning courses. Institutionally administered financial aid is available to distance learners.

Services Distance learners have accessibility to academic advising, bookstore, campus computer network, career placement assistance, e-mail services, library services, tutoring.

Contact Ms. Martha Dixon, Assistant Academic Dean, Distance Learning, Erie Community College, 4041 Southwestern Boulevard, Orchard Park, NY 14127. Telephone: 716-851-1939. Fax: 716-851-1629. E-mail: dixon@ecc.edu.

DEGREES AND AWARDS

AA Liberal Arts and Science/Humanities and Social Science
AAS Business–Business Administration; Business–Office Management; Telecommunications Technology–Verizon
AS Business–Business Administration (Transfer option)
Certificate Computer Applications for the Office

COURSE SUBJECT AREAS OFFERED OUTSIDE OF DEGREE PROGRAMS

Undergraduate—accounting and related services; anthropology; biology; business administration, management and operations; business/corporate communications; business, management, and marketing related; business/managerial economics; business operations support and assistant services; chemistry; clinical psychology; communication and media; computer and information sciences; computer programming; computer science; creative writing; criminal justice and corrections; data processing; developmental and child psychology; dramatic/theater arts and stagecraft; economics; English composition; entrepreneurial and small business operations; finance and financial management services; fine and studio art; geography and cartography; health and physical education/fitness; health/medical preparatory programs; history; hospitality administration; human resources management; information science/studies; languages (Romance languages); liberal arts and sciences, general studies and humanities; management information systems; marketing; mathematics; music; natural resources conservation and research; nursing; nutrition sciences; philosophy; political science and government; psychology; public relations, advertising, and applied communication related; social sciences; sociology; statistics; technical and business writing.

EUGENE BIBLE COLLEGE
Eugene, Oregon
External Studies Department
http://www.ebc.edu

Eugene Bible College was founded in 1925. It is accredited by Association for Biblical Higher Education. It first offered distance learning courses in 1987. In fall 2005, there were 50 students enrolled in distance learning courses. Institutionally administered financial aid is available to distance learners.

Services Distance learners have accessibility to academic advising, bookstore, e-mail services.

Contact Mr. David Earl Sinclair, Director of External Studies, Eugene Bible College, 2155 Bailey Hill Road, Eugene, OR 97405. Telephone: 541-485-1780 Ext. 3206. Fax: 541-343-5801. E-mail: distance-ed@ebc.edu.

DEGREES AND AWARDS
Certificate Bible Studies–One Year Bible Certificate

COURSE SUBJECT AREAS OFFERED OUTSIDE OF DEGREE PROGRAMS
Undergraduate—applied mathematics; biblical and other theological languages and literatures; biblical studies; biological and physical sciences; biology; computer and information sciences; education; educational psychology; English composition; English literature (British and Commonwealth); history; languages (Modern Greek); mathematics; missionary studies and missiology; music; religious education; religious/sacred music; religious studies; school psychology; sociology; speech and rhetoric.

EVERETT COMMUNITY COLLEGE
Everett, Washington
Library/Media/Arts and Distance Learning
http://www.everettcc.edu/distance

Everett Community College was founded in 1941. It is accredited by Northwest Commission on Colleges and Universities. It first offered distance learning courses in 1997. In fall 2005, there were 1,200 students enrolled in distance learning courses. Institutionally administered financial aid is available to distance learners.
Services Distance learners have accessibility to academic advising, bookstore, e-mail services, library services, tutoring.
Contact Sara Frizelle, Director of Distance Learning, Everett Community College, 2000 Tower Street, Everett, WA 98201. Telephone: 425-388-9585. Fax: 425-388-9144. E-mail: distance@everettcc.edu.

DEGREES AND AWARDS
AAS Direct Transfer
AGS General Studies

COURSE SUBJECT AREAS OFFERED OUTSIDE OF DEGREE PROGRAMS
Undergraduate—accounting and related services; allied health and medical assisting services; American literature (United States and Canadian); anthropology; applied mathematics; archeology; business/commerce; computer and information sciences; criminology; economics; English composition; history; human development, family studies, and related services; journalism; liberal arts and sciences, general studies and humanities; library science related; mathematics; music; nutrition sciences; philosophy; physical sciences; psychology; psychology related; science technologies related; science, technology and society; social sciences; sociology; visual and performing arts.
Non-credit—computer and information sciences; computer software and media applications; management information systems.

EVERGREEN VALLEY COLLEGE
San Josè, California
Telecoursè Program
http://www.evc.edu

Evergreen Valley College was founded in 1975. It is accredited by Western Association of Schools and Colleges. It first offered distance learning courses in 1981. In fall 2005, there were 818 students enrolled in distance learning courses. Institutionally administered financial aid is available to distance learners.
Services Distance learners have accessibility to library services, tutoring.
Contact Janice Tomisaka, Program Specialist, Evergreen Valley College, 3095 Yerba Buena Road, San Jose, CA 95135-1598. Telephone: 408-270-6422. Fax: 408-532-1858. E-mail: jan.tomisaka@evc.edu.

DEGREES AND AWARDS
Programs offered do not lead to a degree or other formal award.

COURSE SUBJECT AREAS OFFERED OUTSIDE OF DEGREE PROGRAMS
Undergraduate—anthropology; astronomy and astrophysics; business/commerce; computer and information sciences; English composition; history; languages (Romance languages); library science related; music; political science and government; psychology; sociology.

EXCELSIOR COLLEGE
Albany, New York
Learning Services
http://www.excelsior.edu

Excelsior College was founded in 1970. It is accredited by Middle States Association of Colleges and Schools. It first offered distance learning courses in 1970. In fall 2005, there were 32,281 students enrolled in distance learning courses. Institutionally administered financial aid is available to distance learners.
Services Distance learners have accessibility to academic advising, bookstore, library services, tutoring.
Contact Dr. Murray Block, Interim Provost and Chief Academic Officer, Excelsior College, 7 Columbia Circle, Albany, NY 12203. Telephone: 518-464-8500. Fax: 518-464-8777. E-mail: mblock@excelsior.edu.

DEGREES AND AWARDS
AA Liberal Arts
AAS Administrative/Management Studies; Aviation Studies; Nursing; Technical Studies
AD Occupational Studies in Aviation Studies
AS Business; Computer Software; Electronics Technology; Liberal Arts; Nuclear Technology; Nursing; Science; Technology
BA Liberal Arts; Liberal Studies
BS Accounting NYS CPA Track; Accounting; Business, general; Computer Technology; Criminal Justice; Electronics Engineering Technology; Finance; Global Business; Health Sciences; Hospitality Management; Information Technology; Management Information Systems; Management of Human Resources; Marketing; Nuclear Engineering Technology; Operations Management; Risk Management and Insurance; Science
BSN Nursing
BST Technology
MA Liberal Studies
MBA Business
MS Nursing
See full description on page 374.

FAYETTEVILLE STATE UNIVERSITY
Fayetteville, North Carolina
http://www.uncfsu.edu/conted

Fayetteville State University was founded in 1867. It is accredited by Southern Association of Colleges and Schools. It first offered distance learning courses in 1999. In fall 2005, there were 900 students enrolled in distance learning courses. Institutionally administered financial aid is available to distance learners.
Services Distance learners have accessibility to academic advising, bookstore, campus computer network, career placement assistance, e-mail services, library services.
Contact Ms. Melissa Wells, Administrative Assistant, Extended Learning, Fayetteville State University, Continuing Education Building, 1200 Murchison Road, Fayetteville, NC 28301. Telephone: 910-672-1228. Fax: 910-672-1491. E-mail: mwells@uncfsu.edu.

DEGREES AND AWARDS
Programs offered do not lead to a degree or other formal award.

COURSE SUBJECT AREAS OFFERED OUTSIDE OF DEGREE PROGRAMS
Undergraduate—business/commerce; criminal justice and corrections; education (specific levels and methods); history; nursing; psychology; sociology; special education.

Graduate—business administration, management and operations; criminal justice and corrections; education; history; social work; special education.

FEATHER RIVER COLLEGE
Quincy, California
http://www.frc.edu

Feather River College was founded in 1968. It is accredited by Western Association of Schools and Colleges. It first offered distance learning courses in 2002. In fall 2005, there were 200 students enrolled in distance learning courses. Institutionally administered financial aid is available to distance learners.

Services Distance learners have accessibility to academic advising, bookstore, campus computer network, career placement assistance, e-mail services, library services, tutoring.

Contact Dr. Michael Norman Bagley, Dean of Instruction, Feather River College, 570 Golden Eagle Avenue, Quincy, CA 95971. Telephone: 530-283-0202 Ext. 342. Fax: 530-283-3757. E-mail: mbagley@frc.edu.

DEGREES AND AWARDS

Programs offered do not lead to a degree or other formal award.

COURSE SUBJECT AREAS OFFERED OUTSIDE OF DEGREE PROGRAMS

Undergraduate—allied health and medical assisting services; anthropology; biological and biomedical sciences related; business operations support and assistant services; creative writing; data processing; English composition; health and physical education/fitness; history; insurance; mathematics; psychology; psychology related; sociology.

Non-credit—family and consumer sciences/human sciences; film/video and photographic arts; finance and financial management services; foods, nutrition, and related services; gerontology; health and medical administrative services; historic preservation and conservation; history; human development, family studies, and related services; human resources management; journalism; languages (East Asian); languages (Middle/Near Eastern and Semitic); languages (Slavic, Baltic and Albanian); linguistic, comparative, and related language studies; management information systems; museum studies; music; philosophy; philosophy and religious studies related; psychology; public administration; radio, television, and digital communication; real estate; sales, merchandising, and related marketing operations (general); sales, merchandising, and related marketing operations (specialized); technical and business writing.

FERRIS STATE UNIVERSITY
Big Rapids, Michigan
http://www.ferris.edu/

Ferris State University was founded in 1884. It is accredited by North Central Association of Colleges and Schools. It first offered distance learning courses in 1991. In fall 2005, there were 60 students enrolled in distance learning courses. Institutionally administered financial aid is available to distance learners.

Services Distance learners have accessibility to academic advising, bookstore, campus computer network, career placement assistance, e-mail services, library services, tutoring.

Contact Mr. Steve Cox, Producer and Director, Ferris State University, 1010 Campus Drive, FLITE 460C, Big Rapids, MI 49307. Telephone: 231-591-2721. Fax: 231-591-2785. E-mail: coxs@ferris.edu.

DEGREES AND AWARDS

Programs offered do not lead to a degree or other formal award.

COURSE SUBJECT AREAS OFFERED OUTSIDE OF DEGREE PROGRAMS

Graduate—ophthalmic and optometric support services and allied professions.

FIELDING GRADUATE UNIVERSITY
Santa Barbara, California
http://www.fielding.edu/

Fielding Graduate University was founded in 1974. It is accredited by Western Association of Schools and Colleges. It first offered distance learning courses in 1974. In fall 2005, there were 1,595 students enrolled in distance learning courses. Institutionally administered financial aid is available to distance learners.

Services Distance learners have accessibility to academic advising, bookstore, e-mail services, library services.

Contact Kathy Wells, Admissions Assistant, Fielding Graduate University, 2112 Santa Barbara Street, Santa Barbara, CA 93105-3538. Telephone: 800-340-1099. Fax: 805-687-9793. E-mail: admissions@fielding.edu.

DEGREES AND AWARDS

Certificate Neuropsychology

Certification Organization Development and Organizational Management

MA Collaborative Educational Leadership; Organizational Management/Organizational Development

EdD Educational Leadership and Change

PhD Clinical Psychology; Human and Organizational Development; Media Psychology

FINGER LAKES COMMUNITY COLLEGE
Canandaigua, New York
http://www.flcc.edu

Finger Lakes Community College was founded in 1965. It is accredited by Middle States Association of Colleges and Schools. It first offered distance learning courses in 1970. In fall 2005, there were 105 students enrolled in distance learning courses. Institutionally administered financial aid is available to distance learners.

Services Distance learners have accessibility to academic advising, bookstore, campus computer network, career placement assistance, e-mail services, library services.

Contact Ms. Bonnie Ritts, Director of Admissions, Finger Lakes Community College, 4355 Lake Shore Drive, Canandaigua, NY 14424. Telephone: 585-394-3500 Ext. 7278. Fax: 585-394-5005. E-mail: admissions@flcc.edu.

DEGREES AND AWARDS

Programs offered do not lead to a degree or other formal award.

COURSE SUBJECT AREAS OFFERED OUTSIDE OF DEGREE PROGRAMS

Undergraduate—accounting and computer science; biology; business/commerce; business/corporate communications; computer and information sciences; economics; education; legal studies (non-professional general, undergraduate); marketing; nursing; philosophy; psychology; sales, merchandising, and related marketing operations (specialized); sociology.

Non-credit—computer software and media applications.

FISHER COLLEGE
Boston, Massachusetts

Fisher College was founded in 1903. It is accredited by New England Association of Schools and Colleges. It first offered distance learning courses in 1970. In fall 2005, there were 600 students enrolled in distance learning courses. Institutionally administered financial aid is available to distance learners.

Services Distance learners have accessibility to academic advising, bookstore, career placement assistance, e-mail services, library services.

Contact Michael Wall, Recruitment and Enrollment Manager, Fisher College, 451 Elm Street, North Attleboro, MA 02760. Telephone: 866-309-6539. Fax: 508-695-4604. E-mail: mwall@fisher.edu.

DEGREES AND AWARDS

BS Public Administration; Public Administration

COURSE SUBJECT AREAS OFFERED OUTSIDE OF DEGREE PROGRAMS

Non-credit—business administration, management and operations; computer programming; languages (foreign languages related).

FLORIDA ATLANTIC UNIVERSITY
Boca Raton, Florida
University Resource Management
http://www.itss.fau.edu

Florida Atlantic University was founded in 1961. It is accredited by Southern Association of Colleges and Schools. It first offered distance learning courses in 1996. In fall 2005, there were 2,077 students enrolled in distance learning courses. Institutionally administered financial aid is available to distance learners.

Services Distance learners have accessibility to academic advising, bookstore, campus computer network, e-mail services, library services.

Contact Instructional Technology Support Services, Florida Atlantic University, 777 Glades Road, Boca Raton, FL 33431. Telephone: 561-297-2054. E-mail: itss@fau.edu.

DEGREES AND AWARDS

Certificate Gerontology

MBA Accounting; Management; Taxation–Executive Master of Taxation

MFA Virtual Fine Arts

COURSE SUBJECT AREAS OFFERED OUTSIDE OF DEGREE PROGRAMS

Undergraduate—accounting and related services; biochemistry, biophysics and molecular biology; business/commerce; chemistry; computer science; criminal justice and corrections; economics; education; educational/instructional media design; electrical, electronics and communications engineering; finance and financial management services; geological and earth sciences/geosciences; health professions related; history; industrial and organizational psychology; languages (foreign languages related); management information systems; marketing; mechanical engineering; nursing; ocean engineering; philosophy; political science and government; public administration and social service professions related; social sciences related; sociology.

Graduate—accounting and related services; business administration, management and operations; business/managerial economics; computer science; criminology; economics; educational administration and supervision; educational assessment, evaluation, and research; educational/instructional media design; education related; engineering; finance and financial management services; fine and studio art; health professions related; information science/studies; linguistic, comparative, and related language studies; marketing; mechanical engineering; ocean engineering; public administration; social work; urban studies/affairs.

FLORIDA GULF COAST UNIVERSITY
Fort Myers, Florida
Enrollment Services
http://www.fgcu.edu

Florida Gulf Coast University was founded in 1991. It is accredited by Southern Association of Colleges and Schools. It first offered distance learning courses in 1997. In fall 2005, there were 2,499 students enrolled in distance learning courses. Institutionally administered financial aid is available to distance learners.

Services Distance learners have accessibility to academic advising, bookstore, campus computer network, career placement assistance, e-mail services, library services, tutoring.

Contact Admissions Director, Florida Gulf Coast University, 10501 FGCU Boulevard, South, Fort Myers, FL 33965-6565. Telephone: 239-590-7878. Fax: 239-590-7894. E-mail: admissions@fgcu.edu.

DEGREES AND AWARDS

BS Criminal Justice; Health Science; Legal Studies

MBA Business Administration

MPA Public Administration

MS Geriatric Recreational Therapy; Health Science

COURSE SUBJECT AREAS OFFERED OUTSIDE OF DEGREE PROGRAMS

Undergraduate—accounting and related services; computer science; criminal justice and corrections; educational administration and supervision; education related; environmental/environmental health engineering; finance and financial management services; gerontology; health and medical administrative services; health services/allied health/health sciences; history; human services; information science/studies; management sciences and quantitative methods; marketing; mathematics; nursing; psychology; public administration.

Graduate—education related; legal professions and studies related; public administration.

FLORIDA INSTITUTE OF TECHNOLOGY
Melbourne, Florida
School of Extended Studies–Virtual Campus
http://www.ec.fit.edu

Florida Institute of Technology was founded in 1958. It is accredited by Southern Association of Colleges and Schools. It first offered distance learning courses in 1995. In fall 2005, there were 300 students enrolled in distance learning courses. Institutionally administered financial aid is available to distance learners.

Services Distance learners have accessibility to academic advising, bookstore, career placement assistance, e-mail services, library services.

Contact Vicky W. Knerly, Senior Resident Administrator, Florida Institute of Technology, PO Box 22115, St. Simons Island, GA 31522-8515. Telephone: 912-634-6336. Fax: 912-634-7783. E-mail: vgc@fit.edu.

DEGREES AND AWARDS

MPA Public Administration

MS Acquisition and Contract Management; Human Resources Management; Logistics Management; Material Acquisition Management; Operations Research; Project Management; Systems Management

MSM Management

PMBA Professional Master of Business Administration

COURSE SUBJECT AREAS OFFERED OUTSIDE OF DEGREE PROGRAMS

Graduate—accounting and related services; business administration, management and operations; business/commerce; business/managerial economics; engineering/industrial management; human resources management; information science/studies; management sciences and quantitative methods; marketing; systems engineering; systems science and theory.

Non-credit—finance and financial management services.

See full description on page 376.

FLORIDA STATE UNIVERSITY
Tallahassee, Florida
Office for Distributed and Distance Learning
http://online.fsu.edu

Florida State University was founded in 1851. It is accredited by Southern Association of Colleges and Schools. It first offered distance learning courses in 1987. In fall 2005, there were 1,800 students enrolled in distance learning courses. Institutionally administered financial aid is available to distance learners.

Services Distance learners have accessibility to academic advising, bookstore, campus computer network, career placement assistance, e-mail services, library services, tutoring.

Contact Student Support Services, Florida State University, Academic & Professional Program Services, C3500 University Center, Tallahassee, FL 32306-2550. Telephone: 877-357-8283. Fax: 850-644-5803. E-mail: inquiries@oddl.fsu.edu.

DEGREES AND AWARDS

BS Interdisciplinary Social Science; Software Engineering

BSN Nursing–RN to BSN

MBA Business Administration

MS Criminology and Criminal Justice; Educational Leadership/Administration; Human Resource Development; Information Studies;

Instructional Systems; Management Information Systems; Mathematics Education; Physical Education; Science Education; Special Education
MSM Risk Management/Insurance
MSN Nurse Educator
MSW Social Work

COURSE SUBJECT AREAS OFFERED OUTSIDE OF DEGREE PROGRAMS

Graduate—educational/instructional media design; human resources management; museum studies; special education.
Non-credit—computer software and media applications; finance and financial management services.

See full description on page 378.

FONTBONNE UNIVERSITY
St. Louis, Missouri
http://www.fontbonne.edu/

Fontbonne University was founded in 1917. It is accredited by North Central Association of Colleges and Schools. It first offered distance learning courses in 2000. In fall 2005, there were 500 students enrolled in distance learning courses. Institutionally administered financial aid is available to distance learners.
Services Distance learners have accessibility to academic advising, bookstore, campus computer network, e-mail services, library services, tutoring.
Contact Dr. Tony Teoli, Distance Learning Coordinator, Fontbonne University, 6800 Wydown Boulevard, St. Louis, MO 63105-3098. Telephone: 314-889-1499. E-mail: tteoli@fontbonne.edu.

DEGREES AND AWARDS
Programs offered do not lead to a degree or other formal award.

COURSE SUBJECT AREAS OFFERED OUTSIDE OF DEGREE PROGRAMS

Undergraduate—biological and physical sciences; communication and media; computer software and media applications; economics; English composition; health professions related; mathematics; philosophy; psychology; religious studies.
Graduate—communication disorders sciences and services; computer software and media applications; education (specific subject areas).

FORREST JUNIOR COLLEGE
Anderson, South Carolina
http://www.forrestcollege.com

Forrest Junior College was founded in 1946. It is accredited by Accrediting Council for Independent Colleges and Schools. Institutionally administered financial aid is available to distance learners.
Contact Mrs. Janie Turmon, Admissions Representative, Forrest Junior College, 601 East River Street, Anderson, SC 29624. Telephone: 864-225-7653 Ext. 204. Fax: 864-261-7471. E-mail: janieturmon@forrestcollege.com.

DEGREES AND AWARDS
Programs offered do not lead to a degree or other formal award.

COURSE SUBJECT AREAS OFFERED OUTSIDE OF DEGREE PROGRAMS

Undergraduate—accounting and related services; allied health and medical assisting services; business administration, management and operations; business/commerce; business/corporate communications; business, management, and marketing related; business/managerial economics; business operations support and assistant services; computer and information sciences; computer and information sciences and support services related; computer/information technology administration and management; computer software and media applications; computer systems networking and telecommunications; health aides/attendants/orderlies; health and medical administrative services; human resources management; legal studies (non-professional general, undergraduate); management information systems; sales, merchandising, and related marketing operations (specialized).

FORT HAYS STATE UNIVERSITY
Hays, Kansas
Virtual College
http://www.fhsu.edu/virtualcollege

Fort Hays State University was founded in 1902. It is accredited by North Central Association of Colleges and Schools. It first offered distance learning courses in 1987. In fall 2005, there were 4,033 students enrolled in distance learning courses. Institutionally administered financial aid is available to distance learners.
Services Distance learners have accessibility to academic advising, bookstore, campus computer network, career placement assistance, e-mail services, library services, tutoring.
Contact Judy Waters, Student Services Coordinator, Fort Hays State University, 600 Park Street, Hays, KS 67601-4099. Telephone: 800-628-FHSU. Fax: 785-628-4037. E-mail: virtualcollege@fhsu.edu.

DEGREES AND AWARDS
AGS General Studies
BA Sociology
BBA Management
BGS General Studies; Military specialties
BS Elementary Education; Information Networking and Telecommunications (Computer Networking and Telecommunications concentration); Information Networking and Telecommunications (Web Development concentration); Justice Studies; Organizational Leadership; Technology Leadership
BSN Nursing–RN to BSN
Certificate Community Development; E-Commerce Web Development; Geographic Informations Systems (GIS); Grant Proposal Writing and Program Evaluation; Human Resource Management; Leadership; Life Issues; Management; Post Master's Nursing Administration; Post Master's Nursing Education; Sociology–Applied Sociology; Web Development
Certification Computer Science–Cisco Certified Network Associate Preparation, Military; Computer Science–Cisco Certified Network Associate Preparation, accelerated
MBA Leadership
MLS Liberal Studies
MS Education; Educational Administration; Health and Human Performance; Instructional Technology; Special Education
MSN Nursing Administration; Nursing Education

COURSE SUBJECT AREAS OFFERED OUTSIDE OF DEGREE PROGRAMS

Undergraduate—accounting and computer science; biological and physical sciences; business administration, management and operations; communication and journalism related; communication disorders sciences and services; computer and information sciences; criminal justice and corrections; economics; educational administration and supervision; education related; English; geological and earth sciences/geosciences; health and physical education/fitness; history; languages (foreign languages related); liberal arts and sciences, general studies and humanities; marketing; mathematics and computer science; multi-/interdisciplinary studies related; music; nursing; philosophy; physics; political science and government; psychology; social work; sociology; special education; technology education/industrial arts.
Graduate—education related; education (specific subject areas); health and physical education/fitness; liberal arts and sciences, general studies and humanities; multi-/interdisciplinary studies related; nursing; special education.

FORT VALLEY STATE UNIVERSITY
Fort Valley, Georgia
http://www.fvsu.edu/

Fort Valley State University was founded in 1895. It is accredited by Southern Association of Colleges and Schools. It first offered distance learning courses in 1998. In fall 2005, there were 407 students enrolled in distance learning courses. Institutionally administered financial aid is available to distance learners.
Services Distance learners have accessibility to e-mail services, library services.

Contact Amanda Glover, Distant and Distributed Learning Coordinator, Fort Valley State University, 1005 State University Drive, Information Technology, Fort Valley, GA 31030. Telephone: 478-825-6228. E-mail: glovera@fvsu.edu.

DEGREES AND AWARDS

Programs offered do not lead to a degree or other formal award.

COURSE SUBJECT AREAS OFFERED OUTSIDE OF DEGREE PROGRAMS

Undergraduate—accounting and computer science; accounting and related services; agricultural and food products processing; agricultural/biological engineering and bioengineering; agricultural business and management; animal sciences; behavioral sciences; biology; business, management, and marketing related; business/managerial economics; chemistry; communication and media; computer and information sciences; computer science; criminal justice and corrections; curriculum and instruction; dramatic/theater arts and stagecraft; education; education (specific levels and methods); education (specific subject areas); electrical and electronic engineering technologies; health and physical education/fitness; history; international relations and affairs; languages (foreign languages related); liberal arts and sciences, general studies and humanities; marketing; mathematics; military technologies; political science and government; psychology; social work; sociology.

Graduate—animal sciences; educational psychology; education (specific subject areas); environmental/environmental health engineering; mental and social health services and allied professions.

FRANCISCAN UNIVERSITY OF STEUBENVILLE

Steubenville, Ohio

Distance Learning

http://www.franciscan.edu/distancelearning

Franciscan University of Steubenville was founded in 1946. It is accredited by North Central Association of Colleges and Schools. It first offered distance learning courses in 1995. In fall 2005, there were 300 students enrolled in distance learning courses. Institutionally administered financial aid is available to distance learners.

Services Distance learners have accessibility to academic advising, bookstore, library services.

Contact Ms. Virginia Garrison, Coordinator, Franciscan University of Steubenville, Distance Learning, 1235 University Boulevard, Steubenville, OH 43952. Telephone: 800-466-8336. Fax: 740-284-7037. E-mail: distance@franciscan.edu.

DEGREES AND AWARDS

MA Theology

COURSE SUBJECT AREAS OFFERED OUTSIDE OF DEGREE PROGRAMS

Undergraduate—philosophy; theological and ministerial studies.

Graduate—theological and ministerial studies.

Non-credit—philosophy; theological and ministerial studies.

FRANKLIN PIERCE COLLEGE

Rindge, New Hampshire

http://www.fpc.edu/

Franklin Pierce College was founded in 1962. It is accredited by New England Association of Schools and Colleges. It first offered distance learning courses in 2004. In fall 2005, there were 250 students enrolled in distance learning courses. Institutionally administered financial aid is available to distance learners.

Services Distance learners have accessibility to academic advising, bookstore, campus computer network, career placement assistance, e-mail services, library services, tutoring.

Contact Bobbi Gerry, Director, Online Programs, Franklin Pierce College, 670 North Commercial Street, Manchester, NH 03101. Telephone: 603-899-4344. E-mail: gerryb@fpc.edu.

DEGREES AND AWARDS

AA Criminal Justice; General Studies; Human Services; Management; Marketing

BA Criminal Justice

BS Computer Information Technology; General Studies; Human Services; Management; Marketing

Certificate Accounting; Human Services; Management; Marketing; Paralegal

Graduate Certificate Emerging Network Technologies; Health Practice Management; Human Resource Management; eCommerce

MBA Leadership

MS Information Technology Management

COURSE SUBJECT AREAS OFFERED OUTSIDE OF DEGREE PROGRAMS

Undergraduate—accounting and related services; business administration, management and operations; business/managerial economics; computer and information sciences; computer/information technology administration and management; criminal justice and corrections; economics; finance and financial management services; liberal arts and sciences, general studies and humanities.

Graduate—business/commerce; computer/information technology administration and management; entrepreneurial and small business operations; health professions related; management information systems.

FRANKLIN UNIVERSITY

Columbus, Ohio

Technical and Non-Campus-Based Programs

http://www.franklin.edu

Franklin University was founded in 1902. It is accredited by North Central Association of Colleges and Schools. It first offered distance learning courses in 1996. In fall 2005, there were 4,203 students enrolled in distance learning courses. Institutionally administered financial aid is available to distance learners.

Services Distance learners have accessibility to academic advising, bookstore, campus computer network, career placement assistance, e-mail services, library services, tutoring.

Contact Admissions, Franklin University, 201 South Grant Avenue, Columbus, OH 43215. Telephone: 614-797-4700. Fax: 614-797-4799. E-mail: info@franklin.edu.

DEGREES AND AWARDS

AS Accounting; Business Administration; Computer Science; Information Technology

BS Accounting; Applied Management; Business Administration; Computer Science; Digital Communication; Health Care Management; Information Technology; Management Information Sciences; Management; Public Safety Management

MBA Business Administration–Online MBA

COURSE SUBJECT AREAS OFFERED OUTSIDE OF DEGREE PROGRAMS

Undergraduate—accounting and related services; business administration, management and operations; communication and media; computer science; economics; finance and financial management services; health and medical administrative services; human resources management; information science/studies; marketing; mathematics and computer science; statistics.

Graduate—business administration, management and operations.

See full description on page 380.

FRESNO CITY COLLEGE

Fresno, California

http://www.fresnocitycollege.com

Fresno City College was founded in 1910. It is accredited by Western Association of Schools and Colleges. It first offered distance learning courses in 1999. In fall 2005, there were 794 students enrolled in distance learning courses. Institutionally administered financial aid is available to distance learners.

Services Distance learners have accessibility to academic advising, campus computer network, career placement assistance, e-mail services, library services.

Contact Jon Wilson, Micro Computer Specialist, Fresno City College, 1101 East University Avenue, Fresno, CA 93741. Telephone: 559-442-4600 Ext. 5782. Fax: 559-265-5708. E-mail: jon.wilson@scccd.com.

DEGREES AND AWARDS

Programs offered do not lead to a degree or other formal award.

COURSE SUBJECT AREAS OFFERED OUTSIDE OF DEGREE PROGRAMS

Undergraduate—business administration, management and operations; computer and information sciences; computer systems networking and telecommunications; health/medical preparatory programs; management information systems; technical and business writing.

FROSTBURG STATE UNIVERSITY
Frostburg, Maryland
http://www.frostburg.edu/

Frostburg State University was founded in 1898. It is accredited by Middle States Association of Colleges and Schools. It first offered distance learning courses in 1995. In fall 2005, there were 407 students enrolled in distance learning courses. Institutionally administered financial aid is available to distance learners.

Services Distance learners have accessibility to academic advising, bookstore, campus computer network, career placement assistance, e-mail services, library services.

Contact Mr. Brian K. Wilson, Distance Education Specialist, Frostburg State University, Center for Instructional Technologies, Room 140, Pullen Hall, Frostburg, MD 21532. Telephone: 301-687-4353. Fax: 301-687-3025. E-mail: bwilson@frostburg.edu.

DEGREES AND AWARDS

Programs offered do not lead to a degree or other formal award.

COURSE SUBJECT AREAS OFFERED OUTSIDE OF DEGREE PROGRAMS

Undergraduate—accounting and related services; area, ethnic, cultural, and gender studies related; computer and information sciences; criminal justice and corrections; electrical, electronics and communications engineering; engineering; English; English composition; history; mathematics; mechanical engineering; music; physical sciences; political science and government; psychology; sociology.

Graduate—business administration, management and operations; curriculum and instruction; educational administration and supervision; educational assessment, evaluation, and research; marketing; psychology.

FULTON-MONTGOMERY COMMUNITY COLLEGE
Johnstown, New York
http://fmcc.suny.edu/

Fulton-Montgomery Community College was founded in 1964. It is accredited by Middle States Association of Colleges and Schools. It first offered distance learning courses in 2002. In fall 2005, there were 52 students enrolled in distance learning courses. Institutionally administered financial aid is available to distance learners.

Contact Mr. Reid J. Smalley, Director of Workforce Development, Fulton-Montgomery Community College, 2805 State Highway 67, Johnstown, NY 12095. Telephone: 518-762-4651 Ext. 8102. Fax: 518-762-4334. E-mail: reid.smalley@fmcc.suny.edu.

DEGREES AND AWARDS

Programs offered do not lead to a degree or other formal award.

COURSE SUBJECT AREAS OFFERED OUTSIDE OF DEGREE PROGRAMS

Non-credit—accounting and related services; business administration, management and operations; business/commerce; business, management, and marketing related; computer software and media applications; computer systems networking and telecommunications; education related; entrepreneurial and small business operations; health professions related; health services/allied health/health sciences; languages (foreign languages related).

GADSDEN STATE COMMUNITY COLLEGE
Gadsden, Alabama
Distance Learning
http://www.gadsdenstate.edu/dl/

Gadsden State Community College was founded in 1965. It is accredited by Southern Association of Colleges and Schools. It first offered distance learning courses in 1978. In fall 2005, there were 800 students enrolled in distance learning courses. Institutionally administered financial aid is available to distance learners.

Services Distance learners have accessibility to academic advising, bookstore, campus computer network, career placement assistance, e-mail services, library services.

Contact Ms. Sara W. Brenizer, Associate Dean, Distance Learning, Gadsden State Community College, 147 Allen Hall, PO Box 227, 1001 Wallace Drive, Gadsden, AL 35902. Telephone: 256-439-6833. Fax: 256-549-8466. E-mail: sbrenizer@gadsdenstate.edu.

DEGREES AND AWARDS

AGS General Studies
AS Education, general

COURSE SUBJECT AREAS OFFERED OUTSIDE OF DEGREE PROGRAMS

Undergraduate—accounting and computer science; biology; business administration, management and operations; business/managerial economics; chemistry; civil engineering; computer science; English; history; mathematics; music; nursing; philosophy; political science and government; psychology; sociology; speech and rhetoric.

GALVESTON COLLEGE
Galveston, Texas
Distance Education
http://www.gc.edu

Galveston College was founded in 1967. It is accredited by Southern Association of Colleges and Schools. It first offered distance learning courses in 1987. In fall 2005, there were 248 students enrolled in distance learning courses. Institutionally administered financial aid is available to distance learners.

Services Distance learners have accessibility to academic advising, bookstore, career placement assistance, library services, tutoring.

Contact Ms. Samantha Jolly, Distance Education Specialist, Galveston College, 4015 Avenue Q, Galveston, TX 77550. Telephone: 409-944-1324. Fax: 409-944-1501. E-mail: sjolly@gc.edu.

DEGREES AND AWARDS

Programs offered do not lead to a degree or other formal award.

COURSE SUBJECT AREAS OFFERED OUTSIDE OF DEGREE PROGRAMS

Undergraduate—accounting and computer science; accounting and related services; allied health and medical assisting services; American literature (United States and Canadian); behavioral sciences; biology; business administration, management and operations; chemistry; computer and information sciences; economics; education; English composition; English literature (British and Commonwealth); health professions related; history; information science/studies; nuclear and industrial radiologic technologies; philosophy and religious studies related; political science and government; psychology; social sciences; speech and rhetoric; statistics.

Non-credit—accounting and computer science; accounting and related services; business, management, and marketing related; computer/information technology administration and management; computer programming; family and consumer sciences/human sciences related; legal studies (non-professional general, undergraduate); real estate.

GATEWAY COMMUNITY COLLEGE
New Haven, Connecticut
http://www.gwcc.commnet.edu/

Gateway Community College was founded in 1992. It is accredited by New England Association of Schools and Colleges. It first offered distance learning courses in 1999. In fall 2005, there were 250 students enrolled in distance learning courses. Institutionally administered financial aid is available to distance learners.

Services Distance learners have accessibility to academic advising, career placement assistance, e-mail services, library services, tutoring.

Contact Ms. Catherine Surface, Director of Admissions, Gateway Community College, 60 Sargent Drive, New Haven, CT 06511. Telephone: 203-285-2013. Fax: 203-285-2018. E-mail: csurface@gwcc.commnet.com.

DEGREES AND AWARDS
Programs offered do not lead to a degree or other formal award.

COURSE SUBJECT AREAS OFFERED OUTSIDE OF DEGREE PROGRAMS
Undergraduate—business/commerce; English as a second language; microbiological sciences and immunology; philosophy; political science and government; social sciences.

Non-credit—computer software and media applications; education related; personal and culinary services related.

GEORGE MASON UNIVERSITY
Fairfax, Virginia
http://www.gmu.edu/

George Mason University was founded in 1957. It is accredited by Southern Association of Colleges and Schools. It first offered distance learning courses in 1990. In fall 2005, there were 623 students enrolled in distance learning courses. Institutionally administered financial aid is available to distance learners.

Services Distance learners have accessibility to academic advising, bookstore, campus computer network, career placement assistance, e-mail services, library services.

Contact Miss Cheryl Choy, Special Assistant for Distance and Technical Education in the Office of the Provost, George Mason University, 4400 University Drive, MSN 1D6, Fairfax, VA 22030. E-mail: cchoy@gmu.edu.

DEGREES AND AWARDS
Graduate Certificate Computer Networking; Nonprofit Management; Quality Improvement and Outcomes Management
MA Transportation Policy, Operations, and Logistics
MS Bioscience Management
MSCS Computer Science; Computer Science

COURSE SUBJECT AREAS OFFERED OUTSIDE OF DEGREE PROGRAMS
Undergraduate—computer science; English composition; geography and cartography; technical and business writing.

Graduate—biological and biomedical sciences related; business, management, and marketing related; computer science; computer systems networking and telecommunications; health professions related; nursing; public administration and social service professions related.

GEORGIA COLLEGE & STATE UNIVERSITY
Milledgeville, Georgia
http://www.gcsu.edu/

Georgia College & State University was founded in 1889. It is accredited by Southern Association of Colleges and Schools. It first offered distance learning courses in 1995. In fall 2005, there were 245 students enrolled in distance learning courses. Institutionally administered financial aid is available to distance learners.

Services Distance learners have accessibility to campus computer network, career placement assistance, e-mail services, library services.

Contact Mike Augustine, Director of Admissions, Georgia College & State University, Campus Box 23, Milledgeville, GA 31061. Telephone: 478-445-1283. E-mail: mike.augustine@gcsu.edu.

DEGREES AND AWARDS
MBA Web MBA

COURSE SUBJECT AREAS OFFERED OUTSIDE OF DEGREE PROGRAMS
Undergraduate—health professions related.

Graduate—education; health professions related; management information systems; nursing.

GEORGIA HIGHLANDS COLLEGE
Rome, Georgia
Department of Extended Learning
http://www.floyd.edu/extendedlearning/

Georgia Highlands College was founded in 1970. It is accredited by Southern Association of Colleges and Schools. It first offered distance learning courses in 1977. In fall 2005, there were 770 students enrolled in distance learning courses. Institutionally administered financial aid is available to distance learners.

Services Distance learners have accessibility to academic advising, bookstore, campus computer network, e-mail services, library services.

Contact Jeff Brown, Director of Extended Learning, Georgia Highlands College, Heritage Hall Campus, 415 East Third Avenue, Rome, GA 30162. Telephone: 706-802-5300. Fax: 706-295-6732. E-mail: jbrown@highlands.edu.

DEGREES AND AWARDS
Programs offered do not lead to a degree or other formal award.

COURSE SUBJECT AREAS OFFERED OUTSIDE OF DEGREE PROGRAMS
Undergraduate—cell biology and anatomical sciences; chemistry; developmental and child psychology; English composition; health and physical education/fitness; history; mathematics and statistics related; physiology, pathology and related sciences; sociology.

GEORGIA INSTITUTE OF TECHNOLOGY
Atlanta, Georgia
Center for Distance Learning
http://www.cdl.gatech.edu

Georgia Institute of Technology was founded in 1885. It is accredited by Southern Association of Colleges and Schools. It first offered distance learning courses in 1977. In fall 2005, there were 525 students enrolled in distance learning courses. Institutionally administered financial aid is available to distance learners.

Services Distance learners have accessibility to academic advising, bookstore, campus computer network, e-mail services, library services.

Contact Ms. Tanya Krawiec, Student Support Services Manager, Georgia Institute of Technology, 84 5th Street, NW, Room 013, Atlanta, GA 30308-1031. Telephone: 404-894-3378. Fax: 404-894-8924. E-mail: tanya.krawiec@dlpe.gatech.edu.

DEGREES AND AWARDS
MS Aerospace Engineering; Building Construction; Civil Engineering; Electrical Engineering; Environmental Engineering; Industrial and Systems Engineering; Mechanical Engineering; Medical Physics; Operations Research

COURSE SUBJECT AREAS OFFERED OUTSIDE OF DEGREE PROGRAMS
Graduate—aerospace, aeronautical and astronautical engineering; architectural engineering; architecture related; biomedical/medical engineering; building/construction finishing, management, and inspection; civil engineering; computer engineering; engineering design; engineering/industrial management; environmental/environmental health engineering; mathematics; mechanical engineering.

Non-credit—aerospace, aeronautical and astronautical engineering; civil engineering; computer engineering; environmental/environmental health engineering; mathematics; mechanical engineering.

See full description on page 382.

GEORGIA SOUTHERN UNIVERSITY
Statesboro, Georgia
Distance Learning Center
http://academics.georgiasouthern.edu/dlc/

Georgia Southern University was founded in 1906. It is accredited by Southern Association of Colleges and Schools. It first offered distance learning courses in 1992. In fall 2005, there were 1,432 students enrolled in distance learning courses. Institutionally administered financial aid is available to distance learners.

Services Distance learners have accessibility to academic advising, bookstore, campus computer network, career placement assistance, e-mail services, library services, tutoring.

Contact Mrs. Jennifer Driggers, Instructional Classroom Coordinator, Georgia Southern University, PO Box 8018, Statesboro, GA 30460. Telephone: 912-681-0882. Fax: 912-871-1424. E-mail: jdriggers@georgiasouthern.edu.

DEGREES AND AWARDS

BBA Business Administration
MBA Business Administration
MPA Public Administration

COURSE SUBJECT AREAS OFFERED OUTSIDE OF DEGREE PROGRAMS

Undergraduate—accounting and related services; business administration, management and operations; educational administration and supervision; engineering mechanics; English composition; management sciences and quantitative methods; marketing; mathematics; nursing; political science and government; sociology.

Graduate—accounting and related services; business, management, and marketing related; curriculum and instruction; educational administration and supervision; educational/instructional media design; educational psychology; nursing; public administration and social service professions related.

GLENVILLE STATE COLLEGE
Glenville, West Virginia
http://www.glenville.edu/

Glenville State College was founded in 1872. It is accredited by North Central Association of Colleges and Schools. It first offered distance learning courses in 1997. In fall 2005, there were 271 students enrolled in distance learning courses. Institutionally administered financial aid is available to distance learners.

Services Distance learners have accessibility to campus computer network, e-mail services, library services.

Contact Dr. Kathy Butler, Vice President for Academic Affairs, Glenville State College, 200 High Street, Glenville, WV 26351. Telephone: 304-462-4100. Fax: 304-462-8619. E-mail: kathy.butler@glenville.edu.

DEGREES AND AWARDS

Programs offered do not lead to a degree or other formal award.

COURSE SUBJECT AREAS OFFERED OUTSIDE OF DEGREE PROGRAMS

Undergraduate—biological and biomedical sciences related; computer and information sciences and support services related; computer software and media applications; criminal justice and corrections; economics; education (specific subject areas); engineering technology; English; history; multi-/interdisciplinary studies related; nursing; political science and government; psychology; visual and performing arts.

GOD'S BIBLE SCHOOL AND COLLEGE
Cincinnati, Ohio

God's Bible School and College was founded in 1900. It is accredited by Association for Biblical Higher Education. It first offered distance learning courses in 2001. In fall 2005, there were 25 students enrolled in distance learning courses. Institutionally administered financial aid is available to distance learners.

Services Distance learners have accessibility to academic advising.

Contact Ms. Betty J. Cochran, Aldersgate Distance Education Program Coordinator, God's Bible School and College, 1810 Young Street, Cincinnati, OH 45202. Telephone: 513-721-7944 Ext. 122. Fax: 513-721-1357. E-mail: bcochran@gbs.edu.

DEGREES AND AWARDS

Programs offered do not lead to a degree or other formal award.

COURSE SUBJECT AREAS OFFERED OUTSIDE OF DEGREE PROGRAMS

Undergraduate—biblical and other theological languages and literatures; biblical studies; theological and ministerial studies; theology and religious vocations related.

GOGEBIC COMMUNITY COLLEGE
Ironwood, Michigan
http://www.gogebic.edu

Gogebic Community College was founded in 1932. It is accredited by North Central Association of Colleges and Schools. It first offered distance learning courses in 1992. In fall 2005, there were 196 students enrolled in distance learning courses. Institutionally administered financial aid is available to distance learners.

Services Distance learners have accessibility to academic advising, bookstore, campus computer network, library services.

Contact Ms. Jeanne P. Graham, Director of Admissions and Public Information, Gogebic Community College, E4946 Jackson Road, Ironwood, MI 49938. Telephone: 906-932-4231 Ext. 306. Fax: 906-932-2339. E-mail: jeanneg@gogebic.edu.

DEGREES AND AWARDS

Programs offered do not lead to a degree or other formal award.

COURSE SUBJECT AREAS OFFERED OUTSIDE OF DEGREE PROGRAMS

Undergraduate—accounting and related services; allied health and medical assisting services; biological and physical sciences; business/commerce; business, management, and marketing related; computer and information sciences; computer/information technology administration and management; ecology, evolution, and population biology; English composition; health and medical administrative services; history; liberal arts and sciences, general studies and humanities; psychology; social sciences related; sociology.

GOLDEN WEST COLLEGE
Huntington Beach, California
http://www.gwc.cccd.edu/

Golden West College was founded in 1966. It is accredited by Western Association of Schools and Colleges. It first offered distance learning courses in 1999. In fall 2005, there were 3,500 students enrolled in distance learning courses. Institutionally administered financial aid is available to distance learners.

Services Distance learners have accessibility to academic advising, bookstore, library services, tutoring.

Contact Ms. Juli VanDorn, Online Course Assistant, Golden West College. Telephone: 714-895-8389. E-mail: helpdesk@onlinegwc.cccd.edu.

DEGREES AND AWARDS

Programs offered do not lead to a degree or other formal award.

COURSE SUBJECT AREAS OFFERED OUTSIDE OF DEGREE PROGRAMS

Undergraduate—accounting and computer science; accounting and related services; anthropology; archeology; bilingual, multilingual, and multicultural education; biological and physical sciences; biology; biopsychology; business/commerce; business, management, and marketing related; computer science; computer software and media applications; criminal justice and corrections; criminology; developmental and child psychology; English composition; history; linguistic, comparative, and related language studies; mathematics; philosophy; political science and government; psychology; real estate; sociology.

GORDON-CONWELL THEOLOGICAL SEMINARY
South Hamilton, Massachusetts
Independent Studies Program
http://www.gcts.edu/

Gordon-Conwell Theological Seminary was founded in 1884. It is accredited by New England Association of Schools and Colleges. It first offered distance learning courses in 1986. In fall 2005, there were 640 students enrolled in distance learning courses.

Services Distance learners have accessibility to academic advising, bookstore, career placement assistance, library services.

Contact Mr. Craig F. Bridges, Semlink Coordinator, Gordon-Conwell Theological Seminary, 130 Essex Street, South Hamilton, MA 01982. Telephone: 978-646-4144. Fax: 978-646-4565. E-mail: semlink@gcts.edu.

DEGREES AND AWARDS

Programs offered do not lead to a degree or other formal award.

COURSE SUBJECT AREAS OFFERED OUTSIDE OF DEGREE PROGRAMS

Graduate—biblical and other theological languages and literatures; biblical studies; developmental and child psychology; pastoral counseling and specialized ministries; philosophy and religious studies related; religious education; religious studies; theological and ministerial studies; theology and religious vocations related.

Non-credit—biblical and other theological languages and literatures; biblical studies; developmental and child psychology; pastoral counseling and specialized ministries; philosophy and religious studies related; religious education; religious studies; theological and ministerial studies; theology and religious vocations related.

GOUCHER COLLEGE
Baltimore, Maryland
Center for Graduate and Professional Studies
http://www.goucher.edu

Goucher College was founded in 1885. It is accredited by Middle States Association of Colleges and Schools. It first offered distance learning courses in 1995. In fall 2005, there were 420 students enrolled in distance learning courses. Institutionally administered financial aid is available to distance learners.

Services Distance learners have accessibility to academic advising, bookstore, campus computer network, e-mail services, library services.

Contact Noreen P. Mack, Director for Marketing and Program Development, Goucher College, 1021 Dulaney Valley Road, Baltimore, MD 21204. Telephone: 410-337-6200. Fax: 410-337-6085. E-mail: nmack@goucher.edu.

DEGREES AND AWARDS

Programs offered do not lead to a degree or other formal award.

COURSE SUBJECT AREAS OFFERED OUTSIDE OF DEGREE PROGRAMS

Graduate—education.

GOVERNORS STATE UNIVERSITY
University Park, Illinois
Center for Extended Learning and Communications Services
http://www.govst.edu

Governors State University was founded in 1969. It is accredited by North Central Association of Colleges and Schools. It first offered distance learning courses in 1981. In fall 2005, there were 1,221 students enrolled in distance learning courses. Institutionally administered financial aid is available to distance learners.

Services Distance learners have accessibility to academic advising, bookstore, e-mail services, library services, tutoring.

Contact Veronica Williams, Director, Governors State University, 1 University Parkway, University Park, IL 60466. Telephone: 708-534-4099. Fax: 708-534-8458. E-mail: v-williams@govst.edu.

DEGREES AND AWARDS

BA Individualized Studies

COURSE SUBJECT AREAS OFFERED OUTSIDE OF DEGREE PROGRAMS

Undergraduate—accounting and related services; anthropology; communication and media; developmental and child psychology; English composition; fine and studio art; geography and cartography; marketing; psychology; social work; sociology.

Graduate—anthropology; developmental and child psychology; fine and studio art; social work; sociology.

GRACE COLLEGE
Winona Lake, Indiana
http://www.grace.edu/

Grace College was founded in 1948. It is accredited by North Central Association of Colleges and Schools. It first offered distance learning courses in 1999. In fall 2005, there were 45 students enrolled in distance learning courses. Institutionally administered financial aid is available to distance learners.

Services Distance learners have accessibility to bookstore, career placement assistance, e-mail services, library services.

Contact Mr. Ryan N. Egli, Seminary Recruitment Representative, Grace College, 200 Seminary Drive, Winona Lake, IN 46590. Telephone: 800-544-7223 Ext. 6435. Fax: 574-372-5113. E-mail: gtsrec@grace.edu.

DEGREES AND AWARDS

MA Local Church Ministry

GRAND VIEW COLLEGE
Des Moines, Iowa
Camp Dodge Campus
http://www.gvc.edu

Grand View College was founded in 1896. It is accredited by North Central Association of Colleges and Schools. It first offered distance learning courses in 1994. Institutionally administered financial aid is available to distance learners.

Services Distance learners have accessibility to academic advising, bookstore, campus computer network, career placement assistance, e-mail services, library services.

Contact Ms. Lora Kelly-Benck, Director of Camp Dodge Campus, Grand View College, 1200 Grandview Avenue, Des Moines, IA 50316. Telephone: 515-245-4546. Fax: 515-252-4753. E-mail: lkelly-benck@gvc.edu.

DEGREES AND AWARDS

Programs offered do not lead to a degree or other formal award.

COURSE SUBJECT AREAS OFFERED OUTSIDE OF DEGREE PROGRAMS

Undergraduate—business, management, and marketing related; business/managerial economics; criminal justice and corrections; English; English composition; history; psychology; social psychology; sociology; speech and rhetoric.

GRANITE STATE COLLEGE
Concord, New Hampshire
http://www.cll.edu

Granite State College was founded in 1972. It is accredited by New England Association of Schools and Colleges. It first offered distance learning courses in 1999. In fall 2005, there were 433 students enrolled in distance learning courses. Institutionally administered financial aid is available to distance learners.

Services Distance learners have accessibility to academic advising, bookstore, e-mail services, library services, tutoring.

Contact Ms. Deb Stever, Online Advisor, Granite State College, 2020 Riverside Drive, Room 144, Berlin, NH 03570. Telephone: 603-752-2479. Fax: 603-752-6335. E-mail: deb.stever@granite.edu.

DEGREES AND AWARDS

AA General Studies
AS Business Studies
BA Self-Design
BS Applied Technology; Information Technology; Management; Self-Design
Certificate Computing and Information Technology; Essential Skills for the Workplace; Information Technology Management

COURSE SUBJECT AREAS OFFERED OUTSIDE OF DEGREE PROGRAMS

Undergraduate—behavioral sciences; business administration, management and operations; communication and media; computer/information technology administration and management; computer programming; computer systems analysis; criminal justice and corrections; criminology; education (specific levels and methods); finance and financial management services; health and medical administrative services; history; human development, family studies, and related services; human resources management; human services; liberal arts and sciences, general studies and humanities; management information systems; mathematics; multi-/interdisciplinary studies related; philosophy; psychology related; social sciences; special education.
Graduate—special education.

GRANTHAM UNIVERSITY
Kansas City, Missouri
http://www.grantham.edu/

Grantham University was founded in 1951. It is accredited by Distance Education and Training Council. It first offered distance learning courses in 1990. In fall 2005, there were 9,500 students enrolled in distance learning courses. Institutionally administered financial aid is available to distance learners.
Services Distance learners have accessibility to academic advising, bookstore.
Contact Ms. DeAnn Wandler, Director of Admissions, Grantham University, 7200 NW 86th Street, Kansas City, MO 64153. Telephone: 800-955-2527. Fax: 816-448-3796. E-mail: admissions@grantham.edu.

DEGREES AND AWARDS

AS Business Administration; Computer Engineering Technology; Computer Science; Criminal Justice–Computer Science; Criminal Justice–Homeland Security; Criminal Justice; Electronics Engineering Technology; Engineering Management; General Studies; Information Systems; Interdisciplinary Studies; Software Engineering Technology
BS Business Administration; Computer Engineering Technology; Computer Science; Criminal Justice–Computer Science; Criminal Justice–Homeland Security; Criminal Justice; Electronics Engineering Technology; Engineering Management; General Studies; Information Systems; Interdisciplinary Studies; Software Engineering Technology
MBA Business Administration; Information Management; Project Management
MS Information Management Technology; Information Management–Project Management; Information Technology

COURSE SUBJECT AREAS OFFERED OUTSIDE OF DEGREE PROGRAMS

Undergraduate—accounting and related services; business administration, management and operations; business/commerce; business, management, and marketing related; business/managerial economics; chemistry; computer and information sciences; computer engineering; computer engineering technologies; computer/information technology administration and management; computer programming; computer science; computer software and media applications; computer systems analysis; computer systems networking and telecommunications; criminal justice and corrections; data entry/microcomputer applications; economics; electrical and electronic engineering technologies; electrical, electronics and communications engineering; engineering; English composition; finance and financial management services; history; human resources management; information science/studies; legal studies (non-professional general, undergraduate); management information systems; marketing; mathematics; mathematics and computer science; mathematics and statistics related; physics; psychology; psychology related; sales, merchandising, and related marketing operations (general); sociology; technical and business writing.
Graduate—accounting and related services; business/managerial economics; communications technology; finance and financial management services; management information systems; marketing; systems engineering.

See full description on page 384.

GRATZ COLLEGE
Melrose Park, Pennsylvania
http://www.gratz.edu

Gratz College was founded in 1895. It is accredited by Middle States Association of Colleges and Schools. It first offered distance learning courses in 2000. In fall 2005, there were 75 students enrolled in distance learning courses. Institutionally administered financial aid is available to distance learners.
Services Distance learners have accessibility to academic advising, bookstore, career placement assistance, e-mail services, library services.
Contact Ms. Ronni D. Ticker, Director, Online and Distance Learning, Gratz College, 7605 Old York Road, Melrose Park, PA 19027. Telephone: 215-635-7300 Ext. 115. Fax: 215-635-7399. E-mail: online@gratz.edu.

DEGREES AND AWARDS

CAGS Jewish Early Childhood Education; Jewish Education; Jewish Non-Profit Management; Jewish Studies
MA Jewish Studies

GREENFIELD COMMUNITY COLLEGE
Greenfield, Massachusetts
http://www.gcc.mass.edu/

Greenfield Community College was founded in 1962. It is accredited by New England Association of Schools and Colleges. It first offered distance learning courses in 2002. In fall 2005, there were 45 students enrolled in distance learning courses. Institutionally administered financial aid is available to distance learners.
Services Distance learners have accessibility to campus computer network, e-mail services, library services.
Contact Michelle M. Barthelemy, Coordinator of Distance Learning, Greenfield Community College, One College Drive, East Building, Room 132S, Greenfield, MA 01301. E-mail: online@gcc.mass.edu.

DEGREES AND AWARDS

Programs offered do not lead to a degree or other formal award.

COURSE SUBJECT AREAS OFFERED OUTSIDE OF DEGREE PROGRAMS

Undergraduate—anthropology; biological and physical sciences; computer/information technology administration and management; education; English composition; history; mathematics; psychology; sociology.

GREEN MOUNTAIN COLLEGE
Poultney, Vermont

Green Mountain College was founded in 1834. It is accredited by New England Association of Schools and Colleges. It first offered distance learning courses in 2006. Institutionally administered financial aid is available to distance learners.
Services Distance learners have accessibility to academic advising, bookstore, campus computer network, career placement assistance, e-mail services, library services, tutoring.
Contact Ms. Susan Whiting, Administrative Assistant, Green Mountain College, Office of Graduate Programs, One College Circle, Poultney, VT 05764. Telephone: 802-287-8319. Fax: 802-287-8099. E-mail: whitings@greenmtn.edu.

DEGREES AND AWARDS

MBA Non-Profit Organization Management; Sustainable Business Practices

MS Environmental Studies in Conservation Biology; Self Designed Concentration; Writing and Communictions Concentration

GULF COAST COMMUNITY COLLEGE
Panama City, Florida

Gulf Coast Community College was founded in 1957. It is accredited by Southern Association of Colleges and Schools.
Services Distance learners have accessibility to academic advising, bookstore, campus computer network, e-mail services, library services.
Contact Miss Cindy Lea Mitchell, Administrative Assistant/Distance Education, Gulf Coast Community College, 5230 West U.S. Highway 98, Panama City, FL 32401. Telephone: 850-769-1551 Ext. 5807. Fax: 850-872-3861. E-mail: vcampus@gulfcoast.edu.

DEGREES AND AWARDS
Programs offered do not lead to a degree or other formal award.

COURSE SUBJECT AREAS OFFERED OUTSIDE OF DEGREE PROGRAMS
Undergraduate—biological and physical sciences; chemistry; dental support services and allied professions; developmental and child psychology; economics; English composition; fire protection; health/medical preparatory programs; history; mathematics; music; nursing; physical sciences; psychology; social sciences; sociology; statistics.

HAGERSTOWN COMMUNITY COLLEGE
Hagerstown, Maryland
http://www.hagerstowncc.edu/

Hagerstown Community College was founded in 1946. It is accredited by Middle States Association of Colleges and Schools. It first offered distance learning courses in 1998. In fall 2005, there were 180 students enrolled in distance learning courses. Institutionally administered financial aid is available to distance learners.
Services Distance learners have accessibility to bookstore, library services.
Contact Angela Kelley, Test Center Administrator, Hagerstown Community College, Continuing Education, 11400 Robinwood Drive, Hagerstown, MD 21742. Telephone: 301-790-2800 Ext. 553. Fax: 301-733-4229. E-mail: kelleya@hagerstowncc.edu.

DEGREES AND AWARDS
Programs offered do not lead to a degree or other formal award.

COURSE SUBJECT AREAS OFFERED OUTSIDE OF DEGREE PROGRAMS
Non-credit—accounting and related services; allied health and medical assisting services; business, management, and marketing related; computer programming; computer software and media applications; computer systems networking and telecommunications; culinary arts and related services; publishing.

HALIFAX COMMUNITY COLLEGE
Weldon, North Carolina
Distance Learning
http://www.halifaxcc.edu

Halifax Community College was founded in 1967. It is accredited by Southern Association of Colleges and Schools. It first offered distance learning courses in 1999. In fall 2005, there were 1,049 students enrolled in distance learning courses. Institutionally administered financial aid is available to distance learners.
Services Distance learners have accessibility to career placement assistance, e-mail services, library services.
Contact Beth Gray-Robertson, Director of Distance Learning, Halifax Community College, PO Drawer 809, Weldon , NC 27890. Telephone: 252-536-7299. Fax: 252-536-6347. E-mail: robertsonb@halifaxcc.edu.

DEGREES AND AWARDS
Programs offered do not lead to a degree or other formal award.

COURSE SUBJECT AREAS OFFERED OUTSIDE OF DEGREE PROGRAMS
Undergraduate—accounting and related services; business/commerce; communication and media; computer and information sciences and support services related; computer science; developmental and child psychology; economics; English composition; English literature (British and Commonwealth); fine and studio art; mathematics; religious studies; teaching assistants/aides.
Non-credit—business administration, management and operations; computer software and media applications; computer systems networking and telecommunications; data entry/microcomputer applications; education (specific levels and methods).

HAMLINE UNIVERSITY
St. Paul, Minnesota
http://www.hamline.edu/

Hamline University was founded in 1854. It is accredited by North Central Association of Colleges and Schools. It first offered distance learning courses in 1998. In fall 2005, there were 124 students enrolled in distance learning courses. Institutionally administered financial aid is available to distance learners.
Services Distance learners have accessibility to campus computer network, career placement assistance, e-mail services, library services.
Contact Annette McNamara, Program Administrator, Hamline University, 1536 Hewitt Avenue, A1720, St. Paul, MN 55104-1284. Telephone: 651-523-2175. Fax: 651-523-2489. E-mail: amcnamara@gw.hamline.edu.

DEGREES AND AWARDS
Programs offered do not lead to a degree or other formal award.

COURSE SUBJECT AREAS OFFERED OUTSIDE OF DEGREE PROGRAMS
Undergraduate—history.
Graduate—bilingual, multilingual, and multicultural education; education; educational/instructional media design; education related; education (specific levels and methods); education (specific subject areas); English as a second/foreign language (teaching); English as a second language; mathematics; public administration and social service professions related; special education.
Non-credit—education; educational administration and supervision; educational/instructional media design; education related; education (specific subject areas); English as a second/foreign language (teaching); English as a second language; political science and government; public administration; public administration and social service professions related.

HARFORD COMMUNITY COLLEGE
Bel Air, Maryland
http://www.harford.edu/distlearn/

Harford Community College was founded in 1957. It is accredited by Middle States Association of Colleges and Schools. It first offered distance learning courses in 1999. In fall 2005, there were 1,800 students enrolled in distance learning courses. Institutionally administered financial aid is available to distance learners.
Services Distance learners have accessibility to academic advising, bookstore, campus computer network, career placement assistance, e-mail services, library services, tutoring.
Contact Christel Vonderscheer, Director of Instructional Resources, Harford Community College, 401 Thomas Run Road, Bel Air, MD 21015. Telephone: 410-836-4145. Fax: 410-836-4481. E-mail: cvonders@harford.edu.

DEGREES AND AWARDS
AA General Studies
AS Business Administration

COURSE SUBJECT AREAS OFFERED OUTSIDE OF DEGREE PROGRAMS
Undergraduate—computer and information sciences; computer programming; computer systems networking and telecommunications; edu-

cational psychology; English; English composition; linguistic, comparative, and related language studies; mathematics; psychology; social sciences related.
Non-credit—computer and information sciences; computer programming; computer systems networking and telecommunications.

HARTFORD SEMINARY
Hartford, Connecticut
http://www.hartsem.edu/academic/distance.htm

Hartford Seminary was founded in 1834. It is accredited by New England Association of Schools and Colleges. It first offered distance learning courses in 2002. In fall 2005, there were 30 students enrolled in distance learning courses. Institutionally administered financial aid is available to distance learners.
Services Distance learners have accessibility to academic advising, bookstore, library services, tutoring.
Contact Dr. Scott Thumma, Director of Distance Education, Hartford Seminary, 77 Sherman Street, Hartford, CT 06105. Telephone: 860-509-9571. E-mail: sthumma@hartsem.edu.

DEGREES AND AWARDS
Programs offered do not lead to a degree or other formal award.

COURSE SUBJECT AREAS OFFERED OUTSIDE OF DEGREE PROGRAMS
Graduate—pastoral counseling and specialized ministries; religious studies; sociology.
Non-credit—religious studies.

HARVARD UNIVERSITY
Cambridge, Massachusetts
Division of Continuing Education–Harvard Extension School
http://www.extension.harvard.edu

Harvard University was founded in 1636. It is accredited by New England Association of Schools and Colleges. It first offered distance learning courses in 1996. In fall 2005, there were 1,000 students enrolled in distance learning courses. Institutionally administered financial aid is available to distance learners.
Contact Academic Services, Harvard University, 51 Brattle Street, Cambridge, MA 02138. Telephone: 617-495-4024. E-mail: dce-distance-ed@harvard.edu.

DEGREES AND AWARDS
Programs offered do not lead to a degree or other formal award.

COURSE SUBJECT AREAS OFFERED OUTSIDE OF DEGREE PROGRAMS
Undergraduate—biology; environmental/environmental health engineering; museum studies; philosophy.
Graduate—accounting and computer science; accounting and related services; biology; computer science; environmental/environmental health engineering; languages (Modern Greek); museum studies; philosophy; psychology; religious studies.
Non-credit—biology; computer science; environmental/environmental health engineering; languages (Modern Greek); museum studies; philosophy.

HAYWOOD COMMUNITY COLLEGE
Clyde, North Carolina
http://www.haywood.edu

Haywood Community College was founded in 1964. It is accredited by Southern Association of Colleges and Schools. It first offered distance learning courses in 1992. In fall 2005, there were 550 students enrolled in distance learning courses. Institutionally administered financial aid is available to distance learners.
Services Distance learners have accessibility to academic advising, bookstore, campus computer network, career placement assistance, e-mail services, library services, tutoring.
Contact Debbie Rowland, Coordinator of Admissions, Haywood Community College, 185 Freedlander Drive, Clyde, NC 28716. Telephone: 828-627-4646. Fax: 828-627-4513. E-mail: drowland@haywood.edu.

DEGREES AND AWARDS
AAS Early Childhood Education; Teacher Associate

COURSE SUBJECT AREAS OFFERED OUTSIDE OF DEGREE PROGRAMS
Undergraduate—accounting and related services; anthropology; applied horticulture/horticultural business services; business administration, management and operations; business/commerce; computer and information sciences; computer programming; economics; education; education related; engineering technologies related; English; English composition; fine and studio art; forestry; health and physical education/fitness; history; information science/studies; liberal arts and sciences, general studies and humanities; management information systems; mathematics; mathematics and computer science; political science and government; psychology; religious studies; sociology; teaching assistants/aides; technical and business writing.
Non-credit—computer software and media applications.

HEARTLAND COMMUNITY COLLEGE
Normal, Illinois
http://www.hcc-online.org

Heartland Community College was founded in 1990. It is accredited by North Central Association of Colleges and Schools. It first offered distance learning courses in 1991. In fall 2005, there were 686 students enrolled in distance learning courses. Institutionally administered financial aid is available to distance learners.
Services Distance learners have accessibility to academic advising, bookstore, career placement assistance, library services, tutoring.
Contact Mr. Padriac Sean Shinville, Division Chair, Alternative Learning and Developmental Education, Heartland Community College, 1500 West Raab Road, Normal, IL 61761. Telephone: 309-268-8417. Fax: 309-268-7986. E-mail: padriac.shinville@hcc.cc.il.us.

DEGREES AND AWARDS
Programs offered do not lead to a degree or other formal award.

COURSE SUBJECT AREAS OFFERED OUTSIDE OF DEGREE PROGRAMS
Undergraduate—accounting and related services; American literature (United States and Canadian); business/commerce; communication and media; economics; English composition; foods, nutrition, and related services; history; human development, family studies, and related services; psychology.

HEART OF GEORGIA TECHNICAL COLLEGE
Dublin, Georgia
http://www.hgtc.org

Heart of Georgia Technical College was founded in 1984. It is accredited by Council on Occupational Education. It first offered distance learning courses in 1993. In fall 2005, there were 62 students enrolled in distance learning courses. Institutionally administered financial aid is available to distance learners.
Services Distance learners have accessibility to academic advising, bookstore, campus computer network, career placement assistance, e-mail services, library services, tutoring.
Contact Ms. Lisa Kelly, Admissions Director, Heart of Georgia Technical College, 560 Pinehill Road, Dublin, GA 31021. Telephone: 478-274-7837. Fax: 478-275-6642. E-mail: lisak@hgtc.org.

DEGREES AND AWARDS
Programs offered do not lead to a degree or other formal award.

COURSE SUBJECT AREAS OFFERED OUTSIDE OF DEGREE PROGRAMS
Undergraduate—applied mathematics; business administration, management and operations; computer and information sciences and support services related; computer systems analysis; computer systems net-

working and telecommunications; educational administration and supervision; education related; electrical and electronic engineering technologies; engineering technologies related; English; health professions related; management information systems; mathematics; psychology; teaching assistants/aides; technical and business writing; technology education/industrial arts.

HEBREW COLLEGE
Newton Centre, Massachusetts
http://www.hebrewcollege.edu/online

Hebrew College was founded in 1921. It is accredited by New England Association of Schools and Colleges. It first offered distance learning courses in 1995. In fall 2005, there were 150 students enrolled in distance learning courses. Institutionally administered financial aid is available to distance learners.

Services Distance learners have accessibility to academic advising, bookstore, campus computer network, career placement assistance, library services, tutoring.

Contact Nathan Ehrlich, Dean, Hebrew College Online, Hebrew College, 160 Herrick Road, Newton Centre, MA 02459. Telephone: 617-559-8672. Fax: 617-559-8601. E-mail: nathan@hebrewcollege.edu.

DEGREES AND AWARDS
MA Jewish Studies

COURSE SUBJECT AREAS OFFERED OUTSIDE OF DEGREE PROGRAMS

Undergraduate—biblical and other theological languages and literatures; biblical studies; education related; ethnic, cultural minority, and gender studies; languages (Middle/Near Eastern and Semitic); linguistic, comparative, and related language studies; philosophy and religious studies related; religious studies.

Graduate—biblical and other theological languages and literatures; biblical studies; education related; ethnic, cultural minority, and gender studies; languages (Middle/Near Eastern and Semitic); linguistic, comparative, and related language studies; philosophy and religious studies related; religious studies.

Non-credit—biblical and other theological languages and literatures; biblical studies; education related; ethnic, cultural minority, and gender studies; languages (Middle/Near Eastern and Semitic); linguistic, comparative, and related language studies; philosophy and religious studies related; religious studies.

HILLSBOROUGH COMMUNITY COLLEGE
Tampa, Florida
Distance Learning Office
http://www.hccfl.edu/eCampus

Hillsborough Community College was founded in 1968. It is accredited by Southern Association of Colleges and Schools. It first offered distance learning courses in 1971. In fall 2005, there were 3,000 students enrolled in distance learning courses. Institutionally administered financial aid is available to distance learners.

Services Distance learners have accessibility to academic advising, bookstore, career placement assistance, e-mail services, library services, tutoring.

Contact Melissa Zucal, Distance Learning Manager, Hillsborough Community College, 39 Columbia, Suite 714, Tampa, FL 33606. Telephone: 813-259-6446. Fax: 813-259-6446. E-mail: mzucal@hccfl.edu.

DEGREES AND AWARDS
AS Opticianry

COURSE SUBJECT AREAS OFFERED OUTSIDE OF DEGREE PROGRAMS

Undergraduate—American literature (United States and Canadian); applied mathematics; astronomy and astrophysics; business/commerce; computer and information sciences; computer/information technology administration and management; computer programming; computer science; computer software and media applications; creative writing; developmental and child psychology; economics; English; English composition; finance and financial management services; foods, nutrition, and related services; geological and earth sciences/geosciences; health professions related; human development, family studies, and related services; legal studies (non-professional general, undergraduate); marketing; ophthalmic and optometric support services and allied professions; psychology; sociology.

Non-credit—accounting and related services; crafts, folk art and artisanry; languages (Romance languages).

HOLY APOSTLES COLLEGE AND SEMINARY
Cromwell, Connecticut
http://www.holyapostles.edu

Holy Apostles College and Seminary was founded in 1956. It is accredited by New England Association of Schools and Colleges. It first offered distance learning courses in 1998. In fall 2005, there were 115 students enrolled in distance learning courses. Institutionally administered financial aid is available to distance learners.

Services Distance learners have accessibility to academic advising, e-mail services, library services, tutoring.

Contact Mr. Robert Mish, Distance Learning Coordinator, Holy Apostles College and Seminary, 33 Prospect Hill Road, Cromwell, CT 06416. Telephone: 860-632-3015. Fax: 860-632-3075. E-mail: distancelearn@holyapostles.edu.

DEGREES AND AWARDS
MA Philosophy; Theology

COURSE SUBJECT AREAS OFFERED OUTSIDE OF DEGREE PROGRAMS

Graduate—philosophy and religious studies related.

HOLY NAMES UNIVERSITY
Oakland, California

Holy Names University was founded in 1868. It is accredited by Western Association of Schools and Colleges. It first offered distance learning courses in 1995. In fall 2005, there were 97 students enrolled in distance learning courses. Institutionally administered financial aid is available to distance learners.

Services Distance learners have accessibility to academic advising, bookstore, e-mail services, library services.

Contact Jose Rangel, Office of Admissions, Holy Names University, 3500 Mountain Boulevard, Oakland, CA 94619-1699. Telephone: 510-436-1351. Fax: 510-436-1325. E-mail: admissions@hnu.edu.

DEGREES AND AWARDS
BSN Nursing–Accelerated RN-BSN

HONOLULU COMMUNITY COLLEGE
Honolulu, Hawaii
Distance Learning
http://honolulu.hawaii.edu/distance

Honolulu Community College was founded in 1920. It is accredited by Western Association of Schools and Colleges. It first offered distance learning courses in 1991. In fall 2005, there were 500 students enrolled in distance learning courses. Institutionally administered financial aid is available to distance learners.

Services Distance learners have accessibility to academic advising, bookstore, campus computer network, career placement assistance, e-mail services, library services.

Contact Janice T. Petersen, Distance Learning Coordinator, Honolulu Community College, 874 Dillingham Boulevard, Honolulu, HI 96817. Telephone: 808-845-9437. Fax: 808-847-9679. E-mail: janp@hcc.hawaii.edu.

DEGREES AND AWARDS
Programs offered do not lead to a degree or other formal award.

COURSE SUBJECT AREAS OFFERED OUTSIDE OF DEGREE PROGRAMS

Undergraduate—anthropology; architectural engineering technology; astronomy and astrophysics; chemistry; English; English composition;

fire protection; foods, nutrition, and related services; geological and earth sciences/geosciences; history; liberal arts and sciences, general studies and humanities; microbiological sciences and immunology; philosophy; philosophy and religious studies related; political science and government; psychology; social sciences related; speech and rhetoric.

HOPE INTERNATIONAL UNIVERSITY
Fullerton, California
Distance Learning Department
http://www.hiu.edu

Hope International University was founded in 1928. It is accredited by Western Association of Schools and Colleges. It first offered distance learning courses in 1994. In fall 2005, there were 260 students enrolled in distance learning courses. Institutionally administered financial aid is available to distance learners.

Services Distance learners have accessibility to academic advising, bookstore, career placement assistance, e-mail services, library services.

Contact Wende J. Holtzen, Distance Learning Assistant, Hope International University, 2500 East Nutwood Avenue, Fullerton, CA 92831. Telephone: 714-879-3901 Ext. 1246. Fax: 714-681-7230. E-mail: wholtzen@hiu.edu.

DEGREES AND AWARDS

AA Biblical Studies; Christian Ministry
BS Business Administration and Management; Christian Ministry; Human Development
Certificate Biblical Studies; Christian Ministry
MBA International Development; Management; Nonprofit Management
MSM International Development

COURSE SUBJECT AREAS OFFERED OUTSIDE OF DEGREE PROGRAMS

Undergraduate—biblical studies; history; psychology; religious studies.
Graduate—biblical studies; ethnic, cultural minority, and gender studies; psychology; religious studies.
Non-credit—biblical studies; ethnic, cultural minority, and gender studies; history; psychology; religious studies.

HOUSATONIC COMMUNITY COLLEGE
Bridgeport, Connecticut
http://www.hctc.commnet.edu/

Housatonic Community College was founded in 1965. It is accredited by New England Association of Schools and Colleges. It first offered distance learning courses in 2003. In fall 2005, there were 680 students enrolled in distance learning courses. Institutionally administered financial aid is available to distance learners.

Services Distance learners have accessibility to academic advising, bookstore, campus computer network, e-mail services, library services, tutoring.

Contact Ms. Laurel K. Quinones, Director of Distance Learning, Housatonic Community College, 900 Lafayette Boulevard, Bridgeport, CT 06604. Telephone: 203-332-8571. Fax: 203-332-5247. E-mail: lquinones@hcc.commnet.edu.

DEGREES AND AWARDS

Programs offered do not lead to a degree or other formal award.

COURSE SUBJECT AREAS OFFERED OUTSIDE OF DEGREE PROGRAMS

Undergraduate—American literature (United States and Canadian); behavioral sciences; biology; business administration, management and operations; business/managerial economics; chemistry; communication and journalism related; counseling psychology; developmental and child psychology; economics; English; English composition; English literature (British and Commonwealth); gerontology; history; human development, family studies, and related services; journalism; manufacturing engineering; marketing; mathematics and statistics related; statistics; taxation.
Non-credit—finance and financial management services; health and medical administrative services; taxation.

HOUSTON COMMUNITY COLLEGE SYSTEM
Houston, Texas
Distance Education Department
http://www.distance.hccs.edu

Houston Community College System was founded in 1971. It is accredited by Southern Association of Colleges and Schools. It first offered distance learning courses in 1985. In fall 2005, there were 6,143 students enrolled in distance learning courses. Institutionally administered financial aid is available to distance learners.

Services Distance learners have accessibility to academic advising, bookstore, e-mail services, library services, tutoring.

Contact Eva Gonzalez, Distance Education Associate, Houston Community College System, 3100 Main Street, MC 1740, Houston, TX 77002. Telephone: 713-718-5152. Fax: 713-718-5388. E-mail: eva.gonzalez@hccs.edu.

DEGREES AND AWARDS

Programs offered do not lead to a degree or other formal award.

COURSE SUBJECT AREAS OFFERED OUTSIDE OF DEGREE PROGRAMS

Undergraduate—accounting and related services; American literature (United States and Canadian); anthropology; astronomy and astrophysics; biology; business administration, management and operations; chemistry; community health services; computer/information technology administration and management; computer science; criminology; developmental and child psychology; economics; English composition; English literature (British and Commonwealth); film/video and photographic arts; fine and studio art; fire protection; foods, nutrition, and related services; geography and cartography; history; human development, family studies, and related services; human resources management; human services; languages (Romance languages); management information systems; marketing; mathematics; mathematics and statistics related; philosophy; physical sciences; political science and government; psychology; real estate; social psychology; sociology.

HOWARD COLLEGE
Big Spring, Texas
http://www.howardcollege.edu/

Howard College was founded in 1945. It is accredited by Southern Association of Colleges and Schools. It first offered distance learning courses in 1997. In fall 2005, there were 650 students enrolled in distance learning courses. Institutionally administered financial aid is available to distance learners.

Services Distance learners have accessibility to bookstore, campus computer network, e-mail services, library services.

Contact Stan D. Solis, Director of Distance Learning, Howard College, 1001 Birdwell Lane, Big Spring, TX 79720. Telephone: 432-264-5124. Fax: 432-264-5146. E-mail: ssolis@howardcollege.edu.

DEGREES AND AWARDS

Programs offered do not lead to a degree or other formal award.

COURSE SUBJECT AREAS OFFERED OUTSIDE OF DEGREE PROGRAMS

Undergraduate—accounting and related services; business/commerce; economics; English composition; English literature (British and Commonwealth); foods, nutrition, and related services; mathematics; nursing; psychology; sociology.

HUMBOLDT STATE UNIVERSITY
Arcata, California
http://www.humboldt.edu/

Humboldt State University was founded in 1913. It is accredited by Western Association of Schools and Colleges. It first offered distance learning courses in 1996. In fall 2005, there were 112 students enrolled in distance learning courses. Institutionally administered financial aid is available to distance learners.

Services Distance learners have accessibility to academic advising, bookstore, campus computer network, e-mail services, library services.

Contact Carl Hansen, Director of Extended Education, Humboldt State University, Office of Extended Education, Arcata, CA 95521. Telephone: 707-826-3731. Fax: 707-826-5885. E-mail: hansen@humboldt.edu.

DEGREES AND AWARDS

Programs offered do not lead to a degree or other formal award.

COURSE SUBJECT AREAS OFFERED OUTSIDE OF DEGREE PROGRAMS

Undergraduate—biological and biomedical sciences related; biotechnology; education; forestry; legal professions and studies related; natural resources management and policy.

Graduate—education; educational/instructional media design; film/video and photographic arts.

Non-credit—legal professions and studies related; natural resources management and policy.

ILLINOIS EASTERN COMMUNITY COLLEGES, FRONTIER COMMUNITY COLLEGE

Fairfield, Illinois

http://www.iecc.cc.il.us./fcc

Illinois Eastern Community Colleges, Frontier Community College was founded in 1976. It is accredited by North Central Association of Colleges and Schools. It first offered distance learning courses in 1994. In fall 2005, there were 67 students enrolled in distance learning courses. Institutionally administered financial aid is available to distance learners.

Services Distance learners have accessibility to academic advising, bookstore, campus computer network, career placement assistance, e-mail services, library services, tutoring.

Contact Mr. Jerry Hefley, Dean of the College, Illinois Eastern Community Colleges, Frontier Community College, 2 Frontier Drive, Fairfield, IL 62837. Telephone: 618-842-3711 Ext. 4005. Fax: 618-842-6340. E-mail: hefleyj@iecc.edu.

DEGREES AND AWARDS

Programs offered do not lead to a degree or other formal award.

COURSE SUBJECT AREAS OFFERED OUTSIDE OF DEGREE PROGRAMS

Undergraduate—business/commerce; foods, nutrition, and related services; health and physical education/fitness; marketing; nutrition sciences.

ILLINOIS EASTERN COMMUNITY COLLEGES, LINCOLN TRAIL COLLEGE

Robinson, Illinois

http://www.iecc.cc.il.us/ltc

Illinois Eastern Community Colleges, Lincoln Trail College was founded in 1969. It is accredited by North Central Association of Colleges and Schools. It first offered distance learning courses in 1994. In fall 2005, there were 376 students enrolled in distance learning courses. Institutionally administered financial aid is available to distance learners.

Services Distance learners have accessibility to academic advising, bookstore, campus computer network, career placement assistance, e-mail services, library services, tutoring.

Contact Ms. Penny Quinn, Dean of Instruction, Illinois Eastern Community Colleges, Lincoln Trail College, 11220 State Highway 1, Robinson, IL 62454. Telephone: 618-544-8657 Ext. 1144. Fax: 618-544-7423. E-mail: quinnp@iecc.edu.

DEGREES AND AWARDS

Programs offered do not lead to a degree or other formal award.

COURSE SUBJECT AREAS OFFERED OUTSIDE OF DEGREE PROGRAMS

Undergraduate—astronomy and astrophysics; business/commerce; computer software and media applications; computer systems networking and telecommunications; English composition; health professions related; mathematics; psychology; psychology related.

ILLINOIS EASTERN COMMUNITY COLLEGES, OLNEY CENTRAL COLLEGE

Olney, Illinois

http://www.iecc.cc.il.us/occ/

Illinois Eastern Community Colleges, Olney Central College was founded in 1962. It is accredited by North Central Association of Colleges and Schools. It first offered distance learning courses in 1994. In fall 2005, there were 384 students enrolled in distance learning courses. Institutionally administered financial aid is available to distance learners.

Services Distance learners have accessibility to academic advising, bookstore, campus computer network, career placement assistance, e-mail services, library services, tutoring.

Contact Ms. Lisa Benson, Dean of Instruction, Illinois Eastern Community Colleges, Olney Central College, 305 North West Street, Olney, IL 62450. Telephone: 618-395-7777 Ext. 2002. Fax: 618-395-5212. E-mail: bensonl@iecc.edu.

DEGREES AND AWARDS

Programs offered do not lead to a degree or other formal award.

COURSE SUBJECT AREAS OFFERED OUTSIDE OF DEGREE PROGRAMS

Undergraduate—accounting and related services; business/commerce; communication and media; computer and information sciences; economics; English composition; liberal arts and sciences, general studies and humanities; mathematics; psychology; social sciences.

ILLINOIS EASTERN COMMUNITY COLLEGES, WABASH VALLEY COLLEGE

Mount Carmel, Illinois

http://www.iecc.cc.il.us/wvc

Illinois Eastern Community Colleges, Wabash Valley College was founded in 1960. It is accredited by North Central Association of Colleges and Schools. It first offered distance learning courses in 1994. In fall 2005, there were 213 students enrolled in distance learning courses. Institutionally administered financial aid is available to distance learners.

Services Distance learners have accessibility to academic advising, bookstore, campus computer network, career placement assistance, e-mail services, library services, tutoring.

Contact Mr. Matt Fowler, Dean of Instruction, Illinois Eastern Community Colleges, Wabash Valley College, 2200 College Drive, Mt. Carmel, IL 62863. Telephone: 618-262-8641 Ext. 3213. Fax: 618-262-5614. E-mail: fowlerm@iecc.edu.

DEGREES AND AWARDS

Programs offered do not lead to a degree or other formal award.

COURSE SUBJECT AREAS OFFERED OUTSIDE OF DEGREE PROGRAMS

Undergraduate—accounting and related services; business/commerce; chemistry; history; human resources management; liberal arts and sciences, general studies and humanities; mathematics; mathematics and statistics related; psychology; statistics.

ILLINOIS INSTITUTE OF TECHNOLOGY

Chicago, Illinois

IIT Online

http://www.iit-online.iit.edu

Illinois Institute of Technology was founded in 1890. It is accredited by North Central Association of Colleges and Schools. It first offered distance learning courses in 1976. In fall 2005, there were 969 students enrolled in distance learning courses. Institutionally administered financial aid is available to distance learners.

Services Distance learners have accessibility to academic advising, bookstore, campus computer network, career placement assistance, e-mail services, library services.

Contact Ms. Holli Pryor-Harris, Assistant Dean, Extended Learning, Illinois Institute of Technology, Office of Academic Affairs, Graduate College, 3300 South Federal, Room 110A, Chicago, IL 60616-3793. Telephone: 312-567-3167. Fax: 312-567-7140. E-mail: pryor@iit.edu.

DEGREES AND AWARDS

BA Industrial Facilities Degree Completion; Industrial Logistics Degree Completion; Manufacturing Technology Degree Completion

Graduate Certificate Analytical Method Development; Analytical Spectroscopy; Characterization of Organic and Inorganic Materials; Chromatography; Computer Engineering; Computer and Network Security Technologies; Control Systems; Current Energy Issues; Electronics, advanced; Hazardous Waste Engineering; Indoor Air Quality; Information Systems; Networking and Telecommunications; Particle Processing; Pharmaceutical Processing; Polymer Synthesis and Characterization/Processing; Power Engineering; Process Operations Management; Radiologic Physics; Signal Processing; Software Engineering; Synthesis and Characterization of Inorganic Material; Synthesis and Characterization of Organic Materials; Water and Wastewater Treatment; Wireless Communications

M Ch E Chemical Engineering

MB Biochemistry; Biology; Biotechnology; Cell Biology; Microbiology

MCS Information Systems; Networking and Telecommunications; Software Engineering

MChem Analytical Chemistry; Material and Chemical Synthesis

ME Computer Engineering; Network Engineering; Telecommunications and Software Engineering

MECE Electrical and Computer Engineering

MEE Environmental Engineering

MGE Gas Engineering

MHP Health Physics

MIT Information Technology and Management

MITM Information Technology Management

MITO Industrial Facilities; Industrial Logistics; Manufacturing Technology

MME Manufacturing Engineering

MS Computer Science; Electrical Engineering

COURSE SUBJECT AREAS OFFERED OUTSIDE OF DEGREE PROGRAMS

Undergraduate—applied mathematics; biochemistry, biophysics and molecular biology; biological and physical sciences; biology; cell biology and anatomical sciences; chemical engineering; computer and information sciences; computer engineering; computer programming; computer science; engineering mechanics; mechanical engineering.

Graduate—aerospace, aeronautical and astronautical engineering; biochemistry, biophysics and molecular biology; biological and biomedical sciences related; biological and physical sciences; biomedical/medical engineering; cell biology and anatomical sciences; chemical engineering; chemistry; computer engineering; computer science; computer systems networking and telecommunications; electrical, electronics and communications engineering; environmental/environmental health engineering; food science and technology; industrial and organizational psychology; mechanical engineering; microbiological sciences and immunology.

IMMACULATA UNIVERSITY
Immaculata, Pennsylvania
http://www.immaculata.edu/

Immaculata University was founded in 1920. It is accredited by Middle States Association of Colleges and Schools. It first offered distance learning courses in 1999. In fall 2005, there were 2,100 students enrolled in distance learning courses. Institutionally administered financial aid is available to distance learners.

Services Distance learners have accessibility to academic advising, bookstore, campus computer network, career placement assistance, e-mail services, library services, tutoring.

Contact Dr. Elke Franke, Dean of College of LifeLong Learning, Immaculata University, Box 300, Immaculata, PA 19345-0300. Telephone: 610-647-4400 Ext. 3235. Fax: 610-647-0215. E-mail: efranke@immaculata.edu.

DEGREES AND AWARDS

Programs offered do not lead to a degree or other formal award.

COURSE SUBJECT AREAS OFFERED OUTSIDE OF DEGREE PROGRAMS

Undergraduate—accounting and computer science; accounting and related services; American literature (United States and Canadian); apparel and textiles; biblical and other theological languages and literatures; biological and biomedical sciences related; biological and physical sciences; biology; biology/biotechnology laboratory technician; business administration, management and operations; business/commerce; business/corporate communications; business/managerial economics; cognitive psychology and psycholinguistics; communication and media; computer and information sciences; computer and information sciences and support services related; computer/information technology administration and management; computer science; computer software and media applications; computer systems analysis; counseling psychology; creative writing; English composition; entrepreneurial and small business operations; environmental control technologies; family and consumer economics; family and consumer sciences/human sciences; foods, nutrition, and related services; history; human resources management; international business; management information systems; management sciences and quantitative methods; microbiological sciences and immunology; psychology; religious studies; sales, merchandising, and related marketing operations (specialized); sociology; theology and religious vocations related.

INDEPENDENCE COMMUNITY COLLEGE
Independence, Kansas
Center for Distance Learning
http://www.indycc.edu/

Independence Community College was founded in 1925. It is accredited by North Central Association of Colleges and Schools. It first offered distance learning courses in 1998. In fall 2005, there were 60 students enrolled in distance learning courses. Institutionally administered financial aid is available to distance learners.

Services Distance learners have accessibility to academic advising, bookstore, campus computer network, e-mail services, library services, tutoring.

Contact Stoney Gaddy, Instructor, Independence Community College, PO Box 708, Independence, KS 67301. Telephone: 620-331-4100 Ext. 4306. Fax: 620-331-5344. E-mail: sgaddy@indycc.edu.

DEGREES AND AWARDS

Programs offered do not lead to a degree or other formal award.

COURSE SUBJECT AREAS OFFERED OUTSIDE OF DEGREE PROGRAMS

Undergraduate—accounting and computer science; allied health and medical assisting services; astronomy and astrophysics; biological and physical sciences; computer and information sciences; computer systems networking and telecommunications; English; English composition; fine and studio art; political science and government; sociology.

INDIANA BUSINESS COLLEGE
Indianapolis, Indiana

Indiana Business College was founded in 1902. It is accredited by Accrediting Council for Independent Colleges and Schools. It first offered distance learning courses in 2002. In fall 2005, there were 1,100 students enrolled in distance learning courses. Institutionally administered financial aid is available to distance learners.

Services Distance learners have accessibility to academic advising, bookstore, campus computer network, career placement assistance, library services, tutoring.

Contact Mr. Omar K. Habayeb, Director of Admissions, Distance Learning, Indiana Business College, 550 East Washington Street, Indianapolis, IN 46204. Telephone: 800-999-9229 Ext. 4834. Fax: 866-277-5637. E-mail: omar.habayeb@ibcschools.edu.

DEGREES AND AWARDS

AAS Accounting; Administrative Assistant; Business Administration; Computer Science–CISCO Network Associate; Criminal Justice; Human Resources; Organizational Management

Certificate Medical Transcription

COURSE SUBJECT AREAS OFFERED OUTSIDE OF DEGREE PROGRAMS

Undergraduate—accounting and related services; business administration, management and operations; business, management, and marketing related; computer and information sciences; medical basic sciences; public relations, advertising, and applied communication related; sales, merchandising, and related marketing operations (general); sales, merchandising, and related marketing operations (specialized).

Non-credit—accounting and computer science; accounting and related services; biblical and other theological languages and literatures; biblical studies; business administration, management and operations; business/commerce; business/corporate communications; business, management, and marketing related; business/managerial economics; business operations support and assistant services; communication and journalism related; communication and media; computer and information sciences; computer programming; computer software and media applications; creative writing; dietetics and clinical nutrition services; economics; medical basic sciences; speech and rhetoric; work and family studies.

INDIANA STATE UNIVERSITY
Terre Haute, Indiana
Office of Distance Support Services
http://indstate.edu/distance

Indiana State University was founded in 1865. It is accredited by North Central Association of Colleges and Schools. It first offered distance learning courses in 1969. In fall 2005, there were 2,000 students enrolled in distance learning courses. Institutionally administered financial aid is available to distance learners.

Services Distance learners have accessibility to academic advising, bookstore, campus computer network, career placement assistance, e-mail services, library services.

Contact Distance Support Services, Indiana State University, Erickson Hall, Room 211, Terre Haute, IN 47809. Telephone: 888-237-8080. Fax: 812-237-8540. E-mail: studentservices@indstate.edu.

DEGREES AND AWARDS

AS Aviation Flight Technology, general
BS Business Administration; Career and Technical Education; Community Health Promotion; Criminology; Electronics Technology; Human Resource Development; Industrial Supervision; Industrial Technology; Insurance and Risk Management; Mechanical Engineering Technology; Nursing
Certificate Corrections; Law Enforcement; Private Security and Loss Prevention
License Driver Education Instructor; Education–Middle/Secondary Teaching; School Administration; Visual Impairment; Vocational Business Education
Graduate Certificate Library Media Services; Nursing–Family Nurse Practitioner; Public Administration; Public Personnel Administration; Teaching English as a Second/Foreign Language
MA Criminology
MS Criminology; Electronics and Computer Technology; Health and Safety; Human Resource Development; Nursing–Adult Health Specialization; Nursing–Community Health specialization; Nursing–Family Nurse Practitioner specialization; Nursing–Nursing Administration specialization; Student Affairs and Higher Education
PhD Technology Management

COURSE SUBJECT AREAS OFFERED OUTSIDE OF DEGREE PROGRAMS

Undergraduate—accounting and computer science; accounting and related services; aerospace, aeronautical and astronautical engineering; biological and physical sciences; biology; botany/plant biology; business administration, management and operations; business/commerce; business, management, and marketing related; business operations support and assistant services; chemistry; community health services; computer programming; computer science; construction engineering technology; construction management; criminal justice and corrections; criminology; curriculum and instruction; drafting/design engineering technologies; economics; education; education related; electrical and electronic engineering technologies; engineering-related technologies; English; English composition; finance and financial management services; geography and cartography; health and physical education/fitness; history; human resources management; human services; insurance; library science related; management information systems; marketing; mathematics; mathematics and computer science; mathematics and statistics related; mechanical engineering related technologies; music; nursing; personality psychology; psychology; sociology; technical and business writing; technology education/industrial arts.

Graduate—bilingual, multilingual, and multicultural education; counseling psychology; criminal justice and corrections; criminology; curriculum and instruction; developmental and child psychology; education; educational administration and supervision; educational assessment, evaluation, and research; educational/instructional media design; educational psychology; education related; education (specific levels and methods); education (specific subject areas); electrical and electronic engineering technologies; electrical, electronics and communications engineering; electromechanical and instrumentation and maintenance technologies; English as a second/foreign language (teaching); English as a second language; finance and financial management services; human resources management; industrial and organizational psychology; library science related; nursing; public administration; public administration and social service professions related; school psychology; special education; student counseling and personnel services.

See full description on page 386.

INDIANA TECH
Fort Wayne, Indiana
Independent Study
http://www.indianatech.edu

Indiana Tech was founded in 1930. It is accredited by North Central Association of Colleges and Schools. It first offered distance learning courses in 1982. In fall 2005, there were 120 students enrolled in distance learning courses. Institutionally administered financial aid is available to distance learners.

Services Distance learners have accessibility to academic advising, bookstore, campus computer network, e-mail services.

Contact Mrs. Michelle R. Wood, Director of Independent Study, Indiana Tech, 65 Airport Parkway, Suite 100, Greenwood, IN 46143. Telephone: 800-288-1766 Ext. 5300. Fax: 317-807-0377. E-mail: mrwood@indianatech.edu.

DEGREES AND AWARDS

AS Business Administration; General Studies
BS Business Administration
BSBA Human Resources; Management; Marketing

COURSE SUBJECT AREAS OFFERED OUTSIDE OF DEGREE PROGRAMS

Undergraduate—accounting and related services; business administration, management and operations; business/commerce; computer and information sciences; English composition; psychology; social sciences.

INDIANA UNIVERSITY OF PENNSYLVANIA
Indiana, Pennsylvania
School of Continuing Education
http://www.iup.edu/continuing-ed/

Indiana University of Pennsylvania was founded in 1875. It is accredited by Middle States Association of Colleges and Schools. It first offered distance learning courses in 1990. In fall 2005, there were 772 students enrolled in distance learning courses. Institutionally administered financial aid is available to distance learners.

Services Distance learners have accessibility to academic advising, bookstore, campus computer network, career placement assistance, e-mail services, library services.

Contact Mr. George Rogers, Assistant Dean, College of Continuing Education, Indiana University of Pennsylvania, 104 Keith Hall, 390 Pratt Drive, Indiana, PA 15705. Telephone: 724-357-2292. Fax: 724-357-7597. E-mail: grogers@iup.edu.

DEGREES AND AWARDS

Programs offered do not lead to a degree or other formal award.

COURSE SUBJECT AREAS OFFERED OUTSIDE OF DEGREE PROGRAMS

Undergraduate—accounting and related services; business/commerce; business, management, and marketing related; communications technology; criminology; foods, nutrition, and related services; geological and earth sciences/geosciences; hospitality administration; information science/studies; liberal arts and sciences, general studies and humanities; marketing; mathematics; physics; political science and government; psychology; technical and business writing.
Graduate—educational psychology; education related; engineering technologies related; physics.

INDIANA UNIVERSITY–PURDUE UNIVERSITY FORT WAYNE

Fort Wayne, Indiana
http://www.ipfw.edu/dlearning

Indiana University–Purdue University Fort Wayne was founded in 1917. It is accredited by North Central Association of Colleges and Schools. It first offered distance learning courses in 1996. In fall 2005, there were 2,700 students enrolled in distance learning courses. Institutionally administered financial aid is available to distance learners.
Services Distance learners have accessibility to bookstore, campus computer network, e-mail services, library services.
Contact Deborah Hein, Program Assistant, Indiana University–Purdue University Fort Wayne, 2101 East Coliseum Boulevard, Fort Wayne, IN 46805. Telephone: 260-481-6111. Fax: 260-481-6949. E-mail: dlearn@ipfw.edu.

DEGREES AND AWARDS

Programs offered do not lead to a degree or other formal award.

COURSE SUBJECT AREAS OFFERED OUTSIDE OF DEGREE PROGRAMS

Undergraduate—accounting and related services; biology; business/commerce; communication and media; comparative literature; computer science; economics; education; engineering/industrial management; English composition; history; journalism; mathematics; nursing; philosophy; political science and government; psychology; sociology.
Graduate—business administration, management and operations; educational administration and supervision; nursing.
Non-credit—business/corporate communications; business, management, and marketing related; business operations support and assistant services; computer software and media applications; computer systems networking and telecommunications.

INDIANA UNIVERSITY SYSTEM

Bloomington, Indiana
School of Continuing Studies
http://scs.indiana.edu

Indiana University System is accredited by North Central Association of Colleges and Schools. It first offered distance learning courses in 1995. In fall 2005, there were 4,000 students enrolled in distance learning courses. Institutionally administered financial aid is available to distance learners.
Services Distance learners have accessibility to academic advising, bookstore, campus computer network, e-mail services, library services.
Contact Peer Advisor, Indiana University System, Owen Hall 001, 790 East Kirkwood Avenue, Bloomington, IN 47405-7101. Telephone: 800-334-1011. Fax: 812-855-8680. E-mail: scs@indiana.edu.

DEGREES AND AWARDS

AA General Studies
BGS General Studies Degree program
Certificate Accounting–Healthcare Accounting and Financial Management; Distance Education
MS Adult Education

COURSE SUBJECT AREAS OFFERED OUTSIDE OF DEGREE PROGRAMS

Undergraduate—liberal arts and sciences, general studies and humanities.
Graduate—education related.
Non-credit—accounting and related services; education (specific levels and methods); taxation.

See full description on page 388.

INDIANA WESLEYAN UNIVERSITY

Marion, Indiana
Center for Distributed Learning
http://www.IWUonline.com

Indiana Wesleyan University was founded in 1920. It is accredited by North Central Association of Colleges and Schools. It first offered distance learning courses in 1996. In fall 2005, there were 2,800 students enrolled in distance learning courses. Institutionally administered financial aid is available to distance learners.
Services Distance learners have accessibility to academic advising, bookstore, library services, tutoring.
Contact Mr. Dennis Zuber, Online Enrollment Services, Indiana Wesleyan University, 1900 West 50th Street, Marion, IN 46953. Telephone: 888-IWU-2day. Fax: 765-677-2601. E-mail: info@iwuonline.com.

DEGREES AND AWARDS

AS Accounting; Business; Criminal Justice; General Studies
BS Accounting (Bachelor completion); Business Information Systems (Bachelor completion); Criminal Justice (Bachelor completion); General Studies; Management (Bachelor completion); Nursing (RN to BS completion)
BSBA Business Administration (Bachelor completion)
Certificate Communications; Criminal Justice; Human Services; Religious Studies
License Exceptional Needs with Mild Interventions (Special Ed)
MA Ministry (Ministerial Leadership and Youth Ministry concentrations)
MBA Business Administration
MEd Education
MSM Management
MSN Nursing Education and Nursing Administration majors

COURSE SUBJECT AREAS OFFERED OUTSIDE OF DEGREE PROGRAMS

Undergraduate—anthropology; biblical and other theological languages and literatures; biblical studies; communication and media; computer and information sciences; computer software and media applications; criminal justice and corrections; criminology; English composition; fine and studio art; history; liberal arts and sciences, general studies and humanities; mathematics; music; philosophy and religious studies related; psychology.
Graduate—educational psychology.

INTERNATIONAL INSTITUTE OF THE AMERICAS

Phoenix, Arizona
http://www.iia.edu

International Institute of the Americas was founded in 1979. It is accredited by Accrediting Council for Independent Colleges and Schools. It first offered distance learning courses in 1998. In fall 2005, there were 81 students enrolled in distance learning courses. Institutionally administered financial aid is available to distance learners.
Services Distance learners have accessibility to academic advising, bookstore, campus computer network, career placement assistance, e-mail services, library services.
Contact Ms. Mia Sciandra, Online Admissions Representative, International Institute of the Americas, 5242 West Camelback Road, Glendale, AZ 85301. Telephone: 623-463-6800 Ext. 6870. Fax: 623-463-6858. E-mail: msciandra@iia.edu.

DEGREES AND AWARDS

AA Health Technology Management–Medical Assistant; Health Technology Management–Patient Care Technician
AAB Business Operations–Accounting; Business Operations–Business Technology
BA Management

COURSE SUBJECT AREAS OFFERED OUTSIDE OF DEGREE PROGRAMS
Undergraduate—business administration, management and operations.

INTERNATIONAL INSTITUTE OF THE AMERICAS
Phoenix, Arizona
http://iia-online.com
International Institute of the Americas was founded in 1979. It is accredited by Accrediting Council for Independent Colleges and Schools. It first offered distance learning courses in 2000. In fall 2005, there were 100 students enrolled in distance learning courses. Institutionally administered financial aid is available to distance learners.
Services Distance learners have accessibility to academic advising, bookstore, campus computer network, career placement assistance, e-mail services, library services, tutoring.
Contact Ms. Mia Sciandra, Online Admissions Representative, International Institute of the Americas, 5242 West Camelback Road, Glendale, AZ 85301. Telephone: 623-463-6800 Ext. 6870. Fax: 623-463-6858. E-mail: msciandra@iia.edu.

DEGREES AND AWARDS
AA Business Operations–Business Technology
BA Management

COURSE SUBJECT AREAS OFFERED OUTSIDE OF DEGREE PROGRAMS
Undergraduate—accounting and related services; business administration, management and operations; business/commerce; business/corporate communications; business/managerial economics; communication and media; computer and information sciences; computer and information sciences and support services related; computer science; economics.

IONA COLLEGE
New Rochelle, New York
Iona College was founded in 1940. It is accredited by Middle States Association of Colleges and Schools. It first offered distance learning courses in 1999. In fall 2005, there were 188 students enrolled in distance learning courses. Institutionally administered financial aid is available to distance learners.
Services Distance learners have accessibility to academic advising, bookstore, campus computer network, career placement assistance, e-mail services, library services, tutoring.
Contact Mr. Thomas Weede, Director of Admissions, Iona College, Admissions, 715 North Avenue, New Rochelle, NY 10801. Telephone: 914-633-2502. Fax: 914-633-2642. E-mail: tweede@iona.edu.

DEGREES AND AWARDS
Programs offered do not lead to a degree or other formal award.

COURSE SUBJECT AREAS OFFERED OUTSIDE OF DEGREE PROGRAMS
Undergraduate—business administration, management and operations; business/corporate communications; business, management, and marketing related; business operations support and assistant services; communication and journalism related; computer and information sciences and support services related; entrepreneurial and small business operations; finance and financial management services; human resources management; legal professions and studies related; liberal arts and sciences, general studies and humanities; management information systems; marketing; philosophy and religious studies related; psychology.
Graduate—business administration, management and operations; business/commerce; business/corporate communications; business, management, and marketing related; education; educational administration and supervision; educational/instructional media design; education (specific levels and methods); education (specific subject areas); finance and financial management services; health professions related; human resources management; international business; legal professions and studies related; management information systems; marketing; psychology; public relations, advertising, and applied communication related.

IOWA STATE UNIVERSITY OF SCIENCE AND TECHNOLOGY
Ames, Iowa
Continuing Education and Conference Services
http://www.lifelearner.iastate.edu
Iowa State University of Science and Technology was founded in 1858. It is accredited by North Central Association of Colleges and Schools. It first offered distance learning courses in 1969. In fall 2005, there were 1,185 students enrolled in distance learning courses. Institutionally administered financial aid is available to distance learners.
Services Distance learners have accessibility to academic advising, bookstore, campus computer network, career placement assistance, e-mail services, library services.
Contact Lynette Spicer, Communication Specialist, Iowa State University of Science and Technology, Extension 4-H Youth Building, Ames, IA 50011-3630. Telephone: 515-294-1327. Fax: 515-294-7767. E-mail: lspicer@iastate.edu.

DEGREES AND AWARDS
Certificate Information Assurance; Power Systems Engineering
Graduate Certificate Environmental Engineering; Family Financial Planning; Gerontology; Systems Engineering
MAg Agriculture
MCP Community and Regional Planning
ME Systems Engineering
MS Agronomy; Computer Engineering; Electrical Engineering; Family and Consumer Sciences; Industrial Engineering; Interdisciplinary Studies, Community Development specialization; Mechanical Engineering; Seed Technology and Business; Statistics
PhD Food Service and Lodging Management

COURSE SUBJECT AREAS OFFERED OUTSIDE OF DEGREE PROGRAMS
Undergraduate—agriculture; atmospheric sciences and meteorology; biochemistry, biophysics and molecular biology; biology; criminal justice and corrections; economics; food science and technology; human development, family studies, and related services; mathematics and computer science; sociology.
Graduate—agricultural business and management; atmospheric sciences and meteorology; biochemistry, biophysics and molecular biology; civil engineering; family and consumer economics; food science and technology; foods, nutrition, and related services.

IOWA WESTERN COMMUNITY COLLEGE
Council Bluffs, Iowa
http://iwcc.edu
Iowa Western Community College was founded in 1966. It is accredited by North Central Association of Colleges and Schools. It first offered distance learning courses in 1983. In fall 2005, there were 1,150 students enrolled in distance learning courses. Institutionally administered financial aid is available to distance learners.
Services Distance learners have accessibility to academic advising, bookstore, campus computer network, e-mail services, library services, tutoring.
Contact Barb Vredeveld, Director, Iowa Western Community College, 2700 College Road, Box 4-C, Council Bluffs, IA 51502. Telephone: 712-325-3400. Fax: 712-325-3717. E-mail: bvredeveld@iwcc.edu.

DEGREES AND AWARDS
AS Liberal Arts and Studies

COURSE SUBJECT AREAS OFFERED OUTSIDE OF DEGREE PROGRAMS
Undergraduate—accounting and computer science; accounting and related services; agricultural business and management; air transportation; allied health and medical assisting services; American literature (United States and Canadian); anthropology; applied mathematics; astronomy and astrophysics; atmospheric sciences and meteorology; biological and biomedical sciences related; biology; business administration, management and operations; business/commerce; business/corporate communications; business, management, and marketing related;

chemistry; communication and media; computer and information sciences; computer programming; computer science; computer software and media applications; creative writing; criminal justice and corrections; criminology; data entry/microcomputer applications; dramatic/theater arts and stagecraft; economics; education; electrical and electronic engineering technologies; English; English composition; English language and literature related; entrepreneurial and small business operations; finance and financial management services; fine and studio art; geography and cartography; health and physical education/fitness; history; human development, family studies, and related services; human services; journalism; legal studies (non-professional general, undergraduate); liberal arts and sciences, general studies and humanities; marketing; mathematics; mathematics and statistics related; philosophy; philosophy and religious studies related; physical sciences; physical sciences related; political science and government; psychology; public relations, advertising, and applied communication related; sales, merchandising, and related marketing operations (general); social sciences; sociology; speech and rhetoric; statistics.

ITAWAMBA COMMUNITY COLLEGE

Fulton, Mississippi

Itawamba Community College was founded in 1947. It is accredited by Southern Association of Colleges and Schools. It first offered distance learning courses in 2000. In fall 2005, there were 2,000 students enrolled in distance learning courses. Institutionally administered financial aid is available to distance learners.

Services Distance learners have accessibility to academic advising, bookstore, e-mail services, library services.

Contact Dr. Ellene McCrimon, Dean of Distance Learning, Itawamba Community College, 2176 South Eason Boulevard, Tupelo, MS 38804. Telephone: 662-620-5350. Fax: 662-620-5354. E-mail: emmccrimon@iccms.edu.

DEGREES AND AWARDS

Programs offered do not lead to a degree or other formal award.

COURSE SUBJECT AREAS OFFERED OUTSIDE OF DEGREE PROGRAMS

Undergraduate—accounting and computer science; accounting and related services; agriculture; allied health and medical assisting services; American literature (United States and Canadian); applied mathematics; communication and media; communications technology; computer programming; computer science; criminology; developmental and child psychology; economics; English composition; English literature (British and Commonwealth); health services/allied health/health sciences; history; languages (foreign languages related); legal professions and studies related; management information systems; marketing; mathematics; mathematics and computer science; mathematics and statistics related; music; natural sciences; nursing; nutrition sciences; philosophy; physical sciences; physics; psychology; religious studies; social sciences; social sciences related; sociology; statistics; technology education/industrial arts; theology and religious vocations related; visual and performing arts.

IVY TECH COMMUNITY COLLEGE–BLOOMINGTON

Bloomington, Indiana

http://www.ivytech.edu/bloomington/

Ivy Tech Community College–Bloomington was founded in 2001. It is accredited by North Central Association of Colleges and Schools. In fall 2005, there were 566 students enrolled in distance learning courses. Institutionally administered financial aid is available to distance learners.

Services Distance learners have accessibility to academic advising, bookstore, campus computer network, career placement assistance, e-mail services, library services.

Contact Neil Frederick, Assistant Director of Admissions, Ivy Tech Community College–Bloomington, 200 Daniels Way, Bloomington, IN 47404-0393. Telephone: 812-330-6026. Fax: 812-330-6200. E-mail: nfrederi@ivytech.edu.

DEGREES AND AWARDS

AAS Computer Information Systems; Early Childhood Education; Human Services; Office Administration; Paralegal

AS Computer Information Systems; General Studies; Human Services; Library Assistant; Paralegal

COURSE SUBJECT AREAS OFFERED OUTSIDE OF DEGREE PROGRAMS

Undergraduate—business administration, management and operations; business operations support and assistant services; criminal justice and corrections; mathematics.

IVY TECH COMMUNITY COLLEGE–CENTRAL INDIANA

Indianapolis, Indiana

http://www.ivytech.edu/indianapolis/

Ivy Tech Community College–Central Indiana was founded in 1963. It is accredited by North Central Association of Colleges and Schools. It first offered distance learning courses in 1995. In fall 2005, there were 834 students enrolled in distance learning courses. Institutionally administered financial aid is available to distance learners.

Services Distance learners have accessibility to academic advising, bookstore, career placement assistance, e-mail services, library services, tutoring.

Contact Tracy Funk, Director of Admissions, Ivy Tech Community College–Central Indiana, 50 West Fall Creek Parkway North Drive, Indianapolis, IN 46208-4777. Telephone: 317-921-4371. Fax: 317-921-4753. E-mail: tfunk@ivytech.edu.

DEGREES AND AWARDS

AAS Computer Information Systems; Early Childhood Education; Human Services; Office Administration; Paralegal

AS Computer Information Systems; General Studies; Human Services; Library Assistant; Paralegal

COURSE SUBJECT AREAS OFFERED OUTSIDE OF DEGREE PROGRAMS

Undergraduate—business operations support and assistant services; criminal justice and corrections; mathematics.

IVY TECH COMMUNITY COLLEGE–COLUMBUS

Columbus, Indiana

http://www.ivytech.edu/columbus/

Ivy Tech Community College–Columbus was founded in 1963. It is accredited by North Central Association of Colleges and Schools. It first offered distance learning courses in 1995. In fall 2005, there were 357 students enrolled in distance learning courses. Institutionally administered financial aid is available to distance learners.

Services Distance learners have accessibility to academic advising, bookstore, campus computer network, career placement assistance, e-mail services, library services.

Contact Neil S. Bagadiong, Director of Admissions/Assistant to the Dean of Student Affairs, Ivy Tech Community College–Columbus, 4475 Central Avenue, Columbus, IN 47203-1868. Telephone: 812-374-5129 Ext.. Fax: 812-372-0311. E-mail: nbagadio@ivytech.edu.

DEGREES AND AWARDS

AAS Computer Information Systems; Early Childhood Education; Human Services; Office Administration; Paralegal

AS Computer Information Systems; General Studies; Human Services; Library Assistant; Paralegal

COURSE SUBJECT AREAS OFFERED OUTSIDE OF DEGREE PROGRAMS

Undergraduate—business administration, management and operations; business operations support and assistant services; mathematics.

IVY TECH COMMUNITY COLLEGE–EAST CENTRAL
Muncie, Indiana
http://www.ivytech.edu/muncie/

Ivy Tech Community College–East Central was founded in 1968. It is accredited by North Central Association of Colleges and Schools. It first offered distance learning courses in 1995. In fall 2005, there were 625 students enrolled in distance learning courses. Institutionally administered financial aid is available to distance learners.

Services Distance learners have accessibility to academic advising, bookstore, campus computer network, career placement assistance, e-mail services, library services.

Contact Corey A. Sharp, Admissions Advisor, Ivy Tech Community College–East Central, 4301 South Cowan Road, Muncie, IN 47302-9448. Telephone: 765-289-2291. Fax: 765-289-2292. E-mail: csharp@ivytech.edu.

DEGREES AND AWARDS
AAS Computer Information Systems; Early Childhood Education; Human Services; Office Administration; Paralegal Studies
AS Computer Information Systems; General Studies; Human Services; Library Technical Assistant; Paralegal Studies

COURSE SUBJECT AREAS OFFERED OUTSIDE OF DEGREE PROGRAMS
Undergraduate—business administration, management and operations; business operations support and assistant services; criminal justice and corrections; mathematics; psychology.

IVY TECH COMMUNITY COLLEGE–KOKOMO
Kokomo, Indiana
http://www.ivytech.edu/kokomo/

Ivy Tech Community College–Kokomo was founded in 1968. It is accredited by North Central Association of Colleges and Schools. It first offered distance learning courses in 1995. In fall 2005, there were 297 students enrolled in distance learning courses. Institutionally administered financial aid is available to distance learners.

Services Distance learners have accessibility to academic advising, bookstore, campus computer network, career placement assistance, e-mail services, library services.

Contact Suzanne Dillman, Director of Admissions, Ivy Tech Community College–Kokomo, 1815 East Morgan Street, Kokomo, IN 46903-1373. Telephone: 765-459-0561 Ext. 318. Fax: 765-454-5111. E-mail: sdillman@ivytech.edu.

DEGREES AND AWARDS
AAS Computer Information Systems; Early Childhood Education; Human Services; Office Administration; Paralegal Studies
AS Computer Information Systems; General Studies; Human Services; Library Technical Assistant; Paralegal

COURSE SUBJECT AREAS OFFERED OUTSIDE OF DEGREE PROGRAMS
Undergraduate—criminal justice and corrections; English composition; history; quality control and safety technologies.

IVY TECH COMMUNITY COLLEGE–LAFAYETTE
Lafayette, Indiana
http://www.ivytech.edu/lafayette/

Ivy Tech Community College–Lafayette was founded in 1968. It is accredited by North Central Association of Colleges and Schools. It first offered distance learning courses in 1995. In fall 2005, there were 305 students enrolled in distance learning courses. Institutionally administered financial aid is available to distance learners.

Services Distance learners have accessibility to academic advising, bookstore, campus computer network, career placement assistance, e-mail services, library services.

Contact Judy Doppelfeld, Director of Admissions, Ivy Tech Community College–Lafayette, 3101 South Creasy Lane, Lafayette, IN 47903. Telephone: 765-772-9116. Fax: 765-772-9107. E-mail: jdoppelf@ivytech.edu.

DEGREES AND AWARDS
AAS Computer Information Systems; Early Childhood Education; Human Services; Office Administration; Paralegal Studies
AS Computer Information Systems; General Studies; Human Services; Library Technical Assistant; Paralegal Studies

IVY TECH COMMUNITY COLLEGE–NORTH CENTRAL
South Bend, Indiana
Instructional Technology
http://www.ivytech.edu/southbend/

Ivy Tech Community College–North Central was founded in 1968. It is accredited by North Central Association of Colleges and Schools. It first offered distance learning courses in 1989. In fall 2005, there were 755 students enrolled in distance learning courses. Institutionally administered financial aid is available to distance learners.

Services Distance learners have accessibility to academic advising, bookstore, campus computer network, career placement assistance, e-mail services, library services.

Contact Pam Decker, Director of Admissions, Ivy Tech Community College–North Central, 220 Dean Johnson Boulevard, South Bend, IN 46601. Telephone: 574-289-7001. Fax: 574-236-7177. E-mail: pdecker@ivytech.edu.

DEGREES AND AWARDS
AAS Computer Information Systems; Early Childhood Education; Human Services; Office Administration; Paralegal Studies
AS Computer Information Systems; General Studies; Human Services; Library Technical Assistant; Paralegal Studies

COURSE SUBJECT AREAS OFFERED OUTSIDE OF DEGREE PROGRAMS
Undergraduate—biology; economics; English composition; philosophy; political science and government; psychology; sales, merchandising, and related marketing operations (general); sociology; visual and performing arts related.

IVY TECH COMMUNITY COLLEGE–NORTHEAST
Fort Wayne, Indiana
http://www.ivytech.edu/fortwayne/

Ivy Tech Community College–Northeast was founded in 1969. It is accredited by North Central Association of Colleges and Schools. It first offered distance learning courses in 1995. In fall 2005, there were 525 students enrolled in distance learning courses. Institutionally administered financial aid is available to distance learners.

Services Distance learners have accessibility to academic advising, bookstore, campus computer network, career placement assistance, e-mail services, library services.

Contact Steve Scheer, Director of Admissions, Ivy Tech Community College–Northeast, 3800 North Anthony Boulevard, Fort Wayne, IN 46805-1489. Telephone: 260-480-4221. Fax: 260-480-4177. E-mail: sscheer@ivytech.edu.

DEGREES AND AWARDS
AAS Computer Information Systems; Early Childhood Education; Human Services; Office Administration; Paralegal Studies
AS Computer Information Systems; General Studies; General Studies; Human Services; Library Technical Assistant; Paralegal Studies

COURSE SUBJECT AREAS OFFERED OUTSIDE OF DEGREE PROGRAMS
Undergraduate—construction engineering technology; fire protection.

IVY TECH COMMUNITY COLLEGE–NORTHWEST
Gary, Indiana
http://www.ivytech.edu/gary

Ivy Tech Community College–Northwest was founded in 1963. It is accredited by North Central Association of Colleges and Schools. It first offered distance learning courses in 1995. In fall 2005, there were 972 students enrolled in distance learning courses. Institutionally administered financial aid is available to distance learners.

Services Distance learners have accessibility to academic advising, bookstore, campus computer network, career placement assistance, e-mail services, library services.

Contact Twilla Lewis, Associate Dean of Student Affairs, Ivy Tech Community College–Northwest, 1440 East 35th Avenue, Gary, IN 46409-1499. Telephone: 219-981-1111 Ext. 273. Fax: 219-981-4415. E-mail: tlewis@ivytech.edu.

DEGREES AND AWARDS

AAS Computer Information Systems; Early Childhood Education; Human Services; Office Administration; Paralegal Studies
AS Computer Information Systems; General Studies; Human Services; Library Technical Assistant; Paralegal Studies

COURSE SUBJECT AREAS OFFERED OUTSIDE OF DEGREE PROGRAMS

Undergraduate—accounting and related services; business administration, management and operations; business operations support and assistant services; economics; English composition; fire protection; history; hospitality administration; marketing; mathematics; nursing; physical sciences; psychology; sociology.

IVY TECH COMMUNITY COLLEGE–SOUTHEAST

Madison, Indiana

http://www.ivytech.edu/madison/

Ivy Tech Community College–Southeast was founded in 1963. It is accredited by North Central Association of Colleges and Schools. It first offered distance learning courses in 1995. In fall 2005, there were 321 students enrolled in distance learning courses. Institutionally administered financial aid is available to distance learners.
Services Distance learners have accessibility to academic advising, bookstore, campus computer network, career placement assistance, e-mail services, library services.
Contact Cindy Hutcherson, Assistant Director of Admissions and Career Counselor, Ivy Tech Community College–Southeast, 590 Ivy Tech Drive, Madison, IN 47250-1881. Telephone: 812-265-2580. Fax: 812-265-4028. E-mail: chutcher@ivytech.edu.

DEGREES AND AWARDS

AAS Computer Information Systems; Early Childhood Education; Human Services; Office Administration; Paralegal
AS Computer Information Systems; General Studies; Human Services; Library Assistant; Paralegal

COURSE SUBJECT AREAS OFFERED OUTSIDE OF DEGREE PROGRAMS

Undergraduate—business administration, management and operations; business operations support and assistant services; criminal justice and corrections.

IVY TECH COMMUNITY COLLEGE–SOUTHERN INDIANA

Sellersburg, Indiana

http://www.ivytech.edu/sellersburg/

Ivy Tech Community College–Southern Indiana was founded in 1968. It is accredited by North Central Association of Colleges and Schools. It first offered distance learning courses in 1995. In fall 2005, there were 349 students enrolled in distance learning courses. Institutionally administered financial aid is available to distance learners.
Services Distance learners have accessibility to academic advising, bookstore, campus computer network, career placement assistance, e-mail services, library services.
Contact Pat Fawcett, Interim Dean of Enrollment Services, Ivy Tech Community College–Southern Indiana, 8204 Highway 311, Sellersburg, IN 47172-1897. Telephone: 812-246-3301. Fax: 812-246-9905. E-mail: pfawcett@ivytech.edu.

DEGREES AND AWARDS

AAS Computer Information Systems; Early Childhood Education; Human Services; Office Administration; Paralegal
AS Computer Information Systems; General Studies; Human Services; Library Assistant; Paralegal

COURSE SUBJECT AREAS OFFERED OUTSIDE OF DEGREE PROGRAMS

Undergraduate—business administration, management and operations; business operations support and assistant services; criminal justice and corrections; mathematics; sociology.

IVY TECH COMMUNITY COLLEGE–SOUTHWEST

Evansville, Indiana

http://www.ivytech.edu/evansville/

Ivy Tech Community College–Southwest was founded in 1963. It is accredited by North Central Association of Colleges and Schools. It first offered distance learning courses in 1995. In fall 2005, there were 368 students enrolled in distance learning courses. Institutionally administered financial aid is available to distance learners.
Services Distance learners have accessibility to academic advising, bookstore, campus computer network, career placement assistance, e-mail services, library services.
Contact Denise Johnson-Kincade, Assistant Director, Ivy Tech Community College–Southwest, 3501 First Avenue, Evansville, IN 47710-3398. Telephone: 812-429-1430. Fax: 812-246-9905 Ext.. E-mail: ajohnson@ivytech.edu.

DEGREES AND AWARDS

AAS Computer Information Systems; Early Childhood Education; Human Services; Office Administration; Paralegal
AS Computer Information Systems; General Studies; Human Services; Library Assistant; Paralegal

COURSE SUBJECT AREAS OFFERED OUTSIDE OF DEGREE PROGRAMS

Undergraduate—business administration, management and operations; business operations support and assistant services; criminal justice and corrections; mathematics.

IVY TECH COMMUNITY COLLEGE–WABASH VALLEY

Terre Haute, Indiana

http://www.ivytech.edu/terrehaute/

Ivy Tech Community College–Wabash Valley was founded in 1966. It is accredited by North Central Association of Colleges and Schools. It first offered distance learning courses in 1995. In fall 2005, there were 1,272 students enrolled in distance learning courses. Institutionally administered financial aid is available to distance learners.
Services Distance learners have accessibility to academic advising, bookstore, campus computer network, career placement assistance, e-mail services, library services.
Contact Michael Fisher, Director of Admissions, Ivy Tech Community College–Wabash Valley, 7999 US Highway 41, Terre Haute, IN 47802-4898. Telephone: 812-298-2300. Fax: 812-299-5723. E-mail: mfisher@ivytech.edu.

DEGREES AND AWARDS

AAS Computer Information Systems; Early Childhood Education; Human Services; Office Administration; Paralegal
AS Computer Information Systems; General Studies; Human Services; Library Assistant; Paralegal

COURSE SUBJECT AREAS OFFERED OUTSIDE OF DEGREE PROGRAMS

Undergraduate—biology; business administration, management and operations; business operations support and assistant services; mathematics; psychology.

IVY TECH COMMUNITY COLLEGE–WHITEWATER

Richmond, Indiana

http://www.ivytech.edu/richmond/

Ivy Tech Community College–Whitewater was founded in 1963. It is accredited by North Central Association of Colleges and Schools. It first offered distance learning courses in 1995. In fall 2005, there were 548 students enrolled in distance learning courses. Institutionally administered financial aid is available to distance learners.
Services Distance learners have accessibility to academic advising, bookstore, career placement assistance, e-mail services, library services, tutoring.

Contact Jeff Plasterer, Director of Admissions, Ivy Tech Community College–Whitewater, 2325 Chester Boulevard, Richmond, IN 47374-1298. Telephone: 765-966-2656 Ext. 1212. Fax: 765-962-8741. E-mail: jplaster@ivytech.edu.

DEGREES AND AWARDS

AAS Computer Information Systems; Early Childhood Education; Human Services; Office Administration; Paralegal
AS Computer Information Systems; General Studies; Human Services; Library Assistant; Paralegal

COURSE SUBJECT AREAS OFFERED OUTSIDE OF DEGREE PROGRAMS

Undergraduate—business administration, management and operations; business operations support and assistant services; criminal justice and corrections; mathematics; psychology.

JACKSON COMMUNITY COLLEGE

Jackson, Michigan
http://www.jccmi.edu/distancelearning

Jackson Community College was founded in 1928. It is accredited by North Central Association of Colleges and Schools. It first offered distance learning courses in 1987. In fall 2005, there were 1,110 students enrolled in distance learning courses. Institutionally administered financial aid is available to distance learners.
Services Distance learners have accessibility to academic advising, bookstore, campus computer network, career placement assistance, e-mail services, library services, tutoring.
Contact Jessie Baldwin, Coordinator of Technical Services, Jackson Community College, 2111 Emmons Road, Jackson, MI 49201. Telephone: 517-796-8604. Fax: 517-796-8603. E-mail: jessie_baldwin@jccmi.edu.

DEGREES AND AWARDS

AA Arts
AAS Business Administration; Diagnostic Medical Sonography Echocardiography; Diagnostic Medical Sonography; Vascular Sonography
AGS General Studies
Certificate Business Administration; Diagnostic Medical Sonography Echocardiography; Diagnostic Medical Sonography; Management; Management; Vascular Technology

COURSE SUBJECT AREAS OFFERED OUTSIDE OF DEGREE PROGRAMS

Undergraduate—allied health diagnostic, intervention, and treatment professions; American literature (United States and Canadian); anthropology; business/commerce; communication and media; computer and information sciences and support services related; computer software and media applications; drafting/design engineering technologies; economics; English; English composition; ethnic, cultural minority, and gender studies; history; marketing; mathematics; nursing; social psychology; sociology.
Non-credit—business administration, management and operations; business/commerce; computer software and media applications; health professions related; personal and culinary services related.

JACKSONVILLE STATE UNIVERSITY

Jacksonville, Alabama
Department of Distance Education
http://distance.jsu.edu

Jacksonville State University was founded in 1883. It is accredited by Southern Association of Colleges and Schools. It first offered distance learning courses in 1994. In fall 2005, there were 7,476 students enrolled in distance learning courses. Institutionally administered financial aid is available to distance learners.
Services Distance learners have accessibility to academic advising, bookstore, campus computer network, career placement assistance, e-mail services, library services, tutoring.
Contact Dr. Franklin L. King, Associate Vice President for Distance Education, Jacksonville State University, Office of Distance Education, 700 Pelham Road North, Jacksonville, AL 36265-1602. Telephone: 256-782-5616. Fax: 256-782-8128. E-mail: fking@jsu.edu.

DEGREES AND AWARDS

BA Liberal Studies
BS Emergency Management (Public Safety Communications minor); Emergency Management–Homeland Security minor
BSN Nursing (STEP Nursing Program)
Certificate Spatial Analysis and Emergency Management
Graduate Certificate Emergency Management
MA Liberal Studies
MBA Business Administration
MEd Physical Education
MPA Business Administration; Emergency Management; Political Science; Spatial Analysis and Management concentration
MS Emergency Management
MSN Nursing

COURSE SUBJECT AREAS OFFERED OUTSIDE OF DEGREE PROGRAMS

Undergraduate—accounting and computer science; accounting and related services; American literature (United States and Canadian); anthropology; applied mathematics; atmospheric sciences and meteorology; behavioral sciences; biological and biomedical sciences related; biological and physical sciences; biology; business administration, management and operations; business/commerce; business, management, and marketing related; business/managerial economics; chemistry; clinical psychology; community health services; computer and information sciences; computer and information sciences and support services related; computer/information technology administration and management; computer programming; computer science; computer software and media applications; computer systems analysis; computer systems networking and telecommunications; criminal justice and corrections; criminology; curriculum and instruction; data processing; developmental and child psychology; economics; education; educational administration and supervision; educational assessment, evaluation, and research; educational/instructional media design; educational psychology; education related; education (specific levels and methods); education (specific subject areas); engineering; English; English composition; English language and literature related; English literature (British and Commonwealth); environmental control technologies; family and consumer sciences/human sciences; family and consumer sciences/human sciences related; finance and financial management services; foods, nutrition, and related services; geography and cartography; geological and earth sciences/geosciences; health and physical education/fitness; health professions related; history; human development, family studies, and related services; information science/studies; liberal arts and sciences, general studies and humanities; management information systems; management sciences and quantitative methods; marketing; mathematics; mathematics and computer science; mathematics and statistics related; medical basic sciences; music; nursing; nutrition sciences; physical sciences; physics; political science and government; psychology; psychology related; psychopharmacology; public administration; public administration and social service professions related; quality control and safety technologies; sales, merchandising, and related marketing operations (general); sales, merchandising, and related marketing operations (specialized); school psychology; security and protective services related; social sciences; social work; sociology; special education; statistics; student counseling and personnel services; technology education/industrial arts.
Graduate—accounting and related services; biology; business administration, management and operations; business/commerce; business/corporate communications; business, management, and marketing related; business/managerial economics; chemistry; clinical psychology; computer and information sciences; computer and information sciences and support services related; computer engineering; computer/information technology administration and management; computer programming; computer science; computer software and media applications; computer systems analysis; computer systems networking and telecommunications; criminal justice and corrections; criminology; curriculum and instruction; developmental and child psychology; economics; education; educational administration and supervision; educational assessment, evaluation, and research; educational/instructional media design; educational psychology; education related; education (specific subject areas); envi-

ronmental control technologies; family and consumer sciences/human sciences related; finance and financial management services; fire protection; geography and cartography; geological and earth sciences/geosciences; health and physical education/fitness; health professions related; human development, family studies, and related services; human resources management; information science/studies; liberal arts and sciences, general studies and humanities; management information systems; management sciences and quantitative methods; marketing; mathematics and computer science; medical basic sciences; nursing; physical sciences; political science and government; psychopharmacology; public administration; public administration and social service professions related; quality control and safety technologies; sales, merchandising, and related marketing operations (general); sales, merchandising, and related marketing operations (specialized); school psychology; security and protective services related; social sciences; social work; sociology; special education; statistics.

JAMES MADISON UNIVERSITY
Harrisonburg, Virginia
Distance Learning Center, Office of Continuing Education
http://jmuonline.jmu.edu

James Madison University was founded in 1908. It is accredited by Southern Association of Colleges and Schools. It first offered distance learning courses in 1996. In fall 2005, there were 380 students enrolled in distance learning courses. Institutionally administered financial aid is available to distance learners.

Services Distance learners have accessibility to academic advising, bookstore, campus computer network, career placement assistance, e-mail services, library services.

Contact Dr. Jim Mazoue, Distance Learning Coordinator, Distributed and Distance Learning, James Madison University, 7D Carrier Library, MSC 1702, Harrisonburg, VA 22807. Telephone: 540-568-2591. Fax: 540-568-6734. E-mail: mazouejg@jmu.edu.

DEGREES AND AWARDS
MBA Information Security
MCC Information Security

COURSE SUBJECT AREAS OFFERED OUTSIDE OF DEGREE PROGRAMS
Undergraduate—accounting and related services; biology/biotechnology laboratory technician; business/commerce; communication and media; communications technology; education (specific levels and methods); English composition; health and physical education/fitness; health professions related; human resources management; linguistic, comparative, and related language studies; philosophy; psychology; statistics; technical and business writing.
Graduate—special education.
Non-credit—allied health diagnostic, intervention, and treatment professions; American literature (United States and Canadian); applied mathematics; archeology; architecture; astronomy and astrophysics; biological and biomedical sciences related; biological and physical sciences; building/construction finishing, management, and inspection; business/commerce; business/corporate communications; business, management, and marketing related; communication and journalism related; communication disorders sciences and services; computer programming; computer science; computer systems networking and telecommunications; construction engineering technology; construction trades related; cosmetology and related personal grooming services; counseling psychology; crafts, folk art and artisanry; creative writing; criminal justice and corrections; culinary arts and related services; data entry/microcomputer applications; education; education (specific levels and methods); English; English as a second language; English composition; entrepreneurial and small business operations; family and consumer sciences/human sciences; film/video and photographic arts; fine and studio art; fire protection; foods, nutrition, and related services; forestry; geography and cartography; geological and earth sciences/geosciences; health aides/attendants/orderlies; health and physical education/fitness; health/medical preparatory programs; history; human resources management; human services; information science/studies; international business; journalism; landscape architecture; languages (Germanic); languages (Romance languages); liberal arts and sciences, general studies and humanities; library assistant; linguistic, comparative, and related language studies; management sciences and quantitative methods; marketing; mathematics and computer science; museum studies; music; natural resources and conservation related; nursing; parks, recreation, and leisure related; physical sciences; physical sciences related; physics; plant sciences; political science and government; precision systems maintenance and repair technologies; public administration; public health; public relations, advertising, and applied communication related; quality control and safety technologies; radio, television, and digital communication; real estate; sales, merchandising, and related marketing operations (general); sales, merchandising, and related marketing operations (specialized); social sciences; special education; speech and rhetoric; student counseling and personnel services; systems engineering; taxation; transportation and materials moving related; urban studies/affairs; visual and performing arts.

JAMES SPRUNT COMMUNITY COLLEGE
Kenansville, North Carolina
James Sprunt Community College Distance Learning
http://www.sprunt.com

James Sprunt Community College was founded in 1964. It is accredited by Southern Association of Colleges and Schools. It first offered distance learning courses in 1999. In fall 2005, there were 225 students enrolled in distance learning courses. Institutionally administered financial aid is available to distance learners.

Services Distance learners have accessibility to academic advising, bookstore, library services.

Contact Mrs. Heather L. Lanier, Distance Learning Coordinator, James Sprunt Community College, 221 James Sprunt Circle, PO Box 398, Kenansville, NC 28349. Telephone: 910-296-1334. Fax: 910-296-0731. E-mail: hlanier@jscc.cc.nc.us.

DEGREES AND AWARDS
Programs offered do not lead to a degree or other formal award.

COURSE SUBJECT AREAS OFFERED OUTSIDE OF DEGREE PROGRAMS
Undergraduate—accounting and computer science; agricultural business and management; agriculture and agriculture operations related; allied health and medical assisting services; animal sciences; business administration, management and operations; business/corporate communications; business operations support and assistant services; communication and journalism related; computer software and media applications; criminal justice and corrections; English composition; English language and literature related; English literature (British and Commonwealth); history; linguistic, comparative, and related language studies; marketing; mathematics; psychology; religious studies; sociology.

JAMESTOWN COMMUNITY COLLEGE
Jamestown, New York
Distance Education
http://www.sunyjcc.edu/online

Jamestown Community College was founded in 1950. It is accredited by Middle States Association of Colleges and Schools. It first offered distance learning courses in 1995. In fall 2005, there were 300 students enrolled in distance learning courses. Institutionally administered financial aid is available to distance learners.

Services Distance learners have accessibility to academic advising, bookstore, campus computer network, career placement assistance, e-mail services, library services, tutoring.

Contact Admissions Office, Jamestown Community College, 525 Falconer Street, PO Box 20, Jamestown, NY 14702-0020. Telephone: 800-388-8557 Ext. 2476. Fax: 716-664-9592. E-mail: admissions@mail.sunyjcc.edu.

DEGREES AND AWARDS
AA Individual Studies
AAS Computer Information Systems; Individual Studies; Information Technology
AS Computer Science; Individual Studies
CCCPE Individual Studies; Information Technology; Psychology of the Workplace

COURSE SUBJECT AREAS OFFERED OUTSIDE OF DEGREE PROGRAMS

Non-credit—accounting and related services; business administration, management and operations; business/commerce; business/corporate communications; business, management, and marketing related; business operations support and assistant services; communication and media; computer and information sciences; computer and information sciences and support services related; computer software and media applications; computer systems networking and telecommunications; creative writing; English composition; entrepreneurial and small business operations; finance and financial management services; food science and technology; health and medical administrative services; human resources management; human services; journalism; liberal arts and sciences, general studies and humanities; linguistic, comparative, and related language studies; marketing; psychology related; real estate; sociology.

JEFFERSON COLLEGE OF HEALTH SCIENCES
Roanoke, Virginia
http://www.jchs.edu/

Jefferson College of Health Sciences was founded in 1982. It is accredited by Southern Association of Colleges and Schools. It first offered distance learning courses in 1999. In fall 2005, there were 400 students enrolled in distance learning courses. Institutionally administered financial aid is available to distance learners.

Services Distance learners have accessibility to academic advising, bookstore, e-mail services, library services.

Contact Elizabeth Claybrook, Educational Resource Associate, Jefferson College of Health Sciences, PO Box 13186, Roanoke, VA 24031. Telephone: 540-985-6971. Fax: 540-985-8512. E-mail: eclaybrook@jchs.edu.

DEGREES AND AWARDS

Programs offered do not lead to a degree or other formal award.

COURSE SUBJECT AREAS OFFERED OUTSIDE OF DEGREE PROGRAMS

Undergraduate—allied health diagnostic, intervention, and treatment professions; business administration, management and operations; community health services; computer software and media applications; English composition; foods, nutrition, and related services; gerontology; health and medical administrative services; health and physical education/fitness; health/medical preparatory programs; health professions related; human resources management; nursing; philosophy; psychology; public health; rehabilitation and therapeutic professions; sociology; statistics; technical and business writing.

Graduate—nursing; philosophy.

Non-credit—allied health diagnostic, intervention, and treatment professions; nursing.

JEFFERSON COMMUNITY COLLEGE
Watertown, New York
Division of Continuing Education
http://www.sunyjefferson.edu

Jefferson Community College was founded in 1961. It is accredited by Middle States Association of Colleges and Schools. It first offered distance learning courses in 1995. In fall 2005, there were 1,000 students enrolled in distance learning courses. Institutionally administered financial aid is available to distance learners.

Services Distance learners have accessibility to academic advising, bookstore, career placement assistance, e-mail services, library services, tutoring.

Contact MaKeever Clarke, Distance Learning Coordinator, Jefferson Community College, 1220 Coffeen Street, Watertown, NY 13601. Telephone: 315-786-6527. Fax: 315-786-0158. E-mail: mclarke@sunyjefferson.edu.

DEGREES AND AWARDS

AA Individual Studies; Liberal Arts–Humanities and Social Science
AAS Individual Studies
AS Business Administration; Criminal Justice; Individual Studies

COURSE SUBJECT AREAS OFFERED OUTSIDE OF DEGREE PROGRAMS

Undergraduate—business administration, management and operations; business, management, and marketing related; economics; English composition; history; mathematics and statistics related; psychology; sociology; technical and business writing.

JEFFERSON DAVIS COMMUNITY COLLEGE
Brewton, Alabama
http://www.jdcc.edu

Jefferson Davis Community College was founded in 1965. It is accredited by Southern Association of Colleges and Schools. It first offered distance learning courses in 1994. In fall 2005, there were 137 students enrolled in distance learning courses. Institutionally administered financial aid is available to distance learners.

Services Distance learners have accessibility to e-mail services, library services.

Contact Kathleen Hall, Dean of Instruction, Jefferson Davis Community College, PO Box 958, Brewton, AL 36427. Telephone: 251-809-1500. Fax: 251-809-1527. E-mail: kathleen.hall@jdcc.edu.

DEGREES AND AWARDS

Programs offered do not lead to a degree or other formal award.

COURSE SUBJECT AREAS OFFERED OUTSIDE OF DEGREE PROGRAMS

Undergraduate—accounting and related services; biology; business, management, and marketing related; computer software and media applications; economics; English composition; health and physical education/fitness.

JOHN A. LOGAN COLLEGE
Carterville, Illinois
Learning Resources
http://www.jalc.edu

John A. Logan College was founded in 1967. It is accredited by North Central Association of Colleges and Schools. It first offered distance learning courses in 1979. In fall 2005, there were 850 students enrolled in distance learning courses. Institutionally administered financial aid is available to distance learners.

Services Distance learners have accessibility to academic advising, campus computer network, career placement assistance, library services, tutoring.

Contact Robert Fester, Advisor and Counselor, John A. Logan College, 700 Logan College Road, Carterville, IL 62918. Telephone: 618-985-2828 Ext. 8385. E-mail: bobfester@jalc.edu.

DEGREES AND AWARDS

Programs offered do not lead to a degree or other formal award.

COURSE SUBJECT AREAS OFFERED OUTSIDE OF DEGREE PROGRAMS

Undergraduate—accounting and related services; allied health diagnostic, intervention, and treatment professions; American Sign Language (ASL); biblical studies; biology; business/commerce; business, management, and marketing related; computer and information sciences; creative writing; data processing; dental support services and allied professions; design and applied arts; dramatic/theater arts and stagecraft; English; English composition; English language and literature related; film/video and photographic arts; fine and studio art; history; liberal arts and sciences, general studies and humanities; marketing; mathematics; political science and government; psychology; technology education/industrial arts; visual and performing arts.

JOHN JAY COLLEGE OF CRIMINAL JUSTICE OF THE CITY UNIVERSITY OF NEW YORK

New York, New York

http://www.jjay.cuny.edu

John Jay College of Criminal Justice of the City University of New York was founded in 1964. It is accredited by Middle States Association of Colleges and Schools. It first offered distance learning courses in 1999. In fall 2005, there were 6,000 students enrolled in distance learning courses. Institutionally administered financial aid is available to distance learners.

Services Distance learners have accessibility to bookstore, campus computer network, e-mail services, library services, tutoring.

Contact Prof. Robert James Hong, Director of Educational Technology, John Jay College of Criminal Justice of the City University of New York, 445 West 59th Street, Room 3410, North Hall, New York, NY 10019-1107. Telephone: 212-237-8849. Fax: 212-237-8919. E-mail: rhong@jjay.cuny.edu.

DEGREES AND AWARDS

Programs offered do not lead to a degree or other formal award.

COURSE SUBJECT AREAS OFFERED OUTSIDE OF DEGREE PROGRAMS

Undergraduate—American literature (United States and Canadian); anthropology; computer/information technology administration and management; criminal justice and corrections; economics; fire protection; health and physical education/fitness; languages (Romance languages); legal studies (non-professional general, undergraduate); political science and government; psychology; public administration; public administration and social service professions related; security and protective services related; technical and business writing.

Graduate—public administration; security and protective services related.

THE JOHNS HOPKINS UNIVERSITY

Baltimore, Maryland

School of Continuing Studies, Electronic and Distance Education

http://webapps.jhu.edu/jhuniverse/academics/distance_education/

The Johns Hopkins University was founded in 1876. It is accredited by Middle States Association of Colleges and Schools. It first offered distance learning courses in 1998. In fall 2005, there were 300 students enrolled in distance learning courses. Institutionally administered financial aid is available to distance learners.

Services Distance learners have accessibility to academic advising, bookstore, campus computer network, e-mail services, library services, tutoring.

Contact Dr. Candice V. Dalrymple, Associate Dean and Director of Center for Educational Resources, The Johns Hopkins University, Administration Office, Milton S. Eisenhower Library, 3400 North Charles Street, Baltimore, MD 21218. Telephone: 410-516-8848. Fax: 410-516-5080. E-mail: cdalrymple@jhu.edu.

DEGREES AND AWARDS

Programs offered do not lead to a degree or other formal award.

COURSE SUBJECT AREAS OFFERED OUTSIDE OF DEGREE PROGRAMS

Undergraduate—biological and physical sciences; biology; finance and financial management services; microbiological sciences and immunology; statistics.

JOHNSON BIBLE COLLEGE

Knoxville, Tennessee

Distance Learning Office

http://www.jbc.edu/mastersnt/

Johnson Bible College was founded in 1893. It is accredited by Association for Biblical Higher Education. It first offered distance learning courses in 1988. In fall 2005, there were 60 students enrolled in distance learning courses. Institutionally administered financial aid is available to distance learners.

Services Distance learners have accessibility to academic advising, bookstore, campus computer network, e-mail services, library services.

Contact Dr. John C. Ketchen, Director of Distance Learning, Johnson Bible College, 7900 Johnson Drive, Knoxville, TN 37998. Telephone: 865-251-2254. Fax: 865-251-2285. E-mail: mketchen@jbc.edu.

DEGREES AND AWARDS

MA New Testament

COURSE SUBJECT AREAS OFFERED OUTSIDE OF DEGREE PROGRAMS

Undergraduate—biblical studies.

Graduate—biblical studies.

JOHNSON COUNTY COMMUNITY COLLEGE

Overland Park, Kansas

http://www.jccc.net

Johnson County Community College was founded in 1967. It is accredited by North Central Association of Colleges and Schools. It first offered distance learning courses in 1975. In fall 2005, there were 4,000 students enrolled in distance learning courses. Institutionally administered financial aid is available to distance learners.

Services Distance learners have accessibility to academic advising, bookstore, campus computer network, career placement assistance, e-mail services, library services, tutoring.

Contact Dr. Bill Lamb, Dean of Liberal Arts and Distance Learning, Johnson County Community College, 12345 College Boulevard, Overland Park, KS 66210-1299. Telephone: 913-469-8500 Ext. 2339. Fax: 913-469-2585. E-mail: blamb@jccc.edu.

DEGREES AND AWARDS

AA Multidisciplinary Study

AGS General Studies

COURSE SUBJECT AREAS OFFERED OUTSIDE OF DEGREE PROGRAMS

Undergraduate—accounting and related services; anthropology; biology; chemistry; computer software and media applications; computer systems networking and telecommunications; economics; English composition; English literature (British and Commonwealth); history; legal support services; marketing; mathematics; psychology; sociology; speech and rhetoric; technical and business writing.

Non-credit—computer software and media applications; health and medical administrative services; health/medical preparatory programs; real estate.

JOHN TYLER COMMUNITY COLLEGE

Chester, Virginia

http://www.jtcc.edu/DistanceEd

John Tyler Community College was founded in 1967. It is accredited by Southern Association of Colleges and Schools. It first offered distance learning courses in 1997. In fall 2005, there were 1,243 students enrolled in distance learning courses. Institutionally administered financial aid is available to distance learners.

Services Distance learners have accessibility to bookstore, e-mail services, library services.

Contact Mrs. Angela Branch, Instructional Center Technician, John Tyler Community College, 800 Charter Colony Parkway, Midlothian, VA 23114-4383. Telephone: 804-594-1625. Fax: 804-594-1591. E-mail: distanceed@jtcc.edu.

DEGREES AND AWARDS

AAS Arts and Sciences Degree for Transfer; Nursing–Online ADN Nursing Program

COURSE SUBJECT AREAS OFFERED OUTSIDE OF DEGREE PROGRAMS

Undergraduate—accounting and related services; American literature (United States and Canadian); biology; business administration, management and operations; chemistry; computer and information sciences; creative writing; criminal justice and corrections; economics; English composition; English literature (British and Commonwealth); funeral service and mortuary science; health services/allied health/health sciences; history; human resources management; mathematics; nursing; philosophy; psychology; religious studies; sociology.

JONES COLLEGE
Jacksonville, Florida
http://www.jones.edu/

Jones College was founded in 1918. It is accredited by Accrediting Council for Independent Colleges and Schools. It first offered distance learning courses in 1998. In fall 2005, there were 400 students enrolled in distance learning courses. Institutionally administered financial aid is available to distance learners.

Services Distance learners have accessibility to academic advising, bookstore, campus computer network, career placement assistance, e-mail services, library services, tutoring.

Contact Mr. Thomas A. Clift, Vice President of Academic Affairs, Dean of Distance Learning, Jones College, 5353 Arlington Expressway, Jacksonville, FL 32211-5588. Telephone: 904-743-1122 Ext. 134. Fax: 904-743-4446. E-mail: tclift@jones.edu.

DEGREES AND AWARDS

AS Business Administration; Computer Information Systems
BS Business Administration; Computer Information Systems

COURSE SUBJECT AREAS OFFERED OUTSIDE OF DEGREE PROGRAMS

Undergraduate—accounting and related services; allied health and medical assisting services; business administration, management and operations; business/commerce; business/corporate communications; business/managerial economics; communication and media; community psychology; computer and information sciences; computer and information sciences and support services related; computer programming; computer software and media applications; computer systems analysis; data processing; economics; English; English composition; English language and literature related; information science/studies; international business; international relations and affairs; legal studies (non-professional general, undergraduate); liberal arts and sciences, general studies and humanities; management information systems; mathematics; mathematics and statistics related; sales, merchandising, and related marketing operations (general); social sciences; social sciences related; sociology; taxation; technical and business writing.

Non-credit—English; mathematics.

See full description on page 390.

J. SARGEANT REYNOLDS COMMUNITY COLLEGE
Richmond, Virginia
Division of Instructional Technologies and Distance Education
http://www.jsr.vccs.edu

J. Sargeant Reynolds Community College was founded in 1972. It is accredited by Southern Association of Colleges and Schools. It first offered distance learning courses in 1980. In fall 2005, there were 1,143 students enrolled in distance learning courses. Institutionally administered financial aid is available to distance learners.

Services Distance learners have accessibility to academic advising, bookstore, e-mail services, library services.

Contact M. R. Macbeth, Coordinator of Center for Distance Education, J. Sargeant Reynolds Community College, Center for Distance Education, PO Box 85622, Richmond, VA 23285-5622. E-mail: mmacbeth@jsr.cc.va.us.

DEGREES AND AWARDS

AAS Early Childhood Development; Respiratory Therapy

COURSE SUBJECT AREAS OFFERED OUTSIDE OF DEGREE PROGRAMS

Undergraduate—accounting and related services; American literature (United States and Canadian); biology; business administration, management and operations; business, management, and marketing related; business operations support and assistant services; chemistry; computer science; computer software and media applications; criminal justice and corrections; developmental and child psychology; economics; education; English composition; food science and technology; health and physical education/fitness; history; human development, family studies, and related services; information science/studies; linguistic, comparative, and related language studies; marketing; mathematics; nursing; philosophy; political science and government; psychology; social sciences related; sociology; speech and rhetoric.

JUDSON COLLEGE
Marion, Alabama
Distance Learning Program
http://www.judson.edu

Judson College was founded in 1838. It is accredited by Southern Association of Colleges and Schools. It first offered distance learning courses in 1976. In fall 2005, there were 100 students enrolled in distance learning courses. Institutionally administered financial aid is available to distance learners.

Services Distance learners have accessibility to academic advising, bookstore, campus computer network, career placement assistance, e-mail services, library services.

Contact Angie M. Teague, Director of Distance Learning, Judson College, 302 Bibb Street, Marion, AL 36756. Telephone: 800-447-9472 Ext. 169. Fax: 334-683-5282. E-mail: ateague@judson.edu.

DEGREES AND AWARDS

BA Business; Criminal Justice; Education–Secondary Education; English; History; Music; Psychology; Religious Studies
BMin Ministry Studies
BS Business; Criminal Justice; Education; Psychology

COURSE SUBJECT AREAS OFFERED OUTSIDE OF DEGREE PROGRAMS

Undergraduate—behavioral sciences; biblical studies; bioethics/medical ethics; biological and physical sciences; business administration, management and operations; creative writing; criminal justice and corrections; developmental and child psychology; ecology, evolution, and population biology; economics; education; education (specific levels and methods); education (specific subject areas); English; English composition; English literature (British and Commonwealth); history; music; philosophy and religious studies related; political science and government; psychology; social sciences; sociology.

JUDSON COLLEGE
Elgin, Illinois
Division of Continuing Education
http://www.judsoncollege.edu

Judson College was founded in 1963. It is accredited by North Central Association of Colleges and Schools. It first offered distance learning courses in 1998. In fall 2005, there were 230 students enrolled in distance learning courses. Institutionally administered financial aid is available to distance learners.

Services Distance learners have accessibility to academic advising, bookstore, campus computer network, career placement assistance, e-mail services, library services, tutoring.

Contact Robert Lindahl, Student Specialist for Customized Learning Center, Judson College, 1151 North State Street, Elgin, IL 60123. Telephone: 847-628-1547. Fax: 847-628-1007. E-mail: rlindahl@judsoncollege.edu.

DEGREES AND AWARDS

BA Management and Leadership

COURSE SUBJECT AREAS OFFERED OUTSIDE OF DEGREE PROGRAMS

Undergraduate—astronomy and astrophysics; biblical studies; communication and media; computer software and media applications; criminal justice and corrections; English; English composition; environmental control technologies; fine and studio art; history; liberal arts and sciences, general studies and humanities; mathematics; political science and government; psychology; public relations, advertising, and applied communication related; sociology; technical and business writing.

KANSAS STATE UNIVERSITY
Manhattan, Kansas
Division of Continuing Education, Continuing Learning
http://www.dce.ksu.edu/distance

Kansas State University was founded in 1863. It is accredited by North Central Association of Colleges and Schools. It first offered distance learning courses in 1971. In fall 2005, there were 7,000 students enrolled in distance learning courses. Institutionally administered financial aid is available to distance learners.

Services Distance learners have accessibility to academic advising, bookstore, campus computer network, career placement assistance, e-mail services, library services.

Contact Daniel Butcher, Bachelor Degree Completion Program Coordinator, Kansas State University, Division of Continuing Education, 13 College Court Building, Manhattan, KS 66506. Telephone: 785-532-5575. Fax: 785-532-5637. E-mail: informationdce@ksu.edu.

DEGREES AND AWARDS

BS Animal Science and Industry; Business, general; Dietetics; Food Science and Industry; Interdisciplinary Social Sciences; Technology Management

Certificate of Completion Early Childhood Education Administration Credential

Certificate Food Science; Occupational Health Psychology; Personal Financial Planning

CAGS Business Administration

CCCPE Conflict Resolution; Conflict Resolution

Graduate Certificate Academic Advising; Food Science

MS Agribusiness; Chemical Engineering; Civil Engineering; Electrical Engineering; Engineering Management; Food Science; Gerontology; Industrial/Organizational Psychology; Mechanical Engineering; Merchandising; Personal Financial Planning; Software Engineering; Youth Development

COURSE SUBJECT AREAS OFFERED OUTSIDE OF DEGREE PROGRAMS

Undergraduate—accounting and computer science; accounting and related services; agricultural and domestic animal services; agricultural and food products processing; agricultural business and management; agricultural production; agriculture; agriculture and agriculture operations related; animal sciences; applied horticulture/horticultural business services; area, ethnic, cultural, and gender studies related; behavioral sciences; biochemistry, biophysics and molecular biology; biological and physical sciences; business administration, management and operations; business/commerce; business, management, and marketing related; chemistry; computer and information sciences; developmental and child psychology; dietetics and clinical nutrition services; English; ethnic, cultural minority, and gender studies; family and consumer sciences/human sciences; family and consumer sciences/human sciences related; finance and financial management services; food science and technology; foods, nutrition, and related services; geography and cartography; history; human development, family studies, and related services; information science/studies; management information systems; marketing; music; natural resources and conservation related; natural resources conservation and research; natural resources management and policy; natural sciences; nutrition sciences; physical sciences; physical sciences related; political science and government; psychology; social psychology; social sciences; social sciences related; sociology; statistics.

Graduate—agricultural and food products processing; agricultural business and management; agricultural public services; agriculture; agriculture and agriculture operations related; animal sciences; apparel and textiles; chemical engineering; civil engineering; community health services; community organization and advocacy; community psychology; computer engineering; computer science; computer software and media applications; electrical, electronics and communications engineering; engineering; engineering/industrial management; engineering related; engineering science; family and consumer sciences/human sciences; family and consumer sciences/human sciences related; family psychology; finance and financial management services; gerontology; human resources management; industrial and organizational psychology; mechanical engineering; mechanical engineering related technologies; plant sciences; psychology; quality control and safety technologies.

Non-credit—agricultural and food products processing; agriculture; education; educational administration and supervision; educational assessment, evaluation, and research; educational psychology; education related; education (specific levels and methods); education (specific subject areas); family and consumer economics; family and consumer sciences/human sciences; family and consumer sciences/human sciences related; family psychology; finance and financial management services; food science and technology; foods, nutrition, and related services; social sciences related; work and family studies.

See full description on page 392.

KAPLAN UNIVERSITY
Davenport, Iowa
Kaplan University Online
http://www.kaplancollegeia.com/

Kaplan University was founded in 1937. It is accredited by North Central Association of Colleges and Schools. It first offered distance learning courses in 1999. In fall 2005, there were 25,122 students enrolled in distance learning courses. Institutionally administered financial aid is available to distance learners.

Services Distance learners have accessibility to academic advising, bookstore, e-mail services, library services, tutoring.

Contact Information, Kaplan University, 6301 Kaplan University Ave, Fort Lauderdale, FL 33309. Telephone: 866-527-5268. E-mail: infoku @kaplan.edu.

DEGREES AND AWARDS

AAS Business Administration/Accounting; Business Administration/ Management; Computer Information Systems; Computer Information Systems/Java; Computer Information Systems/Networking; Computer Information Systems/Programming; Computer Information Systems/Web Development; Computer Information Systems/Wireless Networking; Criminal Justice; Criminal Justice/Corrections; Criminal Justice/Law Enforcement; Criminal Justice/Private Security

AS Interdisciplinary Studies; Interdisciplinary Studies/Educational Paraprofessional (Teacher's Aide)

BS Business Security and Assurance; Business; Business/Accounting; Business/Finance; Business/Management of Information Systems; Criminal Justice; Criminal Justice/Corrections; Criminal Justice/Crime Analysis; Criminal Justice/Crime Scene Investigation; Criminal Justice/Forensic Psychology; Criminal Justice/Fraud Examination and Investigation; Criminal Justice/Law Enforcement; Criminal Justice/Private Security; IT/Database; IT/Multimedia and Animation; IT/Networking; IT/Programming; IT/Web Development; Information Technology; Management; Management/ E-Business; Management/Health Care Management; Management/Human Resources Management; Management/Sales and Marketing; Paralegal Studies; Paralegal Studies/Alternative Dispute Resolution; Paralegal Studies/Office Management; Paralegal Studies/Personal Injury

BSN Nursing–RN to BSN Completion

Certificate Case Management; Executive Coaching; Financial Planning; Geriatric Care Management; Information Technology Pathway Certificate; Internet and Website Development; Introduction to Computer Programming Language; Iowa Teacher Intern certificate; Legal Nurse Consulting; Life Care Planning; Nursing–Forensic Nursing; Private Security; Professional Development for Teachers; Project Management; Project Management; Risk Management

MA Teaching and Learning

MAT Teaching Literacy and Language–Grades 6-12; Teaching Literacy and Language–Grades K-6; Teaching Mathematics–Grades 6-8; Teaching Mathematics–Grades 9-12; Teaching Mathematics–Grades K-5; Teaching Science–Grades 6-12; Teaching Students with Special Needs; Teaching With Technology

MBA Business Administration; Entrepreneurship; Finance; Human Resources Management; Information Technology; Management, Communication and Quality; Marketing

MEd Secondary Education

MS Criminal Justice; Criminal Justice/Global Issues in Criminal Justice; Criminal Justice/Law; Criminal Justice/Leadership and Executive Management; Criminal Justice/Policing

COURSE SUBJECT AREAS OFFERED OUTSIDE OF DEGREE PROGRAMS

Non-credit—business administration, management and operations; business/corporate communications; business/managerial economics; finance and financial management services; gerontology; health professions related.

See full description on page 394.

KAUAI COMMUNITY COLLEGE
Lihue, Hawaii
University Center-Kauai
http://www.kauaicc.hawaii.edu

Kauai Community College was founded in 1965. It is accredited by Western Association of Schools and Colleges. It first offered distance learning courses in 1988. In fall 2005, there were 160 students enrolled in distance learning courses. Institutionally administered financial aid is available to distance learners.

Services Distance learners have accessibility to academic advising, bookstore, e-mail services, library services.

Contact Ms. Alison Shigematsu, Educational Specialist, Kauai Community College, 3-1901 Kaumualii Highway, Lihue, HI 96766-9591. Telephone: 808-245-8330. Fax: 808-245-8232. E-mail: ashigema@hawaii.edu.

DEGREES AND AWARDS

Programs offered do not lead to a degree or other formal award.

COURSE SUBJECT AREAS OFFERED OUTSIDE OF DEGREE PROGRAMS

Undergraduate—computer and information sciences; English composition; journalism; languages (Romance languages); linguistic, comparative, and related language studies.

KEAN UNIVERSITY
Union, New Jersey
http://www.kean.edu/

Kean University was founded in 1855. It is accredited by Middle States Association of Colleges and Schools. It first offered distance learning courses in 1998. In fall 2005, there were 642 students enrolled in distance learning courses. Institutionally administered financial aid is available to distance learners.

Services Distance learners have accessibility to bookstore, campus computer network, e-mail services, library services.

Contact Ms. Maria Perez, Coordinator of Academic Technology, Kean University, 1000 Morris Avenue, Union, NJ 07083. Telephone: 908-737-4652. Fax: 908-737-4659. E-mail: mperez@kean.edu.

DEGREES AND AWARDS

Programs offered do not lead to a degree or other formal award.

COURSE SUBJECT AREAS OFFERED OUTSIDE OF DEGREE PROGRAMS

Undergraduate—biology; business administration, management and operations; criminal justice and corrections; education (specific levels and methods); education (specific subject areas); health and medical administrative services; history; marketing; mathematics; parks, recreation and leisure facilities management; political science and government; psychology; sociology.

Graduate—educational administration and supervision; education (specific levels and methods); special education.

Non-credit—accounting and related services; business administration, management and operations; business, management, and marketing related; communication and journalism related; computer and information sciences; computer programming; computer software and media applications; creative writing; education; family and consumer sciences/human sciences; film/video and photographic arts; finance and financial management services; fine and studio art; health and physical education/fitness; languages (foreign languages related); legal professions and studies related; mathematics; parks, recreation and leisure; personal and culinary services related; philosophy; technical and business writing; work and family studies.

KEISER COLLEGE
Fort Lauderdale, Florida
http://online.keisercollege.edu

Keiser College was founded in 1977. It is accredited by Accrediting Bureau of Health Education Schools. It first offered distance learning courses in 1999. Institutionally administered financial aid is available to distance learners.

Services Distance learners have accessibility to academic advising, bookstore, campus computer network, career placement assistance, e-mail services, library services, tutoring.

Contact Admissions Counselor, Keiser College, 1500 NW 49th Street, Fort Lauderdale, FL 33309. Telephone: 866-534-7371. Fax: 954-351-4030. E-mail: admissions@keisercollege.edu.

DEGREES AND AWARDS

AA Accounting; Business Administration; Business; Criminal Justice; Health Service Administration; Homeland Security; Paralegal Studies
AS Computer Networking and Security Management; Medical Assisting
BA Business Administration; Criminal Justice
BS Management of Information Systems

COURSE SUBJECT AREAS OFFERED OUTSIDE OF DEGREE PROGRAMS

Undergraduate—accounting and related services; allied health and medical assisting services; business administration, management and operations; computer/information technology administration and management; computer systems networking and telecommunications; criminal justice and corrections; health and medical administrative services; legal studies (non-professional general, undergraduate).

See full description on page 396.

KENTUCKY STATE UNIVERSITY
Frankfort, Kentucky
KSU Distance Learning
http://www.kysu.edu

Kentucky State University was founded in 1886. It is accredited by Southern Association of Colleges and Schools. It first offered distance learning courses in 1997. In fall 2005, there were 600 students enrolled in distance learning courses. Institutionally administered financial aid is available to distance learners.

Services Distance learners have accessibility to academic advising, e-mail services, library services.

Contact Dr. E. Terry Magel, Director of Continuing and Distance Education, Kentucky State University, 400 East Main Street, Academic Services Building, 523, Frankfort, KY 40601. Telephone: 502-597-5611. Fax: 502-597-5046. E-mail: terry.magel@kysu.edu.

DEGREES AND AWARDS

BA Psychology; Public Administration
MS Aquaculture

COURSE SUBJECT AREAS OFFERED OUTSIDE OF DEGREE PROGRAMS

Undergraduate—accounting and related services; biological and physical sciences; business administration, management and operations; computer and information sciences; computer programming; drafting/design engineering technologies; economics; English; English composition; linguistic, comparative, and related language studies; management information systems; psychology; public administration and social service professions related; sales, merchandising, and related marketing operations (general); social work; sociology; speech and rhetoric.

Graduate—biological and physical sciences; public administration and social service professions related.

KETTERING UNIVERSITY
Flint, Michigan
Graduate School
http://graduate.kettering.edu

Kettering University was founded in 1919. It is accredited by North Central Association of Colleges and Schools. It first offered distance learning courses in 1982. In fall 2005, there were 700 students enrolled in distance learning courses. Institutionally administered financial aid is available to distance learners.

Services Distance learners have accessibility to academic advising, bookstore, campus computer network, e-mail services, library services.

Contact Joanne Allen, Publications Coordinator, Kettering University, 1700 West Third Avenue, Flint, MI 48504-4898. Telephone: 866-584-7237 Ext. 5. Fax: 810-762-9935. E-mail: gradoff@kettering.edu.

DEGREES AND AWARDS
MS Information Technology; Manufacturing Management; Manufacturing Operations; Operations Management
MSE Engineering–Electrical and Computer Engineering concentration; Engineering–Manufacturing Engineering concentration; Engineering–Mechanical Design concentration
MSEM Engineering Management

COURSE SUBJECT AREAS OFFERED OUTSIDE OF DEGREE PROGRAMS
Non-credit—business administration, management and operations; business, management, and marketing related; computer/information technology administration and management; electrical, electronics and communications engineering; engineering; engineering design; engineering related; engineering-related fields; industrial engineering; management information systems; management sciences and quantitative methods; manufacturing engineering; mathematics and statistics related; mechanical engineering; quality control and safety technologies.

LACKAWANNA COLLEGE
Scranton, Pennsylvania
Distance Learning Center
http://www.lackawanna.edu

Lackawanna College was founded in 1894. It is accredited by Middle States Association of Colleges and Schools. It first offered distance learning courses in 1994. In fall 2005, there were 11 students enrolled in distance learning courses. Institutionally administered financial aid is available to distance learners.

Services Distance learners have accessibility to academic advising, bookstore, career placement assistance, library services.

Contact Mr. Griffith R. Lewis, Senior Director, MIS, Lackawanna College, 501 Vine Street, Scranton, PA 18509. Telephone: 570-961-7853. Fax: 570-961-7877. E-mail: lewisg@lackawanna.edu.

DEGREES AND AWARDS
Programs offered do not lead to a degree or other formal award.

COURSE SUBJECT AREAS OFFERED OUTSIDE OF DEGREE PROGRAMS
Undergraduate—business administration, management and operations.

LAKE SUPERIOR COLLEGE
Duluth, Minnesota
http://www.lsc.mnscu.edu/online/

Lake Superior College was founded in 1995. It is accredited by North Central Association of Colleges and Schools. It first offered distance learning courses in 1997. In fall 2005, there were 1,800 students enrolled in distance learning courses. Institutionally administered financial aid is available to distance learners.

Services Distance learners have accessibility to academic advising, bookstore, campus computer network, career placement assistance, e-mail services, library services, tutoring.

Contact Melissa Leno, Enrollment Services Specialist, Lake Superior College, 2101 Trinity Road, Duluth, MN 55811. Telephone: 218-733-5903. E-mail: m.leno@lsc.edu.

DEGREES AND AWARDS
AA Liberal Education
AAS Accountant; Paralegal Studies
AS Business Administration; Paralegal Studies
Certificate Bookkeeping–Professional Bookkeeper; Microcomputer Office Specialist

COURSE SUBJECT AREAS OFFERED OUTSIDE OF DEGREE PROGRAMS
Undergraduate—accounting and related services; anthropology; astronomy and astrophysics; biological and physical sciences; business/commerce; business/corporate communications; business operations support and assistant services; communication and media; computer and information sciences; computer software and media applications; economics; English composition; fine and studio art; geography and cartography; geological and earth sciences/geosciences; health/medical preparatory programs; health professions related; history; liberal arts and sciences, general studies and humanities; mathematics; philosophy and religious studies related; physical sciences; political science and government; psychology; sociology; technical and business writing.

LAMAR STATE COLLEGE–PORT ARTHUR
Port Arthur, Texas
Academic Division
http://www.pa.lamar.edu/

Lamar State College–Port Arthur was founded in 1909. It is accredited by Southern Association of Colleges and Schools. It first offered distance learning courses in 1996. In fall 2005, there were 600 students enrolled in distance learning courses. Institutionally administered financial aid is available to distance learners.

Services Distance learners have accessibility to academic advising, campus computer network, e-mail services, library services.

Contact Dr. Charles Gongre, Dean of Academic Programs, Lamar State College–Port Arthur, PO Box 310, Port Arthur, TX 77641. Telephone: 409-984-6229. Fax: 409-984-6000. E-mail: charles.gongre@lamarpa.edu.

DEGREES AND AWARDS
Programs offered do not lead to a degree or other formal award.

COURSE SUBJECT AREAS OFFERED OUTSIDE OF DEGREE PROGRAMS
Undergraduate—astronomy and astrophysics; biblical and other theological languages and literatures; business administration, management and operations; computer and information sciences; computer programming; computer science; computer software and media applications; computer systems networking and telecommunications; data entry/microcomputer applications; economics; foods, nutrition, and related services; health professions related; mathematics; philosophy; philosophy and religious studies related; psychology.

Non-credit—allied health and medical assisting services; allied health diagnostic, intervention, and treatment professions; alternative and complementary medical support services; alternative and complementary medicine and medical systems; American literature (United States and Canadian); business administration, management and operations; business/commerce; business, management, and marketing related; business/managerial economics; business operations support and assistant services; computer and information sciences; computer/information technology administration and management; computer programming; computer science; computer software and media applications; computer systems analysis; computer systems networking and telecommunications; creative writing; data entry/microcomputer applications; data processing; entrepreneurial and small business operations; finance and financial management services; health aides/attendants/orderlies; human resources management; information science/studies; management information systems; marketing; public relations, advertising, and applied communication related; sales, merchandising, and related marketing operations (general); sales, merchandising, and related marketing operations (specialized); technical and business writing.

LAMAR UNIVERSITY
Beaumont, Texas
Division of Continuing and Distance Education
http://dept.lamar.edu/cde

Lamar University was founded in 1923. It is accredited by Southern Association of Colleges and Schools. It first offered distance learning courses in 1994. In fall 2005, there were 2,000 students enrolled in distance learning courses. Institutionally administered financial aid is available to distance learners.
Services Distance learners have accessibility to academic advising, bookstore, campus computer network, career placement assistance, e-mail services, library services.
Contact Dr. Paula Nichols, Director of Distance Education, Lamar University, Center for Distance Education, PO Box 10794, Beaumont, TX 77710. Telephone: 409-880-1847. Fax: 409-880-1856. E-mail: paula.nichols@lamar.edu.

DEGREES AND AWARDS
Programs offered do not lead to a degree or other formal award.

COURSE SUBJECT AREAS OFFERED OUTSIDE OF DEGREE PROGRAMS
Undergraduate—computer science; geological and earth sciences/ geosciences; history; mathematics; nutrition sciences; political science and government; psychology.

LANSING COMMUNITY COLLEGE
Lansing, Michigan
Virtual College
http://www.lcc.edu/online/

Lansing Community College was founded in 1957. It is accredited by North Central Association of Colleges and Schools. It first offered distance learning courses in 1979. In fall 2005, there were 3,029 students enrolled in distance learning courses. Institutionally administered financial aid is available to distance learners.
Services Distance learners have accessibility to academic advising, bookstore, campus computer network, e-mail services, library services, tutoring.
Contact Ms. Michelle Detering, Learning Support Coordinator–Help Services, Lansing Community College, 9000 Information Services and College Development, PO Box 40010, Lansing, MI 48901-7210. Telephone: 517-483-5324. Fax: 517-483-1758. E-mail: deterim@lcc.edu.

DEGREES AND AWARDS
AD Business; Criminal Justice, Law Enforcement; E-Business; General Studies; International Business
Certificate of Achievement E-Business
Certificate of Completion Computer Programmer/Analyst; Correctional Officer; Information Technology Basics; Microsoft Office Specialist Certification Preparation

COURSE SUBJECT AREAS OFFERED OUTSIDE OF DEGREE PROGRAMS
Undergraduate—accounting and related services; architecture; astronomy and astrophysics; biology; chemistry; computer and information sciences; computer programming; creative writing; design and applied arts; English composition; geography and cartography; history; legal studies (non-professional general, undergraduate); linguistic, comparative, and related language studies; mathematics; mathematics and statistics related; music; natural resources conservation and research; psychology; sales, merchandising, and related marketing operations (general); social psychology; sociology; speech and rhetoric.

LAURA AND ALVIN SIEGAL COLLEGE OF JUDAIC STUDIES
Beachwood, Ohio
http://www.siegalcollege.edu/

Laura and Alvin Siegal College of Judaic Studies was founded in 1963. It is accredited by North Central Association of Colleges and Schools. It first offered distance learning courses in 1995. In fall 2005, there were 70 students enrolled in distance learning courses. Institutionally administered financial aid is available to distance learners.
Services Distance learners have accessibility to academic advising, bookstore, career placement assistance, library services.
Contact Ms. Ruth Kronick, Director of Student Services, Laura and Alvin Siegal College of Judaic Studies, 26500 Shaker Boulevard, Beachwood, OH 44122. Telephone: 216-464-4050 Ext. 101. Fax: 216-464-5827. E-mail: rkronick@siegalcollege.edu.

DEGREES AND AWARDS
MAR Jewish Studies
MCP/MPH Education Administration; Hebrew Language and Literature

COURSE SUBJECT AREAS OFFERED OUTSIDE OF DEGREE PROGRAMS
Undergraduate—education; ethnic, cultural minority, and gender studies; languages (Middle/Near Eastern and Semitic); religious education; religious studies.
Graduate—education; ethnic, cultural minority, and gender studies; languages (Middle/Near Eastern and Semitic); religious education; religious studies.
Non-credit—education; ethnic, cultural minority, and gender studies; languages (Middle/Near Eastern and Semitic); religious education; religious studies.

LAURENTIAN UNIVERSITY
Sudbury, Ontario, Canada
Centre for Continuing Education
http://cce.laurentian.ca

Laurentian University was founded in 1960. It is provincially chartered. It first offered distance learning courses in 1972. In fall 2005, there were 6,000 students enrolled in distance learning courses. Institutionally administered financial aid is available to distance learners.
Services Distance learners have accessibility to academic advising, bookstore, campus computer network, career placement assistance, e-mail services, library services, tutoring.
Contact Ms. Ruby Gervais, Senior Program Manager/Academic Advisor, Laurentian University, 935 Ramsey Lake Road, Sudbury, ON P3E 2C6, Canada. Telephone: 705-675-1151 Ext. 3942. Fax: 705-675-4897. E-mail: rgervais@laurentian.ca.

DEGREES AND AWARDS
BA Folklore et Ethnologie de l'amerique Francaise; Gerontology; Law and Justice (in development); Native Studies (Honours); Native Studies; Psychologie; Psychology; Religious Studies; Sciences Religieuses; Sociology (in development); Women's Studies
BS Liberal Science
BSN Nursing–BSN for Registered Nurses
BSW Service Social (en franþais); Social Work–Native Human Services
Certificate Family Life Studies and Human Sexuality; Folklore et Ethnologie de l'amerique Francaise; Gerontology; Law and Justice; Women's Studies

LAWRENCE TECHNOLOGICAL UNIVERSITY
Southfield, Michigan
http://www.ltu.edu/

Lawrence Technological University was founded in 1932. It is accredited by North Central Association of Colleges and Schools. It first offered distance learning courses in 1998. In fall 2005, there were 444 students enrolled in distance learning courses. Institutionally administered financial aid is available to distance learners.
Services Distance learners have accessibility to academic advising, campus computer network, career placement assistance, e-mail services, library services, tutoring.
Contact Dr. Pam Lowry, Director of Veraldi Instructional Tech Resource Center, Lawrence Technological University, 21000 West Ten Mile Road, Southfield, MI 48075. Telephone: 248-204-3653. Fax: 248-204-3755. E-mail: lowry@ltu.edu.

DEGREES AND AWARDS
Programs offered do not lead to a degree or other formal award.

COURSE SUBJECT AREAS OFFERED OUTSIDE OF DEGREE PROGRAMS

Undergraduate—business administration, management and operations; communications technology; engineering related; marketing; mathematics.

Graduate—business administration, management and operations; education (specific levels and methods); human resources management; information science/studies; international business; marketing.

LEHIGH CARBON COMMUNITY COLLEGE
Schnecksville, Pennsylvania
Office of Distance Learning
http://www.lccc.edu/distancelearning.html

Lehigh Carbon Community College was founded in 1967. It is accredited by Middle States Association of Colleges and Schools. It first offered distance learning courses in 1995. In fall 2005, there were 2,800 students enrolled in distance learning courses. Institutionally administered financial aid is available to distance learners.

Services Distance learners have accessibility to academic advising, bookstore, e-mail services, library services, tutoring.

Contact Beverly J. Benfer, Director of Distance Learning and Instructional Technology, Lehigh Carbon Community College, 4525 Education Park Drive, Schnecksville, PA 18078. Telephone: 610-799-1591. Fax: 610-799-1527. E-mail: bbenfer@lccc.edu.

DEGREES AND AWARDS

AA Liberal Arts

COURSE SUBJECT AREAS OFFERED OUTSIDE OF DEGREE PROGRAMS

Undergraduate—accounting and related services; American literature (United States and Canadian); astronomy and astrophysics; biology; business administration, management and operations; business, management, and marketing related; business operations support and assistant services; computer and information sciences; criminal justice and corrections; criminology; curriculum and instruction; developmental and child psychology; economics; education; educational psychology; education related; education (specific levels and methods); English composition; finance and financial management services; geography and cartography; health and medical administrative services; health and physical education/fitness; health professions related; history; human development, family studies, and related services; human resources management; liberal arts and sciences, general studies and humanities; marketing; mathematics; music; philosophy; physics; political science and government; psychology; psychology related; social sciences; social sciences related; sociology; speech and rhetoric; technical and business writing.

LEHIGH UNIVERSITY
Bethlehem, Pennsylvania
Office of Distance Learning
http://www.distance.lehigh.edu

Lehigh University was founded in 1865. It is accredited by Middle States Association of Colleges and Schools. It first offered distance learning courses in 1992. In fall 2005, there were 700 students enrolled in distance learning courses. Institutionally administered financial aid is available to distance learners.

Services Distance learners have accessibility to academic advising, bookstore, campus computer network, career placement assistance, e-mail services, library services, tutoring.

Contact Lisa Moughan, Marketing Coordinator, Lehigh University, 436 Brodhead Avenue, Bethlehem, PA 18015. Telephone: 610-758-4372. Fax: 610-758-4190. E-mail: lim2@lehigh.edu.

DEGREES AND AWARDS

Certificate Project Management; Supply Chain Management
Graduate Certificate Regulatory Affairs
MBA Business Administration
ME Chemical Engineering; Polymer Science and Engineering
MME Mechanical Engineering (MS or MEng)
MS Chemistry; Manufacturing Systems Engineering; Molecular Biology; Polymer Science and Engineering; Quality Engineering
MSIS Information and Systems Engineering (MS or MEng)

COURSE SUBJECT AREAS OFFERED OUTSIDE OF DEGREE PROGRAMS

Graduate—biological and physical sciences; business administration, management and operations; cell biology and anatomical sciences; chemical engineering; chemistry; polymer/plastics engineering.

Non-credit—business administration, management and operations; business/corporate communications; chemical engineering; chemistry; engineering/industrial management; polymer/plastics engineering.

LENOIR COMMUNITY COLLEGE
Kinston, North Carolina
Distance Learning Services
http://sun2.lenoir.cc.nc.us/~disted/index.html

Lenoir Community College was founded in 1960. It is accredited by Southern Association of Colleges and Schools. It first offered distance learning courses in 1997. In fall 2005, there were 666 students enrolled in distance learning courses. Institutionally administered financial aid is available to distance learners.

Services Distance learners have accessibility to academic advising, bookstore, e-mail services, library services.

Contact Mr. Lee E. Wetherington, Distance Education Coordinator, Lenoir Community College, Kinston, NC 28502-0188. Telephone: 252-527-6223 Ext. 500. E-mail: disted@lenoircc.edu.

DEGREES AND AWARDS

AA the Arts
AAS Accounting; Business Administration; Court Reporting and Captioning; Global Logistics

COURSE SUBJECT AREAS OFFERED OUTSIDE OF DEGREE PROGRAMS

Undergraduate—biology; education related; English; fine and studio art; history; linguistic, comparative, and related language studies; mathematics and statistics related; psychology.

LESLEY UNIVERSITY
Cambridge, Massachusetts
http://www.lesley.edu/online_learning/tie/index.html

Lesley University was founded in 1909. It is accredited by New England Association of Schools and Colleges. It first offered distance learning courses in 1996. In fall 2005, there were 450 students enrolled in distance learning courses. Institutionally administered financial aid is available to distance learners.

Services Distance learners have accessibility to academic advising, bookstore, campus computer network, career placement assistance, e-mail services, library services, tutoring.

Contact Dr. Maureen Yoder, Director of Online Learning, Lesley University, 29 Everett Street, Cambridge, MA 02138. Telephone: 617-349-8421. Fax: 617-349-8391. E-mail: myoder@mail.lesley.edu.

DEGREES AND AWARDS

MEd Science in Education; Technology in Education

COURSE SUBJECT AREAS OFFERED OUTSIDE OF DEGREE PROGRAMS

Graduate—curriculum and instruction; education.

LETOURNEAU UNIVERSITY
Longview, Texas
Graduate and Adult Continuing Studies
http://www.letu.edu/

LeTourneau University was founded in 1946. It is accredited by Southern Association of Colleges and Schools. It first offered distance learning courses in 1999. In fall 2005, there were 1,187 students enrolled in distance learning courses. Institutionally administered financial aid is available to distance learners.

Services Distance learners have accessibility to academic advising, bookstore, campus computer network, e-mail services, library services.

Contact Chris Fonatine, Assistant Vice President for Enrollment Management and Market Research, LeTourneau University, PO Box 7668, Longview, TX 75607-7668. Telephone: 903-233-3250 Ext. 3254. Fax: 903-233-3227. E-mail: chrisfontaine@letu.edu.

DEGREES AND AWARDS

BBA Business Administration–Accelerated Online Bachelors of Business Administration
MBA Business Administration; Educational Leadership

COURSE SUBJECT AREAS OFFERED OUTSIDE OF DEGREE PROGRAMS

Undergraduate—biblical studies; biology; communication and media; computer science; education; English; English composition; history; psychology.
Graduate—business, management, and marketing related; educational administration and supervision.

LEWIS AND CLARK COMMUNITY COLLEGE
Godfrey, Illinois
http://www.lc.edu

Lewis and Clark Community College was founded in 1970. It is accredited by North Central Association of Colleges and Schools. It first offered distance learning courses in 1980. In fall 2005, there were 2,800 students enrolled in distance learning courses. Institutionally administered financial aid is available to distance learners.
Services Distance learners have accessibility to academic advising, bookstore, career placement assistance, e-mail services, library services, tutoring.
Contact Mrs. Mary C. Hales, Dean of Business, Continuing Education, and Workforce Development, Lewis and Clark Community College, 5800 Godfrey Road, Godfrey, IL 62035. Telephone: 618-468-4900. Fax: 618-468-7171. E-mail: mhales@lc.edu.

DEGREES AND AWARDS

Certificate of Completion Case Management for Aging Clients

COURSE SUBJECT AREAS OFFERED OUTSIDE OF DEGREE PROGRAMS

Undergraduate—accounting and related services; astronomy and astrophysics; biological and biomedical sciences related; biology; business administration, management and operations; business/managerial economics; business operations support and assistant services; communication and media; computer and information sciences; criminal justice and corrections; criminology; data entry/microcomputer applications; data processing; developmental and child psychology; economics; fine and studio art; history; marketing; mathematics; music; psychology; speech and rhetoric; teaching assistants/aides.
Non-credit—computer software and media applications; curriculum and instruction.

LEWIS-CLARK STATE COLLEGE
Lewiston, Idaho
Center for Individualized Programs
http://www.lcsc.edu/dl

Lewis-Clark State College was founded in 1893. It is accredited by Northwest Commission on Colleges and Universities. It first offered distance learning courses in 1995. In fall 2005, there were 804 students enrolled in distance learning courses. Institutionally administered financial aid is available to distance learners.
Services Distance learners have accessibility to academic advising, bookstore, campus computer network, career placement assistance, e-mail services, library services.
Contact Ms. Kristy A. Roberts, Director, Distance Learning, Lewis-Clark State College, 500 Eighth Avenue, Lewiston, ID 83501. Telephone: 208-792-2239. Fax: 208-792-2444. E-mail: kroberts@lcsc.edu.

DEGREES AND AWARDS

Programs offered do not lead to a degree or other formal award.

COURSE SUBJECT AREAS OFFERED OUTSIDE OF DEGREE PROGRAMS

Undergraduate—accounting and computer science; business administration, management and operations; business operations support and assistant services; communication and media; computer and information sciences; education; English composition; human development, family studies, and related services; liberal arts and sciences, general studies and humanities; management information systems; psychology; social sciences.

LIBERTY UNIVERSITY
Lynchburg, Virginia
Distance Learning Program
http://www.liberty.edu

Liberty University was founded in 1971. It is accredited by Southern Association of Colleges and Schools. It first offered distance learning courses in 1985. In fall 2005, there were 6,269 students enrolled in distance learning courses. Institutionally administered financial aid is available to distance learners.
Services Distance learners have accessibility to academic advising, bookstore, campus computer network, career placement assistance, e-mail services, library services, tutoring.
Contact Mrs. Wendy Morales, Director of Admissions, Liberty University, 1971 University Boulevard, Lynchburg, VA 24502-2269. Telephone: 800-424-9595. Fax: 800-628-7977. E-mail: dlpadmissions@liberty.edu.

DEGREES AND AWARDS

AA Accounting; Business; Criminal Justice; General Studies; Management Information Systems; Psychology; Religion
BS Accounting; Business; Criminal Justice; Management Information Systems; Multidisciplinary Studies–Education concentration; Multidisciplinary Studies; Psychology; Religion
BSN Nursing–RN to BSN
MA Christian Leadership; Evangelism and Church Growth; Human Services; Marriage and Family Therapy; Pastoral Counseling; Professional Counseling; Worship Studies
MAR Religion
MBA Business Administration
MDiv Divinity
MEd Education
MS Accounting
MSM Management
MSN Nursing
DMin Ministry
EdD Education
PhD Counseling

COURSE SUBJECT AREAS OFFERED OUTSIDE OF DEGREE PROGRAMS

Undergraduate—accounting and related services; biblical studies; biology; business/commerce; developmental and child psychology; economics; education; educational psychology; English composition; gerontology; marketing; philosophy; psychology; social psychology; taxation; theology and religious vocations related.
Graduate—biblical studies; business administration, management and operations; counseling psychology; curriculum and instruction; educational administration and supervision; education related; psychology; religious studies; school psychology; special education; theological and ministerial studies; theology and religious vocations related.

See full description on page 398.

LIFE PACIFIC COLLEGE
San Dimas, California
School of Distance Learning
http://www.lifepacific.edu/distance

Life Pacific College was founded in 1923. It is accredited by ABHE—formerly AABC. It first offered distance learning courses in 1941. In fall 2005, there were 350 students enrolled in distance learning courses. Institutionally administered financial aid is available to distance learners.
Services Distance learners have accessibility to academic advising, bookstore, career placement assistance, library services.

Contact Brian Tomhave, Director, Life Pacific College, 1100 West Covina Boulevard, San Dimas, CA 91773. Telephone: 909-599-5433 Ext. 359. Fax: 909-706-3099. E-mail: distance@lifepacific.edu.

DEGREES AND AWARDS

AA Biblical Studies
BA Ministry and Leadership degree completion program

COURSE SUBJECT AREAS OFFERED OUTSIDE OF DEGREE PROGRAMS

Undergraduate—biblical studies; philosophy and religious studies related; theological and ministerial studies.
Non-credit—biblical and other theological languages and literatures; biblical studies; religious studies.

LIMESTONE COLLEGE
Gaffney, South Carolina
The Block Program
http://www.limestonevirtualcampus.net

Limestone College was founded in 1845. It is accredited by Southern Association of Colleges and Schools. It first offered distance learning courses in 1997. In fall 2005, there were 1,590 students enrolled in distance learning courses. Institutionally administered financial aid is available to distance learners.
Services Distance learners have accessibility to academic advising, bookstore, campus computer network, career placement assistance, e-mail services, library services.
Contact Mr. C. R. Horton, Director of the Extended Campus Program, Limestone College, 1115 College Drive, Gaffney, SC 29340-3799. Telephone: 864-488-4586. Fax: 864-487-8706. E-mail: chorton@limestone.edu.

DEGREES AND AWARDS

AA Business Administration; Computer Science Internet Management; Computer Science Management Information Systems; Computer Science Programming; Liberal Studies
BA Criminal Justice; Human Resource Development; Liberal Studies; Psychology
BS Business Administration–Accounting; Business Administration–Computer Programming; Business Administration–Computer Software Applications; Business Administration–General Business; Business Administration–Management; Computer Science Computer and Information Systems Security; Computer Science Information Technology; Computer Science Internet Management–Database; Computer Science Internet Management–E-commerce; Computer Science Internet Management–Operations Management; Computer Science Internet Management–Web Development; Computer Science Internet Management, general; Computer Science Programming; Liberal Studies

COURSE SUBJECT AREAS OFFERED OUTSIDE OF DEGREE PROGRAMS

Undergraduate—accounting and related services; American literature (United States and Canadian); astronomy and astrophysics; biblical studies; biology; business administration, management and operations; business/commerce; business/corporate communications; comparative literature; computer and information sciences; computer and information sciences and support services related; computer/information technology administration and management; computer programming; computer science; computer software and media applications; computer systems analysis; computer systems networking and telecommunications; creative writing; criminal justice and corrections; data entry/microcomputer applications; data processing; dramatic/theater arts and stagecraft; economics; education (specific levels and methods); English; English composition; English language and literature related; finance and financial management services; geography and cartography; gerontology; history; human resources management; human services; information science/studies; international business; legal studies (non-professional general, undergraduate); management information systems; management sciences and quantitative methods; marketing; mathematics; music; philosophy; political science and government; psychology; psychology related; religious studies; sales, merchandising, and related marketing operations (general); social psychology; social work; sociology; statistics; technical and business writing.

LINN-BENTON COMMUNITY COLLEGE
Albany, Oregon
Media Services
http://www.linnbenton.edu

Linn-Benton Community College was founded in 1966. It is accredited by Northwest Commission on Colleges and Universities. It first offered distance learning courses in 1979. In fall 2005, there were 735 students enrolled in distance learning courses. Institutionally administered financial aid is available to distance learners.
Services Distance learners have accessibility to academic advising, bookstore, career placement assistance, e-mail services, library services.
Contact Christine Baker, Outreach Coordinator, Linn-Benton Community College, Admissions and Records, 6500 Pacific Boulevard, SW, Albany, OR 97321. Telephone: 541-917-4811. Fax: 541-917-4868. E-mail: admissions@linnbenton.edu.

DEGREES AND AWARDS

Programs offered do not lead to a degree or other formal award.

COURSE SUBJECT AREAS OFFERED OUTSIDE OF DEGREE PROGRAMS

Undergraduate—American literature (United States and Canadian); applied mathematics; business administration, management and operations; business/commerce; business/managerial economics; computer software and media applications; creative writing; criminal justice and corrections; economics; English as a second language; health and medical administrative services; health and physical education/fitness; human development, family studies, and related services; journalism; liberal arts and sciences, general studies and humanities; mathematics; public relations, advertising, and applied communication related; technical and business writing.
Non-credit—English as a second language; mathematics; personal and culinary services related.

LIPSCOMB UNIVERSITY
Nashville, Tennessee
http://www.lipscomb.edu/

Lipscomb University was founded in 1891. It is accredited by Southern Association of Colleges and Schools. It first offered distance learning courses in 1999. In fall 2005, there were 78 students enrolled in distance learning courses. Institutionally administered financial aid is available to distance learners.
Services Distance learners have accessibility to bookstore, campus computer network, career placement assistance, e-mail services, library services.
Contact Mr. Al Austelle, Director of the Center for Instructional Technology, Lipscomb University, 3901 Granny White Pike, Nashville, TN 37204-3951. Telephone: 615-279-5703. Fax: 615-279-6559. E-mail: al.austelle@lipscomb.edu.

DEGREES AND AWARDS

Programs offered do not lead to a degree or other formal award.

COURSE SUBJECT AREAS OFFERED OUTSIDE OF DEGREE PROGRAMS

Undergraduate—biblical studies; English; languages (foreign languages related).
Graduate—biblical studies; business administration, management and operations.

LOCK HAVEN UNIVERSITY OF PENNSYLVANIA
Lock Haven, Pennsylvania
http://www.lhup.edu/cde

Lock Haven University of Pennsylvania was founded in 1870. It is accredited by Middle States Association of Colleges and Schools. It first offered distance learning courses in 1995. In fall 2005, there were 346 students enrolled in distance learning courses. Institutionally administered financial aid is available to distance learners.
Services Distance learners have accessibility to academic advising, bookstore, campus computer network, e-mail services, library services.

Contact Dr. Ellen P. O'Hara-Mays, Director of Learning Technologies and Distance Education, Lock Haven University of Pennsylvania, Court House Annex 311, Lock Haven, PA 17745. Telephone: 570-893-2072. Fax: 570-893-2638. E-mail: poharama@lhup.edu.

DEGREES AND AWARDS
AA Criminal Justice
AS Nursing; Surgical Technology
MEd Alternative Education; Teaching and Learning
MHS Physician Assistant
MLA Liberal Arts

COURSE SUBJECT AREAS OFFERED OUTSIDE OF DEGREE PROGRAMS
Undergraduate—applied mathematics; bioethics/medical ethics; comparative literature; computer programming; criminology; English composition; fine and studio art; history; music; sociology.
Graduate—education; health professions related; liberal arts and sciences, general studies and humanities.
Non-credit—allied health and medical assisting services; business/commerce; computer and information sciences and support services related; construction trades; education; legal professions and studies related.

See full description on page 400.

LOS ANGELES HARBOR COLLEGE
Wilmington, California
Distance Education Programs
http://www.lahc.cc.ca.us/acad.htm#onlinecourses

Los Angeles Harbor College was founded in 1949. It is accredited by Western Association of Schools and Colleges. It first offered distance learning courses in 1996. In fall 2005, there were 1,000 students enrolled in distance learning courses. Institutionally administered financial aid is available to distance learners.
Services Distance learners have accessibility to bookstore, e-mail services, library services.
Contact Dr. Robert Richards, Associate Dean, Academic Affairs, Los Angeles Harbor College, 1111 Figueroa Place, Wilmington, CA 90744. Telephone: 310-233-4021. Fax: 310-233-4488. E-mail: richarr@lahc.edu.

DEGREES AND AWARDS
Programs offered do not lead to a degree or other formal award.

COURSE SUBJECT AREAS OFFERED OUTSIDE OF DEGREE PROGRAMS
Undergraduate—accounting and related services; business/commerce; computer and information sciences; computer programming; criminal justice and corrections; criminology; economics; English; English composition; English language and literature related; nursing; political science and government; psychology; sociology.

LOUISIANA STATE UNIVERSITY AND AGRICULTURAL AND MECHANICAL COLLEGE
Baton Rouge, Louisiana
Division of Continuing Education, Extended Learning and Independent Study
http://www.lsu.edu/

Louisiana State University and Agricultural and Mechanical College was founded in 1860. It is accredited by Southern Association of Colleges and Schools. It first offered distance learning courses in 1984. Institutionally administered financial aid is available to distance learners.
Services Distance learners have accessibility to academic advising, bookstore, campus computer network, career placement assistance, e-mail services, library services.
Contact Kiedi A. Mabile, Coordinator, Continuing Education, Extended Learning, Louisiana State University and Agricultural and Mechanical College, 1209 Pleasant Hall, Baton Rouge, LA 70803. Telephone: 225-578-7031. Fax: 225-578-7470. E-mail: kmabile@doce.lsu.edu.

DEGREES AND AWARDS
MA Liberal Arts (Military History)
MS Library and Information Sciences
MSW Social Work

COURSE SUBJECT AREAS OFFERED OUTSIDE OF DEGREE PROGRAMS
Undergraduate—accounting and related services; American literature (United States and Canadian); anthropology; area, ethnic, cultural, and gender studies related; biological and physical sciences; business, management, and marketing related; communication and journalism related; computer and information sciences; economics; education; English composition; English language and literature related; English literature (British and Commonwealth); ethnic, cultural minority, and gender studies; family and consumer economics; geography and cartography; geological and earth sciences/geosciences; health and physical education/fitness; information science/studies; journalism; languages (foreign languages related); library science; mathematics; military studies; music; philosophy and religious studies related; physical sciences; social sciences related; social work; speech and rhetoric.
Graduate—agriculture and agriculture operations related; civil engineering; environmental/environmental health engineering; human resources management.

LOUISIANA STATE UNIVERSITY AND AGRICULTURAL AND MECHANICAL COLLEGE
Baton Rouge, Louisiana
Independent Study
http://www.is.lsu.edu

Louisiana State University and Agricultural and Mechanical College was founded in 1860. It is accredited by Southern Association of Colleges and Schools. It first offered distance learning courses in 1941. In fall 2005, there were 7,500 students enrolled in distance learning courses. Institutionally administered financial aid is available to distance learners.
Services Distance learners have accessibility to bookstore, e-mail services, library services.
Contact Student Services Coordinator, Louisiana State University and Agricultural and Mechanical College, Office of Independent Study, 1225 Pleasant Hall, Baton Rouge, LA 70803. Telephone: 800-234-5046. Fax: 225-578-3090. E-mail: iservices@doce.lsu.edu.

DEGREES AND AWARDS
Programs offered do not lead to a degree or other formal award.

COURSE SUBJECT AREAS OFFERED OUTSIDE OF DEGREE PROGRAMS
Undergraduate—accounting and related services; anthropology; biology; business administration, management and operations; cell biology and anatomical sciences; communication and media; community health services; comparative literature; criminology; curriculum and instruction; developmental and child psychology; dramatic/theater arts and stagecraft; ecology, evolution, and population biology; economics; educational assessment, evaluation, and research; educational psychology; education (specific levels and methods); English; English composition; English language and literature related; English literature (British and Commonwealth); ethnic, cultural minority, and gender studies; finance and financial management services; fine and studio art; fire protection; geography and cartography; geological and earth sciences/geosciences; health and physical education/fitness; history; journalism; languages (classics and classical); languages (Germanic); languages (Romance languages); legal studies (non-professional general, undergraduate); library science related; linguistic, comparative, and related language studies; management information systems; management sciences and quantitative methods; marketing; mathematics; mathematics and statistics related; mechanical engineering; military studies; music; philosophy; philosophy and religious studies related; physical sciences; physics; physiology, pathology and related sciences; political science and government; psychology; psychology related; school psychology; social sciences; social sciences related; sociology; speech and rhetoric; statistics; technical and business writing.
Graduate—human services.

Non-credit—accounting and related services; biology; English composition; mathematics.

LOUISIANA STATE UNIVERSITY AT EUNICE
Eunice, Louisiana
Continuing Education
http://www.lsue.edu/elearning

Louisiana State University at Eunice was founded in 1967. It is accredited by Southern Association of Colleges and Schools. It first offered distance learning courses in 1996. In fall 2005, there were 321 students enrolled in distance learning courses. Institutionally administered financial aid is available to distance learners.

Services Distance learners have accessibility to academic advising, bookstore, campus computer network, career placement assistance, e-mail services, library services.

Contact Ms. Jane M. Spradling, Assistant Director of Continuing Education, Louisiana State University at Eunice, PO Box 1129, Eunice, LA 70535. Telephone: 337-550-1445. Fax: 337-550-1393. E-mail: janaejio@lsue.edu.

DEGREES AND AWARDS

Programs offered do not lead to a degree or other formal award.

COURSE SUBJECT AREAS OFFERED OUTSIDE OF DEGREE PROGRAMS

Undergraduate—American literature (United States and Canadian); business administration, management and operations; business operations support and assistant services; computer software and media applications; education; English composition; fire protection; hospitality administration; information science/studies; marketing; psychology.

Non-credit—computer software and media applications.

LOUISIANA TECH UNIVERSITY
Ruston, Louisiana
Center for Instructional Technology and Distance Learning
http://www.latech.edu/citdl

Louisiana Tech University was founded in 1894. It is accredited by Southern Association of Colleges and Schools. It first offered distance learning courses in 1998. In fall 2005, there were 740 students enrolled in distance learning courses. Institutionally administered financial aid is available to distance learners.

Services Distance learners have accessibility to academic advising, bookstore, campus computer network, e-mail services, library services.

Contact Mr. David R. Cargill, Director of Center for Instructional Technology and Distance Learning, Louisiana Tech University, PO Box 10167, 100 Railroad Avenue, PML 1014, Ruston, LA 71272. Telephone: 318-257-2912. Fax: 318-257-2731. E-mail: david@latech.edu.

DEGREES AND AWARDS

MHSA Health Information–Master of Health Information (MHIM); Health Information–Master of Health Information (MHIM)

COURSE SUBJECT AREAS OFFERED OUTSIDE OF DEGREE PROGRAMS

Undergraduate—architecture; biological and biomedical sciences related; economics; educational administration and supervision; forestry; health professions related; journalism; mathematics; political science and government; technical and business writing.

Graduate—biomedical/medical engineering; educational administration and supervision; English; foods, nutrition, and related services; history; human development, family studies, and related services.

LURLEEN B. WALLACE COMMUNITY COLLEGE
Andalusia, Alabama

Lurleen B. Wallace Community College was founded in 1969. It is accredited by Southern Association of Colleges and Schools. It first offered distance learning courses in 2001. In fall 2005, there were 150 students enrolled in distance learning courses. Institutionally administered financial aid is available to distance learners.

Services Distance learners have accessibility to academic advising, bookstore, campus computer network, career placement assistance, library services.

Contact Mr. James G. Aplin, Assistant Dean of Instructional and Information Technology, Lurleen B. Wallace Community College, PO Box 1418, Andalusia, AL 36420. Telephone: 334-881-2227. Fax: 334-881-2300. E-mail: jgaplin@lbwcc.edu.

DEGREES AND AWARDS

AA Arts

LUTHERAN THEOLOGICAL SEMINARY AT GETTYSBURG
Gettysburg, Pennsylvania
http://www.ltsg.edu/

Lutheran Theological Seminary at Gettysburg was founded in 1826. It is accredited by Middle States Association of Colleges and Schools. It first offered distance learning courses in 2000. In fall 2005, there were 40 students enrolled in distance learning courses. Institutionally administered financial aid is available to distance learners.

Services Distance learners have accessibility to bookstore, e-mail services, library services.

Contact Dr. Marty Stevens, PhD, Registrar, Lutheran Theological Seminary at Gettysburg, 61 Seminary Ridge, Gettysburg, PA 17325. Telephone: 717-334-6286 Ext. 3006. Fax: 717-334-3469. E-mail: mstevens@ltsg.edu.

DEGREES AND AWARDS

Programs offered do not lead to a degree or other formal award.

COURSE SUBJECT AREAS OFFERED OUTSIDE OF DEGREE PROGRAMS

Graduate—biblical and other theological languages and literatures; biblical studies; religious education; religious/sacred music; religious studies; theological and ministerial studies; theology and religious vocations related.

Non-credit—theological and ministerial studies; theology and religious vocations related.

LUTHER RICE UNIVERSITY
Lithonia, Georgia

Luther Rice University was founded in 1962. It is accredited by Transnational Association of Christian Colleges and Schools. It first offered distance learning courses in 1962. In fall 2005, there were 557 students enrolled in distance learning courses. Institutionally administered financial aid is available to distance learners.

Services Distance learners have accessibility to academic advising, bookstore, career placement assistance, library services.

Contact Admissions, Luther Rice University, 3038 Evans Mill Road, Lithonia , GA 30038. Telephone: 770-484-1204. Fax: 770-484-1155. E-mail: admissions@lru.edu.

DEGREES AND AWARDS

BA Religion
MA Christian Studies; Discipleship Counseling; Leadership
DMin Church Ministries

LYNN UNIVERSITY
Boca Raton, Florida
The Institute for Distance Learning
http://www.lynn.edu/distancelearning

Lynn University was founded in 1962. It is accredited by Southern Association of Colleges and Schools. It first offered distance learning courses in 1998. In fall 2005, there were 1,000 students enrolled in distance learning courses. Institutionally administered financial aid is available to distance learners.

Services Distance learners have accessibility to academic advising, bookstore, campus computer network, career placement assistance, e-mail services, library services.

Contact Juliet Juan, Technology Support, Lynn University, 3601 North Military Trail, Boca Raton, FL 33431. Telephone: 561-237-7850. Fax: 561-237-7537. E-mail: jjuan@lynn.edu.

DEGREES AND AWARDS
BA Behavioral Science
BS Business; Criminal Justice
MBA Business Administration
MS Criminal Justice Administration

See full description on page 402.

MACON STATE COLLEGE
Macon, Georgia
Office of Distance Learning
http://www.maconstate.edu

Macon State College was founded in 1968. It is accredited by Southern Association of Colleges and Schools. It first offered distance learning courses in 1997. In fall 2005, there were 1,568 students enrolled in distance learning courses. Institutionally administered financial aid is available to distance learners.

Services Distance learners have accessibility to academic advising, bookstore, campus computer network, career placement assistance, e-mail services, library services, tutoring.

Contact Mr. Geoffrey Dyer, Director, Academic Systems, Macon State College, 100 College Station Drive, Macon, GA 31206-5145. Telephone: 478-471-2860. Fax: 478-471-2896. E-mail: gdyer@mail.maconstate.edu.

DEGREES AND AWARDS
Programs offered do not lead to a degree or other formal award.

COURSE SUBJECT AREAS OFFERED OUTSIDE OF DEGREE PROGRAMS

Undergraduate—accounting and computer science; business/commerce; business/corporate communications; computer and information sciences; computer programming; computer software and media applications; computer systems analysis; computer systems networking and telecommunications; English composition; health and medical administrative services; health services/allied health/health sciences; mathematics; psychology; statistics.

Non-credit—business/corporate communications; computer engineering technologies; computer software and media applications; computer systems networking and telecommunications; English; graphic communications.

MADISON AREA TECHNICAL COLLEGE
Madison, Wisconsin
Instructional Media/Distance Education Department
http://www.matcmadison.edu

Madison Area Technical College was founded in 1911. It is accredited by North Central Association of Colleges and Schools. It first offered distance learning courses in 1994. In fall 2005, there were 6,600 students enrolled in distance learning courses. Institutionally administered financial aid is available to distance learners.

Services Distance learners have accessibility to bookstore, e-mail services, library services.

Contact Lisa Franklin, Administrative Assistant for Distance Learning, Madison Area Technical College, 3550 Anderson Street, Madison, WI 53704. Telephone: 608-246-6288. Fax: 608-246-6287. E-mail: lfranklin@matcmadison.edu.

DEGREES AND AWARDS
AD Accounting
AS Administrative Assistant
ASM Supervisory Management/Leadership Development
Certificate Quality Management
Diploma Business Software Applications Specialist
Specialized diploma Optometric Technician

COURSE SUBJECT AREAS OFFERED OUTSIDE OF DEGREE PROGRAMS

Undergraduate—business administration, management and operations; business operations support and assistant services; computer and information sciences; computer/information technology administration and management; computer programming; computer software and media applications; computer systems networking and telecommunications; criminal justice and corrections; drafting/design engineering technologies; English composition; human development, family studies, and related services; liberal arts and sciences, general studies and humanities; management information systems; marketing; mathematics and statistics related; ophthalmic and optometric support services and allied professions; parks, recreation and leisure; real estate; sales, merchandising, and related marketing operations (general); sales, merchandising, and related marketing operations (specialized); statistics.

MADONNA UNIVERSITY
Livonia, Michigan
Office of Continuing Education and Professional Studies
http://www.madonna.edu

Madonna University was founded in 1947. It is accredited by North Central Association of Colleges and Schools. It first offered distance learning courses in 1983. In fall 2005, there were 500 students enrolled in distance learning courses. Institutionally administered financial aid is available to distance learners.

Services Distance learners have accessibility to academic advising, bookstore, campus computer network, career placement assistance, e-mail services, library services, tutoring.

Contact Ms. Joan M. Stephens, Director, Madonna University, 36600 Schoolcraft Road, Livonia, MI 48150. Telephone: 800-852-4951 Ext. 5732. Fax: 734-432-5732. E-mail: jstephens@madonna.edu.

DEGREES AND AWARDS
Programs offered do not lead to a degree or other formal award.

COURSE SUBJECT AREAS OFFERED OUTSIDE OF DEGREE PROGRAMS

Undergraduate—accounting and computer science; business, management, and marketing related; computer and information sciences; criminal justice and corrections; education; English composition; gerontology; history; liberal arts and sciences, general studies and humanities; mental and social health services and allied professions; nursing; psychology; public relations, advertising, and applied communication related; religious studies.

Graduate—accounting and computer science; accounting and related services; business administration, management and operations; business/commerce; business, management, and marketing related; nursing.

Non-credit—criminal justice and corrections; gerontology; liberal arts and sciences, general studies and humanities.

MALONE COLLEGE
Canton, Ohio
Malone College Online Learning
http://www.malone-online.org

Malone College was founded in 1892. It is accredited by North Central Association of Colleges and Schools. It first offered distance learning courses in 1999. In fall 2005, there were 350 students enrolled in distance learning courses. Institutionally administered financial aid is available to distance learners.

Services Distance learners have accessibility to academic advising, bookstore, career placement assistance, e-mail services, library services.

Contact Sharon Purvis, Online Coordinator, Malone College, 515 25th Street, NW, Canton, OH 44709. Telephone: 330-471-8423. Fax: 330-471-8570. E-mail: inquiry@malone-online.org.

DEGREES AND AWARDS
BA Business Management

COURSE SUBJECT AREAS OFFERED OUTSIDE OF DEGREE PROGRAMS

Undergraduate—biblical studies; biology; business/commerce; communication and media; developmental and child psychology; English composition; English literature (British and Commonwealth); fine and studio art; health and physical education/fitness; history; philosophy; political science and government; psychology; social sciences related; sociology.

Graduate—biblical studies.

MANHATTANVILLE COLLEGE
Purchase, New York

Manhattanville College was founded in 1841. It is accredited by Middle States Association of Colleges and Schools. It first offered distance learning courses in 1999. Institutionally administered financial aid is available to distance learners.

Services Distance learners have accessibility to academic advising, bookstore, campus computer network, career placement assistance, e-mail services, library services, tutoring.

Contact Dr. David C. Adams, Associate Professor, Manhattanville College, Department of Economics, Finance, and Management, 2900 Purchase Street, Purchase, NY 10577. Telephone: 914-323-7122. E-mail: adamsd @mville.edu.

DEGREES AND AWARDS
Programs offered do not lead to a degree or other formal award.

COURSE SUBJECT AREAS OFFERED OUTSIDE OF DEGREE PROGRAMS
Undergraduate—business administration, management and operations; entrepreneurial and small business operations; human resources management.

MANSFIELD UNIVERSITY OF PENNSYLVANIA
Mansfield, Pennsylvania
Center for Lifelong Learning
http://cll.mansfield.edu

Mansfield University of Pennsylvania was founded in 1857. It is accredited by Middle States Association of Colleges and Schools. It first offered distance learning courses in 1995. In fall 2005, there were 276 students enrolled in distance learning courses. Institutionally administered financial aid is available to distance learners.

Services Distance learners have accessibility to academic advising, bookstore, campus computer network, career placement assistance, e-mail services, library services, tutoring.

Contact Brian Barden, Director of Enrollment Management, Mansfield University of Pennsylvania, Alumni Hall, Mansfield University, Mansfield, PA 16933. Telephone: 570-662-4813. Fax: 570-662-4121. E-mail: bbarden@mansfield.edu.

DEGREES AND AWARDS
BA Art History
BSN Nursing–RN to BSN
MEd Art Education
MSE Library and Information Technologies–School Library and Information Technologies
MSN Nursing Education

COURSE SUBJECT AREAS OFFERED OUTSIDE OF DEGREE PROGRAMS
Undergraduate—accounting and related services; business administration, management and operations; computer and information sciences; criminal justice and corrections; economics; English; mathematics; nursing; sociology.

MARANATHA BAPTIST BIBLE COLLEGE
Watertown, Wisconsin
http://www.mbbc.edu/

Maranatha Baptist Bible College was founded in 1968. It is accredited by North Central Association of Colleges and Schools. It first offered distance learning courses in 2001. In fall 2005, there were 25 students enrolled in distance learning courses. Institutionally administered financial aid is available to distance learners.

Services Distance learners have accessibility to academic advising, campus computer network, e-mail services.

Contact Mr. Steven D. Carlson, Assistant Registrar, Maranatha Baptist Bible College, 745 West Main Street, Watertown, WI 53094. Telephone: 920-206-2344. Fax: 920-261-9109. E-mail: scarlson@mbbc.edu.

DEGREES AND AWARDS
Programs offered do not lead to a degree or other formal award.

COURSE SUBJECT AREAS OFFERED OUTSIDE OF DEGREE PROGRAMS
Undergraduate—American literature (United States and Canadian); biblical studies; educational/instructional media design.
Graduate—biblical studies; pastoral counseling and specialized ministries; religious studies.

MARION TECHNICAL COLLEGE
Marion, Ohio
http://www.mtc.edu

Marion Technical College was founded in 1971. It is accredited by North Central Association of Colleges and Schools. It first offered distance learning courses in 1995. In fall 2005, there were 100 students enrolled in distance learning courses. Institutionally administered financial aid is available to distance learners.

Services Distance learners have accessibility to academic advising, campus computer network, career placement assistance, e-mail services, library services.

Contact Vicky Wood, Dean of Business and Instructional Technologies, Marion Technical College, 1467 Mount Vernon Avenue, Marion, OH 43302. Telephone: 740-389-4636 Ext. 265. Fax: 740-389-6136. E-mail: woodv@mtc.edu.

DEGREES AND AWARDS
Programs offered do not lead to a degree or other formal award.

COURSE SUBJECT AREAS OFFERED OUTSIDE OF DEGREE PROGRAMS
Undergraduate—business operations support and assistant services; clinical/medical laboratory science and allied professions; computer software and media applications; English composition; legal studies (non-professional general, undergraduate); management information systems; mathematics.

MARIST COLLEGE
Poughkeepsie, New York
School of Management
http://www.marist.edu/management

Marist College was founded in 1929. It is accredited by Middle States Association of Colleges and Schools. It first offered distance learning courses in 1998. In fall 2005, there were 250 students enrolled in distance learning courses. Institutionally administered financial aid is available to distance learners.

Services Distance learners have accessibility to academic advising, bookstore, campus computer network, career placement assistance, e-mail services, library services.

Contact Ms. Anu Ailawadhi, Director of Graduate Admissions, Marist College, School of Graduate and Continuing Education, Poughkeepsie, NY 12601. Telephone: 845-575-3800. Fax: 845-575-3166. E-mail: anu.ailawadhi@marist.edu.

DEGREES AND AWARDS
MBA Business Administration
MPA Public Administration

COURSE SUBJECT AREAS OFFERED OUTSIDE OF DEGREE PROGRAMS
Undergraduate—accounting and related services; business, management, and marketing related; economics; finance and financial management services; legal studies (non-professional general, undergraduate); statistics.
Graduate—accounting and related services; business administration, management and operations; business, management, and marketing related; business/managerial economics; management sciences and quantitative methods; sales, merchandising, and related marketing operations (specialized).

See full description on page 404.

MARQUETTE UNIVERSITY
Milwaukee, Wisconsin
http://www.marquette.edu/online

Marquette University was founded in 1881. It is accredited by North Central Association of Colleges and Schools. It first offered distance learning courses in 1997. In fall 2005, there were 75 students enrolled in distance learning courses. Institutionally administered financial aid is available to distance learners.

Services Distance learners have accessibility to academic advising, bookstore, campus computer network, e-mail services, library services.

Contact Heidi Schweizer, Director of Center for Electronic Learning, Marquette University, PO Box 1881, Schroeder Health Complex 199E, School of Education, Milwaukee, WI 53201. Telephone: 414-288-8811. Fax: 414-288-3945. E-mail: heidi.schweizer@marquette.edu.

DEGREES AND AWARDS
Certification Education–6-12 Alternative Certification

MA Education–Instructional Leadership

COURSE SUBJECT AREAS OFFERED OUTSIDE OF DEGREE PROGRAMS
Undergraduate—education.

Graduate—education.

Non-credit—education.

MARSHALL UNIVERSITY
Huntington, West Virginia
Distributed Education Technology
http://www.marshall.edu/muonline

Marshall University was founded in 1837. It is accredited by North Central Association of Colleges and Schools. It first offered distance learning courses in 1986. In fall 2005, there were 5,661 students enrolled in distance learning courses. Institutionally administered financial aid is available to distance learners.

Services Distance learners have accessibility to academic advising, bookstore, campus computer network, e-mail services, library services, tutoring.

Contact Crystal Stewart, Program Specialist, Marshall University, One John Marshall Drive, CB 216, Huntington, WV 25755-2140. Telephone: 304-696-2970. Fax: 304-696-2973. E-mail: stewar14@marshall.edu.

DEGREES AND AWARDS
AGS General Studies

BA Regents Bachelor of Arts degree

Certification Public Library Technology (PLT)

MEd Elementary or Secondary Education

COURSE SUBJECT AREAS OFFERED OUTSIDE OF DEGREE PROGRAMS
Undergraduate—accounting and related services; business administration, management and operations; business/managerial economics; chemistry; communication and journalism related; communication and media; computer and information sciences; computer and information sciences and support services related; computer engineering; developmental and child psychology; economics; English composition; geography and cartography; history; journalism; management information systems; marketing; mathematics; mathematics and computer science; mathematics and statistics related; nursing; philosophy; psychology; social work; sociology; statistics; visual and performing arts.

Graduate—accounting and related services; computer and information sciences; marketing; social work; sociology; technology education/industrial arts; visual and performing arts.

MARYGROVE COLLEGE
Detroit, Michigan
Master in the Art of Teaching Program
http://www.marygrove.edu

Marygrove College was founded in 1905. It is accredited by North Central Association of Colleges and Schools. It first offered distance learning courses in 1989. In fall 2005, there were 4,000 students enrolled in distance learning courses. Institutionally administered financial aid is available to distance learners.

Services Distance learners have accessibility to academic advising, bookstore, campus computer network, e-mail services, library services, tutoring.

Contact Ms. Sherry Quinn, Admissions Coordinator, Marygrove College, 8425 West McNichols, Detroit, MI 48221. Telephone: 313-927-1509. Fax: 313-927-1530. E-mail: squinn@marygrove.edu.

DEGREES AND AWARDS
MA Educational Administration

MAT Teacher Education

COURSE SUBJECT AREAS OFFERED OUTSIDE OF DEGREE PROGRAMS
Undergraduate—education (specific subject areas).

Graduate—education (specific subject areas).

MARYLHURST UNIVERSITY
Marylhurst, Oregon
Department of Distance Learning
http://online.marylhurst.edu

Marylhurst University was founded in 1893. It is accredited by Northwest Commission on Colleges and Universities. It first offered distance learning courses in 1996. In fall 2005, there were 525 students enrolled in distance learning courses. Institutionally administered financial aid is available to distance learners.

Services Distance learners have accessibility to academic advising, bookstore, campus computer network, career placement assistance, library services.

Contact Barb Fournier, Staff Assistant, Marylhurst University, 17600 Pacific Highway, PO Box 261, Marylhurst, OR 97036. Telephone: 800-634-9982 Ext. 4084. Fax: 503-534-4084. E-mail: bfournier@marylhurst.edu.

DEGREES AND AWARDS
BA Interdisciplinary Studies

BS Business and Leadership; Real Estate

MBA Business Administration

COURSE SUBJECT AREAS OFFERED OUTSIDE OF DEGREE PROGRAMS
Undergraduate—American literature (United States and Canadian); creative writing; English composition; English literature (British and Commonwealth); film/video and photographic arts; history; human development, family studies, and related services; liberal arts and sciences, general studies and humanities; mathematics and statistics related; music; natural sciences; nutrition sciences; philosophy and religious studies related; political science and government; religious education.

Graduate—multi-/interdisciplinary studies related; philosophy and religious studies related; theological and ministerial studies.

Non-credit—communication and media; ethnic, cultural minority, and gender studies; mathematics; philosophy and religious studies related; psychology related; social and philosophical foundations of education.

MARYVILLE UNIVERSITY OF SAINT LOUIS
St. Louis, Missouri
http://www.maryville.edu/

Maryville University of Saint Louis was founded in 1872. It is accredited by North Central Association of Colleges and Schools. It first offered distance learning courses in 2000. In fall 2005, there were 300 students enrolled in distance learning courses. Institutionally administered financial aid is available to distance learners.

Services Distance learners have accessibility to campus computer network, e-mail services.

Contact Ms. Chris Bretz, Coordinator, CEDL, Maryville University of Saint Louis, St. Louis, MO 63141. E-mail: cbretz@maryville.edu.

DEGREES AND AWARDS

Programs offered do not lead to a degree or other formal award.

COURSE SUBJECT AREAS OFFERED OUTSIDE OF DEGREE PROGRAMS

Undergraduate—data processing; information science/studies.

Non-credit—accounting and related services; business administration, management and operations; communications technology; computer and information sciences; computer software and media applications; computer systems analysis; computer systems networking and telecommunications; crafts, folk art and artisanry; creative writing; data entry/microcomputer applications; data processing; entrepreneurial and small business operations; human development, family studies, and related services; human resources management; information science/studies; journalism; management information systems; public relations, advertising, and applied communication related.

MASSASOIT COMMUNITY COLLEGE

Brockton, Massachusetts

http://www.massasoit.mass.edu/acad_depts/dist_learn/dist_learn.htm

Massasoit Community College was founded in 1966. It is accredited by New England Association of Schools and Colleges. It first offered distance learning courses in 1998. In fall 2005, there were 385 students enrolled in distance learning courses. Institutionally administered financial aid is available to distance learners.

Services Distance learners have accessibility to bookstore, campus computer network, e-mail services, library services.

Contact Candy Center, Dean of e-Learning and Non-Traditional Programs, Massasoit Community College, 1 Massasoit Boulevard, Brockton, MA 02302. Telephone: 508-588-9100 Ext. 1615. Fax: 508-427-1250. E-mail: ccenter@massasoit.mass.edu.

DEGREES AND AWARDS

Programs offered do not lead to a degree or other formal award.

COURSE SUBJECT AREAS OFFERED OUTSIDE OF DEGREE PROGRAMS

Undergraduate—accounting and related services; anthropology; biological and physical sciences; business administration, management and operations; business/commerce; business/corporate communications; chemistry; computer and information sciences; computer software and media applications; film/video and photographic arts; geography and cartography; history; human development, family studies, and related services; international business; mathematics; music; philosophy; physical sciences; psychology; psychology related; sales, merchandising, and related marketing operations (specialized); sociology; speech and rhetoric; statistics.

Non-credit—business/commerce; communication and media; computer and information sciences; computer software and media applications; creative writing; gerontology; health professions related; human resources management; journalism; peace studies and conflict resolution; precision systems maintenance and repair technologies; sales, merchandising, and related marketing operations (general); sales, merchandising, and related marketing operations (specialized); social sciences; taxation.

MASTER'S COLLEGE AND SEMINARY

Toronto, Ontario, Canada

http://www.mcs.edu/

Master's College and Seminary was founded in 1939. It is provincially chartered. It first offered distance learning courses in 1996. In fall 2005, there were 264 students enrolled in distance learning courses. Institutionally administered financial aid is available to distance learners.

Services Distance learners have accessibility to academic advising, bookstore, e-mail services, library services.

Contact Rev. Luc Lombardi, Associate Dean, Master's College and Seminary, 3080 Yonge Street, Box 70, Suite 3040, Toronto, ON M4N 3N1, Canada. Telephone: 800-295-6368 Ext. 224. E-mail: luc.lombardi@mcs.edu.

DEGREES AND AWARDS

AA Religious Education–Bachelor of Religious Education–Pastoral Ministry

CWC Christian Ministry

Diploma Ministry–Ministerial Diploma

COURSE SUBJECT AREAS OFFERED OUTSIDE OF DEGREE PROGRAMS

Undergraduate—biblical and other theological languages and literatures; biblical studies; counseling psychology; ethnic, cultural minority, and gender studies; missionary studies and missiology; pastoral counseling and specialized ministries; philosophy and religious studies related; psychology related; religious education; religious studies; theological and ministerial studies; theology and religious vocations related.

MAYVILLE STATE UNIVERSITY

Mayville, North Dakota

Enrollment Services Office

http://www.mayvillestate.edu

Mayville State University was founded in 1889. It is accredited by North Central Association of Colleges and Schools. It first offered distance learning courses in 1999. In fall 2005, there were 264 students enrolled in distance learning courses. Institutionally administered financial aid is available to distance learners.

Services Distance learners have accessibility to academic advising, bookstore, campus computer network, career placement assistance, e-mail services, library services.

Contact Ms. Lisa Ziegler, Coordinator of Office of Worldwide Learning, Mayville State University, 330 Third Street, NE, Mayville, ND 58257. Telephone: 701-788-4667. Fax: 701-788-4748. E-mail: lisa_ziegler@mayvillestate.edu.

DEGREES AND AWARDS

AA Early Childhood Education Associate

BA Early Childhood Education

BS Business Administration (Bachelor of Applied Science); Business Administration; Computer Information Systems (Bachelor of Applied Science)

COURSE SUBJECT AREAS OFFERED OUTSIDE OF DEGREE PROGRAMS

Undergraduate—accounting and related services; biology; business administration, management and operations; chemistry; education; English composition; human development, family studies, and related services; library science.

MCMURRY UNIVERSITY

Abilene, Texas

McMurry University was founded in 1923. It is accredited by Southern Association of Colleges and Schools. It first offered distance learning courses in 2000. In fall 2005, there were 225 students enrolled in distance learning courses. Institutionally administered financial aid is available to distance learners.

Services Distance learners have accessibility to academic advising, bookstore, e-mail services, library services.

Contact Dr. Alicia T. Wyatt, Associate Professor, McMurry University, Box 218, McMurry Station, Abilene, TX 79697. E-mail: awyatt@mcm.edu.

DEGREES AND AWARDS

Programs offered do not lead to a degree or other formal award.

COURSE SUBJECT AREAS OFFERED OUTSIDE OF DEGREE PROGRAMS

Undergraduate—biblical studies; business administration, management and operations; curriculum and instruction; education (specific levels and methods); religious studies.

MEDICAL COLLEGE OF WISCONSIN
Milwaukee, Wisconsin
Master of Public Health Degree Programs
http://instruct.mcw.edu/prevmed

Medical College of Wisconsin was founded in 1913. It is accredited by North Central Association of Colleges and Schools. It first offered distance learning courses in 1986. In fall 2005, there were 137 students enrolled in distance learning courses. Institutionally administered financial aid is available to distance learners.

Services Distance learners have accessibility to academic advising, bookstore, campus computer network, career placement assistance, e-mail services, library services.

Contact Beverly Carlson, Program Coordinator, MPH Degree Program, Medical College of Wisconsin, Division of Public Health, 8701 Watertown Plank Road, Milwaukee, WI 53226. Telephone: 414-456-4510. Fax: 414-456-6160. E-mail: mph@mcw.edu.

DEGREES AND AWARDS

MPH Occupational Medicine; Preventive Medicine, general

COURSE SUBJECT AREAS OFFERED OUTSIDE OF DEGREE PROGRAMS

Graduate—public health.

MEMORIAL UNIVERSITY OF NEWFOUNDLAND
St. John's, Newfoundland and Labrador, Canada
Distance Education and Learning Technologies
http://www.distance.mun.ca

Memorial University of Newfoundland was founded in 1925. It is provincially chartered. It first offered distance learning courses in 1969. In fall 2005, there were 2,960 students enrolled in distance learning courses. Institutionally administered financial aid is available to distance learners.

Services Distance learners have accessibility to academic advising, bookstore, e-mail services, library services.

Contact Renee Elliott, Manager, Client Relations, Memorial University of Newfoundland, G. A. Hickman Building, ED-2000, St. John's, NF A1B 3X8, Canada. Telephone: 709-737-8700. Fax: 709-737-4070. E-mail: distance@mun.ca.

DEGREES AND AWARDS

BBA Business Administration
BN Nursing–Post-RN
BS Maritime Studies–Bachelor of Maritime Studies (BMS); Technology–Bachelor Technology (BTech)
Certificate Business Administration; Career Development; Criminology; Library Studies; Newfoundland Studies; Public Administration
Diploma Business Administration
MEd Counseling Psychology; Curriculum Teaching and Learning Studies; Educational Leadership Studies; Information Technology; Postsecondary Studies
MN Nursing
MSW Social Work

COURSE SUBJECT AREAS OFFERED OUTSIDE OF DEGREE PROGRAMS

Undergraduate—anthropology; biology; business administration, management and operations; computer science; economics; education; education related; engineering; English; library science; mathematics; nursing; philosophy; political science and government; psychology; religious studies; social work; sociology; statistics.

Graduate—criminology; education related; library science; nursing; social work.

MERCER COUNTY COMMUNITY COLLEGE
Trenton, New Jersey
http://www.mccc.edu/

Mercer County Community College was founded in 1966. It is accredited by Middle States Association of Colleges and Schools. It first offered distance learning courses in 1998. In fall 2005, there were 1,416 students enrolled in distance learning courses. Institutionally administered financial aid is available to distance learners.

Services Distance learners have accessibility to academic advising, bookstore, career placement assistance, library services.

Contact Jennie DeLapo, Program Assistant, Mercer County Community College, 1200 Old Trenton Road, West Windsor, NJ 08550. Telephone: 609-586-4800 Ext. 3317. E-mail: delapo@mccc.edu.

DEGREES AND AWARDS

Programs offered do not lead to a degree or other formal award.

COURSE SUBJECT AREAS OFFERED OUTSIDE OF DEGREE PROGRAMS

Undergraduate—accounting and related services; anthropology; business/commerce; computer and information sciences; computer software and media applications; economics; English composition; health and physical education/fitness; history; mathematics; philosophy; psychology related; sociology.

Non-credit—computer systems networking and telecommunications; finance and financial management services; technical and business writing.

MERCY COLLEGE
Dobbs Ferry, New York
MerLIN
http://merlin.mercy.edu

Mercy College was founded in 1951. It is accredited by Middle States Association of Colleges and Schools. It first offered distance learning courses in 1990. In fall 2005, there were 1,378 students enrolled in distance learning courses. Institutionally administered financial aid is available to distance learners.

Services Distance learners have accessibility to academic advising, bookstore, campus computer network, career placement assistance, e-mail services, library services, tutoring.

Contact Mr. John DiElsi, Dean, Mercy Online, Mercy College, 555 Broadway, Dobbs Ferry, NY 10522. Telephone: 914-674-7527. Fax: 914-674-7240. E-mail: jdielsi@mercy.edu.

DEGREES AND AWARDS

AA Liberal Arts and Sciences
AAS Banking; Business
AS Accounting; Liberal Arts and Sciences
BA Behavioral Science; English; History; Psychology
BS Behavioral Science; Business Administration; Computer Information Systems; Computer Science; Corporate Communications; Criminal Justice; English; Envionmental Health and Safety Management; Health Science; History; Mathematics; Nursing; Organizational Management; Psychology; Spanish
MA English Literature
MBA Business Administration
MHRM Human Resource Management
MNE Nursing Education
MPA Health Services Management
MS Banking; Counseling; Direct Marketing; Health Services Management; Internet Business Systems; Organizational Leadership
MSN Nursing Administration

COURSE SUBJECT AREAS OFFERED OUTSIDE OF DEGREE PROGRAMS

Undergraduate—accounting and related services; area, ethnic, cultural, and gender studies related; biology; business administration, management and operations; business/commerce; communications technology; community organization and advocacy; comparative literature; computer and information sciences; computer science; creative writing; criminal justice and corrections; developmental and child psychology; educational administration and supervision; educational psychology; English; English composition; English literature (British and Common-

wealth); environmental/environmental health engineering; fine and studio art; health professions related; health services/allied health/health sciences; history; human services; international business; languages (foreign languages related); legal studies (non-professional general, undergraduate); liberal arts and sciences, general studies and humanities; management information systems; management sciences and quantitative methods; marketing; mathematics and statistics related; nursing; public administration and social service professions related; public health; social psychology; sociology; statistics.
Graduate—American literature (United States and Canadian); business administration, management and operations; business/commerce; business/corporate communications; business, management, and marketing related; business/managerial economics; community health services; comparative literature; computer and information sciences; computer and information sciences and support services related; computer/information technology administration and management; computer science; computer software and media applications; computer systems analysis; counseling psychology; English; English language and literature related; English literature (British and Commonwealth); health services/allied health/health sciences; human services; management information systems; management sciences and quantitative methods; marketing; peace studies and conflict resolution; psychology; psychology related; sales, merchandising, and related marketing operations (specialized); social sciences related.

MESALANDS COMMUNITY COLLEGE
Tucumcari, New Mexico
http://www.mesalands.edu

Mesalands Community College was founded in 1979. It is accredited by North Central Association of Colleges and Schools. It first offered distance learning courses in 1997. In fall 2005, there were 125 students enrolled in distance learning courses. Institutionally administered financial aid is available to distance learners.
Services Distance learners have accessibility to academic advising, bookstore, campus computer network, library services, tutoring.
Contact Ms. Nancy C. Nydam, Distance Education Coordinator, Mesalands Community College, 911 South Tenth Street, Tucumcari, NM 88401. Telephone: 505-461-4413 Ext. 118. Fax: 505-461-1901. E-mail: nancyn@mesalands.edu.

DEGREES AND AWARDS
Programs offered do not lead to a degree or other formal award.

COURSE SUBJECT AREAS OFFERED OUTSIDE OF DEGREE PROGRAMS
Undergraduate—accounting and related services; agricultural business and management; animal sciences; astronomy and astrophysics; business/commerce; computer and information sciences; computer science; economics; education; English; geography and cartography; geological and earth sciences/geosciences; history; human resources management; marketing; mathematics; music; physical sciences; sociology; teaching assistants/aides.

MESA STATE COLLEGE
Grand Junction, Colorado
Continuing Education Center
http://www2.mesastate.edu

Mesa State College was founded in 1925. It is accredited by North Central Association of Colleges and Schools. It first offered distance learning courses in 1996. In fall 2005, there were 300 students enrolled in distance learning courses. Institutionally administered financial aid is available to distance learners.
Services Distance learners have accessibility to academic advising, bookstore, campus computer network, career placement assistance, e-mail services, library services, tutoring.
Contact Rance Larsen, Director of Admissions, Mesa State College, 1100 North Avenue, Grand Junction, CO 81501. Telephone: 800-982-6372. Fax: 970-248-1464. E-mail: admissions@mesastate.edu.

DEGREES AND AWARDS
Programs offered do not lead to a degree or other formal award.

COURSE SUBJECT AREAS OFFERED OUTSIDE OF DEGREE PROGRAMS
Undergraduate—accounting and computer science; biology; education; electrical, electronics and communications engineering; English; history; management sciences and quantitative methods; mathematics; nursing; parks, recreation and leisure; political science and government; psychology; visual and performing arts.

METROPOLITAN STATE UNIVERSITY
St. Paul, Minnesota
http://www.metrostate.edu

Metropolitan State University was founded in 1971. It is accredited by North Central Association of Colleges and Schools. It first offered distance learning courses in 1994. In fall 2005, there were 1,018 students enrolled in distance learning courses. Institutionally administered financial aid is available to distance learners.
Services Distance learners have accessibility to academic advising, bookstore, career placement assistance, e-mail services, library services, tutoring.
Contact Ms. Monir Johnson, Director of Admissions, Metropolitan State University, 700 East 7th Street, St. Paul, MN 55106. Telephone: 651-793-1303. Fax: 651-793-1310. E-mail: monir.johnson@metrostate.edu.

DEGREES AND AWARDS
BA Individualized Studies
BS Business Administration; Management; Marketing; Organizational Administration
Certificate Nursing–Continence Care Nurse; Nursing–Ostomy Care Nurse; Nursing–Wound Care Nurse; Nursing–Wound Ostomy Continence Nurse
MS Public and Non-Profit Management–Master of Public and Non-Profit Management
MSN Nursing

COURSE SUBJECT AREAS OFFERED OUTSIDE OF DEGREE PROGRAMS
Undergraduate—accounting and related services; anthropology; business administration, management and operations; communication and journalism related; criminal justice and corrections; dramatic/theater arts and stagecraft; economics; English composition; English language and literature related; finance and financial management services; history; hospitality administration; human resources management; human services; information science/studies; international business; legal studies (non-professional general, undergraduate); management information systems; marketing; mathematics; multi-/interdisciplinary studies related; music; nursing; philosophy; physics; political science and government; psychology; public administration; statistics.
Graduate—business administration, management and operations; criminal justice and corrections; economics; management information systems; marketing; nursing; public administration.

MGH INSTITUTE OF HEALTH PROFESSIONS
Boston, Massachusetts
http://www.mghihp.edu

MGH Institute of Health Professions was founded in 1977. It is accredited by New England Association of Schools and Colleges. It first offered distance learning courses in 2000. In fall 2005, there were 273 students enrolled in distance learning courses. Institutionally administered financial aid is available to distance learners.
Services Distance learners have accessibility to academic advising, bookstore, campus computer network, e-mail services, library services, tutoring.
Contact Ms. Terry Lavin, Director of Admissions, MGH Institute of Health Professions, 36 1st Avenue, Boston, MA 02129-4557. Telephone: 617-726-6069. Fax: 617-726-8010. E-mail: tlavin@mghihp.edu.

DEGREES AND AWARDS
Graduate Certificate Clinical Investigation
MS Clinical Investigations
DPT Physical Therapy–Transitional Doctor of Physical Therapy

COURSE SUBJECT AREAS OFFERED OUTSIDE OF DEGREE PROGRAMS

Graduate—communication disorders sciences and services; health professions related; nursing.

MIAMI DADE COLLEGE
Miami, Florida
Virtual College
http://www.mdc.edu/vcollege/

Miami Dade College was founded in 1960. It is accredited by Southern Association of Colleges and Schools. It first offered distance learning courses in 1997. In fall 2005, there were 3,910 students enrolled in distance learning courses. Institutionally administered financial aid is available to distance learners.

Services Distance learners have accessibility to academic advising, bookstore, library services.

Contact Lloyd Hollingsworth, Student Services Coordinator, Miami Dade College, 300 NE 2nd Avenue, Miami, FL 33132-2297. Telephone: 305-237-3873. Fax: 305-237-3863. E-mail: lholling@mdc.edu.

DEGREES AND AWARDS

AA Pre-Bachelor of Arts

COURSE SUBJECT AREAS OFFERED OUTSIDE OF DEGREE PROGRAMS

Undergraduate—accounting and related services; American literature (United States and Canadian); atmospheric sciences and meteorology; biblical studies; biological and biomedical sciences related; biological and physical sciences; biology; business administration, management and operations; computer and information sciences; economics; education; English; English composition; health and medical administrative services; human development, family studies, and related services; international relations and affairs; liberal arts and sciences, general studies and humanities; library science related; management sciences and quantitative methods; marketing; mathematics; nursing; philosophy and religious studies related; physical sciences related; political science and government; psychology; religious studies; social sciences; speech and rhetoric; statistics; taxation.

Non-credit—health professions related.

MICHIGAN STATE UNIVERSITY COLLEGE OF LAW
East Lansing, Michigan

Michigan State University College of Law was founded in 1891. It is accredited by Association of American Law Schools. It first offered distance learning courses in 1999. Institutionally administered financial aid is available to distance learners.

Services Distance learners have accessibility to academic advising, career placement assistance, e-mail services, library services.

Contact Theresa Allen, Michigan State University College of Law, 230 Law College Building, East Lansing, MI 48824. Telephone: 517-432-6827. E-mail: allenthe@law.msu.edu.

DEGREES AND AWARDS

Programs offered do not lead to a degree or other formal award.

COURSE SUBJECT AREAS OFFERED OUTSIDE OF DEGREE PROGRAMS

Graduate—legal professions and studies related; legal research and advanced professional studies; legal support services.

Non-credit—legal professions and studies related; legal research and advanced professional studies; legal studies (non-professional general, undergraduate); legal support services.

MIDDLESEX COMMUNITY COLLEGE
Middletown, Connecticut
http://www.mxctc.commnet.edu/

Middlesex Community College was founded in 1966. It is accredited by New England Association of Schools and Colleges. It first offered distance learning courses in 1999. In fall 2005, there were 200 students enrolled in distance learning courses. Institutionally administered financial aid is available to distance learners.

Services Distance learners have accessibility to academic advising, bookstore, campus computer network, e-mail services, library services, tutoring.

Contact Dr. Yi Guan-Raczkowski, Director of Distance Learning, Middlesex Community College, 100 Training Hill Road, Middletown, CT 06457. Telephone: 860-343-5783. E-mail: yguan@mxcc.commnet.edu.

DEGREES AND AWARDS

Programs offered do not lead to a degree or other formal award.

COURSE SUBJECT AREAS OFFERED OUTSIDE OF DEGREE PROGRAMS

Undergraduate—accounting and computer science; biology; business administration, management and operations; communication and media; computer and information sciences; economics; education; psychology; sociology.

MIDDLESEX COMMUNITY COLLEGE
Bedford, Massachusetts
http://online.middlesex.mass.edu

Middlesex Community College was founded in 1970. It is accredited by New England Association of Schools and Colleges. It first offered distance learning courses in 1996. In fall 2005, there were 1,331 students enrolled in distance learning courses. Institutionally administered financial aid is available to distance learners.

Services Distance learners have accessibility to academic advising, bookstore, campus computer network, e-mail services, library services, tutoring.

Contact Mr. Sanford A. Arbogast, Instructional Technology Analyst, Middlesex Community College, Academic Resources Building, Springs Road, Bedford, MA 01730. Telephone: 781-280-3739. Fax: 781-280-3771. E-mail: arbogasts@middlesex.mass.edu.

DEGREES AND AWARDS

AA Liberal Arts and Sciences

AAS Liberal Studies

ABA Business Administration Career; Small Business Administration

AS Business Administration Transfer; Fire Protection

Certificate Small Business Management; Web Publishing

COURSE SUBJECT AREAS OFFERED OUTSIDE OF DEGREE PROGRAMS

Undergraduate—accounting and related services; area, ethnic, cultural, and gender studies related; biological and biomedical sciences related; biology; business administration, management and operations; business/commerce; business/corporate communications; business/managerial economics; communications technology; community psychology; computer and information sciences; computer and information sciences and support services related; computer programming; computer science; computer software and media applications; criminal justice and corrections; data entry/microcomputer applications; dental support services and allied professions; developmental and child psychology; economics; educational psychology; English; English composition; English language and literature related; English literature (British and Commonwealth); ethnic, cultural minority, and gender studies; fine and studio art; fire protection; foods, nutrition, and related services; geography and cartography; history; human resources management; languages (foreign languages related); legal studies (non-professional general, undergraduate); liberal arts and sciences, general studies and humanities; linguistic, comparative, and related language studies; marketing; mathematics; mathematics and computer science; mathematics and statistics related; philosophy; philosophy and religious studies related; physical sciences; political science and government; psychology; public relations, advertising, and applied communication related; social psychology; social sciences; social sciences related; sociology; statistics; taxation; technical and business writing.

Non-credit—business administration, management and operations; business/commerce; computer software and media applications; computer systems analysis; creative writing; finance and financial management services; fine and studio art; gerontology; technical and business writing.

MIDDLE TENNESSEE STATE UNIVERSITY
Murfreesboro, Tennessee
Division of Continuing Studies
http://www.mtsu.edu/learn

Middle Tennessee State University was founded in 1911. It is accredited by Southern Association of Colleges and Schools. It first offered distance learning courses in 1994. In fall 2005, there were 3,094 students enrolled in distance learning courses. Institutionally administered financial aid is available to distance learners.

Services Distance learners have accessibility to academic advising, bookstore, campus computer network, e-mail services, library services, tutoring.

Contact Dr. Dianna Rust, Director, Academic Outreach and Distance Learning, Middle Tennessee State University, 1301 East Main Street, MTSU Box X109, Murfreesboro, TN 37132. Telephone: 615-898-5611. Fax: 615-896-7925. E-mail: drust@mtsu.edu.

DEGREES AND AWARDS

BS Liberal Studies; Professional Studies, Information Technology concentration; Professional Studies, Organizational Leadership concentration

BSN Nursing

MEd Teaching and Learning, advanced studies

MPS Professional Studies, Strategic Leadership concentration

MS Mathematics

MSN Nursing

COURSE SUBJECT AREAS OFFERED OUTSIDE OF DEGREE PROGRAMS

Undergraduate—accounting and related services; aerospace, aeronautical and astronautical engineering; agricultural business and management; American literature (United States and Canadian); area, ethnic, cultural, and gender studies related; astronomy and astrophysics; business administration, management and operations; business/corporate communications; communication and media; criminal justice and corrections; economics; education; educational psychology; English; English composition; food science and technology; geological and earth sciences/geosciences; health and physical education/fitness; human resources management; journalism; liberal arts and sciences, general studies and humanities; mathematics; nursing; political science and government; radio, television, and digital communication; sales, merchandising, and related marketing operations (general); social sciences; social work; sociology.

Graduate—aerospace, aeronautical and astronautical engineering; economics; educational assessment, evaluation, and research; marketing; mathematics; nursing.

Non-credit—allied health and medical assisting services; area, ethnic, cultural, and gender studies related; bilingual, multilingual, and multicultural education; business administration, management and operations; business/commerce; business/corporate communications; business, management, and marketing related; business/managerial economics; city/urban, community and regional planning; computer and information sciences; computer/information technology administration and management; computer programming; computer science; computer software and media applications; computer systems networking and telecommunications; crafts, folk art and artisanry; culinary arts and related services; dance; dramatic/theater arts and stagecraft; engineering/industrial management; English as a second language; fine and studio art; human resources management; industrial and organizational psychology; linguistic, comparative, and related language studies; management information systems; nursing; real estate; sales, merchandising, and related marketing operations (specialized); wildlife and wildlands science and management.

MIDLAND COLLEGE
Midland, Texas
Distance Learning Program
http://www.midland.ed

Midland College was founded in 1969. It is accredited by Southern Association of Colleges and Schools. It first offered distance learning courses in 1996. In fall 2005, there were 1,800 students enrolled in distance learning courses. Institutionally administered financial aid is available to distance learners.

Services Distance learners have accessibility to academic advising, bookstore, campus computer network, career placement assistance, e-mail services, library services, tutoring.

Contact Mr. Trey Wetendorf, Director, Admissions and Recruitment, Midland College, 3600 North Garfield Street, Midland, TX 79705. Telephone: 432-685-5502. Fax: 432-685-4623. E-mail: twetendorf@midland.edu.

DEGREES AND AWARDS

AAS Fire Science/Fire Administrator

COURSE SUBJECT AREAS OFFERED OUTSIDE OF DEGREE PROGRAMS

Undergraduate—accounting and related services; business/commerce; business/corporate communications; business/managerial economics; business operations support and assistant services; computer and information sciences; computer software and media applications; developmental and child psychology; education (specific levels and methods); English; English composition; gerontology; health and medical administrative services; health and physical education/fitness; health professions related; history; journalism; languages (Romance languages); legal studies (non-professional general, undergraduate); mathematics and statistics related; music; philosophy and religious studies related; social psychology; sociology; speech and rhetoric; statistics.

Non-credit—computer and information sciences; computer and information sciences and support services related; computer systems analysis; computer systems networking and telecommunications; gerontology.

MID MICHIGAN COMMUNITY COLLEGE
Harrison, Michigan
http://www.midmich.cc.mi.us/distanced

Mid Michigan Community College was founded in 1965. It is accredited by North Central Association of Colleges and Schools. It first offered distance learning courses in 1999. In fall 2005, there were 1,107 students enrolled in distance learning courses. Institutionally administered financial aid is available to distance learners.

Services Distance learners have accessibility to academic advising, bookstore, campus computer network, career placement assistance, e-mail services, library services.

Contact Ms. JoDell Richmond, Administrative Specialist, Mid Michigan Community College, 5805 East Pickard, Mount Pleasant, MI 48858. Telephone: 989-773-6622 Ext. 299. Fax: 989-772-2386. E-mail: jrichmond@midmich.edu.

DEGREES AND AWARDS

Programs offered do not lead to a degree or other formal award.

COURSE SUBJECT AREAS OFFERED OUTSIDE OF DEGREE PROGRAMS

Undergraduate—accounting and related services; allied health and medical assisting services; biological and physical sciences; biology; business/commerce; business operations support and assistant services; computer and information sciences; computer programming; computer science; computer software and media applications; economics; English; English composition; geological and earth sciences/geosciences; history; mathematics and statistics related; philosophy; political science and government; psychology; social sciences.

MIDSTATE COLLEGE
Peoria, Illinois
http://www.midstate.edu/

Midstate College was founded in 1888. It is accredited by North Central Association of Colleges and Schools. It first offered distance learning courses in 1999. In fall 2005, there were 232 students enrolled in distance learning courses. Institutionally administered financial aid is available to distance learners.

Services Distance learners have accessibility to academic advising, bookstore, career placement assistance, e-mail services, library services, tutoring.

Contact Ms. Jessica Hancock, Director of Admissions, Midstate College, 411 West Northmoor Road, Peoria, IL 61614. Telephone: 309-692-4092 Ext. 1090. Fax: 309-692-3893. E-mail: admissions@midstate.edu.

DEGREES AND AWARDS
BBA Business Administration

COURSE SUBJECT AREAS OFFERED OUTSIDE OF DEGREE PROGRAMS
Undergraduate—accounting and related services; allied health and medical assisting services; applied mathematics; business, management, and marketing related; computer and information sciences; computer software and media applications; English composition; psychology.

MID-STATE TECHNICAL COLLEGE
Wisconsin Rapids, Wisconsin
Information Services
http://www.mstc.edu/academics/distance/cbt.htm

Mid-State Technical College was founded in 1917. It is accredited by North Central Association of Colleges and Schools. It first offered distance learning courses in 1996. Institutionally administered financial aid is available to distance learners.

Services Distance learners have accessibility to academic advising, bookstore, e-mail services, library services.

Contact Dr. John Higgs, Dean, Business Division, Mid-State Technical College, 500 32nd Street North, Wisconsin Rapids, WI 54494. Telephone: 715-422-5356. Fax: 715-422-5609. E-mail: john.higgs@mstc.edu.

DEGREES AND AWARDS
AD Supervisory Management

COURSE SUBJECT AREAS OFFERED OUTSIDE OF DEGREE PROGRAMS
Undergraduate—business administration, management and operations; computer and information sciences; computer and information sciences and support services related; sociology; systems engineering.

MIDWAY COLLEGE
Midway, Kentucky
http://www.midway.edu/

Midway College was founded in 1847. It is accredited by Southern Association of Colleges and Schools. It first offered distance learning courses in 2003. In fall 2005, there were 125 students enrolled in distance learning courses. Institutionally administered financial aid is available to distance learners.

Services Distance learners have accessibility to academic advising, bookstore, e-mail services.

Contact Patti Kirk, Admissions Counselor/Recruiter, Midway College, 512 East Stephens Street, Midway, KY 40347. Telephone: 800-952-4122. E-mail: midwayonlinecollege@midway.edu.

DEGREES AND AWARDS
Programs offered do not lead to a degree or other formal award.

COURSE SUBJECT AREAS OFFERED OUTSIDE OF DEGREE PROGRAMS
Undergraduate—accounting and related services; computer science; finance and financial management services; mathematics.

MILLERSVILLE UNIVERSITY OF PENNSYLVANIA
Millersville, Pennsylvania
MU Online
http://muweb.millersville.edu/~muonline

Millersville University of Pennsylvania was founded in 1855. It is accredited by Middle States Association of Colleges and Schools. It first offered distance learning courses in 1998. In fall 2005, there were 317 students enrolled in distance learning courses. Institutionally administered financial aid is available to distance learners.

Services Distance learners have accessibility to academic advising, bookstore, campus computer network, career placement assistance, e-mail services, library services.

Contact Ms. Loreal L. Maguire, Assistant Director, Professional Training and Education, Millersville University of Pennsylvania, PO Box 1002, Millersville, PA 17551. Telephone: 717-872-3030. Fax: 717-871-2022. E-mail: loreal.maguire@millersville.edu.

DEGREES AND AWARDS
Programs offered do not lead to a degree or other formal award.

COURSE SUBJECT AREAS OFFERED OUTSIDE OF DEGREE PROGRAMS
Undergraduate—atmospheric sciences and meteorology; business administration, management and operations; chemistry; communication and media; economics; education; education (specific subject areas); English composition; health and physical education/fitness; linguistic, comparative, and related language studies; music; nursing; psychology; sociology; special education.

Graduate—business administration, management and operations; education; education (specific subject areas); English composition; health and physical education/fitness; linguistic, comparative, and related language studies; nursing; special education; technology education/industrial arts.

MILWAUKEE SCHOOL OF ENGINEERING
Milwaukee, Wisconsin
MSOE-TV
http://www.msoe.edu/admiss

Milwaukee School of Engineering was founded in 1903. It is accredited by North Central Association of Colleges and Schools. It first offered distance learning courses in 1989. In fall 2005, there were 107 students enrolled in distance learning courses. Institutionally administered financial aid is available to distance learners.

Services Distance learners have accessibility to academic advising, bookstore, campus computer network, career placement assistance, e-mail services, library services.

Contact Mr. Kent Peterson, Manager of Internet Services, Milwaukee School of Engineering, 1025 North Broadway, Milwaukee, WI 53202-3109. Telephone: 414-277-7176. Fax: 414-277-7453. E-mail: peterson@msoe.edu.

DEGREES AND AWARDS
Programs offered do not lead to a degree or other formal award.

COURSE SUBJECT AREAS OFFERED OUTSIDE OF DEGREE PROGRAMS
Undergraduate—business, management, and marketing related; computer and information sciences; management information systems.

Graduate—business administration, management and operations.

MINNEAPOLIS COLLEGE OF ART AND DESIGN
Minneapolis, Minnesota
MCAD Distance Learning
http://online.mcad.edu

Minneapolis College of Art and Design was founded in 1886. It is accredited by North Central Association of Colleges and Schools. It first offered distance learning courses in 1995. In fall 2005, there were 150 students enrolled in distance learning courses. Institutionally administered financial aid is available to distance learners.

Services Distance learners have accessibility to bookstore, campus computer network, e-mail services, library services, tutoring.

Contact Rebecca J. Alm, Director of Distance Learning, Minneapolis College of Art and Design, 2501 Stevens Avenue, South, Minneapolis, MN 55404. Telephone: 612-874-3658. Fax: 612-874-3704. E-mail: rebecca_alm@mcad.edu.

DEGREES AND AWARDS

Programs offered do not lead to a degree or other formal award.

COURSE SUBJECT AREAS OFFERED OUTSIDE OF DEGREE PROGRAMS

Undergraduate—design and applied arts; film/video and photographic arts; fine and studio art; visual and performing arts; visual and performing arts related.

Graduate—design and applied arts; film/video and photographic arts; fine and studio art; visual and performing arts; visual and performing arts related.

Non-credit—design and applied arts; film/video and photographic arts; fine and studio art; visual and performing arts; visual and performing arts related.

MINNESOTA SCHOOL OF BUSINESS–RICHFIELD
Richfield, Minnesota
http://www.msbcollege.edu

Minnesota School of Business–Richfield was founded in 1877. It is accredited by Accrediting Council for Independent Colleges and Schools. It first offered distance learning courses in 2000. In fall 2005, there were 990 students enrolled in distance learning courses. Institutionally administered financial aid is available to distance learners.

Services Distance learners have accessibility to academic advising, campus computer network, career placement assistance, e-mail services, library services, tutoring.

Contact Jeff Myhre, Director, Minnesota School of Business–Richfield, 1401 West 76th Street, Suite 500, Richfield, MN 55423. Telephone: 612-861-2000. Fax: 800-752-4223. E-mail: jmyhre@msbcollege.edu.

DEGREES AND AWARDS

AAS Accounting; Business Administration
BS Accounting; Business Administration
MBA Business Administration

COURSE SUBJECT AREAS OFFERED OUTSIDE OF DEGREE PROGRAMS

Undergraduate—accounting and related services; animal sciences; biology; business administration, management and operations; communication and media; computer science; entrepreneurial and small business operations; health and medical administrative services; international business; legal professions and studies related; legal studies (nonprofessional general, undergraduate); liberal arts and sciences, general studies and humanities; mathematics; taxation; technical and business writing; veterinary biomedical and clinical sciences.

Graduate—business administration, management and operations.

MINOT STATE UNIVERSITY–BOTTINEAU CAMPUS
Bottineau, North Dakota
http://www.misu-b.nodak.edu

Minot State University–Bottineau Campus was founded in 1906. It is accredited by North Central Association of Colleges and Schools. It first offered distance learning courses in 2000. In fall 2005, there were 170 students enrolled in distance learning courses. Institutionally administered financial aid is available to distance learners.

Services Distance learners have accessibility to academic advising, bookstore, library services.

Contact Kayla O'Toole, Training Coordinator, Minot State University–Bottineau Campus, 105 Simrall Boulevard, Bottineau, ND 58318. Telephone: 888-918-5623. E-mail: kayle.otoole@misu.nodak.edu.

DEGREES AND AWARDS

AA Liberal Arts
AAS Accounting Technician; Administrative Assistant; Medical Assistant; Medical Secretary; Paraeducation; Recreation Management

Certificate of Completion Grounds Worker Skills, basic; Medical Coding; Medical Transcription; Recreation Management

Diploma Bookkeeping; Greenhouse Technology; Landscape Technician; Medical Assistant; Medical Coding; Medical Transcription; Reception Services; Urban Forestry Technology

COURSE SUBJECT AREAS OFFERED OUTSIDE OF DEGREE PROGRAMS

Undergraduate—allied health and medical assisting services; applied horticulture/horticultural business services; biological and biomedical sciences related; business, management, and marketing related; business operations support and assistant services; health and medical administrative services; liberal arts and sciences, general studies and humanities; medical basic sciences; teaching assistants/aides.

MISSISSIPPI STATE UNIVERSITY
Mississippi State, Mississippi
Division of Continuing Education
http://www.distance.msstate.edu

Mississippi State University was founded in 1878. It is accredited by Southern Association of Colleges and Schools. It first offered distance learning courses in 1987. In fall 2005, there were 1,000 students enrolled in distance learning courses. Institutionally administered financial aid is available to distance learners.

Services Distance learners have accessibility to academic advising, bookstore, campus computer network, career placement assistance, e-mail services, library services.

Contact Dr. Laura A. Crittenden, Manager, Office of Academic Outreach, Mississippi State University, Division of Academic Outreach and Continuing Education, 1 Barr Avenue, PO Box 5247, Mississippi State, MS 39762-5247. Telephone: 662-325-2677. Fax: 662-325-0930. E-mail: lcrittenden@aoce.msstate.edu.

DEGREES AND AWARDS

BS Elementary Education; Geosciences, Broadcast Meteorology; Geosciences, Operational Meteorology; Interdisciplinary Studies

Certificate Discovery Teacher Training

MAT Community College Leadership

MBA Business Administration

MS Food Science, Nutrition, and Health Promotion; Geosciences, Teachers in Geoscience; Industrial Engineering; Public Policy Administration; Workforce Education Leadership

PhD Community College Leadership

COURSE SUBJECT AREAS OFFERED OUTSIDE OF DEGREE PROGRAMS

Undergraduate—accounting and computer science; accounting and related services; biological and physical sciences; biology; communication and journalism related; communication and media; computer and information sciences; computer science; counseling psychology; curriculum and instruction; developmental and child psychology; educational/instructional media design; educational psychology; education related; education (specific levels and methods); education (specific subject areas); fine and studio art; forestry; geological and earth sciences/geosciences; human development, family studies, and related services; insurance; landscape architecture; mathematics; multi-/interdisciplinary studies related; physical sciences related; physics; special education; statistics; technology education/industrial arts; zoology/animal biology.

Graduate—agriculture; business administration, management and operations; business/commerce; business/managerial economics; chemical engineering; civil engineering; computer engineering; computer science; counseling psychology; curriculum and instruction; educational administration and supervision; educational assessment, evaluation, and research; educational/instructional media design; educational psychology; education (specific subject areas); electrical, electronics and communications engineering; engineering; engineering technologies related; health professions related; public administration.

MISSOURI STATE UNIVERSITY
Springfield, Missouri
College of Continuing Education and the Extended University
http://ce.smsu.edu

Missouri State University was founded in 1905. It is accredited by North Central Association of Colleges and Schools. It first offered distance learning courses in 1974. In fall 2005, there were 3,000 students enrolled in distance learning courses. Institutionally administered financial aid is available to distance learners.

Services Distance learners have accessibility to academic advising, bookstore, campus computer network, career placement assistance, e-mail services, library services.

Contact Dr. Diana Garland, EdD, Associate Director, Academic Outreach, Missouri State University, College of Continuing Education and the Extended University, Academic Outreach, 901 South National, Springfield, MO 65897. Telephone: 877-678-2005. Fax: 417-836-6016. E-mail: dianagarland@missouristate.edu.

DEGREES AND AWARDS
BS Business Completion Program, general; Elementary Education; Industrial Technology–Bachelor of Applied Science in Industrial Technology (two-year completion)
BSN Nursing
Certificate Manufacturing Management
Certification Education–Missouri Visual Impairment Certification Training program
Graduate Certificate Instructional Technology Specialist; Project Management; Sports Management
MBA Business Administration
MBA/M Ag Business Administration–Accelerated foundation course program
MS Administrative Studies; Computer Information Systems; Elementary Education
MSW Social Work
PMC Nurse Educator

COURSE SUBJECT AREAS OFFERED OUTSIDE OF DEGREE PROGRAMS
Undergraduate—accounting and related services; agricultural business and management; anthropology; apparel and textiles; astronomy and astrophysics; chemistry; communication and journalism related; computer and information sciences; creative writing; developmental and child psychology; economics; English language and literature related; film/video and photographic arts; finance and financial management services; health and physical education/fitness; history; human development, family studies, and related services; industrial production technologies; marketing; mathematics and statistics related; music; nursing; physics; political science and government; religious studies; social work; sociology; special education.

Graduate—accounting and related services; communication and media; computer and information sciences; criminal justice and corrections; curriculum and instruction; economics; education; educational administration and supervision; education (specific levels and methods); education (specific subject areas); finance and financial management services; health and physical education/fitness; history; industrial production technologies; legal research and advanced professional studies; marketing; nursing; political science and government; psychology; religious studies; sales, merchandising, and related marketing operations (specialized); social work; taxation.

Non-credit—information science/studies; management information systems; mental and social health services and allied professions.

MITCHELL TECHNICAL INSTITUTE
Mitchell, South Dakota
http://mti.tec.sd.us/

Mitchell Technical Institute was founded in 1968. It is accredited by North Central Association of Colleges and Schools. It first offered distance learning courses in 1994. In fall 2005, there were 260 students enrolled in distance learning courses. Institutionally administered financial aid is available to distance learners.

Services Distance learners have accessibility to academic advising, career placement assistance, e-mail services.

Contact John J. Heemstra, Telecommunications Coordinator, Mitchell Technical Institute, 821 North Capital, Mitchell, SD 57301. Telephone: 605-995-3065. Fax: 605-995-3067. E-mail: john.heemstra@mitchelltech.edu.

DEGREES AND AWARDS
Programs offered do not lead to a degree or other formal award.

COURSE SUBJECT AREAS OFFERED OUTSIDE OF DEGREE PROGRAMS
Undergraduate—accounting and computer science; business, management, and marketing related; computer and information sciences; computer software and media applications; culinary arts and related services; curriculum and instruction.

Non-credit—business, management, and marketing related; business operations support and assistant services; computer and information sciences; computer software and media applications; data entry/microcomputer applications; entrepreneurial and small business operations; health professions related; heating, air conditioning, ventilation and refrigeration maintenance technology; quality control and safety technologies.

MOBERLY AREA COMMUNITY COLLEGE
Moberly, Missouri
http://www.macc.edu/

Moberly Area Community College was founded in 1927. It is accredited by North Central Association of Colleges and Schools. It first offered distance learning courses in 1995. In fall 2005, there were 371 students enrolled in distance learning courses. Institutionally administered financial aid is available to distance learners.

Services Distance learners have accessibility to academic advising, bookstore, campus computer network, career placement assistance, e-mail services, library services.

Contact Dr. James Grant, Dean of Student Services, Moberly Area Community College, 101 College Avenue, Moberly, MO 65270. Telephone: 660-263-4110 Ext. 239. Fax: 660-263-2406. E-mail: jamesg@macc.edu.

DEGREES AND AWARDS
AAS Computer Information Systems

COURSE SUBJECT AREAS OFFERED OUTSIDE OF DEGREE PROGRAMS
Undergraduate—accounting and related services; biology; business administration, management and operations; computer science; electrical and electronic engineering technologies; English; fine and studio art; geography and cartography; history; human development, family studies, and related services; mathematics; psychology; social sciences related; sociology; speech and rhetoric.

MOHAWK VALLEY COMMUNITY COLLEGE
Utica, New York
Educational Technology
http://www.mvcc.edu

Mohawk Valley Community College was founded in 1946. It is accredited by Middle States Association of Colleges and Schools. It first offered distance learning courses in 1997. In fall 2005, there were 1,100 students enrolled in distance learning courses. Institutionally administered financial aid is available to distance learners.

Services Distance learners have accessibility to bookstore, campus computer network, e-mail services, library services, tutoring.

Contact Mr. Keith Lynip, Director of Distance Learning, Mohawk Valley Community College, 1101 Sherman Drive, Utica, NY 13501. Telephone: 315-731-5753. E-mail: klynip@mvcc.edu.

DEGREES AND AWARDS
AAS Graphic Design
Certificate School Facilities Management; School Transportation Management

COURSE SUBJECT AREAS OFFERED OUTSIDE OF DEGREE PROGRAMS

Undergraduate—accounting and related services; American literature (United States and Canadian); business/commerce; business/managerial economics; computer and information sciences; computer software and media applications; criminal justice and corrections; criminology; culinary arts and related services; design and applied arts; developmental and child psychology; education; electrical and electronic engineering technologies; English composition; English literature (British and Commonwealth); film/video and photographic arts; foods, nutrition, and related services; hospitality administration; management information systems; mathematics; nursing; philosophy and religious studies related; psychology; sales, merchandising, and related marketing operations (general); sales, merchandising, and related marketing operations (specialized); social sciences; social work; sociology; special education; transportation and materials moving related.

Non-credit—accounting and related services; business administration, management and operations; business/commerce; business/corporate communications; business, management, and marketing related; business/managerial economics; computer and information sciences; computer and information sciences and support services related; computer engineering; computer/information technology administration and management; computer programming; computer science; computer software and media applications; computer systems analysis; computer systems networking and telecommunications; management information systems; management sciences and quantitative methods; marketing; sales, merchandising, and related marketing operations (general); sales, merchandising, and related marketing operations (specialized).

MONMOUTH UNIVERSITY
West Long Branch, New Jersey
http://www.monmouth.edu/

Monmouth University was founded in 1933. It is accredited by Middle States Association of Colleges and Schools. It first offered distance learning courses in 1998. In fall 2005, there were 139 students enrolled in distance learning courses. Institutionally administered financial aid is available to distance learners.

Services Distance learners have accessibility to academic advising, bookstore, campus computer network, career placement assistance, e-mail services, library services.

Contact Robert D. Mc Caig, EdD, Vice President for Enrollment Management, Monmouth University, 400 Cedar Avenue, West Long Branch, NJ 07764-1898. Telephone: 732-571-3413. Fax: 732-263-5101. E-mail: rmccaig@monmouth.edu.

DEGREES AND AWARDS

Programs offered do not lead to a degree or other formal award.

COURSE SUBJECT AREAS OFFERED OUTSIDE OF DEGREE PROGRAMS

Undergraduate—education; health professions related; nursing.

Graduate—criminal justice and corrections; education; liberal arts and sciences, general studies and humanities; nursing; social work.

MONROE COMMUNITY COLLEGE
Rochester, New York
http://www.monroecc.edu/

Monroe Community College was founded in 1961. It is accredited by Middle States Association of Colleges and Schools. It first offered distance learning courses in 1997. In fall 2005, there were 2,153 students enrolled in distance learning courses. Institutionally administered financial aid is available to distance learners.

Services Distance learners have accessibility to academic advising, campus computer network, career placement assistance, e-mail services, library services.

Contact Online Learning, Monroe Community College, 1000 East Henrietta Road, Rochester, NY 14623-5780. E-mail: registration@monroecc.edu.

DEGREES AND AWARDS

AAS Criminal Justice

AS Business Administration; Liberal Arts; Physical Education Studies

Certificate of Completion Coaching–New York State Coaching certification

Certificate Dental Assisting

COURSE SUBJECT AREAS OFFERED OUTSIDE OF DEGREE PROGRAMS

Undergraduate—accounting and related services; American literature (United States and Canadian); biology; business/commerce; communication and media; criminal justice and corrections; dental support services and allied professions; English composition; liberal arts and sciences, general studies and humanities; mathematics; psychology; public relations, advertising, and applied communication related; social sciences.

MONTANA STATE UNIVERSITY
Bozeman, Montana
Extended University/Burns Technology Center
http://www.montana.edu/distance

Montana State University was founded in 1893. It is accredited by Northwest Commission on Colleges and Universities. It first offered distance learning courses in 1992. In fall 2005, there were 1,000 students enrolled in distance learning courses. Institutionally administered financial aid is available to distance learners.

Services Distance learners have accessibility to academic advising, bookstore, campus computer network, e-mail services, library services.

Contact Kelly Boyce, Program Manager, Montana State University, EPS 128, Bozeman, MT 59717. Telephone: 406-994-6812. Fax: 406-994-7856. E-mail: kboyce@montana.edu.

DEGREES AND AWARDS

Certification Library Media Certification

MN Nursing

MS Family and Financial Planning; Mathematics; Science Education

COURSE SUBJECT AREAS OFFERED OUTSIDE OF DEGREE PROGRAMS

Graduate—astronomy and astrophysics; biological and physical sciences; biology; education (specific subject areas); foods, nutrition, and related services; health and physical education/fitness; library science related; mathematics; mathematics and statistics related; microbiological sciences and immunology; physics; soil sciences; statistics.

MONTANA STATE UNIVERSITY–BILLINGS
Billings, Montana
http://www.msubonline.org

Montana State University–Billings was founded in 1927. It is accredited by Northwest Commission on Colleges and Universities. It first offered distance learning courses in 1998. In fall 2005, there were 1,700 students enrolled in distance learning courses. Institutionally administered financial aid is available to distance learners.

Services Distance learners have accessibility to academic advising, bookstore, career placement assistance, e-mail services, library services, tutoring.

Contact Mr. Kurt Laudicina, Admissions Counselor for MSU-B Online University, Montana State University–Billings, McMullen Hall 100, 1500 North 30th Street, Billings, MT 59101. Telephone: 406-896-5911. Fax: 406-657-2302. E-mail: inquiry@msubonline.org.

DEGREES AND AWARDS

AAS Accounting Technology

BA Business Administration; Communication/Organizational Communications/Mass Communication/Public Relations

BS Liberal Studies–Management and Communication concentration; Public Relations

MHA Health Administration

MS Public Relations

COURSE SUBJECT AREAS OFFERED OUTSIDE OF DEGREE PROGRAMS

Undergraduate—accounting and related services; biology; business administration, management and operations; business/commerce; business/corporate communications; communication and media; communications technology; curriculum and instruction; dramatic/theater arts and stagecraft; economics; education; English composition; fine and studio art; geography and cartography; history; human resources management; industrial and organizational psychology; liberal arts and sciences, general studies and humanities; marketing; mathematics; physics; psychology; public relations, advertising, and applied communication related; special education; statistics.

Graduate—communication and media; counseling psychology; curriculum and instruction; education; health and medical administrative services; public relations, advertising, and applied communication related; rehabilitation and therapeutic professions.

See full description on page 406.

MONTANA TECH OF THE UNIVERSITY OF MONTANA

Butte, Montana

Office of Extended Studies

http://www.mtech.edu

Montana Tech of The University of Montana was founded in 1895. It is accredited by Northwest Commission on Colleges and Universities. It first offered distance learning courses in 1996. In fall 2005, there were 350 students enrolled in distance learning courses. Institutionally administered financial aid is available to distance learners.

Services Distance learners have accessibility to academic advising, bookstore, campus computer network, career placement assistance, e-mail services, library services.

Contact Ms. Kaila Minehan, Administrative Support, Montana Tech of The University of Montana, 1300 West Park Street, Butte, MT 59701-8997. Telephone: 800-445-8324 Ext. 2. Fax: 406-496-4710. E-mail: admissions@mtech.edu.

DEGREES AND AWARDS

BS Occupational Safety and Health
MPM Project Engineering and Management
MS Industrial Hygiene

COURSE SUBJECT AREAS OFFERED OUTSIDE OF DEGREE PROGRAMS

Undergraduate—business/commerce; computer software and media applications; English composition; health professions related; mathematics; nursing; philosophy; psychology; sociology; technical and business writing.

Graduate—engineering/industrial management; health professions related; public health.

MONTGOMERY COMMUNITY COLLEGE

Troy, North Carolina

http://www.montgomery.cc.nc.us/

Montgomery Community College was founded in 1967. It is accredited by Southern Association of Colleges and Schools. It first offered distance learning courses in 2000. In fall 2005, there were 250 students enrolled in distance learning courses. Institutionally administered financial aid is available to distance learners.

Services Distance learners have accessibility to academic advising, bookstore, campus computer network, career placement assistance, library services, tutoring.

Contact Dean Thomas M. Sargent, Dean of Education Technology, Montgomery Community College, 1011 Page Street, Troy, NC 27371. Telephone: 910-576-6222 Ext. 217. Fax: 910-576-2176. E-mail: sargentt@montgomery.edu.

DEGREES AND AWARDS

AAB Business Administration
AAS Criminal Justice

COURSE SUBJECT AREAS OFFERED OUTSIDE OF DEGREE PROGRAMS

Undergraduate—American literature (United States and Canadian); business administration, management and operations; business/commerce; business operations support and assistant services; computer and information sciences; computer software and media applications; criminal justice and corrections; English; English composition; human resources management; liberal arts and sciences, general studies and humanities; medical basic sciences; psychology; religious education; sociology; technical and business writing.

Non-credit—allied health and medical assisting services; biblical studies; business administration, management and operations; business/corporate communications; computer and information sciences; computer software and media applications; English; English composition.

MOODY BIBLE INSTITUTE

Chicago, Illinois

Moody Bible Institute External Studies Division

http://www.moody.edu/

Moody Bible Institute was founded in 1886. It is accredited by Association for Biblical Higher Education. It first offered distance learning courses in 1941. In fall 2005, there were 5,000 students enrolled in distance learning courses. Institutionally administered financial aid is available to distance learners.

Services Distance learners have accessibility to academic advising, e-mail services, library services.

Contact Eric Johnson, Moody Bible Institute, 820 North LaSalle Boulevard, Chicago, IL 60610. Telephone: 800-758-6352. Fax: 312-329-2081. E-mail: mdlc@moody.edu.

DEGREES AND AWARDS

ABS Biblical Studies
BS Biblical Studies
Certificate Biblical Studies

COURSE SUBJECT AREAS OFFERED OUTSIDE OF DEGREE PROGRAMS

Undergraduate—biblical and other theological languages and literatures; biblical studies; counseling psychology; English composition; languages (classics and classical); philosophy; philosophy and religious studies related; physical sciences; psychology; religious education; religious studies; theological and ministerial studies; theology and religious vocations related.

Graduate—biblical studies; religious studies; theological and ministerial studies; theology and religious vocations related.

Non-credit—biblical studies; religious studies; theological and ministerial studies.

MORAVIAN THEOLOGICAL SEMINARY

Bethlehem, Pennsylvania

Moravian Theological Seminary was founded in 1807. It is accredited by Middle States Association of Colleges and Schools. It first offered distance learning courses in 1999. Institutionally administered financial aid is available to distance learners.

Services Distance learners have accessibility to academic advising, campus computer network, e-mail services, library services.

Contact Ms. Melissa Johnson, Director of Admissions, Moravian Theological Seminary, 1200 Main Street, Bethlehem , PA 18018. Telephone: 610-861-1512. Fax: 610-861-1569. E-mail: melissajohnson@moravian.edu.

DEGREES AND AWARDS

Programs offered do not lead to a degree or other formal award.

COURSE SUBJECT AREAS OFFERED OUTSIDE OF DEGREE PROGRAMS

Graduate—pastoral counseling and specialized ministries; theological and ministerial studies.

Non-credit—pastoral counseling and specialized ministries; theological and ministerial studies; theology and religious vocations related.

MOTLOW STATE COMMUNITY COLLEGE
Tullahoma, Tennessee
Academic Affairs
http://www.mscc.edu

Motlow State Community College was founded in 1969. It is accredited by Southern Association of Colleges and Schools. It first offered distance learning courses in 1996. In fall 2005, there were 562 students enrolled in distance learning courses. Institutionally administered financial aid is available to distance learners.

Services Distance learners have accessibility to academic advising, bookstore, campus computer network, career placement assistance, e-mail services, library services, tutoring.

Contact Dr. Mary McLemore, Vice President for Academic Affairs, Motlow State Community College, PO Box 8500, Lynchburg, TN 37352. Telephone: 931-393-1696. Fax: 931-393-1681. E-mail: mmclemore@mscc.edu.

DEGREES AND AWARDS

AAS Business Technology

COURSE SUBJECT AREAS OFFERED OUTSIDE OF DEGREE PROGRAMS

Undergraduate—computer and information sciences; management information systems; mathematics; statistics.

MOUNTAIN EMPIRE COMMUNITY COLLEGE
Big Stone Gap, Virginia
Office of Continuing and Distance Education
http://www.me.vccs.edu/distance/index.html

Mountain Empire Community College was founded in 1972. It is accredited by Southern Association of Colleges and Schools. It first offered distance learning courses in 1979. In fall 2005, there were 900 students enrolled in distance learning courses. Institutionally administered financial aid is available to distance learners.

Services Distance learners have accessibility to academic advising, bookstore, campus computer network, career placement assistance, e-mail services, library services, tutoring.

Contact Susan Kennedy, Coordinator of Distance Education, Mountain Empire Community College, 3441 Mountain Empire Road, Big Stone Gap, VA 24219. Telephone: 276-523-7488. Fax: 276-523-7486. E-mail: skennedy@me.vccs.edu.

DEGREES AND AWARDS

AAS Accounting; Administrative Support Technology Medical Office Specialist; Administrative Support Technology; Business Administration; Correctional Services; General Studies; Liberal Arts; Water/Wastewater specialization

Certificate Career Studies Certificate–Accounting; Career Studies Certificate–Child Development; Career Studies Certificate–Computer Software Specialist; Career Studies Certificate–Geographical Information Systems; Career Studies Certificate–Health Information Technology; Career Studies Certificate–Legal Office Assisting; Career Studies Certificate–Medical Records Clerk; Career Studies Certificate–Medical Transcriptionist; Career Studies Certificate–Office Automation Specialist; Career Studies Certificate–Personal Computing for Home and Office; Career Studies Certificate–Polysomnography; Career Studies Certificate–Wastewater Plant Operator; Career Studies Certificate–Water Plant Operator; Career Studies Certificate–Word Processing; Clerical Assistant

COURSE SUBJECT AREAS OFFERED OUTSIDE OF DEGREE PROGRAMS

Undergraduate—accounting and related services; astronomy and astrophysics; atmospheric sciences and meteorology; biology; business/commerce; communication and media; computer and information sciences; criminal justice and corrections; criminology; developmental and child psychology; economics; English composition; fine and studio art; geological and earth sciences/geosciences; health and physical education/fitness; history; human development, family studies, and related services; languages (Romance languages); legal studies (non-professional general, undergraduate); linguistic, comparative, and related language studies; marketing; mathematics; music; psychology; religious studies; sociology; speech and rhetoric.

MOUNT ALLISON UNIVERSITY
Sackville, New Brunswick, Canada
Continuing and Distance Education
http://www.mta.ca/conted/index.html

Mount Allison University was founded in 1839. It is provincially chartered. It first offered distance learning courses in 1965. In fall 2005, there were 400 students enrolled in distance learning courses. Institutionally administered financial aid is available to distance learners.

Services Distance learners have accessibility to academic advising, bookstore, campus computer network, e-mail services, library services.

Contact Ms. Heather Patterson, Director, Mount Allison University, Continuous Learning, 65 York Street, Sackville, NB E4L 1E4, Canada. Telephone: 506-364-2266. Fax: 506-364-2272. E-mail: hpatters@mta.ca.

DEGREES AND AWARDS

Programs offered do not lead to a degree or other formal award.

COURSE SUBJECT AREAS OFFERED OUTSIDE OF DEGREE PROGRAMS

Undergraduate—American literature (United States and Canadian); economics; English; English language and literature related; English literature (British and Commonwealth); history; mathematics and statistics related; political science and government; psychology; religious education; religious studies; statistics.

Non-credit—creative writing; languages (foreign languages related).

MOUNT SAINT VINCENT UNIVERSITY
Halifax, Nova Scotia, Canada
Distance Learning and Continuing Education
http://www.msvu.ca/distance

Mount Saint Vincent University was founded in 1873. It is provincially chartered. It first offered distance learning courses in 1980. In fall 2005, there were 3,000 students enrolled in distance learning courses. Institutionally administered financial aid is available to distance learners.

Services Distance learners have accessibility to academic advising, bookstore, campus computer network, e-mail services, library services.

Contact Receptionist, Mount Saint Vincent University, 166 Bedford Highway, Halifax, NS B3M 2J6, Canada. Telephone: 902-457-6511. Fax: 902-443-2135. E-mail: distance@msvu.ca.

DEGREES AND AWARDS

BA Liberal Arts and General Studies
BBA Business Administration; Marketing
BTHM Tourism and Hospitality Management
Certificate Accounting; Gerontology; Information Technology Management
MEd Education

COURSE SUBJECT AREAS OFFERED OUTSIDE OF DEGREE PROGRAMS

Undergraduate—accounting and computer science; accounting and related services; behavioral sciences; business, management, and marketing related; communication and media; computer and information sciences; data entry/microcomputer applications; dietetics and clinical nutrition services; economics; education; education (specific subject areas); English; English literature (British and Commonwealth); entrepreneurial and small business operations; family and consumer sciences/human sciences related; finance and financial management services; foods, nutrition, and related services; gerontology; hospitality administration; international business; languages (foreign languages related); legal studies (non-professional general, undergraduate); marketing; mathematics; nutrition sciences; peace studies and conflict resolution; physiological psychology/psychobiology; psychology related; public relations, advertising, and applied communication related; religious education.

Non-credit—creative writing; mathematics.

MT. SAN ANTONIO COLLEGE
Walnut, California
Distance Learning
http://vclass.mtsac.edu

Mt. San Antonio College was founded in 1946. It is accredited by Western Association of Schools and Colleges. It first offered distance learning courses in 1993. In fall 2005, there were 1,799 students enrolled in distance learning courses. Institutionally administered financial aid is available to distance learners.

Services Distance learners have accessibility to academic advising, bookstore, campus computer network, e-mail services, library services, tutoring.

Contact Kerry C. Stern, Dean, Mt. San Antonio College, Learning Resources, 1100 North Grand Avenue, Walnut, CA 91789. Telephone: 909-594-5611 Ext. 5658. Fax: 909-468-3992. E-mail: kstern@mtsac.edu.

DEGREES AND AWARDS

Programs offered do not lead to a degree or other formal award.

COURSE SUBJECT AREAS OFFERED OUTSIDE OF DEGREE PROGRAMS

Undergraduate—accounting and related services; anthropology; biology; business administration, management and operations; chemistry; computer and information sciences; creative writing; economics; English as a second language; English composition; journalism; legal studies (non-professional general, undergraduate); philosophy; psychology; real estate; religious studies; sales, merchandising, and related marketing operations (specialized); sociology.

Non-credit—computer software and media applications.

MOUNT WACHUSETT COMMUNITY COLLEGE
Gardner, Massachusetts
Division of Continuing Education
http://www.mwcc.edu

Mount Wachusett Community College was founded in 1963. It is accredited by New England Association of Schools and Colleges. It first offered distance learning courses in 1994. In fall 2005, there were 874 students enrolled in distance learning courses. Institutionally administered financial aid is available to distance learners.

Services Distance learners have accessibility to academic advising, bookstore, campus computer network, career placement assistance, e-mail services, library services, tutoring.

Contact Ms. Debora Brennan, Distance Learning Administrative Assistant, Mount Wachusett Community College, 444 Green Street, Gardner, MA 01440. Telephone: 978-630-9275. Fax: 978-630-9537. E-mail: dbrennan@mwcc.mass.edu.

DEGREES AND AWARDS

AS Business Administration; Computer Information Systems; General Studies; Human Services; Paralegal Studies

COURSE SUBJECT AREAS OFFERED OUTSIDE OF DEGREE PROGRAMS

Undergraduate—biology; business administration, management and operations; communication and journalism related; computer programming; computer software and media applications; criminal justice and corrections; criminology; economics; English composition; film/video and photographic arts; history; human development, family studies, and related services; human resources management; human services; journalism; legal professions and studies related; management information systems; marketing; mathematics; mathematics and statistics related; mental and social health services and allied professions; nursing; political science and government; psychology; social sciences; sociology; statistics.

Non-credit—business operations support and assistant services; computer software and media applications; forestry.

MURRAY STATE UNIVERSITY
Murray, Kentucky
Continuing Education
http://ceao.murraystate.edu

Murray State University was founded in 1922. It is accredited by Southern Association of Colleges and Schools. It first offered distance learning courses in 1990. In fall 2005, there were 3,714 students enrolled in distance learning courses. Institutionally administered financial aid is available to distance learners.

Services Distance learners have accessibility to academic advising, bookstore, campus computer network, e-mail services, library services.

Contact Crystal Riley, Coordinator of Distance Learning, Murray State University, 303 Sparks Hall, CEAO, Murray, KY 42071-0009. Telephone: 800-669-7654. Fax: 270-809-3593. E-mail: crystal.riley@murraystate.edu.

DEGREES AND AWARDS

BBA Business–Bachelor of Science in Business

BGS Independent Studies–Bachelor of Independent Studies/General Studies

BS Telecommunications Systems Management

Endorsement English as a Second Language; Gifted and Talented

COURSE SUBJECT AREAS OFFERED OUTSIDE OF DEGREE PROGRAMS

Undergraduate—agricultural business and management; agriculture; agriculture and agriculture operations related; animal sciences; anthropology; business administration, management and operations; business/commerce; communication disorders sciences and services; computer and information sciences; computer programming; computer science; computer systems networking and telecommunications; education; English composition; geography and cartography; geological and earth sciences/geosciences; graphic communications; history; human development, family studies, and related services; journalism; legal studies (non-professional general, undergraduate); mathematics and statistics related; music; nursing; philosophy; philosophy and religious studies related; public relations, advertising, and applied communication related; radio, television, and digital communication; social sciences; social sciences related; social work; sociology.

Graduate—bilingual, multilingual, and multicultural education; communication disorders sciences and services; computer systems networking and telecommunications; educational administration and supervision; English as a second/foreign language (teaching); English as a second language; human services; marketing; nursing; quality control and safety technologies; special education.

MYERS UNIVERSITY
Cleveland, Ohio
COOL Program (College Options On-Line)
http://www.dnmyers.edu/online

Myers University was founded in 1848. It is accredited by North Central Association of Colleges and Schools. It first offered distance learning courses in 1976. In fall 2005, there were 414 students enrolled in distance learning courses. Institutionally administered financial aid is available to distance learners.

Services Distance learners have accessibility to academic advising, bookstore, campus computer network, career placement assistance, e-mail services, library services, tutoring.

Contact Ms. Brooke A. Scharlott, Associate Dean, Online Learning Center, Myers University, 3813 Euclid Avenue, Cleveland, OH 44115. Telephone: 866-388-1578. Fax: 585-388-1518. E-mail: bscharlott@myers.edu.

DEGREES AND AWARDS

BS Criminal Justice Administration; Health Services Management; Information Technology

BSBA Accounting; Corporate Management; Finance; Forensic Accounting; Human Resource Management; Industrial Management; Management Information Systems; Marketing; Small Business Entrepreneurship

COURSE SUBJECT AREAS OFFERED OUTSIDE OF DEGREE PROGRAMS

Undergraduate—accounting and related services; American literature (United States and Canadian); anthropology; applied mathematics; biological and physical sciences; business administration, management and operations; business/commerce; business/corporate communications; business, management, and marketing related; business/managerial economics; communication and media; computer and information sciences; computer and information sciences and support services related; computer engineering; computer/information technology administration and management; computer programming; computer science; computer software and media applications; computer systems analysis; computer systems networking and telecommunications; criminal justice and corrections; criminology; data entry/microcomputer applications; economics; English composition; entrepreneurial and small business operations; finance and financial management services; geography and cartography; history; human resources management; information science/studies; international business; legal studies (non-professional general, undergraduate); management information systems; management sciences and quantitative methods; marketing; mathematics; military studies; political science and government; psychology; public administration; public relations, advertising, and applied communication related; sales, merchandising, and related marketing operations (specialized); sociology.

Graduate—business administration, management and operations; business/commerce.

NAROPA UNIVERSITY

Boulder, Colorado

Outreach Office

http://www.naropa.edu/distance

Naropa University was founded in 1974. It is accredited by North Central Association of Colleges and Schools. It first offered distance learning courses in 1999. In fall 2005, there were 200 students enrolled in distance learning courses. Institutionally administered financial aid is available to distance learners.

Services Distance learners have accessibility to academic advising, bookstore, career placement assistance, e-mail services, library services.

Contact Jeff Mohler, Registration Coordinator, Naropa University, 2130 Arapahoe Avenue, Boulder, CO 80302. Telephone: 303-546-3509. E-mail: registrar@ecampus.naropa.edu.

DEGREES AND AWARDS

MA Transpersonal Psychology with Ecopsychology concentration; Transpersonal Psychology
MAE Contemplative Education
MFA Creative Writing

COURSE SUBJECT AREAS OFFERED OUTSIDE OF DEGREE PROGRAMS

Undergraduate—American literature (United States and Canadian); anthropology; area, ethnic, cultural, and gender studies related; clinical psychology; community psychology; comparative literature; counseling psychology; creative writing; developmental and child psychology; ethnic, cultural minority, and gender studies; experimental psychology; gerontology; liberal arts and sciences, general studies and humanities; multi-/interdisciplinary studies related; peace studies and conflict resolution; philosophy and religious studies related; psychology; religious studies.

Graduate—anthropology; area, ethnic, cultural, and gender studies related; education; English; languages (East Asian); liberal arts and sciences, general studies and humanities; multi-/interdisciplinary studies related; psychology related; religious education.

Non-credit—area, ethnic, cultural, and gender studies related; area studies; creative writing; education; educational psychology; education related; ethnic, cultural minority, and gender studies; human development, family studies, and related services; peace studies and conflict resolution; philosophy; philosophy and religious studies related; psychology; psychology related; religious education; religious/sacred music; religious studies; theological and ministerial studies; theology and religious vocations related.

See full description on page 408.

NASSAU COMMUNITY COLLEGE

Garden City, New York

College of the Air

http://www.ncc.edu

Nassau Community College was founded in 1959. It is accredited by Middle States Association of Colleges and Schools. It first offered distance learning courses in 1991. In fall 2005, there were 1,600 students enrolled in distance learning courses. Institutionally administered financial aid is available to distance learners.

Services Distance learners have accessibility to academic advising, bookstore, campus computer network, e-mail services, library services.

Contact Prof. Arthur L. Friedman, EdD, Coordinator, Distance Education, Nassau Community College, 1 Education Drive, Garden City, NY 11530-6793. Telephone: 516-572-7883. Fax: 516-572-0690. E-mail: friedma@ncc.edu.

DEGREES AND AWARDS

Programs offered do not lead to a degree or other formal award.

COURSE SUBJECT AREAS OFFERED OUTSIDE OF DEGREE PROGRAMS

Undergraduate—accounting and related services; anthropology; apparel and textiles; astronomy and astrophysics; atmospheric sciences and meteorology; biology; business administration, management and operations; business/commerce; computer and information sciences; developmental and child psychology; economics; English composition; English language and literature related; entrepreneurial and small business operations; geological and earth sciences/geosciences; health and physical education/fitness; history; languages (Romance languages); legal studies (non-professional general, undergraduate); marketing; mathematics; mathematics and statistics related; music; physical sciences related; psychology; psychology related; sociology; statistics.

Non-credit—mathematics.

NATIONAL-LOUIS UNIVERSITY

Chicago, Illinois

http://www.nl.edu/

National-Louis University was founded in 1886. It is accredited by North Central Association of Colleges and Schools. It first offered distance learning courses in 1998. In fall 2005, there were 25 students enrolled in distance learning courses. Institutionally administered financial aid is available to distance learners.

Services Distance learners have accessibility to academic advising, bookstore, campus computer network, e-mail services, library services, tutoring.

Contact Dr. Linda Sweeney, EdD, Program Director, Online Master's Programs, National-Louis University, 122 South Michigan Avenue, 3rd Floor, Chicago, IL 60603. Telephone: 800-443-5522 Ext. 3036. Fax: 312-261-3057. E-mail: lsweeney@nl.edu.

DEGREES AND AWARDS

MEd Adult, Continuing, and Literacy Education

NATIONAL UNIVERSITY

La Jolla, California

NU Online

http://www.online.nu.edu

National University was founded in 1971. It is accredited by Western Association of Schools and Colleges. It first offered distance learning courses in 1994. In fall 2005, there were 13,768 students enrolled in distance learning courses. Institutionally administered financial aid is available to distance learners.

Services Distance learners have accessibility to academic advising, bookstore, campus computer network, career placement assistance, e-mail services, library services, tutoring.

Contact Mr. James Wilson, Director of Student Services, National University, 4141 Camino del Rio South, San Diego, CA 92108. Telephone: 800-NAT-UNIV Ext. 7288. Fax: 858-563 7211. E-mail: jwilson @nu.edu.

DEGREES AND AWARDS
AA General Studies–Associate of Arts
BA Early Childhood Development; English–Single Subject Preparation in English; English; Global Studies; History; Psychology
BBA Business Administration
BS Accountancy; Allied Health; Construction Engineering; Criminal Justice Administration; Information Systems; Information Technology Management; Nursing; Organizational Behavior
Certificate Early Childhood Special Education
Certification Administrative Services Certificate; Education–Level I Education Specialist Credential: Mild/Mod; Education–TED Multiple or Single Subject Teaching Credential
EMBA Executive Master of Business Administration (Spanish Version)
MA English; Human Behavior; Human Resource Management and Organizational Development; Management
MAT Teaching
MBA Business Administration
MEd Cross Cultural Teaching
MFA Creative Writing; Digital Cinema
MPA Public Administration–Master of Public Administration
MS Computer Science; Educational Administration and Administrative Services; Educational Technology; Educational and Instructional Technology; Electronic Business; Engineering Management; Forensic Sciences–Master of Forensic Sciences; Homeland Security and Safety Engineering; Information Systems; Organizational Leadership; Special Education and Level I Specialist Credential Mild/Moderate; Technology Management

COURSE SUBJECT AREAS OFFERED OUTSIDE OF DEGREE PROGRAMS
Undergraduate—accounting and related services; allied health and medical assisting services; biological and physical sciences; building/construction finishing, management, and inspection; business administration, management and operations; business/commerce; communications technology; computer software and media applications; construction engineering technology; counseling psychology; criminal justice and corrections; developmental and child psychology; education; English; history; information science/studies; international/global studies; management sciences and quantitative methods; nursing; psychology; public administration.
Graduate—accounting and related services; business administration, management and operations; business/commerce; computer and information sciences; creative writing; criminology; education; educational administration and supervision; educational/instructional media design; education (specific subject areas); human resources management; public administration; special education; technology education/industrial arts.

NAUGATUCK VALLEY COMMUNITY COLLEGE
Waterbury, Connecticut
http://www.nvcc.commnet.edu

Naugatuck Valley Community College was founded in 1992. It is accredited by New England Association of Schools and Colleges. It first offered distance learning courses in 2003. In fall 2005, there were 250 students enrolled in distance learning courses. Institutionally administered financial aid is available to distance learners.
Services Distance learners have accessibility to academic advising, campus computer network, e-mail services, library services.
Contact Ms. Stacy Williams, Distance Learning Coordinator, Naugatuck Valley Community College, 750 Chase Parkway, Waterbury, CT 06708. Telephone: 203-575-8182. E-mail: swilliams@nvcc.commnet.edu.

DEGREES AND AWARDS
Programs offered do not lead to a degree or other formal award.

COURSE SUBJECT AREAS OFFERED OUTSIDE OF DEGREE PROGRAMS
Undergraduate—accounting and related services; business administration, management and operations; business operations support and assistant services; computer and information sciences; criminal justice and corrections; culinary arts and related services; fine and studio art; health professions related; human development, family studies, and related services; liberal arts and sciences, general studies and humanities; music; nursing; sales, merchandising, and related marketing operations (specialized); social work; vehicle maintenance and repair technologies; visual and performing arts related.
Non-credit—accounting and related services; crafts, folk art and artisanry; dance; data entry/microcomputer applications; data processing; English as a second language; health and physical education/fitness; health/medical preparatory programs; real estate.

NEUMANN COLLEGE
Aston, Pennsylvania
neumannonline.org
http://www.neumann.edu/

Neumann College was founded in 1965. It is accredited by Middle States Association of Colleges and Schools. It first offered distance learning courses in 1998. In fall 2005, there were 200 students enrolled in distance learning courses. Institutionally administered financial aid is available to distance learners.
Services Distance learners have accessibility to academic advising, bookstore, campus computer network, career placement assistance, e-mail services, library services, tutoring.
Contact Dr. Patricia Szymurski, Dean, Division of Continuing Adult and Professional Studies, Neumann College, One Neumann Drive, Aston, PA 19014-1298. Telephone: 610-558-5530. Fax: 610-361-5490. E-mail: szymurst@neumann.edu.

DEGREES AND AWARDS
AA Liberal Studies
MS Management Science

COURSE SUBJECT AREAS OFFERED OUTSIDE OF DEGREE PROGRAMS
Undergraduate—criminology; English; English literature (British and Commonwealth); human resources management; mathematics and statistics related; psychology; religious studies; technical and business writing.

NEW ENGLAND COLLEGE OF FINANCE
Boston, Massachusetts
http://www.finance.edu/

New England College of Finance was founded in 1909. It is accredited by New England Association of Schools and Colleges. It first offered distance learning courses in 2002. In fall 2005, there were 350 students enrolled in distance learning courses. Institutionally administered financial aid is available to distance learners.
Services Distance learners have accessibility to academic advising, bookstore, library services.
Contact Kim Simon, Senior Enrollment Manager, New England College of Finance, 10 High Street, Suite 204, Boston, MA 02110. Telephone: 617-951-2350 Ext. 237. Fax: 617-951-2533. E-mail: k.simon@finance.edu.

DEGREES AND AWARDS
AS Business Administration
CCCPE Accounting and Finance; Banking Studies; Branch Management; Commercial Lending; Financial Services Studies; Forensic Accounting; Leadership Versatility in Financial Services; Leadership Versatility in Retail Banking; Mutual Funds and Investments; NECF-UC Berkeley Accelerated Program in Financial Services

COURSE SUBJECT AREAS OFFERED OUTSIDE OF DEGREE PROGRAMS
Undergraduate—accounting and related services; American literature (United States and Canadian); business administration, management and operations; business, management, and marketing related; business operations support and assistant services; computer and information sciences; economics; English; finance and financial management services; history; insurance; mathematics and statistics related; personality psychology; statistics.
Graduate—accounting and related services; business administration, management and operations; business/commerce; business, management, and marketing related; business/managerial economics; finance and financial management services; international business.

Non-credit—accounting and related services; business administration, management and operations; business/commerce; business, management, and marketing related; business/managerial economics; business operations support and assistant services; finance and financial management services.

NEW ENGLAND INSTITUTE OF TECHNOLOGY
Warwick, Rhode Island
http://blackboard.neit.edu

New England Institute of Technology was founded in 1940. It is accredited by New England Association of Schools and Colleges. It first offered distance learning courses in 1996. In fall 2005, there were 80 students enrolled in distance learning courses. Institutionally administered financial aid is available to distance learners.

Services Distance learners have accessibility to academic advising, e-mail services, library services.

Contact Mr. Michael Caruso, Admissions Officer, New England Institute of Technology, 2500 Post Road, Warwick, RI 02886. Telephone: 401-739-5000 Ext. 3411. E-mail: mcaruso@neit.edu.

DEGREES AND AWARDS
Programs offered do not lead to a degree or other formal award.

COURSE SUBJECT AREAS OFFERED OUTSIDE OF DEGREE PROGRAMS
Undergraduate—English composition; mathematics; physics; psychology.

NEW JERSEY CITY UNIVERSITY
Jersey City, New Jersey
Continuing Education
http://newlearning.njcu.edu

New Jersey City University was founded in 1927. It is accredited by Middle States Association of Colleges and Schools. It first offered distance learning courses in 1997. In fall 2005, there were 1,450 students enrolled in distance learning courses. Institutionally administered financial aid is available to distance learners.

Services Distance learners have accessibility to e-mail services, library services.

Contact Marie A. Fosello, Director of Online Learning, New Jersey City University, 2039 Kennedy Boulevard, Jersey City, NJ 07305-1597. Telephone: 201-200-3449. Fax: 201-200-2188. E-mail: conted@njcu.edu.

DEGREES AND AWARDS
MA Educational Technology
MS Finance

COURSE SUBJECT AREAS OFFERED OUTSIDE OF DEGREE PROGRAMS
Undergraduate—accounting and related services; business/commerce; criminal justice and corrections; economics; international relations and affairs; mathematics; physics; political science and government; public health.
Graduate—accounting and related services; business administration, management and operations; criminology; educational administration and supervision; educational/instructional media design; public health; special education.

NEW JERSEY INSTITUTE OF TECHNOLOGY
Newark, New Jersey
Continuing Professional Education
http://cpe.njit.edu/

New Jersey Institute of Technology was founded in 1881. It is accredited by Middle States Association of Colleges and Schools. It first offered distance learning courses in 1985. In fall 2005, there were 8,000 students enrolled in distance learning courses. Institutionally administered financial aid is available to distance learners.

Services Distance learners have accessibility to academic advising, bookstore, campus computer network, career placement assistance, e-mail services, library services, tutoring.

Contact Ellen Schreihoffer, Director of Extended Learning Delivery, New Jersey Institute of Technology, University Heights, Newark, NJ 07102. Telephone: 973-596-6093. Fax: 973-596-3288. E-mail: el@njit.edu.

DEGREES AND AWARDS
BS Information Technology–Bachelor of Science in Information Technology (BSIT)
Graduate Certificate Data Mining; Emergency Management; Enterprise Systems Architecture; Information Management for Managers; Information Systems Implementation; Information Systems Implementation; Internet Systems Engineering; Management of Technology; Managment Essentials; Network Security and Information Assurance; Object-Oriented Design; Pharmaceutical Managment; Practice of Technical Communications; Programming Environment Tools; Project Management; Telecommunications Networking; User Centered Design
MS Engineering Management; Professional and Technical Communications

COURSE SUBJECT AREAS OFFERED OUTSIDE OF DEGREE PROGRAMS
Undergraduate—computer and information sciences; computer science; computer systems networking and telecommunications; engineering; information science/studies; management information systems; technical and business writing.
Graduate—business administration, management and operations; business, management, and marketing related; communication and journalism related; computer/information technology administration and management; computer science; computer systems networking and telecommunications; engineering technologies related; information science/studies; technical and business writing.

See full description on page 410.

NEWMAN THEOLOGICAL COLLEGE
Edmonton, Alberta, Canada
http://www.newman.edu

Newman Theological College was founded in 1969. It is provincially chartered. It first offered distance learning courses in 1987. In fall 2005, there were 76 students enrolled in distance learning courses.

Services Distance learners have accessibility to bookstore, campus computer network, library services.

Contact Carol Anne Seed, Associate Registrar, Newman Theological College, 15611 St. Albert Trail, Edmonton, AB T6V 1H3, Canada. Telephone: 780-447-2993. Fax: 780-447-2685. E-mail: registrar@newman.edu.

DEGREES AND AWARDS
Certificate Theological Studies
Advanced Graduate Diploma Religious Education

COURSE SUBJECT AREAS OFFERED OUTSIDE OF DEGREE PROGRAMS
Undergraduate—theological and ministerial studies.
Graduate—religious education.

NEWMAN UNIVERSITY
Wichita, Kansas
Community Education
http://www.newmanu.edu

Newman University was founded in 1933. It is accredited by North Central Association of Colleges and Schools. It first offered distance learning courses in 1987. In fall 2005, there were 250 students enrolled in distance learning courses. Institutionally administered financial aid is available to distance learners.

Services Distance learners have accessibility to bookstore, campus computer network, e-mail services, library services.

Contact Norman Correll, Director of Distance Learning, Newman University, 3100 McCormick Avenue, Wichita, KS 67213. Telephone: 316-942-4291 Ext. 2222. Fax: 316-942-4483. E-mail: cornelln@newmanu.edu.

DEGREES AND AWARDS

BA Pastoral Ministry
BS Teacher Education
MSE Education–Graduate Teacher Education
MSW Social Work–Master of Social Work

NEW MEXICO INSTITUTE OF MINING AND TECHNOLOGY
Socorro, New Mexico
Distance Education Department
http://www.nmt.edu/~eodi

New Mexico Institute of Mining and Technology was founded in 1889. It is accredited by North Central Association of Colleges and Schools. It first offered distance learning courses in 2000. In fall 2005, there were 80 students enrolled in distance learning courses. Institutionally administered financial aid is available to distance learners.

Services Distance learners have accessibility to academic advising, bookstore, campus computer network, career placement assistance, e-mail services, library services, tutoring.

Contact Mrs. Wendi Rae Carrillo, Student Support Specialist, New Mexico Institute of Mining and Technology, 801 Leroy Place, Socorro, NM 87801. Telephone: 505-835-6908. Fax: 505-835-5541. E-mail: wcarrillo@admin.nmt.edu.

DEGREES AND AWARDS

Programs offered do not lead to a degree or other formal award.

COURSE SUBJECT AREAS OFFERED OUTSIDE OF DEGREE PROGRAMS

Graduate—computer science; education (specific subject areas); engineering mechanics; environmental/environmental health engineering; management sciences and quantitative methods; materials engineering; mathematics; mechanical engineering.

NEW MEXICO JUNIOR COLLEGE
Hobbs, New Mexico
http://www.nmjc.edu

New Mexico Junior College was founded in 1965. It is accredited by North Central Association of Colleges and Schools. It first offered distance learning courses in 2001. In fall 2005, there were 150 students enrolled in distance learning courses. Institutionally administered financial aid is available to distance learners.

Services Distance learners have accessibility to academic advising, bookstore, campus computer network, e-mail services, library services.

Contact Mrs. Lisa Hardison, Dean, New Mexico Junior College, 5317 Lovington Highway, Hobbs, NM 88240. Telephone: 505-492-2641. Fax: 505-392-5757. E-mail: lhardison@nmjc.edu.

DEGREES AND AWARDS

Programs offered do not lead to a degree or other formal award.

COURSE SUBJECT AREAS OFFERED OUTSIDE OF DEGREE PROGRAMS

Undergraduate—accounting and computer science; allied health and medical assisting services; American literature (United States and Canadian); biblical and other theological languages and literatures; business administration, management and operations; communication and media; computer software and media applications; criminal justice and corrections; design and applied arts; economics; education related; English composition; geological and earth sciences/geosciences; history; mathematics; mathematics and statistics related.

NEW MEXICO STATE UNIVERSITY
Las Cruces, New Mexico
Office of Distance Education and Weekend College
http://www.nmsu.edu/distance

New Mexico State University was founded in 1888. It is accredited by North Central Association of Colleges and Schools. It first offered distance learning courses in 1989. In fall 2005, there were 2,612 students enrolled in distance learning courses. Institutionally administered financial aid is available to distance learners.

Services Distance learners have accessibility to academic advising, bookstore, campus computer network, career placement assistance, e-mail services, library services.

Contact Dr. Roberta Derlin, Associate Vice Provost for Distance Education, New Mexico State University, Box 3WEC, Las Cruces, NM 88003. Telephone: 505-646-5095. Fax: 505-646-2044. E-mail: rderlin@nmsu.edu.

DEGREES AND AWARDS

BA Human and Community Services–Bachelor of Human and Community Services; Sociology
BBA Business Administration
BS Elementary Education; Hotel, Restaurant and Tourism Management; Information and Communication Technology–Bachelor of Information and Communication Technology
BSN Nursing
Certificate Teaching and Learning–Online Teaching and Learning
Endorsement Information Technology Coordinator; Reading
License Educational Administrative Licensure; Elementary Licensure (Post BA); School Counseling Licensure; Special Education Alternative Licensure
MA Agricultural and Extension Educator; Education; Educational Administration
MAT Teaching–Master of Arts in Teaching
MCJ Criminal Justice
MS Industrial Engineering–Master of Science in Industrial Engineering; Industrial Engineering
MSN Psychiatric-Mental Health
MSW Social Work
EdD Educational Administration (Educational Leadership)
PhD Curriculum and Instruction–Learning Technologies emphasis

COURSE SUBJECT AREAS OFFERED OUTSIDE OF DEGREE PROGRAMS

Undergraduate—business administration, management and operations; business/commerce; community health services; human services; sociology.

Graduate—criminal justice and corrections; education related; industrial engineering; manufacturing engineering; mechanical engineering.

NEW MEXICO STATE UNIVERSITY–ALAMOGORDO
Alamogordo, New Mexico
http://alamo.nmsu.edu/

New Mexico State University–Alamogordo was founded in 1958. It is accredited by North Central Association of Colleges and Schools. It first offered distance learning courses in 1997. In fall 2005, there were 362 students enrolled in distance learning courses. Institutionally administered financial aid is available to distance learners.

Services Distance learners have accessibility to academic advising, bookstore, campus computer network, e-mail services, library services.

Contact Dr. Debra Teachman, Campus Academic Officer, New Mexico State University–Alamogordo, NMSU-Alamogordo, Academic Office, Alamogordo, NM 88310. Telephone: 505-439-3621. Fax: 505-439-3622. E-mail: teachman@nmsua.nmsu.edu.

DEGREES AND AWARDS

Programs offered do not lead to a degree or other formal award.

COURSE SUBJECT AREAS OFFERED OUTSIDE OF DEGREE PROGRAMS

Undergraduate—applied mathematics; biomedical/medical engineering; chemistry; computer and information sciences; economics; English composition; legal studies (non-professional general, undergraduate); liberal arts and sciences, general studies and humanities; philosophy; psychology.

NEW MEXICO STATE UNIVERSITY–CARLSBAD
Carlsbad, New Mexico
http://cavern.nmsu.edu/

New Mexico State University–Carlsbad was founded in 1950. It is accredited by North Central Association of Colleges and Schools. It first offered distance learning courses in 1998. In fall 2005, there were 75 students enrolled in distance learning courses. Institutionally administered financial aid is available to distance learners.

Services Distance learners have accessibility to academic advising, bookstore, campus computer network, career placement assistance, e-mail services, library services, tutoring.

Contact Denise K. Alaniz, Distance Education Coordinator, New Mexico State University–Carlsbad, Office 1A, Distance Educaton, 1500 University Drive, Carlsbad, NM 88220. Telephone: 505-234-9256. Fax: 505-885-4951. E-mail: dalaniz@cavern.nmsu.edu.

DEGREES AND AWARDS

BA Criminal Justice–Bachelor of Criminal Justice; Sociology
BBA Business, general
BHS Human and Community Services–Bachelor of Human and Community Services
BS Education–Elementary Education licensure; Information Communication Technology–Bachelor of Information Communication Technology
BSN Nursing–BSN Completion program
License Educational Administrative Licensure; School Counceling Licensure
MA Curriculum and Instruction
MAE Educational Management and Development
MCJ Criminal Justice–Master of Criminal Justice

COURSE SUBJECT AREAS OFFERED OUTSIDE OF DEGREE PROGRAMS

Undergraduate—accounting and computer science; business administration, management and operations; business, management, and marketing related; communication and media; computer and information sciences; criminal justice and corrections; economics; education; English; health services/allied health/health sciences; history; languages (foreign languages related); liberal arts and sciences, general studies and humanities; mathematics; natural sciences; nursing; physical sciences; social sciences.
Non-credit—accounting and related services; applied horticulture/horticultural business services; bilingual, multilingual, and multicultural education; business administration, management and operations; business operations support and assistant services; computer and information sciences; computer programming; creative writing; criminal justice and corrections; entrepreneurial and small business operations; gerontology; health professions related; human development, family studies, and related services; management information systems; marketing.

THE NEW SCHOOL
New York, New York
The New School Online
http://www.dialnsa.edu

The New School was founded in 1919. It first offered distance learning courses in 1994. In fall 2005, there were 1,555 students enrolled in distance learning courses. Institutionally administered financial aid is available to distance learners.
Services Distance learners have accessibility to academic advising, bookstore, campus computer network, e-mail services, library services, tutoring.
Contact Gerianne Brusati, Associate Director of Admissions, The New School, 66 West 12th Street, Room 401, New York, NY 10011. Telephone: 212-229-5630. Fax: 212-989-3887. E-mail: brusatig@newschool.edu.

DEGREES AND AWARDS

BA Liberal Arts
Certificate English Language Teaching
Graduate Certificate Media Management program
MA Media Studies

COURSE SUBJECT AREAS OFFERED OUTSIDE OF DEGREE PROGRAMS

Undergraduate—apparel and textiles; business administration, management and operations; communication and journalism related; communication and media; creative writing; design and applied arts; English composition; liberal arts and sciences, general studies and humanities.
Graduate—communication and media; English as a second/foreign language (teaching); marketing.
Non-credit—communication and media; creative writing; English composition; liberal arts and sciences, general studies and humanities.

NEW YORK INSTITUTE OF TECHNOLOGY
Old Westbury, New York
On-Line Campus
http://www.nyit.edu

New York Institute of Technology was founded in 1955. It is accredited by Middle States Association of Colleges and Schools. It first offered distance learning courses in 1984. In fall 2005, there were 2,727 students enrolled in distance learning courses. Institutionally administered financial aid is available to distance learners.
Services Distance learners have accessibility to academic advising, bookstore, campus computer network, career placement assistance, e-mail services, library services.
Contact Ms. Kathleen Lyons, Assistant Director of Admissions, New York Institute of Technology, Carleton Avenue, PO Box 9029, Central Islip, NY 11729-9029. Telephone: 631-348-3200. Fax: 631-348-0912. E-mail: klyons@nyit.edu.

DEGREES AND AWARDS

BA Interdisciplinary Studies
BPS Hospitality Management; Interdisciplinary Studies
BS Business Administration; Community Mental Health; Criminal Justice; Interdisciplinary Studies; Psychology; Sociology
MBA Business
MS Energy Management

COURSE SUBJECT AREAS OFFERED OUTSIDE OF DEGREE PROGRAMS

Undergraduate—accounting and related services; anthropology; biology; business administration, management and operations; business, management, and marketing related; communication and media; creative writing; criminal justice and corrections; design and applied arts; economics; English; English composition; English language and literature related; environmental control technologies; finance and financial management services; journalism; legal studies (non-professional general, undergraduate); marketing; mechanical engineering; philosophy; philosophy and religious studies related; political science and government; social psychology; social work; sociology; speech and rhetoric; statistics.
Graduate—accounting and related services; business administration, management and operations; educational/instructional media design; management information systems; marketing.
Non-credit—computer and information sciences; computer and information sciences and support services related; computer/information technology administration and management; computer software and media applications; culinary arts and related services.

NIAGARA UNIVERSITY
Niagara Falls, New York

Niagara University was founded in 1856. It is accredited by Middle States Association of Colleges and Schools. It first offered distance learning courses in 2003. In fall 2005, there were 141 students enrolled in distance learning courses. Institutionally administered financial aid is available to distance learners.
Services Distance learners have accessibility to academic advising, bookstore, e-mail services, library services.
Contact Office of Admission, Niagara University, Niagara University, NY 14109. E-mail: admissions@niagara.edu.

DEGREES AND AWARDS

Programs offered do not lead to a degree or other formal award.

COURSE SUBJECT AREAS OFFERED OUTSIDE OF DEGREE PROGRAMS

Undergraduate—fine and studio art; hospitality administration; languages (foreign languages related); social work.
Graduate—accounting and computer science; business, management, and marketing related; finance and financial management services.
Non-credit—accounting and computer science; business administration, management and operations; computer software and media applications; health and medical administrative services.

NIPISSING UNIVERSITY
North Bay, Ontario, Canada
Center for Continuing Business Education
http://www.nipissingu.ca/ccbe

Nipissing University was founded in 1992. It is provincially chartered. It first offered distance learning courses in 1997. In fall 2005, there were 325 students enrolled in distance learning courses. Institutionally administered financial aid is available to distance learners.

Services Distance learners have accessibility to academic advising, e-mail services, library services, tutoring.

Contact Emily Sykes, Program Secretary, Nipissing University, 100 College Drive, Box 5002, North Bay, ON P1B 8L7, Canada. Telephone: 705-474-3450 Ext. 4343. Fax: 705-475-0264. E-mail: ccbe@nipissingu.ca.

DEGREES AND AWARDS

BComm Financial Services

COURSE SUBJECT AREAS OFFERED OUTSIDE OF DEGREE PROGRAMS

Undergraduate—accounting and related services; business administration, management and operations; business/commerce; business, management, and marketing related; economics; finance and financial management services; human resources management; international business; management sciences and quantitative methods; marketing.

NORTH AMERICAN BAPTIST SEMINARY
Sioux Falls, South Dakota

North American Baptist Seminary was founded in 1858. It is accredited by North Central Association of Colleges and Schools. It first offered distance learning courses in 2000. In fall 2005, there were 15 students enrolled in distance learning courses. Institutionally administered financial aid is available to distance learners.

Services Distance learners have accessibility to academic advising, bookstore, campus computer network, e-mail services, library services.

Contact Mr. Bryce H. Eben, Director of Enrollment Development, North American Baptist Seminary, 1525 South Grange Avenue, Sioux Falls, SD 57105. Telephone: 605-336-6588 Ext. 706. Fax: 605-335-9090. E-mail: beben@nabs.edu.

DEGREES AND AWARDS

Programs offered do not lead to a degree or other formal award.

COURSE SUBJECT AREAS OFFERED OUTSIDE OF DEGREE PROGRAMS

Graduate—education (specific subject areas); religious/sacred music; theological and ministerial studies; theology and religious vocations related.

NORTH ARKANSAS COLLEGE
Harrison, Arkansas
Articulated Programs and Distance Learning
http://pioneer.northark.net/

North Arkansas College was founded in 1974. It is accredited by North Central Association of Colleges and Schools. It first offered distance learning courses in 1988. In fall 2005, there were 410 students enrolled in distance learning courses. Institutionally administered financial aid is available to distance learners.

Services Distance learners have accessibility to bookstore, campus computer network, e-mail services, library services.

Contact Mr. John P. Walsh, Director of Distance Education, North Arkansas College, 1515 Pioneer Drive, Harrison, AR 72601. Telephone: 870-391-3308. Fax: 870-391-3250. E-mail: jwalsh@northark.edu.

DEGREES AND AWARDS

Programs offered do not lead to a degree or other formal award.

COURSE SUBJECT AREAS OFFERED OUTSIDE OF DEGREE PROGRAMS

Undergraduate—accounting and related services; agricultural business and management; agricultural production; anthropology; biological and physical sciences; business/corporate communications; computer/information technology administration and management; economics; education related; English composition; fine and studio art; history; human resources management; management information systems; mathematics; nursing; psychology; social sciences related; technical and business writing.

Non-credit—computer and information sciences and support services related; computer/information technology administration and management; computer software and media applications.

NORTH CAROLINA STATE UNIVERSITY
Raleigh, North Carolina
Distance Education
http://distance.ncsu.edu

North Carolina State University was founded in 1887. It is accredited by Southern Association of Colleges and Schools. It first offered distance learning courses in 1976. In fall 2005, there were 3,526 students enrolled in distance learning courses. Institutionally administered financial aid is available to distance learners.

Services Distance learners have accessibility to academic advising, bookstore, campus computer network, career placement assistance, e-mail services, library services, tutoring.

Contact Lily Leegstra, Program Coordinator, North Carolina State University, Campus Box 7113, Raleigh, NC 27695-7113. Telephone: 919-515-9030. Fax: 919-515-6668. E-mail: lily_leegstra@ncsu.edu.

DEGREES AND AWARDS

Certificate Computer Programming; HACCP/Food Safety Managers

Graduate Certificate Biological and Agricultural Engineering; Community College Teaching; Geographic Information Systems; Horticulture Science

MCE Chemical Engineering; Civil Engineering

MCS Computer Science

ME Engineering Online

MEd Curriculum and Instruction; Training and Development

MS Wood and Paper Science

MSAE Aerospace Engineering

MSE Agricultural Teacher Education

MSME Mechanical Engineering

MT Textiles Off-Campus programs (TOP)

COURSE SUBJECT AREAS OFFERED OUTSIDE OF DEGREE PROGRAMS

Undergraduate—accounting and related services; agricultural and domestic animal services; agricultural and food products processing; agricultural production; agriculture; American literature (United States and Canadian); animal sciences; anthropology; apparel and textiles; biological and physical sciences; business/commerce; business, management, and marketing related; chemistry; computer programming; educational psychology; education (specific subject areas); English; English as a second/foreign language (teaching); English composition; forestry; genetics; health and physical education/fitness; history; languages (Modern Greek); languages (Romance languages); languages (South Asian); mathematics; multi-/interdisciplinary studies related; music; nutrition sciences; parks, recreation and leisure facilities management; philosophy; physics; political science and government; psychology; soil sciences; technical and business writing; textile sciences and engineering; zoology/animal biology.

Graduate—agricultural and food products processing; agriculture; agriculture and agriculture operations related; biological and physical sciences; chemical engineering; civil engineering; computer engineering; curriculum and instruction; educational administration and supervision; education (specific subject areas); engineering; information science/studies; textile sciences and engineering.

NORTH CENTRAL TEXAS COLLEGE
Gainesville, Texas
http://www.nctc.edu

North Central Texas College was founded in 1924. It is accredited by Southern Association of Colleges and Schools. It first offered distance learning courses in 1999. In fall 2005, there were 843 students enrolled in distance learning courses. Institutionally administered financial aid is available to distance learners.

Services Distance learners have accessibility to academic advising, bookstore, library services.

Contact Debbie J. Huffman, Director of e-Learning, North Central Texas College, 1525 West California Street, Gainesville, TX 76240. Telephone: 940-668-7731 Ext. 4475. Fax: 940-668-6490. E-mail: dhuffman@nctc.edu.

DEGREES AND AWARDS

Programs offered do not lead to a degree or other formal award.

COURSE SUBJECT AREAS OFFERED OUTSIDE OF DEGREE PROGRAMS

Undergraduate—biology; business, management, and marketing related; business operations support and assistant services; computer/information technology administration and management; computer systems networking and telecommunications; criminology; economics; education; English; English composition; English literature (British and Commonwealth); fine and studio art; history; mathematics; nutrition sciences; political science and government; psychology; sociology; speech and rhetoric.

NORTH DAKOTA STATE COLLEGE OF SCIENCE
Wahpeton, North Dakota
http://www.ndscs.edu/

North Dakota State College of Science was founded in 1903. It is accredited by North Central Association of Colleges and Schools. It first offered distance learning courses in 1968. In fall 2005, there were 434 students enrolled in distance learning courses. Institutionally administered financial aid is available to distance learners.

Services Distance learners have accessibility to academic advising, bookstore, career placement assistance, e-mail services, library services, tutoring.

Contact Ms. Margaret Wall, Distance Education Director, North Dakota State College of Science, 800 Sixth Street North, Wahpeton, ND 58076-0002. Telephone: 701-671-2430. Fax: 701-671-2416. E-mail: margaret.wall@ndscs.nodak.edu.

DEGREES AND AWARDS

AAS Administrative Assistant; Architectural Drafting and Estimating Technology; Business Management–eBusiness emphasis; Health Information Technician; Pharmacy Technician

AS Nursing–Practical Nursing

Certificate Computer Information Systems–Web Design; HIT–Medical Coding; Medical Transcription

COURSE SUBJECT AREAS OFFERED OUTSIDE OF DEGREE PROGRAMS

Undergraduate—accounting and related services; allied health and medical assisting services; applied mathematics; biology; business administration, management and operations; business, management, and marketing related; chemistry; computer and information sciences; computer and information sciences and support services related; computer/information technology administration and management; computer programming; developmental and child psychology; drafting/design engineering technologies; economics; English; English composition; foods, nutrition, and related services; health and medical administrative services; health and physical education/fitness; health professions related; history; marketing; mathematics; microbiological sciences and immunology; psychology; psychology related; social sciences; sociology; technical and business writing.

NORTH DAKOTA STATE UNIVERSITY
Fargo, North Dakota
Division of Distance and Continuing Education
http://www.ndsu.edu/dce

North Dakota State University was founded in 1890. It is accredited by North Central Association of Colleges and Schools. It first offered distance learning courses in 1998. Institutionally administered financial aid is available to distance learners.

Services Distance learners have accessibility to academic advising, bookstore, career placement assistance, e-mail services, library services, tutoring.

Contact Karen Murie, Distance Learning Coordinator, North Dakota State University, PO Box 5819, University Station, Fargo, ND 58105. Telephone: 701-231-7015. Fax: 701-231-7016. E-mail: karen.murie@ndsu.edu.

DEGREES AND AWARDS

CAGS Family Financial Planning; Food Protection; Gerontology; Merchandising; Software Engineering
MS Family Financial Planning; Gerontology; Merchandising

COURSE SUBJECT AREAS OFFERED OUTSIDE OF DEGREE PROGRAMS

Undergraduate—applied mathematics; clinical psychology; communication and media; computer and information sciences; data entry/microcomputer applications; developmental and child psychology; education; foods, nutrition, and related services; hospitality administration; human development, family studies, and related services; mathematics.

Graduate—clinical psychology; communication and media; computer engineering; curriculum and instruction; education; educational administration and supervision; educational/instructional media design; education (specific levels and methods); family and consumer economics; human development, family studies, and related services; psychology; special education.

Non-credit—aerospace, aeronautical and astronautical engineering; allied health and medical assisting services; business/commerce; business operations support and assistant services; clinical psychology; computer and information sciences; computer programming; computer science; computer software and media applications; data entry/microcomputer applications; human development, family studies, and related services.

NORTHEAST STATE TECHNICAL COMMUNITY COLLEGE
Blountville, Tennessee
Evening and Distance Education
http://northeaststate.edu

Northeast State Technical Community College was founded in 1966. It is accredited by Southern Association of Colleges and Schools. It first offered distance learning courses in 1996. In fall 2005, there were 2,350 students enrolled in distance learning courses. Institutionally administered financial aid is available to distance learners.

Services Distance learners have accessibility to academic advising, bookstore, campus computer network, career placement assistance, e-mail services, library services.

Contact Ms. Tammy B. Street, Coordinator of Distance Education Programs and Services, Northeast State Technical Community College, PO Box 246, Blountville , TN 37617. Telephone: 423-354-2497. Fax: 423-323-0224. E-mail: tbstreet@northeaststate.edu.

DEGREES AND AWARDS

Programs offered do not lead to a degree or other formal award.

COURSE SUBJECT AREAS OFFERED OUTSIDE OF DEGREE PROGRAMS

Undergraduate—accounting and related services; astronomy and astrophysics; biological and physical sciences; business administration, management and operations; chemistry; computer and information sciences; economics; education; English; English composition; history; mathematics; music; political science and government; psychology; social sciences; speech and rhetoric.

NORTHERN ARIZONA UNIVERSITY
Flagstaff, Arizona
NAU Distance Learning
http://www.distance.nau.edu

Northern Arizona University was founded in 1899. It is accredited by North Central Association of Colleges and Schools. It first offered distance learning courses in 1977. In fall 2005, there were 5,950 students enrolled in distance learning courses. Institutionally administered financial aid is available to distance learners.

Services Distance learners have accessibility to academic advising, bookstore, campus computer network, career placement assistance, e-mail services, library services, tutoring.

Contact Distance Learning Service Center, Northern Arizona University, PO Box 4117, Flagstaff, AZ 86011-4117. Telephone: 800-426-8315. Fax: 928-523-1169. E-mail: distance.programs@nau.edu.

DEGREES AND AWARDS

BA Psychology; Spanish

BEd Career and Technical Education (BS Ed.); Elementary Education (BS Ed.); Secondary Education (BS Ed.); Special and Elementary Education (BS Ed.)

BLS BAILS Arts and Letters; BAILS Criminal Justice; BAILS Enterprise in Society; BAILS Learning and Pedagogy; BAILS Mathematics/Statistics; BAILS Organizational Communication; BAILS Parks and Recreation Management; BAILS Psychology; BAILS Sociology; Environmental Sciences

BS BAILS Environmental Sciences; Criminal Justice; Dental Hygiene Completion Program; Health Promotion; Hotel and Restaurant Management; Interior Design; Management (BSBA); Nursing–Accelerated Option; Nursing; Parks and Recreation Management

BSAST Computer Technology (BAS); Early Childhood (BAS); Health Promotion (BAS); Justice Systems and Policy Planning (BAS); Public Agency Services (BAS)

BSN Nursing–RN to BSN

BSW Social Work

Certificate Educational Technology; Elementary Education Postdegree; International Tourism Management; Parks and Recreation Management; Restaurant Management; Secondary Education Postdegree; Special Education Postdegree

Certification Principalship; Professional Writing; Superintendency; Supervisory

Endorsement Bilingual Education Endorsement; English as a Second Language; Gifted Education; Middle School Education; Reading

Graduate Certificate Public Management

MA Applied Communication; Counseling; English

MAT Mathematics; Teaching English as a Second Language

MEd Bilingual/Multicultural Education; Career and Technical Education; Counseling/Human Relations; Counseling/School Counseling; Early Childhood Education; Educational Leadership; Educational Technology; Elementary Education; Secondary Education with Certification Emphasis; Secondary Education; Special Education

MEngr Engineering

MS Nursing

EdD Educational Leadership

COURSE SUBJECT AREAS OFFERED OUTSIDE OF DEGREE PROGRAMS

Undergraduate—art history, criticism and conservation; curriculum and instruction; environmental/environmental health engineering; marketing/marketing management; social work; sociology.

Graduate—curriculum and instruction; physical therapy.

See full description on page 412.

NORTHERN KENTUCKY UNIVERSITY
Highland Heights, Kentucky
Educational Outreach
http://dl.nku.edu

Northern Kentucky University was founded in 1968. It is accredited by Southern Association of Colleges and Schools. It first offered distance learning courses in 1983. In fall 2005, there were 1,000 students enrolled in distance learning courses. Institutionally administered financial aid is available to distance learners.

Services Distance learners have accessibility to academic advising, bookstore, campus computer network, e-mail services, library services.

Contact Debbie Poweleit, Associate Director of Educational Outreach, Northern Kentucky University, Educational Outreach, FH 305A, Highland Heights, KY 41099-5700. Telephone: 859-572-1500. Fax: 859-572-5174. E-mail: dl@nku.edu.

DEGREES AND AWARDS

BA Organizational Leadership

BSN Nursing–RN-BSN

MAE MAEd

MSN Nursing

COURSE SUBJECT AREAS OFFERED OUTSIDE OF DEGREE PROGRAMS

Undergraduate—entrepreneurial and small business operations; liberal arts and sciences, general studies and humanities.

Graduate—education related; engineering technologies related.

NORTHERN VIRGINIA COMMUNITY COLLEGE
Annandale, Virginia
Extended Learning Institute
http://eli.nvcc.edu

Northern Virginia Community College was founded in 1965. It is accredited by Southern Association of Colleges and Schools. It first offered distance learning courses in 1975. In fall 2005, there were 6,000 students enrolled in distance learning courses. Institutionally administered financial aid is available to distance learners.

Services Distance learners have accessibility to academic advising, bookstore, campus computer network, e-mail services, library services, tutoring.

Contact Jayne Townend, Admissions and Records, Northern Virginia Community College, 8333 Little River Turnpike, Annandale, VA 22003-3796. Telephone: 703-323-3368. Fax: 703-323-3392. E-mail: jtownend@nvcc.edu.

DEGREES AND AWARDS

AA Liberal Arts

AAS Business Management–Public Management specialization; Business Management

AS Business Administration; General Studies

Specialized diploma Information Systems Technology

COURSE SUBJECT AREAS OFFERED OUTSIDE OF DEGREE PROGRAMS

Undergraduate—accounting and related services; biology; creative writing; developmental and child psychology; dramatic/theater arts and stagecraft; English composition; film/video and photographic arts; finance and financial management services; fine and studio art; geography and cartography; history; journalism; languages (Romance languages); legal studies (non-professional general, undergraduate); management information systems; marketing; mathematics and statistics related; mechanical engineering; philosophy and religious studies related; sociology; statistics.

NORTH GEORGIA COLLEGE & STATE UNIVERSITY
Dahlonega, Georgia
E-Learning/Opportunity Services
http://www.ngcsu.edu

North Georgia College & State University was founded in 1873. It is accredited by Southern Association of Colleges and Schools. It first offered distance learning courses in 1995. In fall 2005, there were 400 students enrolled in distance learning courses. Institutionally administered financial aid is available to distance learners.

Services Distance learners have accessibility to academic advising, career placement assistance, e-mail services, library services, tutoring.

Contact Justin White, Coordinator of Student Environments, North Georgia College & State University, Health and Natural Sciences Building, 82 College Circle, Dahlonega, GA 30597. Telephone: 706-864-1844. Fax: 706-864-1886. E-mail: jawhite@ngcsu.edu.

DEGREES AND AWARDS
Programs offered do not lead to a degree or other formal award.

COURSE SUBJECT AREAS OFFERED OUTSIDE OF DEGREE PROGRAMS
Undergraduate—computer and information sciences; education (specific levels and methods); education (specific subject areas); engineering related; gerontology; international and comparative education; international relations and affairs; linguistic, comparative, and related language studies; military studies; nursing; psychology; sociology.

Graduate—educational administration and supervision; educational assessment, evaluation, and research; education (specific levels and methods); education (specific subject areas); gerontology; international and comparative education; nursing; psychology; public administration; public administration and social service professions related; sociology.

Non-credit—communications technology; computer and information sciences; computer software and media applications; educational/instructional media design; military studies.

NORTH IDAHO COLLEGE
Coeur d'Alene, Idaho
http://www.nic.edu

North Idaho College was founded in 1933. It is accredited by Northwest Commission on Colleges and Universities. It first offered distance learning courses in 1997. In fall 2005, there were 600 students enrolled in distance learning courses. Institutionally administered financial aid is available to distance learners.

Services Distance learners have accessibility to academic advising, bookstore, campus computer network, career placement assistance, e-mail services, library services, tutoring.

Contact Dr. Candace Wheeler, Director of Distance Education, North Idaho College, 1000 West Garden Avenue, Coeur d'Alene, ID 83814. Telephone: 208-769-3436. Fax: 208-769-7728. E-mail: candace_wheeler@nic.edu.

DEGREES AND AWARDS
AS General Program

COURSE SUBJECT AREAS OFFERED OUTSIDE OF DEGREE PROGRAMS
Undergraduate—accounting and related services; allied health and medical assisting services; American literature (United States and Canadian); anthropology; area, ethnic, cultural, and gender studies related; biology; business/commerce; communication and media; English composition; fine and studio art; human development, family studies, and related services; mathematics; philosophy; political science and government; psychology; sociology.

Non-credit—accounting and computer science; accounting and related services; allied health and medical assisting services; allied health diagnostic, intervention, and treatment professions; alternative and complementary medicine and medical systems; American literature (United States and Canadian); applied mathematics; behavioral sciences; business administration, management and operations; business/commerce; communication and journalism related; communication and media; communications technologies and support services related; computer and information sciences; computer and information sciences and support services related; computer/information technology administration and management; computer programming; computer software and media applications; computer systems networking and telecommunications; creative writing; entrepreneurial and small business operations; film/video and photographic arts; languages (classics and classical); publishing; technical and business writing.

NORTH LAKE COLLEGE
Irving, Texas

North Lake College was founded in 1977. It is accredited by Southern Association of Colleges and Schools. It first offered distance learning courses in 2000. In fall 2005, there were 1,586 students enrolled in distance learning courses. Institutionally administered financial aid is available to distance learners.

Services Distance learners have accessibility to academic advising, bookstore, campus computer network, career placement assistance, e-mail services, library services, tutoring.

Contact Ms. Shirley Thompson, Professor, North Lake College, Irving , TX 75052. E-mail: sthompson@dcccd.edu.

DEGREES AND AWARDS
Programs offered do not lead to a degree or other formal award.

COURSE SUBJECT AREAS OFFERED OUTSIDE OF DEGREE PROGRAMS
Undergraduate—biology; business, management, and marketing related; communications technology; English; mathematics; psychology; statistics.

NORTH SEATTLE COMMUNITY COLLEGE
Seattle, Washington
Distance Learning Office
http://www.virtualcollege.org

North Seattle Community College was founded in 1970. It is accredited by Northwest Commission on Colleges and Universities. It first offered distance learning courses in 1994. In fall 2005, there were 750 students enrolled in distance learning courses. Institutionally administered financial aid is available to distance learners.

Services Distance learners have accessibility to academic advising, bookstore, campus computer network, career placement assistance, e-mail services, library services, tutoring.

Contact Carol Howe, Program Coordinator, North Seattle Community College, 9600 College Way North, 3NC1443, Seattle, WA 98103. Telephone: 206-527-3738. Fax: 206-985-3984. E-mail: chowe@sccd.ctc.edu.

DEGREES AND AWARDS
AA General Studies

COURSE SUBJECT AREAS OFFERED OUTSIDE OF DEGREE PROGRAMS
Undergraduate—accounting and related services; anthropology; astronomy and astrophysics; biological and physical sciences; business/commerce; communication and media; computer programming; computer software and media applications; computer systems networking and telecommunications; economics; English composition; film/video and photographic arts; geological and earth sciences/geosciences; human development, family studies, and related services; journalism; library science related; mathematics; music; philosophy; psychology.

NORTHWEST CHRISTIAN COLLEGE
Eugene, Oregon
http://www.nwcc.edu/

Northwest Christian College was founded in 1895. It is accredited by Northwest Commission on Colleges and Universities. It first offered distance learning courses in 1999. In fall 2005, there were 36 students enrolled in distance learning courses. Institutionally administered financial aid is available to distance learners.

Services Distance learners have accessibility to academic advising, bookstore, career placement assistance, e-mail services, library services.

Contact Dr. Randy Jones, Dean of Admissions, Northwest Christian College, 828 East 11th Avenue, Eugene, OR 97401. Telephone: 541-684-7201. Fax: 541-684-7317. E-mail: admissions@nwcc.edu.

DEGREES AND AWARDS

Programs offered do not lead to a degree or other formal award.

COURSE SUBJECT AREAS OFFERED OUTSIDE OF DEGREE PROGRAMS

Undergraduate—biblical studies; education (specific levels and methods).

NORTHWESTERN COLLEGE
St. Paul, Minnesota
Center for Distance Education
http://distance.nwc.edu

Northwestern College was founded in 1902. It is accredited by North Central Association of Colleges and Schools. It first offered distance learning courses in 1994. In fall 2005, there were 800 students enrolled in distance learning courses. Institutionally administered financial aid is available to distance learners.

Services Distance learners have accessibility to academic advising, bookstore, campus computer network, career placement assistance, e-mail services, library services, tutoring.

Contact Betty Piper, Assistant Director, Northwestern College, 3003 Snelling Avenue North, St. Paul, MN 55113. Telephone: 800-308-5495. Fax: 651-631-5133. E-mail: distance@nwc.edu.

DEGREES AND AWARDS

AA Biblical Studies
BA Biblical Studies; Intercultural Ministries degree completion
Certificate Bible

COURSE SUBJECT AREAS OFFERED OUTSIDE OF DEGREE PROGRAMS

Undergraduate—archeology; astronomy and astrophysics; biblical studies; chemistry; communication and media; computer software and media applications; ethnic, cultural minority, and gender studies; history; languages (Modern Greek); liberal arts and sciences, general studies and humanities; mathematics; missionary studies and missiology; philosophy and religious studies related; psychology; religious/sacred music; religious studies; speech and rhetoric; theological and ministerial studies; theology and religious vocations related.

See full description on page 414.

NORTHWESTERN CONNECTICUT COMMUNITY COLLEGE
Winsted, Connecticut
http://www.commnet.edu/nwctc

Northwestern Connecticut Community College was founded in 1965. It is accredited by New England Association of Schools and Colleges. It first offered distance learning courses in 1997. In fall 2005, there were 194 students enrolled in distance learning courses. Institutionally administered financial aid is available to distance learners.

Services Distance learners have accessibility to e-mail services, library services, tutoring.

Contact Beverly J. King, Education Technology Specialist, Northwestern Connecticut Community College, Park Place East, Winsted, CT 06098. Telephone: 860-738-6323. E-mail: bking@nwcc.commnet.edu.

DEGREES AND AWARDS

AS Educational Technology

COURSE SUBJECT AREAS OFFERED OUTSIDE OF DEGREE PROGRAMS

Undergraduate—allied health and medical assisting services; biological and physical sciences; computer and information sciences; English composition; geography and cartography; history; philosophy; psychology; sociology.

Non-credit—computer and information sciences; computer software and media applications; technical and business writing.

NORTHWESTERN MICHIGAN COLLEGE
Traverse City, Michigan
Distance Education Services
http://www.nmc.edu/flo/

Northwestern Michigan College was founded in 1951. It is accredited by North Central Association of Colleges and Schools. It first offered distance learning courses in 1982. In fall 2005, there were 1,029 students enrolled in distance learning courses. Institutionally administered financial aid is available to distance learners.

Services Distance learners have accessibility to academic advising, bookstore, campus computer network, career placement assistance, e-mail services, library services, tutoring.

Contact Janet Oliver, Director, Northwestern Michigan College, Educational Media Technologies, 1701 East Front Street, Traverse City, MI 49686. Telephone: 231-995-1076. Fax: 231-995-1080. E-mail: joliver@nmc.edu.

DEGREES AND AWARDS

AAS Education, general transfer

AD Nursing

COURSE SUBJECT AREAS OFFERED OUTSIDE OF DEGREE PROGRAMS

Undergraduate—accounting and related services; anthropology; biology; business administration, management and operations; business/corporate communications; business, management, and marketing related; chemistry; computer and information sciences; computer and information sciences and support services related; computer programming; computer software and media applications; computer systems networking and telecommunications; creative writing; criminal justice and corrections; economics; English composition; English language and literature related; history; legal studies (non-professional general, undergraduate); mathematics and statistics related; music; nursing; pharmacology and toxicology; philosophy; physics; psychology; psychology related; sociology; statistics; technical and business writing.

NORTHWESTERN OKLAHOMA STATE UNIVERSITY
Alva, Oklahoma
http://www.nwalva.edu/

Northwestern Oklahoma State University was founded in 1897. It is accredited by North Central Association of Colleges and Schools. It first offered distance learning courses in 2004. In fall 2005, there were 923 students enrolled in distance learning courses. Institutionally administered financial aid is available to distance learners.

Services Distance learners have accessibility to bookstore, campus computer network, e-mail services, library services.

Contact Dr. Nancy J. Knous, Coordinator of Distance Learning, Northwestern Oklahoma State University, 709 Oklahoma Boulevard, Alva, OK 73717. Telephone: 580-327-8443. Fax: 580-327-8431. E-mail: njknous@nwosu.edu.

DEGREES AND AWARDS

Programs offered do not lead to a degree or other formal award.

COURSE SUBJECT AREAS OFFERED OUTSIDE OF DEGREE PROGRAMS

Undergraduate—accounting and computer science; accounting and related services; business administration, management and operations; business/commerce; business/corporate communications; criminal justice and corrections; curriculum and instruction; education; English; English literature (British and Commonwealth); public relations, advertising, and applied communication related; social psychology; sociology.

Graduate—bilingual, multilingual, and multicultural education; business administration, management and operations; educational administration and supervision; education related.

NORTHWESTERN STATE UNIVERSITY OF LOUISIANA
Natchitoches, Louisiana
http://www.nsula.edu/ece

Northwestern State University of Louisiana was founded in 1884. It is accredited by Southern Association of Colleges and Schools. It first offered distance learning courses in 1997. In fall 2005, there were 3,915 students enrolled in distance learning courses. Institutionally administered financial aid is available to distance learners.

Services Distance learners have accessibility to academic advising, bookstore, campus computer network, career placement assistance, e-mail services, library services, tutoring.

Contact Mrs. Darlene Williams, Director of Electronic and Continuing Education, Northwestern State University of Louisiana, Electronic and Continuing Education, 201 Williamson Hall, Natchitoches, LA 71497. Telephone: 318-357-6355. Fax: 318-357-5573. E-mail: darlene@nsula.edu.

DEGREES AND AWARDS
AA Criminal Justice
AGS General Studies
BA Criminal Justice
BS Psychology; RT to BSRT
BSN Nursing–RN to BSN
Certification School Media Specialist
Advanced Graduate Diploma Educational Leadership and Instruction
MA Adult Education; Art
MAE Educational Technology
MSE Health and Human Performance

COURSE SUBJECT AREAS OFFERED OUTSIDE OF DEGREE PROGRAMS
Undergraduate—accounting and related services; biological and physical sciences; business administration, management and operations; business, management, and marketing related; chemistry; communication and journalism related; computer and information sciences; computer software and media applications; creative writing; criminal justice and corrections; economics; educational/instructional media design; education related; education (specific levels and methods); English; English composition; family and consumer sciences/human sciences; finance and financial management services; fine and studio art; health and physical education/fitness; history; journalism; library science related; marketing; mathematics; nursing; physical sciences; psychology; social work; technical and business writing; zoology/animal biology.
Graduate—educational administration and supervision; educational assessment, evaluation, and research; educational/instructional media design; educational psychology; education related; psychology; special education.

NORTHWESTERN UNIVERSITY
Evanston, Illinois
Communication Systems Strategy and Management Program
http://www.communication.northwestern.edu/mscstrategy

Northwestern University was founded in 1851. It is accredited by North Central Association of Colleges and Schools. It first offered distance learning courses in 2004. In fall 2005, there were 13 students enrolled in distance learning courses. Institutionally administered financial aid is available to distance learners.

Services Distance learners have accessibility to academic advising, bookstore, campus computer network, career placement assistance, e-mail services, library services.

Contact Ms. Donna J. Weirich, Director, Northwestern University, Frances Searle Building, 2240 Campus Drive, 2-118, Evanston, IL 60208. Telephone: 847-491-3848. Fax: 847-467-1036. E-mail: dweirich@northwestern.edu.

DEGREES AND AWARDS
MSC Business Strategy
See full description on page 416.

NORTHWEST MISSOURI STATE UNIVERSITY
Maryville, Missouri
Center for Information Technology in Education
http://www.NorthwestOnline.org

Northwest Missouri State University was founded in 1905. It is accredited by North Central Association of Colleges and Schools. It first offered distance learning courses in 1999. In fall 2005, there were 950 students enrolled in distance learning courses. Institutionally administered financial aid is available to distance learners.

Services Distance learners have accessibility to academic advising, bookstore, campus computer network, career placement assistance, e-mail services, library services.

Contact Dr. Roger Von Holzen, Director of Center for Information Technology in Education, Northwest Missouri State University, OL 246, Maryville, MO 64468. Telephone: 660-562-1532. Fax: 660-562-1049. E-mail: rvh@nwmissouri.edu.

DEGREES AND AWARDS
BS Accounting; Business Management; Computer Science; Management Information Systems; Office Information Systems
MS Applied Computer Science; Geographic Information Science
MSE Special Education; Teaching–Instructional Technology

COURSE SUBJECT AREAS OFFERED OUTSIDE OF DEGREE PROGRAMS
Undergraduate—communication and media; computer and information sciences; dramatic/theater arts and stagecraft; geography and cartography; history; linguistic, comparative, and related language studies; mathematics; music; philosophy; political science and government; psychology.
Graduate—computer and information sciences; computer and information sciences and support services related; computer/information technology administration and management; education; educational/instructional media design; geography and cartography; special education.
Non-credit—educational/instructional media design; geography and cartography.

NORTHWOOD UNIVERSITY
Midland, Michigan
University College
http://www.northwoodonline.org

Northwood University was founded in 1959. It is accredited by North Central Association of Colleges and Schools. It first offered distance learning courses in 1965. In fall 2005, there were 300 students enrolled in distance learning courses. Institutionally administered financial aid is available to distance learners.

Services Distance learners have accessibility to academic advising, bookstore, campus computer network, career placement assistance, e-mail services, library services, tutoring.

Contact Marcella A. Matzke, Program Center Manager, Northwood University, 4000 Whiting Drive, Midland, MI 48640. Telephone: 800-445-5873. Fax: 989-837-4457. E-mail: matzke@northwood.edu.

DEGREES AND AWARDS
Programs offered do not lead to a degree or other formal award.

COURSE SUBJECT AREAS OFFERED OUTSIDE OF DEGREE PROGRAMS
Undergraduate—business, management, and marketing related.

NOVA SCOTIA AGRICULTURAL COLLEGE
Truro, Nova Scotia, Canada
Center for Continuing and Distance Education
http://www.nsac.ns.ca

Nova Scotia Agricultural College was founded in 1905. It is provincially chartered. It first offered distance learning courses in 1996. In fall 2005, there were 60 students enrolled in distance learning courses. Institutionally administered financial aid is available to distance learners.

Services Distance learners have accessibility to academic advising, bookstore, e-mail services, library services.

Contact Mrs. Pamela Doyle, Administrative Assistant, Nova Scotia Agricultural College, PO Box 550, 23 Sheep Hill Lane, Truro, NS B2N 5E3, Canada. Telephone: 902-893-6666. Fax: 902-895-5528. E-mail: cde@nsac.ca.

DEGREES AND AWARDS

Programs offered do not lead to a degree or other formal award.

COURSE SUBJECT AREAS OFFERED OUTSIDE OF DEGREE PROGRAMS

Undergraduate—agricultural business and management; agricultural production; agriculture; animal sciences; plant sciences.

Non-credit—agriculture; animal sciences; plant sciences.

NOVA SOUTHEASTERN UNIVERSITY

Fort Lauderdale, Florida

Graduate School of Computer and Information Sciences

http://www.scis.nova.edu/

Nova Southeastern University was founded in 1964. It is accredited by Southern Association of Colleges and Schools. It first offered distance learning courses in 1983. In fall 2005, there were 1,200 students enrolled in distance learning courses. Institutionally administered financial aid is available to distance learners.

Services Distance learners have accessibility to academic advising, bookstore, campus computer network, career placement assistance, e-mail services, library services.

Contact Program Counselor, Nova Southeastern University, Recruitment Office, Carl DeSantis Building, 4th Floor, 3301 College Avenue, Fort Lauderdale, FL 33314. Telephone: 800-986-2247. Fax: 954-262-3915. E-mail: scisinfo@nova.edu.

DEGREES AND AWARDS

MS Computer Information Systems; Computer Science; Computing Technology in Education; Information Security; Management Information Systems

PhD Computer Information Systems; Computer Science; Computing Technology in Education; Information Systems

COURSE SUBJECT AREAS OFFERED OUTSIDE OF DEGREE PROGRAMS

Graduate—computer and information sciences; computer and information sciences and support services related; computer/information technology administration and management; computer programming; computer science; computer software and media applications; computer systems analysis; computer systems networking and telecommunications; educational/instructional media design; education related; management information systems; medical illustration and informatics; systems science and theory; technology education/industrial arts.

See full description on page 418.

ODESSA COLLEGE

Odessa, Texas

Division of Distance Education

http://www.odessa.edu

Odessa College was founded in 1946. It is accredited by Southern Association of Colleges and Schools. It first offered distance learning courses in 1986. In fall 2005, there were 2,673 students enrolled in distance learning courses. Institutionally administered financial aid is available to distance learners.

Services Distance learners have accessibility to academic advising, bookstore, campus computer network, career placement assistance, e-mail services, library services.

Contact Wilma Chastain, Director of Distance Learning, Odessa College, 201 West University, Odessa, TX 79764. Telephone: 432-335-6317. Fax: 432-335-6667. E-mail: wchastain@odessa.edu.

DEGREES AND AWARDS

ASAST Occupational Safety and Health Technology

COURSE SUBJECT AREAS OFFERED OUTSIDE OF DEGREE PROGRAMS

Undergraduate—accounting and related services; biology; business/commerce; business operations support and assistant services; computer and information sciences; developmental and child psychology; English composition; environmental control technologies; environmental/environmental health engineering; mathematics; social psychology; sociology.

Non-credit—business administration, management and operations; business, management, and marketing related; computer software and media applications; creative writing; linguistic, comparative, and related language studies; sales, merchandising, and related marketing operations (specialized).

OHIO COLLEGE OF MASSOTHERAPY

Akron, Ohio

Ohio College of Massotherapy was founded in 1973. It is accredited by Accrediting Commission of Career Schools and Colleges of Technology. It first offered distance learning courses in 2001. In fall 2005, there were 75 students enrolled in distance learning courses. Institutionally administered financial aid is available to distance learners.

Services Distance learners have accessibility to academic advising, bookstore, career placement assistance, tutoring.

Contact Admissions, Ohio College of Massotherapy, 225 Heritage Woods Drive, Akron, OH 44321. Telephone: 888-888-4325. E-mail: admissions@ocm.edu.

DEGREES AND AWARDS

AAS Massage Therapy–Distance Education

THE OHIO STATE UNIVERSITY

Columbus, Ohio

Technology Enhanced Learning and Research (TELR)

http://telr.ohio-state.edu

The Ohio State University was founded in 1870. It is accredited by North Central Association of Colleges and Schools. It first offered distance learning courses in 1995. In fall 2005, there were 3,500 students enrolled in distance learning courses. Institutionally administered financial aid is available to distance learners.

Services Distance learners have accessibility to academic advising, bookstore, campus computer network, e-mail services, library services, tutoring.

Contact Prof. Susan E. Metros, Deputy CIO and Executive Director for e-Learning, The Ohio State University, Technology Enhanced Learning and Research, 1971 Neil Avenue, BSE 480, Columbus, OH 43210. Telephone: 614-688-8482. Fax: 614-292-7081. E-mail: metros.1@osu.edu.

DEGREES AND AWARDS

EMBA Business Administration

PharmD NonTraditional PharmD

COURSE SUBJECT AREAS OFFERED OUTSIDE OF DEGREE PROGRAMS

Undergraduate—business/commerce; engineering related; family and consumer economics; forestry; linguistic, comparative, and related language studies; plant sciences; political science and government; social work; visual and performing arts related.

Graduate—business administration, management and operations; educational administration and supervision; education related; engineering related; mechanical engineering; nuclear engineering; nursing; plant sciences; social work.

Non-credit—gerontology; mental and social health services and allied professions; special education.

OKLAHOMA STATE UNIVERSITY
Stillwater, Oklahoma
Distance Learning
http://ueied.ue.okstate.edu/dl/index.htm

Oklahoma State University was founded in 1890. It is accredited by North Central Association of Colleges and Schools. It first offered distance learning courses in 1945. In fall 2005, there were 2,000 students enrolled in distance learning courses. Institutionally administered financial aid is available to distance learners.

Services Distance learners have accessibility to academic advising, bookstore, campus computer network, library services.

Contact Cecilia Boardman, Senior Office Assistant, Oklahoma State University, 309 Wes Watkins Center, Stillwater, OK 74078. Telephone: 405-744-6390. Fax: 405-744-3420. E-mail: ics-inf@okstate.edu.

DEGREES AND AWARDS

Programs offered do not lead to a degree or other formal award.

COURSE SUBJECT AREAS OFFERED OUTSIDE OF DEGREE PROGRAMS

Undergraduate—accounting and related services; American literature (United States and Canadian); animal sciences; anthropology; applied horticulture/horticultural business services; business administration, management and operations; business/corporate communications; communication disorders sciences and services; counseling psychology; creative writing; economics; education related; electrical and electronic engineering technologies; engineering technologies related; English composition; English literature (British and Commonwealth); finance and financial management services; fire protection; foods, nutrition, and related services; geography and cartography; geological and earth sciences/geosciences; health and physical education/fitness; history; journalism; languages (Germanic); languages (Romance languages); legal studies (non-professional general, undergraduate); management information systems; marketing; mathematics and statistics related; music; political science and government; psychology; sales, merchandising, and related marketing operations (general); sociology; statistics; technical and business writing.

Non-credit—fire protection.

OLD DOMINION UNIVERSITY
Norfolk, Virginia
Office of Distance Learning and Extended Education
http://www.dl.odu.edu

Old Dominion University was founded in 1930. It is accredited by Southern Association of Colleges and Schools. It first offered distance learning courses in 1984. In fall 2005, there were 5,571 students enrolled in distance learning courses. Institutionally administered financial aid is available to distance learners.

Services Distance learners have accessibility to academic advising, bookstore, campus computer network, career placement assistance, e-mail services, library services.

Contact Mrs. Anita Wiggins Bailey, Enrollment Services Specialist, Old Dominion University, Gornto TELETECHNET Center, Norfolk, VA 23529. Telephone: 800-968-2638. Fax: 757-683-5492. E-mail: awiggins@odu.edu.

DEGREES AND AWARDS

BA Criminal Justice
BHS Health Sciences
BS Computer Science; Criminal Justice; Education–Teacher Preparation; Human Services Counseling; Occupational and Technical Studies
BSBA Accounting, Finance, Information Systems, Marketing; Management
BSET Civil Engineering Technology; Electrical Engineering Technology; Engineering Technology, general; Mechanical Engineering Technology
BSN Nursing
MEM Engineering Management
MS Community Health; Education–Pre-K through 6; Occupational and Technical Studies; Special Education
MSN Nursing–Nurse Leader and Nurse Educator options

COURSE SUBJECT AREAS OFFERED OUTSIDE OF DEGREE PROGRAMS

Undergraduate—accounting and related services; business/corporate communications; business/managerial economics; communication and media; community health services; computer and information sciences; computer science; computer systems networking and telecommunications; criminal justice and corrections; education related; engineering technologies related; finance and financial management services; industrial and organizational psychology; journalism; management information systems; management sciences and quantitative methods; marketing; nursing; philosophy; social psychology; sociology.

Graduate—accounting and related services; aerospace, aeronautical and astronautical engineering; education related; environmental/environmental health engineering; finance and financial management services; management information systems; marketing; mechanical engineering; nursing.

ORAL ROBERTS UNIVERSITY
Tulsa, Oklahoma
http://www.oru.edu/

Oral Roberts University was founded in 1963. It is accredited by North Central Association of Colleges and Schools. It first offered distance learning courses in 1975. In fall 2005, there were 117 students enrolled in distance learning courses. Institutionally administered financial aid is available to distance learners.

Services Distance learners have accessibility to academic advising, bookstore, campus computer network, career placement assistance, e-mail services, library services, tutoring.

Contact Mr. Gary Brougher, SLLE Representative, Oral Roberts University, School of LifeLong Education, 7777 South Lewis Avenue, Tulsa, OK 74171. Telephone: 800-643-7976. Fax: 918-495-6055. E-mail: gbrougher@oru.edu.

DEGREES AND AWARDS

BS Business Administration; Christian Care and Counseling; Church Ministries; Elementary Education with certification; Liberal Studies
MA Practical Theology
MAE Christian School Administration; Christian School Curriculum; Christian School Postsecondary Administration; Early Childhood Education; Public School Administration; Teaching English as a Second Language (TESL); Teaching with certification
MAM Nonprofit Management
MBA Business Administration
MDiv Divinity
MM Management–Master of Management
DMin Ministry
EdD Christian School Administration (PK–12); Education–Postsecondary School Administration; Public School Administration

COURSE SUBJECT AREAS OFFERED OUTSIDE OF DEGREE PROGRAMS

Undergraduate—biblical studies; biology; English; history; liberal arts and sciences, general studies and humanities; mathematics; political science and government.

Non-credit—biblical studies; theological and ministerial studies.

ORANGE COAST COLLEGE
Costa Mesa, California
http://www.orangecoastcollege.com

Orange Coast College was founded in 1947. It is accredited by Western Association of Schools and Colleges. It first offered distance learning courses in 1998. In fall 2005, there were 1,814 students enrolled in distance learning courses. Institutionally administered financial aid is available to distance learners.

Services Distance learners have accessibility to bookstore, library services.

Contact Dr. Nancy Kidder, Administrative Dean of Admissions and Records and International Programs, Orange Coast College, 2701 Fairview Road, Costa Mesa, CA 92626. Telephone: 714-432-0202. E-mail: nkidder@mail.occ.cccd.edu.

DEGREES AND AWARDS

Programs offered do not lead to a degree or other formal award.

COURSE SUBJECT AREAS OFFERED OUTSIDE OF DEGREE PROGRAMS

Undergraduate—accounting and related services; allied health and medical assisting services; anthropology; apparel and textiles; architecture; biology; business, management, and marketing related; business operations support and assistant services; computer and information sciences; computer/information technology administration and management; computer programming; computer software and media applications; construction engineering technology; dance; drafting/design engineering technologies; electrical/electronics maintenance and repair technology; electromechanical and instrumentation and maintenance technologies; English composition; food science and technology; foods, nutrition, and related services; health and medical administrative services; health professions related; heating, air conditioning, ventilation and refrigeration maintenance technology; hospitality administration; human development, family studies, and related services; music; real estate; sales, merchandising, and related marketing operations (specialized).

OREGON INSTITUTE OF TECHNOLOGY
Klamath Falls, Oregon
http://www.oit.edu/dist

Oregon Institute of Technology was founded in 1947. It is accredited by Northwest Commission on Colleges and Universities. It first offered distance learning courses in 1997. In fall 2005, there were 624 students enrolled in distance learning courses. Institutionally administered financial aid is available to distance learners.

Services Distance learners have accessibility to academic advising, bookstore, campus computer network, career placement assistance, e-mail services, library services.

Contact Beth Murphy, Director, Distance Education, Oregon Institute of Technology, 3201 Campus Drive, Klamath Falls, OR 97601. Telephone: 541-885-1141. Fax: 541-885-1139. E-mail: beth.murphy@oit.edu.

DEGREES AND AWARDS

BS Dental Hygiene–Degree Completion in Dental Hygiene; Information Technology Online; Radiological Science–Degree Completion in Radiological Science; Respiratory Care; Ultrasound–degree completion in Ultrasound with option in Echocardiography; Ultrasound–degree completion in Ultrasound with option in Vascular Technology

COURSE SUBJECT AREAS OFFERED OUTSIDE OF DEGREE PROGRAMS

Undergraduate—accounting and related services; allied health diagnostic, intervention, and treatment professions; anthropology; business administration, management and operations; business/commerce; computer and information sciences; computer/information technology administration and management; dental support services and allied professions; economics; engineering/industrial management; human development, family studies, and related services; management information systems; mathematics; psychology; social sciences; technical and business writing.

OREGON STATE UNIVERSITY
Corvallis, Oregon
Extended Campus
http://ecampus.oregonstate.edu

Oregon State University was founded in 1868. It is accredited by Northwest Commission on Colleges and Universities. It first offered distance learning courses in 1986. In fall 2005, there were 2,324 students enrolled in distance learning courses. Institutionally administered financial aid is available to distance learners.

Services Distance learners have accessibility to academic advising, bookstore, campus computer network, career placement assistance, e-mail services, library services, tutoring.

Contact Ecampus Student Services Center, Oregon State University, OSU Extended Campus, 4943 The Valley Library, Corvallis, OR 97331-4504. Telephone: 800-667-1465. Fax: 541-737-2734. E-mail: ecampus @oregonstate.edu.

DEGREES AND AWARDS

BA Liberal Studies
BS Agriculture, general; Environmental Sciences; Liberal Studies; Natural Resources
Certificate Geographic Information Sciences
Endorsement ESOL/Bilingual Education
License Continuing Teaching Licensure
Graduate Certificate Health Management and Policy; Sustainable Natural Resources; Teaching English as a Second Language
MAT Early Childhood/Elementary Education
MEd Adult Education; Education
MHP Radiation Health Physics
MS Radiation Health Physics
EdD Concentration in Community College Leadership
PhD Concentration in Community College Leadership; Radiation Health Physics

COURSE SUBJECT AREAS OFFERED OUTSIDE OF DEGREE PROGRAMS

Undergraduate—agricultural business and management; agriculture; agriculture and agriculture operations related; American literature (United States and Canadian); anthropology; area, ethnic, cultural, and gender studies related; atmospheric sciences and meteorology; botany/plant biology; business/commerce; business/corporate communications; chemistry; communication and media; creative writing; ecology, evolution, and population biology; economics; education; education related; English; English composition; ethnic, cultural minority, and gender studies; fishing and fisheries sciences and management; forestry; geological and earth sciences/geosciences; health and medical administrative services; health services/allied health/health sciences; history; liberal arts and sciences, general studies and humanities; mathematics and statistics related; natural resources and conservation related; natural resources conservation and research; natural resources management and policy; philosophy; philosophy and religious studies related; plant sciences; political science and government; psychology; sales, merchandising, and related marketing operations (general); science, technology and society; social sciences related; sociology; soil sciences; statistics; technical and business writing; wildlife and wildlands science and management.

Graduate—education; educational administration and supervision; education related; education (specific levels and methods); education (specific subject areas); English as a second/foreign language (teaching); English as a second language; environmental/environmental health engineering; foods, nutrition, and related services; geography and cartography; geological and earth sciences/geosciences; health and medical administrative services; health professions related; natural resources conservation and research; natural resources management and policy; nuclear and industrial radiologic technologies; public health.

Non-credit—business, management, and marketing related; communication and media; computer software and media applications; English; English as a second language; family and consumer economics; film/video and photographic arts; fine and studio art; health and medical administrative services; human resources management; languages (Romance languages); linguistic, comparative, and related language studies; pharmacy, pharmaceutical sciences, and administration; psychology; sales, merchandising, and related marketing operations (specialized).

See full description on page 420.

OUACHITA TECHNICAL COLLEGE
Malvern, Arkansas
http://www.otcweb.edu

Ouachita Technical College was founded in 1972. It is accredited by North Central Association of Colleges and Schools. It first offered distance learning courses in 1998. In fall 2005, there were 269 students enrolled in distance learning courses. Institutionally administered financial aid is available to distance learners.

Services Distance learners have accessibility to academic advising, bookstore, campus computer network, career placement assistance, e-mail services, library services, tutoring.

Contact Mr. Mark Burris, Distance Learning Coordinator, Ouachita Technical College, One College Circle, Malvern, AR 72104. Telephone: 501-337-5000 Ext. 1103. Fax: 501-337-9382. E-mail: mburris@otcweb.edu.

DEGREES AND AWARDS

AA Education, general
AAS Criminal Justice

COURSE SUBJECT AREAS OFFERED OUTSIDE OF DEGREE PROGRAMS

Undergraduate—behavioral sciences; biological and physical sciences; biology; business administration, management and operations; computer and information sciences; computer software and media applications; computer systems networking and telecommunications; criminal justice and corrections; English composition; history; human resources management; liberal arts and sciences, general studies and humanities; mathematics; philosophy; political science and government; psychology; social sciences; sociology.

OXNARD COLLEGE
Oxnard, California
http://www.oxnardcollege.edu

Oxnard College was founded in 1975. It is accredited by Western Association of Schools and Colleges. It first offered distance learning courses in 1997. In fall 2005, there were 98 students enrolled in distance learning courses. Institutionally administered financial aid is available to distance learners.

Services Distance learners have accessibility to academic advising, bookstore, e-mail services, library services.

Contact Mr. Robert Tholl, Dean, Liberal Studies, Oxnard College, 4000 South Rose Avenue, Oxnard, CA 93033. Telephone: 805-986-5804. Fax: 805-986-5927. E-mail: rtholl@vcccd.edu.

DEGREES AND AWARDS

Programs offered do not lead to a degree or other formal award.

COURSE SUBJECT AREAS OFFERED OUTSIDE OF DEGREE PROGRAMS

Undergraduate—accounting and related services; American literature (United States and Canadian); anthropology; applied mathematics; area, ethnic, cultural, and gender studies related; area studies; astronomy and astrophysics; bilingual, multilingual, and multicultural education; biological and biomedical sciences related; biology; botany/plant biology; business administration, management and operations; business/commerce; business/corporate communications; business, management, and marketing related; business operations support and assistant services; chemistry; clinical psychology; communication and media; computer and information sciences; computer engineering; computer/information technology administration and management; computer programming; computer science; computer software and media applications; computer systems analysis; computer systems networking and telecommunications; creative writing; criminal justice and corrections; culinary arts and related services; data entry/microcomputer applications; dental support services and allied professions; developmental and child psychology; dramatic/theater arts and stagecraft; economics; education; English; English as a second language; English composition; environmental control technologies; film/video and photographic arts; fine and studio art; fire protection; geological and earth sciences/geosciences; heating, air conditioning, ventilation and refrigeration maintenance technology; history; human development, family studies, and related services; human services; international business; languages (foreign languages related); legal studies (non-professional general, undergraduate); library science related; marketing; mathematics; mechanic and repair technologies related; microbiological sciences and immunology; music; philosophy; physical sciences; physics; political science and government; psychology; public health; public relations, advertising, and applied communication related; radio, television, and digital communication; sales, merchandising, and related marketing operations (specialized); social psychology; sociology; special education; speech and rhetoric; taxation; technical and business writing.

OZARKA COLLEGE
Melbourne, Arkansas
http://www.ozarka.edu

Ozarka College was founded in 1973. It is accredited by North Central Association of Colleges and Schools. It first offered distance learning courses in 1999. In fall 2005, there were 643 students enrolled in distance learning courses. Institutionally administered financial aid is available to distance learners.

Services Distance learners have accessibility to academic advising, campus computer network, e-mail services, library services.

Contact Mr. Ron Helm, Office of Admissions, Ozarka College, 218 College Drive, Melbourne, AR 72556. Telephone: 870-368-7371 Ext. 2028. Fax: 870-368-4733. E-mail: admissions@ozarka.edu.

DEGREES AND AWARDS

Programs offered do not lead to a degree or other formal award.

COURSE SUBJECT AREAS OFFERED OUTSIDE OF DEGREE PROGRAMS

Undergraduate—allied health and medical assisting services; business administration, management and operations; business operations support and assistant services; computer and information sciences; criminal justice and corrections; culinary arts and related services; data entry/microcomputer applications; education (specific subject areas); human development, family studies, and related services; management information systems; nursing.

Non-credit—business/commerce; computer and information sciences; computer/information technology administration and management; computer programming; computer systems analysis; computer systems networking and telecommunications; creative writing.

OZARK CHRISTIAN COLLEGE
Joplin, Missouri

Ozark Christian College was founded in 1942. It is accredited by Association for Biblical Higher Education. Institutionally administered financial aid is available to distance learners.

Services Distance learners have accessibility to academic advising, bookstore.

Contact Mrs. Amy Hunt, Administrative Assistant, Admissions, Ozark Christian College, 1111 North Main, Joplin, MO 64801. Telephone: 417-624-2518 Ext. 2022. Fax: 417-624-0090. E-mail: hunt.amy@occ.edu.

DEGREES AND AWARDS

Programs offered do not lead to a degree or other formal award.

COURSE SUBJECT AREAS OFFERED OUTSIDE OF DEGREE PROGRAMS

Undergraduate—biblical and other theological languages and literatures; biblical studies; history; intercultural/multicultural and diversity studies; philosophy and religious studies related; religious education; religious studies; theological and ministerial studies; theology and religious vocations related.

OZARKS TECHNICAL COMMUNITY COLLEGE
Springfield, Missouri
http://www.otc.cc.mo.us/

Ozarks Technical Community College was founded in 1990. It is accredited by North Central Association of Colleges and Schools. It first offered distance learning courses in 2000. In fall 2005, there were 2,000 students enrolled in distance learning courses. Institutionally administered financial aid is available to distance learners.

Services Distance learners have accessibility to academic advising, bookstore, career placement assistance, e-mail services, library services, tutoring.

Contact Mr. Carleton DeWitt Salley, Jr., Director of Online Teaching and Learning, Ozarks Technical Community College, 1001 East Chestnut Expressway, Springfield, MO 65802. Telephone: 417-447-8199. Fax: 417-447-8153. E-mail: salleyc@otc.edu.

DEGREES AND AWARDS

Programs offered do not lead to a degree or other formal award.

COURSE SUBJECT AREAS OFFERED OUTSIDE OF DEGREE PROGRAMS

Undergraduate—accounting and computer science; allied health and medical assisting services; anthropology; area, ethnic, cultural, and gender studies related; behavioral sciences; biochemistry, biophysics and molecular biology; biological and physical sciences; business administration, management and operations; business/commerce; business/corporate communications; business, management, and marketing related; cell biology and anatomical sciences; communication and media; computer and information sciences; creative writing; criminal justice and corrections; criminology; culinary arts and related services; data processing; developmental and child psychology; dramatic/theater arts and stagecraft; economics; education; educational/instructional media design; educational psychology; education related; English; English composition; family and consumer economics; foods, nutrition, and related services; geography and cartography; history; human resources management; languages (Germanic); liberal arts and sciences, general studies and humanities; mathematics; music; philosophy; philosophy and religious studies related; political science and government; psychology; religious studies; school psychology; social psychology; social sciences; sociology; speech and rhetoric; technical and business writing; technology education/industrial arts; theology and religious vocations related; urban studies/affairs; visual and performing arts related; work and family studies.

PACE UNIVERSITY

New York, New York

Online Pace

http://www.online.pace.edu

Pace University was founded in 1906. It is accredited by Middle States Association of Colleges and Schools. It first offered distance learning courses in 1997. In fall 2005, there were 2,000 students enrolled in distance learning courses. Institutionally administered financial aid is available to distance learners.

Services Distance learners have accessibility to academic advising, bookstore, campus computer network, career placement assistance, e-mail services, library services, tutoring.

Contact Ms. Christine Moloughney, Coordinator of Online Support Services, Pace University, One Pace Plaza, New York, NY 10038. Telephone: 212-346-1471. E-mail: cmoloughney@pace.edu.

DEGREES AND AWARDS

AS Applied Information Technology, Telecommunications Degree
BS Communication Studies–Professional Communication Studies; Professional Technology Studies; Telecommunications
Specialized diploma Computing–Doctor of Professional Studies in Computing
Graduate Certificate Business Aspects of Publishing; Internet Technologies; Internet Technology; Telecommunications
MBA Business Administration–e.MBA
MS Internet Technology for E-Commerce; Publishing

COURSE SUBJECT AREAS OFFERED OUTSIDE OF DEGREE PROGRAMS

Undergraduate—accounting and related services; anthropology; biology; business administration, management and operations; business/commerce; communication and media; computer and information sciences and support services related; computer programming; computer science; computer software and media applications; computer systems networking and telecommunications; criminal justice and corrections; criminology; education; education (specific subject areas); English; finance and financial management services; fine and studio art; history; information science/studies; international business; legal studies (non-professional general, undergraduate); linguistic, comparative, and related language studies; marketing; mathematics; mathematics and statistics related; nursing; physical sciences; political science and government; psychology; science, technology and society; sociology; statistics; visual and performing arts.

Graduate—bilingual, multilingual, and multicultural education; business administration, management and operations; business/commerce; computer and information sciences; computer and information sciences and support services related; computer/information technology administration and management; computer programming; computer software and media applications; computer systems analysis; computer systems networking and telecommunications; education; educational administration and supervision; educational/instructional media design; education related; information science/studies; marketing; nursing; public administration; publishing.

Non-credit—business/commerce; computer and information sciences; education; liberal arts and sciences, general studies and humanities; nursing; personal and culinary services related.

PACIFIC GRADUATE SCHOOL OF PSYCHOLOGY

Palo Alto, California

Master's Degree (M.S.) in Psychology

http://www.pgsp.edu/distance.htm

Pacific Graduate School of Psychology was founded in 1975. It is accredited by Western Association of Schools and Colleges. It first offered distance learning courses in 1999. In fall 2005, there were 26 students enrolled in distance learning courses. Institutionally administered financial aid is available to distance learners.

Services Distance learners have accessibility to academic advising, e-mail services, library services.

Contact Ms. Elizabeth Hilt, Vice President of Enrollment Management, Pacific Graduate School of Psychology, 935 East Meadow Drive, Palo Alto, CA 94303. Telephone: 800-818-6136. Fax: 650-493-6147. E-mail: ehit@pgsp.edu.

DEGREES AND AWARDS

MS Psychology

COURSE SUBJECT AREAS OFFERED OUTSIDE OF DEGREE PROGRAMS

Graduate—psychology.

See full description on page 422.

PACIFIC UNION COLLEGE

Angwin, California

http://www.puc.edu/

Pacific Union College was founded in 1882. It is accredited by Western Association of Schools and Colleges. It first offered distance learning courses in 2001. In fall 2005, there were 56 students enrolled in distance learning courses. Institutionally administered financial aid is available to distance learners.

Services Distance learners have accessibility to academic advising, bookstore, campus computer network, e-mail services, library services, tutoring.

Contact Nancy Lecourt, PhD, Academic Dean, Pacific Union College, One Angwin Avenue, Angwin, CA 94508. Telephone: 707-965-6234. E-mail: nlecourt@puc.edu.

DEGREES AND AWARDS

Programs offered do not lead to a degree or other formal award.

COURSE SUBJECT AREAS OFFERED OUTSIDE OF DEGREE PROGRAMS

Undergraduate—chemistry; computer and information sciences; mathematics; music; nursing; religious studies.

PALM BEACH COMMUNITY COLLEGE

Lake Worth, Florida

http://www.pbcc.edu/dl

Palm Beach Community College was founded in 1933. It is accredited by Southern Association of Colleges and Schools. It first offered distance learning courses in 1997. In fall 2005, there were 5,500 students enrolled in distance learning courses. Institutionally administered financial aid is available to distance learners.

Services Distance learners have accessibility to academic advising, bookstore, career placement assistance, library services.

Contact Ms. Anne Guiler, Distance Learning Coordinator, Palm Beach Community College, 3000 Saint Lucie Avenue, Boca Raton, FL 33431. Telephone: 561-868-4088. E-mail: guilera@pbcc.edu.

DEGREES AND AWARDS

AA General Studies

COURSE SUBJECT AREAS OFFERED OUTSIDE OF DEGREE PROGRAMS

Undergraduate—accounting and related services; anthropology; astronomy and astrophysics; biological and physical sciences; business/commerce; chemistry; communication and media; computer and information sciences; developmental and child psychology; economics; education; electrical and electronic engineering technologies.

PALOMAR COLLEGE
San Marcos, California
Educational Television
http://www.palomar.edu

Palomar College was founded in 1946. It is accredited by Western Association of Schools and Colleges. It first offered distance learning courses in 1975. In fall 2005, there were 4,756 students enrolled in distance learning courses. Institutionally administered financial aid is available to distance learners.

Services Distance learners have accessibility to academic advising, bookstore, campus computer network, career placement assistance, e-mail services, library services, tutoring.

Contact Mrs. Michelle Grace, Educational TV Senior Office Specialist, Palomar College, 1140 West Mission Road, San Marcos, CA 92069. Telephone: 760-744-1150 Ext. 2431. Fax: 760-761-3519. E-mail: mgrace@palomar.edu.

DEGREES AND AWARDS

Programs offered do not lead to a degree or other formal award.

COURSE SUBJECT AREAS OFFERED OUTSIDE OF DEGREE PROGRAMS

Undergraduate—accounting and related services; American Sign Language (ASL); anthropology; area, ethnic, cultural, and gender studies related; behavioral sciences; bilingual, multilingual, and multicultural education; biology; botany/plant biology; business administration, management and operations; business/commerce; business, management, and marketing related; business operations support and assistant services; cell biology and anatomical sciences; chemistry; communication and journalism related; communication and media; computer and information sciences; computer and information sciences and support services related; computer programming; computer science; computer software and media applications; counseling psychology; criminal justice and corrections; data entry/microcomputer applications; developmental and child psychology; economics; educational/instructional media design; English; English composition; ethnic, cultural minority, and gender studies; family and consumer economics; family and consumer sciences/human sciences; family and consumer sciences/human sciences related; finance and financial management services; fine and studio art; fire protection; foods, nutrition, and related services; geological and earth sciences/geosciences; graphic communications; health and physical education/fitness; history; human development, family studies, and related services; information science/studies; international business; journalism; languages (American Indian/Native American); languages (Romance languages); legal professions and studies related; legal research and advanced professional studies; legal studies (non-professional general, undergraduate); legal support services; liberal arts and sciences, general studies and humanities; library assistant; library science; library science related; marketing; music; natural sciences; nutrition sciences; philosophy; philosophy and religious studies related; psychology; psychology related; real estate; sales, merchandising, and related marketing operations (general); social psychology; social sciences; sociology; statistics.

PARKLAND COLLEGE
Champaign, Illinois
Distance Education
http://online.parkland.edu

Parkland College was founded in 1967. It is accredited by North Central Association of Colleges and Schools. It first offered distance learning courses in 1988. In fall 2005, there were 1,639 students enrolled in distance learning courses. Institutionally administered financial aid is available to distance learners.

Services Distance learners have accessibility to academic advising, bookstore, campus computer network, career placement assistance, e-mail services, library services, tutoring.

Contact Haiti Eastin, Online Student Support Coordinator, Parkland College, 2400 West Bradley Avenue, Champaign, IL 61821. Telephone: 217-353-2342. E-mail: heastin@parkland.edu.

DEGREES AND AWARDS

AA Early Childhood Education, Elementary Education, Secondary Education, Special Education, and Mass Communication (Integrated) concentrations; History, Liberal Arts and Sciences, Mass Communications (Advertising/Public Relations; Journalism), Political Science, and Psychology concentrations

AAS Business Management

AGS General Studies

AS Business Administration and Business Education concentrations

Certificate Independent Business Management

COURSE SUBJECT AREAS OFFERED OUTSIDE OF DEGREE PROGRAMS

Undergraduate—accounting and related services; agricultural business and management; anthropology; astronomy and astrophysics; biology; cell biology and anatomical sciences; chemistry; communication and media; computer and information sciences; computer programming; computer software and media applications; developmental and child psychology; dramatic/theater arts and stagecraft; economics; English composition; fine and studio art; health and physical education/fitness; history; journalism; legal studies (non-professional general, undergraduate); marketing; mathematics and statistics related; music; philosophy; physics; political science and government; psychology; social psychology; social sciences related; sociology; speech and rhetoric; statistics.

PARK UNIVERSITY
Parkville, Missouri
School for Extended Learning
http://www.park.edu/online

Park University was founded in 1875. It is accredited by North Central Association of Colleges and Schools. It first offered distance learning courses in 1996. In fall 2005, there were 5,500 students enrolled in distance learning courses. Institutionally administered financial aid is available to distance learners.

Services Distance learners have accessibility to academic advising, bookstore, career placement assistance, e-mail services, library services, tutoring.

Contact Ms. Nancy Eastman, Enrollment Management, Park University, 8700 NW River Park Drive, Parkville, MO 64152-3795. Telephone: 816-584-6524. Fax: 816-741-5133. E-mail: neastman@park.edu.

DEGREES AND AWARDS

BS Criminal Justice Administration; Management; Management/Computer Information Systems; Management/Human Resources; Management/Marketing; Social Psychology

MBA Business Administration; Health Care/Health Services Management; International Business

MEd Education, general; Law–School Law; Multi-Cultural Education; Teaching At-Risk Students

MPA Disaster and Emergency Management; Government–Business Relations; Nonprofit and Community Services Management; Public Management

COURSE SUBJECT AREAS OFFERED OUTSIDE OF DEGREE PROGRAMS

Undergraduate—accounting and related services; American literature (United States and Canadian); area, ethnic, cultural, and gender studies related; biblical studies; biology; business administration, management and operations; business/commerce; business/corporate communications; business, management, and marketing related; communication and journalism related; communication and media; computer and information sciences; computer programming; creative writing; criminal justice and corrections; criminology; economics; education related; English; English composition; finance and financial management services; geography and cartography; geological and earth sciences/geosciences; health and medical administrative services; history; human resources management; management information systems; marketing; mathematics; philosophy and religious studies related; political science and government; psychology; sales, merchandising, and related marketing operations (general); social psychology; statistics.

Graduate—business administration, management and operations; business, management, and marketing related; computer and information sciences; education; educational administration and supervision; international business; public administration; public administration and social service professions related.

See full description on page 424.

PASCO-HERNANDO COMMUNITY COLLEGE
New Port Richey, Florida
http://www.phcc.edu

Pasco-Hernando Community College was founded in 1972. It is accredited by Southern Association of Colleges and Schools. It first offered distance learning courses in 1993. In fall 2005, there were 3,758 students enrolled in distance learning courses. Institutionally administered financial aid is available to distance learners.

Services Distance learners have accessibility to academic advising, campus computer network, library services.

Contact Ms. Debra Bullard, Director of Admissions and Student Records, Pasco-Hernando Community College, 10230 Ridge Road, New Port Richey, FL 34654-5199. Telephone: 727-816-3261. Fax: 727-816-3389. E-mail: bullard@phcc.edu.

DEGREES AND AWARDS

Programs offered do not lead to a degree or other formal award.

COURSE SUBJECT AREAS OFFERED OUTSIDE OF DEGREE PROGRAMS

Undergraduate—biology; business administration, management and operations; business/commerce; computer programming; computer software and media applications; computer systems networking and telecommunications; education (specific levels and methods); English composition; English literature (British and Commonwealth); health and physical education/fitness; history; physical sciences; political science and government; psychology; religious studies; social sciences related; sociology; speech and rhetoric.

Non-credit—business/corporate communications; computer and information sciences; computer programming; computer software and media applications; education; education related; family and consumer economics; health professions related; insurance; personal and culinary services related; sales, merchandising, and related marketing operations (specialized); technical and business writing.

PASSAIC COUNTY COMMUNITY COLLEGE
Paterson, New Jersey
http://www.pccc.cc.nj.us/

Passaic County Community College was founded in 1968. It is accredited by Middle States Association of Colleges and Schools. It first offered distance learning courses in 1998. In fall 2005, there were 750 students enrolled in distance learning courses. Institutionally administered financial aid is available to distance learners.

Services Distance learners have accessibility to academic advising, bookstore, e-mail services, library services, tutoring.

Contact Mr. Rick Perdew, Coordinator of Instructional Technology, Passaic County Community College, 1 College Boulevard, Paterson, NJ 07505-1179. Telephone: 973-684-5790. Fax: 973-684-5413. E-mail: rperdew@pccc.edu.

DEGREES AND AWARDS

AA Humanities option; Humanities option
AAS Health Information Technology

COURSE SUBJECT AREAS OFFERED OUTSIDE OF DEGREE PROGRAMS

Undergraduate—business/commerce; communication and media; computer and information sciences; criminal justice and corrections; English; fire protection; health professions related; history; mathematics and statistics related; physical sciences; psychology; sociology; statistics.

PATRICK HENRY COLLEGE
Purcellville, Virginia
http://www.phc.edu/distancelearning

Patrick Henry College was founded in 1999. It is accredited by American Academy for Liberal Education. It first offered distance learning courses in 2001. In fall 2005, there were 145 students enrolled in distance learning courses. Institutionally administered financial aid is available to distance learners.

Services Distance learners have accessibility to academic advising, bookstore, library services.

Contact Mr. Richard Shipe, Director of Distance Learning, Patrick Henry College, One Patrick Henry Circle, Purcellville, VA 20132. Telephone: 540-338-1776. Fax: 540-338-8708. E-mail: rgshipe@phc.edu.

DEGREES AND AWARDS

Programs offered do not lead to a degree or other formal award.

COURSE SUBJECT AREAS OFFERED OUTSIDE OF DEGREE PROGRAMS

Undergraduate—biblical studies; biology; economics; English composition; history; languages (classics and classical); legal studies (nonprofessional general, undergraduate); liberal arts and sciences, general studies and humanities; music; philosophy; philosophy and religious studies related; political science and government; public policy analysis.

PATRICK HENRY COMMUNITY COLLEGE
Martinsville, Virginia
Learning Resource Center
http://www.ph.vccs.edu

Patrick Henry Community College was founded in 1962. It is accredited by Southern Association of Colleges and Schools. It first offered distance learning courses in 1981. In fall 2005, there were 1,800 students enrolled in distance learning courses. Institutionally administered financial aid is available to distance learners.

Services Distance learners have accessibility to academic advising, bookstore, campus computer network, career placement assistance, e-mail services, library services, tutoring.

Contact Mark Nelson, Distance Learning Webmaster, Patrick Henry Community College, PO Box 5311, Martinsville, VA 24115. Telephone: 276-656-0275. Fax: 276-656-0353. E-mail: mnelson@ph.vccs.edu.

DEGREES AND AWARDS

AAS Information Systems Technology
AS Business Administration; General Studies
Certificate Career Studies–Allied Health; Career Studies–Management Assistant; Career Studies–Medical Transcriptionist; Career Studies–Office Assisting; Career Studies–Wellness; Clerical Studies

COURSE SUBJECT AREAS OFFERED OUTSIDE OF DEGREE PROGRAMS

Undergraduate—accounting and related services; biological and physical sciences; business administration, management and operations; communication and media; computer/information technology administration and management; computer systems networking and telecommunications; developmental and child psychology; economics; English composition;

English literature (British and Commonwealth); fine and studio art; health and physical education/fitness; history; management information systems; mathematics; psychology; religious studies; sociology.

PEIRCE COLLEGE
Philadelphia, Pennsylvania
Peirce College Non-Traditional Education
http://www.peirce.edu

Peirce College was founded in 1865. It is accredited by Middle States Association of Colleges and Schools. It first offered distance learning courses in 1997. In fall 2005, there were 1,565 students enrolled in distance learning courses. Institutionally administered financial aid is available to distance learners.

Services Distance learners have accessibility to academic advising, bookstore, career placement assistance, library services, tutoring.

Contact Ms. Nadine M. Maher, Dean, Enrollment Management, Peirce College, 1420 Pine Street, Philadelphia, PA 19102. Telephone: 888-467-3472 Ext. 9800. Fax: 215-670-9366. E-mail: info@peirce.edu.

DEGREES AND AWARDS

AS Business Administration–Accounting concentration; Business Administration–Business Law concentration; Business Administration–Entrepreneurship/Small Business Management concentration; Business Administration–Human Resource Management concentration; Business Administration–Management concentration; Business Administration–Marketing concentration; Information Technology with Desktop Applications for Business; Information Technology with Network Security; Information Technology with Programming Application Development; Information Technology–Information Security concentration; Information Technology–Networking concentration; Information Technology–Technology Management concentration; Paralegal Studies

BS Business Administration–Accounting concentration; Business Administration–Business Law concentration; Business Administration–Entrepreneurship/Small Business Management concentration; Business Administration–Human Resource Management concentration; Business Administration–Management concentration; Business Administration–Marketing concentration; Business Administration–Real Estate Management concentration; Information Technology with Desktop Applications for Business; Information Technology with Programming and Application Development; Information Technology–Information Security concentration; Information Technology–Network Security concentration; Information Technology–Networking concentration; Information Technology–Technology Management concentration; Paralegal Studies

Certificate Business Administration Business Law; Certified Information Systems Security Professional (CISSP); Information Technology Help Desk Technician; Information Technology with .NET Technology; Information Technology with Programming; Information Technology with Windows Network Operating System; Paralegal Studies; Systems Security Certified Practitioner (SSCP)

COURSE SUBJECT AREAS OFFERED OUTSIDE OF DEGREE PROGRAMS

Undergraduate—accounting and related services; business administration, management and operations; business/commerce; business, management, and marketing related; computer and information sciences and support services related; computer/information technology administration and management; computer programming; computer software and media applications; computer systems networking and telecommunications; entrepreneurial and small business operations; human resources management; information science/studies; legal studies (non-professional general, undergraduate); management information systems; marketing; real estate; sales, merchandising, and related marketing operations (general); security and protective services related.

See full description on page 426.

PENINSULA COLLEGE
Port Angeles, Washington
http://pc.ctc.edu/

Peninsula College was founded in 1961. It is accredited by Northwest Commission on Colleges and Universities. It first offered distance learning courses in 1994. In fall 2005, there were 1,018 students enrolled in distance learning courses. Institutionally administered financial aid is available to distance learners.

Services Distance learners have accessibility to academic advising, bookstore, career placement assistance, library services, tutoring.

Contact Vicki Sievert, Distance Learning Coordinator, Peninsula College, 1502 East Lauridsen Boulevard, Port Angeles, WA 98362. Telephone: 360-417-6272. Fax: 360-417-6295. E-mail: vickis@pcadmin.ctc.edu.

DEGREES AND AWARDS

AA Liberal Arts

AAS Criminal Justice

COURSE SUBJECT AREAS OFFERED OUTSIDE OF DEGREE PROGRAMS

Undergraduate—accounting and related services; allied health and medical assisting services; American literature (United States and Canadian); anthropology; astronomy and astrophysics; biblical and other theological languages and literatures; biochemistry, biophysics and molecular biology; biological and physical sciences; business administration, management and operations; business, management, and marketing related; chemistry; communication and journalism related; computer and information sciences; criminal justice and corrections; dental support services and allied professions; developmental and child psychology; economics; education; English composition; English literature (British and Commonwealth); entrepreneurial and small business operations; family psychology; geological and earth sciences/geosciences; health and physical education/fitness; health professions related; history; human development, family studies, and related services; journalism; liberal arts and sciences, general studies and humanities; mathematics; mathematics and computer science; music; natural sciences; nursing; nutrition sciences; pharmacology and toxicology; philosophy; physical sciences; political science and government; psychology; social sciences; sociology.

PENN FOSTER CAREER SCHOOL
Scranton, Pennsylvania
Center for Degree Studies
http://www.EducationDirect.com

Penn Foster Career School was founded in 1975. It is accredited by Distance Education and Training Council. It first offered distance learning courses in 1975. Institutionally administered financial aid is available to distance learners.

Services Distance learners have accessibility to academic advising, career placement assistance, e-mail services, library services, tutoring.

Contact Ms. Linda K. Smith, Manager of Data Processing, Penn Foster Career School, 925 Oak Street, Scranton, PA 18515. Telephone: 570-342-7701. E-mail: linda.smith@thomson.com.

DEGREES AND AWARDS

AS Accounting (ASB); Business Management–ASB; Business Management–Finance option ASB; Business Management–Marketing option ASB; Civil Engineering Technology; Computer Science–Applied Computer Science ASB; Criminal Justice; Early Childhood Education; Electrical Engineering Technology AST; Electronics Technology AST; Health Information Technology; Hospitality Management (ASB); Industrial Engineering Technology AST; Internet Technology Multimedia and Design AST; Internet Technology Web Programming; Internet Technology–E-Commerce Administration AST; Mechanical Engineering Technology AST; Paralegal Studies; Veterinary Technician

COURSE SUBJECT AREAS OFFERED OUTSIDE OF DEGREE PROGRAMS

Non-credit—accounting and related services; allied health and medical assisting services; business operations support and assistant services; carpentry; computer programming; foods, nutrition, and related services; health and medical administrative services; human development, family studies, and related services; journalism; teaching assistants/aides.

PENNSYLVANIA COLLEGE OF TECHNOLOGY
Williamsport, Pennsylvania
http://www.pct.edu/

Pennsylvania College of Technology was founded in 1965. It is accredited by Middle States Association of Colleges and Schools. It first offered distance learning courses in 1996. In fall 2005, there were 500 students enrolled in distance learning courses. Institutionally administered financial aid is available to distance learners.

Services Distance learners have accessibility to academic advising, bookstore, campus computer network, career placement assistance, e-mail services, library services, tutoring.

Contact Paula Neal, Distance Learning Services Assistant, Pennsylvania College of Technology, One College Avenue, DIF #50, Williamsport, PA 17701. Telephone: 570-320-8019. Fax: 570-321-5559. E-mail: distancelearning@pct.edu.

DEGREES AND AWARDS
BS Applied Health Studies; Automotive Technology Management; Dental Hygiene; Technology Management
BSN Nursing

COURSE SUBJECT AREAS OFFERED OUTSIDE OF DEGREE PROGRAMS
Undergraduate—accounting and related services; architecture; biological and biomedical sciences related; biology; building/construction finishing, management, and inspection; business/commerce; business/corporate communications; chemistry; computer and information sciences; construction engineering technology; dental support services and allied professions; English language and literature related; environmental/environmental health engineering; finance and financial management services; fine and studio art; geological and earth sciences/geosciences; health professions related; history; international business; marketing; mathematics; nursing; philosophy and religious studies related; statistics.

See full description on page 428.

THE PENNSYLVANIA STATE UNIVERSITY UNIVERSITY PARK CAMPUS
State College, Pennsylvania
Department of Distance Education/World Campus
http://www.worldcampus.psu.edu

The Pennsylvania State University University Park Campus was founded in 1855. It is accredited by Middle States Association of Colleges and Schools. It first offered distance learning courses in 1999. In fall 2005, there were 25,454 students enrolled in distance learning courses. Institutionally administered financial aid is available to distance learners.

Services Distance learners have accessibility to academic advising, bookstore, campus computer network, e-mail services, library services.

Contact The Pennsylvania State University University Park Campus.

DEGREES AND AWARDS
AAS Letters, Arts, and Sciences
ABA Business Administration
AD Hotel, Restaurant, and Institutional Management; Human Development and Family Studies
AS Dietetic Food Systems Management, Dietetic Technician Emphasis; Dietetic Food Systems Management, School Food Service Emphasis; Information Sciences and Technology
BA Law and Society; Letters, Arts, and Sciences
BN Nursing–RN to BS
BS Criminal Justice; Organizational Leadership; Turfgrass Science
Certificate Adult Development and Aging Services; Autism; Business Management; Business Management; Children, Youth, and Family Services; Communications Studies; Family Literacy; Hospitality Management; Hotel, Restaurant, and Institutional Management; Human Resources; Information Science and Technology; Labor Studies and Industrial Relations; Organizational Communication; Reading Instruction for Special Education–RISE; School Food Service Management; Turfgrass Management; Turfgrass Management, advanced; Weather Forecasting; Writing Social Commentary
Certification SNA Level 3 Certification Module
Graduate Certificate Applied Behavior Analysis for Special Education; Bioterrorism Preparedness; Children's Literature; Disaster Readiness; Institutional Research; Project Management; Project Management, advanced; Supply Chain and Information Systems
MA Geographic Information Systems
MBA Business Administration (iMBA)
ME Oil and Gas Engineering Management
MEd Adult Education; Curriculum and Instruction Teacher Leadership; Curriculum and Instruction–Children's Literature; Instructional Systems Educational Technology
MPM Project Management
MS/MPH Homeland Security in Public Health Preparedness

COURSE SUBJECT AREAS OFFERED OUTSIDE OF DEGREE PROGRAMS
Undergraduate—accounting and related services; animal sciences; anthropology; biological and physical sciences; biology; business administration, management and operations; business/commerce; business/corporate communications; chemistry; communication and media; comparative literature; creative writing; criminal justice and corrections; economics; educational assessment, evaluation, and research; English composition; entrepreneurial and small business operations; ethnic, cultural minority, and gender studies; finance and financial management services; fine and studio art; foods, nutrition, and related services; gerontology; health and medical administrative services; health and physical education/fitness; history; hospitality administration; human development, family studies, and related services; human resources management; industrial and organizational psychology; information science/studies; journalism; languages (Germanic); languages (Romance languages); linguistic, comparative, and related language studies; management information systems; marketing; mathematics; mathematics and statistics related; music; philosophy; physics; physiology, pathology and related sciences; plant sciences; political science and government; psychology; religious studies; sales, merchandising, and related marketing operations (general); science, technology and society; sociology; speech and rhetoric; statistics; technical and business writing; visual and performing arts; wildlife and wildlands science and management.

Graduate—business administration, management and operations; business/managerial economics; city/urban, community and regional planning; communication and journalism related; curriculum and instruction; educational/instructional media design; electromechanical and instrumentation and maintenance technologies; engineering/industrial management; environmental control technologies; environmental design; management sciences and quantitative methods; mental and social health services and allied professions; sales, merchandising, and related marketing operations (general); statistics; transportation and materials moving related.

Non-credit—business administration, management and operations; business/corporate communications; engineering related; environmental design; geography and cartography; human resources management; wildlife and wildlands science and management.

PEPPERDINE UNIVERSITY
Los Angeles, California
Program in Educational Technology
http://gsep.pepperdine.edu/

Pepperdine University was founded in 1937. It is accredited by Western Association of Schools and Colleges. It first offered distance learning courses in 1995. In fall 2005, there were 150 students enrolled in distance learning courses. Institutionally administered financial aid is available to distance learners.

Services Distance learners have accessibility to academic advising, bookstore, campus computer network, career placement assistance, e-mail services, library services, tutoring.

Contact Ms. Bonita Campbell, Enrollment Specialist, Pepperdine University, Graduate School of Education and Psychology, 6100 Center Drive, Los Angeles, CA 90045. Telephone: 800-347-4849. E-mail: gsep@pepperdine.edu.

DEGREES AND AWARDS
MA Educational Technology
EdD Educational Technology

PFEIFFER UNIVERSITY
Misenheimer, North Carolina
http://www.pfeiffer.edu/

Pfeiffer University was founded in 1885. It is accredited by Southern Association of Colleges and Schools. It first offered distance learning courses in 1999. In fall 2005, there were 225 students enrolled in distance learning courses. Institutionally administered financial aid is available to distance learners.

Services Distance learners have accessibility to academic advising, bookstore, campus computer network, e-mail services, library services, tutoring.

Contact Robert K. Spear, Director of MBA Program, Pfeiffer University, 4701 Park Road, Charlotte, NC 28209. Telephone: 704-945-7303. Fax: 704-521-8617. E-mail: rks@pfeiffer.edu.

DEGREES AND AWARDS
MBA Business Administration
MBA/MHA Business Administration/Health Administration
MBA/MS Business Administration/Organizational Change and Leadership
MHA Health Administration
MS Organizational Change and Leadership

PHILADELPHIA UNIVERSITY
Philadelphia, Pennsylvania
http://www.philau.edu/

Philadelphia University was founded in 1884. It is accredited by Middle States Association of Colleges and Schools. It first offered distance learning courses in 1998. In fall 2005, there were 145 students enrolled in distance learning courses. Institutionally administered financial aid is available to distance learners.

Services Distance learners have accessibility to academic advising, campus computer network, career placement assistance, e-mail services, library services, tutoring.

Contact Mr. William Firman, Director of Graduate Admissions, Philadelphia University, School House Lane and Henry Avenue, Philadelphia, PA 19144. Telephone: 215-951-2943. Fax: 610-902-8508. E-mail: firmanw@philau.edu.

DEGREES AND AWARDS
Certificate Nurse-Midwifery
MBA Textile and Apparel Marketing
MS Disaster Medicine and Management; Midwifery

COURSE SUBJECT AREAS OFFERED OUTSIDE OF DEGREE PROGRAMS
Undergraduate—accounting and related services; business administration, management and operations; economics; finance and financial management services; legal studies (non-professional general, undergraduate); management information systems; management sciences and quantitative methods; marketing; operations research; statistics.

Graduate—accounting and related services; apparel and textiles; finance and financial management services; international business; management information systems; management sciences and quantitative methods; marketing; statistics.

PIEDMONT TECHNICAL COLLEGE
Greenwood, South Carolina
Division of Instructional Technology
http://www.ptc.edu/dl

Piedmont Technical College was founded in 1966. It is accredited by Southern Association of Colleges and Schools. It first offered distance learning courses in 1995. In fall 2005, there were 2,000 students enrolled in distance learning courses. Institutionally administered financial aid is available to distance learners.

Services Distance learners have accessibility to academic advising, bookstore, campus computer network, career placement assistance, e-mail services, library services, tutoring.

Contact Dr. Daniel D. Koenig, Associate Vice President for Instructional Support and Technology, Piedmont Technical College, 620 North Emerald Road, PO Drawer 1467, Greenwood, SC 29648. Telephone: 864-941-8446. Fax: 864-941-8703. E-mail: koenig.d@ptc.edu.

DEGREES AND AWARDS
AA Liberal Arts
AD Business–Associate in Business, Major in General Business; Business–Associate in Business, Major in Office Systems Technology

COURSE SUBJECT AREAS OFFERED OUTSIDE OF DEGREE PROGRAMS
Undergraduate—American literature (United States and Canadian); biology; business administration, management and operations; business/commerce; cell biology and anatomical sciences; chemistry; communication and media; computer science; English composition; English literature (British and Commonwealth); fine and studio art; history; languages (Romance languages); legal studies (non-professional general, undergraduate); management information systems; mathematics and statistics related; music; philosophy and religious studies related; plant sciences; political science and government; psychology; sociology; speech and rhetoric; statistics.

PINE TECHNICAL COLLEGE
Pine City, Minnesota
Distance Education Center
http://www.ptc.tec.mn.us

Pine Technical College was founded in 1965. It is accredited by North Central Association of Colleges and Schools. It first offered distance learning courses in 1985. In fall 2005, there were 200 students enrolled in distance learning courses. Institutionally administered financial aid is available to distance learners.

Services Distance learners have accessibility to academic advising, bookstore, campus computer network, e-mail services, library services, tutoring.

Contact Nancy Mach, Dean of Student Services, Pine Technical College, 900 4th Street, SE, Pine City, MN 55063. Telephone: 320-629-5173. Fax: 320-629-5101. E-mail: machn@pinetech.edu.

DEGREES AND AWARDS
Programs offered do not lead to a degree or other formal award.

COURSE SUBJECT AREAS OFFERED OUTSIDE OF DEGREE PROGRAMS
Undergraduate—accounting and related services; American Sign Language (ASL); business, management, and marketing related; health professions related; public administration and social service professions related.

PLYMOUTH STATE UNIVERSITY
Plymouth, New Hampshire

Plymouth State University was founded in 1871. It is accredited by New England Association of Schools and Colleges. It first offered distance learning courses in 2000. In fall 2005, there were 52 students enrolled in distance learning courses.

Services Distance learners have accessibility to academic advising, bookstore, campus computer network, e-mail services, library services.

Contact Ms. Stacey L Curdie, Director of Online Education, Plymouth State University, MSC 10, 17 High Street, Plymouth, NH 03264. Telephone: 603-535-3221. E-mail: scurdie@plymouth.edu.

DEGREES AND AWARDS
Programs offered do not lead to a degree or other formal award.

COURSE SUBJECT AREAS OFFERED OUTSIDE OF DEGREE PROGRAMS
Undergraduate—business administration, management and operations; communication and media; English; geography and cartography; linguistic, comparative, and related language studies; music.

Graduate—computer and information sciences; education; educational assessment, evaluation, and research.

PORTLAND COMMUNITY COLLEGE
Portland, Oregon
Distance Learning Department
http://www.distance.pcc.edu

Portland Community College was founded in 1961. It is accredited by Northwest Commission on Colleges and Universities. It first offered distance learning courses in 1981. In fall 2005, there were 5,732 students enrolled in distance learning courses. Institutionally administered financial aid is available to distance learners.

Services Distance learners have accessibility to academic advising, bookstore, career placement assistance, e-mail services, library services.

Contact Dennis Hitchcox, Programming Coordinator, Distance Education, Portland Community College, PO Box 19000, Portland, OR 97280-0990. Telephone: 503-977-4655. Fax: 503-977-4858. E-mail: dhitchco@pcc.edu.

DEGREES AND AWARDS

Programs offered do not lead to a degree or other formal award.

COURSE SUBJECT AREAS OFFERED OUTSIDE OF DEGREE PROGRAMS

Undergraduate—accounting and related services; aerospace, aeronautical and astronautical engineering; allied health and medical assisting services; anthropology; biology; business administration, management and operations; business, management, and marketing related; business operations support and assistant services; computer and information sciences; computer and information sciences and support services related; computer science; computer software and media applications; dental support services and allied professions; developmental and child psychology; economics; education; English composition; fire protection; foods, nutrition, and related services; geography and cartography; health and physical education/fitness; health professions related; history; human development, family studies, and related services; marketing; mathematics; mathematics and statistics related; music; nursing; physical sciences related; psychology; real estate; social sciences; sociology; statistics; technical and business writing.

Non-credit—computer/information technology administration and management; computer programming; computer software and media applications; computer systems networking and telecommunications; creative writing; education related; health professions related; languages (foreign languages related); legal professions and studies related; pharmacy, pharmaceutical sciences, and administration; psychology related.

PORTLAND STATE UNIVERSITY
Portland, Oregon
Independent Study
http://www.istudy.pdx.edu

Portland State University was founded in 1946. It is accredited by Northwest Commission on Colleges and Universities. In fall 2005, there were 3,000 students enrolled in distance learning courses. Institutionally administered financial aid is available to distance learners.

Services Distance learners have accessibility to bookstore, library services.

Contact Rebecca Robinson, Director, Portland State University, PO Box 1491, Portland, OR 97207-1491. Telephone: 800-547-8887 Ext. 8485. Fax: 503-725-4880. E-mail: robinsonr@pdx.edu.

DEGREES AND AWARDS

Programs offered do not lead to a degree or other formal award.

COURSE SUBJECT AREAS OFFERED OUTSIDE OF DEGREE PROGRAMS

Undergraduate—chemistry; criminal justice and corrections; economics; English; English composition; geological and earth sciences/geosciences; history; mathematics and statistics related; psychology; sociology; statistics.

PRESCOTT COLLEGE
Prescott, Arizona
http://www.prescott.edu/

Prescott College was founded in 1966. It is accredited by North Central Association of Colleges and Schools. It first offered distance learning courses in 1978. In fall 2005, there were 600 students enrolled in distance learning courses. Institutionally administered financial aid is available to distance learners.

Services Distance learners have accessibility to academic advising, career placement assistance, e-mail services, library services, tutoring.

Contact Melanie Lefever, Assistant Director of Admissions, Prescott College, Admissions, 220 Grove Avenue, Prescott, AZ 86301. Telephone: 877-350-2100 Ext. 2106. Fax: 928-776-5242. E-mail: admissions@prescott.edu.

DEGREES AND AWARDS

BA Adventure Education; Art; Business; Communications; Computer Information Systems; Counseling Psychology/Human Services; Creative Writing; Criminal Justice; Cultural and Regional Studies; Education; Elementary Education; Environmental Studies; History; Humanities; Journalism; Management; Music; Natural Resources and Conservation; Political Science; Special Education; Sustainable Community Development; Theater

Certification Teacher Certification

MA Adventure Education; Alternative Energy Systems; Anthropology; Art History; Art Therapy; Arts Management; Bilingual Education; Counseling and Psychology; Counseling–School Guidance Counseling; Cultural Studies; Ecology; Education; Educational Administration; Environmental Education; Environmental Education; Environmental Studies; Equine Assisted Mental Health; Film and Cinema Studies; Fire Science; Foreign Languages; Gay and Lesbian Studies; Gender Studies; Higher Education Administration; Humanities; Land Use Planning; Mental Health Counseling; Museum Studies; Natural Resources and Conservation; Peace Studies; Philosophy; Photography; Playwriting and Screenwriting; Religious Studies; Sustainability Education; Sustainable Community Development; Wetlands Management; Wildlife Management

PhD Education–Sustainability Education

COURSE SUBJECT AREAS OFFERED OUTSIDE OF DEGREE PROGRAMS

Undergraduate—accounting and related services; bilingual, multilingual, and multicultural education; business administration, management and operations; communication and media; community organization and advocacy; counseling psychology; creative writing; education; English; ethnic, cultural minority, and gender studies; history; human development, family studies, and related services; human services; liberal arts and sciences, general studies and humanities; natural resources conservation and research; parks, recreation and leisure; philosophy and religious studies related; psychology; visual and performing arts; wildlife and wildlands science and management.

Graduate—area, ethnic, cultural, and gender studies related; city/urban, community and regional planning; clinical psychology; communication and media; community organization and advocacy; creative writing; education; ethnic, cultural minority, and gender studies; history; human development, family studies, and related services; human services; movement and mind-body therapies; natural resources and conservation related; natural resources management and policy; parks, recreation and leisure facilities management; peace studies and conflict resolution; philosophy and religious studies related; psychology; visual and performing arts; wildlife and wildlands science and management.

See full description on page 430.

PRESENTATION COLLEGE
Aberdeen, South Dakota
http://www.presentation.edu/

Presentation College was founded in 1951. It is accredited by North Central Association of Colleges and Schools. It first offered distance learning courses in 1994. In fall 2005, there were 317 students enrolled in distance learning courses. Institutionally administered financial aid is available to distance learners.

Services Distance learners have accessibility to academic advising, bookstore, campus computer network, career placement assistance, e-mail services, library services, tutoring.

Contact JoEllen Lindner, Dean of Admissions, Presentation College, 1500 North Main Street, Aberdeen, SD 57401. Telephone: 605-229-8492. Fax: 605-229-8425. E-mail: joellen.lindner@presentation.edu.

DEGREES AND AWARDS

AS Medical Office Administration
BS Business Completion; Nursing–AD-LPN to BSN Nursing Completion; Nursing–LPN Certificate to BSN Nursing Completion; Nursing–RN to BSN Nursing completion; Radiologic Technology Completion Program; Social Work Completion
Certificate Medical Transcription

COURSE SUBJECT AREAS OFFERED OUTSIDE OF DEGREE PROGRAMS

Undergraduate—American Sign Language (ASL); psychology; statistics.

PROVIDENCE COLLEGE AND THEOLOGICAL SEMINARY
Otterburne, Manitoba, Canada
Department of Continuing Education
http://www.prov.ca

Providence College and Theological Seminary was founded in 1925. It is provincially chartered. It first offered distance learning courses in 1975. In fall 2005, there were 100 students enrolled in distance learning courses. Institutionally administered financial aid is available to distance learners.
Services Distance learners have accessibility to academic advising, bookstore, campus computer network, career placement assistance, e-mail services, library services.
Contact Ms. Joy Lise, Director of Enrollment, Providence College and Theological Seminary, General Delivery, Otterburne, MB R0A 1G0, Canada. Telephone: 204-433-7488 Ext. 247. Fax: 204-433-7158. E-mail: info@prov.ca.

DEGREES AND AWARDS

Programs offered do not lead to a degree or other formal award.

COURSE SUBJECT AREAS OFFERED OUTSIDE OF DEGREE PROGRAMS

Undergraduate—biblical and other theological languages and literatures; biblical studies; communication and media; theological and ministerial studies; theology and religious vocations related.
Graduate—area, ethnic, cultural, and gender studies related; biblical and other theological languages and literatures; biblical studies; business operations support and assistant services; counseling psychology; education related; missionary studies and missiology; pastoral counseling and specialized ministries; religious studies; theological and ministerial studies; theology and religious vocations related.
Non-credit—area, ethnic, cultural, and gender studies related; biblical and other theological languages and literatures; biblical studies; counseling psychology; education related; human resources management; missionary studies and missiology; pastoral counseling and specialized ministries; religious/sacred music; theological and ministerial studies; theology and religious vocations related.

PUEBLO COMMUNITY COLLEGE
Pueblo, Colorado

Pueblo Community College was founded in 1933. It is accredited by North Central Association of Colleges and Schools. It first offered distance learning courses in 1993. In fall 2005, there were 800 students enrolled in distance learning courses. Institutionally administered financial aid is available to distance learners.
Services Distance learners have accessibility to academic advising, bookstore, campus computer network, career placement assistance, e-mail services, library services, tutoring.
Contact Ms. JoAnne Dionese, Administrative Assistant, Pueblo Community College, Distance Learning Office, 900 West Orman Avenue, Pueblo, CO 81004-1499. Telephone: 719-549-3343. Fax: 719-549-3419. E-mail: joanne.dionese@pueblocc.edu.

DEGREES AND AWARDS

AA General Studies
AAS Applied Science; Business; Library Technician
AGS General Studies
AS General Studies
Certificate Early Childhood program; Library Technician

COURSE SUBJECT AREAS OFFERED OUTSIDE OF DEGREE PROGRAMS

Undergraduate—accounting and computer science; accounting and related services; American literature (United States and Canadian); anthropology; astronomy and astrophysics; biological and physical sciences; biology; business administration, management and operations; business, management, and marketing related; chemistry; computer and information sciences; computer systems analysis; computer systems networking and telecommunications; creative writing; criminal justice and corrections; developmental and child psychology; economics; education; engineering design; English; English composition; English language and literature related; geography and cartography; geological and earth sciences/geosciences; health professions related; history; liberal arts and sciences, general studies and humanities; library assistant; marketing; mathematics; music; nursing; nutrition sciences; philosophy; physical sciences; physics; physiology, pathology and related sciences; psychology; social sciences; sociology; speech and rhetoric; statistics.

PULASKI TECHNICAL COLLEGE
North Little Rock, Arkansas
http://www.pulaskitech.edu

Pulaski Technical College was founded in 1945. It is accredited by North Central Association of Colleges and Schools. It first offered distance learning courses in 1999. In fall 2005, there were 1,458 students enrolled in distance learning courses. Institutionally administered financial aid is available to distance learners.
Services Distance learners have accessibility to bookstore, library services, tutoring.
Contact Ms. Amy Baldwin, Distance Education Coordinator, Pulaski Technical College, 3000 West Scenic Drive, North Little Rock, AR 72118. Telephone: 501-812-2262. Fax: 501-812-2340. E-mail: abaldwin@pulaskitech.edu.

DEGREES AND AWARDS

AA General Program

COURSE SUBJECT AREAS OFFERED OUTSIDE OF DEGREE PROGRAMS

Undergraduate—accounting and computer science; American literature (United States and Canadian); biology; business/commerce; business operations support and assistant services; computer and information sciences; computer systems networking and telecommunications; education; English composition; legal professions and studies related; mathematics; philosophy; psychology; social sciences.

PURDUE UNIVERSITY
West Lafayette, Indiana
Krannert Executive Education Programs
http://www2.krannert.purdue.edu/

Purdue University was founded in 1869. It is accredited by North Central Association of Colleges and Schools. It first offered distance learning courses in 1983. In fall 2005, there were 220 students enrolled in distance learning courses. Institutionally administered financial aid is available to distance learners.
Services Distance learners have accessibility to academic advising, bookstore, campus computer network, tutoring.
Contact Erika C. Steuterman, Director, Executive Master's Programs, Purdue University, KCTR 206, 425 West State Street, West Lafayette, IN 47907-2056. Telephone: 765-494-7700. Fax: 765-494-0862. E-mail: keepinfo@mgmt.purdue.edu.

DEGREES AND AWARDS
MBA Business Administration–Executive Master of Business Administration; International Masters in Management program (IMM)
See full description on page 432.

PURDUE UNIVERSITY CALUMET
Hammond, Indiana

Purdue University Calumet was founded in 1951. It is accredited by North Central Association of Colleges and Schools. It first offered distance learning courses in 2002. In fall 2005, there were 1,397 students enrolled in distance learning courses. Institutionally administered financial aid is available to distance learners.
Services Distance learners have accessibility to academic advising, bookstore, campus computer network, career placement assistance, e-mail services, library services, tutoring.
Contact Bela Bowley, Director, Extended and Distance Education, Purdue University Calumet, Lawshe Hall, Room 342A, 2200 169th Street, Hammond, IN 46323. Telephone: 219-989-4187. E-mail: bowleyb@calumet.purdue.edu.

DEGREES AND AWARDS
Programs offered do not lead to a degree or other formal award.

COURSE SUBJECT AREAS OFFERED OUTSIDE OF DEGREE PROGRAMS
Undergraduate—anthropology; behavioral sciences; communication and media; computer and information sciences; economics; English; foods, nutrition, and related services; health and physical education/fitness; nursing; psychology; sociology.
Graduate—computer science; engineering; mathematics; nursing; statistics.

QUEEN'S UNIVERSITY AT KINGSTON
Kingston, Ontario, Canada
Continuing and Distance Studies
http://www.queensu.ca/cds

Queen's University at Kingston was founded in 1841. It is provincially chartered. It first offered distance learning courses in 1941. In fall 2005, there were 2,500 students enrolled in distance learning courses. Institutionally administered financial aid is available to distance learners.
Services Distance learners have accessibility to academic advising, bookstore, campus computer network, career placement assistance, e-mail services, library services, tutoring.
Contact Wilma Fernetich, Distance Education Advisor, Queen's University at Kingston, Kingston, ON K7L 2N6, Canada. Telephone: 613-533-6000 Ext. 77770. Fax: 613-533-6805. E-mail: fernetic@post.queensu.ca.

DEGREES AND AWARDS
Programs offered do not lead to a degree or other formal award.

COURSE SUBJECT AREAS OFFERED OUTSIDE OF DEGREE PROGRAMS
Undergraduate—biology; creative writing; dramatic/theater arts and stagecraft; English composition; English literature (British and Commonwealth); ethnic, cultural minority, and gender studies; geography and cartography; history; languages (Germanic); nutrition sciences; pharmacology and toxicology; philosophy; political science and government; psychology; religious studies; social psychology; sociology; statistics.

QUINEBAUG VALLEY COMMUNITY COLLEGE
Danielson, Connecticut
http://www.qvcc.commnet.edu/

Quinebaug Valley Community College was founded in 1971. It is accredited by New England Association of Schools and Colleges. It first offered distance learning courses in 1998. In fall 2005, there were 243 students enrolled in distance learning courses. Institutionally administered financial aid is available to distance learners.
Services Distance learners have accessibility to academic advising, library services, tutoring.
Contact Dr. Toni T. Moumouris, Enrollment and Transition Counselor, Quinebaug Valley Community College, 742 Upper Maple Street, Danielson, CT 06239. Telephone: 860-774-1130 Ext. 318. Fax: 860-779-2998. E-mail: tmoumouris@qvcc.commnet.edu.

DEGREES AND AWARDS
Certificate Health Information Management Technology

COURSE SUBJECT AREAS OFFERED OUTSIDE OF DEGREE PROGRAMS
Undergraduate—biological and physical sciences; business, management, and marketing related; education; English language and literature related; health and medical administrative services; history; liberal arts and sciences, general studies and humanities; political science and government; sociology.
Non-credit—accounting and computer science; allied health and medical assisting services; building/construction finishing, management, and inspection; computer software and media applications; engineering-related fields; health and medical administrative services; legal professions and studies related; sales, merchandising, and related marketing operations (general); technology education/industrial arts.

RADFORD UNIVERSITY
Radford, Virginia
http://www.radford.edu/

Radford University was founded in 1910. It is accredited by Southern Association of Colleges and Schools. It first offered distance learning courses in 1995. In fall 2005, there were 500 students enrolled in distance learning courses. Institutionally administered financial aid is available to distance learners.
Services Distance learners have accessibility to academic advising, bookstore, campus computer network, career placement assistance, e-mail services, library services, tutoring.
Contact Ellen Taylor, Director of Extended Education, Radford University, Office of Extended Education, Radford, VA 24142. Telephone: 540-831-5845. Fax: 540-831-6061. E-mail: eltaylor@radford.edu.

DEGREES AND AWARDS
Programs offered do not lead to a degree or other formal award.

COURSE SUBJECT AREAS OFFERED OUTSIDE OF DEGREE PROGRAMS
Graduate—allied health diagnostic, intervention, and treatment professions; business administration, management and operations; business/commerce; business/corporate communications; business/managerial economics; communication and media; community health services; criminology; curriculum and instruction; educational administration and supervision; education (specific levels and methods); finance and financial management services; health and medical administrative services; health/medical preparatory programs; health professions related; nursing.
Non-credit—accounting and related services; business administration, management and operations; business, management, and marketing related; computer and information sciences; computer and information sciences and support services related; computer software and media applications; nursing; public health; sales, merchandising, and related marketing operations (specialized).

RANDOLPH COMMUNITY COLLEGE
Asheboro, North Carolina
Virtual Campus
http://www.virtualrandolph.org

Randolph Community College was founded in 1962. It is accredited by Southern Association of Colleges and Schools. It first offered distance learning courses in 1998. In fall 2005, there were 1,200 students enrolled in distance learning courses. Institutionally administered financial aid is available to distance learners.
Services Distance learners have accessibility to academic advising, bookstore, e-mail services, library services.
Contact Deborah M. Kennedy, Virtual Campus Content Coordinator, Randolph Community College, 629 Industrial Park Avenue, PO Box

1009, Asheboro, NC 27205. Telephone: 336-633-0263. Fax: 336-629-4695. E-mail: dmkennedy@randolph.edu.

DEGREES AND AWARDS

AA College Transfer
AAS Accounting; Business Administration; Criminal Justice; Information Systems; Office Systems Technology

COURSE SUBJECT AREAS OFFERED OUTSIDE OF DEGREE PROGRAMS

Undergraduate—accounting and related services; allied health and medical assisting services; computer and information sciences; computer software and media applications; criminal justice and corrections; economics; education (specific subject areas); English composition; ethnic, cultural minority, and gender studies; finance and financial management services; history; human development, family studies, and related services; legal studies (non-professional general, undergraduate); marketing; music; philosophy and religious studies related; psychology; sociology.
Non-credit—accounting and related services; allied health and medical assisting services; allied health diagnostic, intervention, and treatment professions; business operations support and assistant services; clinical/medical laboratory science and allied professions; computer software and media applications; gerontology; medical basic sciences; pharmacy, pharmaceutical sciences, and administration.

RAPPAHANNOCK COMMUNITY COLLEGE
Glenns, Virginia
Flexible Learning Opportunities (FLO)
http://www.rcc.vccs.edu

Rappahannock Community College was founded in 1970. It is accredited by Southern Association of Colleges and Schools. It first offered distance learning courses in 1995. In fall 2005, there were 1,200 students enrolled in distance learning courses. Institutionally administered financial aid is available to distance learners.
Services Distance learners have accessibility to academic advising, bookstore, campus computer network, career placement assistance, e-mail services, library services, tutoring.
Contact Kristy Walker, Assistant for Distance Learning and Technology, Rappahannock Community College, 52 Campus Drive, Warsaw, VA 22572. Telephone: 804-333-6786. Fax: 804-333-6784. E-mail: kwalker@rcc.vccs.edu.

DEGREES AND AWARDS

AAS General Studies
Certificate Administrative Support; Bookkeeping/Accounting

COURSE SUBJECT AREAS OFFERED OUTSIDE OF DEGREE PROGRAMS

Undergraduate—accounting and related services; allied health and medical assisting services; American literature (United States and Canadian); business administration, management and operations; business/corporate communications; community health services; criminal justice and corrections; English composition; fine and studio art; health and physical education/fitness; history; mathematics; psychology; religious studies; sociology.
Non-credit—real estate.

RARITAN VALLEY COMMUNITY COLLEGE
Somerville, New Jersey
Distance Learning
http://www.raritanval.edu/newhometest/frameset/virtualcampus.html

Raritan Valley Community College was founded in 1965. It is accredited by Middle States Association of Colleges and Schools. It first offered distance learning courses in 1997. In fall 2005, there were 1,800 students enrolled in distance learning courses. Institutionally administered financial aid is available to distance learners.
Services Distance learners have accessibility to academic advising, bookstore, campus computer network, career placement assistance, e-mail services, library services, tutoring.
Contact Chuck Chulvick, Vice President of Learning and Technology Services, Raritan Valley Community College, PO Box 3300, Somerville, NJ 08876. Telephone: 908-526-1200 Ext. 8409. Fax: 908-429-0034. E-mail: cchulvic@raritanval.edu.

DEGREES AND AWARDS

AS Business Administration; Management Information Systems

COURSE SUBJECT AREAS OFFERED OUTSIDE OF DEGREE PROGRAMS

Undergraduate—American literature (United States and Canadian); anthropology; applied mathematics; area, ethnic, cultural, and gender studies related; astronomy and astrophysics; business administration, management and operations; business, management, and marketing related; computer and information sciences; computer and information sciences and support services related; computer/information technology administration and management; computer programming; computer software and media applications; computer systems networking and telecommunications; creative writing; criminal justice and corrections; criminology; economics; English; English composition; English language and literature related; history; human development, family studies, and related services; legal studies (non-professional general, undergraduate); marketing; mathematics; mathematics and statistics related; nursing; psychology; psychology related; sales, merchandising, and related marketing operations (general); social sciences; social work; sociology; statistics.
Non-credit—allied health and medical assisting services.

RASMUSSEN COLLEGE EDEN PRARIE
Eden Prarie, Minnesota
Rasmussen College Online
http://www.rasmussen.edu/

Rasmussen College Eden Prarie was founded in 1904. It is accredited by Accrediting Council for Independent Colleges and Schools. It first offered distance learning courses in 2001. In fall 2005, there were 1,000 students enrolled in distance learning courses. Institutionally administered financial aid is available to distance learners.
Services Distance learners have accessibility to academic advising, bookstore, campus computer network, career placement assistance, e-mail services, library services, tutoring.
Contact Joe Camolillia, Director of Admissions, Rasmussen College Eden Prarie, 851 Trafalgar Court, Suite 420, Maitland, FL 32751. Telephone: 866-932-3347 Ext. 5385. Fax: 866-874-4888. E-mail: joe.camolillia@rasmussen.edu.

DEGREES AND AWARDS

AAS Accounting–Financial Accounting; Business Management, Accounting; Business Management, Banking and Finance; Business Management, Business Administration; Business Management, Child Care; Business Management, Human Resources; Business Management, Internet Marketing; Business Management, Sales and Marketing; Criminal Justice; Health Information Technician (Records Management/Coding)

COURSE SUBJECT AREAS OFFERED OUTSIDE OF DEGREE PROGRAMS

Undergraduate—accounting and computer science; accounting and related services; allied health and medical assisting services; allied health diagnostic, intervention, and treatment professions; alternative and complementary medical support services; American literature (United States and Canadian); applied mathematics; area, ethnic, cultural, and gender studies related; area studies; behavioral sciences; business administration, management and operations; business/commerce; business, management, and marketing related; business/managerial economics; business operations support and assistant services; cognitive science; communication and journalism related; communication and media; communications technologies and support services related; communications technology; community psychology; comparative literature; computer and information sciences; computer and information sciences and support services related; computer/information technology administration and management; computer science; computer software and media applications; computer systems networking and telecommunications; criminal justice and corrections; criminology; data processing; developmental and child psychology; economics; English; English composition; English language and literature related; ethnic, cultural minority, and gender studies; family psychology; film/video and photographic arts; finance and financial management services; health and medical administrative services; health/medical preparatory programs; health professions related; health services/allied health/health sciences; liberal arts and sciences, general studies and humanities; marketing; mathematics; mathematics and statistics related; physiology, pathology and related sciences; psychology; psychology related; psychopharmacology; sales, merchandising, and related marketing operations (general); sales, merchandising, and related marketing operations (specialized); social sciences; technology education/industrial arts.

READING AREA COMMUNITY COLLEGE
Reading, Pennsylvania
http://www.racc.edu

Reading Area Community College was founded in 1971. It is accredited by Middle States Association of Colleges and Schools. It first offered distance learning courses in 1986. In fall 2005, there were 463 students enrolled in distance learning courses. Institutionally administered financial aid is available to distance learners.

Services Distance learners have accessibility to bookstore, campus computer network, e-mail services, library services.

Contact Mrs. Carol A. Alspach, Coordinator of Special Programs, Reading Area Community College, 10 South Second Street, PO Box 1706, Reading, PA 19603. Telephone: 610-607-6219. Fax: 610-372-4264. E-mail: calspach@racc.edu.

DEGREES AND AWARDS

AGS General Studies; General Studies; General Studies; General Studies; General Studies; General Studies

COURSE SUBJECT AREAS OFFERED OUTSIDE OF DEGREE PROGRAMS

Undergraduate—accounting and related services; anthropology; biological and biomedical sciences related; business administration, management and operations; business/commerce; computer and information sciences; developmental and child psychology; economics; English composition; human development, family studies, and related services; languages (Romance languages); mathematics; psychology; sociology.

RED ROCKS COMMUNITY COLLEGE
Lakewood, Colorado
Learning and Resource Center
http://www.rrcc.edu/online

Red Rocks Community College was founded in 1969. It is accredited by North Central Association of Colleges and Schools. It first offered distance learning courses in 1980. In fall 2005, there were 1,200 students enrolled in distance learning courses. Institutionally administered financial aid is available to distance learners.

Services Distance learners have accessibility to academic advising, bookstore, library services.

Contact Rebecca Woulfe, Director of eLearning, Red Rocks Community College, 13300 West 6th Avenue, Lakewood, CO 80228. Telephone: 303-914-6444. Fax: 303-914-6716. E-mail: rebecca.woulfe@rrcc.edu.

DEGREES AND AWARDS

AAS Building Code Enforcement; Business; Construction Technology–Construction Electrician emphasis; Construction Technology–Power Technology emphasis; Emergency Management and Planning; Fire Science Management

COURSE SUBJECT AREAS OFFERED OUTSIDE OF DEGREE PROGRAMS

Undergraduate—accounting and related services; applied mathematics; building/construction finishing, management, and inspection; computer and information sciences; computer programming; computer science; computer software and media applications; computer systems analysis; computer systems networking and telecommunications; data processing; developmental and child psychology; education related; English as a second language; English composition; fine and studio art; fire protection; geography and cartography; history; mathematics; music; social psychology; sociology; visual and performing arts related.

REGENT UNIVERSITY
Virginia Beach, Virginia
Distance Education
http://www.regent.edu

Regent University was founded in 1977. It is accredited by Southern Association of Colleges and Schools. It first offered distance learning courses in 1989. In fall 2005, there were 2,365 students enrolled in distance learning courses. Institutionally administered financial aid is available to distance learners.

Services Distance learners have accessibility to academic advising, bookstore, campus computer network, career placement assistance, e-mail services, library services.

Contact Mr. Jerrod Fishback, Central Enrollment Management, Regent University, 1000 Regent University Drive, SC 218, Virginia Beach, VA 23464. Telephone: 800-373-5504. Fax: 757-226-4381. E-mail: admissions@regent.edu.

DEGREES AND AWARDS

BA Communications; Religious Studies

BS Global Business; Interdisciplinary Studies; Organizational Leadership and Management; Political Science; Psychology

Certificate TESOL

Graduate Certificate Business Essentials; Entrepreneurship; Finance; Human Resource Management; International Business; Leadership–Certificate of Graduate Studies; Marketing; Not-for-Profit Management; Organizational Change and Development; e-Business

MA Biblical Studies; Cinema Arts; Communication; Government; Human Services Counseling; Journalism; Management; Organizational Leadership; Practical Theology; Strategic Foresight; Television Arts; Theater Arts

MBA Business Administration

MDiv Practical Theology

MEd Christian School Program; Cross-Categorical Special Education; Educational Leadership; Individualized Degree Program; Master Teacher Program; Student Affairs; TESOL

DMin Leadership and Renewal

DSL Strategic Leadership

EdD Education Doctorate

PhD Counseling Education and Supervision; Organizational Leadership; Renewal Studies

COURSE SUBJECT AREAS OFFERED OUTSIDE OF DEGREE PROGRAMS

Undergraduate—business administration, management and operations; business/commerce; business, management, and marketing related; communication and journalism related; communication and media; communications technology; education; English; film/video and photographic arts; history; international business; mathematics; natural sciences; physical sciences; political science and government; psychology; social sciences; theological and ministerial studies; theology and religious vocations related; visual and performing arts.

Graduate—accounting and related services; biblical studies; business administration, management and operations; business/commerce; business, management, and marketing related; communication and journalism related; communication and media; communications technology; counseling psychology; education; English as a second language; international business; pastoral counseling and specialized ministries; political science and government; psychology; public administration; public policy analysis; theological and ministerial studies; theology and religious vocations related; visual and performing arts.

Non-credit—accounting and related services; business administration, management and operations; business/commerce; business, management, and marketing related; communication and journalism related; education; educational administration and supervision; education related; English as a second language; film/video and photographic arts; human resources management; international business; international/global studies; international relations and affairs; pastoral counseling and specialized ministries; public policy analysis; religious education; religious studies; theology and religious vocations related; visual and performing arts.

See full description on page 434.

REGIONS UNIVERSITY
Montgomery, Alabama
Extended Learning Program
http://www.regionsuniversity.edu

Regions University was founded in 1967. It is accredited by Southern Association of Colleges and Schools. It first offered distance learning courses in 1993. In fall 2005, there were 725 students enrolled in distance learning courses. Institutionally administered financial aid is available to distance learners.

Services Distance learners have accessibility to academic advising, bookstore, library services, tutoring.

Contact Rick Johnson, Director of Enrollment Management, Regions University, 1200 Taylor Road, Montgomery, AL 36117-3553. Telephone: 800-351-4040 Ext. 7513. Fax: 334-387-3878. E-mail: rickjohnson@southernchristian.edu.

DEGREES AND AWARDS

AA Liberal Studies
BA Biblical Studies
BS Business Administration/General Business; Business Administration/Information Communication; Business Administration/Information Systems Management; Human Development; Human Resource Leadership; Liberal Studies; Management Communication; Ministry/Bible; Public Safety and Criminal Justice
MA Behavioral Leadership and Management; Biblical Studies; Marriage and Family Therapy; Practical Theology; Professional Counseling
MDiv Marriage and Family Therapy; Ministerial Leadership; Ministry; Pastoral Counseling; Professional Counseling
MS Leadership and Management; Ministerial Leadership; Pastoral Counseling
DMin Christian Ministry; Family Therapy
PhD Biblical Studies; Family Therapy

COURSE SUBJECT AREAS OFFERED OUTSIDE OF DEGREE PROGRAMS

Undergraduate—human services; liberal arts and sciences, general studies and humanities; missionary studies and missiology; pastoral counseling and specialized ministries; philosophy and religious studies related; religious studies; theological and ministerial studies.

Graduate—human services; missionary studies and missiology; pastoral counseling and specialized ministries; philosophy and religious studies related; religious studies; theological and ministerial studies.

Non-credit—human services; liberal arts and sciences, general studies and humanities; missionary studies and missiology; pastoral counseling and specialized ministries; philosophy and religious studies related; religious studies; theological and ministerial studies.

See full description on page 436.

REND LAKE COLLEGE
Ina, Illinois
Learning Resource Center
http://www.rlc.edu

Rend Lake College was founded in 1967. It is accredited by North Central Association of Colleges and Schools. It first offered distance learning courses in 1995. In fall 2005, there were 885 students enrolled in distance learning courses. Institutionally administered financial aid is available to distance learners.

Services Distance learners have accessibility to academic advising, bookstore, campus computer network, career placement assistance, e-mail services, library services, tutoring.

Contact Karla J. Lewis, Coordinator of Distance Learning and Media Technology, Rend Lake College, Learning Resource Center, 468 North Ken Gray Parkway, Ina, IL 62846. Telephone: 618-437-5321 Ext. 1299. Fax: 618-437-5598. E-mail: klewis@rlc.edu.

DEGREES AND AWARDS

Programs offered do not lead to a degree or other formal award.

COURSE SUBJECT AREAS OFFERED OUTSIDE OF DEGREE PROGRAMS

Undergraduate—agriculture; anthropology; astronomy and astrophysics; biology; business/commerce; business/corporate communications; clinical child psychology; computer science; English; English composition; geological and earth sciences/geosciences; health and physical education/fitness; health services/allied health/health sciences; history; liberal arts and sciences, general studies and humanities; mathematics; microbiological sciences and immunology; music; nursing; nutrition sciences; philosophy and religious studies related; plant sciences; political science and government; psychology; real estate; religious studies; social sciences; sociology; speech and rhetoric; work and family studies.

Non-credit—accounting and related services; business administration, management and operations; business operations support and assistant services; computer software and media applications; entrepreneurial and small business operations; human resources management; sales, merchandising, and related marketing operations (general).

THE RICHARD STOCKTON COLLEGE OF NEW JERSEY
Pomona, New Jersey
Office of Distance Education
http://www.stockton.edu

The Richard Stockton College of New Jersey was founded in 1969. It is accredited by Middle States Association of Colleges and Schools. It first offered distance learning courses in 1996. In fall 2005, there were 1,500 students enrolled in distance learning courses. Institutionally administered financial aid is available to distance learners.

Services Distance learners have accessibility to campus computer network, e-mail services, library services.

Contact Dennis Fotia, Distance Education Coordinator, The Richard Stockton College of New Jersey, PO Box 195, Pomona, NJ 08240-0195. Telephone: 609-652-4580. Fax: 609-626-5562. E-mail: dennis.fotia@stockton.edu.

DEGREES AND AWARDS

Programs offered do not lead to a degree or other formal award.

COURSE SUBJECT AREAS OFFERED OUTSIDE OF DEGREE PROGRAMS

Undergraduate—allied health and medical assisting services; anthropology; applied mathematics; business administration, management and operations; English composition; ethnic, cultural minority, and gender studies; film/video and photographic arts; gerontology; health professions related; journalism; liberal arts and sciences, general studies and humanities; marketing; nursing; psychology; sociology.

Graduate—allied health and medical assisting services; business, management, and marketing related; information science/studies; nursing.

RIO HONDO COLLEGE
Whittier, California
http://www.riohondo.edu/

Rio Hondo College was founded in 1960. It is accredited by Western Association of Schools and Colleges. It first offered distance learning courses in 1998. In fall 2005, there were 2,397 students enrolled in distance learning courses. Institutionally administered financial aid is available to distance learners.

Services Distance learners have accessibility to academic advising, bookstore, campus computer network, library services, tutoring.

Contact Antonio Flores, Dean of Admissions and Records, Rio Hondo College, 3600 Workman Mill Road, Whittier, CA 90601. Telephone: 562-692-0921 Ext. 3146. E-mail: aflores@riohondo.edu.

DEGREES AND AWARDS

Programs offered do not lead to a degree or other formal award.

COURSE SUBJECT AREAS OFFERED OUTSIDE OF DEGREE PROGRAMS

Undergraduate—accounting and related services; American literature (United States and Canadian); anthropology; archeology; business, management, and marketing related; comparative literature; computer and information sciences; computer programming; economics; education related; English; English composition; fine and studio art; fire protection; geological and earth sciences/geosciences; health and medical administrative services; health and physical education/fitness; history; international business; languages (Romance languages); library science related; mathematics; political science and government; psychology; sociology.

ROCHESTER INSTITUTE OF TECHNOLOGY
Rochester, New York
Graduate Enrollment Services
http://www.rit.edu/online

Rochester Institute of Technology was founded in 1829. It is accredited by Middle States Association of Colleges and Schools. It first offered distance learning courses in 1979. In fall 2005, there were 1,600 students enrolled in distance learning courses. Institutionally administered financial aid is available to distance learners.

Services Distance learners have accessibility to academic advising, bookstore, campus computer network, e-mail services, library services.

Contact Ms. Diane Ellison, Director, Office of Part-time and Graduate Enrollment Services, Rochester Institute of Technology, Bausch & Lomb Center, 58 Lomb Memorial Drive, Rochester, NY 14623. Telephone: 585-475-2229. Fax: 585-475-7164. E-mail: opes@rit.edu.

DEGREES AND AWARDS

BS Arts and Science–Applied Arts and Science; Electrical/Mechanical Engineering Technology; Safety Technology; Telecommunications Technology

Certificate Disaster and Emergency Management; E-business; Health Systems Administration; Industrial Environmental Management; International Logistics and Transportation Management; Introduction to Programming–NTID; Public Relations Communications–Professional Writing; Quality Implementation; Quality Management, basic; Reliability Maintenance; Safety and Health Technology; Structural Design; Technical Communication, basic; Technical Communications, advanced; Telecommunications–Data Communications; Telecommunications–Network Management; Telecommunications–Voice Communications

Graduate Certificate Elements of Health Care Leadership; Health Information Resources; Health Systems Finance; Human Resource Development; Learning and Knowledge Management Systems; Senior Living Management; Statistical Methods for Product and Process Improvement; Statistical Quality; Technical Information Design

MS Applied Statistics; Cross Disciplinary Professional Studies; Environmental Health and Safety Management; Health Systems Administration; Imaging Science; Information Technology; Learning and Knowledge Management Systems; Microelectronics Manufacturing Engineering; Print Media; Software Development and Management; Telecommunications Engineering Technology

COURSE SUBJECT AREAS OFFERED OUTSIDE OF DEGREE PROGRAMS

Undergraduate—anthropology; business administration, management and operations; chemistry; engineering mechanics; English composition; mechanical engineering; political science and government; psychology; sociology.

ROGER WILLIAMS UNIVERSITY
Bristol, Rhode Island
School of Continuing Studies
http://www.rwu.edu/Academics/Academic+Programs/School+of+Continuing+Studies/

Roger Williams University was founded in 1956. It is accredited by New England Association of Schools and Colleges. It first offered distance learning courses in 1974. In fall 2005, there were 234 students enrolled in distance learning courses. Institutionally administered financial aid is available to distance learners.

Services Distance learners have accessibility to academic advising, bookstore, campus computer network, career placement assistance, e-mail services, library services.

Contact John Stout, Dean, School of Continuing Studies, Roger Williams University, 150 Washington Street, Providence, RI 02903. Telephone: 401-254-3530. Fax: 401-254-3560. E-mail: jstout@rwu.edu.

DEGREES AND AWARDS

Programs offered do not lead to a degree or other formal award.

COURSE SUBJECT AREAS OFFERED OUTSIDE OF DEGREE PROGRAMS

Undergraduate—criminal justice and corrections; criminology; finance and financial management services; health and medical administrative services; health services/allied health/health sciences; history; industrial production technologies; legal studies (non-professional general, undergraduate); physical sciences related; public administration; public administration and social service professions related; sociology.

ROOSEVELT UNIVERSITY
Chicago, Illinois
Distance Learning
http://www.roosevelt.edu/ruonline

Roosevelt University was founded in 1945. It is accredited by North Central Association of Colleges and Schools. It first offered distance learning courses in 2001. In fall 2005, there were 1,000 students enrolled in distance learning courses. Institutionally administered financial aid is available to distance learners.

Services Distance learners have accessibility to academic advising, bookstore, campus computer network, career placement assistance, e-mail services, library services.

Contact Dr. Karen S. Gersten, Associate Provost for Academic Programs and Faculty Development, Roosevelt University, Office of the Provost, 430 South Michigan Avenue, Chicago, IL 60605. Telephone: 312-341-2337. Fax: 312-341-2013. E-mail: kgersten@roosevelt.edu.

DEGREES AND AWARDS

BPS Organizational Leadership

Certificate Organizational Leadership

Graduate Certificate E-Learning; Instructional Design; Training and Development

MA Training and Development

COURSE SUBJECT AREAS OFFERED OUTSIDE OF DEGREE PROGRAMS

Undergraduate—accounting and related services; business administration, management and operations; business/commerce; business/corporate communications; criminal justice and corrections; education; education (specific subject areas); English composition; hospitality administration; intercultural/multicultural and diversity studies; legal studies (non-professional general, undergraduate); liberal arts and sciences, general studies and humanities; multi-/interdisciplinary studies related; personality psychology; physical sciences; psychology; social sciences; sociology.

Graduate—business/corporate communications; communications technology; education; education related; hospitality administration; legal professions and studies related.

ROSALIND FRANKLIN UNIVERSITY OF MEDICINE AND SCIENCE
North Chicago, Illinois
http://www.rosalindfranklin.edu

Rosalind Franklin University of Medicine and Science was founded in 1912. It is accredited by North Central Association of Colleges and Schools. It first offered distance learning courses in 1993. In fall 2005, there were 146 students enrolled in distance learning courses. Institutionally administered financial aid is available to distance learners.

Services Distance learners have accessibility to academic advising, bookstore, campus computer network, e-mail services, library services, tutoring.

Contact Ms. Laura Nelson, Administrative Assistant, Rosalind Franklin University of Medicine and Science, 3333 Green Bay Road, North Chicago, IL 60064-3095. Telephone: 847-578-3310. E-mail: distance.education@rosalindfranklin.edu.

DEGREES AND AWARDS

CAGS Healthcare Management; Women's Health

MS Clinical Laboratory Sciences (advanced and categorical); Clinical Laboratory Sciences (entry-level); Clinical Nutrition/Nutrition Education; Healthcare Management; Women's Health

DPT Physical Therapy–Post-Professional Doctor of Physical Therapy

RUSH UNIVERSITY
Chicago, Illinois

Rush University was founded in 1969. It is accredited by North Central Association of Colleges and Schools. It first offered distance learning courses in 1998. In fall 2005, there were 50 students enrolled in distance learning courses. Institutionally administered financial aid is available to distance learners.

Services Distance learners have accessibility to campus computer network, e-mail services.

Contact Ms. Hicela C. Woods, Director, Rush University, College Admission Services, 600 South Paulina, Suite 440, Chicago, IL 60612. Telephone: 312-942-7100. Fax: 312-942-2219. E-mail: hicela_castruita @rush.edu.

DEGREES AND AWARDS

BSN Nursing; Nursing

RYERSON UNIVERSITY
Toronto, Ontario, Canada
Distance Education
http://www.ryerson.ca/ce/de

Ryerson University was founded in 1948. It is provincially chartered. It first offered distance learning courses in 1999. In fall 2005, there were 4,606 students enrolled in distance learning courses. Institutionally administered financial aid is available to distance learners.

Services Distance learners have accessibility to academic advising, bookstore, campus computer network, career placement assistance, e-mail services, library services, tutoring.

Contact Martha Ireland, Manager, Support Services, Ryerson University, G. Raymond Chang School of Continuing Education, Distance Education, 350 Victoria Street, Toronto, ON M5B 2K3, Canada. Telephone: 416-979-5000 Ext. 7874. Fax: 416-979-5136. E-mail: mireland@ ryerson.ca.

DEGREES AND AWARDS

Programs offered do not lead to a degree or other formal award.

COURSE SUBJECT AREAS OFFERED OUTSIDE OF DEGREE PROGRAMS

Undergraduate—accounting and related services; business administration, management and operations; business/commerce; business/ corporate communications; business/managerial economics; communication and media; community health services; computer/information technology administration and management; criminal justice and corrections; economics; English; entrepreneurial and small business operations; finance and financial management services; foods, nutrition, and related services; geography and cartography; gerontology; health professions related; history; hospitality administration; human development, family studies, and related services; human resources management; legal studies (non-professional general, undergraduate); liberal arts and sciences, general studies and humanities; management information systems; management sciences and quantitative methods; marketing; nursing; philosophy; political science and government; psychology; public administration; public administration and social service professions related; public relations, advertising, and applied communication related; publishing; sales, merchandising, and related marketing operations (general); social sciences; sociology.

SACRAMENTO CITY COLLEGE
Sacramento, California
Courses by Television
http://www.scc.losrios.edu/de

Sacramento City College was founded in 1916. It is accredited by Western Association of Schools and Colleges. It first offered distance learning courses in 1986. In fall 2005, there were 1,958 students enrolled in distance learning courses. Institutionally administered financial aid is available to distance learners.

Services Distance learners have accessibility to academic advising, bookstore, campus computer network, career placement assistance, e-mail services, library services, tutoring.

Contact Jane Phillips, Student Coordinator of Distance Education, Sacramento City College, Learning Resources, Sacramento, CA 95822. Telephone: 916-558-2361. E-mail: phillije@exi.scc.losrios.edu.

DEGREES AND AWARDS

Programs offered do not lead to a degree or other formal award.

COURSE SUBJECT AREAS OFFERED OUTSIDE OF DEGREE PROGRAMS

Undergraduate—accounting and related services; biology; computer and information sciences; computer and information sciences and support services related; computer programming; computer software and media applications; creative writing; English composition; family and consumer sciences/human sciences; geography and cartography; gerontology; health professions related; history; journalism; library science related; mathematics; philosophy and religious studies related; physiology, pathology and related sciences; political science and government; psychology; real estate; sociology.

SACRED HEART UNIVERSITY
Fairfield, Connecticut
University College/ Continuing Education
http://onlinelearning.sacredheart.edu

Sacred Heart University was founded in 1963. It is accredited by New England Association of Schools and Colleges. It first offered distance learning courses in 1997. In fall 2005, there were 592 students enrolled in distance learning courses. Institutionally administered financial aid is available to distance learners.

Services Distance learners have accessibility to academic advising, bookstore, campus computer network, career placement assistance, e-mail services, library services, tutoring.

Contact David M. Demers, PhD, Director, Instructional Technology, Sacred Heart University, 5151 Park Avenue, Fairfield, CT 06825. Telephone: 203-365-7613. Fax: 203-365-7695. E-mail: demersd@ sacredheart.edu.

DEGREES AND AWARDS

BSN Nursing

MSHA Geriatric Rehabilitation and Wellness

MSN Nursing–Patient Care Services Administration–Family Nurse Practitioner

COURSE SUBJECT AREAS OFFERED OUTSIDE OF DEGREE PROGRAMS

Undergraduate—biological and physical sciences; business administration, management and operations; chemistry; communication and media; computer and information sciences; computer science; English composition; English language and literature related; fine and studio art; health professions related; history; international business; languages (foreign languages related); liberal arts and sciences, general studies and humanities; linguistic, comparative, and related language studies; marketing; music; philosophy; philosophy and religious studies related; physical sciences; political science and government; religious education; religious studies; social sciences related.

Graduate—accounting and related services; business administration, management and operations; computer science; economics; education; finance and financial management services; gerontology; health professions related; marketing; mathematics; nursing.

SADDLEBACK COLLEGE
Mission Viejo, California
Office of Instruction
http://www.saddlebackcollege.edu

Saddleback College was founded in 1967. It is accredited by Western Association of Schools and Colleges. It first offered distance learning courses in 1975. In fall 2005, there were 3,000 students enrolled in distance learning courses. Institutionally administered financial aid is available to distance learners.

Services Distance learners have accessibility to academic advising, bookstore, campus computer network, career placement assistance, e-mail services, library services.

Contact Ms. Sheri L. Nelson, Senior Administrative Assistant, Saddleback College, AGB 117, 28000 Marguerite Parkway, Mission Viejo, CA 92692. Telephone: 949-582-4515. Fax: 949-347-0438. E-mail: snelson @saddleback.edu.

DEGREES AND AWARDS

Programs offered do not lead to a degree or other formal award.

COURSE SUBJECT AREAS OFFERED OUTSIDE OF DEGREE PROGRAMS

Undergraduate—accounting and computer science; accounting and related services; anthropology; business, management, and marketing related; business/managerial economics; communication and journalism related; computer science; developmental and child psychology; health/medical preparatory programs; history; human development, family studies, and related services; international business; library science related; management information systems; marketing; music; nursing; political science and government; real estate; sales, merchandising, and related marketing operations (general); social sciences related; sociology.

ST. CLAIR COUNTY COMMUNITY COLLEGE
Port Huron, Michigan
http://www.SC4.edu/

St. Clair County Community College was founded in 1923. It is accredited by North Central Association of Colleges and Schools. It first offered distance learning courses in 2000. In fall 2005, there were 600 students enrolled in distance learning courses. Institutionally administered financial aid is available to distance learners.

Services Distance learners have accessibility to academic advising, bookstore, career placement assistance, e-mail services, library services, tutoring.

Contact Linda Davis, Associate Dean of eLearning and Instructional Technology, St. Clair County Community College, 323 Erie Street, PO Box 5015, Port Huron, MI 48061-5015. Telephone: 810-989-5765. E-mail: ldavis@sc4.edu.

DEGREES AND AWARDS

Programs offered do not lead to a degree or other formal award.

COURSE SUBJECT AREAS OFFERED OUTSIDE OF DEGREE PROGRAMS

Undergraduate—accounting and related services; astronomy and astrophysics; business administration, management and operations; business/corporate communications; chemistry; communication and journalism related; computer and information sciences; creative writing; economics; education (specific levels and methods); electrical and electronic engineering technologies; English composition; geography and cartography; history; mathematics; nursing; political science and government; psychology; social sciences; sociology; speech and rhetoric; statistics.

ST. CLOUD STATE UNIVERSITY
St. Cloud, Minnesota
Center for Continuing Studies
http://www.stcloudstate.edu/~ccs/

St. Cloud State University was founded in 1869. It is accredited by North Central Association of Colleges and Schools. It first offered distance learning courses in 1975. In fall 2005, there were 3,000 students enrolled in distance learning courses. Institutionally administered financial aid is available to distance learners.

Services Distance learners have accessibility to bookstore, campus computer network, e-mail services, library services.

Contact Ms. Patricia Aceves, Director of Distributed Learning, St. Cloud State University, 720 4th Avenue South, St. Cloud, MN 56301. Telephone: 320-308-3081. Fax: 320-308-5041. E-mail: paceves@stcloudstate.edu.

DEGREES AND AWARDS

AA Liberal Arts
BA Criminal Justice Studies
BGS Community Psychology; Self-Designed
BSAST Aviation Maintenance Management
MA Teaching English as a Second Language
MBA Business Administration
MS Behavior Analysis; Criminal Justice Studies; Educational Administration; Environmental and Technological Studies

COURSE SUBJECT AREAS OFFERED OUTSIDE OF DEGREE PROGRAMS

Undergraduate—aerospace, aeronautical and astronautical engineering; American literature (United States and Canadian); anthropology; astronomy and astrophysics; biology; botany/plant biology; chemistry; communication and media; counseling psychology; creative writing; criminal justice and corrections; economics; educational administration and supervision; English; English as a second language; English composition; environmental/environmental health engineering; history; management information systems; mathematics; philosophy; physics; psychology; social sciences related; sociology; special education; speech and rhetoric; statistics.

Graduate—behavioral sciences; community psychology; criminal justice and corrections; English as a second language; psychology related; statistics.

ST. EDWARD'S UNIVERSITY
Austin, Texas
New College
http://www.stedwards.edu

St. Edward's University was founded in 1885. It is accredited by Southern Association of Colleges and Schools. It first offered distance learning courses in 1994. In fall 2005, there were 300 students enrolled in distance learning courses. Institutionally administered financial aid is available to distance learners.

Services Distance learners have accessibility to academic advising, bookstore, campus computer network, career placement assistance, e-mail services, library services, tutoring.

Contact Ms. Bridget Sowinski, Coordinator, Center for Academic Progress, St. Edward's University, Center for Academic Progress, 3001 South Congress Avenue, Austin, TX 78704-6489. Telephone: 512-428-0161. Fax: 512-428-1032. E-mail: bridgets@stedwards.edu.

DEGREES AND AWARDS

Programs offered do not lead to a degree or other formal award.

COURSE SUBJECT AREAS OFFERED OUTSIDE OF DEGREE PROGRAMS

Undergraduate—accounting and related services; anthropology; business administration, management and operations; business/corporate communications; business, management, and marketing related; business/managerial economics; communication and media; computer systems analysis; criminal justice and corrections; economics; education; English; geography and cartography; history; human resources management; human services; philosophy; philosophy and religious studies related; public administration; sales, merchandising, and related marketing operations (general); social sciences related.

Graduate—accounting and related services; business administration, management and operations; business/corporate communications; business/managerial economics; computer/information technology administration and management; computer systems analysis; counseling psychology; entrepreneurial and small business operations; human resources management; human services; liberal arts and sciences, general studies and humanities; marketing; peace studies and conflict resolution; public relations, advertising, and applied communication related; sales, merchandising, and related marketing operations (general); sales, merchandising, and related marketing operations (specialized).

Non-credit—business administration, management and operations; computer/information technology administration and management; computer systems analysis.

SAINT FRANCIS MEDICAL CENTER COLLEGE OF NURSING
Peoria, Illinois

Saint Francis Medical Center College of Nursing was founded in 1986. It is accredited by North Central Association of Colleges and Schools. It first offered distance learning courses in 2000. In fall 2005, there were 58 students enrolled in distance learning courses. Institutionally administered financial aid is available to distance learners.

Services Distance learners have accessibility to academic advising, campus computer network, e-mail services, library services.

Contact Mrs. Janice E. Farquharson, Director of Admissions, Registrar, Saint Francis Medical Center College of Nursing, 511 NE Greenleaf Street, Peoria, IL 61603. Telephone: 309-624-8980. Fax: 309-624-8973. E-mail: janice.e.farquharson@osfhealthcare.org.

DEGREES AND AWARDS

MSN Nursing

COURSE SUBJECT AREAS OFFERED OUTSIDE OF DEGREE PROGRAMS

Undergraduate—nursing.
Graduate—nursing.

ST. JOHNS RIVER COMMUNITY COLLEGE
Palatka, Florida
Continuing Education
http://www.sjrcc.cc.fl.us/

St. Johns River Community College was founded in 1958. It is accredited by Southern Association of Colleges and Schools. It first offered distance learning courses in 1996. In fall 2005, there were 2,000 students enrolled in distance learning courses. Institutionally administered financial aid is available to distance learners.

Services Distance learners have accessibility to academic advising, bookstore, campus computer network, career placement assistance, e-mail services, library services, tutoring.

Contact Dr. Melanie A. Brown, Dean of Distance Learning, St. Johns River Community College, 5001 St. Johns Avenue, Palatka, FL 32177. Telephone: 386-312-4211. Fax: 386-312-4027. E-mail: opencampus@sjrcc.edu.

DEGREES AND AWARDS

Programs offered do not lead to a degree or other formal award.

COURSE SUBJECT AREAS OFFERED OUTSIDE OF DEGREE PROGRAMS

Undergraduate—developmental and child psychology; English composition; sociology.

ST. JOHN'S UNIVERSITY
Queens, New York
The School of Education

St. John's University was founded in 1870. It is accredited by Middle States Association of Colleges and Schools. It first offered distance learning courses in 1994. In fall 2005, there were 916 students enrolled in distance learning courses. Institutionally administered financial aid is available to distance learners.

Services Distance learners have accessibility to academic advising, bookstore, campus computer network, career placement assistance, e-mail services, library services.

Contact Kelly K. Ronayne, Assistant Dean, St. John's University, 8000 Utopia Parkway, Newman Hall, 106, Queens, NY 11439. Telephone: 718-990-2304. Fax: 718-990-2343. E-mail: graded@stjohns.edu.

DEGREES AND AWARDS

Advanced Graduate Diploma Professional Diploma in Educational Administration and Supervision
MSE Educational Administration and Supervision
PMC Educational Administration–School District Administrator

COURSE SUBJECT AREAS OFFERED OUTSIDE OF DEGREE PROGRAMS

Graduate—education; educational administration and supervision; educational assessment, evaluation, and research; educational/instructional media design; education related; education (specific levels and methods); education (specific subject areas).

ST. JOHN'S UNIVERSITY
Queens, New York
http://www.stjohns.edu/distancelearning

St. John's University was founded in 1870. It is accredited by Middle States Association of Colleges and Schools. It first offered distance learning courses in 1994. In fall 2005, there were 999 students enrolled in distance learning courses. Institutionally administered financial aid is available to distance learners.

Services Distance learners have accessibility to academic advising, bookstore, campus computer network, career placement assistance, e-mail services, library services, tutoring.

Contact Dr. Jeffery E. Olson, Associate Vice President, Online Learning and Services, St. John's University, 8000 Utopia Parkway, Queens, NY 11439. Telephone: 718-990-5705. Fax: 718-990-5689. E-mail: distancelearning@stjohns.edu.

DEGREES AND AWARDS

AA Liberal Studies
AS Business; Criminal Justice
BA Liberal Studies
BS Administrative Studies; Criminal Justice
MSE School Building Leader in Educational Administration and Supervision
PMC School District Leader Professional Diploma

COURSE SUBJECT AREAS OFFERED OUTSIDE OF DEGREE PROGRAMS

Undergraduate—business administration, management and operations; communication and journalism related; computer science; criminal justice and corrections; economics; education; English; history; languages (Romance languages); legal studies (non-professional general, undergraduate); marketing; mathematics; pharmacy, pharmaceutical sciences, and administration; physics; political science and government; science technologies related; sociology; theology and religious vocations related.
Graduate—business, management, and marketing related; economics; education; educational administration and supervision; education (specific subject areas); library science.

ST. JOSEPH'S COLLEGE, NEW YORK
Brooklyn, New York

St. Joseph's College, New York was founded in 1916. It is accredited by Middle States Association of Colleges and Schools. It first offered distance learning courses in 1999. In fall 2005, there were 250 students enrolled in distance learning courses. Institutionally administered financial aid is available to distance learners.

Services Distance learners have accessibility to academic advising, bookstore, career placement assistance, e-mail services, library services, tutoring.

Contact Ms. Shannon M. O'Neill, Assistant to the Dean, St. Joseph's College, New York, 155 West Roe Boulevard, Patchogue, NY 11772. Telephone: 631-447-3254. Fax: 631-447-3624. E-mail: smoneill@sjcny.edu.

DEGREES AND AWARDS

BS Organizational Management

SAINT JOSEPH'S COLLEGE OF MAINE
Standish, Maine
Graduate & Professional Studies
http://www.sjcme.edu/gps

Saint Joseph's College of Maine was founded in 1912. It is accredited by New England Association of Schools and Colleges. It first offered distance learning courses in 1976. In fall 2005, there were 4,000 students enrolled in distance learning courses. Institutionally administered financial aid is available to distance learners.

Services Distance learners have accessibility to academic advising, bookstore, campus computer network, career placement assistance, e-mail services, library services, tutoring.

Contact Lynne Robinson, Director of Admissions, Saint Joseph's College of Maine, 278 Whites Bridge Road, Standish, ME 04084-5263. Telephone: 800-752-4723. Fax: 207-892-7480. E-mail: info@sjcme.edu.

DEGREES AND AWARDS

AS Adult Education and Training; Business Administration; Criminal Justice; General Studies; Human Services; Information Technology Management; Management; Psychology

BA Adult Religious Education

BLS Christian Tradition

BS General Studies; Health Care Administration; Long-Term Care Administration; Radiological Sciences

BSBA Business Administration

BSN Nursing

BSPA Professional Arts

Certificate Adult Education and Training; Business Administration; Christian Tradition; Health Care Management; Health Care Management, advanced; Information Technology Management; Long-Term Care Administration; Long-Term Care Administration, advanced; Professional Studies

Graduate Certificate Nursing Administration and Leadership; Nursing and Healthcare Education

MBA Quality Leadership

MBA/MSN Health Services Administration and Nursing Dual degree

MHSA Health Services Administration

MSE Education

MSN Nursing

COURSE SUBJECT AREAS OFFERED OUTSIDE OF DEGREE PROGRAMS

Undergraduate—accounting and related services; biblical studies; business administration, management and operations; communication and media; computer/information technology administration and management; criminology; developmental and child psychology; educational assessment, evaluation, and research; education (specific subject areas); English composition; health and medical administrative services; human services; industrial and organizational psychology; marketing; multi-/interdisciplinary studies related; nursing; pastoral counseling and specialized ministries; philosophy and religious studies related; religious education; social psychology; sociology.

Graduate—accounting and related services; business administration, management and operations; business/corporate communications; business, management, and marketing related; business/managerial economics; curriculum and instruction; educational administration and supervision; educational assessment, evaluation, and research; education (specific subject areas); entrepreneurial and small business operations; health and medical administrative services; management sciences and quantitative methods; marketing; nursing; public administration; sales, merchandising, and related marketing operations (specialized).

Non-credit—biblical studies; pastoral counseling and specialized ministries; religious studies.

See full description on page 438.

SAINT JOSEPH'S UNIVERSITY
Philadelphia, Pennsylvania
http://www.sju.edu/www/PHARMACEUTICAL_MARKETING/distance.htm

Saint Joseph's University was founded in 1851. It is accredited by Middle States Association of Colleges and Schools. It first offered distance learning courses in 2001. In fall 2005, there were 80 students enrolled in distance learning courses. Institutionally administered financial aid is available to distance learners.

Services Distance learners have accessibility to e-mail services, library services.

Contact Terese Waldron, Director of Graduate Business Distance Learning Programs, Saint Joseph's University, 5600 City Avenue, Philadelphia, PA 19083. Telephone: 610-660-3150. Fax: 610-660-3160. E-mail: twaldron@sju.edu.

DEGREES AND AWARDS

MBA Pharmaceutical Marketing

COURSE SUBJECT AREAS OFFERED OUTSIDE OF DEGREE PROGRAMS

Undergraduate—business administration, management and operations; chemistry; education; finance and financial management services; legal professions and studies related; marketing; mathematics; philosophy; political science and government; psychology; sociology; theology and religious vocations related.

Graduate—education; food science and technology; health and medical administrative services; marketing; psychology.

SAINT LEO UNIVERSITY
Saint Leo, Florida
Center for Distance Learning
http://www.saintleo.edu/col

Saint Leo University was founded in 1889. It is accredited by Southern Association of Colleges and Schools. It first offered distance learning courses in 1998. In fall 2005, there were 7,378 students enrolled in distance learning courses. Institutionally administered financial aid is available to distance learners.

Services Distance learners have accessibility to academic advising, bookstore, campus computer network, career placement assistance, e-mail services, library services, tutoring.

Contact Ms. Ruth Turner, Admissions Coordinator, Saint Leo University, Center for Online Learning, MC 2260, PO Box 6665, Saint Leo, FL 33574. Telephone: 877-856-2144 Ext. 7347. Fax: 352-588-4793. E-mail: coladmission2@saintleo.edu.

DEGREES AND AWARDS

AA Liberal Arts

AAB Business Administration

BA Accounting; Business Administration; Criminal Justice

BS Computer Information Systems

CAGS Criminal Justice

MAT Education–Master of Arts in Teaching Blended

MBA Business Administration–Master of Business Administration with Concentration

MEd Education–Master of Education—Exceptional Student Education Concentration

MS Criminal Justice

COURSE SUBJECT AREAS OFFERED OUTSIDE OF DEGREE PROGRAMS

Undergraduate—accounting and related services; biological and biomedical sciences related; business administration, management and operations; business/corporate communications; computer and information sciences; computer and information sciences and support services related; computer programming; computer software and media applications; computer systems analysis; computer systems networking and telecommunications; criminal justice and corrections; criminology; English; English composition; fine and studio art; human resources management; liberal arts and sciences, general studies and humanities; management sciences and quantitative methods; marketing; mathematics; philosophy;

philosophy and religious studies related; physical sciences; psychology; public administration; social sciences related; taxation.

ST. LOUIS COMMUNITY COLLEGE SYSTEM
St. Louis, Missouri
Telelearning Services
http://stlcc.edu/distance

St. Louis Community College System is accredited by North Central Association of Colleges and Schools. It first offered distance learning courses in 1973. In fall 2005, there were 6,016 students enrolled in distance learning courses. Institutionally administered financial aid is available to distance learners.

Services Distance learners have accessibility to academic advising, bookstore, career placement assistance, library services.

Contact Dr. Daniel A. Bain, Director of Telelearning Services, St. Louis Community College System, 300 South Broadway, St. Louis, MO 63102. Telephone: 314-539-5056. Fax: 314-539-5125. E-mail: dbain@stlcc.edu.

DEGREES AND AWARDS

AA General Program; Transfer Studies, general
AAS Information Reporting Technology

COURSE SUBJECT AREAS OFFERED OUTSIDE OF DEGREE PROGRAMS

Undergraduate—accounting and computer science; American literature (United States and Canadian); biological and physical sciences; communication and journalism related; computer and information sciences; computer and information sciences and support services related; computer software and media applications; data entry/microcomputer applications; funeral service and mortuary science; history; languages (Romance languages); marketing; mathematics; sociology.

Non-credit—business administration, management and operations; business/commerce; business, management, and marketing related; management information systems.

See full description on page 440.

SAINT MARY-OF-THE-WOODS COLLEGE
Saint Mary-of-the-Woods, Indiana
Woods External Degree Program
http://www.smwc.edu/

Saint Mary-of-the-Woods College was founded in 1840. It is accredited by North Central Association of Colleges and Schools. It first offered distance learning courses in 1973. In fall 2005, there were 1,300 students enrolled in distance learning courses. Institutionally administered financial aid is available to distance learners.

Services Distance learners have accessibility to academic advising, bookstore, career placement assistance, e-mail services, library services, tutoring.

Contact Mrs. Sara Lindsey, Associate Director of Distance Education Admission, Saint Mary-of-the-Woods College, Office of Distance Education Admission, 122 Guerin Hall, Saint Mary-of-the-Woods, IN 47876. Telephone: 800-499-0373. Fax: 812-535-5010. E-mail: wedadms@smwc.edu.

DEGREES AND AWARDS

AA Humanities; Paralegal Studies
AS Accounting; Business, general; Early Childhood/Child Development; Gerontology
BA English; History and Political Studies; Humanities; Journalism; Mathematics; Paralegal Studies; Professional Writing; Social Science/History; Theology
BS Accounting Information Systems; Accounting; Business Administration; Computer Information Systems; Digital Media Communication; Education–Kindergarten-Elementary Education; Education–Middle School/High School Special Education; Education–Preschool-Grade 3 Education/Mild Intervention; Gerontology; Human Resource Management; Human Services; Marketing; Not-for-Profit Child Care Administration; Not-for-Profit Financial Administration; Not-for-Profit Human Services; Not-for-Profit Public Relations; Psychology; Secondary Education–English; Secondary Education–Mathematics; Secondary Education–Social Studies
Certificate Gerontology; Paralegal Studies; Theology
MA Art Therapy; Earth Literacy; Music Therapy; Pastoral Theology

COURSE SUBJECT AREAS OFFERED OUTSIDE OF DEGREE PROGRAMS

Undergraduate—accounting and related services; business administration, management and operations; business/commerce; computer and information sciences; creative writing; education; education related; education (specific levels and methods); education (specific subject areas); gerontology; history; human resources management; human services; journalism; liberal arts and sciences, general studies and humanities; marketing; mathematics; political science and government; psychology; social sciences related; special education; technical and business writing; theology and religious vocations related.

Graduate—music; natural resources and conservation related; theological and ministerial studies.

See full description on page 442.

ST. MARY'S UNIVERSITY OF SAN ANTONIO
San Antonio, Texas
Graduate School
http://www.stmarytx.edu

St. Mary's University of San Antonio was founded in 1852. It is accredited by Southern Association of Colleges and Schools. It first offered distance learning courses in 1997. In fall 2005, there were 51 students enrolled in distance learning courses. Institutionally administered financial aid is available to distance learners.

Services Distance learners have accessibility to academic advising, bookstore, campus computer network, career placement assistance, e-mail services, library services.

Contact Dr. Henry Flores, Dean of the Graduate School, St. Mary's University of San Antonio, One Camino Santa Maria, Box 43, San Antonio, TX 78228. Telephone: 210-436-3101. E-mail: hflores@stmarytx.edu.

DEGREES AND AWARDS

MA Community Counseling; International Relations; Theology

ST. PETERSBURG COLLEGE
St. Petersburg, Florida
Electronic Campus
http://e.spcollege.edu

St. Petersburg College was founded in 1927. It is accredited by Southern Association of Colleges and Schools. It first offered distance learning courses in 1970. In fall 2005, there were 13,000 students enrolled in distance learning courses. Institutionally administered financial aid is available to distance learners.

Services Distance learners have accessibility to academic advising, bookstore, career placement assistance, e-mail services, library services, tutoring.

Contact Dr. James Connolly, eCampus Director, St. Petersburg College, PO Box 13489, St. Petersburg, FL 33733. Telephone: 727-394-6006. E-mail: connolly.james@spcollege.edu.

DEGREES AND AWARDS

AA General Program
AS Crime Scene Technology; Emergency Administration and Management; Funeral Services; Medical Laboratory Technology; Veterinary Technology
BA Dental Hygiene; Technology Management
Certificate Computer Related Crime Investigations; Crime Scene Technology; Critical Care (Advanced Technical Certification); Emergency Administration and Management; Fire Inspector I; Fire Inspector II; Fire Investigator I; Fire Investigator II; Fire Officer I; Fire Officer II; Nursing–Perioperative Nursing; Quality Assurance and Software Testing; Veterinary Hospital Management; Veterinary Hospital Manager

COURSE SUBJECT AREAS OFFERED OUTSIDE OF DEGREE PROGRAMS

Undergraduate—accounting and related services; American literature (United States and Canadian); anthropology; archeology; area studies; astronomy and astrophysics; biblical studies; biological and physical sciences; biology; business administration, management and operations; business/commerce; business/corporate communications; chemistry; communication and media; computer science; economics; education; educational assessment, evaluation, and research; educational/instructional media design; educational psychology; English as a second language; entrepreneurial and small business operations; finance and financial management services; fine and studio art; funeral service and mortuary science; geography and cartography; history; liberal arts and sciences, general studies and humanities; linguistic, comparative, and related language studies; mathematics; microbiological sciences and immunology; music; philosophy; political science and government; psychology; social psychology.

SALEM COMMUNITY COLLEGE
Carneys Point, New Jersey
http://www.salemcc.edu

Salem Community College was founded in 1972. It is accredited by Middle States Association of Colleges and Schools. It first offered distance learning courses in 1997. In fall 2005, there were 175 students enrolled in distance learning courses. Institutionally administered financial aid is available to distance learners.

Services Distance learners have accessibility to academic advising, bookstore, campus computer network, e-mail services, library services, tutoring.

Contact Ms. Karen Mattison, Director of Instruction, Salem Community College, 460 Hollywood Avenue, Carneys Point, NJ 08069. Telephone: 856-351-2672. E-mail: mattison@salemcc.edu.

DEGREES AND AWARDS

Programs offered do not lead to a degree or other formal award.

COURSE SUBJECT AREAS OFFERED OUTSIDE OF DEGREE PROGRAMS

Undergraduate—business administration, management and operations; computer/information technology administration and management; computer systems networking and telecommunications; economics; history; human development, family studies, and related services; psychology; sociology; speech and rhetoric.

Non-credit—business/corporate communications; education (specific subject areas).

SALVE REGINA UNIVERSITY
Newport, Rhode Island
Extension Study
http://www.salve.edu

Salve Regina University was founded in 1934. It is accredited by New England Association of Schools and Colleges. It first offered distance learning courses in 1985. In fall 2005, there were 350 students enrolled in distance learning courses. Institutionally administered financial aid is available to distance learners.

Services Distance learners have accessibility to academic advising, bookstore, campus computer network, career placement assistance, e-mail services, library services.

Contact Maureen E. Moriarty, Director of Extension Studies, Salve Regina University, 100 Ochre Point Avenue, Newport, RI 02840-4192. Telephone: 401-341-2212. Fax: 401-341-2931. E-mail: moriartm@salve.edu.

DEGREES AND AWARDS

BS Business
Certificate Management
MA Humanities; International Relations; Rehabilitation Counseling
MBA Business Administration
MS Administration of Justice; Management

COURSE SUBJECT AREAS OFFERED OUTSIDE OF DEGREE PROGRAMS

Graduate—business administration, management and operations; business/commerce; health and medical administrative services; international relations and affairs; rehabilitation and therapeutic professions.

Non-credit—business/commerce; health and medical administrative services; human resources management.

See full description on page 444.

SAM HOUSTON STATE UNIVERSITY
Huntsville, Texas
Correspondence Course Division
http://www.shsu.edu/~cor_www

Sam Houston State University was founded in 1879. It is accredited by Southern Association of Colleges and Schools. It first offered distance learning courses in 1953. In fall 2005, there were 1,300 students enrolled in distance learning courses. Institutionally administered financial aid is available to distance learners.

Services Distance learners have accessibility to bookstore, e-mail services, library services.

Contact Gail M. Wright, Correspondence Course Coordinator, Sam Houston State University, Box 2536, Huntsville, TX 77341-2536. Telephone: 936-294-1003. Fax: 936-294-3703. E-mail: cor_gmw@shsu.edu.

DEGREES AND AWARDS

Programs offered do not lead to a degree or other formal award.

COURSE SUBJECT AREAS OFFERED OUTSIDE OF DEGREE PROGRAMS

Undergraduate—accounting and related services; agricultural business and management; anthropology; business, management, and marketing related; chemistry; creative writing; economics; English; family and consumer economics; film/video and photographic arts; finance and financial management services; geological and earth sciences/geosciences; gerontology; health professions related; history; legal studies (nonprofessional general, undergraduate); marketing; mathematics and statistics related; nutrition sciences; philosophy; political science and government; psychology; sociology.

SAMUEL MERRITT COLLEGE
Oakland, California
Academic Affairs
http://www.samuelmerritt.edu

Samuel Merritt College was founded in 1909. It is accredited by Western Association of Schools and Colleges. It first offered distance learning courses in 2001. In fall 2005, there were 17 students enrolled in distance learning courses. Institutionally administered financial aid is available to distance learners.

Services Distance learners have accessibility to academic advising, bookstore, campus computer network, e-mail services, library services, tutoring.

Contact Mr. John Garten-Shuman, Vice President of Enrollment Services, Samuel Merritt College, Bechtel Hall, 450 30th Street, Oakland, CA 94609. Telephone: 800-607-6377. Fax: 510-869-6525. E-mail: jgartens@samuelmerritt.edu.

DEGREES AND AWARDS

MSN Nursing

SAN BERNARDINO VALLEY COLLEGE
San Bernardino, California
Distance Education Office
http://www.valleycollege.net

San Bernardino Valley College was founded in 1926. It is accredited by Western Association of Schools and Colleges. It first offered distance learning courses in 1986. In fall 2005, there were 2,158 students enrolled in distance learning courses. Institutionally administered financial aid is available to distance learners.

Services Distance learners have accessibility to bookstore, campus computer network, career placement assistance, e-mail services, library services, tutoring.

Contact Mr. Chuck Dean, Computer Technician, San Bernardino Valley College, 441 West 8th Street, San Bernardino, CA 92401. Telephone: 909-384-4318. Fax: 909-885-3035. E-mail: cdean@sbccd.cc.ca.us.

DEGREES AND AWARDS

AA Liberal Arts

COURSE SUBJECT AREAS OFFERED OUTSIDE OF DEGREE PROGRAMS

Undergraduate—accounting and related services; anthropology; astronomy and astrophysics; biology; business administration, management and operations; chemistry; communication and journalism related; economics; English; fine and studio art; human development, family studies, and related services; liberal arts and sciences, general studies and humanities; mathematics and statistics related; philosophy and religious studies related; political science and government; psychology related; radio, television, and digital communication; social sciences related; sociology; speech and rhetoric.

SAN DIEGO STATE UNIVERSITY
San Diego, California
Academic Affairs
http://www.sdsu.edu/dl

San Diego State University was founded in 1897. It is accredited by Western Association of Schools and Colleges. It first offered distance learning courses in 1984. In fall 2005, there were 971 students enrolled in distance learning courses. Institutionally administered financial aid is available to distance learners.

Services Distance learners have accessibility to academic advising, bookstore, e-mail services, library services, tutoring.

Contact Ms. Francesca Ringland, Director, Credit Community Education, College of Education, San Diego State University, 5500 Campanile Drive, San Diego, CA 92182-8010. Telephone: 619-594-2193. E-mail: ringland@mail.sdsu.edu.

DEGREES AND AWARDS

Certificate Instructional Technology

MA Education Leadership

MAE Educational Technology

MS Biomedical Quality Systems; Regulatory Affairs; Rehabilitation Counseling

COURSE SUBJECT AREAS OFFERED OUTSIDE OF DEGREE PROGRAMS

Undergraduate—building/construction finishing, management, and inspection; business/commerce; educational/instructional media design; education related; education (specific levels and methods); education (specific subject areas); ethnic, cultural minority, and gender studies; geological and earth sciences/geosciences; history; parks, recreation, and leisure related; physiology, pathology and related sciences.

Graduate—educational administration and supervision; educational/instructional media design; education (specific levels and methods).

Non-credit—business/commerce; computer programming; computer software and media applications; education; English as a second language; English composition; film/video and photographic arts; geological and earth sciences/geosciences; history.

SAN FRANCISCO STATE UNIVERSITY
San Francisco, California
Multimedia Studies Program
http://www.sfsu.edu/

San Francisco State University was founded in 1899. It is accredited by Western Association of Schools and Colleges. It first offered distance learning courses in 1999. In fall 2005, there were 32 students enrolled in distance learning courses. Institutionally administered financial aid is available to distance learners.

Services Distance learners have accessibility to academic advising, bookstore.

Contact Richard Sinrich, Online Program Coordinator, San Francisco State University, Multimedia Studies Program Online, College of Extended Learning, 425 Market Street, San Francisco, CA 94105-2406. Telephone: 415-405-3344. Fax: 415-405-7760. E-mail: rsinrich@sfsu.edu.

DEGREES AND AWARDS

Programs offered do not lead to a degree or other formal award.

COURSE SUBJECT AREAS OFFERED OUTSIDE OF DEGREE PROGRAMS

Non-credit—computer software and media applications; education (specific levels and methods).

SAN JOAQUIN DELTA COLLEGE
Stockton, California
Instructional Development
http://www.deltacollege.edu

San Joaquin Delta College was founded in 1935. It is accredited by Western Association of Schools and Colleges. It first offered distance learning courses in 1976. In fall 2005, there were 6,432 students enrolled in distance learning courses. Institutionally administered financial aid is available to distance learners.

Services Distance learners have accessibility to academic advising, bookstore, e-mail services, library services, tutoring.

Contact Dr. Kathleen A. Hart, Dean of Research, Planning, and Regional Education, San Joaquin Delta College, 5151 Pacific Avenue, Stockton, CA 95207. Telephone: 209-954-5039. Fax: 209-954-5600. E-mail: khart@deltacollege.edu.

DEGREES AND AWARDS

Certificate Early Childhood Education Assistant; Merchandising; Supervision and Management

ATC Liberal Arts and Science

COURSE SUBJECT AREAS OFFERED OUTSIDE OF DEGREE PROGRAMS

Undergraduate—accounting and related services; American literature (United States and Canadian); anthropology; astronomy and astrophysics; biblical and other theological languages and literatures; business/commerce; business/corporate communications; chemistry; computer science; computer software and media applications; computer systems networking and telecommunications; creative writing; criminal justice and corrections; design and applied arts; education related; English composition; finance and financial management services; health and physical education/fitness; history; human development, family studies, and related services; legal studies (non-professional general, undergraduate); mathematics and statistics related; nursing; philosophy and religious studies related; political science and government; psychology; sales, merchandising, and related marketing operations (general); sociology; statistics.

SAVANNAH COLLEGE OF ART AND DESIGN
Savannah, Georgia
http://www.scad.edu

Savannah College of Art and Design was founded in 1978. It is accredited by Southern Association of Colleges and Schools. It first offered distance learning courses in 2003. In fall 2005, there were 24 students enrolled in distance learning courses. Institutionally administered financial aid is available to distance learners.

Services Distance learners have accessibility to academic advising, bookstore, campus computer network, career placement assistance, e-mail services, library services, tutoring.

Contact Ms. Eve Seibert, Director of Recruitment, Savannah College of Art and Design, PO Box 3146, Savannah, GA 31402-3146. Telephone: 912-525-5100. Fax: 912-525-5986. E-mail: eseibert@scad.edu.

DEGREES AND AWARDS

Certificate Digital Publishing

Graduate Certificate Digital Publishing; Historic Preservation; Interactive Design

MA Graphic Design; Historic Preservation

See full description on page 446.

SAYBROOK GRADUATE SCHOOL AND RESEARCH CENTER

San Francisco, California

http://www.saybrook.edu/

Saybrook Graduate School and Research Center was founded in 1970. It is accredited by Western Association of Schools and Colleges. It first offered distance learning courses in 1971. In fall 2005, there were 525 students enrolled in distance learning courses. Institutionally administered financial aid is available to distance learners.

Services Distance learners have accessibility to academic advising, bookstore, campus computer network, library services.

Contact Ms. Maria Delos Reyes, Admissions, Saybrook Graduate School and Research Center, 747 Front Street, Third Floor, San Francisco, CA 94111. Telephone: 800-825-4480. Fax: 415-433-9271. E-mail: admissions@saybrook.edu.

DEGREES AND AWARDS

Graduate Certificate Building a Sustainable World; Community Health and Development; Creativity Studies; Expressive Arts for Healing and Social Change; Leading Organizational Transformation; Organizational Consulting; Peace and Conflict Resolution (International focus); Socially Engaged Spirituality; Violence Prevention and Response

MA Human Science; Marriage and Family Therapy; Organizational Systems; Psychology

PhD Doctoral Completion program; Human Science; Organizational Studies; Police and Public Safety Psychology (CopDoc); Psychology

COURSE SUBJECT AREAS OFFERED OUTSIDE OF DEGREE PROGRAMS

Graduate—agriculture; allied health diagnostic, intervention, and treatment professions; alternative and complementary medical support services; alternative and complementary medicine and medical systems; business administration, management and operations; clinical child psychology; clinical psychology; cognitive science; community health services; community organization and advocacy; community psychology; counseling psychology; criminal justice and corrections; developmental and child psychology; educational administration and supervision; environmental psychology; ethnic, cultural minority, and gender studies; family and consumer sciences/human sciences; family psychology; gerontology; health psychology; housing and human environments; human development, family studies, and related services; industrial and organizational psychology; intercultural/multicultural and diversity studies; operations research; peace studies and conflict resolution; physiology, pathology and related sciences; psychology; psychology related; public administration and social service professions related; rehabilitation and therapeutic professions; social psychology; social sciences related; somatic bodywork and related therapeutic services; theological and ministerial studies; urban studies/affairs.

Non-credit—business administration, management and operations; educational administration and supervision; industrial and organizational psychology; psychology; psychology related; public administration and social service professions related; theology and religious vocations related.

See full description on page 448.

SCHENECTADY COUNTY COMMUNITY COLLEGE

Schenectady, New York

http://www.sunysccc.edu

Schenectady County Community College was founded in 1969. It is accredited by Middle States Association of Colleges and Schools. It first offered distance learning courses in 1998. In fall 2005, there were 512 students enrolled in distance learning courses. Institutionally administered financial aid is available to distance learners.

Services Distance learners have accessibility to academic advising, bookstore, campus computer network, e-mail services, library services, tutoring.

Contact Shirlee Dufort, Associate for Continuing Education, Schenectady County Community College, 78 Washington Avenue, Schenectady, NY 12305. Telephone: 518-381-1315. E-mail: dufortsa@gw.sunysccc.edu.

DEGREES AND AWARDS

Programs offered do not lead to a degree or other formal award.

COURSE SUBJECT AREAS OFFERED OUTSIDE OF DEGREE PROGRAMS

Undergraduate—accounting and related services; astronomy and astrophysics; biology; business administration, management and operations; computer software and media applications; criminal justice and corrections; culinary arts and related services; English composition; entrepreneurial and small business operations; fire protection; history; hospitality administration; human development, family studies, and related services; legal studies (non-professional general, undergraduate); mathematics; music; nutrition sciences; psychology; sociology; technical and business writing.

SCHILLER INTERNATIONAL UNIVERSITY

Largo, Florida

http://www.schiller.edu/

Schiller International University was founded in 1991. It is accredited by Accrediting Council for Independent Colleges and Schools. It first offered distance learning courses in 1999. In fall 2005, there were 98 students enrolled in distance learning courses. Institutionally administered financial aid is available to distance learners.

Services Distance learners have accessibility to academic advising, bookstore, career placement assistance, e-mail services, library services.

Contact Ms. Susan Russeff, Associate Director of Admissions, Schiller International University, 300 East Bay Drive, Largo, FL 33770. Telephone: 727-736-5082 Ext. 239. Fax: 727-734-0359. E-mail: admissions @schiller.edu.

DEGREES AND AWARDS

BBA International Business; International Hotel and Tourism Management

MBA Financial Planning; International Hotel and Tourism Management; Management of Information Technology

MBAIB International Business

COURSE SUBJECT AREAS OFFERED OUTSIDE OF DEGREE PROGRAMS

Undergraduate—accounting and related services; business administration, management and operations; business/commerce; business/corporate communications; business/managerial economics; English composition; history; human resources management; international business; international relations and affairs; marketing; mathematics; physical sciences; psychology; statistics.

Graduate—accounting and related services; business administration, management and operations; business/corporate communications; business/managerial economics; computer/information technology administration and management; finance and financial management services; hospitality administration; human resources management; industrial and organizational psychology; international business; legal research and advanced professional studies; marketing; sales, merchandising, and related marketing operations (specialized); statistics.

See full description on page 450.

SCHOOLCRAFT COLLEGE

Livonia, Michigan

Distance Learning Office

http://www.schoolcraft.edu/distance

Schoolcraft College was founded in 1961. It is accredited by North Central Association of Colleges and Schools. It first offered distance learning courses in 1982. In fall 2005, there were 3,500 students enrolled in distance learning courses. Institutionally administered financial aid is available to distance learners.

Services Distance learners have accessibility to academic advising, bookstore, campus computer network, career placement assistance, library services, tutoring.

Contact Marc R. Robinson, Director, Distance Learning, Schoolcraft College, Distance Learning Department, 18600 Haggerty Road, Livonia, MI 48152-2696. Telephone: 734-462-4532. Fax: 734-462-4589. E-mail: mrobinso@schoolcraft.edu.

DEGREES AND AWARDS

AA Liberal Arts
AAS Aviation Management; Business,general; Homeland Security
AGS Liberal Arts
Certificate Aviation Management

COURSE SUBJECT AREAS OFFERED OUTSIDE OF DEGREE PROGRAMS

Undergraduate—accounting and related services; allied health and medical assisting services; American literature (United States and Canadian); anthropology; astronomy and astrophysics; biological and biomedical sciences related; biological and physical sciences; biology; business/commerce; business, management, and marketing related; business/managerial economics; business operations support and assistant services; communication and journalism related; communication and media; computer and information sciences; computer programming; computer science; computer software and media applications; criminal justice and corrections; culinary arts and related services; developmental and child psychology; economics; engineering; English; English composition; English language and literature related; entrepreneurial and small business operations; fine and studio art; geography and cartography; health professions related; health services/allied health/health sciences; history; journalism; marketing; mathematics; music; philosophy; philosophy and religious studies related; physical sciences; physics; psychology; public relations, advertising, and applied communication related; security and protective services related; social sciences; social sciences related; sociology; speech and rhetoric; technical and business writing.
Non-credit—community health services; computer programming; computer software and media applications.

SEATTLE CENTRAL COMMUNITY COLLEGE
Seattle, Washington
Distance Learning Program
http://www.seattlecentral.edu/distance

Seattle Central Community College was founded in 1966. It is accredited by Northwest Commission on Colleges and Universities. It first offered distance learning courses in 1990. In fall 2005, there were 700 students enrolled in distance learning courses. Institutionally administered financial aid is available to distance learners.
Services Distance learners have accessibility to academic advising, bookstore, campus computer network, e-mail services, library services.
Contact Ms. Queenie L. Baker, Director, Seattle Central Community College, 1701 Broadway, NP304, Seattle, WA 98122-2400. Telephone: 800-510-1724. Fax: 206-287-5562. E-mail: qbaker@sccd.ctc.edu.

DEGREES AND AWARDS

AA General Program; Liberal Arts

COURSE SUBJECT AREAS OFFERED OUTSIDE OF DEGREE PROGRAMS

Undergraduate—accounting and related services; anthropology; developmental and child psychology; English composition; film/video and photographic arts; geography and cartography; journalism; languages (foreign languages related); mathematics and statistics related; medieval and Renaissance studies; philosophy and religious studies related; sociology; statistics.

SEATTLE PACIFIC UNIVERSITY
Seattle, Washington
School of Education
http://www.spu.edu/connection

Seattle Pacific University was founded in 1891. It is accredited by Northwest Commission on Colleges and Universities. It first offered distance learning courses in 1984. In fall 2005, there were 441 students enrolled in distance learning courses. Institutionally administered financial aid is available to distance learners.
Services Distance learners have accessibility to bookstore, campus computer network, e-mail services, library services.
Contact Megan Bartlett, Distance Learning Program Coordinator, Seattle Pacific University, 3307 Third Avenue West, Suite 215, Seattle, WA 98119-1950. Telephone: 800-482-3848. Fax: 206-281-2271. E-mail: connect@spu.edu.

DEGREES AND AWARDS

Programs offered do not lead to a degree or other formal award.

COURSE SUBJECT AREAS OFFERED OUTSIDE OF DEGREE PROGRAMS

Undergraduate—linguistic, comparative, and related language studies.
Graduate—astronomy and astrophysics; bilingual, multilingual, and multicultural education; computer software and media applications; curriculum and instruction; education; education (specific levels and methods); education (specific subject areas); English as a second/foreign language (teaching); geography and cartography; history; library science; mathematics; parks, recreation and leisure; special education.

SEMINOLE COMMUNITY COLLEGE
Sanford, Florida
Distance Learning Department
http://www.scc-fl.edu/dl

Seminole Community College was founded in 1966. It is accredited by Southern Association of Colleges and Schools. It first offered distance learning courses in 1970. In fall 2005, there were 3,100 students enrolled in distance learning courses. Institutionally administered financial aid is available to distance learners.
Services Distance learners have accessibility to academic advising, bookstore, career placement assistance, e-mail services, library services.
Contact Mrs. Lillie Gibson, Distance Learning Support Specialist, Seminole Community College, 100 Weldon Boulevard, Sanford, FL 32773. Telephone: 407-328-2424. Fax: 407-328-2233. E-mail: gibsonl@scc-fl.edu.

DEGREES AND AWARDS

AA Accounting; Advertising and Public Relations; Anthropology Pre-Major; Business, general; Economics (Business track); Economics (Liberal Arts track); General Studies; Interpersonal Communications; Journalism; Management Information Systems; Organizational Communication; Psychology; Public Relations and Organizational Communication; Social Work; Sociology
AS Computer Programming and Analysis (C++ Programming Specialization); Computer Programming and Analysis Visual Basic Programming Specialization; Computer Programming and Analysis; Programming and Analysis (WWW Programming Specialization); e-Business Technology (Security Specialization); e-Business Technology (Software Specialization); e-Business Technology (Technology Specialization)
Certificate Computer Programming; Computer Science–Microsoft Certified Systems Administrator
Technical Certificate Accounting Applications; Computer Science–Microsoft Certified Systems Engineer; Office Software Applications; Office Support; e-Business Software (Database track); e-Business Software (Web Design track); e-Business Technology (Microsoft track)

COURSE SUBJECT AREAS OFFERED OUTSIDE OF DEGREE PROGRAMS

Undergraduate—accounting and computer science; accounting and related services; allied health and medical assisting services; anthropology; applied mathematics; area, ethnic, cultural, and gender studies related; astronomy and astrophysics; atmospheric sciences and meteorology; behavioral sciences; biological and biomedical sciences related; biological and physical sciences; biology; biology/biotechnology laboratory technician; business administration, management and operations; business/commerce; business/corporate communications; business, management, and marketing related; business operations support and assistant services; communication and journalism related; communication and media; community health services; computer and information sciences; computer and information sciences and support services related; computer engineering; computer engineering technologies; computer/information technology administration and management; computer programming; computer science; computer software and media applications; computer systems analysis; computer systems networking and telecommunications; construction engineering; construction engineering technology; criminal justice and corrections; criminology; data entry/microcomputer applications; data processing; developmental and child psychology; ecology, evolution, and population biology; economics; education; education related; education (specific subject areas); electrical and electronic engineering technologies; electrical/electronics maintenance and repair technology; English; English composition; family psychology; fire protection; geography and cartography; geological and earth sciences/geosciences; health and medical administrative services; health/medical preparatory programs; health professions related; history; human development, family studies, and related services; legal professions and studies related; legal research and advanced professional studies; legal studies (non-professional general, undergraduate); legal support services; liberal arts and sciences, general studies and humanities; library science; library science related; management information systems; marketing; mathematics; mathematics and computer science; mathematics and statistics related; music; nutrition sciences; physical sciences; physical sciences related; political science and government; psychology; psychology related; public health; social psychology; social sciences; social sciences related; sociology; speech and rhetoric; statistics; technical and business writing.

Non-credit—education (specific levels and methods); health and medical administrative services; security and protective services related.

SETON HALL UNIVERSITY
South Orange, New Jersey
MA in Counseling
http://www.shu.edu/

Seton Hall University was founded in 1856. It is accredited by Middle States Association of Colleges and Schools. It first offered distance learning courses in 1998. Institutionally administered financial aid is available to distance learners.

Services Distance learners have accessibility to academic advising, bookstore, campus computer network, career placement assistance, e-mail services, library services.

Contact Ms. Rosalie Maiorella, Program Administrator, Seton Hall University, 400 South Orange Avenue, South Orange, NJ 07079. Telephone: 973-313-6239. E-mail: setonworldwide@shu.edu.

DEGREES AND AWARDS

MA Counseling

See full description on page 460.

SETON HALL UNIVERSITY
South Orange, New Jersey
MA Education Leadership Management and Policy
http://www.shu.edu/

Seton Hall University was founded in 1856. It is accredited by Middle States Association of Colleges and Schools. It first offered distance learning courses in 1998. Institutionally administered financial aid is available to distance learners.

Services Distance learners have accessibility to academic advising, bookstore, campus computer network, career placement assistance, e-mail services, library services.

Contact Ms. Cindy Jimenez, Program Coordinator, Seton Hall University, 400 South Orange Avenue, South Orange, NJ 07079. Telephone: 973-761-9087. Fax: 973-761-9325. E-mail: setonworldwide@shu.edu.

DEGREES AND AWARDS

MA Education Leadership, Management, and Policy (ELMP)

See full description on page 452.

SETON HALL UNIVERSITY
South Orange, New Jersey
MA in Health Administration
http://www.shu.edu/

Seton Hall University was founded in 1856. It is accredited by Middle States Association of Colleges and Schools. It first offered distance learning courses in 1998. Institutionally administered financial aid is available to distance learners.

Contact Ms. Cindy Jimenez, Program Coordinator, Seton Hall University, 400 South Orange Avenue, South Orange, NJ 07079. Telephone: 973-761-9087. Fax: 973-761-9325. E-mail: setonworldwide@shu.edu.

DEGREES AND AWARDS

MHA Healthcare Administration

See full description on page 458.

SETON HALL UNIVERSITY
South Orange, New Jersey
MA in Strategic Communication and Leadership
http://www.shu.edu/

Seton Hall University was founded in 1856. It is accredited by Middle States Association of Colleges and Schools. It first offered distance learning courses in 1998. Institutionally administered financial aid is available to distance learners.

Services Distance learners have accessibility to academic advising, bookstore, campus computer network, career placement assistance, e-mail services, library services.

Contact Ms. Cindy Jimenez, Program Coordinator, Seton Hall University, 400 South Orange Avenue, South Orange, NJ 07079. Telephone: 973-761-9087. Fax: 973-761-9325. E-mail: setonworldwide@shu.edu.

DEGREES AND AWARDS

MA Strategic Communication and Leadership

See full description on page 454.

SETON HALL UNIVERSITY
South Orange, New Jersey
BSN-MSN
http://www.shu.edu/

Seton Hall University was founded in 1856. It is accredited by Middle States Association of Colleges and Schools. It first offered distance learning courses in 1998. Institutionally administered financial aid is available to distance learners.

Services Distance learners have accessibility to academic advising, bookstore, campus computer network, career placement assistance, e-mail services, library services.

Contact Ms. Cindy Jimenez, Program Coordinator, Seton Hall University, 400 South Orange Avenue, South Orange, NJ 07079. Telephone: 973-761-9087. Fax: 973-761-9325. E-mail: setonworldwide@shu.edu.

DEGREES AND AWARDS

BSN Nursing–RN to BSN

MSN Nursing

See full description on page 456.

SHASTA BIBLE COLLEGE
Redding, California
Individualized Distance Learning
http://www.shasta.edu

Shasta Bible College was founded in 1971. It is accredited by Transnational Association of Christian Colleges and Schools. It first offered distance learning courses in 1999. In fall 2005, there were 20 students enrolled in distance learning courses. Institutionally administered financial aid is available to distance learners.

Services Distance learners have accessibility to academic advising, bookstore, campus computer network, career placement assistance, e-mail services.

Contact Pastor George Gunn, Dean of Admissions and Records, Shasta Bible College, 2951 Goodwater Avenue, Redding, CA 96002. Telephone: 530-221-4275. Fax: 530-221-6929. E-mail: ggunn@shasta.edu.

DEGREES AND AWARDS

Programs offered do not lead to a degree or other formal award.

COURSE SUBJECT AREAS OFFERED OUTSIDE OF DEGREE PROGRAMS

Undergraduate—education related; religious studies.
Graduate—educational administration and supervision.
Non-credit—biblical studies.

SHAWNEE COMMUNITY COLLEGE
Ullin, Illinois
Learning Resources
http://www.shawneecc.edu/

Shawnee Community College was founded in 1967. It is accredited by North Central Association of Colleges and Schools. It first offered distance learning courses in 1994. In fall 2005, there were 560 students enrolled in distance learning courses.

Services Distance learners have accessibility to bookstore, e-mail services, library services.

Contact Russ Stoup, Director of Learning Resources and Instructional Technology, Shawnee Community College, 8364 Shawnee College Road, Ullin, IL 62992. Telephone: 618-634-3200. Fax: 618-634-3215. E-mail: russs@shawneecc.edu.

DEGREES AND AWARDS

Programs offered do not lead to a degree or other formal award.

COURSE SUBJECT AREAS OFFERED OUTSIDE OF DEGREE PROGRAMS

Undergraduate—accounting and related services; anthropology; biology; developmental and child psychology; English composition; legal studies (non-professional general, undergraduate); sociology.

SHAWNEE STATE UNIVERSITY
Portsmouth, Ohio
Department of Nursing
http://www.shawnee.edu/acadamics/hsc/nurs/index.html

Shawnee State University was founded in 1986. It is accredited by North Central Association of Colleges and Schools. In fall 2005, there were 50 students enrolled in distance learning courses. Institutionally administered financial aid is available to distance learners.

Services Distance learners have accessibility to bookstore, e-mail services, library services.

Contact Dr. Mattie Burton, Chair, Nursing, Shawnee State University, 940 Second Street, Health Sciences Building, Room 121, Portsmouth, OH 45662. Telephone: 740-351-3378. E-mail: mburton@shawnee.edu.

DEGREES AND AWARDS

Programs offered do not lead to a degree or other formal award.

COURSE SUBJECT AREAS OFFERED OUTSIDE OF DEGREE PROGRAMS

Undergraduate—nursing.

SHENANDOAH UNIVERSITY
Winchester, Virginia
School of Continuing Education
http://www.su.edu/cont-ed

Shenandoah University was founded in 1875. It is accredited by Southern Association of Colleges and Schools. It first offered distance learning courses in 1988. In fall 2005, there were 1,500 students enrolled in distance learning courses. Institutionally administered financial aid is available to distance learners.

Services Distance learners have accessibility to academic advising, bookstore, career placement assistance, e-mail services, library services.

Contact Dr. R. T. Good, Dean of the School of Continuing Education, Shenandoah University, 1460 University Drive, Winchester, VA 22601. Telephone: 540-665-4643. Fax: 540-665-3496. E-mail: rgood@su.edu.

DEGREES AND AWARDS

Programs offered do not lead to a degree or other formal award.

COURSE SUBJECT AREAS OFFERED OUTSIDE OF DEGREE PROGRAMS

Undergraduate—computer and information sciences; computer engineering; computer software and media applications; computer systems networking and telecommunications; education.
Graduate—education; educational administration and supervision; educational psychology; education related.
Non-credit—computer and information sciences; computer engineering technologies; computer programming; computer systems analysis; education; legal professions and studies related; veterinary biomedical and clinical sciences.

SHIPPENSBURG UNIVERSITY OF PENNSYLVANIA
Shippensburg, Pennsylvania
Extended Studies
http://www.ship.edu/extended/

Shippensburg University of Pennsylvania was founded in 1871. It is accredited by Middle States Association of Colleges and Schools. It first offered distance learning courses in 1998. In fall 2005, there were 106 students enrolled in distance learning courses. Institutionally administered financial aid is available to distance learners.

Services Distance learners have accessibility to academic advising, bookstore, campus computer network, career placement assistance, e-mail services, library services, tutoring.

Contact Dr. Anthony S. Winter, Interim Dean of Extended Studies, Shippensburg University of Pennsylvania, 1871 Old Main Drive, Shippensburg, PA 17257-2299. Telephone: 717-477-1348. Fax: 717-477-4050. E-mail: extended@ship.edu.

DEGREES AND AWARDS

MBA Business Administration
MSIS Information Systems

COURSE SUBJECT AREAS OFFERED OUTSIDE OF DEGREE PROGRAMS

Undergraduate—accounting and related services; communication and media; computer science; criminal justice and corrections; economics; education; English; finance and financial management services; fine and studio art; geography and cartography; gerontology; history; information science/studies; international business; management information systems; management sciences and quantitative methods; marketing; mathematics; music; philosophy; physics; political science and government; psychology; social work; sociology; speech and rhetoric.
Graduate—accounting and related services; business administration, management and operations; communication and media; criminal justice and corrections; English; entrepreneurial and small business operations; gerontology; history; information science/studies; international business; management information systems; political science and government; psychology; social work; sociology.

SHORELINE COMMUNITY COLLEGE
Shoreline, Washington
http://success.shoreline.edu/distance/

Shoreline Community College was founded in 1964. It is accredited by Northwest Commission on Colleges and Universities. It first offered distance learning courses in 1997. In fall 2005, there were 755 students enrolled in distance learning courses. Institutionally administered financial aid is available to distance learners.

Services Distance learners have accessibility to academic advising, bookstore, e-mail services, library services.

Contact Dr. Ann Garnsey-Harter, Director of Distance Learning, Shoreline Community College, Distance Learning Services, 16101 Greenwood Avenue North, Shoreline, WA 98133. Telephone: 206-546-6966. Fax: 206-546-4604. E-mail: dl@shoreline.edu.

DEGREES AND AWARDS
Certificate of Completion Accounting Clerk; Accounts Receivable/Payable Clerk; Payroll Clerk
Certificate Accounting; Purchasing Management; Speech Language Pathology Assistant

COURSE SUBJECT AREAS OFFERED OUTSIDE OF DEGREE PROGRAMS
Undergraduate—accounting and related services; area, ethnic, cultural, and gender studies related; biological and biomedical sciences related; business administration, management and operations; business/commerce; business/corporate communications; computer and information sciences; creative writing; criminal justice and corrections; education; English; English as a second language; English composition; geography and cartography; geological and earth sciences/geosciences; health professions related; history; international business; library science related; marketing; mathematics; music; nutrition sciences; pharmacy, pharmaceutical sciences, and administration; philosophy; psychology; sociology.
Non-credit—curriculum and instruction.

SIMMONS COLLEGE
Boston, Massachusetts

Simmons College was founded in 1899. It is accredited by New England Association of Schools and Colleges. It first offered distance learning courses in 2001. In fall 2005, there were 350 students enrolled in distance learning courses. Institutionally administered financial aid is available to distance learners.
Services Distance learners have accessibility to academic advising, bookstore, campus computer network, e-mail services, library services, tutoring.
Contact Ms. Yolanda Mendez Rainey, Administrative Assistant, Simmons College, School for Health Studies, 300 The Fenway, Boston, MA 02115-5898. Telephone: 617-521-2652. Fax: 617-521-3137. E-mail: yolanda.rainey@simmons.edu.

DEGREES AND AWARDS
CAGS Clinical Genetics; Health Professions Education; Sports Nutrition
DPT Bridge Doctor of Physical Therapy

COURSE SUBJECT AREAS OFFERED OUTSIDE OF DEGREE PROGRAMS
Non-credit—developmental and child psychology; statistics.

SIMPSON COLLEGE
Indianola, Iowa
Division of Adult Learning
http://www.simpson.edu/dal

Simpson College was founded in 1860. It is accredited by North Central Association of Colleges and Schools. It first offered distance learning courses in 1996. In fall 2005, there were 250 students enrolled in distance learning courses. Institutionally administered financial aid is available to distance learners.
Services Distance learners have accessibility to academic advising, bookstore, campus computer network, career placement assistance, e-mail services, library services.
Contact Walter Pearson, Director, Simpson College, 701 North C Street, Indianola, IA 50125. Telephone: 515-961-1615. Fax: 515-961-1498. E-mail: pearsonw@simpson.edu.

DEGREES AND AWARDS
Programs offered do not lead to a degree or other formal award.

COURSE SUBJECT AREAS OFFERED OUTSIDE OF DEGREE PROGRAMS
Undergraduate—accounting and related services; communication and media; computer science; criminal justice and corrections; English; finance and financial management services; human resources management; journalism; liberal arts and sciences, general studies and humanities; marketing.
Graduate—education (specific subject areas).

SINCLAIR COMMUNITY COLLEGE
Dayton, Ohio
Distance Learning Division
http://www.sinclair.edu/distance

Sinclair Community College was founded in 1887. It is accredited by North Central Association of Colleges and Schools. It first offered distance learning courses in 1979. In fall 2005, there were 5,000 students enrolled in distance learning courses. Institutionally administered financial aid is available to distance learners.
Services Distance learners have accessibility to academic advising, bookstore, e-mail services, library services.
Contact Ms. Linda M. Stowe, Coordinator of Distance Learning Services, Sinclair Community College, Distance Learning and Instructional Support Division, Room 14-223, 444 West Third Street, Dayton, OH 45402. Telephone: 937-512-2694. Fax: 937-512-2891. E-mail: linda.stowe@sinclair.edu.

DEGREES AND AWARDS
AA Liberal Arts and Sciences
AS Business Administration; Liberal Arts and Sciences
Certificate Programmer Analyst–Fast Track--Programmer Analyst Short-Term Certificate; Software Applications for the Professional; Web Programming–Visual Basic or Java Track Short-Term certificate
Certification Human Services Short-Term Certificate; Medical Office Coding Specialist; Radiologic Technology Continuing Education Units (CEUs)

COURSE SUBJECT AREAS OFFERED OUTSIDE OF DEGREE PROGRAMS
Undergraduate—accounting and computer science; architectural engineering; behavioral sciences; business administration, management and operations; business, management, and marketing related; business operations support and assistant services; chemistry; civil engineering technology; communication and media; computer and information sciences; computer programming; computer software and media applications; computer systems networking and telecommunications; creative writing; developmental and child psychology; drafting/design engineering technologies; economics; English composition; entrepreneurial and small business operations; film/video and photographic arts; fine and studio art; history; human services; legal studies (non-professional general, undergraduate); liberal arts and sciences, general studies and humanities; marketing; mathematics; psychology; social psychology; sociology; speech and rhetoric; technical and business writing.
Non-credit—health professions related.

SKIDMORE COLLEGE
Saratoga Springs, New York
University Without Walls
http://www.skidmore.edu/uww

Skidmore College was founded in 1903. It is accredited by Middle States Association of Colleges and Schools. It first offered distance learning courses in 1971. In fall 2005, there were 200 students enrolled in distance learning courses. Institutionally administered financial aid is available to distance learners.
Services Distance learners have accessibility to academic advising, bookstore, campus computer network, career placement assistance, e-mail services, library services.
Contact Tracy Riley, Administrative Assistant, Skidmore College, University Without Walls, 815 North Broadway, Saratoga Springs, NY 12866. Telephone: 518-580-5450. Fax: 518-580-5449. E-mail: uww@skidmore.edu.

DEGREES AND AWARDS
BA American Studies; Anthropology; Art History; Asian Studies; Biology; Chemistry; Classics; Computer Science; Economics; English; Environmental Studies; Foreign Languages and Literature; French; German; Government; History; Individualized Studies; International Affairs; Mathematics; Music; Philosophy; Physics; Psychology; Psychology-Sociology; Religious Studies; Sociology; Sociology-Anthropology; Spanish; Theater; Women's Studies

BS Art (studio); Business and Management; Dance; Educational Administration; Exercise Science; Individualized Studies

COURSE SUBJECT AREAS OFFERED OUTSIDE OF DEGREE PROGRAMS

Undergraduate—liberal arts and sciences, general studies and humanities.

See full description on page 462.

SKIDMORE COLLEGE
Saratoga Springs, New York
Graduate Programs
http://www.skidmore.edu/mals

Skidmore College was founded in 1903. It is accredited by Middle States Association of Colleges and Schools. It first offered distance learning courses in 1992. In fall 2005, there were 51 students enrolled in distance learning courses. Institutionally administered financial aid is available to distance learners.

Services Distance learners have accessibility to academic advising, bookstore, campus computer network, e-mail services, library services, tutoring.

Contact Dr. Erica Bastress-Dukehart, Director of Master of Arts in Liberal Studies, Skidmore College, 815 North Broadway, Saratoga Springs, NY 12866. Telephone: 518-580-5480. Fax: 518-580-5486. E-mail: bastress@skidmore.edu.

DEGREES AND AWARDS

Programs offered do not lead to a degree or other formal award.

COURSE SUBJECT AREAS OFFERED OUTSIDE OF DEGREE PROGRAMS

Graduate—liberal arts and sciences, general studies and humanities.

SNOW COLLEGE
Ephraim, Utah
Snow College Outreach Education
http://www.snow.edu/

Snow College was founded in 1888. It is accredited by Northwest Commission on Colleges and Universities. It first offered distance learning courses in 1979. In fall 2005, there were 47 students enrolled in distance learning courses. Institutionally administered financial aid is available to distance learners.

Services Distance learners have accessibility to academic advising, bookstore, campus computer network, career placement assistance, e-mail services, library services, tutoring.

Contact Ms. Wendy Christensen, Continuing Education Coordinator, Snow College, 150 East College Avenue, Ephraim, UT 84627. Telephone: 435-283-7320. Fax: 435-283-7149. E-mail: wendy.christensen@snow.edu.

DEGREES AND AWARDS

Programs offered do not lead to a degree or other formal award.

COURSE SUBJECT AREAS OFFERED OUTSIDE OF DEGREE PROGRAMS

Undergraduate—accounting and computer science; American Sign Language (ASL); anthropology; applied mathematics; behavioral sciences; business administration, management and operations; communication and media; computer software and media applications; criminal justice and corrections; dramatic/theater arts and stagecraft; education; foods, nutrition, and related services; history; human development, family studies, and related services; languages (foreign languages related); mathematics; nursing; philosophy; sociology.

SOLANO COMMUNITY COLLEGE
Suisun City, California
http://www.solano.cc.ca.us/

Solano Community College was founded in 1945. It is accredited by Western Association of Schools and Colleges. It first offered distance learning courses in 1976. In fall 2005, there were 2,558 students enrolled in distance learning courses. Institutionally administered financial aid is available to distance learners.

Services Distance learners have accessibility to academic advising, bookstore, e-mail services, library services.

Contact Mrs. Sarah Nordin, Online Coordinator, Solano Community College, 4000 Suisun Valley Road, Fairfield, CA 94534-3197. Telephone: 707-864-7000 Ext. 276. Fax: 707-864-7190. E-mail: sarah.nordin@solano.edu.

DEGREES AND AWARDS

AS Criminal Justice, Corrections; Criminal Justice, Law Enforcement

COURSE SUBJECT AREAS OFFERED OUTSIDE OF DEGREE PROGRAMS

Undergraduate—accounting and related services; biological and physical sciences; business administration, management and operations; business/commerce; business/managerial economics; computer and information sciences; computer and information sciences and support services related; computer programming; computer science; computer software and media applications; computer systems networking and telecommunications; creative writing; criminal justice and corrections; criminology; data entry/microcomputer applications; developmental and child psychology; economics; electrical and electronic engineering technologies; English composition; fire protection; geography and cartography; geological and earth sciences/geosciences; health and physical education/fitness; health/medical preparatory programs; history; music; nursing; political science and government; psychology; social sciences related; sociology; student counseling and personnel services.

SONOMA STATE UNIVERSITY
Rohnert Park, California
Liberal Studies Special Sessions Degree Programs
http://www.sonoma.edu/exed/Degrees/dindex.html

Sonoma State University was founded in 1960. It is accredited by Western Association of Schools and Colleges. It first offered distance learning courses in 1996. In fall 2005, there were 120 students enrolled in distance learning courses. Institutionally administered financial aid is available to distance learners.

Services Distance learners have accessibility to academic advising, bookstore, campus computer network, career placement assistance, e-mail services, library services.

Contact Beth Warner, Administrative Coordinator, Sonoma State University, 1801 East Cotati Avenue, Rohnert Park, CA 94928-3609. Telephone: 707-664-3977. Fax: 707-664-2613. E-mail: beth.warner@sonoma.edu.

DEGREES AND AWARDS

BA Liberal Studies

MA Interdisciplinary Studies–Action for a Viable Future

COURSE SUBJECT AREAS OFFERED OUTSIDE OF DEGREE PROGRAMS

Undergraduate—educational/instructional media design.

Non-credit—business administration, management and operations; business/corporate communications; business, management, and marketing related; computer/information technology administration and management; computer software and media applications; computer systems networking and telecommunications.

SOUTH CENTRAL COLLEGE
North Mankato, Minnesota
http://southcentral.edu

South Central College was founded in 1946. It is accredited by North Central Association of Colleges and Schools. It first offered distance learning courses in 2001. In fall 2005, there were 500 students enrolled in distance learning courses. Institutionally administered financial aid is available to distance learners.

Services Distance learners have accessibility to academic advising, bookstore, campus computer network, e-mail services, library services.

Contact Linda Beer, Registrar, South Central College, 1920 Lee Boulevard, North Mankato, MN 56003. Telephone: 507-389-7351. Fax: 507-388-9951. E-mail: linda.beer@southcentral.edu.

DEGREES AND AWARDS

AAS Community Supports for People with Disabilities; Legal Administrative Assistant; Medical Laboratory Technician Fast Track; Medical Laboratory Technician

Certificate Community Supports for People with Disabilities; Phlebotomy; Web Programmer

Diploma Community Supports for People with Disabilities; Legal Adminstrative Assistant

COURSE SUBJECT AREAS OFFERED OUTSIDE OF DEGREE PROGRAMS

Undergraduate—accounting and related services; business/corporate communications; business, management, and marketing related; clinical/ medical laboratory science and allied professions; community organization and advocacy; computer and information sciences; computer software and media applications; data entry/microcomputer applications; education; health aides/attendants/orderlies; human development, family studies, and related services; human services; liberal arts and sciences, general studies and humanities; nursing; sales, merchandising, and related marketing operations (general).

SOUTH DAKOTA SCHOOL OF MINES AND TECHNOLOGY

Rapid City, South Dakota

http://www.sdsmt.edu

South Dakota School of Mines and Technology was founded in 1885. It is accredited by North Central Association of Colleges and Schools. It first offered distance learning courses in 2001. In fall 2005, there were 88 students enrolled in distance learning courses. Institutionally administered financial aid is available to distance learners.

Services Distance learners have accessibility to academic advising, bookstore, campus computer network, e-mail services.

Contact Distance Learning Contact, South Dakota School of Mines and Technology, 501 East St. Joseph Street, Rapid City, SD 57701. Telephone: 605-394-2400. Fax: 605-394-6131.

DEGREES AND AWARDS

Programs offered do not lead to a degree or other formal award.

COURSE SUBJECT AREAS OFFERED OUTSIDE OF DEGREE PROGRAMS

Undergraduate—chemistry; geography and cartography; liberal arts and sciences, general studies and humanities.

Graduate—engineering related; management sciences and quantitative methods.

SOUTHEAST ARKANSAS COLLEGE

Pine Bluff, Arkansas

http://www.seark.edu/

Southeast Arkansas College was founded in 1991. It is accredited by North Central Association of Colleges and Schools. It first offered distance learning courses in 1995. In fall 2005, there were 719 students enrolled in distance learning courses. Institutionally administered financial aid is available to distance learners.

Services Distance learners have accessibility to e-mail services, library services.

Contact Daytra Demmings, Coordinator of Distance Learning, Southeast Arkansas College, 1900 Hazel Street, Pine Bluff, AR 71603. Telephone: 870-543-5992. Fax: 870-543-5937. E-mail: ddemmings@seark.edu.

DEGREES AND AWARDS

Programs offered do not lead to a degree or other formal award.

COURSE SUBJECT AREAS OFFERED OUTSIDE OF DEGREE PROGRAMS

Undergraduate—anthropology; applied mathematics; business administration, management and operations; business/commerce; business/ corporate communications; business, management, and marketing related; business/managerial economics; computer/information technology administration and management; computer programming; computer science; computer software and media applications; computer systems analysis; computer systems networking and telecommunications; criminal justice and corrections; criminology; data entry/microcomputer applications; economics; English; English composition; entrepreneurial and small business operations; fire protection; foods, nutrition, and related services; geography and cartography; health and physical education/fitness; health professions related; history; insurance; international business; marketing; mathematics; mathematics and computer science; mathematics and statistics related; nursing; psychology; real estate; sociology; statistics.

SOUTHEAST COMMUNITY COLLEGE, BEATRICE CAMPUS

Beatrice, Nebraska

http://online.scc.cc.ne.us

Southeast Community College, Beatrice Campus was founded in 1976. It is accredited by North Central Association of Colleges and Schools. It first offered distance learning courses in 1996. In fall 2005, there were 2,000 students enrolled in distance learning courses. Institutionally administered financial aid is available to distance learners.

Services Distance learners have accessibility to academic advising, bookstore, career placement assistance, library services, tutoring.

Contact Bob Morgan, Assistant Campus Director and Director of Distance Learning, Southeast Community College, Beatrice Campus, 4771 West Scott Road, Beatrice, NE 68310. Telephone: 402-228-3468 Ext. 272. Fax: 402-228-2218. E-mail: bmorgan@southeast.edu.

DEGREES AND AWARDS

AA Early Childhood

AAS Business Administration; Radiologic Technology Program; Respiratory Care; Surgical Technology

Certification Food Service Training Program

License Nursing Home Administration

COURSE SUBJECT AREAS OFFERED OUTSIDE OF DEGREE PROGRAMS

Undergraduate—accounting and related services; biological and biomedical sciences related; business administration, management and operations; business/commerce; business/corporate communications; economics; English; English composition; foods, nutrition, and related services; health and medical administrative services; health professions related; history; human services; liberal arts and sciences, general studies and humanities; mathematics; philosophy; psychology; sales, merchandising, and related marketing operations (specialized); social psychology; speech and rhetoric; technical and business writing.

Non-credit—management sciences and quantitative methods; mathematics.

SOUTHEAST COMMUNITY COLLEGE, LINCOLN CAMPUS

Lincoln, Nebraska

Academic Education

http://www.southeast.edu/

Southeast Community College, Lincoln Campus was founded in 1973. It is accredited by North Central Association of Colleges and Schools. It first offered distance learning courses in 1996. In fall 2005, there were 2,000 students enrolled in distance learning courses. Institutionally administered financial aid is available to distance learners.

Services Distance learners have accessibility to academic advising, bookstore, campus computer network, career placement assistance, library services, tutoring.

Contact Bob Morgan, Assistant Campus Director and Director of Distance Learning, Southeast Community College, Lincoln Campus, 4771 West Scott Road, Beatrice, NE 68310. Telephone: 402-228-3468 Ext. 272. Fax: 402-228-2218. E-mail: bmorgan@southeast.edu.

DEGREES AND AWARDS

AA Early Childhood

AAS Business Administration; Radiological Technology; Respiratory Care; Surgical Technology

Certification Food Service Training Program

License Nursing Home Administration

COURSE SUBJECT AREAS OFFERED OUTSIDE OF DEGREE PROGRAMS

Undergraduate—accounting and related services; biological and biomedical sciences related; business administration, management and operations; business/commerce; business/corporate communications; economics; education (specific levels and methods); English; English composition; foods, nutrition, and related services; health and medical administrative services; health professions related; history; human services; languages (Romance languages); legal studies (non-professional general, undergraduate); liberal arts and sciences, general studies and humanities; mathematics; philosophy; philosophy and religious studies related; psychology; sales, merchandising, and related marketing operations (specialized); social psychology; sociology; speech and rhetoric; technical and business writing.

Non-credit—management sciences and quantitative methods; mathematics.

SOUTHEAST COMMUNITY COLLEGE, MILFORD CAMPUS

Milford, Nebraska

Southeast Community College, Milford Campus was founded in 1941. It is accredited by North Central Association of Colleges and Schools. It first offered distance learning courses in 1996. In fall 2005, there were 2,000 students enrolled in distance learning courses. Institutionally administered financial aid is available to distance learners.

Services Distance learners have accessibility to academic advising, bookstore, career placement assistance, library services, tutoring.

Contact Bob Morgan, Assistant Campus Director and Director of Distance Learning, Southeast Community College, Milford Campus, 4771 West Scott Road, Beatrice, NE 68310. Telephone: 402-228-3468 Ext. 272. Fax: 402-228-2218. E-mail: bmorgan@southeast.edu.

DEGREES AND AWARDS

AA Early Childhood
AAS Business Administration; Radiologic Technology Program; Respiratory Care; Surgical Technology
Certification Food Service Training Program
License Nursing Home Administration

COURSE SUBJECT AREAS OFFERED OUTSIDE OF DEGREE PROGRAMS

Undergraduate—accounting and related services; biological and biomedical sciences related; business administration, management and operations; business/commerce; business/corporate communications; economics; English; English composition; foods, nutrition, and related services; health and medical administrative services; health professions related; history; human services; liberal arts and sciences, general studies and humanities; mathematics; philosophy; psychology; sales, merchandising, and related marketing operations (specialized); social psychology; speech and rhetoric; technical and business writing.

Non-credit—management sciences and quantitative methods; mathematics.

SOUTHERN ARKANSAS UNIVERSITY TECH

Camden, Arkansas

Southern Arkansas University Tech was founded in 1967. It is accredited by North Central Association of Colleges and Schools. It first offered distance learning courses in 1995. In fall 2005, there were 750 students enrolled in distance learning courses. Institutionally administered financial aid is available to distance learners.

Services Distance learners have accessibility to academic advising, bookstore, campus computer network, e-mail services, library services, tutoring.

Contact Robert D. Gunnels, Vice Chancellor for Instruction, Southern Arkansas University Tech, PO Box 3499, Camden, AR 71711. Telephone: 870-574-4521. Fax: 870-574-4477. E-mail: rgunnels@sautech.edu.

DEGREES AND AWARDS

AS Business Administration

COURSE SUBJECT AREAS OFFERED OUTSIDE OF DEGREE PROGRAMS

Undergraduate—accounting and related services; biological and physical sciences; business administration, management and operations; computer science; computer systems networking and telecommunications; curriculum and instruction; education; English; geography and cartography; health and physical education/fitness; history; mathematics; philosophy; political science and government; psychology.

SOUTHERN ILLINOIS UNIVERSITY CARBONDALE

Carbondale, Illinois
Office of Distance Education
http://www.dce.siu.edu/siuconnected

Southern Illinois University Carbondale was founded in 1869. It is accredited by North Central Association of Colleges and Schools. It first offered distance learning courses in 1981. In fall 2005, there were 752 students enrolled in distance learning courses. Institutionally administered financial aid is available to distance learners.

Services Distance learners have accessibility to bookstore, campus computer network, e-mail services, library services, tutoring.

Contact Dr. Susan Edgren, Assistant Director, Southern Illinois University Carbondale, Washington Square C, Mailcode 6705, Carbondale, IL 62901-6705. Telephone: 618-453-5659. Fax: 618-453-5668. E-mail: sedgren@siu.edu.

DEGREES AND AWARDS

BS Information Systems Technology

COURSE SUBJECT AREAS OFFERED OUTSIDE OF DEGREE PROGRAMS

Undergraduate—agricultural business and management; agricultural mechanization; agriculture; American literature (United States and Canadian); Army J.R.O.T.C/R.O.T.C; biological and biomedical sciences related; biological and physical sciences; biology; business/commerce; business, management, and marketing related; computer and information sciences; computer/information technology administration and management; criminal justice and corrections; criminology; educational administration and supervision; educational psychology; education related; education (specific subject areas); English; finance and financial management services; geography and cartography; health/medical preparatory programs; history; information science/studies; insurance; journalism; landscape architecture; languages (East Asian); languages (Romance languages); management sciences and quantitative methods; marketing; mathematics; mathematics and statistics related; music; philosophy; philosophy and religious studies related; plant sciences; political science and government; quality control and safety technologies; real estate; religious studies; sales, merchandising, and related marketing operations (general); social sciences; sociology.

Graduate—education; rehabilitation and therapeutic professions.

Non-credit—marketing.

SOUTHERN ILLINOIS UNIVERSITY EDWARDSVILLE

Edwardsville, Illinois
Office of Continuing Education
http://www.siue.edu/CE/

Southern Illinois University Edwardsville was founded in 1957. It is accredited by North Central Association of Colleges and Schools. It first offered distance learning courses in 1994. In fall 2005, there were 187 students enrolled in distance learning courses. Institutionally administered financial aid is available to distance learners.

Services Distance learners have accessibility to academic advising, bookstore, campus computer network, career placement assistance, e-mail services, library services, tutoring.

Contact Lynn Heidinger-Brown, Director of Continuing Education, Southern Illinois University Edwardsville, Campus Box 1084, Edwardsville, IL 62026. Telephone: 618-650-3210. Fax: 618-650-2629. E-mail: lhbrown@siue.edu.

DEGREES AND AWARDS
BS Nursing–RN to BS
BSN Nursing

COURSE SUBJECT AREAS OFFERED OUTSIDE OF DEGREE PROGRAMS
Undergraduate—nursing.
Graduate—business/commerce; education; nursing.

SOUTHERN METHODIST UNIVERSITY
Dallas, Texas
School of Engineering–Distance Learning
http://www.engr.smu.edu

Southern Methodist University was founded in 1911. It is accredited by Southern Association of Colleges and Schools. It first offered distance learning courses in 1968. In fall 2005, there were 550 students enrolled in distance learning courses. Institutionally administered financial aid is available to distance learners.

Services Distance learners have accessibility to academic advising, bookstore, campus computer network, career placement assistance, e-mail services, library services.

Contact Mr. Jim Dees, Senior Director of Graduate Student Experience and Enrollment Management, Southern Methodist University, PO Box 750335, Dallas, TX 75275-0335. Telephone: 214-768-1456. Fax: 214-768-3778. E-mail: jdees@engr.smu.edu.

DEGREES AND AWARDS
MS Computer Engineering; Computer Science; Environmental Engineering; Environmental Science (Environmental Systems Management major); Environmental Science (Hazardous and Waste Materials Management major); Environmental Science; Facilities Management; Information Engineering and Management; Manufacturing Systems Management; Operations Research; Packaging of Electronic and Optical Devices; Security Engineering; Software Engineering; Systems Engineering; Telecommunications
MSCE Civil Engineering
MSEE Electrical Engineering
MSEM Engineering Management
MSME Mechanical Engineering

COURSE SUBJECT AREAS OFFERED OUTSIDE OF DEGREE PROGRAMS
Graduate—architectural engineering; business administration, management and operations; civil engineering; computer and information sciences; computer and information sciences and support services related; computer engineering; computer engineering technologies; computer/information technology administration and management; computer science; computer software and media applications; computer systems networking and telecommunications; electrical and electronic engineering technologies; electrical, electronics and communications engineering; engineering design; engineering/industrial management; engineering mechanics; engineering physics; engineering related; engineering-related fields; engineering-related technologies; engineering science; engineering technologies related; engineering technology; environmental/environmental health engineering; industrial engineering; information science/studies; mechanical engineering; mechanical engineering related technologies; systems engineering.

See full description on page 464.

SOUTHERN NEW HAMPSHIRE UNIVERSITY
Manchester, New Hampshire
SNHU Online
http://www.snhu.edu/Prospective_Student/distance_ed.html

Southern New Hampshire University was founded in 1932. It is accredited by New England Association of Schools and Colleges. It first offered distance learning courses in 1996. In fall 2005, there were 12,000 students enrolled in distance learning courses. Institutionally administered financial aid is available to distance learners.

Services Distance learners have accessibility to academic advising, bookstore, campus computer network, career placement assistance, e-mail services, library services, tutoring.

Contact Ms. Voula Annas, Manager of Marketing and Recruitment, SNHU Online, Southern New Hampshire University, 2500 North River Road, Manchester, NH 03106. Telephone: 866-860-0449. Fax: 603-645-9706. E-mail: online@snhu.edu.

DEGREES AND AWARDS
AA Liberal Arts
AS Accounting; Business Administration; Information Technology; Marketing
BA English Language and Literature; Psychology; Social Science
BS Accounting; Accounting/Finance; Business Administration; Business Studies; Economics/Finance; Information Technology; International Business; Management Advisory Services; Marketing; Technical Management
Certificate Accounting; Human Resources Management; Software Development
Graduate Certificate International Business
MBA Business Administration–Global MBA
MEd Child Development; Child Development
MS Business Education; Hospitality Administration; Organizational Leadership

See full description on page 466.

SOUTHERN OREGON UNIVERSITY
Ashland, Oregon
Extended Campus Programs
http://www.sou.edu/ecp/distlearn

Southern Oregon University was founded in 1926. It is accredited by Northwest Commission on Colleges and Universities. It first offered distance learning courses in 1992. In fall 2005, there were 150 students enrolled in distance learning courses. Institutionally administered financial aid is available to distance learners.

Services Distance learners have accessibility to academic advising, bookstore, campus computer network, e-mail services, library services.

Contact P.J. Mau, Program Assistant, Southern Oregon University, Distance Learning, 1250 Siskiyou Boulevard, Ashland, OR 97520. Telephone: 800-552-5388. Fax: 541-552-6047. E-mail: maup@sou.edu.

DEGREES AND AWARDS
BS Business Administration; Criminology and Criminal Justice; Early Childhood Education
MS Education–Secondary Education; Special Education

COURSE SUBJECT AREAS OFFERED OUTSIDE OF DEGREE PROGRAMS
Undergraduate—business, management, and marketing related; criminal justice and corrections; criminology.
Graduate—education (specific subject areas).

SOUTHERN POLYTECHNIC STATE UNIVERSITY
Marietta, Georgia
http://eu.spsu.edu/DistanceLearning/index.htm

Southern Polytechnic State University was founded in 1948. It is accredited by Southern Association of Colleges and Schools. It first offered distance learning courses in 1995. In fall 2005, there were 300 students enrolled in distance learning courses. Institutionally administered financial aid is available to distance learners.

Services Distance learners have accessibility to academic advising, bookstore, career placement assistance, e-mail services, library services.

Contact Dean Dawn Ramsey, Dean of Extended University, Southern Polytechnic State University, 1100 South Marietta Parkway, Atrium Building, Suite J-330, Marietta, GA 30060-2855. Telephone: 678-915-4287. Fax: 678-915-3576. E-mail: dramsey@spsu.edu.

DEGREES AND AWARDS
BS Information Technology
Certificate Specialty Construction
Graduate Certificate Communications Management; Content Development; Instructional Design; Technical Communication; Visual Communication and Graphics

MS Quality Assurance; Systems Engineering

COURSE SUBJECT AREAS OFFERED OUTSIDE OF DEGREE PROGRAMS

Undergraduate—building/construction finishing, management, and inspection; civil engineering technology; communication and journalism related; computer science; educational/instructional media design; electrical and electronic engineering technologies; engineering design; information science/studies; speech and rhetoric; statistics; textile sciences and engineering.
Graduate—communication and journalism related; computer and information sciences; computer engineering; computer programming; computer science; computer systems analysis; computer systems networking and telecommunications.
Non-credit—computer programming.

See full description on page 468.

SOUTHERN UNIVERSITY AT SHREVEPORT
Shreveport, Louisiana

Southern University at Shreveport was founded in 1964. It is accredited by Southern Association of Colleges and Schools. In fall 2005, there were 670 students enrolled in distance learning courses. Institutionally administered financial aid is available to distance learners.
Services Distance learners have accessibility to academic advising, bookstore, campus computer network, career placement assistance, e-mail services, library services, tutoring.
Contact Dr. Ilko Iliev, Education Department Chairperson, Southern University at Shreveport, 3050 Martin Luther King, Jr. Drive, Shreveport, LA 71107. Telephone: 318-674-3356. E-mail: iiliev@susla.edu.

DEGREES AND AWARDS

Programs offered do not lead to a degree or other formal award.

COURSE SUBJECT AREAS OFFERED OUTSIDE OF DEGREE PROGRAMS

Undergraduate—accounting and related services; allied health and medical assisting services; biology; business, management, and marketing related; chemistry; computer science; dental support services and allied professions; economics; English; hospitality administration; mathematics; political science and government; psychology.

SOUTH PIEDMONT COMMUNITY COLLEGE
Polkton, North Carolina
http://www.spcc.edu

South Piedmont Community College was founded in 1962. It is accredited by Southern Association of Colleges and Schools. It first offered distance learning courses in 1982. In fall 2005, there were 800 students enrolled in distance learning courses. Institutionally administered financial aid is available to distance learners.
Services Distance learners have accessibility to academic advising, bookstore, library services.
Contact Ms. Judith A. Smith, Associate Vice President, Distance Learning/ Special Projects, South Piedmont Community College, 680 Highway 74 West, PO Box 126, Polkton, NC 28135. Telephone: 704-272-5397. E-mail: j-smith@spcc.edu.

DEGREES AND AWARDS

Programs offered do not lead to a degree or other formal award.

COURSE SUBJECT AREAS OFFERED OUTSIDE OF DEGREE PROGRAMS

Undergraduate—accounting and computer science; accounting and related services; behavioral sciences; biology; business administration, management and operations; business/commerce; business, management, and marketing related; computer and information sciences; computer and information sciences and support services related; computer/information technology administration and management; computer programming; computer software and media applications; computer systems analysis; computer systems networking and telecommunications; criminal justice and corrections; design and applied arts; dietetics and clinical nutrition services; economics; education; educational administration and supervision; education (specific levels and methods); education (specific subject areas); English; English composition; finance and financial management services; foods, nutrition, and related services; health professions related; history; human development, family studies, and related services; intercultural/multicultural and diversity studies; legal professions and studies related; mathematics and statistics related; psychology; sales, merchandising, and related marketing operations (general); sociology; teaching assistants/aides.
Non-credit—health aides/attendants/orderlies.

SOUTH PLAINS COLLEGE
Levelland, Texas
http://www.spc.cc.tx.us/

South Plains College was founded in 1958. It is accredited by Southern Association of Colleges and Schools. It first offered distance learning courses in 1994. In fall 2005, there were 1,600 students enrolled in distance learning courses. Institutionally administered financial aid is available to distance learners.
Services Distance learners have accessibility to academic advising, bookstore, e-mail services, library services, tutoring.
Contact Ms. Andrea Rangel, Dean of Admissions and Records, South Plains College, 1401 South College Avenue, Levelland, TX 79336. Telephone: 806-894-9611 Ext. 2370. E-mail: arangel@southplainscollege.edu.

DEGREES AND AWARDS

Programs offered do not lead to a degree or other formal award.

COURSE SUBJECT AREAS OFFERED OUTSIDE OF DEGREE PROGRAMS

Undergraduate—accounting and related services; agricultural business and management; agriculture and agriculture operations related; American literature (United States and Canadian); anthropology; applied mathematics; area, ethnic, cultural, and gender studies related; area studies; behavioral sciences; biology; botany/plant biology; business administration, management and operations; business/corporate communications; computer and information sciences; computer programming; economics; education; English; English composition; English language and literature related; English literature (British and Commonwealth); ethnic, cultural minority, and gender studies; history; mathematics; psychology; social sciences.

SOUTHWESTERN ASSEMBLIES OF GOD UNIVERSITY
Waxahachie, Texas
School of Distance Education
http://www.sagu.edu

Southwestern Assemblies of God University was founded in 1927. It is accredited by Association for Biblical Higher Education. It first offered distance learning courses in 1983. In fall 2005, there were 572 students enrolled in distance learning courses. Institutionally administered financial aid is available to distance learners.
Services Distance learners have accessibility to academic advising, bookstore, campus computer network, career placement assistance, e-mail services, library services, tutoring.
Contact Mr. Jeff Francis, Distance Education Admissions Counselor, Southwestern Assemblies of God University, 1200 Sycamore Street, Waxahachie, TX 75165. Telephone: 972-825-4772. Fax: 972-923-8123. E-mail: jfrancis@sagu.edu.

DEGREES AND AWARDS

AA Bible; Business Administration; Business, general; Early Childhood Education; Education; English; General Studies; Media; Psychology; Social Studies
BA Business; Church Ministries; Education; English; History; Professional Studies
BS Business; Church Ministries; Education; English; History; Professional Studies
MA Human Services Counseling; Theological Studies
MEd Education

MS Human Services Counseling; Theological Studies

COURSE SUBJECT AREAS OFFERED OUTSIDE OF DEGREE PROGRAMS

Undergraduate—accounting and related services; Air Force J.R.O.T.C/ R.O.T.C; biblical studies; biology; business administration, management and operations; business/commerce; creative writing; curriculum and instruction; developmental and child psychology; education; educational administration and supervision; education related; education (specific subject areas); English composition; history; human resources management; missionary studies and missiology; multi-/interdisciplinary studies related; music; pastoral counseling and specialized ministries; psychology; religious education; religious/sacred music; religious studies; social psychology; social sciences; social sciences related; sociology; theological and ministerial studies; theology and religious vocations related.

Graduate—biblical studies; counseling psychology; education; educational administration and supervision; education related; education (specific subject areas); missionary studies and missiology; religious education; religious studies; theological and ministerial studies; theology and religious vocations related.

SOUTHWESTERN BAPTIST THEOLOGICAL SEMINARY

Fort Worth, Texas

Department of Continuing Education

http://swbts.edu

Southwestern Baptist Theological Seminary was founded in 1908. It is accredited by Southern Association of Colleges and Schools. It first offered distance learning courses in 1993. In fall 2005, there were 227 students enrolled in distance learning courses. Institutionally administered financial aid is available to distance learners.

Services Distance learners have accessibility to academic advising, bookstore, campus computer network, career placement assistance, e-mail services, library services.

Contact Dr. Jim Wicker, Director of Distance Learning, Southwestern Baptist Theological Seminary, PO Box 22147, Fort Worth, TX 76122. Telephone: 817-923-1921 Ext. 6805. Fax: 817-921-8760. E-mail: jwicker@swbts.edu.

DEGREES AND AWARDS

Programs offered do not lead to a degree or other formal award.

COURSE SUBJECT AREAS OFFERED OUTSIDE OF DEGREE PROGRAMS

Undergraduate—biblical studies; religious education; religious studies; theological and ministerial studies.

Graduate—biblical and other theological languages and literatures; biblical studies; educational administration and supervision; educational assessment, evaluation, and research; educational/instructional media design; educational psychology; education related; human development, family studies, and related services; linguistic, comparative, and related language studies; pastoral counseling and specialized ministries; philosophy and religious studies related; psychology; psychology related; religious education; religious/sacred music; religious studies; theological and ministerial studies; theology and religious vocations related.

SOUTHWESTERN COLLEGE

Winfield, Kansas

Southwestern College Online

http://www.sckans.edu/online

Southwestern College was founded in 1885. It is accredited by North Central Association of Colleges and Schools. It first offered distance learning courses in 2001. In fall 2005, there were 1,118 students enrolled in distance learning courses. Institutionally administered financial aid is available to distance learners.

Services Distance learners have accessibility to academic advising, bookstore, career placement assistance, library services.

Contact Candyce Duggan, Director of SC Online, Southwestern College, 2040 South Rock Road, Wichita, KS 67207. Telephone: 888-684-5335 Ext. 112. Fax: 316-688-5218. E-mail: online@sckans.edu.

DEGREES AND AWARDS

BA Pastoral Studies

BS Accounting; Business Administration; Business Quality Management; Computer Operations Technology; Computer Programming Technology; Criminal Justice; Human Resource Development; Nursing–RN to BSN; Operations Management; Security Management

MA Specialized Ministries–Youth and Young Adult Ministry

MBA Business Administration

MS Leadership; Security Administration

COURSE SUBJECT AREAS OFFERED OUTSIDE OF DEGREE PROGRAMS

Undergraduate—business/commerce; computer/information technology administration and management; economics; English; English composition; industrial production technologies; liberal arts and sciences, general studies and humanities; nursing; philosophy; social sciences.

Graduate—business administration, management and operations; education.

SOUTHWESTERN COMMUNITY COLLEGE

Creston, Iowa

http://www.swcc.cc.ia.us/

Southwestern Community College was founded in 1966. It is accredited by North Central Association of Colleges and Schools. It first offered distance learning courses in 2000. In fall 2005, there were 135 students enrolled in distance learning courses. Institutionally administered financial aid is available to distance learners.

Services Distance learners have accessibility to academic advising, bookstore, campus computer network, e-mail services, library services, tutoring.

Contact Doug Greene, Director of Distance Learning, Southwestern Community College, 1501 West Townline Street, Creston, IA 50801. Telephone: 641-782-7081 Ext. 324. Fax: 641-782-3312. E-mail: greene @swcciowa.edu.

DEGREES AND AWARDS

AA Liberal Arts

COURSE SUBJECT AREAS OFFERED OUTSIDE OF DEGREE PROGRAMS

Undergraduate—accounting and related services; area studies; biology; cell biology and anatomical sciences; English composition; fine and studio art; geography and cartography; journalism; mathematics and statistics related; music; philosophy and religious studies related; sociology.

SOUTHWESTERN OREGON COMMUNITY COLLEGE

Coos Bay, Oregon

http://www.socc.edu

Southwestern Oregon Community College was founded in 1961. It is accredited by Northwest Commission on Colleges and Universities. It first offered distance learning courses in 1999. In fall 2005, there were 700 students enrolled in distance learning courses. Institutionally administered financial aid is available to distance learners.

Services Distance learners have accessibility to academic advising, bookstore, campus computer network, e-mail services, library services.

Contact Karen Helland, Instructional Director Learning Resources and Development, Southwestern Oregon Community College, 1988 Newmark, Coos Bay, OR 97420. Telephone: 541-888-7212. Fax: 541-888-7601. E-mail: khelland@socc.edu.

DEGREES AND AWARDS

AD Early Childhood Education

COURSE SUBJECT AREAS OFFERED OUTSIDE OF DEGREE PROGRAMS

Undergraduate—allied health and medical assisting services; business/commerce; chemistry; communication and media; comparative literature; computer engineering; computer science; computer software and media applications; criminal justice and corrections; curriculum and instruction; developmental and child psychology; human development, family studies, and related services; human services; marketing; psychology; psychology related; social psychology; social work; sociology; teaching assistants/aides; technical and business writing.

SOUTHWEST GEORGIA TECHNICAL COLLEGE
Thomasville, Georgia

Southwest Georgia Technical College was founded in 1963. It is accredited by Council on Occupational Education. It first offered distance learning courses in 2001. In fall 2005, there were 243 students enrolled in distance learning courses. Institutionally administered financial aid is available to distance learners.

Services Distance learners have accessibility to academic advising, bookstore, career placement assistance, e-mail services, library services, tutoring.

Contact Mrs. Carla W. Barrow, GVTC Coordinator, Southwest Georgia Technical College, 15689 US Highway 19 North, Thomasville, GA 31792. Telephone: 229-227-2680. Fax: 229-225-5289. E-mail: cbarrow@southwestgatech.edu.

DEGREES AND AWARDS

Programs offered do not lead to a degree or other formal award.

COURSE SUBJECT AREAS OFFERED OUTSIDE OF DEGREE PROGRAMS

Undergraduate—accounting and computer science; applied mathematics; business/commerce; business, management, and marketing related; computer and information sciences; computer/information technology administration and management; computer programming; computer software and media applications; computer systems networking and telecommunications; criminal justice and corrections; criminology; data processing; economics; education (specific levels and methods); English; English composition; mathematics; psychology; sociology.

Non-credit—real estate.

SOUTHWEST VIRGINIA COMMUNITY COLLEGE
Richlands, Virginia
Audiovisual and Distance Education Services
http://desweb.sw.edu

Southwest Virginia Community College was founded in 1968. It is accredited by Southern Association of Colleges and Schools. It first offered distance learning courses in 1991. In fall 2005, there were 1,800 students enrolled in distance learning courses. Institutionally administered financial aid is available to distance learners.

Services Distance learners have accessibility to academic advising, bookstore, campus computer network, career placement assistance, e-mail services, library services, tutoring.

Contact Thomas A. Cash, Director of Distance and Distributed Learning, Southwest Virginia Community College, PO Box SVCC, Richlands, VA 24641. Telephone: 276-964-7280. Fax: 276-964-7686. E-mail: tom.cash@sw.edu.

DEGREES AND AWARDS

AAS Arts and Science Degree Program; Arts and Science Degree Program
AS General Studies
Certificate Network and Internet Administration

COURSE SUBJECT AREAS OFFERED OUTSIDE OF DEGREE PROGRAMS

Undergraduate—creative writing; developmental and child psychology; English composition; history; languages (Romance languages); mathematics and statistics related; sociology; statistics.

Non-credit—computer and information sciences and support services related.

SOUTHWEST WISCONSIN TECHNICAL COLLEGE
Fennimore, Wisconsin
http://www.swtc.edu/

Southwest Wisconsin Technical College was founded in 1967. It is accredited by North Central Association of Colleges and Schools. It first offered distance learning courses in 1989. In fall 2005, there were 700 students enrolled in distance learning courses. Institutionally administered financial aid is available to distance learners.

Services Distance learners have accessibility to bookstore, e-mail services, library services, tutoring.

Contact Kristal Davenport, Instructional Technology Support Specialist, Southwest Wisconsin Technical College, 1800 Bronson Boulevard, Fennimore, WI 53809. Telephone: 608-822-2426. Fax: 608-822-6019. E-mail: kdavenport@swtc.edu.

DEGREES AND AWARDS

Diploma Medical Transcription
Technical Certificate Medical Coding Specialist

COURSE SUBJECT AREAS OFFERED OUTSIDE OF DEGREE PROGRAMS

Undergraduate—accounting and related services; allied health and medical assisting services; applied mathematics; business/corporate communications; communication and journalism related; communication and media; computer and information sciences; computer programming; computer software and media applications; computer systems networking and telecommunications; cosmetology and related personal grooming services; culinary arts and related services; curriculum and instruction; economics; educational/instructional media design; foods, nutrition, and related services; health/medical preparatory programs; hospitality administration; human resources management; management information systems; mathematics; nursing; psychology; social sciences; sociology; statistics.

SPARTANBURG TECHNICAL COLLEGE
Spartanburg, South Carolina
http://dl.stcsc.edu

Spartanburg Technical College was founded in 1961. It is accredited by Southern Association of Colleges and Schools. It first offered distance learning courses in 1997. In fall 2005, there were 622 students enrolled in distance learning courses. Institutionally administered financial aid is available to distance learners.

Services Distance learners have accessibility to academic advising, bookstore, e-mail services, library services, tutoring.

Contact Mr. Mark Roseveare, Director of STCOnline, Spartanburg Technical College, PO Box 4386, Business I-85 and New Cut Road, Spartanburg, SC 29305-4386. Telephone: 864-592-4763. Fax: 864-592-4941. E-mail: rosevearem@stcsc.edu.

DEGREES AND AWARDS

AA Arts
AD Interpreter Training (General Technology–AD in Occupational Technology); Management

COURSE SUBJECT AREAS OFFERED OUTSIDE OF DEGREE PROGRAMS

Undergraduate—accounting and related services; applied mathematics; business administration, management and operations; business/commerce; computer software and media applications; data entry/microcomputer applications; English; English composition; mathematics; psychology; sales, merchandising, and related marketing operations (general); sociology; statistics.

SPERTUS INSTITUTE OF JEWISH STUDIES
Chicago, Illinois
http://www.spertus.edu/

Spertus Institute of Jewish Studies was founded in 1924. It is accredited by North Central Association of Colleges and Schools. It first offered distance learning courses in 1994. In fall 2005, there were 250 students enrolled in distance learning courses. Institutionally administered financial aid is available to distance learners.

Services Distance learners have accessibility to academic advising, library services.

Contact Simona Funnye, Admissions, Spertus Institute of Jewish Studies, 618 South Michigan Avenue, Chicago, IL 60605. Telephone: 888-322-1769. Fax: 312-922-6406. E-mail: college@spertus.edu.

DEGREES AND AWARDS

MS Jewish Education–Master of Science in Jewish Education (MSJE)
MSJS Jewish Studies
DJS Jewish Studies

STANFORD UNIVERSITY
Stanford, California
Stanford Center for Professional Development
http://scpd.stanford.edu

Stanford University was founded in 1891. It is accredited by Western Association of Schools and Colleges. It first offered distance learning courses in 1969. In fall 2005, there were 1,500 students enrolled in distance learning courses. Institutionally administered financial aid is available to distance learners.
Services Distance learners have accessibility to academic advising, bookstore, campus computer network, e-mail services, library services.
Contact Carleen Wayne, Stanford University, 496 Lomita Hall, Room 300, Stanford, CA 94305-4036. Telephone: 650-725-3000. Fax: 650-725-2868. E-mail: carleen1@stanford.edu.

DEGREES AND AWARDS

Graduate Certificate Artificial Intelligence; Biodesign; Bioinformatics; Cardiovascular Bioengineering; Clinical Informatics; Computer Architecture; Computer Hardware and VLSI Design; Computer Languages and Operating Systems; Computer Science–Foundations in Computer Science; Control and System Engineering; Data Mining and Applications (Statistics); Databases; Decision Analysis; Design for Customer Value and Market Success; Digital Communication; Electronic Circuits; Electronic Devices and Technology; Engineering Mechanics–Mathematical Foundations and Applications; Guidance and Control (Aeronautics and Astronautics); International Security; Management Science and Engineering; Nanoscale Materials Science; Networking (Electrical Engineering); Optics, Imaging, and Communications; Product Creation and Innovative Manufacturing; Quantitative Methods in Finance and Risk Management (Statistics); Risk Analysis (Management Science and Engineering); Signal Processing; Software Systems; Software Systems, advanced; Spacecraft Design and Operation proficiency; Telecommunications; Wireless Personal Communication
MS Aeronautics and Astronautics; Biomedical Informatics; Computer Science; Electrical Engineering; Engineering–Computational and Mathematical Engineering; Management Science and Engineering; Mechanical Engineering

COURSE SUBJECT AREAS OFFERED OUTSIDE OF DEGREE PROGRAMS

Non-credit—biomedical/medical engineering; biotechnology; business administration, management and operations; business/managerial economics; civil engineering; computer science; computer systems networking and telecommunications; construction engineering technology; electrical, electronics and communications engineering; engineering/industrial management; entrepreneurial and small business operations; finance and financial management services; management sciences and quantitative methods; systems engineering.

STANLY COMMUNITY COLLEGE
Albemarle, North Carolina
http://www.stanly.edu

Stanly Community College was founded in 1971. It is accredited by Southern Association of Colleges and Schools. It first offered distance learning courses in 1990. In fall 2005, there were 2,100 students enrolled in distance learning courses. Institutionally administered financial aid is available to distance learners.
Services Distance learners have accessibility to academic advising, bookstore, campus computer network, career placement assistance, e-mail services, library services.
Contact Marlene Saunders, Director of Distance Learning, Stanly Community College, 141 College Drive, Albemarle, NC 28001. Telephone: 704-991-0258. Fax: 704-982-0819. E-mail: saundem@stanly.edu.

DEGREES AND AWARDS

AA the Arts
AAS Accounting; Business Administration; Criminal Justice Technology; Early Childhood Associate

COURSE SUBJECT AREAS OFFERED OUTSIDE OF DEGREE PROGRAMS

Undergraduate—accounting and related services; allied health diagnostic, intervention, and treatment professions; applied mathematics; biological and biomedical sciences related; biology; business administration, management and operations; computer and information sciences; computer and information sciences and support services related; computer systems networking and telecommunications; criminal justice and corrections; developmental and child psychology; economics; English composition; finance and financial management services; human development, family studies, and related services; human services; management information systems; marketing; mathematics; nursing; philosophy and religious studies related; political science and government; psychology; religious studies; sociology.

STATE UNIVERSITY OF NEW YORK AT BUFFALO
Buffalo, New York
Millard Fillmore College Distance Learning Office
http://www.mfc.buffalo.edu

State University of New York at Buffalo was founded in 1846. It is accredited by Middle States Association of Colleges and Schools. It first offered distance learning courses in 1994. In fall 2005, there were 1,000 students enrolled in distance learning courses. Institutionally administered financial aid is available to distance learners.
Services Distance learners have accessibility to academic advising, bookstore, campus computer network, e-mail services, library services.
Contact Mr. Larry Gingrich, Associate Dean, State University of New York at Buffalo, 128 Parker Hall, Buffalo, NY 14214-3007. Telephone: 716-829-3131. Fax: 716-829-2475. E-mail: gingrich@buffalo.edu.

DEGREES AND AWARDS

Programs offered do not lead to a degree or other formal award.

COURSE SUBJECT AREAS OFFERED OUTSIDE OF DEGREE PROGRAMS

Undergraduate—computer/information technology administration and management; computer systems networking and telecommunications; English composition; entrepreneurial and small business operations; legal studies (non-professional general, undergraduate); public relations, advertising, and applied communication related.
Graduate—education (specific subject areas).

STATE UNIVERSITY OF NEW YORK AT BUFFALO
Buffalo, New York
Adult Education & Human Resource Development
http://www.buffalo.edu/

State University of New York at Buffalo was founded in 1846. It is accredited by Middle States Association of Colleges and Schools. It first offered distance learning courses in 1995. In fall 2005, there were 850 students enrolled in distance learning courses. Institutionally administered financial aid is available to distance learners.
Services Distance learners have accessibility to academic advising, bookstore, campus computer network, career placement assistance, e-mail services, library services.
Contact Mr. Larry R. Gingrich, Associate Dean, State University of New York at Buffalo, 3435 Main Street, 128 Parker Hall, Buffalo, NY 14214. Telephone: 716-829-3131. Fax: 716-829-2475. E-mail: gingrich@buffalo.edu.

DEGREES AND AWARDS

Programs offered do not lead to a degree or other formal award.

COURSE SUBJECT AREAS OFFERED OUTSIDE OF DEGREE PROGRAMS

Undergraduate—computer/information technology administration and management; data entry/microcomputer applications; health professions related; human resources management; international business; legal professions and studies related; nutrition sciences; psychology.

Non-credit—accounting and computer science; business, management, and marketing related; computer and information sciences; human resources management; legal professions and studies related.

STATE UNIVERSITY OF NEW YORK AT NEW PALTZ

New Paltz, New York

Center for Continuing and Professional Education

http://www.newpaltz.edu

State University of New York at New Paltz was founded in 1828. It is accredited by Middle States Association of Colleges and Schools. It first offered distance learning courses in 1995. In fall 2005, there were 230 students enrolled in distance learning courses. Institutionally administered financial aid is available to distance learners.

Services Distance learners have accessibility to bookstore, campus computer network, e-mail services, library services.

Contact Helise Winters, Director, Extension and Distance Learning, State University of New York at New Paltz, 1 Hawk Drive, Suite 9, New Paltz, NY 12561-2443. Telephone: 845-257-2894. Fax: 845-257-2899. E-mail: edl@newpaltz.edu.

DEGREES AND AWARDS

Programs offered do not lead to a degree or other formal award.

COURSE SUBJECT AREAS OFFERED OUTSIDE OF DEGREE PROGRAMS

Undergraduate—American literature (United States and Canadian); anthropology; communication and media; comparative literature; computer science; curriculum and instruction; developmental and child psychology; economics; English composition; English literature (British and Commonwealth); geography and cartography; geological and earth sciences/geosciences; history; industrial and organizational psychology; philosophy; psychology; public relations, advertising, and applied communication related; social and philosophical foundations of education; sociology.

Graduate—computer science; education.

STATE UNIVERSITY OF NEW YORK AT OSWEGO

Oswego, New York

Office of Distance Learning

http://www.oswego.edu

State University of New York at Oswego was founded in 1861. It is accredited by Middle States Association of Colleges and Schools. It first offered distance learning courses in 1995. In fall 2005, there were 700 students enrolled in distance learning courses. Institutionally administered financial aid is available to distance learners.

Services Distance learners have accessibility to academic advising, bookstore, campus computer network, career placement assistance, e-mail services, library services, tutoring.

Contact Allison Finsterwalder, Associate Director, State University of New York at Oswego, Continuing Education, 100 Sheldon Hall, Oswego, NY 13126. Telephone: 315-312-2270. Fax: 315-312-3078. E-mail: ced @oswego.edu.

DEGREES AND AWARDS

BA Communications; Public Justice
BS Vocational Teacher Preparation

COURSE SUBJECT AREAS OFFERED OUTSIDE OF DEGREE PROGRAMS

Undergraduate—anthropology; archeology; biology; business administration, management and operations; business/managerial economics; chemistry; communication and journalism related; communication and media; computer and information sciences; computer science; computer systems networking and telecommunications; counseling psychology; criminal justice and corrections; developmental and child psychology; dramatic/theater arts and stagecraft; economics; educational psychology; education (specific subject areas); geological and earth sciences/geosciences; health services/allied health/health sciences; history; information science/studies; journalism; philosophy and religious studies related; psychology; public relations, advertising, and applied communication related; sociology.

Graduate—accounting and related services; anthropology; business administration, management and operations; counseling psychology; curriculum and instruction; economics; education; education (specific subject areas); gerontology; information science/studies; psychology.

See full description on page 472.

STATE UNIVERSITY OF NEW YORK AT PLATTSBURGH

Plattsburgh, New York

Distance Learning Office

http://www.plattsburgh.edu/cll

State University of New York at Plattsburgh was founded in 1889. It is accredited by Middle States Association of Colleges and Schools. It first offered distance learning courses in 1990. In fall 2005, there were 873 students enrolled in distance learning courses. Institutionally administered financial aid is available to distance learners.

Services Distance learners have accessibility to academic advising, bookstore, campus computer network, e-mail services, library services, tutoring.

Contact Mr. Michael J. Bozonie, Associate Dean, Library and Information Services, State University of New York at Plattsburgh, Feinberg Library, 2 Draper Avenue, Plattsburgh, NY 12901. E-mail: michael.bozonie@plattsburgh.edu.

DEGREES AND AWARDS

BS Nursing

COURSE SUBJECT AREAS OFFERED OUTSIDE OF DEGREE PROGRAMS

Undergraduate—area, ethnic, cultural, and gender studies related; biochemistry, biophysics and molecular biology; biology; biopsychology; business administration, management and operations; computer and information sciences; education; education related; entrepreneurial and small business operations; ethnic, cultural minority, and gender studies; geological and earth sciences/geosciences; health and physical education/fitness; health professions related; library science related; marketing; nursing; political science and government; psychology related; sales, merchandising, and related marketing operations (specialized); social sciences; sociology; statistics.

Graduate—business administration, management and operations; education; educational administration and supervision; educational/instructional media design; education related; entrepreneurial and small business operations; special education.

STATE UNIVERSITY OF NEW YORK COLLEGE AT CORTLAND

Cortland, New York

http://www.cortland.edu/

State University of New York College at Cortland was founded in 1868. It is accredited by Middle States Association of Colleges and Schools. It first offered distance learning courses in 1996. In fall 2005, there were 118 students enrolled in distance learning courses. Institutionally administered financial aid is available to distance learners.

Services Distance learners have accessibility to academic advising, bookstore, campus computer network, career placement assistance, e-mail services, library services.

Contact Mark Yacavone, Director of Admissions, State University of New York College at Cortland, PO Box 2000, Miller Building, Cortland, NY 13045. Telephone: 607-753-4711. Fax: 607-753-5998. E-mail: admissions@cortland.edu.

DEGREES AND AWARDS

Programs offered do not lead to a degree or other formal award.

COURSE SUBJECT AREAS OFFERED OUTSIDE OF DEGREE PROGRAMS

Graduate—computer science; English language and literature related; psychology.

STATE UNIVERSITY OF NEW YORK COLLEGE AT POTSDAM

Potsdam, New York

http://www.potsdam.edu/

State University of New York College at Potsdam was founded in 1816. It is accredited by Middle States Association of Colleges and Schools. It first offered distance learning courses in 2002. In fall 2005, there were 20 students enrolled in distance learning courses. Institutionally administered financial aid is available to distance learners.

Services Distance learners have accessibility to academic advising, bookstore, campus computer network, e-mail services, library services.

Contact Ms. Lee Ghostlaw, Staff Assistant, Continuing Education, State University of New York College at Potsdam, 44 Pierrepont Avenue, Potsdam, NY 13676. Telephone: 315-267-2166. Fax: 315-267-3088. E-mail: ghostllk@potsdam.edu.

DEGREES AND AWARDS

Programs offered do not lead to a degree or other formal award.

COURSE SUBJECT AREAS OFFERED OUTSIDE OF DEGREE PROGRAMS

Undergraduate—behavioral sciences; biology; business administration, management and operations; business, management, and marketing related; business/managerial economics; communication and journalism related; community health services; data processing; economics; education (specific subject areas); entrepreneurial and small business operations; geography and cartography; management information systems; music; physical sciences; psychology; sociology.

Graduate—education (specific levels and methods).

Non-credit—accounting and related services; business administration, management and operations; business/commerce; communication and media; computer and information sciences; computer programming; computer software and media applications; creative writing; culinary arts and related services; data entry/microcomputer applications; entrepreneurial and small business operations; finance and financial management services; languages (Romance languages); linguistic, comparative, and related language studies; sales, merchandising, and related marketing operations (specialized).

STATE UNIVERSITY OF NEW YORK COLLEGE OF AGRICULTURE AND TECHNOLOGY AT MORRISVILLE

Morrisville, New York

http://www.morrisville.edu/

State University of New York College of Agriculture and Technology at Morrisville was founded in 1908. It is accredited by Middle States Association of Colleges and Schools. It first offered distance learning courses in 1997. In fall 2005, there were 142 students enrolled in distance learning courses. Institutionally administered financial aid is available to distance learners.

Services Distance learners have accessibility to academic advising, bookstore, campus computer network, e-mail services, library services.

Contact Office of the Registrar, State University of New York College of Agriculture and Technology at Morrisville, Morrisville, NY 13408. Telephone: 315-684-6066. Fax: 315-684-6024. E-mail: registrar@morrisville.edu.

DEGREES AND AWARDS

Programs offered do not lead to a degree or other formal award.

COURSE SUBJECT AREAS OFFERED OUTSIDE OF DEGREE PROGRAMS

Undergraduate—accounting and related services; agricultural business and management; agriculture; business/commerce; computer/information technology administration and management; computer software and media applications; creative writing; English composition; hospitality administration; management sciences and quantitative methods; mathematics; technical and business writing.

STATE UNIVERSITY OF NEW YORK EMPIRE STATE COLLEGE

Saratoga Springs, New York

Center for Distance Learning

http://www.esc.edu/cdl

State University of New York Empire State College was founded in 1971. It is accredited by Middle States Association of Colleges and Schools. It first offered distance learning courses in 1979. In fall 2005, there were 4,900 students enrolled in distance learning courses. Institutionally administered financial aid is available to distance learners.

Services Distance learners have accessibility to academic advising, bookstore, campus computer network, career placement assistance, e-mail services, library services, tutoring.

Contact Ms. Kathleen Schechner, Outreach Specialist, State University of New York Empire State College, 111 West Avenue, Saratoga Springs, NY 12866. Telephone: 518-587-2100 Ext. 2556. Fax: 518-587-2660. E-mail: kathy.schechner@esc.edu.

DEGREES AND AWARDS

AA Business, Management, and Economics; Community and Human Services; Cultural Studies; Educational Studies; Historical Studies; Human Development; Interdisciplinary Studies; Labor Studies; Science, Math, and Technology; Social Theory, Social Structure, and Change; the Arts

AS Business, Management, and Economics; Community and Human Services; Cultural Studies; Educational Studies; Historical Studies; Human Development; Interdisciplinary Studies; Labor Studies; Science, Math, and Technology; Social Theory, Social Structure, and Change; the Arts

BA Business, Management, and Economics; Community and Human Services; Cultural Studies; Educational Studies; Historical Studies; Human Development; Interdisciplinary Studies; Labor Studies; Science, Math, and Technology; Social Theory, Social Structure, and Change; the Arts

BPS Business, Management, and Economics

BS Business, Management, and Economics; Community and Human Services; Community and Human Services; Cultural Studies; Educational Studies; Historical Studies; Human Development; Interdisciplinary Studies; Labor Studies; Science, Math, and Technology; Social Theory, Social Structure, and Change; the Arts

MA Liberal Studies; Policy Studies

MBA Business Administration

COURSE SUBJECT AREAS OFFERED OUTSIDE OF DEGREE PROGRAMS

Undergraduate—accounting and related services; biology; English composition; finance and financial management services; fire protection; history; international business; legal studies (non-professional general, undergraduate); management information systems; mathematics and statistics related; social psychology; sociology; statistics.

Graduate—business/commerce; political science and government; social sciences.

See full description on page 470.

STATE UNIVERSITY OF NEW YORK, FREDONIA

Fredonia, New York

Office of Lifelong Learning/SUNY Learning Network

http://sln.suny.edu

State University of New York, Fredonia was founded in 1826. It is accredited by Middle States Association of Colleges and Schools. It first offered distance learning courses in 1998. In fall 2005, there were 52 students enrolled in distance learning courses. Institutionally administered financial aid is available to distance learners.

Services Distance learners have accessibility to academic advising, bookstore, campus computer network, career placement assistance, e-mail services, library services.

Contact Mr. Grant Umberger, Associate Director of Lifelong Learning, State University of New York, Fredonia, Office of Lifelong Learning,

2142 Fenton Hall, Fredonia, NY 14063. Telephone: 716-673-3177. Fax: 716-673-3712. E-mail: grant.umberger@fredonia.edu.

DEGREES AND AWARDS

Programs offered do not lead to a degree or other formal award.

COURSE SUBJECT AREAS OFFERED OUTSIDE OF DEGREE PROGRAMS

Undergraduate—biological and biomedical sciences related; business, management, and marketing related; computer and information sciences and support services related; political science and government.
Graduate—education.

STEPHEN F. AUSTIN STATE UNIVERSITY
Nacogdoches, Texas
http://oit.sfasu.edu/

Stephen F. Austin State University was founded in 1923. It is accredited by Southern Association of Colleges and Schools. It first offered distance learning courses in 1993. In fall 2005, there were 1,700 students enrolled in distance learning courses. Institutionally administered financial aid is available to distance learners.
Services Distance learners have accessibility to academic advising, bookstore, campus computer network, career placement assistance, e-mail services, library services, tutoring.
Contact Andra Floyd, Distance Education Support Specialist, Stephen F. Austin State University, SFA Box 13038, Nacogdoches, TX 75962. Telephone: 936-468-1919. Fax: 936-468-1308. E-mail: sfaonline@sfasu.edu.

DEGREES AND AWARDS

BS Interdisciplinary Studies
Certificate Elementary Education (Post-Baccalaureate Certification)
MA Music Education
MS Resource Interpretation

COURSE SUBJECT AREAS OFFERED OUTSIDE OF DEGREE PROGRAMS

Undergraduate—accounting and related services; agriculture; astronomy and astrophysics; business administration, management and operations; business/corporate communications; curriculum and instruction; economics; educational psychology; family and consumer economics; finance and financial management services; hospitality administration; music; psychology; sales, merchandising, and related marketing operations (specialized); social work; special education; technical and business writing.
Graduate—educational administration and supervision; educational psychology; education related; education (specific levels and methods); forestry; music; psychology; special education.

STEPHENS COLLEGE
Columbia, Missouri
Division of Graduate and Continuing Studies
http://www.stephens.edu/admission/nontraditional/

Stephens College was founded in 1833. It is accredited by North Central Association of Colleges and Schools. It first offered distance learning courses in 1970. In fall 2005, there were 200 students enrolled in distance learning courses. Institutionally administered financial aid is available to distance learners.
Services Distance learners have accessibility to academic advising, bookstore, e-mail services, library services.
Contact Ms. Mellodie Wilson, Associate Director, Stephens College, 1200 East Broadway, Box 2083, Columbia, MO 65215. Telephone: 800-388-7579. Fax: 573-876-7290. E-mail: online@stephens.edu.

DEGREES AND AWARDS

BS Business Administration; Health Information Administration
Certificate Health Information Administration
MBA Clinical Information Systems Management; Customized Emphasis
MEd Curriculum & Instruction

COURSE SUBJECT AREAS OFFERED OUTSIDE OF DEGREE PROGRAMS

Undergraduate—accounting and related services; business/commerce; computer and information sciences; creative writing; developmental and child psychology; economics; English; health and medical administrative services; history; mathematics; philosophy; psychology; religious studies; social sciences.
Graduate—accounting and related services; entrepreneurial and small business operations; finance and financial management services; marketing; statistics.

STEVENS INSTITUTE OF TECHNOLOGY
Hoboken, New Jersey
Graduate School
http://www.webcampus.stevens.edu

Stevens Institute of Technology was founded in 1870. It is accredited by Middle States Association of Colleges and Schools. It first offered distance learning courses in 1999. In fall 2005, there were 2,500 students enrolled in distance learning courses. Institutionally administered financial aid is available to distance learners.
Services Distance learners have accessibility to academic advising, bookstore, campus computer network, career placement assistance, e-mail services, library services, tutoring.
Contact Robert Zotti, Program Director, Online Learning, Stevens Institute of Technology, Hoboken, NJ 07030. Telephone: 800-496-4935. Fax: 201-216-5011. E-mail: webcampus@stevens.edu.

DEGREES AND AWARDS

Graduate Certificate Atmospheric and Environmental Science and Engineering; Computer Graphics; Cyber Security; Database Systems; Digital Signal Processing; Elements of Computer Science; Financial Engineering; Human Resources Management; Management Information Systems; Multimedia Technology; Networked Information Systems; Pharmaceutical Manufacturing Practices; Professional Communications; Project Management; Quantitative Software Engineering; Secure Network Systems Design; Technology Management; Telecommunications Management; Wireless Communications
ME Networked Information Systems
MS Computer Science with CyberSecurity Concentration; Computer Science/Telecom Management with Concentration in Security; Management and Forensics; Microelectronics and Photonics; Project Management; Quantitative Software Engineering; Systems Engineering; Telecommunication Management

COURSE SUBJECT AREAS OFFERED OUTSIDE OF DEGREE PROGRAMS

Graduate—management information systems; management science.
See full description on page 474.

STONY BROOK UNIVERSITY, STATE UNIVERSITY OF NEW YORK
Stony Brook, New York
Electronic Extension Program
http://www.stonybrook.edu/spd/online/

Stony Brook University, State University of New York was founded in 1957. It is accredited by Middle States Association of Colleges and Schools. It first offered distance learning courses in 1996. In fall 2005, there were 600 students enrolled in distance learning courses. Institutionally administered financial aid is available to distance learners.
Services Distance learners have accessibility to academic advising, bookstore, campus computer network, library services.
Contact Kim Giacalone, Assistant Director, Stony Brook University, State University of New York, School of Professional Development, N 213 SBS Building, Stony Brook, NY 11794-4310. Telephone: 631-632-9484. Fax: 631-632-9046. E-mail: kim.giacalone@stonybrook.edu.

DEGREES AND AWARDS

Graduate Certificate Human Resource Management
MA Liberal Studies

COURSE SUBJECT AREAS OFFERED OUTSIDE OF DEGREE PROGRAMS

Graduate—education; educational administration and supervision; English language and literature related; human resources management; liberal arts and sciences, general studies and humanities.

STRAYER UNIVERSITY
Washington, District of Columbia
Strayer Online
http://www.online.strayer.edu

Strayer University was founded in 1892. It is accredited by Middle States Association of Colleges and Schools. It first offered distance learning courses in 1997. In fall 2005, there were 27,000 students enrolled in distance learning courses. Institutionally administered financial aid is available to distance learners.

Services Distance learners have accessibility to academic advising, bookstore, campus computer network, e-mail services, library services, tutoring.

Contact Patty Pellici, Director of Online Operations, Strayer University, PO Box 487, Newington, VA 22122. Telephone: 866-344-3286. Fax: 703-339-4849. E-mail: info@strayer.edu.

DEGREES AND AWARDS

AA Accounting; Acquisition and Contract Management; Business Administration; Computer Information Systems; Computer Networking; Database Technology; Economics; General Studies; Information Systems; Internetworking Technology; Marketing

BBA Acquisition and Contract Management; Banking; E-business; Finance; Hospitality and Tourism Management; Human Resource Management; Legal Studies; Management; Marketing; Retail Management

BS Accounting; Computer Information Systems; Computer Networking; Database Technology; Economics; Information Systems; International Business; Internetworking Technology

Certificate Accounting; Business Administration; Computer Information Systems; Information Systems

Diploma Accounting; Acquisition and Contract Management; Computer Information Systems; Information Systems; Internetworking Technology; Network Security; Web Development

Graduate Certificate Information Systems

MBA Business Administration

MEd Education

MHSA Health Services Administration

MPA Public Administration

MS Communications Technology; Information Systems; Management Information Systems; Professional Accounting

COURSE SUBJECT AREAS OFFERED OUTSIDE OF DEGREE PROGRAMS

Undergraduate—accounting and related services; area, ethnic, cultural, and gender studies related; business/commerce; economics; English; English composition; finance and financial management services; history; information science/studies; international business; legal studies (nonprofessional general, undergraduate); linguistic, comparative, and related language studies; mathematics; political science and government; psychology; sales, merchandising, and related marketing operations (general); sociology.

Graduate—accounting and related services; business/commerce; economics; information science/studies; legal research and advanced professional studies; mathematics.

See full description on page 476.

SULLIVAN UNIVERSITY
Louisville, Kentucky
Program in Dispute Resolution
http://home.sullivan.edu/grad_school/graduate/curriculum/MSDR.htm

Sullivan University was founded in 1864. It is accredited by Southern Association of Colleges and Schools. It first offered distance learning courses in 2002. In fall 2005, there were 60 students enrolled in distance learning courses. Institutionally administered financial aid is available to distance learners.

Services Distance learners have accessibility to academic advising, bookstore, campus computer network, career placement assistance, e-mail services, library services, tutoring.

Contact Mr. Ron Hinson, Director of Graduate Admissions, Sullivan University, The Graduate School, 3101 Bardstown Road, Louisville, KY 40205. Telephone: 800-844-1354 Ext. 477. Fax: 502-456-0016. E-mail: rhinson@sullivan.edu.

DEGREES AND AWARDS

Certificate Dispute Resolution

MS Dispute Resolution, Conflict Management

COURSE SUBJECT AREAS OFFERED OUTSIDE OF DEGREE PROGRAMS

Graduate—bioethics/medical ethics; business administration, management and operations; business/corporate communications; community organization and advocacy; community psychology; construction management; construction trades related; educational administration and supervision; engineering/industrial management; family and consumer sciences/human sciences business services; health and medical administrative services; health professions related; hospitality administration; human resources management; human services; industrial and organizational psychology; insurance; international business; legal research and advanced professional studies; mental and social health services and allied professions; natural resources management and policy; nursing; pastoral counseling and specialized ministries; peace studies and conflict resolution; psychology related; public administration; public administration and social service professions related; public relations, advertising, and applied communication related; real estate; social work; special education.

See full description on page 478.

SYRACUSE UNIVERSITY
Syracuse, New York
University College
http://www.suce.syr.edu/distance

Syracuse University was founded in 1870. It is accredited by Middle States Association of Colleges and Schools. It first offered distance learning courses in 1966. In fall 2005, there were 1,000 students enrolled in distance learning courses. Institutionally administered financial aid is available to distance learners.

Services Distance learners have accessibility to academic advising, bookstore, campus computer network, career placement assistance, e-mail services, library services.

Contact Dr. Geraldine de Berly, Associate Dean, University College, Syracuse University, 700 University Avenue, Suite 403, Syracuse, NY 13244-2530. Telephone: 315-443-5753. Fax: 315-443-4410. E-mail: deberly@uc.syr.edu.

DEGREES AND AWARDS

AA Liberal Arts

BA Liberal Studies

BPS Organizational Leadership

Certificate Organizational Leadership

CAGS Digital Libraries; Information Security Management; Information Security Management; Information Systems and Telecommunications Management; School Media

MA Advertising Design; Illustration

MBA iMBA

MS Communications Management; Information Management; Library and Information Science in School Media; Library and Information Science; Social Sciences; Telecommunications and Network Management

COURSE SUBJECT AREAS OFFERED OUTSIDE OF DEGREE PROGRAMS

Undergraduate—biological and physical sciences; business, management, and marketing related; computer and information sciences; English language and literature related; ethnic, cultural minority, and gender studies; liberal arts and sciences, general studies and humanities; science, technology and society; social sciences; speech and rhetoric; statistics; technical and business writing; visual and performing arts related.

Graduate—anthropology; business administration, management and operations; communication and media; computer and information sciences; computer/information technology administration and management; computer systems networking and telecommunications; ethnic, cultural minority, and gender studies; history; information science/studies; library science; library science related; management information systems; psychology; sociology; visual and performing arts related.

See full description on page 484.

SYRACUSE UNIVERSITY
Syracuse, New York
Martin J. Whitman School of Management
http://whitman.syr.edu/imba

Syracuse University was founded in 1870. It is accredited by Middle States Association of Colleges and Schools. It first offered distance learning courses in 1977. In fall 2005, there were 220 students enrolled in distance learning courses. Institutionally administered financial aid is available to distance learners.

Services Distance learners have accessibility to academic advising, bookstore, campus computer network, career placement assistance, e-mail services, library services.

Contact Pamela Suzadail, Assistant Director, External Programs, Syracuse University, 721 University Avenue, Syracuse, NY 13244-2450. Telephone: 315-443-8384. E-mail: pjsuzada@syr.edu.

DEGREES AND AWARDS

MBA Business Administration

COURSE SUBJECT AREAS OFFERED OUTSIDE OF DEGREE PROGRAMS

Graduate—accounting and related services; business administration, management and operations; business/commerce; business/managerial economics; entrepreneurial and small business operations; finance and financial management services; management information systems; management sciences and quantitative methods; marketing; sales, merchandising, and related marketing operations (general).

See full description on page 482.

SYRACUSE UNIVERSITY
Syracuse, New York
School of Information Studies
http://www.ist.syr.edu

Syracuse University was founded in 1870. It is accredited by Middle States Association of Colleges and Schools. It first offered distance learning courses in 1993. In fall 2005, there were 350 students enrolled in distance learning courses. Institutionally administered financial aid is available to distance learners.

Services Distance learners have accessibility to academic advising, bookstore, campus computer network, career placement assistance, e-mail services, library services, tutoring.

Contact Kathryn Allen, Director of Distance Learning, Syracuse University, School of Information Studies, 114 Hinds Hall, Syracuse, NY 13244. Telephone: 315-443-4251. Fax: 315-443-5673. E-mail: kallen02@syr.edu.

DEGREES AND AWARDS

CAGS Digital Libraries; Information Security Management; Information Systems and Telecommunications Management; School Media

MLIS Library and Information Science

MS Information Management

MTM Telecommunications and Network Management

COURSE SUBJECT AREAS OFFERED OUTSIDE OF DEGREE PROGRAMS

Undergraduate—business administration, management and operations; communications technology; computer systems networking and telecommunications; information science/studies; management information systems; science, technology and society; systems science and theory.

Graduate—communications technology; computer and information sciences; computer/information technology administration and management; computer software and media applications; computer systems analysis; computer systems networking and telecommunications; data processing; information science/studies; library assistant; library science; library science related; management information systems; systems science and theory.

See full description on page 480.

TACOMA COMMUNITY COLLEGE
Tacoma, Washington
Distance Learning Program
http://www.tacoma.ctc.edu/inst_dept/distancelearning/

Tacoma Community College was founded in 1965. It is accredited by Northwest Commission on Colleges and Universities. It first offered distance learning courses in 1975. In fall 2005, there were 2,700 students enrolled in distance learning courses. Institutionally administered financial aid is available to distance learners.

Services Distance learners have accessibility to academic advising, bookstore, library services.

Contact Mr. Andy Duckworth, Coordinator, Distance Learning and Multimedia Services, Tacoma Community College, 6501 South 19th Street, Building 7, Room 25, Tacoma, WA 98466. Telephone: 253-460-3958. Fax: 253-566-6077. E-mail: aduckwor@tcc.ctc.edu.

DEGREES AND AWARDS

Programs offered do not lead to a degree or other formal award.

COURSE SUBJECT AREAS OFFERED OUTSIDE OF DEGREE PROGRAMS

Undergraduate—accounting and related services; allied health and medical assisting services; allied health diagnostic, intervention, and treatment professions; anthropology; applied mathematics; biology; botany/plant biology; business/commerce; chemistry; computer and information sciences; computer programming; computer science; criminal justice and corrections; data entry/microcomputer applications; design and applied arts; engineering; engineering physics; engineering related; English as a second language; English composition; fine and studio art; geography and cartography; geological and earth sciences/geosciences; health and medical administrative services; health professions related; history; human development, family studies, and related services; human services; information science/studies; legal studies (non-professional general, undergraduate); library science; library science related; linguistic, comparative, and related language studies; mathematics; music; nursing; physics; political science and government; psychology; social work; sociology; speech and rhetoric.

Non-credit—business administration, management and operations; computer and information sciences; management information systems.

TAFT COLLEGE
Taft, California
http://www.taftcollege.edu

Taft College was founded in 1922. It is accredited by Western Association of Schools and Colleges. It first offered distance learning courses in 1997. In fall 2005, there were 850 students enrolled in distance learning courses. Institutionally administered financial aid is available to distance learners.

Services Distance learners have accessibility to academic advising, bookstore, campus computer network, e-mail services, library services, tutoring.

Contact Patti Bench, Coordinator of Distance Learning, Taft College, 29 Emmons Park Drive, Taft, CA 93268. Telephone: 661-763-7757. Fax: 661-763-7816. E-mail: pbench@taft.org.

DEGREES AND AWARDS

AA Business Administration; Liberal Arts
AS Business, general; Criminal Justice Administration; Early Childhood Education

COURSE SUBJECT AREAS OFFERED OUTSIDE OF DEGREE PROGRAMS

Undergraduate—accounting and related services; applied mathematics; biological and physical sciences; business administration, management and operations; business/commerce; computer science; creative writing; criminal justice and corrections; economics; English; English composition; English language and literature related; geological and earth sciences/geosciences; history; human development, family studies, and related services; mathematics; mathematics and statistics related; psychology; psychology related; social sciences; social sciences related; sociology; statistics.

TAYLOR UNIVERSITY
Fort Wayne, Indiana
Center for Lifelong Learning
http://cll.taylor.edu

Taylor University was founded in 1938. It is accredited by North Central Association of Colleges and Schools. It first offered distance learning courses in 1941. In fall 2005, there were 458 students enrolled in distance learning courses. Institutionally administered financial aid is available to distance learners.
Services Distance learners have accessibility to academic advising, bookstore, e-mail services, library services.
Contact Kevin J. Mahaffy, Director, Taylor University, Center for Lifelong Learning, 1025 West Rudisill Boulevard, Fort Wayne, IN 46807-2197. Telephone: 260-744-8750. Fax: 260-744-8796. E-mail: info@cll.taylor.edu.

DEGREES AND AWARDS

AA Biblical Studies; Justice Administration — Ministry Concentration; Justice Administration — Public Policy Concentration; Liberal Arts — History concentration; Liberal Arts — Interdisciplinary concentration; Liberal Arts — Social Science concentration
BBA Business Administration
Certificate Biblical Studies; Biblical and Cultural Leadership; Christian Worker; Justice and Ministry; Leadership Development; Missions Studies; Professional Writing

COURSE SUBJECT AREAS OFFERED OUTSIDE OF DEGREE PROGRAMS

Undergraduate—American literature (United States and Canadian); area, ethnic, cultural, and gender studies related; area studies; behavioral sciences; biblical and other theological languages and literatures; biblical studies; biological and physical sciences; biology; business administration, management and operations; business/commerce; business, management, and marketing related; business/managerial economics; communication and journalism related; computer and information sciences; computer/information technology administration and management; computer science; counseling psychology; creative writing; criminal justice and corrections; developmental and child psychology; economics; education; educational/instructional media design; educational psychology; education related; English; English composition; English literature (British and Commonwealth); fine and studio art; geography and cartography; history; information science/studies; journalism; liberal arts and sciences, general studies and humanities; management information systems; marketing; mathematics; medieval and Renaissance studies; missionary studies and missiology; multi-/interdisciplinary studies related; music; pastoral counseling and specialized ministries; peace studies and conflict resolution; philosophy; philosophy and religious studies related; physical sciences; physical sciences related; political science and government; psychology; psychology related; religious education; religious/sacred music; religious studies; social psychology; social sciences; social sciences related; social work; sociology; speech and rhetoric; theological and ministerial studies; theology and religious vocations related.
Non-credit—accounting and related services; applied mathematics; biblical and other theological languages and literatures; biblical studies; business administration, management and operations; business/commerce; business/corporate communications; business, management, and marketing related; business operations support and assistant services; communication and journalism related; communication and media; computer and information sciences; computer and information sciences and support services related; computer/information technology administration and management; computer programming; computer software and media applications; computer systems networking and telecommunications; creative writing; data entry/microcomputer applications; data processing; English composition; entrepreneurial and small business operations; family and consumer economics; human development, family studies, and related services; human resources management; information science/studies; management information systems; marketing; mathematics; mathematics and computer science; public relations, advertising, and applied communication related; religious studies; sales, merchandising, and related marketing operations (general); sales, merchandising, and related marketing operations (specialized); technical and business writing; theological and ministerial studies.

See full description on page 486.

TEMPLE BAPTIST SEMINARY
Chattanooga, Tennessee
Distance Education
http://www.templebaptistseminary.edu/

Temple Baptist Seminary was founded in 1948. It is accredited by Transnational Association of Christian Colleges and Schools. It first offered distance learning courses in 1993. In fall 2005, there were 53 students enrolled in distance learning courses. Institutionally administered financial aid is available to distance learners.
Services Distance learners have accessibility to academic advising, bookstore, campus computer network, career placement assistance, e-mail services, library services.
Contact Ms. Ashley Orme, TBS DE Coordinator, Temple Baptist Seminary, Distance Education Office, 1815 Union Avenue, Chattanooga, TN 37404. Telephone: 423-493-4292. E-mail: tbsde@tntemple.edu.

DEGREES AND AWARDS

Certificate Biblical Studies; Discipleship/Christian Education Studies; Leadership Studies; Missions/Missiological Studies; Pastoral Studies
MABS Biblical Studies–over 20 concentrations available
MDiv Divinity–Master of Divinity–English Bible Track with over 20 concentrations available
MMin Ministry–Master of Ministry–various concentrations available
MRE Religious Education—with 3 distinct Concentrations available
DMin Ministry Studies–6 distinct concentrations available

COURSE SUBJECT AREAS OFFERED OUTSIDE OF DEGREE PROGRAMS

Graduate—biblical studies; missionary studies and missiology; pastoral counseling and specialized ministries; philosophy and religious studies related; religious education.
Non-credit—biblical studies; missionary studies and missiology; pastoral counseling and specialized ministries; philosophy and religious studies related; religious studies.

TENNESSEE TEMPLE UNIVERSITY
Chattanooga, Tennessee
School of External Studies
http://www.tntemple.edu/external_studies/general.htm

Tennessee Temple University was founded in 1946. It is accredited by Transnational Association of Christian Colleges and Schools. It first offered distance learning courses in 1988. In fall 2005, there were 375 students enrolled in distance learning courses. Institutionally administered financial aid is available to distance learners.
Services Distance learners have accessibility to academic advising, bookstore, e-mail services.

Contact Mr. Jeffrey Jackson, Administrative Assistant for Distance Education Program, Tennessee Temple University, 1815 Union Avenue, Chattanooga, TN 37404. Telephone: 800-553-4050 Ext. 4288. Fax: 423-493-4286. E-mail: distance@tntemple.edu.

DEGREES AND AWARDS

AS Biblical Studies
BS Biblical Studies

COURSE SUBJECT AREAS OFFERED OUTSIDE OF DEGREE PROGRAMS

Undergraduate—biblical and other theological languages and literatures; biblical studies; liberal arts and sciences, general studies and humanities; pastoral counseling and specialized ministries; philosophy; political science and government; psychology; religious education; religious studies; sociology.
Graduate—education.

TEXAS A&M UNIVERSITY–COMMERCE
Commerce, Texas
Instructional Technology and Distance Learning
http://www7.tamu-commerce.edu/itde/

Texas A&M University–Commerce was founded in 1889. It is accredited by Southern Association of Colleges and Schools. It first offered distance learning courses in 1993. In fall 2005, there were 2,560 students enrolled in distance learning courses. Institutionally administered financial aid is available to distance learners.
Services Distance learners have accessibility to academic advising, bookstore, campus computer network, career placement assistance, e-mail services, library services, tutoring.
Contact Charlotte A. Larkin, Director of Instructional Technology and Distance Education, Texas A&M University–Commerce, PO Box 3011, Commerce, TX 75429. Telephone: 903-886-5511. Fax: 903-886-5991. E-mail: charlotte_larkin@tamu-commerce.edu.

DEGREES AND AWARDS

Programs offered do not lead to a degree or other formal award.

COURSE SUBJECT AREAS OFFERED OUTSIDE OF DEGREE PROGRAMS

Undergraduate—accounting and computer science; agricultural production; animal sciences; biology; botany/plant biology; business administration, management and operations; business/commerce; business, management, and marketing related; business/managerial economics; communication and media; computer and information sciences; computer science; creative writing; criminal justice and corrections; developmental and child psychology; economics; English; English composition; history; industrial engineering; journalism; management information systems; marketing; mathematics; psychology; social work; sociology.
Graduate—accounting and related services; agriculture; business, management, and marketing related; business/managerial economics; computer and information sciences; construction management; curriculum and instruction; economics; education; educational administration and supervision; educational/instructional media design; English composition; finance and financial management services; industrial engineering; library science related; marketing; psychology; radio, television, and digital communication; social work; special education.
Non-credit—economics; finance and financial management services.

TEXAS A&M UNIVERSITY–KINGSVILLE
Kingsville, Texas
Center for Distance Learning and Continuing Education
http://www.tamuk.edu/distancelearning

Texas A&M University–Kingsville was founded in 1925. It is accredited by Southern Association of Colleges and Schools. It first offered distance learning courses in 1992. In fall 2005, there were 2,150 students enrolled in distance learning courses. Institutionally administered financial aid is available to distance learners.
Services Distance learners have accessibility to academic advising, bookstore, campus computer network, career placement assistance, e-mail services, library services.
Contact Dr. Tadeo Reyna, Jr., Director, Texas A&M University–Kingsville, 700 University Boulevard, MSC 147, Kingsville, TX 78363-8202. Telephone: 361-593-2861 Ext. 2854. Fax: 361-593-2859. E-mail: t-reyna@tamuk.edu.

DEGREES AND AWARDS

Programs offered do not lead to a degree or other formal award.

COURSE SUBJECT AREAS OFFERED OUTSIDE OF DEGREE PROGRAMS

Undergraduate—accounting and computer science; agriculture; bilingual, multilingual, and multicultural education; business/corporate communications; communication disorders sciences and services; computer and information sciences; computer science; criminal justice and corrections; economics; education; English; family and consumer sciences/human sciences; finance and financial management services; geological and earth sciences/geosciences; history; management sciences and quantitative methods; marketing; physics; psychology; sociology.
Graduate—agriculture; bilingual, multilingual, and multicultural education; business administration, management and operations; communication disorders sciences and services; economics; education; educational administration and supervision; English; English as a second language; environmental/environmental health engineering; family and consumer sciences/human sciences; sociology.
Non-credit—computer programming; computer software and media applications.

TEXAS A&M UNIVERSITY–TEXARKANA
Texarkana, Texas
http://www.tamut.edu/

Texas A&M University–Texarkana was founded in 1971. It is accredited by Southern Association of Colleges and Schools. It first offered distance learning courses in 1995. In fall 2005, there were 250 students enrolled in distance learning courses. Institutionally administered financial aid is available to distance learners.
Services Distance learners have accessibility to academic advising, career placement assistance, e-mail services, library services.
Contact Mrs. Patricia Black, Director of Admissions and Registrar, Texas A&M University–Texarkana, PO Box 5518, Texarkana, TX 75505-5518. Telephone: 903-223-3069. Fax: 903-223-3140. E-mail: pat.black@tamut.edu.

DEGREES AND AWARDS

Programs offered do not lead to a degree or other formal award.

COURSE SUBJECT AREAS OFFERED OUTSIDE OF DEGREE PROGRAMS

Undergraduate—accounting and related services; business administration, management and operations; criminal justice and corrections; education (specific subject areas); English; history; marketing; mathematics; political science and government; psychology; sales, merchandising, and related marketing operations (general); sociology.
Graduate—accounting and related services; business administration, management and operations; economics; educational administration and supervision; educational/instructional media design; education related; education (specific levels and methods); management information systems; marketing.

TEXAS CHRISTIAN UNIVERSITY
Fort Worth, Texas
Cyberlearning
http://www.tcuglobal.edu

Texas Christian University was founded in 1873. It is accredited by Southern Association of Colleges and Schools. It first offered distance learning courses in 1999. In fall 2005, there were 118 students enrolled in distance learning courses. Institutionally administered financial aid is available to distance learners.
Services Distance learners have accessibility to academic advising, bookstore, campus computer network, career placement assistance, e-mail services, library services, tutoring.

Contact Mrs. Romana J. Hughes, Director, eLearning Initiatives, Texas Christian University, Box 298970, Fort Worth, TX 76129. Telephone: 817-257-7434. Fax: 817-257-7393. E-mail: r.hughes@tcu.edu.

DEGREES AND AWARDS
Advanced Graduate Diploma Liberal Arts–Master of Liberal Arts
MSN Nursing

COURSE SUBJECT AREAS OFFERED OUTSIDE OF DEGREE PROGRAMS
Undergraduate—biology; dramatic/theater arts and stagecraft; fine and studio art; history.

TEXAS STATE TECHNICAL COLLEGE WACO
Waco, Texas
http://www.waco.tstc.edu/
Texas State Technical College Waco was founded in 1965. It is accredited by Southern Association of Colleges and Schools. It first offered distance learning courses in 1995. In fall 2005, there were 1,000 students enrolled in distance learning courses. Institutionally administered financial aid is available to distance learners.
Services Distance learners have accessibility to academic advising, bookstore, campus computer network, career placement assistance, e-mail services, library services, tutoring.
Contact Lance Zimmerman, Director, Distance Education, Texas State Technical College Waco, 3801 Campus Drive, Waco, TX 76705-1696. Telephone: 800-792-8784 Ext. 3257. Fax: 254-867-3470. E-mail: lance.zimmerman@tstc.edu.

DEGREES AND AWARDS
AAS Web Designer; Web Developer

COURSE SUBJECT AREAS OFFERED OUTSIDE OF DEGREE PROGRAMS
Undergraduate—computer programming; computer science; computer software and media applications; computer systems analysis; computer systems networking and telecommunications; data entry/microcomputer applications; English composition; mathematics.
Non-credit—computer programming; computer software and media applications; personal and culinary services related..

See full description on page 488.

TEXAS STATE UNIVERSITY-SAN MARCOS
San Marcos, Texas
Correspondence and Extension Studies
http://www.ideal.swt.edu/correspondence/
Texas State University-San Marcos was founded in 1899. It is accredited by Southern Association of Colleges and Schools. It first offered distance learning courses in 1953. In fall 2005, there were 1,500 students enrolled in distance learning courses. Institutionally administered financial aid is available to distance learners.
Services Distance learners have accessibility to bookstore, campus computer network, e-mail services, library services, tutoring.
Contact Carolyn Bettelheim, Administrative Assistant, Texas State University-San Marcos, Office of Correspondence Studies, 302 ASB North, 601 University Drive, San Marcos, TX 78666. Telephone: 512-245-2322. Fax: 512-245-8934. E-mail: corrstudy@txstate.edu.

DEGREES AND AWARDS
Programs offered do not lead to a degree or other formal award.

COURSE SUBJECT AREAS OFFERED OUTSIDE OF DEGREE PROGRAMS
Undergraduate—allied health and medical assisting services; American literature (United States and Canadian); behavioral sciences; biological and physical sciences; biology; business/commerce; cell biology and anatomical sciences; community psychology; comparative literature; creative writing; criminology; dance; developmental and child psychology; English; English composition; English language and literature related; English literature (British and Commonwealth); family psychology; fine and studio art; health and medical administrative services; health professions related; history; industrial and organizational psychology; languages (Romance languages); legal professions and studies related; liberal arts and sciences, general studies and humanities; mathematics; mathematics and computer science; music; philosophy; political science and government; psychology; psychology related; social psychology; social sciences; social sciences related; sociology.
Graduate—mathematics.
Non-credit—health and medical administrative services.

TEXAS TECH UNIVERSITY
Lubbock, Texas
Outreach and Distance Education
http://www.ttu.edu/
Texas Tech University was founded in 1923. It is accredited by Southern Association of Colleges and Schools. It first offered distance learning courses in 1941. In fall 2005, there were 1,918 students enrolled in distance learning courses. Institutionally administered financial aid is available to distance learners.
Services Distance learners have accessibility to academic advising, bookstore, campus computer network, e-mail services, library services.
Contact Mrs. Michele L. Moskos, Marketing Director, Division of Outreach and Extended Studies, Texas Tech University, Box 42191, Lubbock, TX 79409-2191. Telephone: 806-742-7200 Ext. 276. Fax: 806-742-7277. E-mail: dldegrees.oes@ttu.edu.

DEGREES AND AWARDS
BGS General Studies
BS Horticulture
Certificate Educational Diagnostician; Orientation and Mobility; Special Education, generic; Visual Impairment
CAGS Autism; Deaf and Hard of Hearing; Dual Impairments; Gerontology
MA Art Education; Technical Communication
MAg Agriculture
ME Engineering
MEd Educational Leadership and Principal Professional Certification Preparation; Instructional Technology (Distance Education emphasis); Language Literacy Education; Special Education
MS Computer Science; Crop Science; Horticulture; Human Development and Family Studies (Gerontology emphasis); Restaurant, Hotel, and Institutional Management; Software Engineering; Systems and Engineering Management
EdD Agricultural Education
PhD Technical Communication and Rhetoric

COURSE SUBJECT AREAS OFFERED OUTSIDE OF DEGREE PROGRAMS
Undergraduate—accounting and related services; agricultural business and management; agriculture; American literature (United States and Canadian); anthropology; applied horticulture/horticultural business services; business administration, management and operations; developmental and child psychology; economics; educational psychology; English composition; English literature (British and Commonwealth); food science and technology; foods, nutrition, and related services; history; journalism; languages (Romance languages); legal studies (non-professional general, undergraduate); liberal arts and sciences, general studies and humanities; marketing; mathematics and statistics related; music; psychology; sales, merchandising, and related marketing operations (specialized); social psychology; sociology; technical and business writing.
Graduate—agriculture; animal sciences; architecture; chemical engineering; civil engineering; computer and information sciences and support services related; computer science; curriculum and instruction; education; educational administration and supervision; educational assessment, evaluation, and research; educational/instructional media design; education related; electrical and electronic engineering technologies; engineering; engineering related; English; English composition; environmental/environmental health engineering; family and consumer economics; gerontology; mathematics; mechanical engineering; music; petroleum engineering; plant sciences; special education; statistics; technical and business writing; textile sciences and engineering; visual and performing arts.

Non-credit—business administration, management and operations; languages (Romance languages).

See full description on page 490.

TEXAS WOMAN'S UNIVERSITY
Denton, Texas
http://www.twuonline.com

Texas Woman's University was founded in 1901. It is accredited by Southern Association of Colleges and Schools. It first offered distance learning courses in 1994. In fall 2005, there were 3,856 students enrolled in distance learning courses. Institutionally administered financial aid is available to distance learners.

Services Distance learners have accessibility to academic advising, bookstore, campus computer network, career placement assistance, e-mail services, library services, tutoring.

Contact Ms. Allison Mabry, Coordinator, eLearning Student Support Services, Texas Woman's University, PO Box 425649, Denton, TX 76204. Telephone: 940-898-3409. Fax: 940-898-3416. E-mail: dl@twu.edu.

DEGREES AND AWARDS

BGS General Studies
BS Health Studies
EMBA Business Administration
MA Occupational Therapy
MAT Teaching
MLS Library Science
MS Deaf Education; Family Studies; Health Studies; Institutional Administration (Nutrition); Speech-Language Pathology
PhD Nursing

COURSE SUBJECT AREAS OFFERED OUTSIDE OF DEGREE PROGRAMS

Undergraduate—business administration, management and operations; communication disorders sciences and services; computer and information sciences; education; English; family and consumer economics; health and physical education/fitness; health services/allied health/health sciences; history; nursing; nutrition sciences; psychology; sociology; visual and performing arts.

Graduate—bilingual, multilingual, and multicultural education; business administration, management and operations; business/commerce; communication disorders sciences and services; computer and information sciences; education; education related; family and consumer economics; health and physical education/fitness; health services/allied health/health sciences; library science; nursing; nutrition sciences; rehabilitation and therapeutic professions; school psychology; sociology; visual and performing arts.

THOMAS EDISON STATE COLLEGE
Trenton, New Jersey
DIAL–Distance and Independent Adult Learning
http://www.tesc.edu

Thomas Edison State College was founded in 1972. It is accredited by Middle States Association of Colleges and Schools. It first offered distance learning courses in 1972. In fall 2005, there were 11,224 students enrolled in distance learning courses. Institutionally administered financial aid is available to distance learners.

Services Distance learners have accessibility to academic advising, library services.

Contact Ms. Renee San Giacomo, Director of Admissions, Thomas Edison State College, 101 West State Street, Trenton, NJ 08608-1176. Telephone: 888-442-8372. Fax: 609-984-8447. E-mail: admissions@tesc.edu.

DEGREES AND AWARDS

AA Liberal Arts/General Studies

AAS Administrative Studies; Applied Electronic Studies; Applied Health Studies; Computer Science–Applied Computer Studies; Mechanics and Maintenance; Occupational Studies

ASAST Air Traffic Control; Architectural Design; Aviation Flight Technology; Aviation Maintenance Technology; Biomedical Electronics; Civil and Construction Engineering Technology; Clinical Lab Science; Computer Science Technology; Electrical Technology; Electronic Engineering Technology; Engineering Graphics; Environmental Sciences; Fire Protection Science; Forestry; Horticulture; Laboratory Animal Science; Manufacturing Engineering Technology; Marine Engineering Technology; Mechanical Engineering Technology; Medical Imaging; Nondestructive Testing Technology; Nuclear Engineering Technology; Nuclear Medicine Technology; Radiation Protection; Radiation Therapy; Respiratory Care; Surveying

ASM Accounting; Administrative Office Management; Banking; Computer Information Systems; Finance; Hospital Health Care Administration; Hotel/Motel/Restaurant Management; Human Resource Management; Insurance; International Business; Management, general; Marketing; Operations Management; Procurement; Public Administration; Purchasing and Materials Management; Real Estate; Retailing Management; Small Business Management/Entrepreneurship; Transportation/Distribution Management

ASNSM Biology; Computer Science; Mathematics

ASPSS Administration of Justice; Child Development Services; Community Services; Emergency Disaster Management; Fitness and Wellness Services; Gerontology; Legal Services; Recreation Services; Social Services for Special Populations; Social Services

BA Anthropology; Art; Biology; Communications; Computer Science; Criminal Justice; Economics; English; Environmental Studies; Foreign Language; History; Humanities; Journalism; Labor Studies; Liberal Studies; Mathematics; Music; Natural Sciences/Mathematics; Philosophy; Photography; Political Science; Psychology; Religion; Social Sciences/History; Sociology; Theater

BS Administration of Justice; Child Development Services; Community Services; Emergency Disaster Management; Gerontology; Health Services Administration; Health Services Education; Health Services; Health and Nutrition Counseling; Legal Services; Mental Health and Rehabilitation Services; Recreation Services; Social Services Administration; Social Services for Special Populations; Social Services

BSAST Air Traffic Control; Architectural Design; Aviation Flight Technology; Aviation Maintenance Technology; Biomedical Electronics; Civil Engineering Technology; Clinical Lab Science; Computer Science Technology; Construction; Cytotechnology; Dental Hygiene; Electrical Technology; Electronic Engineering Technology; Engineering Graphics; Environmental Sciences; Fire Protection Science; Forestry; Horticulture; Laboratory Animal Science; Manufacturing Engineering Technology; Marine Engineering Technology; Mechanical Engineering Technology; Medical Imaging; Nondestructive Testing Technology; Nuclear Engineering Technology; Nuclear Medicine Technology; Perfusion Technology; Radiation Protection; Radiation Therapy; Respiratory Care; Surveying

BSBA Accounting; Administrative Office Management; Advertising Management; Banking; Computer Information Systems; Finance; General Management; Hospital Health Care Administration; Hotel/Motel/Restaurant Management; Human Resources Management; Insurance; International Business; Logistics; Marketing; Operations Management; Organizational Management; Procurement; Public Administration; Purchasing and Materials Management; Real Estate; Retailing Management; Small Business Management/Entrepreneurship; Transportation/Distribution Management

BSN Nursing

MA Professional Studies

MSHRM Human Resources Management

MSM Management

MSN Nursing

See full description on page 492.

THREE RIVERS COMMUNITY COLLEGE
Norwich, Connecticut
http://www.trcc.commnet.edu/

Three Rivers Community College was founded in 1963. It is accredited by New England Association of Schools and Colleges. It first offered distance learning courses in 2000. In fall 2005, there were 320 students enrolled in distance learning courses. Institutionally administered financial aid is available to distance learners.

Services Distance learners have accessibility to bookstore, career placement assistance, library services, tutoring.

Contact Mr. R. Kem Barfield, Director of Distance Learning, Three Rivers Community College, 7 Mahan Drive, Norwich, CT 06360. Telephone: 860-383-5215. E-mail: rbarfield@trcc.commnet.edu.

DEGREES AND AWARDS
AS General Studies
CCCPE Laser and Fiber Optic Technology

COURSE SUBJECT AREAS OFFERED OUTSIDE OF DEGREE PROGRAMS
Undergraduate—accounting and related services; business administration, management and operations; computer and information sciences; environmental/environmental health engineering; history; mathematics; psychology.

Non-credit—allied health and medical assisting services; computer software and media applications.

THREE RIVERS COMMUNITY COLLEGE
Poplar Bluff, Missouri
http://www.trcc.cc.mo.us/

Three Rivers Community College was founded in 1966. It is accredited by North Central Association of Colleges and Schools. It first offered distance learning courses in 1996. In fall 2005, there were 1,000 students enrolled in distance learning courses. Institutionally administered financial aid is available to distance learners.

Services Distance learners have accessibility to academic advising, bookstore, library services.

Contact Cindy Clark, Registrar, Three Rivers Community College, 2080 Three Rivers Boulevard, Poplar Bluff, MO 63901. Telephone: 573-840-9665. Fax: 573-840-9666. E-mail: cclark@trcc.edu.

DEGREES AND AWARDS
Programs offered do not lead to a degree or other formal award.

COURSE SUBJECT AREAS OFFERED OUTSIDE OF DEGREE PROGRAMS
Undergraduate—accounting and computer science; agriculture; allied health and medical assisting services; American literature (United States and Canadian); biology; business administration, management and operations; creative writing; developmental and child psychology; English language and literature related; English literature (British and Commonwealth); history; mathematics; social work; sociology; speech and rhetoric.

THUNDERBIRD, THE GARVIN SCHOOL OF INTERNATIONAL MANAGEMENT
Glendale, Arizona
http://www.thunderbird.edu/globalmba/

Thunderbird, The Garvin School of International Management was founded in 1946. It is accredited by North Central Association of Colleges and Schools. It first offered distance learning courses in 1998. In fall 2005, there were 286 students enrolled in distance learning courses. Institutionally administered financial aid is available to distance learners.

Services Distance learners have accessibility to academic advising, bookstore, campus computer network, career placement assistance, e-mail services, library services, tutoring.

Contact Dr. Bert Valencia, Executive Director, Thunderbird, The Garvin School of International Management, 15249 North 59th Avenue, Glendale, AZ 85306-6000. Telephone: 602-978-7534. Fax: 602-978-7874. E-mail: globalmba@t-bird.edu.

DEGREES AND AWARDS
MBA Global Master of Business Administration On-Demand; Global Master of Business Administration for Latin American Managers

COURSE SUBJECT AREAS OFFERED OUTSIDE OF DEGREE PROGRAMS
Graduate—accounting and related services; business administration, management and operations; business/corporate communications; business, management, and marketing related; international business; management information systems; sales, merchandising, and related marketing operations (specialized).

Non-credit—business administration, management and operations; business/commerce; business/corporate communications; business, management, and marketing related; business/managerial economics; international business; international/global studies; marketing.

TOMPKINS CORTLAND COMMUNITY COLLEGE
Dryden, New York
Instructional and Learning Resources
http://www.sunytccc.edu/e-tc3/e-tc3.asp

Tompkins Cortland Community College was founded in 1968. It is accredited by Middle States Association of Colleges and Schools. It first offered distance learning courses in 1997. In fall 2005, there were 1,772 students enrolled in distance learning courses. Institutionally administered financial aid is available to distance learners.

Services Distance learners have accessibility to bookstore, career placement assistance, library services, tutoring.

Contact Eric Machan Howd, Coordinator of Online Learning Services, Tompkins Cortland Community College, 170 North Street, PO Box 139, Dryden, NY 13053. Telephone: 607-844-8211 Ext. 4297. Fax: 607-844-6540. E-mail: howde@tc3.edu.

DEGREES AND AWARDS
AAS Business Administration–Applied Management; Chemical Dependency Studies Counseling; Hotel and Restaurant Management; Paralegal Studies

COURSE SUBJECT AREAS OFFERED OUTSIDE OF DEGREE PROGRAMS
Undergraduate—accounting and related services; business/commerce; business/corporate communications; communication and media; computer and information sciences; computer programming; computer software and media applications; developmental and child psychology; English; English as a second language; English composition; fine and studio art; hospitality administration; international business; legal studies (non-professional general, undergraduate); management sciences and quantitative methods; marketing; mathematics; mental and social health services and allied professions; nursing; psychology; psychology related; social psychology; sociology; visual and performing arts.

Non-credit—business, management, and marketing related; business operations support and assistant services; computer software and media applications; computer systems networking and telecommunications; data processing.

TOURO UNIVERSITY INTERNATIONAL
Cypress, California
http://www.tourou.edu/

Touro University International first offered distance learning courses in 1999. In fall 2005, there were 6,500 students enrolled in distance learning courses. Institutionally administered financial aid is available to distance learners.

Services Distance learners have accessibility to academic advising, bookstore, campus computer network, e-mail services, library services.

Contact Wei Ren, Registrar, Touro University International, 5665 Plaza Drive, 3rd Floor, Cypress, CA 90630. Telephone: 714-816-0366. Fax: 714-827-7407. E-mail: registration@tourou.edu.

DEGREES AND AWARDS
BS Business Administration; Computer Science; Health Sciences; Information Technology Management
MAE Education

MBA Business Administration
MHS Health Sciences
MS Information Technology Management
PhD Business Administration; Educational Leadership; Health Sciences

COURSE SUBJECT AREAS OFFERED OUTSIDE OF DEGREE PROGRAMS

Undergraduate—accounting and related services; business administration, management and operations; business/corporate communications; business, management, and marketing related; computer/information technology administration and management; computer science; criminal justice and corrections; English composition; health professions related; health services/allied health/health sciences; history; international business; mathematics and computer science; philosophy; political science and government; psychology; sociology; statistics.

Graduate—accounting and related services; business administration, management and operations; business/commerce; computer/information technology administration and management; criminal justice and corrections; education; education (specific subject areas); entrepreneurial and small business operations; health professions related; human resources management; international business; management information systems; public health; statistics.

See full description on page 494.

TREASURE VALLEY COMMUNITY COLLEGE
Ontario, Oregon
Division of Extended Learning
http://www.tvcc.cc

Treasure Valley Community College was founded in 1962. It is accredited by Northwest Commission on Colleges and Universities. It first offered distance learning courses in 1985. In fall 2005, there were 400 students enrolled in distance learning courses. Institutionally administered financial aid is available to distance learners.

Services Distance learners have accessibility to academic advising, bookstore, campus computer network, e-mail services, library services.

Contact Linda C. Simmons, Director, Continuing/Community Education, Treasure Valley Community College, 650 College Boulevard, Ontario, OR 97914. Telephone: 541-881-8822 Ext. 358. Fax: 541-881-2721. E-mail: lsimmons@tvcc.cc.

DEGREES AND AWARDS

Programs offered do not lead to a degree or other formal award.

COURSE SUBJECT AREAS OFFERED OUTSIDE OF DEGREE PROGRAMS

Undergraduate—biology; business/commerce; chemistry; computer and information sciences and support services related; computer programming; creative writing; health and physical education/fitness; mathematics and statistics related; music; nutrition sciences; physical sciences; psychology; psychology related; sociology.

Non-credit—real estate.

TRI-COUNTY COMMUNITY COLLEGE
Murphy, North Carolina
http://www.tccc.cc.nc.us/

Tri-County Community College was founded in 1964. It is accredited by Southern Association of Colleges and Schools. It first offered distance learning courses in 1997. In fall 2005, there were 100 students enrolled in distance learning courses. Institutionally administered financial aid is available to distance learners.

Services Distance learners have accessibility to academic advising, bookstore.

Contact Mr. Wes Chastain, Distance Learning Coordinator/Technician, Tri-County Community College, 4600 East US 64, Murphy, NC 28906. Telephone: 828-837-6810. Fax: 828-837-3266. E-mail: wchastain@tricountycc.edu.

DEGREES AND AWARDS

Programs offered do not lead to a degree or other formal award.

COURSE SUBJECT AREAS OFFERED OUTSIDE OF DEGREE PROGRAMS

Undergraduate—accounting and computer science; accounting and related services; business administration, management and operations; business, management, and marketing related; computer and information sciences; computer science; computer systems analysis; data entry/microcomputer applications; economics; English; history; marketing; social psychology; social sciences; sociology.

Non-credit—accounting and computer science; accounting and related services; business administration, management and operations; computer and information sciences; computer and information sciences and support services related; computer programming; computer science.

TRINITY EPISCOPAL SCHOOL FOR MINISTRY
Ambridge, Pennsylvania

Trinity Episcopal School for Ministry was founded in 1975. It is accredited by Association of Theological Schools in the United States and Canada. It first offered distance learning courses in 1997. In fall 2005, there were 110 students enrolled in distance learning courses. Institutionally administered financial aid is available to distance learners.

Services Distance learners have accessibility to academic advising, bookstore, campus computer network, career placement assistance, e-mail services, library services, tutoring.

Contact Mr. Travis S. Hines, Director, Center for Distance Learning, Trinity Episcopal School for Ministry, 311 11th Street, Ambridge, PA 15003. Telephone: 724-266-3838 Ext. 228. Fax: 724-266-4617. E-mail: thines@tesm.edu.

DEGREES AND AWARDS

Diploma Anglican Studies; Christian Studies, basic

COURSE SUBJECT AREAS OFFERED OUTSIDE OF DEGREE PROGRAMS

Graduate—biblical and other theological languages and literatures; biblical studies; missionary studies and missiology; religious studies; theological and ministerial studies; theology and religious vocations related.

Non-credit—biblical studies; missionary studies and missiology; religious studies; theological and ministerial studies; theology and religious vocations related.

TRI-STATE UNIVERSITY
Angola, Indiana
http://www.tristate.edu/

Tri-State University was founded in 1884. It is accredited by North Central Association of Colleges and Schools. It first offered distance learning courses in 1995. In fall 2005, there were 95 students enrolled in distance learning courses. Institutionally administered financial aid is available to distance learners.

Services Distance learners have accessibility to bookstore, e-mail services, library services.

Contact Mr. Scott Goplin, Dean of Admission, Tri-State University, 1 University Avenue, Angola, IN 46703. Telephone: 260-665-4132. Fax: 260-665-4578. E-mail: admit@tristate.edu.

DEGREES AND AWARDS

Programs offered do not lead to a degree or other formal award.

COURSE SUBJECT AREAS OFFERED OUTSIDE OF DEGREE PROGRAMS

Undergraduate—accounting and related services; business administration, management and operations; business/commerce; economics; fine and studio art; geological and earth sciences/geosciences; history; legal studies (non-professional general, undergraduate); liberal arts and sciences, general studies and humanities; marketing; social sciences.

TRITON COLLEGE
River Grove, Illinois
Alternative Learning at Triton
http://www.triton.edu

Triton College was founded in 1964. It is accredited by North Central Association of Colleges and Schools. It first offered distance learning courses in 1997. In fall 2005, there were 1,032 students enrolled in distance learning courses. Institutionally administered financial aid is available to distance learners.

Services Distance learners have accessibility to academic advising, bookstore, campus computer network, e-mail services, library services, tutoring.

Contact Mr. Douglas Olson, Dean, Student Services, Triton College, 2000 Fifth Avenue, River Grove, IL 60171. Telephone: 708-456-0300 Ext. 3230. Fax: 708-582-3162. E-mail: dolson@triton.edu.

DEGREES AND AWARDS
AA the Arts
AAS General Program

COURSE SUBJECT AREAS OFFERED OUTSIDE OF DEGREE PROGRAMS
Undergraduate—accounting and related services; anthropology; architecture; area studies; astronomy and astrophysics; biology; chemistry; clinical/medical laboratory science and allied professions; developmental and child psychology; drafting/design engineering technologies; dramatic/theater arts and stagecraft; economics; educational psychology; English composition; fine and studio art; health and physical education/fitness; history; languages (Romance languages); legal studies (non-professional general, undergraduate); liberal arts and sciences, general studies and humanities; linguistic, comparative, and related language studies; marketing; music; nursing; philosophy; philosophy and religious studies related; psychology; real estate; social psychology; social sciences; sociology; speech and rhetoric; statistics.

Non-credit—communication and journalism related; computer and information sciences; languages (foreign languages related); medical basic sciences.

TROY UNIVERSITY
Troy, Alabama
eCampus/Graduate
http://www.tsulearn.net

Troy University was founded in 1887. It is accredited by Southern Association of Colleges and Schools. It first offered distance learning courses in 1998. In fall 2005, there were 1,200 students enrolled in distance learning courses. Institutionally administered financial aid is available to distance learners.

Services Distance learners have accessibility to academic advising, bookstore, career placement assistance, e-mail services, library services.

Contact Dr. Barbara Echord, Director of Student Services, Troy University, eCampus Online Programs, 304 Wallace Hall, Troy, AL 36082. Telephone: 334-670-5875. Fax: 334-670-5679. E-mail: bechord@troy.edu.

DEGREES AND AWARDS
MBA Business Administration
MPA Public Administration
MS Criminal Justice; Human Resource Management; International Relations; Management; Postsecondary Education

TUNXIS COMMUNITY COLLEGE
Farmington, Connecticut
http://www.tunxis.commnet.edu/tole

Tunxis Community College was founded in 1969. It is accredited by New England Association of Schools and Colleges. It first offered distance learning courses in 1996. In fall 2005, there were 1,800 students enrolled in distance learning courses. Institutionally administered financial aid is available to distance learners.

Services Distance learners have accessibility to academic advising, bookstore, campus computer network, e-mail services, library services, tutoring.

Contact Peter McCluskey, Director of Admissions, Tunxis Community College, 271 Scott Swamp Road, Farmington, CT 06032. Telephone: 860-255-3563. E-mail: tx-admissions@txcc.commnet.edu.

DEGREES AND AWARDS
AA Criminal Justice; General Studies/Liberal Arts

Certificate Corrections Pre-Certification

COURSE SUBJECT AREAS OFFERED OUTSIDE OF DEGREE PROGRAMS
Undergraduate—anthropology; area, ethnic, cultural, and gender studies related; business administration, management and operations; communication and media; computer and information sciences; computer systems networking and telecommunications; criminal justice and corrections; criminology; dental support services and allied professions; developmental and child psychology; English; English composition; history; industrial and organizational psychology; linguistic, comparative, and related language studies; management information systems; music; philosophy; psychology; sociology.

Non-credit—business/commerce; computer and information sciences; criminal justice and corrections; education related; information science/studies.

TYLER JUNIOR COLLEGE
Tyler, Texas
Learning Resources
http://www.tjc.edu/academics/distance-learning.htm

Tyler Junior College was founded in 1926. It is accredited by Southern Association of Colleges and Schools. It first offered distance learning courses in 1969. In fall 2005, there were 2,300 students enrolled in distance learning courses. Institutionally administered financial aid is available to distance learners.

Services Distance learners have accessibility to academic advising, bookstore, career placement assistance, e-mail services, library services, tutoring.

Contact Gay Howard, Secretary of Learning Resources, Tyler Junior College, PO Box 9020, Tyler, TX 75711. Telephone: 903-510-2529. Fax: 903-510-2643. E-mail: ghow@tjc.edu.

DEGREES AND AWARDS
Programs offered do not lead to a degree or other formal award.

COURSE SUBJECT AREAS OFFERED OUTSIDE OF DEGREE PROGRAMS
Undergraduate—accounting and related services; American literature (United States and Canadian); astronomy and astrophysics; biology; business administration, management and operations; business/commerce; business/corporate communications; business operations support and assistant services; cell biology and anatomical sciences; computer and information sciences; computer and information sciences and support services related; computer/information technology administration and management; computer programming; computer science; computer software and media applications; computer systems analysis; computer systems networking and telecommunications; creative writing; criminal justice and corrections; economics; education; educational/instructional media design; English composition; fine and studio art; fire protection; history; languages (Romance languages); legal studies (non-professional general, undergraduate); legal support services; liberal arts and sciences, general studies and humanities; mathematics and statistics related; music; political science and government; psychology; sociology.

Non-credit—accounting and related services; business administration, management and operations; business/commerce; computer and information sciences; computer programming; computer software and media applications; educational/instructional media design; information science/studies; management information systems.

UNION THEOLOGICAL SEMINARY AND PRESBYTERIAN SCHOOL OF CHRISTIAN EDUCATION

Richmond, Virginia

http://www.union-psce.edu

Union Theological Seminary and Presbyterian School of Christian Education was founded in 1812. It is accredited by Southern Association of Colleges and Schools. It first offered distance learning courses in 1988. In fall 2005, there were 75 students enrolled in distance learning courses. Institutionally administered financial aid is available to distance learners.

Services Distance learners have accessibility to academic advising, e-mail services, library services.

Contact Mr. Phil Hargrove, Director of Admissions, Union Theological Seminary and Presbyterian School of Christian Education, 3401 Brook Road, Richmond, VA 23227. Telephone: 804-355-0671 Ext. 222. Fax: 804-355-3919. E-mail: amontague@union-psce.edu.

DEGREES AND AWARDS

MACE Christian Education

COURSE SUBJECT AREAS OFFERED OUTSIDE OF DEGREE PROGRAMS

Graduate—religious education; theology and religious vocations related.

Non-credit—religious education; religious studies; theology and religious vocations related.

UNITED STATES SPORTS ACADEMY

Daphne, Alabama

Continuing Education and Distance Learning

http://www.ussa.edu

United States Sports Academy was founded in 1972. It is accredited by Southern Association of Colleges and Schools. It first offered distance learning courses in 1995. In fall 2005, there were 900 students enrolled in distance learning courses. Institutionally administered financial aid is available to distance learners.

Services Distance learners have accessibility to academic advising, bookstore, campus computer network, e-mail services, library services.

Contact Ms. Bobbie Spurgeon-Harris, Director of Student Services, United States Sports Academy, One Academy Drive, Daphne, AL 36526-7055. Telephone: 800-223-2668 Ext. 147. Fax: 251-625-1035. E-mail: spurgeon@ussa.edu.

DEGREES AND AWARDS

BS Sports Coaching; Sports Management

Certification Coaching–National Coaching certification; International Sport Diploma; Sports Coaching (International Certification); Sports Coaching; Sports Management (International Certification); Sports Management; Sports Medicine

MSS Fitness Management; Sports Coaching; Sports Management; Sports Medicine; Sports Studies

DSM Sports Management–Sports Medicine emphasis; Sports Management

COURSE SUBJECT AREAS OFFERED OUTSIDE OF DEGREE PROGRAMS

Undergraduate—business, management, and marketing related; health and physical education/fitness.

Graduate—business administration, management and operations; entrepreneurial and small business operations; health and physical education/ fitness; marketing.

Non-credit—business, management, and marketing related; health and physical education/fitness; parks, recreation and leisure; parks, recreation and leisure facilities management; parks, recreation, and leisure related.

See full description on page 496.

THE UNIVERSITY OF AKRON

Akron, Ohio

Information Services

http://www.uakron.edu

The University of Akron was founded in 1870. It is accredited by North Central Association of Colleges and Schools. It first offered distance learning courses in 1994. In fall 2005, there were 22,525 students enrolled in distance learning courses. Institutionally administered financial aid is available to distance learners.

Services Distance learners have accessibility to academic advising, bookstore, campus computer network, career placement assistance, e-mail services, library services, tutoring.

Contact Holly Harris-Bane, Associate Vice President, Strategic Initiatives and Engagement, The University of Akron, Buchtel Hall 102, Akron, OH 44325-4703. Telephone: 330-972-7508. Fax: 330-972-8699. E-mail: harrisb@uakron.edu.

DEGREES AND AWARDS

Programs offered do not lead to a degree or other formal award.

COURSE SUBJECT AREAS OFFERED OUTSIDE OF DEGREE PROGRAMS

Undergraduate—accounting and related services; allied health and medical assisting services; anthropology; archeology; astronomy and astrophysics; audiovisual communications technologies; behavioral sciences; bilingual, multilingual, and multicultural education; biochemistry, biophysics and molecular biology; biological and physical sciences; biology; botany/plant biology; business administration, management and operations; business/commerce; business/corporate communications; business, management, and marketing related; business/managerial economics; business operations support and assistant services; chemistry; communication and journalism related; communication and media; community health services; community organization and advocacy; computer and information sciences; computer science; computer software and media applications; computer systems networking and telecommunications; creative writing; criminal justice and corrections; criminology; curriculum and instruction; design and applied arts; economics; education; educational administration and supervision; educational assessment, evaluation, and research; educational/instructional media design; education related; education (specific levels and methods); education (specific subject areas); engineering related; English as a second/foreign language (teaching); English composition; English language and literature related; English literature (British and Commonwealth); finance and financial management services; fire protection; geography and cartography; geological and earth sciences/geosciences; health and medical administrative services; history; hospitality administration; human resources management; journalism; languages (East Asian); languages (Germanic); liberal arts and sciences, general studies and humanities; linguistic, comparative, and related language studies; mathematics; mathematics and computer science; medical basic sciences; microbiological sciences and immunology; music; nursing; pharmacy, pharmaceutical sciences, and administration; philosophy; philosophy and religious studies related; physical sciences; physical sciences related; political science and government; polymer/plastics engineering; psychology; public administration; public administration and social service professions related; real estate; sales, merchandising, and related marketing operations (general); sales, merchandising, and related marketing operations (specialized); security and protective services related; social and philosophical foundations of education; social work; sociology; special education; speech and rhetoric; statistics; taxation; technical and business writing; technology education/industrial arts; urban studies/affairs; zoology/animal biology.

Graduate—accounting and related services; applied mathematics; bilingual, multilingual, and multicultural education; business administration, management and operations; computer and information sciences; computer software and media applications; counseling psychology; curriculum and instruction; economics; education; educational administration and supervision; educational assessment, evaluation, and research; educational/instructional media design; educational psychology; education related; education (specific levels and methods); education (specific subject areas); engineering; English language and literature related; health professions related; human resources management; human services; information science/studies; legal research and advanced professional studies; mathematics; mathematics and computer science; math-

ematics and statistics related; nursing; political science and government; psychology; psychology related; public administration; public health; school psychology; social and philosophical foundations of education; social psychology; social work; special education; speech and rhetoric; statistics; technology education/industrial arts.
Non-credit—allied health and medical assisting services; area, ethnic, cultural, and gender studies related; communications technology; computer and information sciences; computer and information sciences and support services related; computer/information technology administration and management; computer programming; computer science; computer software and media applications; computer systems analysis; computer systems networking and telecommunications; curriculum and instruction; data entry/microcomputer applications; data processing; educational/instructional media design; education related; education (specific levels and methods); entrepreneurial and small business operations; human resources management; information science/studies; nursing.

THE UNIVERSITY OF ALABAMA
Tuscaloosa, Alabama
College of Continuing Studies
http://academicoutreach.ua.edu

The University of Alabama was founded in 1831. It is accredited by Southern Association of Colleges and Schools. It first offered distance learning courses in 1991. In fall 2005, there were 5,000 students enrolled in distance learning courses. Institutionally administered financial aid is available to distance learners.
Services Distance learners have accessibility to academic advising, bookstore, campus computer network, e-mail services, library services.
Contact Ms. Nina Smith, Program Manager, Adult Student Services, The University of Alabama, Division of Academic Outreach, Box 870388, Tuscaloosa, AL 35487-0388. Telephone: 205-348-0089. Fax: 205-348-0249. E-mail: nsmith@ccs.ua.edu.

DEGREES AND AWARDS
BA Interdisciplinary Studies
BS Commerce and Business Administration (General Business); Human Environmental Sciences–General Studies option; Human Environmental Sciences–Restaurant and Hospitality Management; Interdisciplinary Studies; Mechanical Engineering; Nursing
Certificate Personal Financial Planning and Counseling
MA Health Studies–Health Promotion; Rehabilitation Counseling
MLIS Library and Information Studies–Master of Library and Information Studies
MS Human Environmental Sciences–Food and Nutrition; Human Environmental Sciences–Interactive Technology; Nursing Case Management; Operations Management
MSAE Aerospace Engineering

COURSE SUBJECT AREAS OFFERED OUTSIDE OF DEGREE PROGRAMS
Undergraduate—accounting and related services; American literature (United States and Canadian); astronomy and astrophysics; biological and physical sciences; biology; business/commerce; business, management, and marketing related; communication and media; computer and information sciences; computer science; computer systems networking and telecommunications; creative writing; criminal justice and corrections; economics; education (specific levels and methods); engineering; English; English composition; English language and literature related; English literature (British and Commonwealth); family and consumer economics; family and consumer sciences/human sciences; family and consumer sciences/human sciences business services; family and consumer sciences/human sciences related; finance and financial management services; foods, nutrition, and related services; geography and cartography; health professions related; history; hospitality administration; human development, family studies, and related services; journalism; languages (Romance languages); liberal arts and sciences, general studies and humanities; linguistic, comparative, and related language studies; mathematics; philosophy; philosophy and religious studies related; political science and government; psychology; public relations, advertising, and applied communication related; religious studies; sales, merchandising, and related marketing operations (specialized); social sciences; social sciences related.
Graduate—aerospace, aeronautical and astronautical engineering; computer and information sciences and support services related; engineering mechanics; family and consumer economics; finance and financial management services; health professions related; library science; nursing.
See full description on page 498.

THE UNIVERSITY OF ALABAMA IN HUNTSVILLE
Huntsville, Alabama
Engineering Management Distance Learning Programs
http://www.engdl.uah.edu/

The University of Alabama in Huntsville was founded in 1950. It is accredited by Southern Association of Colleges and Schools. It first offered distance learning courses in 1992. In fall 2005, there were 150 students enrolled in distance learning courses. Institutionally administered financial aid is available to distance learners.
Services Distance learners have accessibility to academic advising, bookstore, e-mail services, library services.
Contact Dr. Dawn R. Utley, Associate Director of Distance Learning, The University of Alabama in Huntsville, N136 Technology Hall, ISEEM Department, Huntsville, AL 35899. Telephone: 256-824-6075. Fax: 256-824-6608. E-mail: utley@ise.uah.edu.

DEGREES AND AWARDS
MSE Engineering Management; Industrial Engineering; Systems Engineering
PhD Industrial and Systems Engineering

COURSE SUBJECT AREAS OFFERED OUTSIDE OF DEGREE PROGRAMS
Graduate—engineering/industrial management; industrial engineering; operations research; quality control and safety technologies; statistics; systems engineering.

UNIVERSITY OF ALASKA ANCHORAGE, KODIAK COLLEGE
Kodiak, Alaska

University of Alaska Anchorage, Kodiak College was founded in 1968. It is accredited by Northwest Commission on Colleges and Universities. In fall 2005, there were 700 students enrolled in distance learning courses. Institutionally administered financial aid is available to distance learners.
Services Distance learners have accessibility to academic advising, bookstore, e-mail services, library services, tutoring.
Contact Jennifer Myrick, Registrar, University of Alaska Anchorage, Kodiak College, 117 Benny Benson Drive, Kodiak, AK 99615. Telephone: 907-486-1235. Fax: 907-486-1264. E-mail: jmyrick@kodiak.alaska.edu.

DEGREES AND AWARDS
Programs offered do not lead to a degree or other formal award.

COURSE SUBJECT AREAS OFFERED OUTSIDE OF DEGREE PROGRAMS
Undergraduate—accounting and computer science.

UNIVERSITY OF ALASKA FAIRBANKS
Fairbanks, Alaska
Center for Distance Education and Independent Learning
http://distance.uaf.edu

University of Alaska Fairbanks was founded in 1917. It is accredited by Northwest Commission on Colleges and Universities. It first offered distance learning courses in 1970. In fall 2005, there were 3,000 students enrolled in distance learning courses. Institutionally administered financial aid is available to distance learners.
Services Distance learners have accessibility to bookstore, campus computer network, e-mail services, library services, tutoring.
Contact Tina Johnson, Communications Coordinator, University of Alaska Fairbanks, PO Box 756700, Fairbanks, AK 99775. Telephone: 907-474-5353. Fax: 907-474-5402. E-mail: distance@uaf.edu.

DEGREES AND AWARDS

Programs offered do not lead to a degree or other formal award.

COURSE SUBJECT AREAS OFFERED OUTSIDE OF DEGREE PROGRAMS

Undergraduate—accounting and related services; American literature (United States and Canadian); anthropology; applied mathematics; bilingual, multilingual, and multicultural education; biology; business administration, management and operations; business/commerce; business, management, and marketing related; communication and journalism related; computer and information sciences; computer science; computer software and media applications; criminal justice and corrections; drafting/design engineering technologies; dramatic/theater arts and stagecraft; economics; education; educational administration and supervision; English; English composition; English language and literature related; ethnic, cultural minority, and gender studies; film/video and photographic arts; fine and studio art; geography and cartography; gerontology; health professions related; health psychology; history; human development, family studies, and related services; human resources management; journalism; languages (classics and classical); languages (Romance languages); legal studies (non-professional general, undergraduate); liberal arts and sciences, general studies and humanities; library science; linguistic, comparative, and related language studies; marketing; mathematics; mathematics and computer science; mathematics and statistics related; music; nutrition sciences; personality psychology; political science and government; psychology; psychometrics and quantitative psychology; public relations, advertising, and applied communication related; radio, television, and digital communication; real estate; social psychology; social sciences; social sciences related; social work; sociology; statistics; technical and business writing; technology education/industrial arts.

Graduate—computer and information sciences; counseling psychology; curriculum and instruction; educational administration and supervision; education related; education (specific levels and methods); family psychology; health psychology; human development, family studies, and related services; intercultural/multicultural and diversity studies; psychology; psychology related.

See full description on page 500.

UNIVERSITY OF ALASKA SOUTHEAST
Juneau, Alaska
Distance Learning at UAS
http://www.uas.alaska.edu/distance

University of Alaska Southeast was founded in 1972. It is accredited by Northwest Commission on Colleges and Universities. It first offered distance learning courses in 1986. In fall 2005, there were 1,021 students enrolled in distance learning courses. Institutionally administered financial aid is available to distance learners.

Services Distance learners have accessibility to academic advising, bookstore, campus computer network, e-mail services, library services, tutoring.

Contact Deema Ferguson, Admissions Clerk, University of Alaska Southeast, 11120 Glacier Highway, Juneau, AK 99801-8625. Telephone: 907-796-6100. Fax: 907-796-6365. E-mail: infoo.uas@uas.alaska.edu.

DEGREES AND AWARDS

AA Education, general
AAS Business Administration; Computer Information and Office Systems; Early Childhood Education; Environmental Technology; Health Information Management
BBA Accounting; Business, general; Management; Marketing
BLS General Studies
Certificate of Completion Administrative Office Support; Child Development Associate; Computer Applications; Computing Skills, basic; Envoronmental Technology; Medical Office Specialist; Web Authoring; Web Foundations
Certificate Accounting Technician; Community Wellness Advocate; Computer Information and Office Systems; Early Childhood Education; Environmental Technology; Health Information Management Coding Specialist; Healthcare Privacy; Small Business Management
Endorsement Early Childhood Education; Educational Technology; Mathematics Education; Reading; Special Education
License Elementary Education
MAT Elementary Education
MBA Business Administration
MEd Early Childhood Education; Educational Technology; Reading
MPA Public Administration

UNIVERSITY OF ALBERTA
Edmonton, Alberta, Canada
Master of Arts in Communications & Technology
http://www.ualberta.ca/

University of Alberta was founded in 1906. It is provincially chartered. It first offered distance learning courses in 2000. In fall 2005, there were 80 students enrolled in distance learning courses. Institutionally administered financial aid is available to distance learners.

Services Distance learners have accessibility to academic advising, bookstore, campus computer network, career placement assistance, e-mail services, library services, tutoring.

Contact Eileen Crookes, Program Coordinator, University of Alberta, 8303-112 Street, Edmonton, AB T6G 2T4, Canada. Telephone: 780-492-1501. Fax: 780-492-0627. E-mail: eileen.crookes@ualberta.ca.

DEGREES AND AWARDS

MA Communications and Technology

COURSE SUBJECT AREAS OFFERED OUTSIDE OF DEGREE PROGRAMS

Graduate—business/corporate communications; communication and journalism related; communication and media; computer/information technology administration and management; computer software and media applications; educational/instructional media design; information science/studies; public relations, advertising, and applied communication related; science, technology and society.

See full description on page 502.

UNIVERSITY OF ARKANSAS
Fayetteville, Arkansas
Division for Continuing Education
http://www.uacted.uark.edu

University of Arkansas was founded in 1871. It is accredited by North Central Association of Colleges and Schools. It first offered distance learning courses in 1998. In fall 2005, there were 1,000 students enrolled in distance learning courses. Institutionally administered financial aid is available to distance learners.

Services Distance learners have accessibility to bookstore, e-mail services, library services.

Contact Gary McHenry, Director, University of Arkansas, Office of Credit Studies, 2 East Center Street, Fayetteville, AR 72701. Telephone: 479-575-3648. Fax: 479-575-7232. E-mail: gmchenry@uark.edu.

DEGREES AND AWARDS

BS Human Resource Development
MBA/M Ed Elementary Education/Reading; Special Education; Workforce Development Education
MBA/MS Agricultural, Food and Life Sciences Non-Thesis (Food Safety emphasis)

COURSE SUBJECT AREAS OFFERED OUTSIDE OF DEGREE PROGRAMS

Undergraduate—curriculum and instruction; developmental and child psychology; dramatic/theater arts and stagecraft; English composition; geography and cartography; history; industrial and organizational psychology; journalism; languages (Germanic); languages (Romance languages); legal studies (non-professional general, undergraduate); mathematics and statistics related; microbiological sciences and immunology; philosophy and religious studies related; social work; sociology.

Graduate—agricultural and food products processing; education (specific subject areas).

UNIVERSITY OF ARKANSAS AT PINE BLUFF
Pine Bluff, Arkansas
http://www.uaex.edu/AQFI

University of Arkansas at Pine Bluff was founded in 1873. It is accredited by North Central Association of Colleges and Schools. It first offered distance learning courses in 1997. Institutionally administered financial aid is available to distance learners.

Services Distance learners have accessibility to academic advising, campus computer network, e-mail services.

Contact Dr. Carole Engle, Director and Chair, University of Arkansas at Pine Bluff, 1200 North University Drive, Mail Slot 4912, Pine Bluff, AR 71601. Telephone: 870-575-8523. Fax: 870-575-4637. E-mail: cengle@uaex.edu.

DEGREES AND AWARDS
Programs offered do not lead to a degree or other formal award.

COURSE SUBJECT AREAS OFFERED OUTSIDE OF DEGREE PROGRAMS
Undergraduate—accounting and related services; agricultural business and management; agriculture; American literature (United States and Canadian); animal sciences; apparel and textiles; architectural engineering; bilingual, multilingual, and multicultural education; biological and physical sciences; biology; business administration, management and operations; business/corporate communications; chemistry; communication and media; computer and information sciences; computer science; economics; education; English; fishing and fisheries sciences and management.

Graduate—education; fishing and fisheries sciences and management.

Non-credit—Air Force J.R.O.T.C/R.O.T.C; bilingual, multilingual, and multicultural education; business operations support and assistant services; carpentry; computer/information technology administration and management.

UNIVERSITY OF BRIDGEPORT
Bridgeport, Connecticut
Office of Distance Learning
http://www.bridgeport.edu/pages/50.asp

University of Bridgeport was founded in 1927. It is accredited by New England Association of Schools and Colleges. It first offered distance learning courses in 1997. In fall 2005, there were 300 students enrolled in distance learning courses. Institutionally administered financial aid is available to distance learners.

Services Distance learners have accessibility to academic advising, bookstore, campus computer network, e-mail services, library services, tutoring.

Contact Claude A. Perrottet, Coordinator of Student Services, University of Bridgeport, 126 Park Avenue, Bridgeport, CT 06604. Telephone: 203-576-4853. Fax: 203-576-4537. E-mail: ubonline@bridgeport.edu.

DEGREES AND AWARDS
BS Dental Hygiene Online (degree completion program)
Certification Marriage Education (for credit); Marriage Education (non-credit)
MS Human Nutrition

COURSE SUBJECT AREAS OFFERED OUTSIDE OF DEGREE PROGRAMS
Undergraduate—area, ethnic, cultural, and gender studies related; business/commerce; business, management, and marketing related; community health services; counseling psychology; dental support services and allied professions; developmental and child psychology; economics; education; entrepreneurial and small business operations; film/video and photographic arts; foods, nutrition, and related services; history; human development, family studies, and related services; human services; legal studies (non-professional general, undergraduate); liberal arts and sciences, general studies and humanities; mathematics and statistics related; music; peace studies and conflict resolution; philosophy; philosophy and religious studies related; political science and government; psychology; public health; religious studies; sales, merchandising, and related marketing operations (general); social psychology; social sciences; sociology; visual and performing arts.

Graduate—biochemistry, biophysics and molecular biology; botany/plant biology; foods, nutrition, and related services.

Non-credit—education related; human development, family studies, and related services.

THE UNIVERSITY OF BRITISH COLUMBIA
Vancouver, British Columbia, Canada
Distance Education and Technology
http://det.ubc.ca

The University of British Columbia was founded in 1915. It is provincially chartered. It first offered distance learning courses in 1949. In fall 2005, there were 4,172 students enrolled in distance learning courses. Institutionally administered financial aid is available to distance learners.

Services Distance learners have accessibility to academic advising, bookstore, campus computer network, career placement assistance, e-mail services, library services, tutoring.

Contact Sonja Fragoso, Student Resource Clerk, The University of British Columbia, Enrolment Services, 1874 East Mall, Room 2016, Brock Hall, Vancouver, BC V6T 1Z1, Canada. Telephone: 604-822-9836. Fax: 604-822-5945. E-mail: sonja.fragoso@ubc.ca.

DEGREES AND AWARDS
Graduate Certificate Rehabilitation Sciences; Technology-Based Distributed Learning; Technology-Based Learning for Schools
MA Educational Technology–Master of Educational Technology

COURSE SUBJECT AREAS OFFERED OUTSIDE OF DEGREE PROGRAMS
Undergraduate—agricultural business and management; agriculture; animal sciences; area studies; civil engineering; computer and information sciences; dental support services and allied professions; education; educational/instructional media design; English; environmental control technologies; ethnic, cultural minority, and gender studies; film/video and photographic arts; foods, nutrition, and related services; forestry; geography and cartography; history; landscape architecture; languages (Romance languages); library science related; medieval and Renaissance studies; metallurgical engineering; music; nursing; philosophy; political science and government; psychology; rehabilitation and therapeutic professions; social work; soil sciences.

Graduate—education; educational/instructional media design; rehabilitation and therapeutic professions.

Non-credit—English composition.

UNIVERSITY OF CALGARY
Calgary, Alberta, Canada
Teaching and Learning Centre at University of Calgary
http://www.commons.ucalgary.ca

University of Calgary was founded in 1945. It is provincially chartered. It first offered distance learning courses in 1977.

Services Distance learners have accessibility to academic advising, bookstore, campus computer network, career placement assistance, e-mail services, library services.

Contact Joanne Carruthers, E-Learning Coordinator, University of Calgary, Teaching and Learning Centre, 540 Bio Science Building, 2500 University Drive, NW, Calgary, AB T2N 1N4, Canada. Telephone: 403-220-7364. Fax: 403-282-0730. E-mail: carruthe@ucalgary.ca.

DEGREES AND AWARDS
BCR Community Rehabilitation
BN Nursing
Certificate Adult Learning; E-Learning; Environmental Management; Human Resource Management; Management, general; Teacher Assistant
MEd Education–Master of Education

COURSE SUBJECT AREAS OFFERED OUTSIDE OF DEGREE PROGRAMS
Undergraduate—nursing; social work.

Graduate—education; educational administration and supervision; educational assessment, evaluation, and research; educational/instructional media design; educational psychology; social work.

Non-credit—education (specific levels and methods).

UNIVERSITY OF CALIFORNIA, BERKELEY
Berkeley, California
Extension Online Programs
http://www.unex.berkeley.edu/

University of California, Berkeley was founded in 1868. It is accredited by Western Association of Schools and Colleges. It first offered distance learning courses in 1992. In fall 2005, there were 5,048 students enrolled in distance learning courses. Institutionally administered financial aid is available to distance learners.

Services Distance learners have accessibility to bookstore.

Contact Online staff, University of California, Berkeley, 1995 University Avenue, Suite 300, Berkeley, CA 94720. Telephone: 510-642-7343. Fax: 510-643-9271. E-mail: online@unex.berkeley.edu.

DEGREES AND AWARDS
Programs offered do not lead to a degree or other formal award.

COURSE SUBJECT AREAS OFFERED OUTSIDE OF DEGREE PROGRAMS
Undergraduate—accounting and related services; American literature (United States and Canadian); anthropology; behavioral sciences; biochemistry, biophysics and molecular biology; biological and physical sciences; biology; business administration, management and operations; business/commerce; business, management, and marketing related; business/managerial economics; cell biology and anatomical sciences; chemistry; communication and journalism related; communication and media; communications technology; comparative literature; computer and information sciences and support services related; computer programming; computer software and media applications; construction management; counseling psychology; creative writing; data entry/microcomputer applications; data processing; developmental and child psychology; economics; education; educational/instructional media design; education related; education (specific subject areas); English; English language and literature related; English literature (British and Commonwealth); entrepreneurial and small business operations; film/video and photographic arts; finance and financial management services; genetics; history; human development, family studies, and related services; human resources management; industrial and organizational psychology; information science/studies; international business; legal studies (nonprofessional general, undergraduate); liberal arts and sciences, general studies and humanities; management sciences and quantitative methods; marketing; mathematics; mathematics and statistics related; nutrition sciences; philosophy; philosophy and religious studies related; physical sciences; physics; physiology, pathology and related sciences; political science and government; psychology; psychology related; public relations, advertising, and applied communication related; quality control and safety technologies; real estate; sales, merchandising, and related marketing operations (general); social psychology; social sciences; social sciences related; sociology; special education; statistics; technical and business writing.

Graduate—accounting and related services; behavioral sciences; biochemistry, biophysics and molecular biology; biology; business administration, management and operations; business, management, and marketing related; business/managerial economics; cell biology and anatomical sciences; chemistry; communication and journalism related; comparative literature; creative writing; economics; educational/instructional media design; English; English language and literature related; English literature (British and Commonwealth); entrepreneurial and small business operations; history; human development, family studies, and related services; human resources management; industrial and organizational psychology; international business; journalism; management sciences and quantitative methods; marketing; mathematics and statistics related; philosophy; philosophy and religious studies related; physical sciences; physics; psychology; quality control and safety technologies; sales, merchandising, and related marketing operations (general); sociology; statistics.

UNIVERSITY OF CALIFORNIA, DAVIS
Davis, California
UC Davis Extension
http://www.extension.ucdavis.edu/distancelearning

University of California, Davis was founded in 1905. It is accredited by Western Association of Schools and Colleges. It first offered distance learning courses in 1987. In fall 2005, there were 573 students enrolled in distance learning courses. Institutionally administered financial aid is available to distance learners.

Services Distance learners have accessibility to academic advising, bookstore, library services.

Contact Bill Heekin, Director of Student Services, University of California, Davis, 1333 Research Park Drive, Davis, CA 95616. Telephone: 530-757-8777. Fax: 530-757-8696. E-mail: bheekin@unexmail.ucdavis.edu.

DEGREES AND AWARDS
Programs offered do not lead to a degree or other formal award.

COURSE SUBJECT AREAS OFFERED OUTSIDE OF DEGREE PROGRAMS
Undergraduate—agriculture and agriculture operations related; computer/information technology administration and management; computer programming; computer science; computer software and media applications; computer systems analysis; computer systems networking and telecommunications; education; education (specific subject areas); food science and technology; linguistic, comparative, and related language studies.

Graduate—agricultural and food products processing.

Non-credit—agriculture and agriculture operations related; computer and information sciences; English composition; linguistic, comparative, and related language studies; management sciences and quantitative methods.

UNIVERSITY OF CALIFORNIA, LOS ANGELES
Los Angeles, California
University Extension
http://www.uclaextension.edu

University of California, Los Angeles was founded in 1919. It is accredited by Western Association of Schools and Colleges. It first offered distance learning courses in 1996. In fall 2005, there were 2,500 students enrolled in distance learning courses. Institutionally administered financial aid is available to distance learners.

Services Distance learners have accessibility to academic advising, bookstore, campus computer network, e-mail services, library services, tutoring.

Contact Mrs. Sandra Saika, Project Representative, University of California, Los Angeles, 10995 LeConte Avenue, Room 714, Los Angeles, CA 90024. Telephone: 310-825-2648. Fax: 310-267-4783. E-mail: ssaika@uclaextension.edu.

DEGREES AND AWARDS
Programs offered do not lead to a degree or other formal award.

COURSE SUBJECT AREAS OFFERED OUTSIDE OF DEGREE PROGRAMS
Graduate—archeology; business administration, management and operations; business/commerce; design and applied arts; economics; film/video and photographic arts; health and physical education/fitness; languages (foreign languages related); liberal arts and sciences, general studies and humanities; mathematics; philosophy and religious studies related; psychology; social sciences; technical and business writing; visual and performing arts.

UNIVERSITY OF CALIFORNIA, RIVERSIDE
Riverside, California
University Extension
http://www.unex.ucr.edu

University of California, Riverside was founded in 1954. It is accredited by Western Association of Schools and Colleges. It first offered distance learning courses in 1994. In fall 2005, there were 150 students enrolled in distance learning courses. Institutionally administered financial aid is available to distance learners.

Services Distance learners have accessibility to academic advising, bookstore, library services.

Contact Jon Kindschy, Director of Sciences, University of California, Riverside, Riverside, CA 92507. Telephone: 951-827-5804 Ext. 1622. E-mail: sciences@ucx.ucr.edu.

DEGREES AND AWARDS

Programs offered do not lead to a degree or other formal award.

COURSE SUBJECT AREAS OFFERED OUTSIDE OF DEGREE PROGRAMS

Non-credit—agriculture and agriculture operations related; applied horticulture/horticultural business services; atmospheric sciences and meteorology; computer software and media applications; education related; geography and cartography; nursing; plant sciences.

UNIVERSITY OF CENTRAL ARKANSAS

Conway, Arkansas

Division of Continuing Education

http://www.uca.edu/aoep

University of Central Arkansas was founded in 1907. It is accredited by North Central Association of Colleges and Schools. It first offered distance learning courses in 1992. In fall 2005, there were 336 students enrolled in distance learning courses. Institutionally administered financial aid is available to distance learners.

Services Distance learners have accessibility to bookstore, career placement assistance, e-mail services, library services.

Contact Sondra Pugh, Extended Study Secretary, University of Central Arkansas, 201 Donaghey Avenue, Brewer-Hegeman Conference Center, Suite 102, Conway, AR 72035. Telephone: 501-450-3118. Fax: 501-450-5277. E-mail: sondrap@mail.uca.edu.

DEGREES AND AWARDS

Programs offered do not lead to a degree or other formal award.

COURSE SUBJECT AREAS OFFERED OUTSIDE OF DEGREE PROGRAMS

Undergraduate—accounting and related services; American literature (United States and Canadian); creative writing; educational psychology; English composition; history; languages (Germanic); mathematics; political science and government; psychology; social psychology; sociology.

Graduate—business, management, and marketing related; computer and information sciences and support services related; curriculum and instruction; educational administration and supervision; education related; geography and cartography; health professions related; library science related; nursing; rehabilitation and therapeutic professions.

Non-credit—business administration, management and operations; computer and information sciences; English; insurance; journalism.

UNIVERSITY OF CENTRAL FLORIDA

Orlando, Florida

Center for Distributed Learning

http://online.ucf.edu

University of Central Florida was founded in 1963. It is accredited by Southern Association of Colleges and Schools. It first offered distance learning courses in 1996. In fall 2005, there were 8,650 students enrolled in distance learning courses. Institutionally administered financial aid is available to distance learners.

Services Distance learners have accessibility to academic advising, bookstore, campus computer network, e-mail services, library services.

Contact Ms. Lori Allison, Coordinator, University of Central Florida, 3100 Technology Parkway, Suite 234, Orlando, FL 32826-3271. Telephone: 407-823-4910. Fax: 407-207-4911. E-mail: lallison@mail.ucf.edu.

DEGREES AND AWARDS

BA Liberal Studies

BS Health Services Administration; Information Systems Technology; Liberal Studies; Radiologic Sciences; Technical Education and Industry Training

BSET Engineering Technology

BSN Nursing

Graduate Certificate Community College Education; Educational Media; Gifted Education; Initial Teacher Professional Preparation; Instructional Design for Simulations; Instructional/Educational Technology; Nonprofit Management; Nursing and Health Professional Education; Pre-Kindergarten Handicapped Endorsement; Professional Writing; Special Education; e-Learning Professional Development

MA Exceptional Education; Instructional Technology/Media–E-Learning Professional track; Instructional Technology/Media–Educational Technology track; Instructional Technology/Media–Instructional Systems track; Vocational Education

MEd Instructional Technology/Media–Educational Media track

MM Nonprofit Management

MS Criminal Justice; Forensic Science–Forensic Analysis track; Forensic Science–Forensic Biochemistry track

MSN Nursing–Leadership and Management track; Nursing–Nurse Educator track

COURSE SUBJECT AREAS OFFERED OUTSIDE OF DEGREE PROGRAMS

Undergraduate—computer and information sciences and support services related; education related; health and medical administrative services; nursing; sociology; statistics.

Graduate—chemistry; educational/instructional media design; education related; health and medical administrative services; nursing; public administration and social service professions related; technical and business writing.

UNIVERSITY OF CENTRAL OKLAHOMA

Edmond, Oklahoma

Distance Learning Technologies

http://www.bronze.ucok.edu/corrstudies

University of Central Oklahoma was founded in 1890. It is accredited by North Central Association of Colleges and Schools. It first offered distance learning courses in 1996. In fall 2005, there were 2,000 students enrolled in distance learning courses. Institutionally administered financial aid is available to distance learners.

Services Distance learners have accessibility to academic advising, bookstore, career placement assistance, e-mail services, library services.

Contact Sandra L. Burkey, Assistant Director, University of Central Oklahoma, 100 North University, Box 159, Edmond, OK 73034. Telephone: 405-974-2529. E-mail: sburkey@ucok.edu.

DEGREES AND AWARDS

Programs offered do not lead to a degree or other formal award.

COURSE SUBJECT AREAS OFFERED OUTSIDE OF DEGREE PROGRAMS

Undergraduate—educational administration and supervision; education related; English; English as a second language; fine and studio art; funeral service and mortuary science; library science; sociology.

Graduate—educational administration and supervision; education related; English; English as a second language; fine and studio art; funeral service and mortuary science; library science; sociology.

Non-credit—computer and information sciences.

UNIVERSITY OF CINCINNATI

Cincinnati, Ohio

Distance Learning Programs

http://www.uc.edu/distance

University of Cincinnati was founded in 1819. It is accredited by North Central Association of Colleges and Schools. It first offered distance learning courses in 1984. In fall 2005, there were 2,950 students enrolled in distance learning courses. Institutionally administered financial aid is available to distance learners.

Services Distance learners have accessibility to academic advising, bookstore, campus computer network, e-mail services, library services, tutoring.

Contact Dr. Melody Clark, Academic Director, Distance Learning, University of Cincinnati, PO Box 210635, Cincinnati, OH 45221-0635. Telephone: 513-556-9154. Fax: 513-556-6050. E-mail: melody.clark@uc.edu.

DEGREES AND AWARDS

AAS Early Childhood Education; Fire Science Technology
BEd Early Childhood Education
BS Addiction Studies; Clinical Laboratory Science; Fire Science Technology; Health Information Management
MEd Curriculum and Instruction (for Health Care Professionals); Educational Leadership
MS Criminal Justice
MSN Nurse Midwifery; Women's Health Nurse Practitioner
PharmD Pharmacy

COURSE SUBJECT AREAS OFFERED OUTSIDE OF DEGREE PROGRAMS

Undergraduate—accounting and related services; business/commerce; communication disorders sciences and services; computer software and media applications; criminal justice and corrections; engineering related; geography and cartography; geological and earth sciences/geosciences; history; philosophy; philosophy and religious studies related; psychology.
Graduate—communication disorders sciences and services; engineering related.
Non-credit—accounting and computer science; accounting and related services; business/commerce; business operations support and assistant services; computer and information sciences; computer programming; publishing; technical and business writing.

UNIVERSITY OF CINCINNATI RAYMOND WALTERS COLLEGE
Cincinnati, Ohio
Outreach and Continuing Education
http://www.rwc.uc.edu/maps/news/courses.htm

University of Cincinnati Raymond Walters College was founded in 1967. It is accredited by North Central Association of Colleges and Schools. It first offered distance learning courses in 1995. In fall 2005, there were 290 students enrolled in distance learning courses. Institutionally administered financial aid is available to distance learners.
Services Distance learners have accessibility to academic advising, bookstore, campus computer network, career placement assistance, e-mail services, library services.
Contact Janice Ooten, Program Manager, University of Cincinnati Raymond Walters College, 9555 Plainfield Road, Cincinnati, OH 45236-1096. Telephone: 513-936-1533. Fax: 513-745-8315. E-mail: janice.ooten@uc.edu.

DEGREES AND AWARDS

Programs offered do not lead to a degree or other formal award.

COURSE SUBJECT AREAS OFFERED OUTSIDE OF DEGREE PROGRAMS

Undergraduate—business administration, management and operations; business/commerce; computer/information technology administration and management; computer software and media applications; English composition; film/video and photographic arts; foods, nutrition, and related services; health professions related; library science; physics; psychology; sociology.

UNIVERSITY OF COLORADO AT BOULDER
Boulder, Colorado
Center for Advanced Engineering and Technology Education (CAETE)
http://caete.colorado.edu

University of Colorado at Boulder was founded in 1876. It is accredited by North Central Association of Colleges and Schools. It first offered distance learning courses in 1983. In fall 2005, there were 400 students enrolled in distance learning courses. Institutionally administered financial aid is available to distance learners.
Services Distance learners have accessibility to academic advising, bookstore, campus computer network, career placement assistance, e-mail services, library services.
Contact Robin M.W. McClanahan, Marketing Manager, University of Colorado at Boulder, CAETE, 435 UCB, Boulder, CO 80309. Telephone: 303-492-0212. Fax: 303-492-5987. E-mail: caete@colorado.edu.

DEGREES AND AWARDS

Graduate Certificate Engineering Management; Managing Applied Research in Technology; Performance Excellence in Technology Management; Power Electronics; Project Management; Quality Systems for Product and Process Engineering; Research and Development; Software Engineering

ME Aerospace Engineering; Computer Science; Electrical and Computer Engineering; Engineering Management; Telecommunications

MS Aerospace Engineering; Electrical and Computer Engineering; Telecommunications

COURSE SUBJECT AREAS OFFERED OUTSIDE OF DEGREE PROGRAMS

Graduate—aerospace, aeronautical and astronautical engineering; biomedical/medical engineering; civil engineering; computer engineering; computer science; computer systems networking and telecommunications; electrical and electronic engineering technologies; engineering/industrial management; environmental/environmental health engineering; mechanical engineering.

Non-credit—aerospace, aeronautical and astronautical engineering; biomedical/medical engineering; civil engineering; computer engineering; computer science; computer systems networking and telecommunications; electrical and electronic engineering technologies; engineering/industrial management; environmental/environmental health engineering; mechanical engineering.

UNIVERSITY OF COLORADO AT COLORADO SPRINGS
Colorado Springs, Colorado
http://www.uccs.edu/~online/

University of Colorado at Colorado Springs was founded in 1965. It is accredited by North Central Association of Colleges and Schools. It first offered distance learning courses in 1996. In fall 2005, there were 610 students enrolled in distance learning courses. Institutionally administered financial aid is available to distance learners.
Services Distance learners have accessibility to academic advising, campus computer network, e-mail services, library services.
Contact Dana Rocha, Director of Extended Studies, University of Colorado at Colorado Springs, 1420 Austin Bluffs Parkway, MH 316, ADM 10, Colorado Springs, CO 80933-7150. Telephone: 719-262-4662. E-mail: drocha@uccs.edu.

DEGREES AND AWARDS

MA Curriculum and Instruction–Educational Leadership; English as a Second Language Education Program; Online Principal Licensure Program and Masters Degree in Curriculum and Instruction

MBA Business Administration

ME Engineering Management; Space Studies; Systems Engineering

MSN Nurse Practitioner and Clinical Specialist

COURSE SUBJECT AREAS OFFERED OUTSIDE OF DEGREE PROGRAMS

Undergraduate—American literature (United States and Canadian); area, ethnic, cultural, and gender studies related; biological and biomedical sciences related; chemistry; communication and media; economics; English composition; geography and cartography; gerontology; health professions related; history; languages (Middle/Near Eastern and Semitic); mathematics; mechanical engineering; military studies; nursing; psychology; sociology.

Graduate—aerospace, aeronautical and astronautical engineering; business/commerce; criminal justice and corrections; educational administration and supervision; health professions related; mechanical engineering; nursing; public administration.

UNIVERSITY OF COLORADO AT DENVER AND HEALTH SCIENCES CENTER—DOWNTOWN DENVER CAMPUS

Denver, Colorado

CU Online

http://cuonline.edu/petersons

University of Colorado at Denver and Health Sciences Center—Downtown Denver Campus was founded in 1912. It is accredited by North Central Association of Colleges and Schools. It first offered distance learning courses in 1996. In fall 2005, there were 2,290 students enrolled in distance learning courses. Institutionally administered financial aid is available to distance learners.

Services Distance learners have accessibility to academic advising, bookstore, career placement assistance, e-mail services, library services, tutoring.

Contact Program Assistant, University of Colorado at Denver and Health Sciences Center—Downtown Denver Campus, Campus Box 198, PO Box 173364, Denver, CO 80217-3364. Telephone: 303-556-6505. Fax: 303-556-6530. E-mail: inquiry@cuonline.edu.

DEGREES AND AWARDS

BA English–Writing; Sociology

Certificate of Achievement World History for Educators

Certificate ALPS International Educational Leadership Program; Designing and Implementing Web-based Learning Environments

Certification Early Literacy Certificate program; Nonprofit Management

License Early Childhood Special Education, Generalist

MA Early Childhood Education; Information and Learning Technologies, School Library; eLearning Design and Implementation

MBA Business Administration

MEngr Geographic Information Systems (GIS)

MPA Public Administration

MS Finance; Information Systems

COURSE SUBJECT AREAS OFFERED OUTSIDE OF DEGREE PROGRAMS

Undergraduate—accounting and related services; American literature (United States and Canadian); anthropology; biochemistry, biophysics and molecular biology; biology; cell biology and anatomical sciences; civil engineering; communication and media; computer programming; creative writing; dramatic/theater arts and stagecraft; economics; electrical, electronics and communications engineering; engineering; engineering science; English; English composition; ethnic, cultural minority, and gender studies; fine and studio art; geography and cartography; geological and earth sciences/geosciences; history; industrial and organizational psychology; languages (classics and classical); liberal arts and sciences, general studies and humanities; linguistic, comparative, and related language studies; mathematics and statistics related; mechanical engineering; music; philosophy and religious studies related; physics; political science and government; psychology; social psychology; sociology; statistics; technical and business writing.

Graduate—accounting and related services; architecture; business administration, management and operations; business/commerce; business/corporate communications; business, management, and marketing related; business/managerial economics; education; education related; electrical, electronics and communications engineering; engineering; engineering design; engineering/industrial management; engineering related; engineering technologies related; history; management information systems; management sciences and quantitative methods; marketing; political science and government; public administration; public administration and social service professions related; public policy analysis; sales, merchandising, and related marketing operations (general); sales, merchandising, and related marketing operations (specialized).

See full description on page 504.

UNIVERSITY OF CONNECTICUT

Storrs, Connecticut

Center for Continuing Studies

http://continuingstudies.uconn.edu/onlinecourses

University of Connecticut was founded in 1881. It is accredited by New England Association of Schools and Colleges. It first offered distance learning courses in 2001. In fall 2005, there were 500 students enrolled in distance learning courses. Institutionally administered financial aid is available to distance learners.

Services Distance learners have accessibility to academic advising, bookstore, campus computer network, career placement assistance, e-mail services, library services, tutoring.

Contact Dr. Judy Buffolino, Director of Distance Education, University of Connecticut, Center for Continuing Studies, Distance Education Office, One Bishop Circle, Unit 4056, Storrs, CT 06269-4056. Telephone: 860-486-1080. Fax: 860-486-0756. E-mail: judy.buffolino@uconn.edu.

DEGREES AND AWARDS

BGS Environmental and Occupational Safety and Health focus; Public Safety/Criminal Justice; Web Technology focus

Certificate Environmental Health and Safety; Occupational Safety and Health

MPS Homeland Security Leadership; Human Resource Management; Humanitarian Services Administration; Occupational Safety and Health Management

COURSE SUBJECT AREAS OFFERED OUTSIDE OF DEGREE PROGRAMS

Undergraduate—area, ethnic, cultural, and gender studies related; behavioral sciences; computer and information sciences and support services related; computer/information technology administration and management; computer programming; computer software and media applications; criminal justice and corrections; ethnic, cultural minority, and gender studies; health professions related; health services/allied health/health sciences; liberal arts and sciences, general studies and humanities; multi-/interdisciplinary studies related; sociology.

Graduate—criminology; health professions related; human resources management; human services; security and protective services related.

Non-credit—health professions related.

See full description on page 506.

UNIVERSITY OF DALLAS

Irving, Texas

Center for Distance Education

http://www.thedallasmba.com

University of Dallas was founded in 1955. It is accredited by American Academy for Liberal Education. It first offered distance learning courses in 1970. In fall 2005, there were 800 students enrolled in distance learning courses. Institutionally administered financial aid is available to distance learners.

Services Distance learners have accessibility to academic advising, bookstore, career placement assistance, library services, tutoring.

Contact Ms. Vanessa Cox, Associate Director of Online Learning, University of Dallas, 1845 East Northgate Drive, Irving, TX 75062-4736. Telephone: 877-408-2335. Fax: 972-721-5265. E-mail: vcox@gsm.udallas.edu.

DEGREES AND AWARDS

Graduate Certificate Accounting; CFP Certified Financial Planning; Corporate Finance; Global Business; Health Services Management; Information Assurance; Information Technology; Interdisciplinary (Custom curriculum); Marketing Management; Not-for-Profit; Project Management; Sports and Entertainment Management; Supply Chain Management/Market Logistics; Telecommunications Management

MBA Accounting; CFP Certified Financial Planning; Corporate Finance; Global Business; Health Services Management; Information Assurance; Information Technology; Interdisciplinary (Custom curriculum); Marketing Management; Not-for-Profit; Project Management; Sports and Entertainment Management; Supply Chain Management/Market Logistics; Telecommunications Management

MM Accounting; CFP Certified Financial Planning; Corporate Finance; Global Business; Health Services Management; Information Assurance; Information Technology; Interdisciplinary (Custom curriculum); Marketing Management; Not-for-Profit; Project Management; Sports and Entertainment Management; Supply Chain Management/Market Logistics; Telecommunications Management

COURSE SUBJECT AREAS OFFERED OUTSIDE OF DEGREE PROGRAMS

Graduate—accounting and related services; business administration, management and operations; computer and information sciences; computer and information sciences and support services related; computer systems analysis; computer systems networking and telecommunications; finance and financial management services; health and medical administrative services; international business; management information systems; marketing; sales, merchandising, and related marketing operations (general); sales, merchandising, and related marketing operations (specialized).

See full description on page 508.

UNIVERSITY OF DELAWARE
Newark, Delaware
Division of Professional and Continuing Studies
http://www.continuingstudies.udel.edu/udonline/

University of Delaware was founded in 1743. It is accredited by Middle States Association of Colleges and Schools. It first offered distance learning courses in 1988. In fall 2005, there were 1,256 students enrolled in distance learning courses. Institutionally administered financial aid is available to distance learners.

Services Distance learners have accessibility to academic advising, bookstore, campus computer network, career placement assistance, e-mail services, library services, tutoring.

Contact Mrs. Melanie Rehberg, Program Manager, University of Delaware, 210 Clayton Hall, Newark, DE 19716. Telephone: 302-831-1079. Fax: 302-831-3292. E-mail: melanier@udel.edu.

DEGREES AND AWARDS

BS Hotel, Restaurant, and Institutional Management; Nursing

MME Mechanical Engineering

MS Health Services Administration

MSEE Electrical Engineering

MSN Nursing–Health Services Administration; Nursing–RN to MSN

COURSE SUBJECT AREAS OFFERED OUTSIDE OF DEGREE PROGRAMS

Undergraduate—accounting and related services; animal sciences; biology; chemical engineering; chemistry; civil engineering; communication and media; criminal justice and corrections; economics; education; engineering science; English; English composition; English language and literature related; foods, nutrition, and related services; history; hospitality administration; human development, family studies, and related services; marketing; mathematics and statistics related; mechanical engineering; music; nursing; philosophy and religious studies related; political science and government; sociology; technical and business writing; urban studies/affairs.

Graduate—chemical engineering; civil engineering; education; engineering mechanics; foods, nutrition, and related services; health professions related; mechanical engineering; nursing; political science and government; public administration.

Non-credit—business, management, and marketing related; foods, nutrition, and related services; hospitality administration; mechanical engineering; nursing.

See full description on page 510.

UNIVERSITY OF DENVER
Denver, Colorado
University College
http://www.universitycollege.du.edu

University of Denver was founded in 1864. It is accredited by North Central Association of Colleges and Schools. It first offered distance learning courses in 1996. In fall 2005, there were 375 students enrolled in distance learning courses. Institutionally administered financial aid is available to distance learners.

Services Distance learners have accessibility to academic advising, bookstore, campus computer network, career placement assistance, e-mail services, library services.

Contact Mr. Mark Guthrie, Director of Enrollment and Advising, University of Denver, 2211 South Josephine, Denver, CO 80208. Telephone: 303-871-7582. Fax: 303-871-3070. E-mail: maguthri@du.edu.

DEGREES AND AWARDS

BA Bachelor of Arts Completion Program

Certificate Alternative Dispute Resolution–Certificate of Advanced Study; Arts and Literature–Certificate of Advanced Study; Broadband–Certificate of Advanced Study; Computer Information Systems–Certificate of Advanced Study; Database Administration–Certificate of Advanced Study; Distributed Object-Oriented Analysis and Design–Certificate of Advanced Study; Environmental Information Management–Certificate of Advanced Study; Environmental Management–Certificate of Advanced Study; Environmental Policy–Certificate of Advanced Study; Environmental Project Management–Certificate of Advanced Study; Environmental, Health, and Safety Management–Certificate of Advanced Study; Geographic Information Systems–Certificate of Advanced Study; Human Resource Administration–Certificate of Advanced Study; Information Security–Certificate of Advanced Study; Information Systems Security–Certificate of Advanced Study; Leadership–Certificate of Advanced Study; Modern Languages–Certificate of Advanced Study; Natural Resource Management–Certificate of Advanced Study; Organizational Security–Certificate of Advanced Study; Project Management–Certificate of Advanced Study; Public Relations and Marketing Communications–Certificate of Advanced Study; Technology Management–Certificate of Advanced Study; Telecommunications Management and Policy–Certificate of Advanced Study; Telecommunications Networks–Certificate of Advanced Study; Telecommunications Technology–Certificate of Advanced Study; Training and Development–Certificate of Advanced Study; Web Design and Development Technologies–Certificate of Advanced Study

MLS Liberal Studies–Master of Liberal Studies

MPS Applied Communication–Master of Professional Studies in Applied Communication; Human Resource Administration–Master of Professional Studies in Human Resource Administration; Organizational Leadership–Master of Professional Studies in Organizational Leadership

MS Computer Information Systems–Master of Applied Science in Computer Information Systems; Environmental Policy and Management–Master of Applied Science in Environmental Policy and Management; Knowledge and Information Technologies–Master of Applied Science in Knowledge and Information Technologies; Security Management–Master of Applied Science in Security Management; Technology Management–Master of Applied Science in Technology Management; Telecommunications–Master of Applied Science in Telecommunications

COURSE SUBJECT AREAS OFFERED OUTSIDE OF DEGREE PROGRAMS

Undergraduate—business/corporate communications; public policy analysis; science, technology and society; social sciences related.

Graduate—business administration, management and operations; communication and media; computer and information sciences; computer and information sciences and support services related; computer/information technology administration and management; computer systems networking and telecommunications; creative writing; liberal arts and sciences, general studies and humanities; linguistic, comparative, and related language studies; natural resources management and policy.

See full description on page 512.

THE UNIVERSITY OF FINDLAY
Findlay, Ohio
Global Campus
http://ufonline.findlay.edu

The University of Findlay was founded in 1882. It is accredited by North Central Association of Colleges and Schools. It first offered distance learning courses in 1998. In fall 2005, there were 1,050 students enrolled in distance learning courses. Institutionally administered financial aid is available to distance learners.

Services Distance learners have accessibility to academic advising, bookstore, campus computer network, career placement assistance, e-mail services, library services, tutoring.

Contact Mrs. Heather L. Riffle, Director, Graduate and Special Programs, The University of Findlay, 1000 North Main Street, Findlay, OH 45840. Telephone: 419-434-4600. Fax: 419-434-5517. E-mail: riffle@findlay.edu.

DEGREES AND AWARDS

BS Business Management; Criminal Justice Administration; Environmental, Safety, and Health Management
MBA Business Administration
MS Environmental, Safety, and Health Management

COURSE SUBJECT AREAS OFFERED OUTSIDE OF DEGREE PROGRAMS

Undergraduate—accounting and related services; biblical studies; business administration, management and operations; business/commerce; business/managerial economics; chemistry; communication and journalism related; computer science; criminal justice and corrections; criminology; economics; ethnic, cultural minority, and gender studies; fine and studio art; history; human resources management; international business; marketing; mathematics; philosophy and religious studies related; religious studies; social sciences; sociology; statistics; visual and performing arts.

Graduate—accounting and related services; business administration, management and operations; business/corporate communications; business/managerial economics; educational assessment, evaluation, and research; educational/instructional media design; environmental control technologies; human resources management; marketing; public administration; sales, merchandising, and related marketing operations (general).

Non-credit—business, management, and marketing related; business/managerial economics; management information systems; management sciences and quantitative methods.

UNIVERSITY OF FLORIDA
Gainesville, Florida
Distance Learning
http://www.distancelearning.ufl.edu

University of Florida was founded in 1853. It is accredited by Southern Association of Colleges and Schools. It first offered distance learning courses in 1996. In fall 2005, there were 4,000 students enrolled in distance learning courses. Institutionally administered financial aid is available to distance learners.

Services Distance learners have accessibility to academic advising, bookstore, campus computer network, career placement assistance, e-mail services, library services, tutoring.

Contact Chris Newsom, Distance Learning Coordinator, University of Florida, 2209 NW 13th Street, Gainesville, FL 32609. Telephone: 352-392-1711 Ext. 218. Fax: 352-392-6950. E-mail: distance@dce.ufl.edu.

DEGREES AND AWARDS

BS Business Administration; Fire and Emergency Services
Certificate Criminal Justice; Executive EMS Officer; Executive Emergency Management Officer; Executive Fire Officer; Geriatric Care Management
Graduate Certificate Construction Project Management; Educational Technology Production; Environmental Policy Management; Forensic DNA and Serology; Forensic Death Investigation; Forensic Drug Chemistry; Forensic Toxicology; Geriatric Care Management; Health Care Risk Management; Instruction and Curriculum; K-12 Technology Integration; Landscape Pest Management; Materials Science and Engineering; Pest Control Technology; Public Health; Sustainable Construction; Teaching and Learning with Technology; Teaching and Learning–Online Teaching and Learning; Urban Pest Management
MA Latin
MBA Business Administration
MCM International Construction Management
MEd Curriculum and Instruction
MHS Occupational Therapy
MS Agricultural Education and Communication; Civil Engineering; Computer Engineering; Electrical and Computer Engineering; Entomology; Materials Science and Engineering; Mechanical and Aerospace Engineering; Pest Management; Pharmaceutical Science–Forensic DNA and Serology; Pharmaceutical Science–Forensic Drug Chemistry; Pharmacy Regulation and Policy; Soil and Water Science–Environmental Science; Veterinary Medical Sciences–Forensic Toxicology; Water, Wastewater, and Stormwater Engineering
MSWREE Water Resources Planning and Management
PhD Audiology; Classical Civilization; Latin and Roman Studies
PharmD Pharmacy, First Professional Degree; Pharmacy, Working Professional

COURSE SUBJECT AREAS OFFERED OUTSIDE OF DEGREE PROGRAMS

Undergraduate—agricultural and domestic animal services; agricultural and food products processing; agricultural business and management; agricultural production; agricultural public services; agriculture; agriculture and agriculture operations related; American literature (United States and Canadian); anthropology; applied horticulture/horticultural business services; applied mathematics; astronomy and astrophysics; biblical studies; biochemistry, biophysics and molecular biology; biology; botany/plant biology; business administration, management and operations; business/commerce; business, management, and marketing related; chemistry; communication and journalism related; communication and media; criminal justice and corrections; criminology; developmental and child psychology; ecology, evolution, and population biology; economics; education; educational assessment, evaluation, and research; educational psychology; education (specific subject areas); English; English as a second/foreign language (teaching); English as a second language; English composition; English language and literature related; entrepreneurial and small business operations; finance and financial management services; fire protection; food science and technology; foods, nutrition, and related services; forestry; geography and cartography; geological and earth sciences/geosciences; gerontology; history; human development, family studies, and related services; human resources management; industrial and organizational psychology; insurance; international business; journalism; languages (classics and classical); languages (Germanic); languages (Romance languages); legal studies (nonprofessional general, undergraduate); liberal arts and sciences, general studies and humanities; linguistic, comparative, and related language studies; management sciences and quantitative methods; marketing; mathematics; mathematics and statistics related; multi-/interdisciplinary studies related; natural resources and conservation related; natural resources management and policy; nutrition sciences; parks, recreation and leisure; parks, recreation and leisure facilities management; parks, recreation, and leisure related; philosophy; philosophy and religious studies related; political science and government; psychology; psychology related; public administration; public relations, advertising, and applied communication related; real estate; religious studies; sales, merchandising, and related marketing operations (general); social and philosophical foundations of education; social psychology; social sciences related; sociology; soil sciences; statistics; technical and business writing; textile sciences and engineering.

Graduate—agricultural business and management; agricultural mechanization; agricultural public services; agriculture; audiovisual communications technologies; biological and biomedical sciences related; biology/biotechnology laboratory technician; building/construction finishing, management, and inspection; business, management, and marketing related; civil engineering; classical and ancient studies; communication and media; communications technology; computer and information sciences; computer engineering; computer science; computer software and media applications; construction management; curriculum and instruction; education; educational administration and supervision; educational assessment, evaluation, and research; educational/instructional media

design; education related; education (specific subject areas); engineering; environmental control technologies; foods, nutrition, and related services; genetics; gerontology; health/medical preparatory programs; materials engineering; materials science; natural resources and conservation related; natural resources management and policy; soil sciences; statistics.
Non-credit—English as a second language; environmental control technologies; foods, nutrition, and related services; gerontology; medical basic sciences; nutrition sciences.

UNIVERSITY OF FLORIDA
Gainesville, Florida
UF EDGE
http://www.ufl.edu/

University of Florida was founded in 1853. It is accredited by Southern Association of Colleges and Schools. It first offered distance learning courses in 1964. In fall 2005, there were 250 students enrolled in distance learning courses. Institutionally administered financial aid is available to distance learners.
Services Distance learners have accessibility to academic advising, bookstore, campus computer network, career placement assistance, library services.
Contact Lisa Boles, Program Assistant, University of Florida, College of Engineering, E-117 CSE, PO Box 116100, Gainesville, FL 32611-6100. Telephone: 352-392-1678. Fax: 352-392-1724. E-mail: lbole@eng.ufl.edu.

DEGREES AND AWARDS
MS Civil Engineering; Computer Engineering (Bioinformatics track); Computer Engineering (General track); Computer Engineering–Bioinformatics; Electrical and Computer Engineering; Environmental Engineering–Water Resources Planning and Management track; Environmental Engineering–Water, Wastewater, and Stormwater Engineering; Materials Science and Engineering; Mechanical and Aerospace Engineering–Fundamentals of Thermal Fluids Transport track; Mechanical and Aerospace Engineering–Solid Mechanics and Design track

COURSE SUBJECT AREAS OFFERED OUTSIDE OF DEGREE PROGRAMS
Graduate—environmental/environmental health engineering; materials science.

See full description on page 514.

UNIVERSITY OF GREAT FALLS
Great Falls, Montana
Center for Distance Learning
http://www.ugf.edu/distancelearning/

University of Great Falls was founded in 1932. It is accredited by Northwest Commission on Colleges and Universities. It first offered distance learning courses in 1979. In fall 2005, there were 488 students enrolled in distance learning courses. Institutionally administered financial aid is available to distance learners.
Services Distance learners have accessibility to academic advising, bookstore, campus computer network, career placement assistance, e-mail services, library services, tutoring.
Contact Jim Gretch, Production Manager, University of Great Falls, 1301 20th Street South, Great Falls, MT 59405. Telephone: 406-791-5320. Fax: 406-791-5394. E-mail: jgretch@ugf.edu.

DEGREES AND AWARDS
BA Criminal Justice; Paralegal Studies; Psychology
MA Criminal Justice Administration; Human Services Administration–Master of Human Services Administration; Secondary Teaching
MSIS Information Systems

COURSE SUBJECT AREAS OFFERED OUTSIDE OF DEGREE PROGRAMS
Undergraduate—American literature (United States and Canadian); biological and physical sciences; computer and information sciences; computer science; computer software and media applications; counseling psychology; criminal justice and corrections; developmental and child psychology; English; fine and studio art; health and physical education/fitness; history; human services; legal studies (non-professional general, undergraduate); liberal arts and sciences, general studies and humanities; mathematics; mathematics and statistics related; natural sciences; philosophy and religious studies related; psychology; social sciences; sociology; technical and business writing; theological and ministerial studies.
Graduate—computer and information sciences; criminal justice and corrections; education (specific levels and methods); human services.

UNIVERSITY OF HAWAII–WEST OAHU
Pearl City, Hawaii
http://www.uhwo.hawaii.edu/distanceed

University of Hawaii–West Oahu was founded in 1976. It is accredited by Western Association of Schools and Colleges. It first offered distance learning courses in 1996. In fall 2005, there were 150 students enrolled in distance learning courses. Institutionally administered financial aid is available to distance learners.
Services Distance learners have accessibility to academic advising, bookstore, campus computer network, career placement assistance, e-mail services, library services, tutoring.
Contact Robyn Oshiro, Student Services Specialist, University of Hawaii–West Oahu, 96-129 Ala Ike, Student Services Office, Pearl City, HI 96782. Telephone: 808-454-4700. Fax: 808-453-6075. E-mail: robyno@hawaii.edu.

DEGREES AND AWARDS
BA Business Administration; Social Sciences–Applied Track; Social Sciences
Certificate Substance Abuse and Addictions Studies

COURSE SUBJECT AREAS OFFERED OUTSIDE OF DEGREE PROGRAMS
Undergraduate—accounting and related services; anthropology; business administration, management and operations; business, management, and marketing related; clinical psychology; counseling psychology; criminal justice and corrections; criminology; developmental and child psychology; economics; history; human resources management; philosophy; political science and government; psychology; psychology related; public administration; public administration and social service professions related; social sciences; social sciences related; sociology; statistics.

UNIVERSITY OF HOUSTON–CLEAR LAKE
Houston, Texas
Distance and Extended Education
http://www.uhcl.edu/disted

University of Houston–Clear Lake was founded in 1971. It is accredited by Southern Association of Colleges and Schools. It first offered distance learning courses in 1995. In fall 2005, there were 1,253 students enrolled in distance learning courses. Institutionally administered financial aid is available to distance learners.
Services Distance learners have accessibility to academic advising, bookstore, campus computer network, career placement assistance, e-mail services, library services, tutoring.
Contact Kate Finstad, Director of Distance and Off-Campus Education, University of Houston–Clear Lake, 2700 Bay Area Boulevard, Box 101, Houston, TX 77058-1098. Telephone: 281-283-3032. Fax: 281-226-7130. E-mail: disted@uhcl.edu.

DEGREES AND AWARDS
MS Instructional Technology; Software Engineering

COURSE SUBJECT AREAS OFFERED OUTSIDE OF DEGREE PROGRAMS
Graduate—business administration, management and operations; computer and information sciences; computer programming; computer science; computer software and media applications; economics; educational/instructional media design; health and medical administrative services; human resources management.

UNIVERSITY OF HOUSTON–DOWNTOWN
Houston, Texas
http://www.uhd.edu/

University of Houston–Downtown was founded in 1974. It is accredited by Southern Association of Colleges and Schools. It first offered distance learning courses in 1994. In fall 2005, there were 1,800 students enrolled in distance learning courses. Institutionally administered financial aid is available to distance learners.

Services Distance learners have accessibility to academic advising, bookstore, campus computer network, e-mail services, library services.

Contact Dr. Gail S.M. Evans, Executive Director of Distance Education, University of Houston–Downtown, One Main Street, Houston, TX 77002. Telephone: 713-221-2735. Fax: 713-221-8922. E-mail: evansg@uhd.edu.

DEGREES AND AWARDS

Programs offered do not lead to a degree or other formal award.

COURSE SUBJECT AREAS OFFERED OUTSIDE OF DEGREE PROGRAMS

Undergraduate—accounting and related services; biological and physical sciences; biology/biotechnology laboratory technician; business administration, management and operations; business/corporate communications; business/managerial economics; computer/information technology administration and management; computer programming; computer science; computer software and media applications; computer systems analysis; computer systems networking and telecommunications; criminal justice and corrections; developmental and child psychology; education; English language and literature related; finance and financial management services; history; industrial and organizational psychology; international business; legal studies (non-professional general, undergraduate); liberal arts and sciences, general studies and humanities; management information systems; marketing; political science and government; sales, merchandising, and related marketing operations (general); sociology; statistics.

Graduate—criminal justice and corrections; education (specific levels and methods).

UNIVERSITY OF HOUSTON–VICTORIA
Victoria, Texas
School of Business Administration

University of Houston–Victoria was founded in 1973. It is accredited by Southern Association of Colleges and Schools. It first offered distance learning courses in 1996. In fall 2005, there were 1,856 students enrolled in distance learning courses. Institutionally administered financial aid is available to distance learners.

Services Distance learners have accessibility to academic advising, bookstore, campus computer network, career placement assistance, e-mail services, library services, tutoring.

Contact Ms. Chari Norgard, Director of Instructional Support Services, University of Houston–Victoria, 3007 North Ben Wilson, Victoria, TX 77901-4450. Telephone: 361-570-4290. Fax: 361-570-4314. E-mail: norgardc@uhv.edu.

DEGREES AND AWARDS

BBA Business, general; Management; Marketing

MBA Business Administration; Global MBA

COURSE SUBJECT AREAS OFFERED OUTSIDE OF DEGREE PROGRAMS

Undergraduate—accounting and related services; biology; computer and information sciences; education; English composition; history; psychology.

Graduate—accounting and related services; communication and media; computer and information sciences; education; psychology.

UNIVERSITY OF HOUSTON–VICTORIA
Victoria, Texas
School of Education and Human Development

University of Houston–Victoria was founded in 1973. It is accredited by Southern Association of Colleges and Schools. It first offered distance learning courses in 1998. In fall 2005, there were 400 students enrolled in distance learning courses. Institutionally administered financial aid is available to distance learners.

Services Distance learners have accessibility to academic advising, bookstore, career placement assistance, e-mail services, library services, tutoring.

Contact Ms. Deborah Elaine Biner, Student Recruitment Coordinator, University of Houston–Victoria, 3007 North Ben Wilson, Victoria, TX 77901. Telephone: 877-970-4848 Ext. 266. Fax: 361-570-4257. E-mail: binerd@uhv.edu.

DEGREES AND AWARDS

Programs offered do not lead to a degree or other formal award.

COURSE SUBJECT AREAS OFFERED OUTSIDE OF DEGREE PROGRAMS

Undergraduate—anthropology; education; educational/instructional media design; education related; education (specific levels and methods); education (specific subject areas); English language and literature related; human development, family studies, and related services; mathematics; natural sciences; physical sciences; physical sciences related; physics; special education.

Graduate—anthropology; counseling psychology; curriculum and instruction; developmental and child psychology; education; educational administration and supervision; educational assessment, evaluation, and research; educational/instructional media design; educational psychology; education related; education (specific levels and methods); education (specific subject areas); English language and literature related; family psychology; geological and earth sciences/geosciences; intercultural/multicultural and diversity studies; mathematics; mathematics and statistics related; multi-/interdisciplinary studies related; natural sciences; physical sciences; physical sciences related; physics; school psychology; special education; student counseling and personnel services; teaching assistants/aides.

UNIVERSITY OF ILLINOIS AT CHICAGO
Chicago, Illinois
Office of External Education
http://www.uic.edu/depts/uionline/

University of Illinois at Chicago was founded in 1946. It is accredited by North Central Association of Colleges and Schools. It first offered distance learning courses in 1998. In fall 2005, there were 4,438 students enrolled in distance learning courses. Institutionally administered financial aid is available to distance learners.

Services Distance learners have accessibility to academic advising, bookstore, campus computer network, e-mail services, library services.

Contact Kristen H. Brown, Senior Program Coordinator, University of Illinois at Chicago, External Education, 1333 South Halsted Street, MC 140, Suite 205, Chicago, IL 60607. Telephone: 312-355-1275. Fax: 312-413-9730. E-mail: khartz@uic.edu.

DEGREES AND AWARDS

Certificate of Achievement Business English Online; Culture of U.S. Business; Marketing Strategy in the Digital Age; Project Management

Certificate of Completion Antithrombosis Therapy Management program; Medical–Graduate Medical Education Core Curriculum; Nonprofit Management; Public Health Preparedness

Certificate Bioinformatics; Blood Bank Technology Specialist Campus Certificate; Electromagnetics Technology Campus Certificate; Emergency Preparedness and Continuity Planning; Engineering Law and Management Campus Certificate; Environmental Health Informatics Campus Certificate; Public Health Informatics Campus Certificate; School Nurse Campus Certificate; Wireless Communication Technology Campus Certificate

MEngr Engineering

MHPE Health Professions Education

MPH Public Health Informatics

COURSE SUBJECT AREAS OFFERED OUTSIDE OF DEGREE PROGRAMS

Graduate—accounting and related services; allied health and medical assisting services; business administration, management and operations; business/commerce; business/corporate communications; business, management, and marketing related; business/managerial economics; chemical engineering; clinical/medical laboratory science and allied professions; economics; education (specific subject areas); electrical and electronic engineering technologies; engineering; engineering related; engineering technology; finance and financial management services; health professions related; health services/allied health/health sciences; information science/studies; international business; marketing; nursing; pharmacy, pharmaceutical sciences, and administration; public health; statistics.

Non-credit—business/commerce; health and medical administrative services; marketing; medical clinical sciences/graduate medical studies; nursing; pharmacy, pharmaceutical sciences, and administration; public administration and social service professions related; public health; technical and business writing.

UNIVERSITY OF ILLINOIS AT SPRINGFIELD
Springfield, Illinois
Office of Technology-Enhanced Learning
http://online.uis.edu

University of Illinois at Springfield was founded in 1969. It is accredited by North Central Association of Colleges and Schools. It first offered distance learning courses in 1984. In fall 2005, there were 1,679 students enrolled in distance learning courses. Institutionally administered financial aid is available to distance learners.

Services Distance learners have accessibility to academic advising, bookstore, campus computer network, career placement assistance, e-mail services, library services, tutoring.

Contact Dr. Ray Schroeder, Director of Office of Technology and Enhanced Learning, University of Illinois at Springfield, OTEL, Brookens, Room 426, One University Plaza, MS BRK 425, Springfield, IL 62703-5407. Telephone: 217-206-7531. Fax: 217-206-7539. E-mail: schroeder.ray@uis.edu.

DEGREES AND AWARDS

BA Economics; English; History; Liberal Studies; Mathematical Sciences; Philosophy

BBA Business Administration

BS Computer Science

MA Environmental Studies–Natural Resources and Sustainable Development concentration; Teacher Leadership

MPA Public Administration

MS Computer Science; Human Services–Social Services Administration concentration; Management Information Systems

COURSE SUBJECT AREAS OFFERED OUTSIDE OF DEGREE PROGRAMS

Undergraduate—accounting and related services; anthropology; business administration, management and operations; chemistry; communication and media; computer science; creative writing; English composition; ethnic, cultural minority, and gender studies; languages (foreign languages related); liberal arts and sciences, general studies and humanities; mathematics; philosophy; psychology; public administration; public policy analysis; sociology.

Graduate—communication and media; computer science; education related; management information systems; philosophy; political science and government; public administration.

UNIVERSITY OF ILLINOIS AT URBANA–CHAMPAIGN
Champaign, Illinois
Graduate School of Library and Information Science
http://www.lis.uiuc.edu/

University of Illinois at Urbana–Champaign was founded in 1867. It is accredited by North Central Association of Colleges and Schools. It first offered distance learning courses in 1996. In fall 2005, there were 250 students enrolled in distance learning courses. Institutionally administered financial aid is available to distance learners.

Services Distance learners have accessibility to academic advising, bookstore, campus computer network, career placement assistance, e-mail services, library services, tutoring.

Contact Valerie Youngen, Admissions Staff, University of Illinois at Urbana–Champaign, 501 East Daniel Street, Champaign, IL 61820. Telephone: 800-982-0914. Fax: 217-244-3302. E-mail: lis-apply@uiuc.edu.

DEGREES AND AWARDS

CAGS Library and Information Science

MS Library and Information Science

COURSE SUBJECT AREAS OFFERED OUTSIDE OF DEGREE PROGRAMS

Graduate—communications technology; computer and information sciences; computer/information technology administration and management; computer software and media applications; educational/instructional media design; library science; science, technology and society.

UNIVERSITY OF ILLINOIS AT URBANA–CHAMPAIGN
Champaign, Illinois
College of Engineering
http://online.engr.uiuc.edu

University of Illinois at Urbana–Champaign was founded in 1867. It is accredited by North Central Association of Colleges and Schools. It first offered distance learning courses in 1998. In fall 2005, there were 180 students enrolled in distance learning courses. Institutionally administered financial aid is available to distance learners.

Services Distance learners have accessibility to academic advising, bookstore, campus computer network, e-mail services, library services.

Contact Mrs. Laura A. Miller, Director of Engineering Online Programs, University of Illinois at Urbana–Champaign, Office of Continuing Engineering Education, 1308 West Green Street, Urbana, IL 61801. Telephone: 217-333-6634. Fax: 217-333-0015. E-mail: ocee@uiuc.edu.

DEGREES AND AWARDS

Graduate Certificate Computer Security; Environmental and Water Resources Engineering; Information Systems; Materials Engineering; Materials Failure Analysis; Networks and Distributed Systems; Software Engineering; Strategic Technology Management; System Software; Systems Engineering

MCC Computer Science–Master of Computer Science

MSME Mechanical Engineering

COURSE SUBJECT AREAS OFFERED OUTSIDE OF DEGREE PROGRAMS

Graduate—civil engineering; computer science; computer systems analysis; computer systems networking and telecommunications; data processing; engineering; entrepreneurial and small business operations; genetics; management sciences and quantitative methods; materials engineering; materials science; mathematics; mechanical engineering; systems engineering.

Non-credit—genetics; management sciences and quantitative methods; mechanical engineering.

THE UNIVERSITY OF IOWA
Iowa City, Iowa
Center for Credit Programs
http://www.continuetolearn.uiowa.edu/ccp

The University of Iowa was founded in 1847. It is accredited by North Central Association of Colleges and Schools. In fall 2005, there were 3,000 students enrolled in distance learning courses. Institutionally administered financial aid is available to distance learners.

Services Distance learners have accessibility to academic advising, bookstore, e-mail services, library services.

Contact Dian Gottlob, Educational Coordinator, The University of Iowa, Center for Credit Programs, 116 International Center, Iowa City, IA 52242. Telephone: 800-272-6430. Fax: 319-335-2740. E-mail: dian-gottlob@uiowa.edu.

DEGREES AND AWARDS
BLS Liberal Studies

COURSE SUBJECT AREAS OFFERED OUTSIDE OF DEGREE PROGRAMS
Undergraduate—area studies; behavioral sciences; creative writing; education; ethnic, cultural minority, and gender studies; fine and studio art; gerontology; history; journalism; languages (classics and classical); languages (Romance languages); liberal arts and sciences, general studies and humanities; mathematics; nursing; psychology; religious studies; social work; sociology.

Graduate—creative writing; economics; education; ethnic, cultural minority, and gender studies; fine and studio art; gerontology; history; journalism; mathematics; nursing; psychology; religious studies; social work; sociology.

See full description on page 516.

UNIVERSITY OF LA VERNE
La Verne, California
Distance Learning Center
http://www.ulv.edu/dlc/dlc.html

University of La Verne was founded in 1891. It is accredited by Western Association of Schools and Colleges. It first offered distance learning courses in 1996. In fall 2005, there were 1,300 students enrolled in distance learning courses. Institutionally administered financial aid is available to distance learners.

Services Distance learners have accessibility to academic advising, bookstore, campus computer network, career placement assistance, e-mail services, library services, tutoring.

Contact Mrs. Alene Harrison, ULV Online Registrar, University of La Verne, 1950 3rd Street, La Verne, CA 91750. Telephone: 800-695-4858 Ext. 5301. Fax: 909-981-8695. E-mail: harrisoa@ulv.edu.

DEGREES AND AWARDS
BS Criminology; Organizational Management; Public Administration
MBA Business Administration

COURSE SUBJECT AREAS OFFERED OUTSIDE OF DEGREE PROGRAMS
Undergraduate—anthropology; biology; business administration, management and operations; chemistry; communication and media; creative writing; criminology; developmental and child psychology; English composition; history; liberal arts and sciences, general studies and humanities; music; philosophy; physical sciences; psychology; public administration; public administration and social service professions related; speech and rhetoric.

Graduate—business administration, management and operations; business/commerce.

Non-credit—biological and physical sciences; curriculum and instruction; education; education related; education (specific subject areas); history; museum studies; music; natural resources and conservation related; natural resources conservation and research; parks, recreation, and leisure related; physical sciences.

UNIVERSITY OF LETHBRIDGE
Lethbridge, Alberta, Canada
http://www.uleth.ca/

University of Lethbridge was founded in 1967. It is provincially chartered. It first offered distance learning courses in 2001. In fall 2005, there were 223 students enrolled in distance learning courses. Institutionally administered financial aid is available to distance learners.

Services Distance learners have accessibility to academic advising, bookstore, campus computer network, career placement assistance, e-mail services, library services, tutoring.

Contact Inquiries, University of Lethbridge, 4401 University Drive, Lethbridge, AB T1K 3M4, Canada. Telephone: 403-329-2233. E-mail: inquiries@uleth.ca.

DEGREES AND AWARDS
Programs offered do not lead to a degree or other formal award.

COURSE SUBJECT AREAS OFFERED OUTSIDE OF DEGREE PROGRAMS
Undergraduate—computer software and media applications; education related; health services/allied health/health sciences.

Graduate—education; educational assessment, evaluation, and research; education related.

UNIVERSITY OF MAINE
Orono, Maine
Continuing Education Division
http://Learnonline.umaine.edu

University of Maine was founded in 1865. It is accredited by New England Association of Schools and Colleges. It first offered distance learning courses in 1989. In fall 2005, there were 2,548 students enrolled in distance learning courses. Institutionally administered financial aid is available to distance learners.

Services Distance learners have accessibility to academic advising, bookstore, campus computer network, e-mail services, library services.

Contact James F. Toner, Associate Director, University of Maine, 5713 Chadbourne Hall, Orono, ME 04469-5713. Telephone: 207-581-3142. Fax: 207-581-3141. E-mail: jim.toner@umit.maine.edu.

DEGREES AND AWARDS
BUS University Studies
Certificate Maine Studies

COURSE SUBJECT AREAS OFFERED OUTSIDE OF DEGREE PROGRAMS
Undergraduate—accounting and related services; area studies; biology; civil engineering technology; communication disorders sciences and services; computer and information sciences and support services related; creative writing; developmental and child psychology; education (specific subject areas); English as a second/foreign language (teaching); English as a second language; English composition; ethnic, cultural minority, and gender studies; languages (foreign languages related); mechanical engineering; music; nursing; plant sciences; psychology; public administration; social psychology; sociology; special education; technical and business writing; visual and performing arts.

Graduate—animal sciences; anthropology; business/commerce; civil engineering; education; liberal arts and sciences, general studies and humanities; mechanical engineering; social work.

THE UNIVERSITY OF MAINE AT AUGUSTA
Augusta, Maine
University of Maine System Network for Education and Technology (UNET)
http://www.uma.maine.edu

The University of Maine at Augusta was founded in 1965. It is accredited by New England Association of Schools and Colleges. It first offered distance learning courses in 1986. In fall 2005, there were 2,300 students enrolled in distance learning courses. Institutionally administered financial aid is available to distance learners.

Services Distance learners have accessibility to academic advising, bookstore, campus computer network, e-mail services, library services, tutoring.

Contact Sheri Fraser, Director of Admissions and Advising, The University of Maine at Augusta, 46 University Drive, Augusta, ME 04330. Telephone: 207-621-3390. Fax: 207-621-3333. E-mail: fraser@maine.edu.

DEGREES AND AWARDS

AA Liberal Arts; Social Services
AS Business Administration; Liberal Studies; Library and Information Services
BS Accounting; Applied Science–Bachelor of Applied Science; Library and Information Services; Management; Mental Health and Human Services

COURSE SUBJECT AREAS OFFERED OUTSIDE OF DEGREE PROGRAMS

Undergraduate—accounting and related services; American literature (United States and Canadian); anthropology; applied mathematics; business administration, management and operations; business/commerce; business/corporate communications; business, management, and marketing related; communication and media; community health services; comparative literature; computer and information sciences; computer software and media applications; counseling psychology; creative writing; criminal justice and corrections; developmental and child psychology; economics; English; English composition; finance and financial management services; history; human development, family studies, and related services; human resources management; human services; liberal arts and sciences, general studies and humanities; library science related; mathematics; mental and social health services and allied professions; music; nursing; philosophy; physical sciences; political science and government; psychology; social sciences; sociology; statistics; taxation; technical and business writing.

UNIVERSITY OF MAINE AT FORT KENT
Fort Kent, Maine

University of Maine at Fort Kent was founded in 1878. It is accredited by New England Association of Schools and Colleges. It first offered distance learning courses in 1989. In fall 2005, there were 575 students enrolled in distance learning courses. Institutionally administered financial aid is available to distance learners.
Services Distance learners have accessibility to academic advising, bookstore, campus computer network, career placement assistance, e-mail services, library services, tutoring.
Contact Donald K. Eno, Academic Outreach Coordinator, University of Maine at Fort Kent, 23 University Drive, Fort Kent, ME 04743. Telephone: 207-834-7835. E-mail: deno@maine.edu.

DEGREES AND AWARDS

AA General Studies with Criminal Justice Sequence
BSN Nursing–RN to BSN
BUS University Studies

COURSE SUBJECT AREAS OFFERED OUTSIDE OF DEGREE PROGRAMS

Undergraduate—anthropology; astronomy and astrophysics; behavioral sciences; business/commerce; communication and media; creative writing; criminal justice and corrections; developmental and child psychology; education (specific levels and methods); English; geological and earth sciences/geosciences; health professions related; history; liberal arts and sciences, general studies and humanities; music; nursing; philosophy; political science and government; psychology; public administration; sociology.

UNIVERSITY OF MAINE AT PRESQUE ISLE
Presque Isle, Maine
http://www.umpi.maine.edu/

University of Maine at Presque Isle was founded in 1903. It is accredited by New England Association of Schools and Colleges. It first offered distance learning courses in 2001. In fall 2005, there were 165 students enrolled in distance learning courses.
Services Distance learners have accessibility to campus computer network, e-mail services.
Contact Mr. Ed A. Dery, ITV Coordinator, University of Maine at Presque Isle, 181 Maine Street, Presque Isle, ME 04769. Telephone: 207-768-9648. Fax: 207-764-5833. E-mail: dery@umpi.maine.edu.

DEGREES AND AWARDS

Programs offered do not lead to a degree or other formal award.

COURSE SUBJECT AREAS OFFERED OUTSIDE OF DEGREE PROGRAMS

Undergraduate—English composition; special education.

UNIVERSITY OF MANAGEMENT AND TECHNOLOGY
Arlington, Virginia
http://www.umtweb.edu

University of Management and Technology was founded in 1998. It is accredited by Distance Education and Training Council. It first offered distance learning courses in 1998. In fall 2005, there were 4,000 students enrolled in distance learning courses. Institutionally administered financial aid is available to distance learners.
Services Distance learners have accessibility to academic advising, bookstore, library services, tutoring.
Contact Dr. J. Davidson Frame, Academic Dean, University of Management and Technology, 1901 North Fort Myer Drive, Suite 700, Arlington, VA 22209. Telephone: 703-516-0035. Fax: 703-516-0985. E-mail: davidson.frame@umtweb.edu.

DEGREES AND AWARDS

ABA Business Administration
AS Computer Science; General Studies
BBA Information Technology Management; International Management; Management; Marketing Management
BS Computer Science–Information Systems; Computer Science–Information Technology; Computer Science–Software Engineering; Computer Science; General Studies
Certificate Acquisition Management; Project Management
Graduate Certificate Project Management
MBA Management; Project Management
MS Information Technology–IT Management; Information Technology–IT Project Management; Information Technology–Management Information Systems
MSCS Computer Science; Multimedia Technology; Software Engineering
MSM Acquisition Management; Management; Project Management; Public Administration; Telecommunications Management

UNIVERSITY OF MANITOBA
Winnipeg, Manitoba, Canada
Distance and Online Education
http://www.umanitoba.ca/distance

University of Manitoba was founded in 1877. It is provincially chartered. It first offered distance learning courses in 1950. In fall 2005, there were 3,500 students enrolled in distance learning courses. Institutionally administered financial aid is available to distance learners.
Services Distance learners have accessibility to academic advising, bookstore, campus computer network, e-mail services, library services.
Contact Student Support, University of Manitoba, Distance and Online Education, 188D Extended Education Complex, Winnipeg, MB R3T 2N2, Canada. Telephone: 204-474-8012. Fax: 204-474-7660. E-mail: de_info@umanitoba.ca.

DEGREES AND AWARDS

BA General degree studies–3-Year General Degree; Geography
BN Nursing–Baccalaureate Program for Registered Nurses
BSW Social Work
Graduate Certificate Education–Post-Baccalaureate Diploma in Education program

UNIVERSITY OF MARYLAND
Baltimore, Maryland
Master's Program in Nursing
http://nursing.umaryland.edu

University of Maryland was founded in 1807. It is accredited by Middle States Association of Colleges and Schools. It first offered distance learning courses in 1992. In fall 2005, there were 400 students enrolled in distance learning courses. Institutionally administered financial aid is available to distance learners.

Services Distance learners have accessibility to academic advising, bookstore, campus computer network, career placement assistance, e-mail services, library services, tutoring.

Contact Dr. Mary Etta Mills, Associate Dean, Academic Affairs, University of Maryland, 655 West Lombard Street, Room 505K, Baltimore, MD 21201. Telephone: 410-706-3975. E-mail: mills@son.umaryland.edu.

DEGREES AND AWARDS
BSN Nursing–RN to BSN
MS Nursing

COURSE SUBJECT AREAS OFFERED OUTSIDE OF DEGREE PROGRAMS
Undergraduate—nursing.
Graduate—education related; information science/studies; nursing.

UNIVERSITY OF MARYLAND, COLLEGE PARK
College Park, Maryland
Instructional Television System
http://www.itv.umd.edu

University of Maryland, College Park was founded in 1856. It is accredited by Middle States Association of Colleges and Schools. It first offered distance learning courses in 1980. In fall 2005, there were 212 students enrolled in distance learning courses. Institutionally administered financial aid is available to distance learners.

Services Distance learners have accessibility to academic advising, bookstore, campus computer network, e-mail services, library services.

Contact Mr. Marty Ronning, Assistant Director, University of Maryland, College Park, 2104A Martin Hall, College Park, MD 20742-5231. Telephone: 301-405-4899. Fax: 301-314-9639. E-mail: cronning@umd.edu.

DEGREES AND AWARDS
MS Electrical Engineering; Mechanical Engineering; Professional Masters; Reliability Engineering; Systems Engineering

COURSE SUBJECT AREAS OFFERED OUTSIDE OF DEGREE PROGRAMS
Graduate—civil engineering; electrical, electronics and communications engineering; engineering; engineering related; mechanical engineering.

UNIVERSITY OF MARYLAND, COLLEGE PARK
College Park, Maryland
E-Learning
http://www.onlinestudies.umd.edu

University of Maryland, College Park was founded in 1856. It is accredited by Middle States Association of Colleges and Schools. It first offered distance learning courses in 2000. In fall 2005, there were 250 students enrolled in distance learning courses. Institutionally administered financial aid is available to distance learners.

Services Distance learners have accessibility to academic advising, bookstore, library services.

Contact Paul E. Roche, EdD, Senior Project Manager, University of Maryland, College Park, 2103 Reckord Armory, Office of Professional Studies, College Park, MD 20742. Telephone: 301-405-8989. Fax: 301-314-9572. E-mail: proche@umd.edu.

DEGREES AND AWARDS
Graduate Certificate Graduate Certificate in Public Health Informatics
MEngr Professional Master of Engineering in Fire Protection
MLS Life Sciences

See full description on page 520.

UNIVERSITY OF MARYLAND EASTERN SHORE
Princess Anne, Maryland
http://www.umes.edu

University of Maryland Eastern Shore was founded in 1886. It is accredited by Middle States Association of Colleges and Schools. It first offered distance learning courses in 2000. In fall 2005, there were 229 students enrolled in distance learning courses. Institutionally administered financial aid is available to distance learners.

Services Distance learners have accessibility to academic advising, bookstore, campus computer network, career placement assistance, e-mail services, library services, tutoring.

Contact Dr. Andrew T. Carrington, Associate Vive President, Academic Affairs, University of Maryland Eastern Shore, JT Williams Hall, Room #2104, Princess Anne, MD 21853. Telephone: 410-651-8446. Fax: 410-651-6085. E-mail: atcarrington@umes.edu.

DEGREES AND AWARDS
Programs offered do not lead to a degree or other formal award.

COURSE SUBJECT AREAS OFFERED OUTSIDE OF DEGREE PROGRAMS
Undergraduate—agricultural and domestic animal services; agriculture and agriculture operations related; developmental and child psychology; educational/instructional media design; family and consumer sciences/human sciences; hospitality administration; physical sciences related; rehabilitation and therapeutic professions; social sciences; sociology; statistics.
Graduate—counseling psychology; educational assessment, evaluation, and research; fishing and fisheries sciences and management; health and medical administrative services; health professions related; health psychology; pharmacology and toxicology; psychology related; rehabilitation and therapeutic professions.

UNIVERSITY OF MARYLAND UNIVERSITY COLLEGE
Adelphi, Maryland
Undergraduate and Graduate Online Programs
http://www.umuc.edu

University of Maryland University College was founded in 1947. It is accredited by Middle States Association of Colleges and Schools. It first offered distance learning courses in 1972. In fall 2005, there were 26,000 students enrolled in distance learning courses. Institutionally administered financial aid is available to distance learners.

Services Distance learners have accessibility to academic advising, bookstore, campus computer network, career placement assistance, e-mail services, library services, tutoring.

Contact Advisor, University of Maryland University College, 3501 University Boulevard East, Adelphi, MD 20783. Telephone: 800-888-UMUC. E-mail: umucinfo@umuc.edu.

DEGREES AND AWARDS
BA Communication Studies; English; History; Humanities
BS Accounting; Business Administration; Computer Studies; Computer and Information Science; Criminal Justice; Criminal Justice; Criminal Justice; Environmental Management; Finance; Fire Science; Global Business and Public Policy; Human Resource Management; Information Systems Management; Legal Studies; Management Studies; Marketing; Psychology; Social Science
CGMS Accounting and Information Technology; Accounting; Advertising; Bioinformatics; Biotechnology Management; Energy Resources Management and Policy; Environmental Management; Financial Management in Organizations; Foundations for Human Resource Management; Health Care Administration; Homeland Security Management; Information Resources Management; Integrated Direct Marketing; Inte-

grative Supply Chain Management; International Marketing; International Trade; Leadership and Management; Nonprofit and Association Financial Management; Procurement and Contract Management; Project Management; Public Relations; Public Relations; Software Development Management; Systems Analysis; Technology Systems Management; Technology Systems Management; Telecommunications Management
GMBA Business Administration
MBA Business Administration
MDE Distance Education
MEd Education
MS Accounting and Financial Management; Accounting and Information Technology; Biotechnology Studies; Computer Systems Management; E-Commerce; Environmental Management; Financial Management and Information Systems; Health Administration Informatics; Health Care Administration; Information Technology; Management; Software Engineering; Technology Management; Telecommunications Management
DM Management

COURSE SUBJECT AREAS OFFERED OUTSIDE OF DEGREE PROGRAMS

Undergraduate—accounting and related services; anthropology; area studies; biology; business administration, management and operations; chemistry; communication and media; computer and information sciences; criminal justice and corrections; economics; fire protection; gerontology; human resources management; information science/studies; international business; journalism; mathematics; psychology; sales, merchandising, and related marketing operations (general); social sciences; sociology.

Graduate—accounting and related services; business administration, management and operations; business, management, and marketing related; computer/information technology administration and management; computer systems networking and telecommunications; educational/instructional media design; education (specific levels and methods); education (specific subject areas); entrepreneurial and small business operations; health and medical administrative services; human resources management; international business; marketing; public administration; sales, merchandising, and related marketing operations (general).

See full description on page 518.

UNIVERSITY OF MASSACHUSETTS AMHERST
Amherst, Massachusetts
Continuing and Professional Education
http://www.umassulearn.net

University of Massachusetts Amherst was founded in 1863. It is accredited by New England Association of Schools and Colleges. It first offered distance learning courses in 1998. In fall 2005, there were 2,133 students enrolled in distance learning courses. Institutionally administered financial aid is available to distance learners.

Services Distance learners have accessibility to academic advising, bookstore, campus computer network, e-mail services, library services.

Contact Ms. Lucinda Butler, Adviser, University of Massachusetts Amherst, Continuing and Professional Education, 100 Venture Way, Suite 201, Hadley, MA 01035-9430. Telephone: 413-545-3430. Fax: 413-545-3351. E-mail: info@contined.umass.edu.

DEGREES AND AWARDS

BBA Business Administration
BS Hospitality and Tourism Management; Nursing–RN to BS Mobility Online Track
Certificate Arts Management; Business Studies; Casino Management; Criminal Justices Studies; Food Service Management; Hospitality and Tourism Management; Journalism–Online Journalism; Online Program in Basics in Exercise and Nutrition for Health and Human Performance
MBA Business Administration–Online Professional MBA Program (UMass Amherst Degree)
MEd Science Teachers
MS Engineering Management
MS/MPH Nursing/Public Health–MS in Nursing and MS in Public Health

COURSE SUBJECT AREAS OFFERED OUTSIDE OF DEGREE PROGRAMS

Undergraduate—accounting and related services; anthropology; biology; business administration, management and operations; community health services; comparative literature; criminal justice and corrections; education related; English; environmental/environmental health engineering; finance and financial management services; foods, nutrition, and related services; hospitality administration; journalism; legal professions and studies related; management sciences and quantitative methods; marketing; natural resources and conservation related; natural resources conservation and research; philosophy; psychology; sociology; wildlife and wildlands science and management.

Graduate—accounting and related services; biology; chemical engineering; educational administration and supervision; education related; engineering/industrial management; finance and financial management services; health professions related; human resources management; international business; management information systems; marketing; mechanical engineering; nursing; public health; statistics; technical and business writing.

Non-credit—business, management, and marketing related; management sciences and quantitative methods; nutrition sciences.

See full description on page 522.

UNIVERSITY OF MASSACHUSETTS BOSTON
Boston, Massachusetts
Corporate, Continuing and Distance Education
http://www.ccde.umb.edu

University of Massachusetts Boston was founded in 1964. It is accredited by New England Association of Schools and Colleges. It first offered distance learning courses in 2001. In fall 2005, there were 1,163 students enrolled in distance learning courses. Institutionally administered financial aid is available to distance learners.

Services Distance learners have accessibility to academic advising, bookstore, campus computer network, e-mail services, library services.

Contact Ms. Katharine Grant Galaitsis, Director of Online Education, University of Massachusetts Boston, Corporate, Continuing, and Distance Education, 100 Morrissey Boulevard, Boston, MA 02125-3393. Telephone: 617-287-7918. Fax: 617-287-7297. E-mail: kitty.galaitsis@umb.edu.

DEGREES AND AWARDS

BA Completer Program in Community Studies
BS Nursing–RN to BS
Certificate Community, Media, and Technology; Information Technology–Fundamentals of Information Technology
Graduate Certificate Critical and Creative Thinking (Focus on Creativity at Work); Education–Adapting Curriculum Frameworks for All Learners; Gerontology–Management of Aging Services track; Instructional Technology Design; Instructional Technology for Educators
MA Linguistics–Applied Linguistics, ESL concentration
MEd Counseling–Family Therapy Track; Counseling–Mental Health Counseling track; Counseling–Rehabilitation Counseling Track; Counseling–School Guidance track; Instructional Design
MS Gerontology–Management of Aging Services track
PMC Nursing–Gerontological/Adult and Family Nurse Practitioner

COURSE SUBJECT AREAS OFFERED OUTSIDE OF DEGREE PROGRAMS

Undergraduate—anthropology; archeology; biology; business administration, management and operations; classical and ancient studies; communication and media; community organization and advocacy; computer and information sciences; computer/information technology administration and management; computer science; criminal justice and corrections; economics; environmental/environmental health engineering; fine and studio art; history; international relations and affairs; languages (classics and classical); languages (Romance languages); liberal arts and sciences, general studies and humanities; linguistic, comparative, and related language studies; management information systems; marketing; mathematics; music; natural resources and conservation related; nursing; nutrition sciences; political science and government; psychology; social sciences; sociology; statistics; technology education/industrial arts.

Graduate—biological and physical sciences; counseling psychology; criminal justice and corrections; education; educational/instructional media design; educational psychology; education (specific subject areas); English as a second/foreign language (teaching); gerontology; history; international relations and affairs; nursing; peace studies and conflict resolution; school psychology; sociology; special education; statistics; student counseling and personnel services; technology education/industrial arts.

Non-credit—agriculture and agriculture operations related; city/urban, community and regional planning; human services; landscape architecture; natural resources and conservation related; parks, recreation, and leisure related; urban studies/affairs.

UNIVERSITY OF MASSACHUSETTS LOWELL
Lowell, Massachusetts
Continuing Studies and Corporate Education
http://continuinged.uml.edu/online

University of Massachusetts Lowell was founded in 1894. It is accredited by New England Association of Schools and Colleges. It first offered distance learning courses in 1995. In fall 2005, there were 2,400 students enrolled in distance learning courses. Institutionally administered financial aid is available to distance learners.

Services Distance learners have accessibility to academic advising, bookstore, campus computer network, e-mail services, library services.

Contact Catherine A. Kendrick, Director of Corporate and Distance Market Development, University of Massachusetts Lowell, One University Avenue, Lowell, MA 01854-2881. Telephone: 800-480-3190. Fax: 978-934-4064. E-mail: onlinelearning@uml.edu.

DEGREES AND AWARDS

AS Information Technology

BA Liberal Arts (BLA)

BS Information Technology with Business Minor; Information Technology

Certificate Contemporary Communications; Data/Telecommunications; Information Technology; Multimedia Applications; Paralegal Studies; Security Management and Homeland Security; UNIX; Website Design and Development

Graduate Certificate Behavioral Intervention in Autism; Business–Foundations of Business; Clinical Pathology; Domestic Violence Prevention; Forensic Criminology; Plastics Engineering Fundamentals; Security Studies

MA Criminal Justice

MEd Curriculum and Instruction–Science Education concentration; Curriculum and Instruction; Educational Administration; Reading and Language

COURSE SUBJECT AREAS OFFERED OUTSIDE OF DEGREE PROGRAMS

Undergraduate—accounting and computer science; business/commerce; business/corporate communications; communication and media; computer and information sciences; computer programming; computer systems networking and telecommunications; education (specific levels and methods); English composition; ethnic, cultural minority, and gender studies; information science/studies; liberal arts and sciences, general studies and humanities; mathematics and computer science; philosophy; security and protective services related; social sciences related; sociology.

Graduate—accounting and computer science; behavioral sciences; clinical/medical laboratory science and allied professions; criminal justice and corrections; criminology; curriculum and instruction; education; educational administration and supervision; electrical and electronic engineering technologies; finance and financial management services; forensic psychology; health professions related; health services/allied health/health sciences; management information systems; marketing; polymer/plastics engineering; security and protective services related; special education.

Non-credit—educational/instructional media design; education related.

UNIVERSITY OF MEDICINE AND DENTISTRY OF NEW JERSEY
Newark, New Jersey
http://www.umdnj.edu/

University of Medicine and Dentistry of New Jersey was founded in 1970. It is accredited by Middle States Association of Colleges and Schools. It first offered distance learning courses in 1998. In fall 2005, there were 300 students enrolled in distance learning courses. Institutionally administered financial aid is available to distance learners.

Services Distance learners have accessibility to academic advising, bookstore, campus computer network, e-mail services, library services.

Contact Mr. Brian Lewis, Assistant Dean of Enrollment Services, University of Medicine and Dentistry of New Jersey, 65 Bergen Street, Room 149, Newark, NJ 07107. Telephone: 973-972-8575. Fax: 973-972-7463. E-mail: lewisbj@umdnj.edu.

DEGREES AND AWARDS

BS Health Sciences

MS Clinical Nutrition; Health Sciences; Health Systems; Psychiatric Rehabilitation

DH Sc Clinical Nutrition (DCN)

PhD Health Sciences

COURSE SUBJECT AREAS OFFERED OUTSIDE OF DEGREE PROGRAMS

Undergraduate—health professions related; nutrition sciences.

Graduate—health professions related; nutrition sciences.

UNIVERSITY OF MICHIGAN
Ann Arbor, Michigan
Media Union
http://cpd.engin.umich.edu

University of Michigan was founded in 1817. It is accredited by North Central Association of Colleges and Schools. It first offered distance learning courses in 1969. In fall 2005, there were 315 students enrolled in distance learning courses. Institutionally administered financial aid is available to distance learners.

Services Distance learners have accessibility to academic advising, bookstore, campus computer network, e-mail services, library services.

Contact Shannon Leahy Rolston, Student Liaison, University of Michigan, Michigan Interdisciplinary and Professional Engineering, College of Engineering, 273 Chrysler Center, 2121 Bonisteel Boulevard, Ann Arbor, MI 48109-2092. Telephone: 734-647-7188. Fax: 734-647-2243. E-mail: leahysh@umich.edu.

DEGREES AND AWARDS

ME Manufacturing Engineering

MEngr Automotive Engineering; Integrated Microsystems; Pharmaceutical Engineering

COURSE SUBJECT AREAS OFFERED OUTSIDE OF DEGREE PROGRAMS

Graduate—engineering; engineering/industrial management; engineering related; engineering science; engineering technologies related; engineering technology; industrial engineering; manufacturing engineering.

Non-credit—aerospace, aeronautical and astronautical engineering; atmospheric sciences and meteorology; engineering; engineering design; engineering/industrial management; engineering related; engineering-related technologies; engineering science; engineering technologies related; management sciences and quantitative methods; materials engineering; materials science; mechanical engineering; mechanical engineering related technologies; quality control and safety technologies; systems engineering.

UNIVERSITY OF MICHIGAN–DEARBORN
Dearborn, Michigan
http://dln.engin.umd.umich.edu

University of Michigan–Dearborn was founded in 1959. It is accredited by North Central Association of Colleges and Schools. It first offered distance learning courses in 2003. In fall 2005, there were 170 students enrolled in distance learning courses. Institutionally administered financial aid is available to distance learners.

Services Distance learners have accessibility to academic advising, bookstore, campus computer network, e-mail services, library services.

Contact Susan Guinn, Distance Learning Program Manager, University of Michigan–Dearborn, College of Engineering and Computer Science, 4901 Evergreen Road, 2040 PEC, Dearborn, MI 48128-1491. Telephone: 313-593-4000. Fax: 313-593-4070. E-mail: sguinn@umich.edu.

DEGREES AND AWARDS

MS Software Engineering
MSE Automotive Systems Engineering; Computer Engineering
MSEM Engineering Management

COURSE SUBJECT AREAS OFFERED OUTSIDE OF DEGREE PROGRAMS

Undergraduate—computer and information sciences; computer science.
Graduate—computer and information sciences; computer engineering; computer science; engineering; engineering/industrial management; engineering science; mechanical engineering.
Non-credit—engineering science.

UNIVERSITY OF MICHIGAN–FLINT
Flint, Michigan
Distance Learning Program
http://online.umflint.edu/

University of Michigan–Flint was founded in 1956. It is accredited by North Central Association of Colleges and Schools. It first offered distance learning courses in 2000. In fall 2005, there were 1,250 students enrolled in distance learning courses. Institutionally administered financial aid is available to distance learners.

Services Distance learners have accessibility to academic advising, bookstore, campus computer network, career placement assistance, e-mail services, library services, tutoring.

Contact Office of Admissions and Recruitment, University of Michigan–Flint, Room 245, University Pavilion, Flint, MI 48502-1950. Telephone: 800-942-5636 Ext. 23300. Fax: 810-762-3272. E-mail: admin@umflintonline.org.

DEGREES AND AWARDS

BBA Administration
BSN Nursing
MBA Business Administration

COURSE SUBJECT AREAS OFFERED OUTSIDE OF DEGREE PROGRAMS

Undergraduate—accounting and related services; allied health diagnostic, intervention, and treatment professions; business/commerce; computer science; management sciences and quantitative methods; marketing; mathematics; nursing; social work.
Graduate—accounting and related services; business administration, management and operations; human resources management; management sciences and quantitative methods; marketing.
Non-credit—accounting and related services; business administration, management and operations; business/commerce; business/corporate communications; business, management, and marketing related; computer software and media applications; educational administration and supervision; educational assessment, evaluation, and research; educational/instructional media design; education (specific subject areas); management information systems; sales, merchandising, and related marketing operations (specialized); teaching assistants/aides.

UNIVERSITY OF MINNESOTA, CROOKSTON
Crookston, Minnesota
Office of Continuing Education
http://www.crk.umn.edu/cal

University of Minnesota, Crookston was founded in 1966. It is accredited by North Central Association of Colleges and Schools. It first offered distance learning courses in 1990. In fall 2005, there were 415 students enrolled in distance learning courses. Institutionally administered financial aid is available to distance learners.

Services Distance learners have accessibility to academic advising, bookstore, campus computer network, career placement assistance, e-mail services, library services, tutoring.

Contact Michelle A. Christopherson, Director, Center for Adult Learning, University of Minnesota, Crookston, 2900 University Avenue, Crookston, MN 56716-5001. Telephone: 218-281-8679. Fax: 218-281-8040. E-mail: mchristo@umn.edu.

DEGREES AND AWARDS

BS Applied Health–Bachelor of Applied Health Online; Business Online; Manufacturing Management–Bachelor of Manufacturing Management Online
Certificate Hotel, Restaurant, and Institutional Management

COURSE SUBJECT AREAS OFFERED OUTSIDE OF DEGREE PROGRAMS

Undergraduate—accounting and related services; agricultural and food products processing; biology; business administration, management and operations; data entry/microcomputer applications; data processing; economics; English composition; entrepreneurial and small business operations; foods, nutrition, and related services; health and medical administrative services; industrial production technologies; information science/studies; management information systems; marketing; mathematics; microbiological sciences and immunology; philosophy; physics; psychology; sociology; speech and rhetoric; statistics.

UNIVERSITY OF MINNESOTA, MORRIS
Morris, Minnesota
College of Continuing Education-GenEdWeb Program
http://genedweb.mrs.umn.edu

University of Minnesota, Morris was founded in 1959. It is accredited by North Central Association of Colleges and Schools. It first offered distance learning courses in 1997. In fall 2005, there were 78 students enrolled in distance learning courses. Institutionally administered financial aid is available to distance learners.

Services Distance learners have accessibility to academic advising, bookstore, campus computer network, e-mail services, library services, tutoring.

Contact Ms. Karen M. Cusey, Program Associate, University of Minnesota, Morris, 225 Community Services Building, 600 East 4th Street, Morris, MN 56267. Telephone: 800-842-0030. Fax: 320-589-1661. E-mail: genedweb@morris.umn.edu.

DEGREES AND AWARDS

Programs offered do not lead to a degree or other formal award.

COURSE SUBJECT AREAS OFFERED OUTSIDE OF DEGREE PROGRAMS

Undergraduate—developmental and child psychology; economics; education; education (specific subject areas); English composition; history; legal studies (non-professional general, undergraduate); mathematics; multi-/interdisciplinary studies related; political science and government; psychology; sociology; statistics.

UNIVERSITY OF MINNESOTA, TWIN CITIES CAMPUS
Minneapolis, Minnesota
Independent and Distance Learning
http://www.cce.umn.edu/petersons

University of Minnesota, Twin Cities Campus was founded in 1851. It is accredited by North Central Association of Colleges and Schools. It first offered distance learning courses in 1941. In fall 2005, there were 5,500 students enrolled in distance learning courses. Institutionally administered financial aid is available to distance learners.

Services Distance learners have accessibility to bookstore, campus computer network, e-mail services, library services, tutoring.

Contact Information Center Receptionist, University of Minnesota, Twin Cities Campus, College of Continuing Education, Room 101, Wesbrook Hall, 77 Pleasant Street, SE, Minneapolis, MN 55455-0216. Telephone: 800-234-6564. Fax: 612-625-1511. E-mail: info@cce.umn.edu.

DEGREES AND AWARDS

Certificate Applied Business; Paper Science and Engineering

MS Paper Science and Engineering

COURSE SUBJECT AREAS OFFERED OUTSIDE OF DEGREE PROGRAMS

Undergraduate—accounting and related services; agriculture; allied health diagnostic, intervention, and treatment professions; applied horticulture/horticultural business services; biochemistry, biophysics and molecular biology; biology; biology/biotechnology laboratory technician; biopsychology; business administration, management and operations; business/corporate communications; business, management, and marketing related; business/managerial economics; business operations support and assistant services; cell biology and anatomical sciences; communication and journalism related; communication and media; comparative literature; computer software and media applications; computer systems networking and telecommunications; creative writing; developmental and child psychology; ecology, evolution, and population biology; economics; educational psychology; English; English composition; English language and literature related; English literature (British and Commonwealth); entrepreneurial and small business operations; ethnic, cultural minority, and gender studies; family and consumer economics; family and consumer sciences/human sciences; finance and financial management services; fine and studio art; food science and technology; foods, nutrition, and related services; forest engineering; genetics; geological and earth sciences/geosciences; health and medical administrative services; health/medical preparatory programs; health professions related; health services/allied health/health sciences; history; human resources management; journalism; languages (classics and classical); languages (Germanic); languages (Romance languages); languages (Slavic, Baltic and Albanian); liberal arts and sciences, general studies and humanities; linguistic, comparative, and related language studies; marketing; materials science; mathematics; music; nursing; operations research; personality psychology; philosophy; physics; physiology, pathology and related sciences; psychology; public health; public relations, advertising, and applied communication related; publishing; rehabilitation and therapeutic professions; social work; speech and rhetoric; technical and business writing; work and family studies.

Graduate—communication and media; forest engineering; liberal arts and sciences, general studies and humanities; public health; speech and rhetoric.

See full description on page 524.

UNIVERSITY OF MINNESOTA, TWIN CITIES CAMPUS

Minneapolis, Minnesota

School of Nursing

http://www.nursing.umn.edu

University of Minnesota, Twin Cities Campus was founded in 1851. It is accredited by North Central Association of Colleges and Schools. It first offered distance learning courses in 2000. Institutionally administered financial aid is available to distance learners.

Services Distance learners have accessibility to academic advising, bookstore, campus computer network, e-mail services, library services.

Contact Recruiter, University of Minnesota, Twin Cities Campus, 5-150 Weaver Densford Hall, 308 Harvard Street, SE, Minneapolis, MN 55455. Telephone: 612-625-7980. Fax: 612-626-2359. E-mail: sonstudentinfo@umn.edu.

DEGREES AND AWARDS

MS Nurse Midwifery; Nursing–Public Health Nursing; Nursing–Women's Health Care Nurse Practitioner; Psych Mental Health

UNIVERSITY OF MISSOURI–COLUMBIA

Columbia, Missouri

Center for Distance and Independent Study

http://cdis.missouri.edu

University of Missouri–Columbia was founded in 1839. It is accredited by North Central Association of Colleges and Schools. It first offered distance learning courses in 1941. In fall 2005, there were 6,248 students enrolled in distance learning courses. Institutionally administered financial aid is available to distance learners.

Services Distance learners have accessibility to academic advising, bookstore, e-mail services, library services.

Contact Ms. Terrie Nagel, Student Services Advisor, University of Missouri–Columbia, 136 Clark Hall, Columbia, MO 65211-4200. Telephone: 800-609-3727 Ext. 4. Fax: 573-882-6808. E-mail: nagelt@missouri.edu.

DEGREES AND AWARDS

BGS General Studies–Online Bachelor of General Studies Completion program

COURSE SUBJECT AREAS OFFERED OUTSIDE OF DEGREE PROGRAMS

Undergraduate—accounting and related services; agricultural/biological engineering and bioengineering; American literature (United States and Canadian); animal sciences; anthropology; area, ethnic, cultural, and gender studies related; astronomy and astrophysics; atmospheric sciences and meteorology; behavioral sciences; biblical and other theological languages and literatures; biology; business administration, management and operations; business/commerce; business, management, and marketing related; business/managerial economics; classical and ancient studies; computer programming; computer science; creative writing; curriculum and instruction; developmental and child psychology; economics; education; educational psychology; education related; engineering; engineering mechanics; English; English composition; English language and literature related; English literature (British and Commonwealth); ethnic, cultural minority, and gender studies; film/video and photographic arts; geography and cartography; geological and earth sciences/geosciences; gerontology; health and medical administrative services; health and physical education/fitness; health professions related; history; human development, family studies, and related services; human resources management; intercultural/multicultural and diversity studies; international relations and affairs; languages (classics and classical); languages (foreign languages related); languages (Germanic); languages (Romance languages); liberal arts and sciences, general studies and humanities; linguistic, comparative, and related language studies; marketing; mathematics; mathematics and statistics related; mental and social health services and allied professions; parks, recreation and leisure; philosophy; physics; political science and government; psychology; psychology related; social work; sociology; statistics; technical and business writing.

Graduate—animal sciences; business/commerce; counseling psychology; curriculum and instruction; education; educational administration and supervision; educational assessment, evaluation, and research; educational psychology; education related; English; English language and literature related; gerontology; human development, family studies, and related services; human resources management; mental and social health services and allied professions; philosophy; sociology.

Non-credit—city/urban, community and regional planning; fire protection; human resources management; languages (Romance languages); work and family studies.

UNIVERSITY OF MISSOURI–COLUMBIA

Columbia, Missouri

MU Direct: Continuing and Distance Education

http://MUdirect.missouri.edu/mu/pg3.htm

University of Missouri–Columbia was founded in 1839. It is accredited by North Central Association of Colleges and Schools. It first offered distance learning courses in 1990. In fall 2005, there were 1,992 students enrolled in distance learning courses. Institutionally administered financial aid is available to distance learners.

Services Distance learners have accessibility to academic advising, bookstore, campus computer network, e-mail services, library services, tutoring.

Contact Juanita Smarr, Administrative Assistant, University of Missouri–Columbia, 105 Whitten Hall, Columbia, MO 65211-6300. Telephone: 800-545-2604. Fax: 573-882-5071. E-mail: mudirect@missouri.edu.

DEGREES AND AWARDS

BHS Radiologic Sciences Bachelor's Completion Program (Radiography); Respiratory Therapy Bachelor's Completion Program
BSN Nursing–RN to BSN Online Option (Bachelor's Completion Program)
MA Journalism (Media Management); Journalism (Strategic Communications); Library Science
MEd Early Childhood Education; Early Childhood Special Education; Educational Leadership; Gifted Education; Journalism Education; Learning Systems Design and Development; Literacy; Mental Health Practices in Schools; Social Studies; Technology in Schools
MHA Health Services Management (Executive Program)
MS Family Nurse Practitioner; Gerontological Nurse Practitioner; Health Informatics (Executive Program); Leadership in Nursing and Healthcare Systems; Mental Health Nurse Practitioner; Nursing Education; Pediatric Nurse Practitioner; Public Health or School Health Nursing
PhD Architectural Studies

COURSE SUBJECT AREAS OFFERED OUTSIDE OF DEGREE PROGRAMS

Undergraduate—agricultural and food products processing; agricultural business and management; food science and technology; foods, nutrition, and related services; health professions related; nuclear engineering; nursing; plant sciences; real estate.
Graduate—agricultural and food products processing; agricultural business and management; economics; education; educational administration and supervision; educational/instructional media design; educational psychology; education related; education (specific subject areas); food science and technology; foods, nutrition, and related services; health and medical administrative services; information science/studies; journalism; library science; library science related; mental and social health services and allied professions; nuclear engineering; nursing; public relations, advertising, and applied communication related; radio, television, and digital communication; real estate; school psychology; technology education/industrial arts.
Non-credit—agricultural business and management; allied health diagnostic, intervention, and treatment professions; business, management, and marketing related; health professions related; personal and culinary services related; real estate; sales, merchandising, and related marketing operations (specialized).

UNIVERSITY OF MISSOURI–ST. LOUIS
St. Louis, Missouri
Video Instructional Program
http://www.umsl.edu/technology/videosupport/distancelearning/distancelearning.html

University of Missouri–St. Louis was founded in 1963. It is accredited by North Central Association of Colleges and Schools. It first offered distance learning courses in 1988. In fall 2005, there were 954 students enrolled in distance learning courses. Institutionally administered financial aid is available to distance learners.
Services Distance learners have accessibility to academic advising, bookstore, campus computer network, e-mail services, library services.
Contact Ruthann Perkins, Assistant to the Dean, University of Missouri–St. Louis, College of Arts and Sciences, 303 Lucas Hall, One University Boulevard, St. Louis, MO 63121. Telephone: 314-516-5004. Fax: 314-516-5415. E-mail: perkinsr@umsl.edu.

DEGREES AND AWARDS

Programs offered do not lead to a degree or other formal award.

COURSE SUBJECT AREAS OFFERED OUTSIDE OF DEGREE PROGRAMS

Undergraduate—anthropology; biology; developmental and child psychology; history; philosophy; radio, television, and digital communication; sociology.

THE UNIVERSITY OF MONTANA
Missoula, Montana
Continuing Education
http://www.umt.edu/ce/deo/external

The University of Montana was founded in 1893. It is accredited by Northwest Commission on Colleges and Universities. It first offered distance learning courses in 1989. In fall 2005, there were 989 students enrolled in distance learning courses. Institutionally administered financial aid is available to distance learners.
Services Distance learners have accessibility to academic advising, bookstore, campus computer network, career placement assistance, e-mail services, library services.
Contact Ms. Candice Merrill, Program Coordinator, The University of Montana, Extended Degrees, Continuing Education, Missoula, MT 59812. Telephone: 406-243-6431. Fax: 406-243-2047. E-mail: candice.merrill@umontana.edu.

DEGREES AND AWARDS

AAS Surgical Technology
Certificate Customer Relations; Forensic Studies
Endorsement Library Media
MBA Business Administration (Off Campus MBA)
MEd Curriculum Studies; Educational Leadership
MPA Public Administration
EdD Educational Leadership (weekend cohort program)

COURSE SUBJECT AREAS OFFERED OUTSIDE OF DEGREE PROGRAMS

Undergraduate—accounting and related services; anthropology; biology; business/commerce; communication and media; computer science; curriculum and instruction; educational administration and supervision; English composition; environmental psychology; journalism; library science related; mathematics; nursing; philosophy; philosophy and religious studies related; physical sciences; psychology; public administration; public health; science, technology and society; social work; sociology; speech and rhetoric.
Graduate—business administration, management and operations; curriculum and instruction; education; educational administration and supervision; information science/studies; library science related; mathematics; philosophy; political science and government; public administration.

See full description on page 526.

THE UNIVERSITY OF MONTANA–WESTERN
Dillon, Montana
Division of Outreach
http://www.wmc.edu/Academics/Outreach/

The University of Montana–Western was founded in 1893. It is accredited by Northwest Commission on Colleges and Universities. It first offered distance learning courses in 1989. In fall 2005, there were 150 students enrolled in distance learning courses. Institutionally administered financial aid is available to distance learners.
Services Distance learners have accessibility to academic advising, bookstore, career placement assistance, e-mail services, library services.
Contact Vickie Lansing, Director of Continuing Education and Extension Programs, The University of Montana–Western, 710 South Atlantic Street, Dillon, MT 59725. Telephone: 406-683-7537. Fax: 406-683-7809. E-mail: v_lansing@umwestern.edu.

DEGREES AND AWARDS

Programs offered do not lead to a degree or other formal award.

COURSE SUBJECT AREAS OFFERED OUTSIDE OF DEGREE PROGRAMS

Undergraduate—business, management, and marketing related; computer software and media applications; education; education (specific levels and methods); English composition; liberal arts and sciences, general studies and humanities; library science related; philosophy; psychology.

UNIVERSITY OF NEBRASKA AT KEARNEY

Kearney, Nebraska
Division of Continuing Education
http://learn.unk.edu

University of Nebraska at Kearney was founded in 1903. It is accredited by North Central Association of Colleges and Schools. It first offered distance learning courses in 1986. In fall 2005, there were 600 students enrolled in distance learning courses. Institutionally administered financial aid is available to distance learners.

Services Distance learners have accessibility to academic advising, bookstore, campus computer network, career placement assistance, e-mail services, library services, tutoring.

Contact Gloria Vavricka, Director of Off-Campus, University of Nebraska at Kearney, Communications Center, Kearney, NE 68849-4220. Telephone: 308-865-8390. Fax: 308-865-8090. E-mail: vavrickag@unk.edu.

DEGREES AND AWARDS

Endorsement Educational Media Graduate Endorsement; Gifted Graduate Endorsement; Vocational Diversified Occupations Endorsement
MAE Special Education–Gifted Education
MS Biology
MSE Instructional Technology

UNIVERSITY OF NEBRASKA AT OMAHA

Omaha, Nebraska
http://www.unomaha.edu/

University of Nebraska at Omaha was founded in 1908. It is accredited by North Central Association of Colleges and Schools. It first offered distance learning courses in 1996. In fall 2005, there were 762 students enrolled in distance learning courses. Institutionally administered financial aid is available to distance learners.

Services Distance learners have accessibility to academic advising, bookstore, campus computer network, e-mail services, library services.

Contact Shelley Schafer, Manager of Distance Education, University of Nebraska at Omaha, Eppley Administration Building, #110-H, 6001 Dodge Street, Omaha, NE 68123. Telephone: 402-554-4831. Fax: 402-554-3475. E-mail: sschafer@mail.unomaha.edu.

DEGREES AND AWARDS

MPA Public Administration

COURSE SUBJECT AREAS OFFERED OUTSIDE OF DEGREE PROGRAMS

Undergraduate—astronomy and astrophysics; English composition; English language and literature related; history; political science and government; psychology; social psychology; sociology.
Graduate—air transportation; education (specific subject areas); public administration; special education.

UNIVERSITY OF NEBRASKA–LINCOLN

Lincoln, Nebraska
Extended Education and Outreach
http://extended.unl.edu

University of Nebraska–Lincoln was founded in 1869. It is accredited by North Central Association of Colleges and Schools. It first offered distance learning courses in 1941. In fall 2005, there were 4,000 students enrolled in distance learning courses. Institutionally administered financial aid is available to distance learners.

Services Distance learners have accessibility to academic advising, bookstore, campus computer network, career placement assistance, e-mail services, library services, tutoring.

Contact Dr. Robert E. Mathiasen, Distance Services Coordinator/Advisor, University of Nebraska–Lincoln, Extended Education and Outreach, 900 North 21st Street, Room 202, Lincoln, NE 68588-8802. Telephone: 402-472-0400. Fax: 402-472-4345. E-mail: rmathiasen1@unl.edu.

DEGREES AND AWARDS

Endorsement Educational Administration; Special Education; Teaching, Learning, and Teacher Education
Graduate Certificate Educational Technology; Financial Planning–Family Financial Planning; NCA CASI School Improvement Specialist; Youth Development
MA Educational Administration; Journalism and Mass Communications; Textiles, Clothing, and Design
MAg Agriculture
MBA Business Administration
MEd Educational Administration; Special Education; Teaching, Learning, and Teacher Education
MEngr Engineering Management
MS Architecture; Entomology; Family and Consumer Sciences
EdD Educational Administration; Educational Studies
PhD Educational Studies

COURSE SUBJECT AREAS OFFERED OUTSIDE OF DEGREE PROGRAMS

Undergraduate—accounting and related services; agricultural business and management; area studies; biology; curriculum and instruction; developmental and child psychology; ecology, evolution, and population biology; economics; engineering/industrial management; English; English composition; finance and financial management services; fine and studio art; geography and cartography; health and physical education/fitness; history; human development, family studies, and related services; insurance; international business; journalism; marketing; mathematics; mathematics and statistics related; medieval and Renaissance studies; nursing; philosophy; physics; plant sciences; political science and government; psychology; radio, television, and digital communication; real estate; sociology; statistics.
Graduate—accounting and related services; agricultural business and management; curriculum and instruction; international business; journalism; marketing; political science and government; statistics.
Non-credit—business/commerce; English composition; mathematics and statistics related.

UNIVERSITY OF NEBRASKA MEDICAL CENTER

Omaha, Nebraska
CON Rural Nursing Education/CON Graduate Program
http://www.unmc.edu/nursing

University of Nebraska Medical Center was founded in 1869. It is accredited by North Central Association of Colleges and Schools. It first offered distance learning courses in 1970. In fall 2005, there were 425 students enrolled in distance learning courses. Institutionally administered financial aid is available to distance learners.

Services Distance learners have accessibility to academic advising, bookstore, campus computer network, e-mail services, library services.

Contact Ms. Dani Eveloff, Recruitment Coordinator, University of Nebraska Medical Center, 985330 Nebraska Medical Center, College of Nursing, Omaha, NE 68198-5330. Telephone: 402-559-5184.

DEGREES AND AWARDS

BSN Nursing

COURSE SUBJECT AREAS OFFERED OUTSIDE OF DEGREE PROGRAMS

Undergraduate—nursing.
Graduate—nursing.
Non-credit—nursing.

UNIVERSITY OF NEVADA, LAS VEGAS

Las Vegas, Nevada
Distance Education
http://Distance_Ed.unlv.edu

University of Nevada, Las Vegas was founded in 1957. It is accredited by Northwest Commission on Colleges and Universities. It first offered distance learning courses in 1996. In fall 2005, there were 9,000 students enrolled in distance learning courses. Institutionally administered financial aid is available to distance learners.

Services Distance learners have accessibility to academic advising, bookstore, campus computer network, e-mail services, library services.

Contact Barbara Trumble, Program Manager of Distance Education, University of Nevada, Las Vegas, 4505 Maryland Parkway, Box 451038, Las Vegas, NV 89154. Telephone: 702-895-0334. Fax: 702-895-2918. E-mail: distanceeducation@unlv.edu.

DEGREES AND AWARDS

BA Social Science Studies
Graduate Certificate Instructional Technology
See full description on page 528.

UNIVERSITY OF NEVADA, RENO
Reno, Nevada
Independent Study and Division of Continuing Education
http://istudy.unr.edu

University of Nevada, Reno was founded in 1874. It is accredited by Northwest Commission on Colleges and Universities. It first offered distance learning courses in 1944. In fall 2005, there were 3,500 students enrolled in distance learning courses. Institutionally administered financial aid is available to distance learners.
Services Distance learners have accessibility to bookstore, campus computer network, e-mail services, library services.
Contact Carley Ries, Associate Director, University of Nevada, Reno, Independent Learning, Mail Stop 050, Reno, NV 89557. Telephone: 775-784-4652. Fax: 775-784-1280. E-mail: istudy@unr.edu.

DEGREES AND AWARDS

MEd Educational Psychology (Information Technology emphasis)

COURSE SUBJECT AREAS OFFERED OUTSIDE OF DEGREE PROGRAMS

Undergraduate—accounting and related services; American literature (United States and Canadian); anthropology; area, ethnic, cultural, and gender studies related; area studies; business/commerce; business/managerial economics; communication and media; computer and information sciences; counseling psychology; creative writing; criminal justice and corrections; curriculum and instruction; developmental and child psychology; economics; educational psychology; education related; English; English as a second/foreign language (teaching); English composition; fine and studio art; foods, nutrition, and related services; geography and cartography; history; hospitality administration; languages (Germanic); languages (Romance languages); library science; linguistic, comparative, and related language studies; marketing; mathematics; music; psychology; social work; sociology; statistics.
Graduate—counseling psychology; curriculum and instruction; education; education related; library science; psychology related.

UNIVERSITY OF NEW BRUNSWICK FREDERICTON
Fredericton, New Brunswick, Canada
College of Extended Learning
http://www.unb.ca/extend/

University of New Brunswick Fredericton was founded in 1785. It is provincially chartered. It first offered distance learning courses in 1970. In fall 2005, there were 3,478 students enrolled in distance learning courses. Institutionally administered financial aid is available to distance learners.
Services Distance learners have accessibility to academic advising, bookstore, campus computer network, e-mail services, library services, tutoring.
Contact Deborah Brideau, Team Lead Online Programs, University of New Brunswick Fredericton, Distance Education and Off-Campus Services, PO Box 4400, 6 Duffie Drive, Fredericton, NB E3B 5A3, Canada. Telephone: 506-453-4802. Fax: 506-453-3572. E-mail: dbrideau@unb.ca.

DEGREES AND AWARDS

Programs offered do not lead to a degree or other formal award.

COURSE SUBJECT AREAS OFFERED OUTSIDE OF DEGREE PROGRAMS

Undergraduate—accounting and related services; air transportation; biology; business administration, management and operations; business/commerce; cognitive psychology and psycholinguistics; economics; education (specific levels and methods); engineering; English; finance and financial management services; forest engineering; forestry; human resources management; microbiological sciences and immunology; nursing; political science and government; social psychology; sociology; statistics.
Graduate—business, management, and marketing related; education (specific levels and methods).
Non-credit—creative writing; environmental design; environmental/environmental health engineering; health professions related.

UNIVERSITY OF NEW HAMPSHIRE
Durham, New Hampshire
Interactive Instructional Television Center
http://e-learn.unh.edu

University of New Hampshire was founded in 1866. It is accredited by New England Association of Schools and Colleges. It first offered distance learning courses in 1980. In fall 2005, there were 70 students enrolled in distance learning courses. Institutionally administered financial aid is available to distance learners.
Services Distance learners have accessibility to academic advising, bookstore, campus computer network, career placement assistance, e-mail services, library services.
Contact Dr. Kent Chamberlin, Professor, University of New Hampshire, Department of Electrical and Computer Engineering, Kingsbury Hall, Durham, NH 03824. Telephone: 603-862-3766. Fax: 603-862-1832. E-mail: kent.chamberlin@unh.edu.

DEGREES AND AWARDS

Programs offered do not lead to a degree or other formal award.

COURSE SUBJECT AREAS OFFERED OUTSIDE OF DEGREE PROGRAMS

Graduate—computer science; electrical, electronics and communications engineering; health professions related; mechanical engineering; statistics.

UNIVERSITY OF NEW ORLEANS
New Orleans, Louisiana
UNO Metropolitan College
http://alt.uno.edu

University of New Orleans was founded in 1958. It is accredited by Southern Association of Colleges and Schools. It first offered distance learning courses in 1980. In fall 2005, there were 7,000 students enrolled in distance learning courses. Institutionally administered financial aid is available to distance learners.
Services Distance learners have accessibility to academic advising, bookstore, campus computer network, e-mail services, library services, tutoring.
Contact Dr. Darrin Pruitt, Coordinator, Distance Education, University of New Orleans, Lakefront Campus, Education 122, New Orleans, LA 70148. Telephone: 504-280-7100. Fax: 504-280-7317. E-mail: alt@uno.edu.

DEGREES AND AWARDS

Programs offered do not lead to a degree or other formal award.

COURSE SUBJECT AREAS OFFERED OUTSIDE OF DEGREE PROGRAMS

Undergraduate—accounting and computer science; American literature (United States and Canadian); American Sign Language (ASL); anthropology; applied mathematics; architectural engineering; architectural engineering technology; area, ethnic, cultural, and gender studies related; behavioral sciences; bioethics/medical ethics; biological and biomedical sciences related; biological and physical sciences; biology; business administration, management and operations; business/corporate communications; business, management, and marketing related; business/managerial economics; chemistry; city/urban, community and regional planning; civil engineering; classical and ancient studies; community organization and advocacy; comparative literature; computer and information sciences; computer programming; computer science; computer systems analysis; creative writing; curriculum and instruction; developmental and child psychology; economics; education; educational administration and supervision; educational assessment, evaluation, and research; education (specific levels and methods); education (specific subject areas); electrical and electronic engineering technologies; engineering; engineering-related fields; English; English as a second language; English composition; English language and literature related; English literature (British and Commonwealth); entrepreneurial and small business operations; finance and financial management services; geography and cartography; geological and earth sciences/geosciences; geological/geophysical engineering; gerontology; health professions related; history; hospitality administration; human resources management; journalism; languages (foreign languages related); languages (Germanic); languages (Romance languages); liberal arts and sciences, general studies and humanities; linguistic, comparative, and related language studies; management information systems; management sciences and quantitative methods; marketing; mathematics; mathematics and computer science; mathematics and statistics related; mechanical engineering; medieval and Renaissance studies; music; natural resources and conservation related; naval architecture and marine engineering; personality psychology; philosophy; philosophy and religious studies related; physical sciences; physics; political science and government; psychology; psychometrics and quantitative psychology; public administration; public administration and social service professions related; real estate; social sciences; sociology; special education; speech and rhetoric; statistics; systems engineering; technical and business writing; urban studies/affairs.

Graduate—accounting and computer science; American literature (United States and Canadian); American Sign Language (ASL); anthropology; applied mathematics; architectural engineering; architectural engineering technology; area, ethnic, cultural, and gender studies related; behavioral sciences; biological and biomedical sciences related; biological and physical sciences; biology; business administration, management and operations; business/corporate communications; business, management, and marketing related; business/managerial economics; chemistry; city/urban, community and regional planning; civil engineering; classical and ancient studies; comparative literature; computer and information sciences; computer programming; computer science; computer systems analysis; creative writing; curriculum and instruction; developmental and child psychology; dramatic/theater arts and stagecraft; economics; education; educational administration and supervision; educational assessment, evaluation, and research; educational/instructional media design; education (specific levels and methods); education (specific subject areas); electrical and electronic engineering technologies; engineering; engineering-related fields; English; English as a second language; English composition; English language and literature related; English literature (British and Commonwealth); entrepreneurial and small business operations; finance and financial management services; geography and cartography; geological and earth sciences/geosciences; geological/geophysical engineering; gerontology; health professions related; history; hospitality administration; human resources management; journalism; languages (foreign languages related); languages (Germanic); languages (Romance languages); liberal arts and sciences, general studies and humanities; linguistic, comparative, and related language studies; management information systems; management sciences and quantitative methods; marketing; mathematics; mathematics and computer science; mathematics and statistics related; mechanical engineering; medieval and Renaissance studies; music; natural resources and conservation related; naval architecture and marine engineering; personality psychology; philosophy; philosophy and religious studies related; physical sciences; physics; political science and government; psychology; psychometrics and quantitative psychology; public administration; public administration and social service professions related; real estate; social sciences; sociology; special education; speech and rhetoric; statistics; systems engineering; technical and business writing; urban studies/affairs.

UNIVERSITY OF NORTH ALABAMA
Florence, Alabama
Educational Technology Services/Distance Learning
http://distance.una.edu

University of North Alabama was founded in 1830. It is accredited by Southern Association of Colleges and Schools. It first offered distance learning courses in 1997. In fall 2005, there were 1,000 students enrolled in distance learning courses. Institutionally administered financial aid is available to distance learners.

Services Distance learners have accessibility to academic advising, bookstore, career placement assistance, e-mail services, library services, tutoring.

Contact Brenda J. Wilson, Coordinator of Distance Learning, University of North Alabama, Box 5005, Florence, AL 35632-0001. Telephone: 877-765-6110. Fax: 256-765-4863. E-mail: bhwilson@una.edu.

DEGREES AND AWARDS
BSN Nursing–RN to BSN
EMBA Business Administration–Executive Business Administration
MBA Business Administration–Online MBA program

COURSE SUBJECT AREAS OFFERED OUTSIDE OF DEGREE PROGRAMS
Undergraduate—accounting and related services; area studies; business, management, and marketing related; communication and media; computer and information sciences; criminal justice and corrections; education; English; English composition; foods, nutrition, and related services; geography and cartography; gerontology; history; marketing; nursing; philosophy; political science and government; social work; sociology.

Graduate—accounting and related services; area studies; business administration, management and operations; business/commerce; education; English; geography and cartography.

THE UNIVERSITY OF NORTH CAROLINA AT CHAPEL HILL
Chapel Hill, North Carolina
The William and Ida Friday Center for Continuing Education
http://fridaycenter.unc.edu

The University of North Carolina at Chapel Hill was founded in 1789. It is accredited by Southern Association of Colleges and Schools. It first offered distance learning courses in 1941. In fall 2005, there were 3,800 students enrolled in distance learning courses. Institutionally administered financial aid is available to distance learners.

Services Distance learners have accessibility to academic advising, bookstore, career placement assistance, library services.

Contact Carol McDonnell, Student Services Manager, The University of North Carolina at Chapel Hill, CB #1020, Chapel Hill, NC 27599-1020. Telephone: 800-862-5669. Fax: 919-962-5549. E-mail: carol_mcdonnell@unc.edu.

DEGREES AND AWARDS
Programs offered do not lead to a degree or other formal award.

COURSE SUBJECT AREAS OFFERED OUTSIDE OF DEGREE PROGRAMS
Undergraduate—accounting and related services; anthropology; area studies; astronomy and astrophysics; biology; business administration, management and operations; business/corporate communications; chemistry; communication and media; computer and information sciences; creative writing; criminal justice and corrections; dramatic/theater arts and stagecraft; economics; English as a second language; English composition; ethnic, cultural minority, and gender studies; fine and studio art; foods, nutrition, and related services; geography and cartography; geological and earth sciences/geosciences; history; hospitality administration; journalism; languages (classics and classical); languages (foreign languages related); languages (Romance languages); languages (Slavic, Baltic and Albanian); mathematics and statistics related; music; parks, recreation and leisure; philosophy; physics; political science and government; psychology; religious studies; sociology; statistics.

Non-credit—area, ethnic, cultural, and gender studies related; business/corporate communications; business, management, and marketing related; creative writing; ethnic, cultural minority, and gender studies; fine and studio art; history; music; nursing; philosophy; political science and government.

See full description on page 530.

THE UNIVERSITY OF NORTH CAROLINA AT CHAPEL HILL

Chapel Hill, North Carolina

School of Journalism and Mass Communication

The University of North Carolina at Chapel Hill was founded in 1789. It is accredited by Southern Association of Colleges and Schools. It first offered distance learning courses in 2003. In fall 2005, there were 40 students enrolled in distance learning courses. Institutionally administered financial aid is available to distance learners.

Services Distance learners have accessibility to campus computer network, e-mail services, library services.

Contact Ms. Louise Spieler, Assistant Dean for Distance Education and Executive Education, The University of North Carolina at Chapel Hill, School of Journalism and Mass Communication, Campus Box 3365, Chapel Hill, NC 27599. Telephone: 919-843-8137. Fax: 919-843-8138. E-mail: lspieler@unc.edu.

DEGREES AND AWARDS

Programs offered do not lead to a degree or other formal award.

COURSE SUBJECT AREAS OFFERED OUTSIDE OF DEGREE PROGRAMS

Graduate—communication and journalism related; communication and media; journalism; radio, television, and digital communication.

THE UNIVERSITY OF NORTH CAROLINA AT CHARLOTTE

Charlotte, North Carolina

Continuing Education, Extension and Summer Programs

http://www.DistanceEd.uncc.edu

The University of North Carolina at Charlotte was founded in 1946. It is accredited by Southern Association of Colleges and Schools. It first offered distance learning courses in 1985. In fall 2005, there were 396 students enrolled in distance learning courses. Institutionally administered financial aid is available to distance learners.

Services Distance learners have accessibility to academic advising, bookstore, campus computer network, career placement assistance, e-mail services, library services, tutoring.

Contact Mary Faye Englebert, Associate Director, The University of North Carolina at Charlotte, 9201 University City Boulevard, Charlotte, NC 28223. Telephone: 704-687-4594. Fax: 704-687-4305. E-mail: mfengleb@email.uncc.edu.

DEGREES AND AWARDS

BA Elementary Education

BSET Electrical Engineering Technology; Fire Science

BSN Nursing–RN to BSN completion

License Education–Middle and Secondary Education (Teacher Licensure); Special Education–Adapted Curriculum; Special Education–General Curriculum (Teacher Licensure)

Graduate Certificate Child and Family Development–Early Intervention; Education–Academically and Intellectually Gifted; Information Systems and Information Security; Nursing Education

MEd Education–Middle Grades; Educational Administration–School Administration (MSA); Elementary Education; Reading

MSN Nursing–Community Health

COURSE SUBJECT AREAS OFFERED OUTSIDE OF DEGREE PROGRAMS

Undergraduate—education; engineering; nursing.

Graduate—education; information science/studies; nursing.

Non-credit—accounting and computer science; accounting and related services; architecture; building/construction finishing, management, and inspection; business administration, management and operations; business/commerce; business/corporate communications; business, management, and marketing related; business operations support and assistant services; civil engineering; computer software and media applications; counseling psychology; electrical and electronic engineering technologies; engineering; film/video and photographic arts; finance and financial management services; geography and cartography; health and medical administrative services; hospitality administration; human resources management; legal support services; marketing; mechanical engineering; nursing; public administration and social service professions related; sales, merchandising, and related marketing operations (specialized); taxation.

THE UNIVERSITY OF NORTH CAROLINA AT GREENSBORO

Greensboro, North Carolina

Division of Continual Learning and Summer Session

http://www.calldcl.com

The University of North Carolina at Greensboro was founded in 1891. It is accredited by Southern Association of Colleges and Schools. It first offered distance learning courses in 1972. In fall 2005, there were 1,281 students enrolled in distance learning courses. Institutionally administered financial aid is available to distance learners.

Services Distance learners have accessibility to academic advising, bookstore, campus computer network, career placement assistance, e-mail services, library services.

Contact William H. Taylor, Director of Distance Learning and Program Analysis, The University of North Carolina at Greensboro, Division of Continual Learning, 1100 West Market Street, Suite 300, PO Box 26170, Greensboro, NC 27402-6170. Telephone: 336-334-5414. Fax: 336-334-5628. E-mail: whtaylor@uncg.edu.

DEGREES AND AWARDS

BA Liberal Studies (Humanities concentration)

BS Education–Birth-Kindergarten Teacher Licensure

BSN Nursing

Certificate Conflict Resolution; Nonprofit Management (Post-Baccalaureate)

MA Conflict Resolution; Dance Education; Liberal Studies

MEd Curriculum and Instruction; Educational Administration–School Administration; Special Education (Cross-Categorical emphasis)

MLIS Library and Information Studies

MSN Nursing

PMC Counseling–School Counseling, advanced

COURSE SUBJECT AREAS OFFERED OUTSIDE OF DEGREE PROGRAMS

Undergraduate—anthropology; classical and ancient studies; economics; film/video and photographic arts; health professions related; history; human development, family studies, and related services; liberal arts and sciences, general studies and humanities; mathematics and statistics related; philosophy; philosophy and religious studies related; psychology; public health; sociology.

Graduate—curriculum and instruction; dance; education related; English as a second/foreign language (teaching); historic preservation and conservation; international/global studies; languages (Romance languages); liberal arts and sciences, general studies and humanities; library science; library science related; music; peace studies and conflict resolution; special education; student counseling and personnel services.

Non-credit—accounting and related services; business administration, management and operations; computer and information sciences and support services related; computer software and media applications; computer systems analysis; data entry/microcomputer applications; health and medical administrative services; human resources management; legal professions and studies related; legal support services; pharmacy, pharmaceutical sciences, and administration.

THE UNIVERSITY OF NORTH CAROLINA WILMINGTON
Wilmington, North Carolina
Division of Academic Affairs
http://www.uncw.edu/extended_ed/orientation/index.htm

The University of North Carolina Wilmington was founded in 1947. It is accredited by Southern Association of Colleges and Schools. It first offered distance learning courses in 1992. In fall 2005, there were 565 students enrolled in distance learning courses. Institutionally administered financial aid is available to distance learners.

Services Distance learners have accessibility to academic advising, bookstore, campus computer network, career placement assistance, e-mail services, library services.

Contact Dr. Beth A. Barton, Director, The University of North Carolina Wilmington, Administration Building, Room 23, 444 Western Boulevard, Jacksonville, NC 28546. Telephone: 910-455-2310. Fax: 910-451-5266. E-mail: bartonb@uncw.edu.

DEGREES AND AWARDS
Programs offered do not lead to a degree or other formal award.

COURSE SUBJECT AREAS OFFERED OUTSIDE OF DEGREE PROGRAMS
Undergraduate—criminal justice and corrections; education (specific subject areas); history; psychology.

Graduate—liberal arts and sciences, general studies and humanities.

UNIVERSITY OF NORTH DAKOTA
Grand Forks, North Dakota
Division of Continuing Education
http://www.conted.und.edu

University of North Dakota was founded in 1883. It is accredited by North Central Association of Colleges and Schools. It first offered distance learning courses in 1970. In fall 2005, there were 619 students enrolled in distance learning courses. Institutionally administered financial aid is available to distance learners.

Services Distance learners have accessibility to academic advising, bookstore, campus computer network, career placement assistance, e-mail services, library services, tutoring.

Contact Ms. Heidi Flaten, Coordinator, University of North Dakota, UND Continuing Education, Gustafson Hall, Room 205, 3264 Campus Road Stop 9021, Grand Forks, ND 58202-9021. Telephone: 877-450-1842. Fax: 701-777-6401. E-mail: distancedegreeprograms@mail.und.edu.

DEGREES AND AWARDS
BA Social Science
BBA Information Systems
BGS General Studies
BS Chemical Engineering; Civil Engineering; Electrical Engineering; Mechanical Engineering; Nursing
Endorsement English Language Learner/English as a Second Language
Graduate Certificate Autistic Spectrum Disorders; Health Administration
MA Counseling
MBA Business Administration
MEd Education Leadership; Special Education
MPA Public Administration
MS Early Childhood Education; Elementary Education; General Studies (Secondary Education); Space Studies
MSN Nursing–Education specialization
MSW Social Work
EdD Educational Leadership
PhD Higher Education

COURSE SUBJECT AREAS OFFERED OUTSIDE OF DEGREE PROGRAMS
Undergraduate—accounting and related services; anthropology; business administration, management and operations; chemical engineering; chemistry; civil engineering; communication and media; economics; education (specific levels and methods); education (specific subject areas); English composition; geography and cartography; history; industrial and organizational psychology; linguistic, comparative, and related language studies; mathematics; mechanical engineering; nursing; physical sciences; physics; psychology; religious studies; social work; sociology.

Graduate—business administration, management and operations; education (specific subject areas); English as a second/foreign language (teaching); public administration; social work.

Non-credit—computer programming; computer software and media applications; graphic communications; health and medical administrative services; health professions related; heating, air conditioning, ventilation and refrigeration maintenance technology; human resources management; legal support services; mathematics; real estate.

UNIVERSITY OF NORTHERN COLORADO
Greeley, Colorado
Office of Extended Studies
http://www.unco.edu/center/es/main

University of Northern Colorado was founded in 1890. It is accredited by North Central Association of Colleges and Schools. It first offered distance learning courses in 1941. In fall 2005, there were 450 students enrolled in distance learning courses. Institutionally administered financial aid is available to distance learners.

Services Distance learners have accessibility to academic advising, bookstore, campus computer network, career placement assistance, e-mail services, library services.

Contact Receptionist, University of Northern Colorado, Michener Library, Southwest Lower Level, Campus Box 21, Greeley, CO 80639. Telephone: 800-232-1749. Fax: 970-351-2519. E-mail: esinfo@unco.edu.

DEGREES AND AWARDS
BA American Sign Language–English Interpretation
BS Dietetics (degree completion/didactic program in dietetics); Nursing (RN to BS)
Certificate of Completion Speech-Language Pathology–Master's Preparation ('Leveling')
Internship Certificate Dietetics
Graduate Certificate Nursing Education
MA Educational Media and School Library Media Endorsement; Educational Technology; Special Education–Deaf and Hard of Hearing emphasis; Special Education–Visual Impairment emphasis; Speech-Language Pathology
PhD Nursing Education

COURSE SUBJECT AREAS OFFERED OUTSIDE OF DEGREE PROGRAMS
Undergraduate—biology; chemistry; community health services; creative writing; economics; foods, nutrition, and related services; geography and cartography; geological and earth sciences/geosciences; gerontology; health and medical administrative services; health professions related; human services; mathematics; nursing; political science and government; psychology; rehabilitation and therapeutic professions; special education.

Graduate—chemistry; communication disorders sciences and services; educational/instructional media design; education related; gerontology; health and physical education/fitness; legal research and advanced professional studies; marketing; special education.

UNIVERSITY OF NORTHERN IOWA
Cedar Falls, Iowa
Division of Continuing Education
http://www.uni.edu/contined/cp/distance.shtml

University of Northern Iowa was founded in 1876. It is accredited by North Central Association of Colleges and Schools. It first offered distance learning courses in 1941. In fall 2005, there were 1,200 students enrolled in distance learning courses. Institutionally administered financial aid is available to distance learners.

Services Distance learners have accessibility to academic advising, bookstore, campus computer network, career placement assistance, e-mail services, library services.

Contact Dr. Kent Johnson, Associate Director of Continuing Education Credit Programs, University of Northern Iowa, Cedar Falls, IA 50614-0223. Telephone: 319-273-5970. Fax: 319-273-2872. E-mail: kent.johnson@uni.edu.

DEGREES AND AWARDS
BLS Liberal Studies

COURSE SUBJECT AREAS OFFERED OUTSIDE OF DEGREE PROGRAMS
Undergraduate—accounting and related services; area studies; communication and media; criminology; education; English; family and consumer economics; geography and cartography; health and physical education/fitness; history; marketing; mathematics; music; psychology; religious studies; social work; sociology.
Graduate—criminology; education; geography and cartography; history; religious studies; social work; sociology.

UNIVERSITY OF NORTH FLORIDA
Jacksonville, Florida
http://www.unf.edu/

University of North Florida was founded in 1965. It is accredited by Southern Association of Colleges and Schools. It first offered distance learning courses in 1997. In fall 2005, there were 1,022 students enrolled in distance learning courses. Institutionally administered financial aid is available to distance learners.
Services Distance learners have accessibility to academic advising, campus computer network, career placement assistance, e-mail services, library services, tutoring.
Contact Dr. Jace Hargis, Director of Faculty Enhancement, University of North Florida, 4567 St. Johns Bluff Road South, Jacksonville, FL 32224-2465. Telephone: 904-620-1446. E-mail: jhargis@unf.edu.

DEGREES AND AWARDS
Programs offered do not lead to a degree or other formal award.

COURSE SUBJECT AREAS OFFERED OUTSIDE OF DEGREE PROGRAMS
Undergraduate—computer and information sciences; curriculum and instruction; health professions related; nursing; sociology; special education.
Graduate—curriculum and instruction; health professions related; human services; special education.

UNIVERSITY OF NORTH TEXAS
Denton, Texas
Center for Distributed Learning
http://courses.unt.edu

University of North Texas was founded in 1890. It is accredited by Southern Association of Colleges and Schools. It first offered distance learning courses in 1995. In fall 2005, there were 8,269 students enrolled in distance learning courses. Institutionally administered financial aid is available to distance learners.
Services Distance learners have accessibility to academic advising, bookstore, campus computer network, career placement assistance, e-mail services, library services, tutoring.
Contact Dr. Arlita W. Harris, Senior Marketing Specialist, University of North Texas, PO Box 310889, Denton, TX 76203-0889. Telephone: 940-565-2942. E-mail: arlita@unt.edu.

DEGREES AND AWARDS
BAA Applied Technology and Performance Improvement
Certificate E-Commerce; Retailing–Five Course Sequence in Retailing; TESOL Certificate through Distance Learning
Certification Texas Teacher Certification–Secondary Education
Endorsement Gifted and Talented Education
Graduate Certificate Behavior Analysis; Gerontology–Applied Gerontology; Gifted Education; Hospitality Management; Library and Information Sciences; Merchandising; Volunteer and Community Resource Management
MA Anthropology
MBA Management
MEd Education–Secondary Education; Educational Administration
MLS Library Science
MS Computer Education and Cognitive Systems; Educational Administration and Supervision; Educational Psychology; Gerontology–Applied Gerontology; Hospitality Management; Information Sciences; Merchandising; Teaching and Learning with Technology
MSE Applied Technology, Training, and Development

COURSE SUBJECT AREAS OFFERED OUTSIDE OF DEGREE PROGRAMS
Undergraduate—anthropology; apparel and textiles; behavioral sciences; biology; business administration, management and operations; business/commerce; business, management, and marketing related; chemistry; computer and information sciences; computer/information technology administration and management; computer software and media applications; curriculum and instruction; data entry/microcomputer applications; developmental and child psychology; economics; education; educational administration and supervision; educational assessment, evaluation, and research; educational/instructional media design; educational psychology; electrical and electronic engineering technologies; engineering-related technologies; engineering technologies related; family and consumer economics; fine and studio art; food science and technology; geological and earth sciences/geosciences; health and physical education/fitness; history; hospitality administration; human development, family studies, and related services; journalism; library science; library science related; linguistic, comparative, and related language studies; marketing; mathematics; music; nutrition sciences; psychology related; public administration; rehabilitation and therapeutic professions; sales, merchandising, and related marketing operations (specialized); social sciences; social work; sociology; special education; technical and business writing.
Graduate—anthropology; apparel and textiles; behavioral sciences; business administration, management and operations; business, management, and marketing related; chemistry; communications technology; community organization and advocacy; computer and information sciences; computer software and media applications; curriculum and instruction; developmental and child psychology; education; educational administration and supervision; educational assessment, evaluation, and research; educational/instructional media design; educational psychology; education related; electrical and electronic engineering technologies; family and consumer economics; food science and technology; gerontology; health and medical administrative services; hospitality administration; human development, family studies, and related services; human resources management; industrial and organizational psychology; information science/studies; library science; library science related; linguistic, comparative, and related language studies; marketing; rehabilitation and therapeutic professions; sales, merchandising, and related marketing operations (specialized); social and philosophical foundations of education; social sciences; special education.
Non-credit—behavioral sciences; business administration, management and operations; education; educational administration and supervision; educational psychology; gerontology; library science; library science related; marketing; rehabilitation and therapeutic professions; school psychology; special education.

UNIVERSITY OF OKLAHOMA
Norman, Oklahoma
College of Continuing Education
http://www.occe.ou.edu

University of Oklahoma was founded in 1890. It is accredited by North Central Association of Colleges and Schools. It first offered distance learning courses in 1941. In fall 2005, there were 50,000 students enrolled in distance learning courses. Institutionally administered financial aid is available to distance learners.
Services Distance learners have accessibility to academic advising, bookstore, campus computer network, career placement assistance, e-mail services, library services.
Contact Larry D. Hayes, Information Assistant, Office of the Vice President for University Outreach/College of Continuing Education, University of Oklahoma, 1700 Asp Avenue, Norman, OK 73072. Telephone: 800-522-0772 Ext. 4414. Fax: 405-325-7196. E-mail: lhayes@ou.edu.

DEGREES AND AWARDS

BLS Liberal Studies
MA Advanced programs
MLS Liberal Studies
PhD Advanced programs

COURSE SUBJECT AREAS OFFERED OUTSIDE OF DEGREE PROGRAMS

Undergraduate—anthropology; astronomy and astrophysics; business administration, management and operations; business/corporate communications; chemistry; communication and media; dramatic/theater arts and stagecraft; economics; education; engineering; English composition; finance and financial management services; geography and cartography; geological and earth sciences/geosciences; health and physical education/fitness; history; journalism; library science related; marketing; mathematics; philosophy; political science and government; sociology.

See full description on page 532.

UNIVERSITY OF OREGON

Eugene, Oregon
Distance Education
http://de.uoregon.edu

University of Oregon was founded in 1872. It is accredited by Northwest Commission on Colleges and Universities. It first offered distance learning courses in 1996. In fall 2005, there were 750 students enrolled in distance learning courses. Institutionally administered financial aid is available to distance learners.

Services Distance learners have accessibility to academic advising, bookstore, campus computer network, e-mail services, library services.

Contact Sandra Gladney, Program Coordinator, University of Oregon, 1277 University of Oregon, Eugene, OR 97403-1277. Telephone: 541-346-4231. Fax: 541-346-3545. E-mail: disted@uoregon.edu.

DEGREES AND AWARDS

MS Information Management–Applied Information Management

COURSE SUBJECT AREAS OFFERED OUTSIDE OF DEGREE PROGRAMS

Undergraduate—astronomy and astrophysics; economics; English; geography and cartography; geological and earth sciences/geosciences; multi-/interdisciplinary studies related; physics; political science and government; visual and performing arts related.

Graduate—information science/studies; management information systems.

UNIVERSITY OF PHOENIX ONLINE CAMPUS

Phoenix, Arizona
http://www.uoponline.com

University of Phoenix Online Campus was founded in 1989. It is accredited by North Central Association of Colleges and Schools. It first offered distance learning courses in 1989. In fall 2005, there were 186,481 students enrolled in distance learning courses. Institutionally administered financial aid is available to distance learners.

Services Distance learners have accessibility to academic advising, bookstore, campus computer network, library services, tutoring.

Contact Mr. Brian Mayer, Director of Marketing, University of Phoenix Online Campus, Mail Stop AA-B418, 4615 East Elwood Street, Phoenix, AZ 85040-1958. Telephone: 480-557-1510. Fax: 602-838-6364. E-mail: brian.mayer@phoenix.edu.

DEGREES AND AWARDS

AA Accounting; Business; Criminal Justice; General Studies; Health Administration; Information Technology
BEd Education
BS Business Hospitality Management; Business/Accounting; Business/Business Administration; Business/Communication; Business/E-Business; Business/Finance; Business/Global Management; Business/Integrated Supply Chain and Operations Management; Business/Management; Business/Management; Business/Marketing; Business/Public Administration; Business/Retail Management; Criminal Justice Administration; Health Administration; Health Administration/Health Information Systems; Health Administration/Long-Term Care; Human Services/Management; Information Technology; Information Technology/Visual Communication; Nursing; Organizational Security and Management
MA Curriculum and Instruction–Adult Education; Education–Administration and Supervision specialization; Education–Computer Education; Education–Curriculum and Instruction; Education–Early Childhood Education specialization; Education–Elementary or Secondary Teacher Education; Education–Special Education specialization; Education/ESL
MBA Accounting; Business Administration; Business Administration/Marketing; Global Management; Human Resource Management; Technology Management
MBA/MHMS Business Administration/Health Care Management
MHA Health Administration–Master of Health Administration
MISM Information Systems–Master of Information Systems
MM Human Resource Management; Management; Public Administration
MS Administration of Justice and Security
MSN Nursing–Integrative Health Care; Nursing–Master of Business Administration, Health Care Management; Nursing–Nursing/Health Care Education; Nursing
DBA Business Administration
DH Sc Health Administration–Doctor of Health Administration (DHA)
DM Organizational Leadership, Information Systems and Technology specialization; Organizational Management
EdD Educational Leadership; Educational Leadership, Curriculum and Instruction specialization

COURSE SUBJECT AREAS OFFERED OUTSIDE OF DEGREE PROGRAMS

Undergraduate—business operations support and assistant services; human resources management.

Graduate—education; nursing.

See full description on page 534.

UNIVERSITY OF PITTSBURGH

Pittsburgh, Pennsylvania
Office of Extended Education
http://www.pitt.edu/~cgs/uesp.htm

University of Pittsburgh was founded in 1787. It is accredited by Middle States Association of Colleges and Schools. It first offered distance learning courses in 1972. In fall 2005, there were 810 students enrolled in distance learning courses. Institutionally administered financial aid is available to distance learners.

Services Distance learners have accessibility to academic advising, bookstore, campus computer network, career placement assistance, e-mail services, library services.

Contact Mr. Brent Cione, Academic Consultant, University of Pittsburgh, College of General Studies, 4th Floor Cathedral of Learning, 4200 Fifth Avenue, Pittsburgh, PA 15260. Telephone: 412-624-4079. Fax: 412-624-3836. E-mail: cione@cgs.pitt.edu.

DEGREES AND AWARDS

BA Humanities; Social Sciences

COURSE SUBJECT AREAS OFFERED OUTSIDE OF DEGREE PROGRAMS

Undergraduate—astronomy and astrophysics; economics; English composition; mathematics; music; philosophy and religious studies related; political science and government; psychology.

UNIVERSITY OF PITTSBURGH AT BRADFORD

Bradford, Pennsylvania
http://www.upb.pitt.edu/

University of Pittsburgh at Bradford was founded in 1963. It is accredited by Middle States Association of Colleges and Schools. It first offered distance learning courses in 1995. In fall 2005, there were 14 students enrolled in distance learning courses. Institutionally administered financial aid is available to distance learners.

Services Distance learners have accessibility to academic advising, bookstore, campus computer network, career placement assistance, e-mail services, library services.

Contact Mr. Don Lewicki, Director, Computing, Telecommunications, Media Services, University of Pittsburgh at Bradford, 300 Campus Drive, Bradford, PA 16701-2898. Telephone: 814-362-7660. Fax: 814-362-5279. E-mail: lewicki@upb.pitt.edu.

DEGREES AND AWARDS

AA Liberal Studies

COURSE SUBJECT AREAS OFFERED OUTSIDE OF DEGREE PROGRAMS

Undergraduate—biology; business, management, and marketing related; chemistry; computer and information sciences; computer science; criminal justice and corrections; economics; management information systems; marketing; nursing.

UNIVERSITY OF PITTSBURGH AT JOHNSTOWN

Johnstown, Pennsylvania

http://www.upj.pitt.edu

University of Pittsburgh at Johnstown was founded in 1927. It is accredited by Middle States Association of Colleges and Schools. It first offered distance learning courses in 1994. In fall 2005, there were 20 students enrolled in distance learning courses. Institutionally administered financial aid is available to distance learners.

Services Distance learners have accessibility to e-mail services, library services.

Contact Mrs. Judith Freedman, Coordinator of Distance Education and Professional Development, University of Pittsburgh at Johnstown, 114 Blackington Hall, Johnstown, PA 15904. Telephone: 814-269-2099. Fax: 814-269-7075. E-mail: jfreedma@pitt.edu.

DEGREES AND AWARDS

Programs offered do not lead to a degree or other formal award.

COURSE SUBJECT AREAS OFFERED OUTSIDE OF DEGREE PROGRAMS

Graduate—nursing.

UNIVERSITY OF ST. AUGUSTINE FOR HEALTH SCIENCES

St. Augustine, Florida

Division of Distance Education

http://www.usa.edu

University of St. Augustine for Health Sciences was founded in 1978. It is accredited by Distance Education and Training Council. It first offered distance learning courses in 1979. In fall 2005, there were 400 students enrolled in distance learning courses. Institutionally administered financial aid is available to distance learners.

Services Distance learners have accessibility to academic advising, bookstore, e-mail services, library services, tutoring.

Contact Dr. Richard Jensen, Dean of Division of Advanced Studies, University of St. Augustine for Health Sciences, 1 University Boulevard, St. Augustine, FL 32086. Telephone: 904-826-0084 Ext. 262. Fax: 904-826-0085. E-mail: info@usa.edu.

DEGREES AND AWARDS

MHS Health Science–Master of Health Science (MHSc)

DH Sc Health Science

DPT Physical Therapy–Transitional Doctor of Physical Therapy

OTD Occupational Therapy

COURSE SUBJECT AREAS OFFERED OUTSIDE OF DEGREE PROGRAMS

Graduate—rehabilitation and therapeutic professions.

Non-credit—health professions related.

UNIVERSITY OF ST. FRANCIS

Joliet, Illinois

http://www.stfrancis.edu/

University of St. Francis was founded in 1920. It is accredited by North Central Association of Colleges and Schools. It first offered distance learning courses in 1997. In fall 2005, there were 1,453 students enrolled in distance learning courses. Institutionally administered financial aid is available to distance learners.

Services Distance learners have accessibility to academic advising, bookstore, campus computer network, career placement assistance, e-mail services, library services, tutoring.

Contact Ms. Sandra Sloka, Director, Graduate and Degree Completion Admissions, University of St. Francis, 500 Wilcox Street, Joliet, IL 60435. Telephone: 800-735-7500. Fax: 815-740-5032. E-mail: ssloka@stfrancis.edu.

DEGREES AND AWARDS

BS Health Arts; Health Care Leadership; Organizational Leadership; Organizational Management–Applied Organizational Management

BSN Nursing Fast Track

MBA Business Administration

MS Health Services Administration; Training and Development

MSM Management

MSN Nurse Practitioner

COURSE SUBJECT AREAS OFFERED OUTSIDE OF DEGREE PROGRAMS

Undergraduate—business administration, management and operations; English; health professions related; history; nursing; philosophy and religious studies related; social sciences.

Graduate—business administration, management and operations; educational assessment, evaluation, and research; health and medical administrative services; marketing; nursing.

UNIVERSITY OF ST. MICHAEL'S COLLEGE

Toronto, Ontario, Canada

University of St. Michael's College was founded in 1852. It is provincially chartered. It first offered distance learning courses in 2005. In fall 2005, there were 20 students enrolled in distance learning courses. Institutionally administered financial aid is available to distance learners.

Services Distance learners have accessibility to campus computer network, e-mail services, library services.

Contact Dr. Anne Anderson, CSJ, Dean, Faculty of Theology, University of St. Michael's College, 81 St. Mary Street, Toronto, ON M5S 1J4, Canada. Telephone: 416-926-7265. Fax: 416-926-7294. E-mail: anne.anderson@utoronto.ca.

DEGREES AND AWARDS

Programs offered do not lead to a degree or other formal award.

COURSE SUBJECT AREAS OFFERED OUTSIDE OF DEGREE PROGRAMS

Undergraduate—theology and religious vocations related.

Graduate—theology and religious vocations related.

UNIVERSITY OF SAN DIEGO

San Diego, California

http://www.sandiego.edu/

University of San Diego was founded in 1949. It is accredited by Western Association of Schools and Colleges. It first offered distance learning courses in 2000. In fall 2005, there were 2,100 students enrolled in distance learning courses. Institutionally administered financial aid is available to distance learners.

Services Distance learners have accessibility to academic advising, bookstore, e-mail services, library services.

Contact Mal J. Rafferty, Director, Continuing Education, University of San Diego, Manchester Executive Conference Center, 5998 Alcala Park, San Diego, CA 92110-2492. Telephone: 858-573-0122. Fax: 619-260-2961. E-mail: rafferty@sandiego.edu.

DEGREES AND AWARDS
Programs offered do not lead to a degree or other formal award.

COURSE SUBJECT AREAS OFFERED OUTSIDE OF DEGREE PROGRAMS
Undergraduate—education.

UNIVERSITY OF SASKATCHEWAN
Saskatoon, Saskatchewan, Canada
Extension Credit Studies
http://www.extension.usask.ca

University of Saskatchewan was founded in 1907. It is provincially chartered. It first offered distance learning courses in 1941. In fall 2005, there were 1,500 students enrolled in distance learning courses. Institutionally administered financial aid is available to distance learners.

Services Distance learners have accessibility to academic advising, bookstore, campus computer network, e-mail services, library services, tutoring.

Contact Ms. Grace Milashenko, Independent Studies Coordinator, University of Saskatchewan, 117 Science Place, Kirk Hall, Room 330, Saskatoon, SK S7N 5C8, Canada. Telephone: 306-966-5562. Fax: 306-966-5590. E-mail: grace.milashenko@usask.ca.

DEGREES AND AWARDS
Programs offered do not lead to a degree or other formal award.

COURSE SUBJECT AREAS OFFERED OUTSIDE OF DEGREE PROGRAMS
Undergraduate—agriculture; agriculture and agriculture operations related; anthropology; archeology; computer science; curriculum and instruction; economics; education (specific levels and methods); English; English as a second/foreign language (teaching); English literature (British and Commonwealth); geography and cartography; geological and earth sciences/geosciences; history; mathematics; music; nursing; philosophy; psychology; religious studies; sociology.
Graduate—educational psychology; education related.
Non-credit—agricultural business and management; agriculture and agriculture operations related; applied horticulture/horticultural business services; botany/plant biology; educational/instructional media design; education related; education (specific subject areas); English as a second/foreign language (teaching); English as a second language; landscape architecture; soil sciences.

UNIVERSITY OF SIOUX FALLS
Sioux Falls, South Dakota
http://www.usiouxfalls.edu/

University of Sioux Falls was founded in 1883. It is accredited by North Central Association of Colleges and Schools. It first offered distance learning courses in 2000. In fall 2005, there were 114 students enrolled in distance learning courses. Institutionally administered financial aid is available to distance learners.

Services Distance learners have accessibility to academic advising, bookstore, career placement assistance, e-mail services, library services.

Contact Megan Larsen, Registration Clerk, University of Sioux Falls, 1101 West 22nd Street, Jorden Hall, Sioux Falls, SD 57105. Telephone: 605-331-6732. Fax: 605-331-6615. E-mail: megan.larsen@usiouxfalls.edu.

DEGREES AND AWARDS
Programs offered do not lead to a degree or other formal award.

COURSE SUBJECT AREAS OFFERED OUTSIDE OF DEGREE PROGRAMS
Undergraduate—education (specific subject areas); English; fine and studio art; geography and cartography; health and physical education/fitness; health professions related; history; sociology.
Graduate—education; educational administration and supervision; educational assessment, evaluation, and research.

UNIVERSITY OF SOUTH ALABAMA
Mobile, Alabama
USA Online
http://usaonline.southalabama.edu

University of South Alabama was founded in 1963. It is accredited by Southern Association of Colleges and Schools. It first offered distance learning courses in 1999. In fall 2005, there were 1,300 students enrolled in distance learning courses. Institutionally administered financial aid is available to distance learners.

Services Distance learners have accessibility to academic advising, bookstore, e-mail services, library services.

Contact Melissa Jones, Director of Admissions, University of South Alabama, AD 182, Mobile, AL 36688-0002. Telephone: 251-460-6141. Fax: 251-460-7876. E-mail: admiss@usamail.usouthal.edu.

DEGREES AND AWARDS
BSN Nursing
Certification Educational Administration; Educational Media (Library Media)
MEd Educational Leadership; Educational Media (Library Media); Special Education (Gifted)
MS Instructional Design and Development
MSN Nursing

COURSE SUBJECT AREAS OFFERED OUTSIDE OF DEGREE PROGRAMS
Graduate—accounting and related services; business administration, management and operations; educational administration and supervision; educational/instructional media design; education (specific levels and methods); finance and financial management services; nursing; special education.

UNIVERSITY OF SOUTH CAROLINA SUMTER
Sumter, South Carolina
http://www.uscsumter.edu/

University of South Carolina Sumter was founded in 1966. It is accredited by Southern Association of Colleges and Schools. It first offered distance learning courses in 1993. In fall 2005, there were 37 students enrolled in distance learning courses. Institutionally administered financial aid is available to distance learners.

Services Distance learners have accessibility to bookstore, campus computer network, e-mail services, library services.

Contact Mr. Keith Britton, Director of Admissions, University of South Carolina Sumter, 200 Miller Road, Sumter, SC 29150. Telephone: 803-938-3882. Fax: 803-775-2180. E-mail: kbritton@uscsumter.edu.

DEGREES AND AWARDS
Programs offered do not lead to a degree or other formal award.

COURSE SUBJECT AREAS OFFERED OUTSIDE OF DEGREE PROGRAMS
Undergraduate—American literature (United States and Canadian); community health services; education; educational administration and supervision; educational assessment, evaluation, and research; engineering; history; public administration; public health; social and philosophical foundations of education; social psychology; social sciences.
Graduate—business administration, management and operations; educational administration and supervision; education related; nursing; social work; sociology.

UNIVERSITY OF SOUTHERN INDIANA
Evansville, Indiana
Distance Education Programming
http://www.usi.edu/distance

University of Southern Indiana was founded in 1965. It is accredited by North Central Association of Colleges and Schools. It first offered distance learning courses in 1994. In fall 2005, there were 1,564 students enrolled in distance learning courses. Institutionally administered financial aid is available to distance learners.

Services Distance learners have accessibility to academic advising, bookstore, campus computer network, e-mail services, library services.

Contact Dr. Saxon Reasons, Programming Manager, Instructional Technology Services, University of Southern Indiana, 8600 University Boulevard, Evansville, IN 47712. Telephone: 800-813-4238. Fax: 812-465-7131. E-mail: saxrea@usi.edu.

DEGREES AND AWARDS

BS Health Professions and Related Sciences; Radiologic and Imaging Sciences
BSN Nursing
MHA Health Administration
MSN Nursing
MSOT Occupational Therapy

COURSE SUBJECT AREAS OFFERED OUTSIDE OF DEGREE PROGRAMS

Undergraduate—biology; communication and media; computer/information technology administration and management; dental support services and allied professions; economics; education; educational psychology; education (specific levels and methods); English; English composition; English literature (British and Commonwealth); fine and studio art; gerontology; health and medical administrative services; history; journalism; languages (foreign languages related); linguistic, comparative, and related language studies; nursing; political science and government; psychology; public relations, advertising, and applied communication related; radio, television, and digital communication; speech and rhetoric; visual and performing arts.
Graduate—economics; education; education (specific subject areas); health professions related; marketing; nursing; social work.
Non-credit—accounting and computer science; audiovisual communications technologies; communication and journalism related; computer and information sciences; computer software and media applications; film/video and photographic arts; health professions related; human resources management; legal professions and studies related; nursing; sales, merchandising, and related marketing operations (general).

UNIVERSITY OF SOUTHERN MISSISSIPPI
Hattiesburg, Mississippi
Department of Continuing Education
http://www.usm.edu/cice/ce/index.html

University of Southern Mississippi was founded in 1910. It is accredited by Southern Association of Colleges and Schools. It first offered distance learning courses in 1941. In fall 2005, there were 2,672 students enrolled in distance learning courses. Institutionally administered financial aid is available to distance learners.
Services Distance learners have accessibility to academic advising, bookstore, campus computer network, e-mail services, library services.
Contact Dr. Lin Harper, Director, Distance Education and Alternative Learning, University of Southern Mississippi, Distance Education and Alternative Learning, 118 College Drive, #9649, Hattiesburg, MS 39406-0001. Telephone: 601-266-6197. Fax: 601-266-4409. E-mail: lin.harper@usm.edu.

DEGREES AND AWARDS

BS Construction Technology; Construction Technology
MAT Teaching of Languages (MATL)
MEd Music Education–Master of Music Education
MLIS Library Information Science
MS Child and Family Studies; Sport Coaching Education; Sport Management

COURSE SUBJECT AREAS OFFERED OUTSIDE OF DEGREE PROGRAMS

Undergraduate—accounting and related services; anthropology; biblical studies; biology; chemistry; community health services; community organization and advocacy; comparative literature; creative writing; criminal justice and corrections; criminology; educational administration and supervision; educational assessment, evaluation, and research; education related; engineering technologies related; English; English composition; English literature (British and Commonwealth); foods, nutrition, and related services; geography and cartography; health and physical education/fitness; health professions related; human development, family studies, and related services; liberal arts and sciences, general studies and humanities; library science related; linguistic, comparative, and related language studies; management information systems; marketing; mathematics and statistics related; microbiological sciences and immunology; music; nursing; philosophy and religious studies related; social work; sociology; special education; technical and business writing.
Graduate—biochemistry, biophysics and molecular biology; biology; city/urban, community and regional planning; cognitive psychology and psycholinguistics; communication and media; community health services; construction engineering technology; criminal justice and corrections; curriculum and instruction; demography and population; economics; education; educational administration and supervision; educational assessment, evaluation, and research; geography and cartography; health and physical education/fitness; human development, family studies, and related services; linguistic, comparative, and related language studies; marketing; music; nursing; parks, recreation, and leisure related; public health; social and philosophical foundations of education; social work; special education; statistics.

UNIVERSITY OF SOUTH FLORIDA
Tampa, Florida
Educational Outreach
http://www.outreach.usf.edu/dlstudents

University of South Florida was founded in 1956. It is accredited by Southern Association of Colleges and Schools. It first offered distance learning courses in 1983. In fall 2005, there were 13,108 students enrolled in distance learning courses. Institutionally administered financial aid is available to distance learners.
Services Distance learners have accessibility to academic advising, bookstore, campus computer network, career placement assistance, e-mail services, library services.
Contact Office of the Registrar, University of South Florida, 4202 East Fowler Avenue, SVC 1034, Tampa, FL 33620. Telephone: 813-974-2000. Fax: 813-974-5271. E-mail: asktheregistrar@admin.usf.edu.

DEGREES AND AWARDS

BSN Nursing–RN Completion Program for Associate Degree Holding Nurses
Endorsement Non-Degree Gifted Endorsement course work
Graduate Certificate Children's Mental Health; Clinical Investigation; Digital Music Education; Disaster Management; Engineering Technology Management; Entrepreneurship; Gifted Education; Homeland Security; Humanitarian Assistance; Instructional Technology–Distance Education; Instructional Technology–Florida Digital Educator; Instructional Technology–Web Design; Process Engineering; Public Health Generalist; Public Health Policy and Programs; Regulatory Affairs–Medical Devices; Total Quality Management Engineering; Transportation Systems Analysis; Wireless Engineering
MA Career and Technical Education; Gifted Education; Library and Information Science; Music Education
MPH Public Health Practice
MSEE Electrical Engineering (MSEE)
MSEM Engineering Management (MSEM)
MSN Nursing

COURSE SUBJECT AREAS OFFERED OUTSIDE OF DEGREE PROGRAMS

Undergraduate—anthropology; archeology; area, ethnic, cultural, and gender studies related; area studies; biology; chemistry; criminal justice and corrections; curriculum and instruction; education; engineering; English; English composition; ethnic, cultural minority, and gender studies; fine and studio art; geography and cartography; geological and earth sciences/geosciences; history; languages (Romance languages); liberal arts and sciences, general studies and humanities; library science; mathematics; mathematics and computer science; music; natural sciences; nursing; nutrition sciences; philosophy; philosophy and religious studies related; social sciences; sociology.
Graduate—accounting and computer science; biomedical/medical engineering; business administration, management and operations; business, management, and marketing related; business/managerial economics; chemical engineering; chemistry; civil engineering technology; computer and information sciences; computer engineering; computer programming; computer software and media applications; construction engineering;

criminal justice and corrections; criminology; curriculum and instruction; education; educational administration and supervision; educational assessment, evaluation, and research; educational/instructional media design; educational psychology; education (specific levels and methods); education (specific subject areas); electrical and electronic engineering technologies; electrical, electronics and communications engineering; engineering; engineering design; engineering/industrial management; English; English as a second/foreign language (teaching); environmental/environmental health engineering; health services/allied health/health sciences; industrial engineering; information science/studies; languages (Germanic); library science; marketing; materials engineering; mechanical engineering; music; nursing; psychology; public administration; public health; public policy analysis; quality control and safety technologies; social and philosophical foundations of education; special education; systems engineering; visual and performing arts.

UNIVERSITY OF SOUTH FLORIDA
Tampa, Florida
College of Engineering
http://feeds.eng.usf.edu/

University of South Florida was founded in 1956. It is accredited by Southern Association of Colleges and Schools. It first offered distance learning courses in 1984. In fall 2005, there were 400 students enrolled in distance learning courses. Institutionally administered financial aid is available to distance learners.

Services Distance learners have accessibility to academic advising, bookstore, campus computer network, career placement assistance, e-mail services, library services, tutoring.

Contact Russ Fairman, Student Service and Materials Coordinator, University of South Florida, College of Engineering, APEX Department, 4202 East Fowler Avenue, ENB 118, Tampa, FL 33620. Telephone: 813-974-3783. Fax: 813-974-8010. E-mail: apex@eng.usf.edu.

DEGREES AND AWARDS
Graduate Certificate Entrepreneurship; Homeland Security; Technology Management; Total Quality Management; Wireless Engineering
MSE Engineering Management
MSEE Electrical Engineering

COURSE SUBJECT AREAS OFFERED OUTSIDE OF DEGREE PROGRAMS
Undergraduate—engineering.
Graduate—engineering.
Non-credit—engineering.

THE UNIVERSITY OF TENNESSEE
Knoxville, Tennessee
Department of Distance Education and Independent Study
http://www.anywhere.tennessee.edu

The University of Tennessee was founded in 1794. It is accredited by Southern Association of Colleges and Schools. It first offered distance learning courses in 1941. In fall 2005, there were 1,800 students enrolled in distance learning courses. Institutionally administered financial aid is available to distance learners.

Services Distance learners have accessibility to academic advising, bookstore, campus computer network, e-mail services, library services.

Contact Ms. Caroline C. Bowers, Assistant Director, Distance Education, The University of Tennessee, 208 Conference Center Building, 600 Henley Street, Knoxville, TN 37996-4126. Telephone: 800-670-8657. Fax: 865-974-4684. E-mail: cbowers1@utk.edu.

DEGREES AND AWARDS
Graduate Certificate Applied Statistical Strategies; Computational Fluid Dynamics; Engineering Management; Maintenance and Reliability Engineering; Nuclear Criticality Safety
MBA Aerospace; Physician Executive; Professional (weekend) program; Senior Executive
MCE Public Works option
MS Agricultural and Extension Education; Engineering Management; Environmental Engineering; Information Sciences; Nuclear Engineering

COURSE SUBJECT AREAS OFFERED OUTSIDE OF DEGREE PROGRAMS
Undergraduate—accounting and related services; agricultural business and management; American literature (United States and Canadian); anthropology; applied mathematics; astronomy and astrophysics; business administration, management and operations; chemistry; creative writing; curriculum and instruction; economics; education; English; English composition; English language and literature related; English literature (British and Commonwealth); geography and cartography; history; languages (Germanic); languages (Romance languages); liberal arts and sciences, general studies and humanities; linguistic, comparative, and related language studies; mathematics; physics; political science and government; psychology; religious studies; sociology; technical and business writing.
Non-credit—computer/information technology administration and management; creative writing; mathematics.

THE UNIVERSITY OF TENNESSEE AT MARTIN
Martin, Tennessee
Office of Extended Campus and Continuing Education
http://www.utm.edu/~ecce

The University of Tennessee at Martin was founded in 1900. It is accredited by Southern Association of Colleges and Schools. It first offered distance learning courses in 1992. In fall 2005, there were 816 students enrolled in distance learning courses. Institutionally administered financial aid is available to distance learners.

Services Distance learners have accessibility to academic advising, bookstore, campus computer network, career placement assistance, e-mail services, library services.

Contact Dr. Tommy Cates, Director, The University of Tennessee at Martin, Office of Online and University Studies, 227 Administration Building, Martin, TN 38238-5050. Telephone: 731-881-7589. E-mail: tcates@utm.edu.

DEGREES AND AWARDS
BUS University Studies
MBA Business Administration
MS Agricultural Operations Management
MSE Education

COURSE SUBJECT AREAS OFFERED OUTSIDE OF DEGREE PROGRAMS
Undergraduate—accounting and related services; business administration, management and operations; computer science; economics; English composition; English literature (British and Commonwealth); fine and studio art; geological and earth sciences/geosciences; health and physical education/fitness; history; linguistic, comparative, and related language studies; sociology; special education; visual and performing arts.
Graduate—accounting and related services; business administration, management and operations; business/commerce; educational administration and supervision; education (specific subject areas); special education.
Non-credit—accounting and related services; business administration, management and operations; computer and information sciences; crafts, folk art and artisanry; criminal justice and corrections; education; education (specific levels and methods); human development, family studies, and related services.

THE UNIVERSITY OF TEXAS AT ARLINGTON
Arlington, Texas
Center for Distance Education
http://distance.uta.edu

The University of Texas at Arlington was founded in 1895. It is accredited by Southern Association of Colleges and Schools. It first offered distance learning courses in 1973. In fall 2005, there were 2,500 students enrolled in distance learning courses. Institutionally administered financial aid is available to distance learners.

Services Distance learners have accessibility to academic advising, bookstore, campus computer network, e-mail services, library services, tutoring.

Contact Dr. Pete Smith, Assistant Vice President of Academic Affairs, The University of Texas at Arlington, Box 19027, Arlington, TX 76019. Telephone: 817-272-5727. Fax: 817-272-5728. E-mail: info@distance.uta.edu.

DEGREES AND AWARDS

BA Criminology and Criminal Justice (Completion Degree)
MBA Management, general
ME Aerospace Engineering; Computer Science and Engineering; Mechanical Engineering
MEd Curriculum and Instruction/Reading
MPA Public Administration
MS Industrial Engineering
MSCE Civil Engineering
MSEE Electrical Engineering

COURSE SUBJECT AREAS OFFERED OUTSIDE OF DEGREE PROGRAMS

Undergraduate—biology; business, management, and marketing related; communication and journalism related; criminology; dramatic/theater arts and stagecraft; economics; fine and studio art; political science and government; social work; sociology.

Graduate—aerospace, aeronautical and astronautical engineering; curriculum and instruction; engineering mechanics; environmental/environmental health engineering; finance and financial management services; mechanical engineering; political science and government; social work.

THE UNIVERSITY OF TEXAS AT DALLAS
Richardson, Texas
School of Management
http://som.utdallas.edu/globalmba

The University of Texas at Dallas was founded in 1969. It is accredited by Southern Association of Colleges and Schools. It first offered distance learning courses in 1999. In fall 2005, there were 245 students enrolled in distance learning courses. Institutionally administered financial aid is available to distance learners.

Services Distance learners have accessibility to academic advising, bookstore, campus computer network, career placement assistance, e-mail services, library services.

Contact Mr. George E. Barnes, Director of Global MBA Online, The University of Texas at Dallas, PO Box 830688, SM 27, Richardson, TX 75080-0688. Telephone: 972-883-2783. Fax: 972-883-6598. E-mail: gbarnes@utdallas.edu.

DEGREES AND AWARDS

MBA Business Administration–Global MBA Online

COURSE SUBJECT AREAS OFFERED OUTSIDE OF DEGREE PROGRAMS

Graduate—accounting and related services; business administration, management and operations; business/commerce; business/managerial economics; computer software and media applications; finance and financial management services; information science/studies; international business; management sciences and quantitative methods; marketing; taxation.

THE UNIVERSITY OF TEXAS AT TYLER
Tyler, Texas
Interactive Television
http://www.uttyler.edu

The University of Texas at Tyler was founded in 1971. It is accredited by Southern Association of Colleges and Schools. It first offered distance learning courses in 1991. In fall 2005, there were 1,000 students enrolled in distance learning courses. Institutionally administered financial aid is available to distance learners.

Services Distance learners have accessibility to academic advising, bookstore, e-mail services, library services.

Contact Bonnie Purser, Admissions Assistant, The University of Texas at Tyler, Enrollment Management, 3900 University Boulevard, Tyler, TX 75799. Telephone: 903-566-7202. Fax: 903-566-7068. E-mail: bpurser@uttyler.edu.

DEGREES AND AWARDS

BSN Nursing
MBA Business Administration
MS Kinesiology; Technology–Human Resource Development

COURSE SUBJECT AREAS OFFERED OUTSIDE OF DEGREE PROGRAMS

Undergraduate—accounting and related services; anthropology; archeology; biology; business/commerce; business/corporate communications; community health services; computer science; criminal justice and corrections; criminology; curriculum and instruction; education (specific levels and methods); finance and financial management services; fire protection; geography and cartography; health and physical education/fitness; health professions related; history; human resources management; industrial production technologies; marketing; mathematics; nursing; political science and government; psychology; sales, merchandising, and related marketing operations (specialized); sociology; special education; statistics; technology education/industrial arts.

Graduate—business administration, management and operations; computer science; health professions related; human resources management; management sciences and quantitative methods; nursing; public administration; quality control and safety technologies; special education.

THE UNIVERSITY OF TEXAS OF THE PERMIAN BASIN
Odessa, Texas
REACH Program Center
http://www.utpb.edu/reach/

The University of Texas of the Permian Basin was founded in 1969. It is accredited by Southern Association of Colleges and Schools. It first offered distance learning courses in 1996. In fall 2005, there were 1,881 students enrolled in distance learning courses. Institutionally administered financial aid is available to distance learners.

Services Distance learners have accessibility to academic advising, bookstore, e-mail services, library services, tutoring.

Contact MaryAnn Rangel, Administrative Secretary, The University of Texas of the Permian Basin, 4901 East University Drive, Odessa, TX 79762-0001. Telephone: 432-552-2870. Fax: 432-522-2871. E-mail: rangel_a@utpb.edu.

DEGREES AND AWARDS

BA Criminal Justice
MBA Business Administration
MS Kinesiology

COURSE SUBJECT AREAS OFFERED OUTSIDE OF DEGREE PROGRAMS

Undergraduate—accounting and related services; American literature (United States and Canadian); computer and information sciences; criminology; curriculum and instruction; education related; education (specific subject areas); English as a second language; English composition; fine and studio art; health and physical education/fitness; history; human development, family studies, and related services; industrial and organizational psychology; mathematics; philosophy and religious studies related; psychology; sociology; special education; visual and performing arts.

Graduate—criminal justice and corrections; criminology; curriculum and instruction; educational administration and supervision; educational psychology; education (specific levels and methods); education (specific subject areas); English as a second language; health and physical education/fitness; statistics.

THE UNIVERSITY OF TEXAS SYSTEM
Austin, Texas
UT TeleCampus
http://www.telecampus.utsystem.edu

The University of Texas System is accredited by Southern Association of Colleges and Schools. It first offered distance learning courses in 1999. In fall 2005, there were 2,917 students enrolled in distance learning courses. Institutionally administered financial aid is available to distance learners.

Services Distance learners have accessibility to academic advising, bookstore, campus computer network, library services, tutoring.

Contact Dr. Darcy Hardy, Director, The University of Texas System, 702 Colorado, Suite 4.100, Austin, TX 78701. Telephone: 888-TEXAS-16. Fax: 512-499-4715. E-mail: telecampus@utsystem.edu.

DEGREES AND AWARDS

BS Criminal Justice (Completion Degree)

BSAST Health Services Technology (BAT)

BSN Nursing–RN to BSN

Certificate Blood Bank Technology; Border Administration; Border Studies; Chess in Education Online; Paralegal; Physical Therapy (IMPRINTS); Reading Specialist

Certification Education–Alternative Teacher; Education–Master Reading Teacher; Health Science Technology Teacher; Office Education Teacher; Trade & Industrial (T&I)

Endorsement English as a Second Language (ESL)

Graduate Certificate Nursing Education

MAT Science Education

MBA Business Administration and Management

MEd Curriculum and Instruction–Literacy emphasis; Educational Technology; Kinesiology

MFA Creative Writing–Bilingual

MPA Public Administration

MS Human Resource Development; Kinesiology

COURSE SUBJECT AREAS OFFERED OUTSIDE OF DEGREE PROGRAMS

Undergraduate—accounting and related services; biology; clinical/medical laboratory science and allied professions; computer and information sciences; computer and information sciences and support services related; computer systems networking and telecommunications; creative writing; curriculum and instruction; developmental and child psychology; economics; education; educational/instructional media design; education related; education (specific subject areas); English; English as a second language; English composition; English language and literature related; fine and studio art; geological and earth sciences/geosciences; health professions related; history; information science/studies; liberal arts and sciences, general studies and humanities; linguistic, comparative, and related language studies; mathematics; mathematics and statistics related; music; physical sciences; physical sciences related; political science and government; psychology; social and philosophical foundations of education; social sciences; social sciences related; sociology; statistics.

Graduate—allied health and medical assisting services; computer and information sciences; curriculum and instruction; education; educational/instructional media design; educational psychology; education related; education (specific subject areas); English as a second/foreign language (teaching); health professions related; nursing; political science and government; social and philosophical foundations of education; teaching assistants/aides.

Non-credit—allied health and medical assisting services; clinical/medical laboratory science and allied professions; legal support services; political science and government.

See full description on page 536.

UNIVERSITY OF THE INCARNATE WORD
San Antonio, Texas
Universe Online
http://www.uiw.edu/online

University of the Incarnate Word was founded in 1881. It is accredited by Southern Association of Colleges and Schools. It first offered distance learning courses in 2000. In fall 2005, there were 1,000 students enrolled in distance learning courses. Institutionally administered financial aid is available to distance learners.

Services Distance learners have accessibility to academic advising, bookstore, career placement assistance, library services, tutoring.

Contact Dr. Cyndi Wilson Porter, Dean, Virtual University/Director, Universe Online, University of the Incarnate Word, CPO #324, 4301 Broadway, San Antonio, TX 78209. Telephone: 877-827-2709. Fax: 210-829-2756. E-mail: virtual@universe.uiwtx.edu.

DEGREES AND AWARDS

AA Business; Information Systems; Liberal Studies

BA Human Resources; Organizational Development

BAA Applied Arts and Sciences (BAAS)

BBA Business Administration

MA Administration–Communication Arts; Instructional Technology; Organizational Development

MBA General Program; International

See full description on page 538.

UNIVERSITY OF THE SCIENCES IN PHILADELPHIA
Philadelphia, Pennsylvania
http://www.usip.edu

University of the Sciences in Philadelphia was founded in 1821. It is accredited by Middle States Association of Colleges and Schools. It first offered distance learning courses in 2000. In fall 2005, there were 80 students enrolled in distance learning courses. Institutionally administered financial aid is available to distance learners.

Services Distance learners have accessibility to academic advising, bookstore, career placement assistance, e-mail services, library services.

Contact Ms. Joyce D'Angelo, Admission Counselor, College of Graduate Studies, University of the Sciences in Philadelphia, 600 South 43rd Street, Philadelphia, PA 19104-4418. Telephone: 215-596-8937. Fax: 215-895-1185. E-mail: j.dangel@usip.edu.

DEGREES AND AWARDS

MBA Pharmaceutical Business

MS Biomedical Writing

COURSE SUBJECT AREAS OFFERED OUTSIDE OF DEGREE PROGRAMS

Undergraduate—information science/studies.

Graduate—health services/allied health/health sciences; technical and business writing.

THE UNIVERSITY OF TOLEDO
Toledo, Ohio
Division of Distance and eLearning
http://www.dl.utoledo.edu

The University of Toledo was founded in 1872. It is accredited by North Central Association of Colleges and Schools. It first offered distance learning courses in 1995. In fall 2005, there were 3,464 students enrolled in distance learning courses. Institutionally administered financial aid is available to distance learners.

Services Distance learners have accessibility to academic advising, bookstore, campus computer network, career placement assistance, e-mail services, library services, tutoring.

Contact Janet Green, Assistant Director for Marketing and Enrollment Management, The University of Toledo, Distance and eLearning, MS 215, Toledo, OH 43606-3390. Telephone: 419-321-5130. Fax: 419-321-5147. E-mail: utdl@utoledo.edu.

DEGREES AND AWARDS

AAB Accounting Technology; Business Management Technology–FastTrack option; Business Management Technology; Computer Software Specialist; Information Services and Support; Marketing and Sales Technology; Programming and Software Development
AIS Interdisciplinary program in Technical Studies
AS Computer Science and Engineering Technology
BA Adult Liberal Studies
BS Computer Science and Engineering Technology; Health Information Management
Certificate Accounting Technology; Business Management Technology; Computer Software Specialist; Diversity Management; Information Services and Support; Marketing and Sales Technology; Programming and Sofware Development
MLS Liberal Studies
MSE Engineering

COURSE SUBJECT AREAS OFFERED OUTSIDE OF DEGREE PROGRAMS

Undergraduate—allied health and medical assisting services; area, ethnic, cultural, and gender studies related; communication and media; computer and information sciences; computer/information technology administration and management; criminology; curriculum and instruction; developmental and child psychology; economics; education; education related; engineering technologies related; English; English composition; ethnic, cultural minority, and gender studies; film/video and photographic arts; geography and cartography; health professions related; history; human resources management; journalism; legal studies (non-professional general, undergraduate); liberal arts and sciences, general studies and humanities; mathematics; music; nutrition sciences; philosophy; philosophy and religious studies related; political science and government; psychology; public administration and social service professions related; religious studies; social sciences; social work; sociology; statistics; technical and business writing; visual and performing arts related.
Graduate—counseling psychology; curriculum and instruction; education; educational assessment, evaluation, and research; education related; engineering; engineering related; liberal arts and sciences, general studies and humanities; philosophy; political science and government; special education.

See full description on page 540.

UNIVERSITY OF TORONTO
Toronto, Ontario, Canada
School of Continuing Studies
http://learn.utoronto.ca

University of Toronto was founded in 1827. It is provincially chartered. It first offered distance learning courses in 1944. In fall 2005, there were 5,000 students enrolled in distance learning courses. Institutionally administered financial aid is available to distance learners.
Services Distance learners have accessibility to academic advising, bookstore, e-mail services.
Contact Alison Baird, Operations Manager, University of Toronto, School of Continuing Studies, Toronto, ON M5S 2V8, Canada. Telephone: 416-978-7698. Fax: 416-978-5673. E-mail: alison.baird@utoronto.ca.

DEGREES AND AWARDS

Programs offered do not lead to a degree or other formal award.

COURSE SUBJECT AREAS OFFERED OUTSIDE OF DEGREE PROGRAMS

Undergraduate—accounting and related services; business administration, management and operations; business/commerce; business/corporate communications; business/managerial economics; communication and media; computer/information technology administration and management; economics; finance and financial management services; human resources management; information science/studies; languages (foreign languages related); management sciences and quantitative methods; marketing.
Non-credit—accounting and related services; business administration, management and operations; business/corporate communications; business/managerial economics; communication and media; computer/information technology administration and management; economics; finance and financial management services; human resources management; insurance; languages (East Asian); languages (foreign languages related); languages (Germanic); languages (Romance languages); languages (South Asian); management sciences and quantitative methods; marketing.

UNIVERSITY OF TULSA
Tulsa, Oklahoma
College of Business Administration
http://www.imba.utulsa.edu

University of Tulsa was founded in 1894. It is accredited by North Central Association of Colleges and Schools. It first offered distance learning courses in 2000. In fall 2005, there were 70 students enrolled in distance learning courses. Institutionally administered financial aid is available to distance learners.
Services Distance learners have accessibility to academic advising, bookstore, campus computer network, career placement assistance, e-mail services, library services, tutoring.
Contact Candace Sitzer, Enrollment Management Coordinator, University of Tulsa, 600 South College, BAH 217, Tulsa, OK 74104-3189. Telephone: 918-631-2242. Fax: 918-631-2142. E-mail: graduate-business@utulsa.edu.

DEGREES AND AWARDS

M Tax Taxation
MBA MBA Online

COURSE SUBJECT AREAS OFFERED OUTSIDE OF DEGREE PROGRAMS

Graduate—accounting and related services; business administration, management and operations; business/commerce; business, management, and marketing related; business/managerial economics; computer and information sciences; computer/information technology administration and management; computer software and media applications; computer systems networking and telecommunications; economics; entrepreneurial and small business operations; finance and financial management services; human resources management; information science/studies; international business; legal research and advanced professional studies; management information systems; management sciences and quantitative methods; marketing; sales, merchandising, and related marketing operations (general); taxation.

See full description on page 542.

UNIVERSITY OF UTAH
Salt Lake City, Utah
Distance Education
http://continue.utah.edu/distance

University of Utah was founded in 1850. It is accredited by Northwest Commission on Colleges and Universities. It first offered distance learning courses in 1941. In fall 2005, there were 1,000 students enrolled in distance learning courses. Institutionally administered financial aid is available to distance learners.
Services Distance learners have accessibility to bookstore.
Contact Lisa Himonas, Program Coordinator, University of Utah, 1901 East South Campus Drive, Room 1215, Salt Lake City, UT 84112-9359. Telephone: 801-581-8801. Fax: 801-581-6267. E-mail: distance@aoce.utah.edu.

DEGREES AND AWARDS

Programs offered do not lead to a degree or other formal award.

COURSE SUBJECT AREAS OFFERED OUTSIDE OF DEGREE PROGRAMS

Undergraduate—anthropology; area, ethnic, cultural, and gender studies related; biology; chemistry; creative writing; developmental and child psychology; economics; education (specific subject areas); English literature (British and Commonwealth); finance and financial management services; fine and studio art; foods, nutrition, and related services; history;

mathematics; mathematics and statistics related; music; physics; political science and government; psychology; social psychology; social sciences; special education; statistics.
Non-credit—real estate.

UNIVERSITY OF VIRGINIA
Charlottesville, Virginia
Educational Technologies
http://uvacontinuingstudies.info

University of Virginia was founded in 1819. It is accredited by Southern Association of Colleges and Schools. It first offered distance learning courses in 1983. In fall 2005, there were 675 students enrolled in distance learning courses. Institutionally administered financial aid is available to distance learners.
Services Distance learners have accessibility to academic advising, bookstore, e-mail services, library services.
Contact Office of Admissions, University of Virginia, PO Box 400160, Charlottesville, VA 22904. Telephone: 434-982-3200. Fax: 434-924-3587. E-mail: undergrad-admission@virginia.edu.

DEGREES AND AWARDS
ME Engineering

COURSE SUBJECT AREAS OFFERED OUTSIDE OF DEGREE PROGRAMS
Undergraduate—accounting and related services; computer/information technology administration and management.
Graduate—education.
Non-credit—business administration, management and operations; computer/information technology administration and management; human resources management.

THE UNIVERSITY OF VIRGINIA'S COLLEGE AT WISE
Wise, Virginia
http://www.uvawise.edu

The University of Virginia's College at Wise was founded in 1954. It is accredited by Southern Association of Colleges and Schools. It first offered distance learning courses in 1995. In fall 2005, there were 56 students enrolled in distance learning courses. Institutionally administered financial aid is available to distance learners.
Services Distance learners have accessibility to academic advising, bookstore, campus computer network, career placement assistance, e-mail services, library services, tutoring.
Contact Mr. P. Scott Bevins, Director of Institutional Research/External Programs, The University of Virginia's College at Wise, 1 College Avenue, Wise, VA 24219. Telephone: 276-376-1066. Fax: 276-376-4518. E-mail: pb8q@uvawise.edu.

DEGREES AND AWARDS
Programs offered do not lead to a degree or other formal award.

COURSE SUBJECT AREAS OFFERED OUTSIDE OF DEGREE PROGRAMS
Undergraduate—accounting and related services; business administration, management and operations; economics.

UNIVERSITY OF WASHINGTON
Seattle, Washington
Extension
http://onlinelearning.washington.edu/ol/

University of Washington was founded in 1861. It is accredited by Northwest Commission on Colleges and Universities. In fall 2005, there were 9,700 students enrolled in distance learning courses. Institutionally administered financial aid is available to distance learners.
Services Distance learners have accessibility to academic advising, bookstore, campus computer network, e-mail services, library services.
Contact General Information, University of Washington, 4311 11th Avenue, NE, Seattle, WA 98105-4608. Telephone: 800-543-2320. Fax: 206-685-9359. E-mail: onlinelearning@extn.washington.edu.

DEGREES AND AWARDS
Certificate Brain Research in Education; Business Foundations; Computer Programming–C Programming; Computer Programming–C++ Programming; Computer Programming–Java 2 Programming; Construction Management; Curriculum Integration in Action; Data Resource Management; Database Management; Distance Learning Design and Development; Embedded and Real-Time Systems Programming; Facility Management; Fiction Writing; Gerontology; Heavy Construction Project Management; Infrastructure Construction; Internet Programming; Object-Oriented Analysis and Design Using UML; Project Management; Quantitative Construction Management; School Library Media Specialist; Site Planning; Web Administration; Web Consultant for Small Business; Web Technology Essentials
CCCPE Paralegal
MAE Aerospace Engineering
MEE Electrical Engineering
MLIS Library and Information Science
MS Aeronautics and Astronautics; Construction Engineering; Strategic Planning for Critical Infrastructure
MSE Manufacturing Engineering; Materials Science and Engineering
MSME Mechanical Engineering

COURSE SUBJECT AREAS OFFERED OUTSIDE OF DEGREE PROGRAMS
Undergraduate—accounting and related services; American literature (United States and Canadian); anthropology; applied mathematics; archeology; astronomy and astrophysics; atmospheric sciences and meteorology; building/construction finishing, management, and inspection; business/corporate communications; chemistry; cognitive psychology and psycholinguistics; communication and media; computer engineering; computer programming; computer science; construction engineering technology; creative writing; criminology; curriculum and instruction; developmental and child psychology; economics; education; educational psychology; English; English as a second language; English composition; ethnic, cultural minority, and gender studies; geography and cartography; geological and earth sciences/geosciences; gerontology; history; international business; journalism; languages (Modern Greek); languages (Slavic, Baltic and Albanian); library science; marketing; materials engineering; mathematics; mathematics and statistics related; mechanical engineering; pharmacy, pharmaceutical sciences, and administration; philosophy; political science and government; psychology; religious studies; social psychology; sociology; speech and rhetoric; statistics; technical and business writing; urban studies/affairs.
Graduate—building/construction finishing, management, and inspection; city/urban, community and regional planning; civil engineering; computer science; construction engineering technology; electrical and electronic engineering technologies; engineering/industrial management; engineering related; gerontology; library science; library science related; materials engineering; mechanical engineering; political science and government.
Non-credit—business administration, management and operations; city/urban, community and regional planning; computer and information sciences; computer and information sciences and support services related; computer/information technology administration and management; computer programming; computer software and media applications; computer systems analysis; creative writing; English; English as a second language; information science/studies.

See full description on page 544.

UNIVERSITY OF WATERLOO
Waterloo, Ontario, Canada
Distance and Continuing Education
http://dce.uwaterloo.ca

University of Waterloo was founded in 1957. It is provincially chartered. It first offered distance learning courses in 1968. In fall 2005, there were 4,000 students enrolled in distance learning courses. Institutionally administered financial aid is available to distance learners.

Services Distance learners have accessibility to academic advising, bookstore, campus computer network, e-mail services, library services, tutoring.

Contact Information and Student Services, University of Waterloo, Distance and Continuing Education Office, Waterloo, ON N2L 3G1, Canada. Telephone: 519-888-4050. Fax: 519-746-4607. E-mail: distance@uwaterloo.ca.

DEGREES AND AWARDS

BA Economics; English; General Studies, Non-Major; Humanities; Philosophy; Psychology; Religious Studies; Social Development Studies; Social Sciences

BS Science, general non-major

MM Management Sciences–Master of Management Sciences Online (MMSC)

COURSE SUBJECT AREAS OFFERED OUTSIDE OF DEGREE PROGRAMS

Undergraduate—accounting and related services; American literature (United States and Canadian); anthropology; applied mathematics; area, ethnic, cultural, and gender studies related; area studies; astronomy and astrophysics; biblical and other theological languages and literatures; biblical studies; biochemistry, biophysics and molecular biology; biological and biomedical sciences related; biological and physical sciences; biology; business/managerial economics; cell biology and anatomical sciences; chemistry; community organization and advocacy; computer and information sciences; computer science; criminology; dance; developmental and child psychology; ecology, evolution, and population biology; economics; educational psychology; English composition; English literature (British and Commonwealth); ethnic, cultural minority, and gender studies; finance and financial management services; geological and earth sciences/geosciences; gerontology; history; human development, family studies, and related services; insurance; languages (classics and classical); languages (foreign languages related); languages (Germanic); languages (Modern Greek); languages (Romance languages); languages (Slavic, Baltic and Albanian); liberal arts and sciences, general studies and humanities; linguistic, comparative, and related language studies; mathematics; mathematics and statistics related; medieval and Renaissance studies; microbiological sciences and immunology; multi-/interdisciplinary studies related; peace studies and conflict resolution; philosophy; philosophy and religious studies related; physical sciences; physics; physiology, pathology and related sciences; psychology; psychology related; religious studies; social psychology; social sciences; social sciences related; social work; sociology; statistics.

Graduate—management information systems.

Non-credit—chemistry; English composition; mathematics and statistics related; physics.

UNIVERSITY OF WEST FLORIDA
Pensacola, Florida
Online Campus/Academic Technology Center
http://onlinecampus.uwf.edu

University of West Florida was founded in 1963. It is accredited by Southern Association of Colleges and Schools. It first offered distance learning courses in 1995. In fall 2005, there were 2,500 students enrolled in distance learning courses. Institutionally administered financial aid is available to distance learners.

Services Distance learners have accessibility to academic advising, bookstore, campus computer network, e-mail services, library services, tutoring.

Contact Mrs. Sharon Cobb, Program Coordinator, Academic Technology Center, University of West Florida, 11000 University Parkway, Building 77, Room 138A, Pensacola, FL 32514. Telephone: 850-473-7468. Fax: 850-474-2807. E-mail: scobb@uwf.edu.

DEGREES AND AWARDS

BA Career and Technical Studies Education Specialization; Elementary/Special Education, Dual Major; Maritime Studies

BS Engineering Technology Instructional Support; Oceanography

MA Special Education

MEd Career and Technical Education (CTE); Education and Training Management Subspecialty/Human Performance Technology; Education and Training Management Subspecialty/Instructional Technology; Education–Comprehensive Masters in Education; Instructional Technology

MS Criminal Justice Administration (MSA); Education Leadership (MSA); Health Care Administration (MSA); Human Performance Technology (MSA); Public Administration (MSA); Public Health

COURSE SUBJECT AREAS OFFERED OUTSIDE OF DEGREE PROGRAMS

Undergraduate—anthropology; archeology; biological and biomedical sciences related; biology; business/corporate communications; communication and media; communications technology; computer programming; computer science; computer software and media applications; computer systems networking and telecommunications; data entry/microcomputer applications; economics; engineering technologies related; English; English composition; fine and studio art; history; liberal arts and sciences, general studies and humanities; mathematics; mathematics and statistics related; philosophy; physical sciences; physical sciences related; political science and government; religious studies; statistics; technical and business writing.

Graduate—educational/instructional media design.

Non-credit—business, management, and marketing related; communications technology; computer engineering; education related; education (specific subject areas); human resources management; technology education/industrial arts.

UNIVERSITY OF WISCONSIN COLLEGES
Madison, Wisconsin
UWC On-line
http://www.online.uwc.edu

University of Wisconsin Colleges is accredited by North Central Association of Colleges and Schools. It first offered distance learning courses in 1998. In fall 2005, there were 1,400 students enrolled in distance learning courses. Institutionally administered financial aid is available to distance learners.

Services Distance learners have accessibility to academic advising, bookstore, campus computer network, e-mail services, library services, tutoring.

Contact Ms. Leanne Johnson, DE Coordinator, University of Wisconsin Colleges, 780 Regent Street, Suite 130, Madison, WI 53715-2635. Telephone: 608-263-9553. Fax: 608-262-7872. E-mail: ljohnson@uwc.edu.

DEGREES AND AWARDS

AAS Liberal Arts

COURSE SUBJECT AREAS OFFERED OUTSIDE OF DEGREE PROGRAMS

Undergraduate—anthropology; biological and physical sciences; biology; business/commerce; chemistry; communication and journalism related; English; English composition; fine and studio art; geography and cartography; history; journalism; mathematics; mathematics and computer science; music; philosophy; political science and government; psychology; sociology; statistics.

UNIVERSITY OF WISCONSIN–LA CROSSE
La Crosse, Wisconsin
http://www.uwlax.edu/

University of Wisconsin–La Crosse was founded in 1909. It is accredited by North Central Association of Colleges and Schools. It first offered distance learning courses in 1995. In fall 2005, there were 65 students enrolled in distance learning courses. Institutionally administered financial aid is available to distance learners.

Services Distance learners have accessibility to academic advising, bookstore, campus computer network, career placement assistance, e-mail services, library services, tutoring.

Contact Terry Wirkus, DE Site Support Coordinator, University of Wisconsin–La Crosse, 1725 State Street, La Crosse, WI 54601. Telephone: 608-785-8049. Fax: 608-785-8825. E-mail: wirkus.terr@uwlax.edu.

DEGREES AND AWARDS
Programs offered do not lead to a degree or other formal award.

COURSE SUBJECT AREAS OFFERED OUTSIDE OF DEGREE PROGRAMS
Undergraduate—health professions related; linguistic, comparative, and related language studies.

Graduate—accounting and related services; business administration, management and operations; economics; educational psychology; finance and financial management services; microbiological sciences and immunology; parks, recreation and leisure facilities management; sales, merchandising, and related marketing operations (general).

UNIVERSITY OF WISCONSIN–MADISON
Madison, Wisconsin
http://www.wisc.edu/

University of Wisconsin–Madison was founded in 1848. It is accredited by North Central Association of Colleges and Schools. It first offered distance learning courses in 1991. In fall 2005, there were 11,724 students enrolled in distance learning courses.

Services Distance learners have accessibility to academic advising, bookstore, campus computer network, e-mail services, library services.

Contact University of Wisconsin–Madison.

DEGREES AND AWARDS
BS Nursing
Certificate of Completion Distance Education
MEngr Professional Practice; Technical Japanese
MS Computer Engineering; Electrical Engineering; Mechanical Engineering
PharmD Pharmacy

COURSE SUBJECT AREAS OFFERED OUTSIDE OF DEGREE PROGRAMS
Undergraduate—clinical/medical laboratory science and allied professions; computer science; human development, family studies, and related services; human resources management; languages (East Asian); mechanical engineering; nursing; nutrition sciences; social work.

Graduate—civil engineering; clinical/medical laboratory science and allied professions; computer science; educational psychology; engineering; mechanical engineering; pharmacy, pharmaceutical sciences, and administration; social work.

UNIVERSITY OF WISCONSIN–PARKSIDE
Kenosha, Wisconsin
http://www.uwp.edu/

University of Wisconsin–Parkside was founded in 1968. It is accredited by North Central Association of Colleges and Schools. It first offered distance learning courses in 1996. In fall 2005, there were 27 students enrolled in distance learning courses. Institutionally administered financial aid is available to distance learners.

Services Distance learners have accessibility to academic advising, bookstore, campus computer network, career placement assistance, e-mail services, library services, tutoring.

Contact Bradley R. Piazza, Assistant Dean of the School of Business, University of Wisconsin–Parkside, 900 Wood Road, PO Box 2000, Kenosha, WI 53141-2000. Telephone: 262-595-2046. Fax: 262-595-2680. E-mail: bradley.piazza@uwp.edu.

DEGREES AND AWARDS
Programs offered do not lead to a degree or other formal award.

COURSE SUBJECT AREAS OFFERED OUTSIDE OF DEGREE PROGRAMS
Graduate—accounting and computer science; accounting and related services; business administration, management and operations; business, management, and marketing related; business/managerial economics; economics; finance and financial management services; management information systems; management sciences and quantitative methods; sales, merchandising, and related marketing operations (general); statistics.

UNIVERSITY OF WISCONSIN–PLATTEVILLE
Platteville, Wisconsin
Distance Learning Center
http://www.uwplatt.edu/~disted

University of Wisconsin–Platteville was founded in 1866. It is accredited by North Central Association of Colleges and Schools. It first offered distance learning courses in 1978. In fall 2005, there were 1,000 students enrolled in distance learning courses. Institutionally administered financial aid is available to distance learners.

Services Distance learners have accessibility to academic advising, bookstore, campus computer network, career placement assistance, e-mail services, library services.

Contact Heidi Tuescher Gille, University of Wisconsin–Platteville, B12 Karrmann Library, One University Plaza, Platteville, WI 53818. Telephone: 800-362-5460. Fax: 608-342-1071. E-mail: disted@uwplatt.edu.

DEGREES AND AWARDS
BS Business Administration
Certificate Engineering Management; Human Resource Management; International Business; Leadership and Human Performance; Project Management
Advanced Graduate Diploma Criminal Justice
MS Criminal Justice; Engineering; Project Management

COURSE SUBJECT AREAS OFFERED OUTSIDE OF DEGREE PROGRAMS
Undergraduate—accounting and related services; business administration, management and operations; communication and media; economics; finance and financial management services; human resources management; marketing; mathematics; music; sales, merchandising, and related marketing operations (specialized); speech and rhetoric.

Graduate—business/commerce; civil engineering; communication and media; criminal justice and corrections; education (specific levels and methods); management sciences and quantitative methods; mathematics; mechanical engineering; psychology.

UNIVERSITY OF WISCONSIN–PLATTEVILLE
Platteville, Wisconsin
Online Program in Criminal Justice
http://www.uwplatt.edu/~disted/

University of Wisconsin–Platteville was founded in 1866. It is accredited by North Central Association of Colleges and Schools. It first offered distance learning courses in 1978. In fall 2005, there were 1,000 students enrolled in distance learning courses. Institutionally administered financial aid is available to distance learners.

Services Distance learners have accessibility to academic advising, bookstore, campus computer network, career placement assistance, e-mail services, library services.

Contact Dr. Cheryl Banachowski-Fuller, Program Coordinator of Criminal Justice Distance Education Program, University of Wisconsin–Platteville, 1 University Plaza, Platteville, WI 53818. Telephone: 608-342-1652. Fax: 608-342-1986. E-mail: criminaljstc@uwplatt.edu.

DEGREES AND AWARDS

Advanced Graduate Diploma Criminal Justice
MS Criminal Justice

COURSE SUBJECT AREAS OFFERED OUTSIDE OF DEGREE PROGRAMS

Undergraduate—business/corporate communications; business, management, and marketing related; international business.

Graduate—business administration, management and operations; business/commerce; criminal justice and corrections; criminology; political science and government; psychology; sociology.

UNIVERSITY OF WISCONSIN–PLATTEVILLE
Platteville, Wisconsin
Online Program in Project Management
http://www.uwplatt.edu/~disted/

University of Wisconsin–Platteville was founded in 1866. It is accredited by North Central Association of Colleges and Schools. It first offered distance learning courses in 1978. In fall 2005, there were 1,000 students enrolled in distance learning courses. Institutionally administered financial aid is available to distance learners.

Services Distance learners have accessibility to academic advising, bookstore, campus computer network, career placement assistance, e-mail services, library services.

Contact Bill Haskins, Program Coordinator of Project Management Program, University of Wisconsin–Platteville, 1 University Plaza, Platteville, WI 53818. Telephone: 608-342-1961. Fax: 608-342-1466. E-mail: projectmgmt@uwplatt.edu.

DEGREES AND AWARDS

Certificate Project Management
MS Project Management

COURSE SUBJECT AREAS OFFERED OUTSIDE OF DEGREE PROGRAMS

Graduate—accounting and related services; business administration, management and operations; business/commerce; business/corporate communications; mathematics.

Non-credit—quality control and safety technologies.

UNIVERSITY OF WISCONSIN–PLATTEVILLE
Platteville, Wisconsin
Online Program in Engineering
http://www.uwplatt.edu/~disted/

University of Wisconsin–Platteville was founded in 1866. It is accredited by North Central Association of Colleges and Schools. It first offered distance learning courses in 1978. In fall 2005, there were 1,000 students enrolled in distance learning courses. Institutionally administered financial aid is available to distance learners.

Services Distance learners have accessibility to academic advising, bookstore, campus computer network, career placement assistance, e-mail services, library services.

Contact Dr. Lisa Riedle, Program Coordinator of Engineering Distance Education Program, University of Wisconsin–Platteville, 1 University Plaza, Platteville, WI 53818. Telephone: 608-342-1686. Fax: 608-342-1566. E-mail: engineering@uwplatt.edu.

DEGREES AND AWARDS

MS Engineering

COURSE SUBJECT AREAS OFFERED OUTSIDE OF DEGREE PROGRAMS

Graduate—business administration, management and operations; business/commerce; business/corporate communications; computer engineering; electrical, electronics and communications engineering; engineering; engineering design; engineering/industrial management; engineering related; mathematics; statistics.

UNIVERSITY OF WISCONSIN–PLATTEVILLE
Platteville, Wisconsin
Bachelor of Science in Business Administration
http://www.uwplatt.edu/~disted/

University of Wisconsin–Platteville was founded in 1866. It is accredited by North Central Association of Colleges and Schools. It first offered distance learning courses in 1978. In fall 2005, there were 1,000 students enrolled in distance learning courses. Institutionally administered financial aid is available to distance learners.

Services Distance learners have accessibility to academic advising, bookstore, campus computer network, career placement assistance, e-mail services, library services.

Contact Marge Karsten, Chair of Business and Accounting Department, University of Wisconsin–Platteville, 1 University Plaza, Platteville, WI 53818. Telephone: 608-342-1749. Fax: 608-342-1466. E-mail: businessadmn@uwplatt.edu.

DEGREES AND AWARDS

BSBA Business Administration
Certificate Human Resource Management; International Business; Leadership and Human Performance

COURSE SUBJECT AREAS OFFERED OUTSIDE OF DEGREE PROGRAMS

Undergraduate—accounting and related services; business administration, management and operations; business/commerce; business/corporate communications; communication and media; economics; finance and financial management services; human resources management; international business; marketing; mathematics; public relations, advertising, and applied communication related.

Graduate—business administration, management and operations; business/corporate communications.

UNIVERSITY OF WISCONSIN–RIVER FALLS
River Falls, Wisconsin
Outreach Office
http://www.uwrf.edu/ogs

University of Wisconsin–River Falls was founded in 1874. It is accredited by North Central Association of Colleges and Schools. It first offered distance learning courses in 1982. In fall 2005, there were 200 students enrolled in distance learning courses. Institutionally administered financial aid is available to distance learners.

Services Distance learners have accessibility to academic advising, bookstore, career placement assistance, e-mail services, library services, tutoring.

Contact Katrina Larsen, Director of Outreach Programs, University of Wisconsin–River Falls, 410 South 3rd Street, River Falls, WI 54022. Telephone: 715-425-3256. Fax: 715-425-0624. E-mail: katrina.larsen@uwrf.edu.

DEGREES AND AWARDS

Programs offered do not lead to a degree or other formal award.

COURSE SUBJECT AREAS OFFERED OUTSIDE OF DEGREE PROGRAMS

Undergraduate—accounting and computer science; agricultural and food products processing; agricultural business and management; agriculture; astronomy and astrophysics; business administration, management and operations; business/commerce; business, management, and marketing related; communication and media; computer and information sciences; dramatic/theater arts and stagecraft; education (specific subject areas); geological and earth sciences/geosciences; history; liberal arts and sciences, general studies and humanities; political science and government; psychology; sociology; speech and rhetoric.

Graduate—agricultural business and management; biological and biomedical sciences related; biological and physical sciences; city/urban, community and regional planning; community organization and advocacy; counseling psychology; curriculum and instruction; economics; education; education (specific levels and methods); education (specific subject areas); environmental design; food science and technology; geological and earth sciences/geosciences; history; hospitality administration; natural resources and conservation related; natural resources management and policy; parks, recreation and leisure facilities management; political science and government; sales, merchandising, and related marketing operations (specialized); special education; statistics; wildlife and wildlands science and management.

UNIVERSITY OF WISCONSIN–STOUT
Menomonie, Wisconsin
Office of Continuing Education
http://www.uwstout.edu/solutions/ces

University of Wisconsin–Stout was founded in 1891. It is accredited by North Central Association of Colleges and Schools. It first offered distance learning courses in 1980. In fall 2005, there were 3,500 students enrolled in distance learning courses. Institutionally administered financial aid is available to distance learners.

Services Distance learners have accessibility to academic advising, bookstore, campus computer network, career placement assistance, e-mail services, library services.

Contact Sandra White, Credit Outreach Program Manager III, University of Wisconsin–Stout, Outreach Services, 140 Vocational Rehabilitation Building, Menomonie, WI 54751-0790. Telephone: 715-232-2693. Fax: 715-232-3385. E-mail: whites@uwstout.edu.

DEGREES AND AWARDS

BS Career and Technical Education; Management

Certification Reading Teacher Certification

MS Career and Technical Education; Education; Hospitality and Tourism Management; Manufacturing Engineering; Technology Management; Training and Development

COURSE SUBJECT AREAS OFFERED OUTSIDE OF DEGREE PROGRAMS

Undergraduate—business, management, and marketing related; chemistry; developmental and child psychology; economics; education; human resources management.

Graduate—developmental and child psychology; education; human resources management; management sciences and quantitative methods.

Non-credit—computer systems networking and telecommunications; gerontology; human development, family studies, and related services; human resources management.

UNIVERSITY OF WISCONSIN–SUPERIOR
Superior, Wisconsin
http://dlc.uwsuper.edu/

University of Wisconsin–Superior was founded in 1893. It is accredited by North Central Association of Colleges and Schools. It first offered distance learning courses in 1978. In fall 2005, there were 256 students enrolled in distance learning courses. Institutionally administered financial aid is available to distance learners.

Services Distance learners have accessibility to academic advising, bookstore, campus computer network, career placement assistance, e-mail services, library services, tutoring.

Contact Barbara Doherty, Student Services Program Manager, University of Wisconsin–Superior, Distance Learning Center, PO Box 2000, Belknap and Catlin, Superior, WI 54880. Telephone: 715-394-8487. Fax: 715-394-8139. E-mail: dlc@uwsuper.edu.

DEGREES AND AWARDS

BS Elementary Education; Individualized major

COURSE SUBJECT AREAS OFFERED OUTSIDE OF DEGREE PROGRAMS

Undergraduate—accounting and computer science; American literature (United States and Canadian); biology; business administration, management and operations; communication and media; education; English; fine and studio art; mathematics and computer science; physical sciences; social sciences.

Graduate—education; educational administration and supervision; health psychology.

See full description on page 546.

UNIVERSITY OF WISCONSIN–WHITEWATER
Whitewater, Wisconsin

University of Wisconsin–Whitewater was founded in 1868. It is accredited by North Central Association of Colleges and Schools. It first offered distance learning courses in 1980. In fall 2005, there were 1,455 students enrolled in distance learning courses. Institutionally administered financial aid is available to distance learners.

Services Distance learners have accessibility to bookstore, e-mail services, library services.

Contact Lorna Wong, Director, Instructional Technology Services, University of Wisconsin–Whitewater, 800 West Main Street, Whitewater, WI 53190. Telephone: 262-472-7795. E-mail: disted@uww.edu.

DEGREES AND AWARDS

MBA Business Administration–Online Masters of Business Administration

COURSE SUBJECT AREAS OFFERED OUTSIDE OF DEGREE PROGRAMS

Undergraduate—accounting and computer science; anthropology; area, ethnic, cultural, and gender studies related; business administration, management and operations; business, management, and marketing related; communication and journalism related; communication and media; creative writing; curriculum and instruction; economics; education; education related; English; English as a second language; ethnic, cultural minority, and gender studies; history; journalism; languages (foreign languages related); library science; management information systems; marketing; political science and government.

Graduate—accounting and related services; area, ethnic, cultural, and gender studies related; business administration, management and operations; business, management, and marketing related; communication and journalism related; creative writing; economics; English; English as a second language; finance and financial management services; history; journalism; management information systems; marketing; political science and government; psychology related.

UNIVERSITY OF WYOMING
Laramie, Wyoming
Outreach School
http://outreach.uwyo.edu/occ

University of Wyoming was founded in 1886. It is accredited by North Central Association of Colleges and Schools. In fall 2005, there were 3,931 students enrolled in distance learning courses. Institutionally administered financial aid is available to distance learners.

Services Distance learners have accessibility to academic advising, bookstore, campus computer network, career placement assistance, e-mail services, library services, tutoring.

Contact Ms. Judith E. Atencio, Program Manager, Outreach Credit Programs, University of Wyoming, Department 3274, 1000 East University Avenue, Laramie, WY 82071. Telephone: 800-448-7801. Fax: 307-766-4048. E-mail: occ@uwyo.edu.

DEGREES AND AWARDS

BA Criminal Justice; Social Sciences

BS Business Administration; Family and Consumer Sciences (Family and Community Services option); Family and Consumer Sciences (Professional Child Development option); Psychology; Social Sciences

BSN Nursing–RN to BSN

Certificate Family and Consumer Sciences (Early Childhood Program Director's certificate); Land Surveying; Real Estate

Endorsement Early Childhood (Birth to Five); Literacy (Wyoming Reading Endorsement)

MA Education–Adult and Post-Secondary Education; Education–Special Education; Education–Teaching and Learning

MBA Business Administration

MPA Public Administration

MS Education–Instructional Technology; Kinesiology and Health; Nursing–Nurse Educator option; Speech-Language Pathology

MSW Social Work

COURSE SUBJECT AREAS OFFERED OUTSIDE OF DEGREE PROGRAMS

Undergraduate—agriculture; American literature (United States and Canadian); astronomy and astrophysics; biological and biomedical sciences related; botany/plant biology; business/commerce; chemistry; communication and media; criminal justice and corrections; education; English composition; English literature (British and Commonwealth); ethnic, cultural minority, and gender studies; family and consumer economics; foods, nutrition, and related services; geography and cartography; history; liberal arts and sciences, general studies and humanities; mathematics; music; nursing; physics; real estate; social psychology; statistics.

Graduate—business administration, management and operations; education; educational/instructional media design; health professions related; nursing; public administration; social work.

See full description on page 548.

UPPER IOWA UNIVERSITY
Fayette, Iowa
External Degree
http://www.uiu.edu

Upper Iowa University was founded in 1857. It is accredited by North Central Association of Colleges and Schools. It first offered distance learning courses in 1973. In fall 2005, there were 1,800 students enrolled in distance learning courses. Institutionally administered financial aid is available to distance learners.

Services Distance learners have accessibility to academic advising, bookstore, career placement assistance, library services.

Contact Barbara J. Schultz, Director of External Degree, Upper Iowa University, PO Box 1861, Fayette, IA 52142. Telephone: 888-877-3742. Fax: 563-425-5353. E-mail: extdegree@uiu.edu.

DEGREES AND AWARDS

AA Business, general; Liberal Arts

BS Accounting; Business Administration; Criminal Justice; Emergency and Disaster Management; Finance; Health Services Administration; Human Resources Management; Human Services; Interdisciplinary Studies; Management; Marketing; Psychology; Public Administration; Public Administration–Fire Science emphasis; Public Administration–Law Enforcement emphasis; Social Sciences; Technology and Information Management

Certificate Emergency and Disaster Management; Human Resources Management; Marketing; Organizational Communications; Organizational Leadership

COURSE SUBJECT AREAS OFFERED OUTSIDE OF DEGREE PROGRAMS

Undergraduate—accounting and related services; astronomy and astrophysics; biology; business administration, management and operations; communication and media; criminal justice and corrections; English; English composition; history; human resources management; human services; industrial and organizational psychology; international business; legal studies (non-professional general, undergraduate); liberal arts and sciences, general studies and humanities; management information systems; management sciences and quantitative methods; marketing; mathematics; philosophy and religious studies related; political science and government; psychology; psychology related; public administration; public administration and social service professions related; public relations, advertising, and applied communication related; social psychology; sociology; statistics.

Non-credit—accounting and computer science; accounting and related services; biological and physical sciences; biology; communication and media; English composition; history; industrial and organizational psychology; international business; management information systems; marketing; political science and government; psychology; public administration; sociology; statistics.

See full description on page 550.

UTAH STATE UNIVERSITY
Logan, Utah
Independent and Distance Education
http://extension.usu.edu

Utah State University was founded in 1888. It is accredited by Northwest Commission on Colleges and Universities. It first offered distance learning courses in 1983. In fall 2005, there were 7,300 students enrolled in distance learning courses. Institutionally administered financial aid is available to distance learners.

Services Distance learners have accessibility to academic advising, bookstore, campus computer network, e-mail services, library services.

Contact Staff Assistant, Independent and Distance Education, Utah State University, 5055 Old Main Hill, Logan, UT 84322-5055. Telephone: 800-233-2137. Fax: 435-797-1399. E-mail: de-info@ext.usu.edu.

DEGREES AND AWARDS

AAS Office Support Systems; Ornamental Horticulture

AS General Studies

BS Business; Communicative Disorders and Deaf Education (Post Bachelor's); Computer Science; Psychology; Special Education

MEd Elementary or Secondary Education; Health, Physical Education, and Recreation; Instructional Technology–Educational Technology emphasis; Special Education

MFHD Family and Human Development

MS Business Information Systems; Computer Science; English/Technical Writing Specialization Online; FCSEE or AST Specialization; Psychology–School Counseling specialization; Special Education

EdD Education

COURSE SUBJECT AREAS OFFERED OUTSIDE OF DEGREE PROGRAMS

Undergraduate—accounting and related services; anthropology; applied mathematics; biology; business administration, management and operations; business operations support and assistant services; chemistry; communication disorders sciences and services; data entry/microcomputer applications; data processing; economics; English; English literature (British and Commonwealth); family and consumer economics; family and consumer sciences/human sciences; history; human resources management; liberal arts and sciences, general studies and humanities; mathematics; mathematics and statistics related; philosophy; physical sciences; physics; psychology; social psychology; social sciences; social work; sociology; special education; statistics.

Graduate—agriculture and agriculture operations related; business administration, management and operations; computer programming; computer science; computer software and media applications; computer systems analysis; computer systems networking and telecommunications; curriculum and instruction; education; educational administration and supervision; educational assessment, evaluation, and research; educational/instructional media design; educational psychology; education (specific levels and methods); education (specific subject areas); English; family and consumer sciences/human sciences; human development, family studies, and related services; human resources management; library science related; psychology; school psychology; social sciences related; special education.

See full description on page 552.

UTAH VALLEY STATE COLLEGE
Orem, Utah
Department of Distance Education
http://www.uvsc.edu/disted

Utah Valley State College was founded in 1941. It is accredited by Northwest Commission on Colleges and Universities. It first offered distance learning courses in 1988. In fall 2005, there were 10,000 students enrolled in distance learning courses. Institutionally administered financial aid is available to distance learners.

Services Distance learners have accessibility to academic advising, bookstore, campus computer network, career placement assistance, e-mail services, library services, tutoring.

Contact Karen Merrick, Support Center Coordinator, Utah Valley State College, 800 West University Parkway, MS 149, Orem, UT 84058. Telephone: 801-863-HELP. Fax: 801-863-7298. E-mail: dehelp@uvsc.edu.

DEGREES AND AWARDS

AS Communication; Criminal Justice; General Studies
BS Aviation Science

COURSE SUBJECT AREAS OFFERED OUTSIDE OF DEGREE PROGRAMS

Undergraduate—accounting and related services; air transportation; American literature (United States and Canadian); anthropology; astronomy and astrophysics; atmospheric sciences and meteorology; behavioral sciences; biological and physical sciences; biology; business administration, management and operations; business/corporate communications; business, management, and marketing related; communication and journalism related; communication and media; computer and information sciences; creative writing; dramatic/theater arts and stagecraft; electrical/electronics maintenance and repair technology; English; English composition; fire protection; history; hospitality administration; languages (foreign languages related); legal studies (non-professional general, undergraduate); management information systems; ocean engineering; philosophy; political science and government; psychology; public relations, advertising, and applied communication related; social sciences; sociology; zoology/animal biology.
Non-credit—computer and information sciences; computer software and media applications.

UTAH VALLEY STATE COLLEGE
Orem, Utah
Global Aviation Degree Center
http://www.aviationuniversity.com

Utah Valley State College was founded in 1941. It is accredited by Northwest Commission on Colleges and Universities. It first offered distance learning courses in 1997. In fall 2005, there were 1,500 students enrolled in distance learning courses. Institutionally administered financial aid is available to distance learners.
Services Distance learners have accessibility to academic advising, bookstore, campus computer network, career placement assistance, e-mail services, library services, tutoring.
Contact Claire Downing, Coordinator of Global Aviation, Utah Valley State College, 800 West University Parkway, Orem, UT 84058-5999. Telephone: 888-901-7192 Ext. 7816. Fax: 801-764-7815. E-mail: downincl@uvsc.edu.

DEGREES AND AWARDS

AAS Aviation Job Ready Degree
AS Aviation (Baccalaureate Degree transfer)
BS Aviation Professional Pilot

COURSE SUBJECT AREAS OFFERED OUTSIDE OF DEGREE PROGRAMS

Undergraduate—aerospace, aeronautical and astronautical engineering; biology; English composition; English language and literature related; fine and studio art; health and physical education/fitness; history; mathematics; philosophy; physical sciences; social sciences; social sciences related.
Graduate—aerospace, aeronautical and astronautical engineering.

UTICA COLLEGE
Utica, New York

Utica College was founded in 1946. It is accredited by Middle States Association of Colleges and Schools. It first offered distance learning courses in 2000. In fall 2005, there were 329 students enrolled in distance learning courses. Institutionally administered financial aid is available to distance learners.
Services Distance learners have accessibility to academic advising, bookstore, campus computer network, e-mail services, library services, tutoring.
Contact Mr. Cory Berntson, Coordinator, On-Line Programs, Utica College, 1600 Burrstone Road, Office of Graduate and Extended Services, Utica, NY 13502. Telephone: 866-295-3106 Ext. 5314. E-mail: cberntson@utica.edu.

DEGREES AND AWARDS

BS Criminal Justice Economic Crime Investigation; Cybersecurity and Information Assurance
Certificate Financial Crime Investication Certificate Program
MBA Business Administration–Economic Crime and Fraud Management; Business Administration–Professional Accountancy
MS Economic Crime Management
DPT Physical Therapy–Transitional Doctorate of Physical Therapy

COURSE SUBJECT AREAS OFFERED OUTSIDE OF DEGREE PROGRAMS

Undergraduate—biology; economics; English; gerontology; liberal arts and sciences, general studies and humanities; mathematics; psychology.

VALLEY CITY STATE UNIVERSITY
Valley City, North Dakota
North Dakota Interactive Video Network
http://distancelearning.vcsu.edu

Valley City State University was founded in 1890. It is accredited by North Central Association of Colleges and Schools. It first offered distance learning courses in 2000. In fall 2005, there were 95 students enrolled in distance learning courses. Institutionally administered financial aid is available to distance learners.
Services Distance learners have accessibility to academic advising, bookstore, campus computer network, career placement assistance, e-mail services.
Contact Monte Johnson, Registrar, Valley City State University, 101 College Street, SW, Valley City, ND 58072. Telephone: 701-845-7295 Ext. 7297. Fax: 701-845-7299. E-mail: monte.johnson@vcsu.edu.

DEGREES AND AWARDS

Programs offered do not lead to a degree or other formal award.

COURSE SUBJECT AREAS OFFERED OUTSIDE OF DEGREE PROGRAMS

Undergraduate—communication and journalism related; English as a second language; English composition; health and physical education/fitness; library science; psychology; speech and rhetoric; technology education/industrial arts.
Graduate—education; technology education/industrial arts.

VALPARAISO UNIVERSITY
Valparaiso, Indiana
http://www.valpo.edu/

Valparaiso University was founded in 1859. It is accredited by North Central Association of Colleges and Schools. It first offered distance learning courses in 2002. In fall 2005, there were 200 students enrolled in distance learning courses. Institutionally administered financial aid is available to distance learners.
Services Distance learners have accessibility to academic advising, library services.
Contact Janice Pedersen, Coordinator of Academic and Student Services, Valparaiso University, Kretzmann Hall, #116, 1700 Chapel Drive, Valparaiso, IN 46383. Telephone: 800-821-7685. Fax: 219-464-5381. E-mail: graduate.studies@valpo.edu.

DEGREES AND AWARDS

Programs offered do not lead to a degree or other formal award.

COURSE SUBJECT AREAS OFFERED OUTSIDE OF DEGREE PROGRAMS

Undergraduate—communication and media; education; nursing; theology and religious vocations related.
Graduate—communication and media; theology and religious vocations related.

VANCE-GRANVILLE COMMUNITY COLLEGE
Henderson, North Carolina
http://www.vgcc.edu

Vance-Granville Community College was founded in 1969. It is accredited by Southern Association of Colleges and Schools. It first offered distance learning courses in 1998. In fall 2005, there were 1,101 students enrolled in distance learning courses. Institutionally administered financial aid is available to distance learners.

Services Distance learners have accessibility to academic advising, bookstore, library services.

Contact Evelyn Harris, Director of Distance Education, Vance-Granville Community College, PO Box 917, Henderson, NC 27536. Telephone: 252-492-2061. Fax: 252-738-3372. E-mail: harris@vgcc.edu.

DEGREES AND AWARDS

AA General Studies

AAS Business Administration; Business Administration; Information Systems; Information Systems/Network Administration and Support

Certificate Early Childhood Associate–Administration; Early Childhood Associate–General Education; Early Childood Associate–Special Needs

COURSE SUBJECT AREAS OFFERED OUTSIDE OF DEGREE PROGRAMS

Undergraduate—accounting and related services; American literature (United States and Canadian); biology; business administration, management and operations; business operations support and assistant services; computer/information technology administration and management; computer programming; computer systems networking and telecommunications; criminal justice and corrections; criminology; economics; English composition; history; human development, family studies, and related services; human services; information science/studies; liberal arts and sciences, general studies and humanities; marketing; political science and government; psychology; sociology; statistics; teaching assistants/ aides.

Non-credit—accounting and related services; building/construction finishing, management, and inspection; business/commerce; business/ corporate communications; computer and information sciences; computer programming; computer software and media applications; computer systems networking and telecommunications; data entry/microcomputer applications; entrepreneurial and small business operations; personal and culinary services related; sales, merchandising, and related marketing operations (specialized); technical and business writing.

VANGUARD UNIVERSITY OF SOUTHERN CALIFORNIA
Costa Mesa, California
http://www.vanguard.edu/eec

Vanguard University of Southern California was founded in 1920. It is accredited by Western Association of Schools and Colleges. It first offered distance learning courses in 2002. In fall 2005, there were 250 students enrolled in distance learning courses. Institutionally administered financial aid is available to distance learners.

Services Distance learners have accessibility to academic advising, bookstore, career placement assistance, e-mail services, library services, tutoring.

Contact Adm. Bren Martin, Child Development Program, Vanguard University of Southern California, 55 Fair Drive, Costa Mesa, CA 92626. Telephone: 714-668-6196 Ext. 472. Fax: 714-966-5460. E-mail: eecadmissions@vanguard.edu.

DEGREES AND AWARDS

Programs offered do not lead to a degree or other formal award.

COURSE SUBJECT AREAS OFFERED OUTSIDE OF DEGREE PROGRAMS

Undergraduate—curriculum and instruction; education; educational administration and supervision; education related; human development, family studies, and related services.

VERMONT TECHNICAL COLLEGE
Randolph Center, Vermont
http://www.vtc.vsc.edu/

Vermont Technical College was founded in 1866. It is accredited by New England Association of Schools and Colleges. It first offered distance learning courses in 1996. In fall 2005, there were 75 students enrolled in distance learning courses. Institutionally administered financial aid is available to distance learners.

Services Distance learners have accessibility to academic advising, bookstore, campus computer network, e-mail services, library services.

Contact Mr. Michael Dempsey, Registrar, Vermont Technical College, PO Box 500, Randolph Center, VT 05061. Telephone: 802-728-1302. Fax: 802-728-1597. E-mail: mdempsey@vtc.edu.

DEGREES AND AWARDS

Programs offered do not lead to a degree or other formal award.

COURSE SUBJECT AREAS OFFERED OUTSIDE OF DEGREE PROGRAMS

Undergraduate—computer and information sciences; history; social sciences related.

VINCENNES UNIVERSITY
Vincennes, Indiana
Distance Education/Degree Completion
http://www.vinu.edu/distance

Vincennes University was founded in 1801. It is accredited by North Central Association of Colleges and Schools. It first offered distance learning courses in 1989. In fall 2005, there were 1,000 students enrolled in distance learning courses. Institutionally administered financial aid is available to distance learners.

Services Distance learners have accessibility to academic advising, bookstore, campus computer network, career placement assistance, e-mail services, library services, tutoring.

Contact Mr. Donald E. Kaufman, Dean of Continuing Studies, Vincennes University, 1002 North First Street, Classroom Building A, Vincennes, IN 47591. Telephone: 812-888-5343. Fax: 812-888-2054. E-mail: dkaufman@vinu.edu.

DEGREES AND AWARDS

AAS Funeral Service Education; General Studies–Business Studies; General Studies; Law Enforcement Studies; Technology Apprenticeship–General Studies option

AS Behavioral Sciences; Business Administration; General Studies Surgical Technology Degree completion; General Studies; Health Information Management; Law Enforcement Studies; Recreation Management–Therapeutic option; Technology Apprenticeship

Certificate of Completion Administrative Office Technology–Office Software Specialist; Behavioral Science–Substance Abuse Certificate; Community Rehabilitation; Pharmacy Technician

Certificate General Studies–Customized Certificate

Graduate Certificate Surgical Technology Accelerated Option, Certificate of Graduation

COURSE SUBJECT AREAS OFFERED OUTSIDE OF DEGREE PROGRAMS

Undergraduate—accounting and related services; allied health and medical assisting services; applied mathematics; business/commerce; business operations support and assistant services; chemistry; community health services; computer and information sciences; creative writing; criminal justice and corrections; developmental and child psychology; economics; education; English composition; entrepreneurial and small business operations; fire protection; funeral service and mortuary science; history; information science/studies; mathematics; parks, recreation and leisure facilities management; pharmacy, pharmaceutical sciences, and administration; psychology; rehabilitation and therapeutic professions; sales, merchandising, and related marketing operations (specialized); social sciences; social work; sociology; speech and rhetoric.

VIRGINIA POLYTECHNIC INSTITUTE AND STATE UNIVERSITY

Blacksburg, Virginia

Institute for Distance and Distributed Learning

http://iddl.vt.edu

Virginia Polytechnic Institute and State University was founded in 1872. It is accredited by Southern Association of Colleges and Schools. It first offered distance learning courses in 1983. In fall 2005, there were 5,095 students enrolled in distance learning courses. Institutionally administered financial aid is available to distance learners.

Services Distance learners have accessibility to academic advising, bookstore, campus computer network, career placement assistance, e-mail services, library services, tutoring.

Contact Ms. Angie Starr, Online Enrollment Specialist, Virginia Polytechnic Institute and State University, Institute for Distance and Distributed Learning, Blacksburg, VA 24061. Telephone: 540-231-1264. Fax: 540-231-2079. E-mail: vto@vt.edu.

DEGREES AND AWARDS

License Alternative Teaching; Career and Technical Education
Graduate Certificate Computer Engineering; IT Business Information Systems; IT Communication; IT Decision Support Systems; IT Networking; Liberal Arts; Natural Resources; Software Development
MA Instructional Technology–Curriculum and Instruction emphasis
MBA Business Administration
MIT Information Technology
MS Agricultural and Life Sciences; Career and Technical Education; Civil Infrastructure Engineering; Civil and Environmental Engineering; Computer Engineering; Curriculum and Instruction–Health Promotion emphasis; Electrical and Computer Engineering; Engineering Administration; Ocean Engineering; Political Science; Systems Engineering

COURSE SUBJECT AREAS OFFERED OUTSIDE OF DEGREE PROGRAMS

Undergraduate—agriculture; agriculture and agriculture operations related; apparel and textiles; applied horticulture/horticultural business services; civil engineering; communication and media; computer engineering; computer science; education (specific levels and methods); education (specific subject areas); electrical and electronic engineering technologies; engineering; English composition; ethnic, cultural minority, and gender studies; fishing and fisheries sciences and management; geography and cartography; history; hospitality administration; human resources management; languages (Romance languages); linguistic, comparative, and related language studies; marketing; mathematics; music; philosophy; physics; political science and government; religious studies; science technologies related; sociology.

Graduate—accounting and related services; aerospace, aeronautical and astronautical engineering; agriculture and agriculture operations related; applied horticulture/horticultural business services; computer engineering; computer science; curriculum and instruction; educational administration and supervision; education related; education (specific subject areas); English; ethnic, cultural minority, and gender studies; forestry; geography and cartography; management information systems; marketing; mathematics; mechanical engineering; natural resources management and policy; political science and government; public administration; science technologies related; urban studies/affairs; veterinary biomedical and clinical sciences.

Non-credit—applied horticulture/horticultural business services; architecture; business/commerce; computer software and media applications; education; engineering; engineering technologies related; history; music; natural resources conservation and research; public health.

See full description on page 554.

VITERBO UNIVERSITY

La Crosse, Wisconsin

Viterbo University was founded in 1890. It is accredited by North Central Association of Colleges and Schools. It first offered distance learning courses in 2001. In fall 2005, there were 500 students enrolled in distance learning courses. Institutionally administered financial aid is available to distance learners.

Services Distance learners have accessibility to academic advising, bookstore, campus computer network, career placement assistance, e-mail services, library services, tutoring.

Contact Deb Randall Anderson, Viterbo University, School of Adult Learning, 900 Viterbo Drive, La Crosse, WI 54601. Telephone: 608-796-3370. E-mail: drandallanderson@viterbo.edu.

DEGREES AND AWARDS

Programs offered do not lead to a degree or other formal award.

COURSE SUBJECT AREAS OFFERED OUTSIDE OF DEGREE PROGRAMS

Undergraduate—accounting and computer science; biblical studies; business, management, and marketing related; liberal arts and sciences, general studies and humanities; nursing; social sciences.

Graduate—business administration, management and operations; education; nursing; theological and ministerial studies.

WAKE TECHNICAL COMMUNITY COLLEGE

Raleigh, North Carolina

http://www.waketech.edu

Wake Technical Community College was founded in 1958. It is accredited by Southern Association of Colleges and Schools. It first offered distance learning courses in 1986. In fall 2005, there were 3,332 students enrolled in distance learning courses. Institutionally administered financial aid is available to distance learners.

Services Distance learners have accessibility to academic advising, bookstore, career placement assistance, e-mail services, library services, tutoring.

Contact Diana Osborne, Head, Distance Education Support Department, Wake Technical Community College, 9101 Fayetteville Road, Raleigh, NC 27603-5696. Telephone: 919-773-4741. Fax: 919-773-6190. E-mail: dgosborn@waketech.edu.

DEGREES AND AWARDS

AA College/University Transfer
AAS Web Technologies

COURSE SUBJECT AREAS OFFERED OUTSIDE OF DEGREE PROGRAMS

Undergraduate—accounting and related services; allied health and medical assisting services; American literature (United States and Canadian); biology; business/commerce; business operations support and assistant services; computer and information sciences and support services related; computer software and media applications; computer systems networking and telecommunications; criminal justice and corrections; economics; engineering technology; English composition; English literature (British and Commonwealth); geological and earth sciences/geosciences; heating, air conditioning, ventilation and refrigeration maintenance technology; history; marketing; mathematics; philosophy; psychology; social work; sociology.

Non-credit—accounting and related services; business administration, management and operations; computer software and media applications; English as a second language; entrepreneurial and small business operations; film/video and photographic arts; technical and business writing.

WALDEN UNIVERSITY

Minneapolis, Minnesota

http://www.waldenu.edu/

Walden University was founded in 1970. It is accredited by North Central Association of Colleges and Schools. It first offered distance learning courses in 1970. In fall 2005, there were 25,301 students enrolled in distance learning courses. Institutionally administered financial aid is available to distance learners.

Services Distance learners have accessibility to academic advising, bookstore, campus computer network, career placement assistance, e-mail services, library services, tutoring.

Contact Enrollment Advisor, Walden University, 1001 Fleet Street, Baltimore, MD 21202. Telephone: 866-492-5336. E-mail: info@waldenu.edu.

DEGREES AND AWARDS

BS Business Administration Completion–Finance; Business Administration Completion–Human Resource Management; Business Administration Completion–Information Systems; Business Administration Completion–Management; Business Administration Completion–Marketing; Business Administration Completion, general

MBA Business Administration, general; E-Business; Finance; Global Business; Health Services; High-Tech–Technical MBA; Human Resource Management; Knowledge and Learning Management; Management of Technology; Marketing; Nonprofit Management; Risk Management/Insurance

MBA/MPA Dual Degree

MBA/MPH Dual Degree

MPA General Program; Health Services; Homeland Security, Policy, and Coordination; International Nongovernmental Organizations (NGOs); Knowledge Management; Nonprofit Management and Leadership; Public Administration/Public Health–MPH Master of Public Administration and Master of Public Health Dual Degree; Public Management and Leadership; Public Policy; Public Safety Management

MPH Community Health

MS Computer Engineering; Computer Science; Education–Curriculum, Instruction, and Assessment (Grades K–12); Education–Educational Leadership; Education–Elementary Reading and Literacy (Grades K–6); Education–Elementary Reading and Mathematics (Grades K–6); Education–Integrating Technology in the Classroom (Grades 3–12); Education–Literacy and Learning in the Content Areas (Grades 6–12); Education–Mathematics (Grades 6–8); Education–Mathematics (Grades K–5); Education–Middle Level Education (Grades 5–8); Education–Science (Grades K–8); Electrical Engineering–Communications Track; Electrical Engineering–Intigrated Circuits Track; Electrical Engineering–Microelectronic and Semiconductor Engineering; Engineering Management; Mental Health Counseling; Nursing–BSN track, Education; Nursing–BSN track, Leadership and Management; Nursing–RN track, Education; Nursing–RN track, Leadership and Management; Psychology–General; Psychology–Industrial/Organizational Psychology; Software Engineering; Systems Engineering

EdD Administrator Leadership for Teaching and Learning; Teacher Leadership

PhD Applied Management and Decision Sciences–Accounting; Applied Management and Decision Sciences–Engineering Management; Applied Management and Decision Sciences–Finance; Applied Management and Decision Sciences–Information Systems Management; Applied Management and Decision Sciences–Knowledge Management; Applied Management and Decision Sciences–Leadership and Organizational Change; Applied Management and Decision Sciences–Learning Management; Applied Management and Decision Sciences–Operations Research; Applied Management and Decision Sciences–self-designed; Applied Management and Decision Sciences, general; Education–Adult Education Leadership; Education–Community College Leadership; Education–Early Childhood Education; Education–Educational Technology; Education–Higher Education; Education–K-12 Educational Leadership; Education–Self-Designed; Education–Special Education; Education, general; Health Services–Community Health; Health Services–Health Management and Policy; Health Services–Health Promotion and Education; Health Services–Health and Human Behavior; Health Services–self-designed; Health Services, general; Human Services–Clinical Social Work; Human Services–Counseling; Human Services–Criminal Justice; Human Services–Family Studies and Intervention Strategies; Human Services–Human Services Administration; Human Services–Social Policy Analysis and Planning; Human Services–self-designed; Human Services, general; Psychology–Clinical Psychology (Licensure); Psychology–Counseling Psychology (Licensure); Psychology–General Program, Educational Psychology track; Psychology–General Program, Research and Evaluation track; Psychology–Health Psychology; Psychology–Organizational; Psychology–School Psychology (Licensure); Public Health–Community Health Promotion and Education; Public Health–Epidemiology; Public Policy and Administration–Health Services; Public Policy and Administration–Homeland Security, Policy, and Coordination; Public Policy and Administration–International Nongovernmental Organizations (NGOs); Public Policy and Administration–Knowledge Management; Public Policy and Administration–Nonprofit Management and Leadership; Public Policy and Administration–Public Management and Leadership; Public Policy and Administration–Public Policy; Public Policy and Administration–Public Safety Management; Public Policy and Administration, general

See full description on page 556.

WASHBURN UNIVERSITY
Topeka, Kansas
Division of Continuing Education
http://www.washburn.edu/ce

Washburn University was founded in 1865. It is accredited by North Central Association of Colleges and Schools. It first offered distance learning courses in 1999. In fall 2005, there were 2,600 students enrolled in distance learning courses. Institutionally administered financial aid is available to distance learners.

Services Distance learners have accessibility to academic advising, bookstore, campus computer network, career placement assistance, e-mail services, library services.

Contact Dr. Timothy W. Peterson, Dean of Continuing Education, Washburn University, 1700 SW College Avenue, Topeka, KS 66621. Telephone: 785-670-1399. Fax: 785-670-1028. E-mail: tim.peterson@washburn.edu.

DEGREES AND AWARDS

BAA Human Services; Technology Administration

BHS Health Services Administration/Health Services Administration and Medical Imaging

BLS Administrative Communications–Liberal Studies

BS Criminal Justice

BSN Nursing

COURSE SUBJECT AREAS OFFERED OUTSIDE OF DEGREE PROGRAMS

Undergraduate—allied health diagnostic, intervention, and treatment professions; American literature (United States and Canadian); biology; business, management, and marketing related; chemistry; education; English composition; health and physical education/fitness; history; human services; military studies; music; nursing; political science and government; psychology; public administration; social work; sociology; technology education/industrial arts.

Graduate—criminal justice and corrections; education; liberal arts and sciences, general studies and humanities.

Non-credit—human resources management; social sciences related.

WASHINGTON STATE UNIVERSITY
Pullman, Washington
Distance Degree Programs
http://www.distance.wsu.edu

Washington State University was founded in 1890. It is accredited by Northwest Commission on Colleges and Universities. It first offered distance learning courses in 1991. In fall 2005, there were 2,700 students enrolled in distance learning courses. Institutionally administered financial aid is available to distance learners.

Services Distance learners have accessibility to academic advising, bookstore, campus computer network, career placement assistance, e-mail services, library services, tutoring.

Contact Student Services, Washington State University, 104 Van Doren Hall, PO Box 645220, Pullman, WA 99164-5220. Telephone: 800-222-4978. Fax: 509-335-4850. E-mail: distance@wsu.edu.

DEGREES AND AWARDS

BA Business Administration; Criminal Justice; Human Development; Humanities; Social Sciences

BSN Nursing–RN to BS

Certificate Professional Writing

MS Agriculture

COURSE SUBJECT AREAS OFFERED OUTSIDE OF DEGREE PROGRAMS

Undergraduate—English composition.

See full description on page 558.

WASHTENAW COMMUNITY COLLEGE
Ann Arbor, Michigan
Office of Distance Learning
http://www.wccnet.edu

Washtenaw Community College was founded in 1965. It is accredited by North Central Association of Colleges and Schools. It first offered distance learning courses in 1982. In fall 2005, there were 1,100 students enrolled in distance learning courses. Institutionally administered financial aid is available to distance learners.

Services Distance learners have accessibility to academic advising, bookstore, campus computer network, e-mail services, library services, tutoring.

Contact Ms. Michele Meissner, Manager of Instructional Design and Technology, Washtenaw Community College, Ann Arbor, MI 48106. Telephone: 734-477-8724. E-mail: meissner@wccnet.edu.

DEGREES AND AWARDS
Programs offered do not lead to a degree or other formal award.

COURSE SUBJECT AREAS OFFERED OUTSIDE OF DEGREE PROGRAMS
Undergraduate—building/construction finishing, management, and inspection; business administration, management and operations; business operations support and assistant services; clinical psychology; communication and journalism related; communication and media; computer and information sciences; computer programming; computer software and media applications; construction management; dental support services and allied professions; English; English composition; health professions related; legal studies (non-professional general, undergraduate); mathematics; nursing; philosophy; political science and government; psychology; sociology.

WAUKESHA COUNTY TECHNICAL COLLEGE
Pewaukee, Wisconsin
Instructional Resources
http://www.wctc.edu/wctc/distance/

Waukesha County Technical College was founded in 1923. It is accredited by North Central Association of Colleges and Schools. It first offered distance learning courses in 1995. In fall 2005, there were 2,700 students enrolled in distance learning courses.

Services Distance learners have accessibility to academic advising, bookstore, campus computer network, career placement assistance, e-mail services, library services.

Contact Linda Perenchio, Waukesha County Technical College, 800 Main Street, L130, Pewaukee, WI 53072. Telephone: 262-691-5314. Fax: 262-691-5089. E-mail: lperenchio@wctc.edu.

DEGREES AND AWARDS
Programs offered do not lead to a degree or other formal award.

COURSE SUBJECT AREAS OFFERED OUTSIDE OF DEGREE PROGRAMS
Undergraduate—accounting and related services; allied health and medical assisting services; business, management, and marketing related; computer science; computer systems networking and telecommunications; dental support services and allied professions; economics; English composition; finance and financial management services; fire protection; health/medical preparatory programs; international business; marketing; mathematics; medical basic sciences; nursing; pharmacy, pharmaceutical sciences, and administration; psychology; real estate; sociology; teaching assistants/aides.

WAYLAND BAPTIST UNIVERSITY
Plainview, Texas
http://www.wbu.edu/

Wayland Baptist University was founded in 1908. It is accredited by Southern Association of Colleges and Schools. It first offered distance learning courses in 1998. In fall 2005, there were 1,130 students enrolled in distance learning courses. Institutionally administered financial aid is available to distance learners.

Services Distance learners have accessibility to library services.

Contact Dr. David Howle, Virtual Campus Director, Wayland Baptist University, 1900 West 7th Street, CMB 420, Plainview, TX 79072. Telephone: 806-291-1031. Fax: 806-291-1957. E-mail: dhowle@wbu.edu.

DEGREES AND AWARDS
Programs offered do not lead to a degree or other formal award.

COURSE SUBJECT AREAS OFFERED OUTSIDE OF DEGREE PROGRAMS
Undergraduate—accounting and related services; business administration, management and operations; criminal justice and corrections; economics; education related; finance and financial management services; health and medical administrative services; history; management information systems; marketing; music; political science and government; psychology; religious education; religious studies; sociology.

Graduate—accounting and related services; business administration, management and operations; counseling psychology; economics; education related; health and medical administrative services; management information systems; religious education; religious studies.

WAYNE STATE COLLEGE
Wayne, Nebraska
Regional Education and Distance Learning
http://www.wsc.edu

Wayne State College was founded in 1910. It is accredited by North Central Association of Colleges and Schools. It first offered distance learning courses in 1997. In fall 2005, there were 511 students enrolled in distance learning courses. Institutionally administered financial aid is available to distance learners.

Services Distance learners have accessibility to academic advising, bookstore, campus computer network, career placement assistance, e-mail services, library services.

Contact Mr. Roger Feuerbacher, Director of Continuing Education, Wayne State College, 1111 Main Street, Wayne, NE 68787. Telephone: 402-375-7217. Fax: 402-375-7204. E-mail: rofeuer1@wsc.edu.

DEGREES AND AWARDS
Programs offered do not lead to a degree or other formal award.

COURSE SUBJECT AREAS OFFERED OUTSIDE OF DEGREE PROGRAMS
Undergraduate—accounting and related services; business administration, management and operations; chemistry; computer and information sciences; economics; education; education (specific subject areas); English; family and consumer sciences/human sciences; human resources management; industrial production technologies; languages (foreign languages related); mathematics; multi-/interdisciplinary studies related; natural sciences; philosophy; physical sciences; physics.

Graduate—accounting and related services; business administration, management and operations; counseling psychology; economics; education; educational administration and supervision; education (specific subject areas); English; family and consumer sciences/human sciences; human resources management; industrial production technologies; mathematics; multi-/interdisciplinary studies related; special education.

WEBER STATE UNIVERSITY
Ogden, Utah
Distance Learning and Independent Study
http://departments.weber.edu/ce/dl

Weber State University was founded in 1889. It is accredited by Northwest Commission on Colleges and Universities. It first offered distance learning courses in 1990. In fall 2005, there were 8,000 students enrolled in distance learning courses. Institutionally administered financial aid is available to distance learners.

Services Distance learners have accessibility to academic advising, bookstore, campus computer network, career placement assistance, e-mail services, library services, tutoring.

Contact Susan Smith, Office of Distance Learning, Weber State University, 4005 University Circle, Ogden, UT 84408-4005. Telephone: 801-626-6600. Fax: 801-626-8035. E-mail: dist-learn@weber.edu.

DEGREES AND AWARDS

AAS Clinical Laboratory Technician; Health Information Technology
AS Criminal Justice; General Studies
BS Clinical Laboratory Sciences; Health Administrative Services; Health Promotion; Radiological Sciences
Certificate Health Care Coding and Classification; Radiological Sciences

COURSE SUBJECT AREAS OFFERED OUTSIDE OF DEGREE PROGRAMS

Undergraduate—accounting and related services; anthropology; building/construction finishing, management, and inspection; business administration, management and operations; chemistry; communication and media; computer and information sciences; English; English composition; geography and cartography; geological and earth sciences/geosciences; gerontology; health and medical administrative services; history; human development, family studies, and related services; linguistic, comparative, and related language studies; mathematics; microbiological sciences and immunology; music; philosophy; physics; political science and government; psychology; technical and business writing; zoology/animal biology.

See full description on page 560.

WEBSTER UNIVERSITY
St. Louis, Missouri
Academic Distance Learning Center
http://www.webster.edu/worldclassroom

Webster University was founded in 1915. It is accredited by North Central Association of Colleges and Schools. It first offered distance learning courses in 1998. In fall 2005, there were 1,386 students enrolled in distance learning courses. Institutionally administered financial aid is available to distance learners.

Services Distance learners have accessibility to academic advising, bookstore, career placement assistance, e-mail services, library services, tutoring.

Contact Matt Nolan, Director, Graduate and Evening Student Admissions, Webster University, 470 East Lockwood Avenue, St. Louis, MO 63119. Telephone: 314-968-7089. Fax: 314-968-7462. E-mail: nolan@webster.edu.

DEGREES AND AWARDS

Certificate Web Site Design; Web Site Development
Graduate Certificate Decision Support Systems; Global Commerce–MBA Certificate in Global Commerce; Government Contracting; Web Services
MA Business and Organizational Security Management; Media Communication, Communication Management emphasis; Procurement and Acquisitions Management
MAT Educational Technology and Multidisciplinary Studies
MBA Business Administration

COURSE SUBJECT AREAS OFFERED OUTSIDE OF DEGREE PROGRAMS

Undergraduate—computer and information sciences; languages (foreign languages related); philosophy; public relations, advertising, and applied communication related; religious education.

Graduate—business, management, and marketing related; communication and journalism related; computer and information sciences and support services related; education; educational administration and supervision; finance and financial management services; management information systems; marketing; security and protective services related.

WESTCHESTER COMMUNITY COLLEGE
Valhalla, New York
http://www.sunywcc.edu/

Westchester Community College was founded in 1946. It is accredited by Middle States Association of Colleges and Schools. It first offered distance learning courses in 1997. In fall 2005, there were 550 students enrolled in distance learning courses. Institutionally administered financial aid is available to distance learners.

Services Distance learners have accessibility to academic advising, bookstore, library services.

Contact Carol Klein, Acting Distance Learning Coordinator, Westchester Community College, 75 Grasslands Road, Valhalla, NY 10595. Telephone: 914-785-6827. Fax: 914-785-8550. E-mail: carol.klein@sunywcc.edu.

DEGREES AND AWARDS

AA Liberal Arts/Social Science; Liberal Arts/Social Science

COURSE SUBJECT AREAS OFFERED OUTSIDE OF DEGREE PROGRAMS

Undergraduate—accounting and related services; American literature (United States and Canadian); anthropology; behavioral sciences; biological and physical sciences; biology; business/commerce; chemistry; communication and media; computer and information sciences; computer and information sciences and support services related; computer programming; computer science; computer systems networking and telecommunications; criminal justice and corrections; data processing; economics; English; English as a second language; English composition; English language and literature related; geography and cartography; health and physical education/fitness; history; management information systems; mathematics; mathematics and computer science; philosophy; psychology; sales, merchandising, and related marketing operations (specialized); social sciences; sociology; technical and business writing.

WESTERN KENTUCKY UNIVERSITY
Bowling Green, Kentucky
Distance Learning
http://www.wku.edu/reachu

Western Kentucky University was founded in 1906. It is accredited by Southern Association of Colleges and Schools. It first offered distance learning courses in 1999. In fall 2005, there were 3,559 students enrolled in distance learning courses. Institutionally administered financial aid is available to distance learners.

Services Distance learners have accessibility to academic advising, bookstore, career placement assistance, e-mail services, library services.

Contact Ms. Pam Wilson, Coordinator, Distance Learning, Western Kentucky University, Distance Learning, 1906 College Heights Boulevard, 61084, Bowling Green , KY 42101-1084. Telephone: 270-745-2106. Fax: 270-745-2107. E-mail: pam.wilson@wku.edu.

DEGREES AND AWARDS

AAS Paramedicine completion
AS Interdisciplinary Early Childhood Education
BS Computer Information Technology; Consumer and Family Sciences with Child Studies emphasis
Certificate Canadian Studies
Endorsement Gifted and Talented Graduate Teaching Endorsement
Graduate Certificate Women's Studies
MA Exceptional Education
MBA eMBA
MS Communication Disorders; Library Media Education

WESTERN MICHIGAN UNIVERSITY
Kalamazoo, Michigan
Department of Distance Education
http://dde.wmich.edu

Western Michigan University was founded in 1903. It is accredited by North Central Association of Colleges and Schools. It first offered distance learning courses in 1996. In fall 2005, there were 1,766 students enrolled in distance learning courses. Institutionally administered financial aid is available to distance learners.

Services Distance learners have accessibility to academic advising, bookstore, campus computer network, career placement assistance, e-mail services, library services.

Contact Rosemary Nichols, Office Manager, Western Michigan University, Academic Technology and Instructional Services, 1343 Ellsworth Hall, Kalamazoo, MI 49008-5232. Telephone: 269-387-4129. Fax: 269-387-4226. E-mail: rosemary.nicholas@wmich.edu.

DEGREES AND AWARDS

MAE Educational Technology

COURSE SUBJECT AREAS OFFERED OUTSIDE OF DEGREE PROGRAMS

Undergraduate—air transportation; anthropology; apparel and textiles; computer software and media applications; economics; educational administration and supervision; educational/instructional media design; English composition; ethnic, cultural minority, and gender studies; family and consumer economics; family and consumer sciences/human sciences related; geography and cartography; medieval and Renaissance studies; music; rehabilitation and therapeutic professions; religious studies; sales, merchandising, and related marketing operations (specialized); science, technology and society; social work; sociology.

Graduate—computer engineering; computer science; counseling psychology; developmental and child psychology; economics; educational/instructional media design; engineering/industrial management; family and consumer economics; film/video and photographic arts; history; human resources management.

WESTERN NEVADA COMMUNITY COLLEGE

Carson City, Nevada

http://www.wncc.nevada.edu/

Western Nevada Community College was founded in 1971. It is accredited by Northwest Commission on Colleges and Universities. It first offered distance learning courses in 1994. In fall 2005, there were 1,100 students enrolled in distance learning courses. Institutionally administered financial aid is available to distance learners.

Services Distance learners have accessibility to academic advising, bookstore, campus computer network, career placement assistance, e-mail services, library services, tutoring.

Contact Walter Lewis, Administrative Assistant, Distance Education, Western Nevada Community College, 160 Campus Way, Fallon, NV 89406. Telephone: 775-423-7565 Ext. 2249. Fax: 775-423-8029. E-mail: wlewis@wncc.nevada.edu.

DEGREES AND AWARDS

Programs offered do not lead to a degree or other formal award.

COURSE SUBJECT AREAS OFFERED OUTSIDE OF DEGREE PROGRAMS

Undergraduate—accounting and related services; allied health and medical assisting services; biology; business/commerce; carpentry; computer and information sciences; culinary arts and related services; education related; geography and cartography; languages (Romance languages); management sciences and quantitative methods; mechanical engineering; nursing; social psychology; sociology.

WESTERN OKLAHOMA STATE COLLEGE

Altus, Oklahoma

Information Services

http://www.wosc.edu/dl/

Western Oklahoma State College was founded in 1926. It is accredited by North Central Association of Colleges and Schools. It first offered distance learning courses in 1976. In fall 2005, there were 150 students enrolled in distance learning courses. Institutionally administered financial aid is available to distance learners.

Services Distance learners have accessibility to campus computer network, library services.

Contact Kent Brooks, Dean and Chief Technology Officer, Western Oklahoma State College, 2801 North Main, Altus, OK 73521. Telephone: 580-477-7764. Fax: 866-500-1261. E-mail: kent.brooks@wosc.edu.

DEGREES AND AWARDS

AA General Studies
AAS Office Systems Technology

COURSE SUBJECT AREAS OFFERED OUTSIDE OF DEGREE PROGRAMS

Undergraduate—computer and information sciences; crafts, folk art and artisanry; developmental and child psychology; English composition; history; sociology.

WESTERN PIEDMONT COMMUNITY COLLEGE

Morganton, North Carolina

http://www.wp.cc.nc.us/

Western Piedmont Community College was founded in 1964. It is accredited by Southern Association of Colleges and Schools. It first offered distance learning courses in 1995. In fall 2005, there were 1,000 students enrolled in distance learning courses. Institutionally administered financial aid is available to distance learners.

Services Distance learners have accessibility to academic advising, bookstore, campus computer network, career placement assistance, e-mail services, library services.

Contact Susan Williams, Director of Admissions, Western Piedmont Community College, 1001 Burkemont Avenue, Morganton, NC 28655. Telephone: 828-438-6051. Fax: 828-438-6015. E-mail: swilliams@wpcc.edu.

DEGREES AND AWARDS

AAS Business Administration; Paralegal Studies

COURSE SUBJECT AREAS OFFERED OUTSIDE OF DEGREE PROGRAMS

Undergraduate—accounting and computer science; accounting and related services; business administration, management and operations; business/commerce; business/managerial economics; business operations support and assistant services; computer and information sciences; computer programming; computer software and media applications; computer systems networking and telecommunications; criminal justice and corrections; economics; education (specific levels and methods); English composition; fine and studio art; geography and cartography; history; human resources management; management information systems; marketing; nursing; psychology; sociology; taxation.

WESTERN SEMINARY

Portland, Oregon

Center for Lifelong Learning

http://www.westernseminary.edu

Western Seminary was founded in 1927. It is accredited by Northwest Commission on Colleges and Universities. It first offered distance learning courses in 1981. In fall 2005, there were 120 students enrolled in distance learning courses. Institutionally administered financial aid is available to distance learners.

Services Distance learners have accessibility to academic advising, bookstore, career placement assistance, e-mail services, library services.

Contact James Stewart, Director of Distance Education, Western Seminary, 5511 SE Hawthorne Boulevard, Portland, OR 97215. Telephone: 877-517-1800. Fax: 503-517-1801. E-mail: jstewart@westernseminary.edu.

DEGREES AND AWARDS

Programs offered do not lead to a degree or other formal award.

COURSE SUBJECT AREAS OFFERED OUTSIDE OF DEGREE PROGRAMS

Graduate—biblical and other theological languages and literatures; biblical studies; religious education; religious studies; theological and ministerial studies; theology and religious vocations related.

Non-credit—biblical and other theological languages and literatures; biblical studies; religious education; religious studies; theological and ministerial studies; theology and religious vocations related.

WESTERN UNIVERSITY OF HEALTH SCIENCES

Pomona, California

http://www.westernu.edu

Western University of Health Sciences was founded in 1975. It is accredited by Western Association of Schools and Colleges. It first offered distance learning courses in 1997. In fall 2005, there were 70 students enrolled in distance learning courses. Institutionally administered financial aid is available to distance learners.

Services Distance learners have accessibility to academic advising, bookstore, campus computer network, career placement assistance, e-mail services, library services.

Contact Ms. Franchette Padrigon, Student Coordinator, Western University of Health Sciences, College of Graduate Nursing, 309 East Second Street, College Plaza, Pomona, CA 91766. Telephone: 909-469-5523. Fax: 909-469-5521. E-mail: cgn@westernu.edu.

DEGREES AND AWARDS
Certificate Nursing–Family Nurse Practitioner
MSN Nursing

COURSE SUBJECT AREAS OFFERED OUTSIDE OF DEGREE PROGRAMS
Graduate—nursing.
Non-credit—nursing.

WESTERN WASHINGTON UNIVERSITY
Bellingham, Washington
Extended Education and Summer Programs
http://www.ExtendedEd.wwu.edu

Western Washington University was founded in 1893. It is accredited by Northwest Commission on Colleges and Universities. It first offered distance learning courses in 1941. In fall 2005, there were 335 students enrolled in distance learning courses. Institutionally administered financial aid is available to distance learners.

Services Distance learners have accessibility to academic advising, bookstore, campus computer network, career placement assistance, e-mail services, library services, tutoring.

Contact Barbara (Bunny) Starbuck, Distance Learning Assistant, Western Washington University, MS 5293, 516 High Street, Bellingham, WA 98225-5996. Telephone: 360-650-3650. Fax: 360-650-6858. E-mail: eesp.distedpeters@wwu.edu.

DEGREES AND AWARDS
BA Human Services
Certificate Child Care–Birth to Five Care; Emergency Management/Homeland Security

COURSE SUBJECT AREAS OFFERED OUTSIDE OF DEGREE PROGRAMS
Undergraduate—American literature (United States and Canadian); anthropology; area studies; biblical and other theological languages and literatures; communication and journalism related; community health services; creative writing; curriculum and instruction; developmental and child psychology; economics; educational administration and supervision; education (specific levels and methods); education (specific subject areas); engineering technologies related; English; English as a second/foreign language (teaching); English as a second language; ethnic, cultural minority, and gender studies; history; human development, family studies, and related services; human services; languages (East Asian); languages (Modern Greek); languages (Romance languages); library science related; management sciences and quantitative methods; mathematics; medieval and Renaissance studies; music; parks, recreation, and leisure related; psychology; social work; sociology; special education.

WESTERN WYOMING COMMUNITY COLLEGE
Rock Springs, Wyoming
Extended Education
http://www.wwcc.cc.wy.us/dist.htm

Western Wyoming Community College was founded in 1959. It is accredited by North Central Association of Colleges and Schools. It first offered distance learning courses in 1988. In fall 2005, there were 1,200 students enrolled in distance learning courses. Institutionally administered financial aid is available to distance learners.

Services Distance learners have accessibility to academic advising, bookstore, campus computer network, career placement assistance, e-mail services, library services, tutoring.

Contact Ms. Christine Lustik, Director of Distance Education, Western Wyoming Community College, 2500 College Drive, PO Box 428, Rock Springs, WY 82902. Telephone: 307-382-1757. Fax: 307-382-1812. E-mail: clustik@wwcc.wy.edu.

DEGREES AND AWARDS
AA General Program
AAS Office Information Systems
Certification Web Site Development Certificate

COURSE SUBJECT AREAS OFFERED OUTSIDE OF DEGREE PROGRAMS
Undergraduate—accounting and related services; anthropology; applied mathematics; biological and physical sciences; business administration, management and operations; business/commerce; business operations support and assistant services; computer science; computer software and media applications; economics; education (specific levels and methods); English composition; ethnic, cultural minority, and gender studies; philosophy; psychology.

WEST LOS ANGELES COLLEGE
Culver City, California
Distance Learning Center
http://www.wlac.edu/online

West Los Angeles College was founded in 1969. It is accredited by Western Association of Schools and Colleges. It first offered distance learning courses in 1999. In fall 2005, there were 2,145 students enrolled in distance learning courses. Institutionally administered financial aid is available to distance learners.

Services Distance learners have accessibility to academic advising, bookstore, campus computer network, library services.

Contact Mr. Eric Jean Ichon, Distance Learning Coordinator, West Los Angeles College, 9000 Overland Avenue, Culver City, CA 90230. Telephone: 310-287-4305. Fax: 310-841-0396. E-mail: ichone@wlac.edu.

DEGREES AND AWARDS
Programs offered do not lead to a degree or other formal award.

COURSE SUBJECT AREAS OFFERED OUTSIDE OF DEGREE PROGRAMS
Undergraduate—accounting and computer science; air transportation; allied health and medical assisting services; American literature (United States and Canadian); applied mathematics; area, ethnic, cultural, and gender studies related; behavioral sciences; business administration, management and operations; business/commerce; computer/information technology administration and management; computer science; creative writing; criminal justice and corrections; data entry/microcomputer applications; dentistry and oral sciences (advanced/graduate); design and applied arts; dramatic/theater arts and stagecraft; economics; English; English as a second language; English composition; English language and literature related; health and physical education/fitness; health/medical preparatory programs; history; international relations and affairs; library science; mathematics; political science and government; psychology; sales, merchandising, and related marketing operations (specialized); speech and rhetoric; technical and business writing; visual and performing arts.

WEST SHORE COMMUNITY COLLEGE
Scottville, Michigan
http://www.westshore.edu

West Shore Community College was founded in 1967. It is accredited by North Central Association of Colleges and Schools. It first offered distance learning courses in 1998. In fall 2005, there were 230 students enrolled in distance learning courses. Institutionally administered financial aid is available to distance learners.

Services Distance learners have accessibility to academic advising, bookstore, career placement assistance, e-mail services, library services, tutoring.

Contact Patti Davidson, Director of Distance Learning and Information Technology, West Shore Community College, 3000 North Stiles Road, Scottville, MI 49454-0277. Telephone: 231-845-0806. Fax: 231-845-0207. E-mail: pldavidson@westshore.edu.

DEGREES AND AWARDS
AGS General Studies

COURSE SUBJECT AREAS OFFERED OUTSIDE OF DEGREE PROGRAMS

Undergraduate—American literature (United States and Canadian); biology; botany/plant biology; business administration, management and operations; business, management, and marketing related; computer and information sciences; criminal justice and corrections; English composition; geological and earth sciences/geosciences; history; liberal arts and sciences, general studies and humanities; marketing; mathematics; mathematics and statistics related; public relations, advertising, and applied communication related; sociology.

WEST TEXAS A&M UNIVERSITY
Canyon, Texas

West Texas A&M University was founded in 1909. It is accredited by Southern Association of Colleges and Schools. It first offered distance learning courses in 1997. In fall 2005, there were 3,186 students enrolled in distance learning courses. Institutionally administered financial aid is available to distance learners.

Services Distance learners have accessibility to academic advising, bookstore, career placement assistance, e-mail services, library services.

Contact Ms. Lila Vars, Director, Admissions, West Texas A&M University, Office of Admissions, WTAMU Box 60907, Canyon, TX 79016-0001. Telephone: 806-651-2020. Fax: 806-651-5285. E-mail: admissions@wtamu.edu.

DEGREES AND AWARDS

BAA Emergency Management Administration
BGS General Studies
BSN Nursing–RN to BSN degree completion program
MBA Business Administration
MEd Instructional Technology
MS Agricultural Business Economics

COURSE SUBJECT AREAS OFFERED OUTSIDE OF DEGREE PROGRAMS

Undergraduate—education.

Graduate—accounting and computer science; educational assessment, evaluation, and research; education (specific subject areas).

WEST VIRGINIA NORTHERN COMMUNITY COLLEGE
Wheeling, West Virginia
http://www.northern.wvnet.edu/

West Virginia Northern Community College was founded in 1972. It is accredited by North Central Association of Colleges and Schools. It first offered distance learning courses in 1988. In fall 2005, there were 338 students enrolled in distance learning courses. Institutionally administered financial aid is available to distance learners.

Services Distance learners have accessibility to academic advising, bookstore, career placement assistance, e-mail services, library services, tutoring.

Contact Mr. Steve Woodburn, Dean, Wheeling Campus, West Virginia Northern Community College, 1704 Market Street, Wheeling, WV 26003. Telephone: 304-233-5900. E-mail: swoodburn@northern.wvnet.edu.

DEGREES AND AWARDS

Programs offered do not lead to a degree or other formal award.

COURSE SUBJECT AREAS OFFERED OUTSIDE OF DEGREE PROGRAMS

Undergraduate—accounting and related services; biology; criminal justice and corrections; English composition; history; management information systems; mathematics and statistics related; microbiological sciences and immunology; psychology; sociology.

WEST VIRGINIA UNIVERSITY
Morgantown, West Virginia
Extended Learning
http://www.e-learn.wvu.edu

West Virginia University was founded in 1867. It is accredited by North Central Association of Colleges and Schools. It first offered distance learning courses in 1987. In fall 2005, there were 2,207 students enrolled in distance learning courses. Institutionally administered financial aid is available to distance learners.

Services Distance learners have accessibility to academic advising, bookstore, campus computer network, career placement assistance, e-mail services, library services, tutoring.

Contact Ms. Cindy K. Hart, Coordinator of Distance Learning, West Virginia University, One Waterfront Place, Room 1009, PO Box 6808, Morgantown, WV 26506-6808. Telephone: 304-293-3852. Fax: 304-293-3853. E-mail: lkhart@mail.wvu.edu.

DEGREES AND AWARDS

BA Multidisciplinary Studies; Regents Bachelor of Arts
BSN Nursing–RN to BSN
Certificate Integrated Marketing Communications
EMBA Business Administration
MA Special Education
MLS Legal Studies
MS Athletic Coaching; Integrated Marketing Communications; Rehabilitation Counseling; Software Engineering; Sports Management
MSE Physical Education Teacher Education
MSN Nursing
MSOT Occupational Therapy

COURSE SUBJECT AREAS OFFERED OUTSIDE OF DEGREE PROGRAMS

Non-credit—computer software and media applications; education; engineering related; finance and financial management services; forensic psychology; health professions related; health services/allied health/health sciences; legal support services; management information systems; nursing; technology education/industrial arts.

WEST VIRGINIA UNIVERSITY AT PARKERSBURG
Parkersburg, West Virginia
http://www.wvup.edu

West Virginia University at Parkersburg was founded in 1961. It is accredited by North Central Association of Colleges and Schools. It first offered distance learning courses in 1999. In fall 2005, there were 1,034 students enrolled in distance learning courses. Institutionally administered financial aid is available to distance learners.

Services Distance learners have accessibility to bookstore, campus computer network, e-mail services, library services, tutoring.

Contact Theresa Cross, WebCT System Administrator, West Virginia University at Parkersburg, 300 Campus Drive, Parkersburg, WV 26104. Telephone: 304-424-8358. Fax: 304-424-8354. E-mail: theresa.cross@mail.wvu.edu.

DEGREES AND AWARDS

AAS Business Technology; Criminal Justice

COURSE SUBJECT AREAS OFFERED OUTSIDE OF DEGREE PROGRAMS

Undergraduate—accounting and related services; biological and physical sciences; biology; business administration, management and operations; business/commerce; business/corporate communications; business, management, and marketing related; business/managerial economics; business operations support and assistant services; communication and journalism related; community health services; computer and information sciences; computer/information technology administration and management; criminal justice and corrections; dramatic/theater arts and stagecraft; English composition; English language and literature related; health and physical education/fitness; health professions related; history; human resources management; intercultural/multicultural and diversity studies; management information systems; marketing; mathematics; nursing; philosophy; psychology; social sciences; sociology; technology education/industrial arts.

Non-credit—accounting and computer science; business/corporate communications; business operations support and assistant services; communication and media; communications technologies and support services related; computer and information sciences; computer/information technology administration and management; construction trades related; crafts, folk art and artisanry; dance; fishing and fisheries sciences and management; foods, nutrition, and related services; quality control and safety technologies; technical and business writing.

WESTWOOD ONLINE
Denver, Colorado
http://www.westwood.edu

Westwood Online is accredited by Accrediting Commission of Career Schools and Colleges of Technology. It first offered distance learning courses in 2002. In fall 2005, there were 350 students enrolled in distance learning courses. Institutionally administered financial aid is available to distance learners.

Services Distance learners have accessibility to academic advising, bookstore, campus computer network, career placement assistance, e-mail services, library services, tutoring.

Contact Kim Beckman, Area Vice President, Westwood Online, Denver, CO 80221. Telephone: 303-635-7750 Ext. 11510. E-mail: kbeckman@westwood.edu.

DEGREES AND AWARDS

AAS Computer Network Engineering; Graphic Design and Multimedia; Software Engineering

BS Animation; Business Administration–Accounting concentration; Business Administration–Marketing and Sales concentration; Business–Fashion Merchandising; Computer Network Management; Criminal Justice; E-Business Management; Game Art and Design; Game Software Development; Information Systems Security; Visual Communications; Web Design and Multimedia

MBA Business Administration

COURSE SUBJECT AREAS OFFERED OUTSIDE OF DEGREE PROGRAMS

Undergraduate—accounting and related services; business administration, management and operations; computer programming; computer software and media applications; computer systems networking and telecommunications; criminal justice and corrections; design and applied arts.

See full description on page 562.

WHARTON COUNTY JUNIOR COLLEGE
Wharton, Texas
http://www.wcjc.cc.tx.us/

Wharton County Junior College was founded in 1946. It is accredited by Southern Association of Colleges and Schools. It first offered distance learning courses in 1993. Institutionally administered financial aid is available to distance learners.

Services Distance learners have accessibility to bookstore, e-mail services, library services, tutoring.

Contact Ken Rosier, Distance Learning Program Director, Wharton County Junior College, 911 Boling Highway, Wharton, TX 77488. Telephone: 979-532-6944. Fax: 979-532-6567. E-mail: rosierk@wcjc.edu.

DEGREES AND AWARDS

Programs offered do not lead to a degree or other formal award.

COURSE SUBJECT AREAS OFFERED OUTSIDE OF DEGREE PROGRAMS

Undergraduate—accounting and computer science; allied health and medical assisting services; American literature (United States and Canadian); behavioral sciences; biology; business administration, management and operations; business/commerce; business, management, and marketing related; computer and information sciences; computer science; computer software and media applications; computer systems networking and telecommunications; creative writing; criminal justice and corrections; English; English composition; English language and literature related; English literature (British and Commonwealth); geological and earth sciences/geosciences; history; liberal arts and sciences, general studies and humanities; marketing; psychology; sociology; speech and rhetoric.

Non-credit—English as a second language; fire protection.

WHATCOM COMMUNITY COLLEGE
Bellingham, Washington
http://www.whatcom.ctc.edu/

Whatcom Community College was founded in 1970. It is accredited by Northwest Commission on Colleges and Universities. It first offered distance learning courses in 1991. In fall 2005, there were 255 students enrolled in distance learning courses. Institutionally administered financial aid is available to distance learners.

Services Distance learners have accessibility to academic advising, bookstore, campus computer network, library services, tutoring.

Contact Al Epp, Distance Learning Coordinator, Whatcom Community College, 237 West Kellogg Road, Bellingham, WA 98226. Telephone: 360-676-2170 Ext. 3399. Fax: 360-676-2171. E-mail: aepp@whatcom.ctc.edu.

DEGREES AND AWARDS

Programs offered do not lead to a degree or other formal award.

COURSE SUBJECT AREAS OFFERED OUTSIDE OF DEGREE PROGRAMS

Undergraduate—accounting and related services; anthropology; astronomy and astrophysics; biology; business/commerce; chemistry; economics; education; education related; English; English composition; geography and cartography; history; mathematics; music; philosophy; psychology; sociology.

WICHITA STATE UNIVERSITY
Wichita, Kansas
Media Resources Center
http://www.mrc.twsu.edu/mrc/telecourse

Wichita State University was founded in 1895. It is accredited by North Central Association of Colleges and Schools. It first offered distance learning courses in 1982. In fall 2005, there were 689 students enrolled in distance learning courses.

Services Distance learners have accessibility to bookstore, library services.

Contact Mary Morriss, Telecourse Coordinator, Wichita State University, 1845 Fairmount, Wichita, KS 67260-0057. Telephone: 316-978-7766. Fax: 316-978-3560. E-mail: morriss@mrc.twsu.edu.

DEGREES AND AWARDS

Programs offered do not lead to a degree or other formal award.

COURSE SUBJECT AREAS OFFERED OUTSIDE OF DEGREE PROGRAMS

Undergraduate—accounting and related services; anthropology; astronomy and astrophysics; communication and media; comparative literature; family and consumer economics; geography and cartography; gerontology; history; music; psychology; sociology; speech and rhetoric.

WILFRID LAURIER UNIVERSITY
Waterloo, Ontario, Canada
Office of Teaching Support Services
http://www.wlu.ca/pts

Wilfrid Laurier University was founded in 1911. It is provincially chartered. It first offered distance learning courses in 1978. In fall 2005, there were 2,500 students enrolled in distance learning courses. Institutionally administered financial aid is available to distance learners.

Services Distance learners have accessibility to academic advising, bookstore, campus computer network, career placement assistance, e-mail services, library services.

Contact Lisa Fanjoy, Manager, Distance and Continuing Education, Wilfrid Laurier University, Office of Teaching Support Services, 75

University Avenue West, Waterloo, ON N2L 3C5, Canada. Telephone: 519-884-0710 Ext. 4106. Fax: 519-884-6063. E-mail: lfanjoy@wlu.ca.

DEGREES AND AWARDS

BA Psychology; Sociology

COURSE SUBJECT AREAS OFFERED OUTSIDE OF DEGREE PROGRAMS

Undergraduate—accounting and related services; anthropology; astronomy and astrophysics; biology; business/commerce; communication and media; developmental and child psychology; economics; English; English literature (British and Commonwealth); finance and financial management services; fine and studio art; geography and cartography; geological and earth sciences/geosciences; history; languages (Germanic); languages (Romance languages); philosophy; psychology; psychology related; religious studies; social work; sociology; visual and performing arts.
Non-credit—English composition.

WILKES COMMUNITY COLLEGE
Wilkesboro, North Carolina
Individualized Studies Department
http://www.wilkes.cc.nc.us

Wilkes Community College was founded in 1965. It is accredited by Southern Association of Colleges and Schools. It first offered distance learning courses in 1984. In fall 2005, there were 1,624 students enrolled in distance learning courses. Institutionally administered financial aid is available to distance learners.
Services Distance learners have accessibility to academic advising, bookstore, campus computer network, career placement assistance, e-mail services, library services.
Contact Debi McGuire, Director of Distance Learning, Wilkes Community College, PO Box 120, Wilkesboro, NC 28697. Telephone: 336-838-6524. E-mail: debi.mcguire@wilkescc.edu.

DEGREES AND AWARDS

AA Arts
AAS Business Administration

COURSE SUBJECT AREAS OFFERED OUTSIDE OF DEGREE PROGRAMS

Undergraduate—accounting and related services; American literature (United States and Canadian); biology; business administration, management and operations; business/commerce; business, management, and marketing related; business/managerial economics; communication and media; communications technology; computer and information sciences; computer and information sciences and support services related; computer programming; computer science; creative writing; data processing; dramatic/theater arts and stagecraft; education related; English; English composition; English language and literature related; English literature (British and Commonwealth); ethnic, cultural minority, and gender studies; fine and studio art; history; human development, family studies, and related services; management information systems; marketing; mathematics; philosophy and religious studies related; physical sciences; psychology; psychology related; public relations, advertising, and applied communication related; religious studies; sales, merchandising, and related marketing operations (specialized); sociology; technical and business writing.

WILKES UNIVERSITY
Wilkes-Barre, Pennsylvania
http://www.wilkes.edu/

Wilkes University was founded in 1933. It is accredited by Middle States Association of Colleges and Schools.
Services Distance learners have accessibility to academic advising, bookstore, campus computer network, e-mail services, library services.
Contact Mrs. Corina Niculescu-Mihai, Associate Director, Center for Continued Learning, Wilkes University, 84 West South Street, Wilkes-Barre, PA 18766. Telephone: 570-408-4238. Fax: 570-408-7846. E-mail: corina.mihai@wilkes.edu.

DEGREES AND AWARDS

MA Creative Writing
MS School Business Leadership
MSE Classroom Technology; Early Childhood Literacy

WILLIAM RAINEY HARPER COLLEGE
Palatine, Illinois
Learning Resource Center
http://www.harpercollege.edu/doit

William Rainey Harper College was founded in 1965. It is accredited by North Central Association of Colleges and Schools. It first offered distance learning courses in 1984. In fall 2005, there were 1,000 students enrolled in distance learning courses. Institutionally administered financial aid is available to distance learners.
Services Distance learners have accessibility to academic advising, bookstore, campus computer network, e-mail services, library services, tutoring.
Contact Fran Hendrickson, Program Assistant, William Rainey Harper College, 1200 West Algonquin Road, Palatine, IL 60067-7398. Telephone: 847-925-6586. Fax: 847-925-6037. E-mail: fhendric@harpercollege.edu.

DEGREES AND AWARDS

Programs offered do not lead to a degree or other formal award.

COURSE SUBJECT AREAS OFFERED OUTSIDE OF DEGREE PROGRAMS

Undergraduate—accounting and related services; allied health and medical assisting services; allied health diagnostic, intervention, and treatment professions; astronomy and astrophysics; business/commerce; business/corporate communications; business, management, and marketing related; business operations support and assistant services; chemistry; computer and information sciences; computer and information sciences and support services related; computer/information technology administration and management; computer programming; computer science; computer software and media applications; computer systems networking and telecommunications; creative writing; criminal justice and corrections; developmental and child psychology; economics; education; English; English as a second language; English composition; English language and literature related; film/video and photographic arts; finance and financial management services; geography and cartography; health professions related; history; information science/studies; international business; liberal arts and sciences, general studies and humanities; linguistic, comparative, and related language studies; nursing; psychology; real estate; sales, merchandising, and related marketing operations (general); sales, merchandising, and related marketing operations (specialized); social psychology; sociology; technical and business writing.

WILLIAMSON CHRISTIAN COLLEGE
Franklin, Tennessee
http://www.williamsoncc.edu

Williamson Christian College was founded in 1997. It is accredited by Association for Biblical Higher Education. It first offered distance learning courses in 2000. In fall 2005, there were 10 students enrolled in distance learning courses. Institutionally administered financial aid is available to distance learners.
Services Distance learners have accessibility to academic advising, bookstore, career placement assistance, e-mail services, library services.
Contact Ms. Elizabeth Heffington, Registrar, Williamson Christian College, 200 Seaboard Lane, Franklin, TN 37067. Telephone: 615-771-7821. Fax: 615-771-7810. E-mail: elizabeth@williamsoncc.edu.

DEGREES AND AWARDS

BS Leadership and Ministry

COURSE SUBJECT AREAS OFFERED OUTSIDE OF DEGREE PROGRAMS

Undergraduate—biblical studies; religious studies; theological and ministerial studies.

WINSTON-SALEM STATE UNIVERSITY
Winston-Salem, North Carolina
http://www.wssu.edu/dl

Winston-Salem State University was founded in 1892. It is accredited by Southern Association of Colleges and Schools. It first offered distance learning courses in 1996. In fall 2005, there were 275 students enrolled in distance learning courses. Institutionally administered financial aid is available to distance learners.

Services Distance learners have accessibility to academic advising, bookstore, campus computer network, career placement assistance, e-mail services, library services, tutoring.

Contact Ms. Chandra Wells, Coordinator of Student Services, Winston-Salem State University, Office of Distance Learning, Anderson Conference Center, Suite 137, Winston-Salem, NC 27110. Telephone: 336-750-2634. Fax: 336-750-2636. E-mail: wellsc@wssu.edu.

DEGREES AND AWARDS

BS BS—Bachelor of Interdisciplinary Studies (Concentration in Integrative Studies); Clinical Laboratory Science (lateral entry); Education–Birth to Kindergarten Education (lateral entry/certification); Physical Education, Teaching Option (lateral entry)
BSN Nursing–RN to BSN (lateral entry)
Certificate Computer Programming (Post-Baccalaureate); Social Work Paraprofessional

COURSE SUBJECT AREAS OFFERED OUTSIDE OF DEGREE PROGRAMS

Undergraduate—business administration, management and operations; business/commerce; computer programming; curriculum and instruction; developmental and child psychology; education (specific levels and methods); history; liberal arts and sciences, general studies and humanities; microbiological sciences and immunology; music; social and philosophical foundations of education; social work; sociology.

WISCONSIN INDIANHEAD TECHNICAL COLLEGE
Shell Lake, Wisconsin
http://www.witc.edu

Wisconsin Indianhead Technical College was founded in 1912. It is accredited by North Central Association of Colleges and Schools. It first offered distance learning courses in 1991. In fall 2005, there were 611 students enrolled in distance learning courses. Institutionally administered financial aid is available to distance learners.

Services Distance learners have accessibility to bookstore, career placement assistance, e-mail services, library services, tutoring.

Contact Ms. Stephanie DeCicco, Vice President for Learning, Wisconsin Indianhead Technical College, 505 Pine Ridge Drive, Shell Lake, WI 54871. Telephone: 715-468-2815 Ext. 2222. Fax: 715-468-2819. E-mail: sdecicco@witc.edu.

DEGREES AND AWARDS

AD Information Technology–Web Analyst/Programmer

COURSE SUBJECT AREAS OFFERED OUTSIDE OF DEGREE PROGRAMS

Undergraduate—accounting and related services; agricultural and food products processing; agricultural business and management; agriculture; applied mathematics; business administration, management and operations; business/commerce; business operations support and assistant services; communication and media; computer and information sciences; computer programming; foods, nutrition, and related services; human development, family studies, and related services; nursing; public relations, advertising, and applied communication related; sales, merchandising, and related marketing operations (specialized).

Non-credit—accounting and related services; agricultural and food products processing; agricultural business and management; agriculture; applied mathematics; business administration, management and operations; business/commerce; business operations support and assistant services; communication and media; computer and information sciences; computer programming; foods, nutrition, and related services; human development, family studies, and related services; nursing; public relations, advertising, and applied communication related; sales, merchandising, and related marketing operations (specialized).

WOODBURY UNIVERSITY
Burbank, California
http://www.woodbury.edu/

Woodbury University was founded in 1884. It is accredited by Western Association of Schools and Colleges. It first offered distance learning courses in 2004. In fall 2005, there were 10 students enrolled in distance learning courses. Institutionally administered financial aid is available to distance learners.

Services Distance learners have accessibility to academic advising, campus computer network, library services.

Contact Mr. Mauro Diaz, Director of Admissions, Woodbury University, 7500 Glenoaks Boulevard, Burbank, CA 91510. Telephone: 818-767-0888. Fax: 818-767-7520. E-mail: info@woodbury.edu.

DEGREES AND AWARDS

Programs offered do not lead to a degree or other formal award.

COURSE SUBJECT AREAS OFFERED OUTSIDE OF DEGREE PROGRAMS

Undergraduate—economics.

WORCESTER POLYTECHNIC INSTITUTE
Worcester, Massachusetts
Advanced Distance Learning Network
http://www.wpi.edu/+ADLN

Worcester Polytechnic Institute was founded in 1865. It is accredited by New England Association of Schools and Colleges. It first offered distance learning courses in 1979. In fall 2005, there were 350 students enrolled in distance learning courses. Institutionally administered financial aid is available to distance learners.

Services Distance learners have accessibility to academic advising, bookstore, campus computer network, career placement assistance, e-mail services, library services.

Contact Pamela S. Shelley, Assistant Director of Advanced Distance Learning Network, Worcester Polytechnic Institute, 100 Institute Road, Worcester, MA 01609-2280. Telephone: 508-831-5220. Fax: 508-831-5881. E-mail: adln@wpi.edu.

DEGREES AND AWARDS

CGMS Management
Graduate Certificate Environmental Engineering; Fire Protection Engineering
MBA Technology Management
MS Environmental Engineering; Fire Protection Engineering

COURSE SUBJECT AREAS OFFERED OUTSIDE OF DEGREE PROGRAMS

Graduate—business administration, management and operations; computer systems networking and telecommunications; environmental/environmental health engineering; fire protection; international business; marketing; sales, merchandising, and related marketing operations (general); systems science and theory.

WRIGHT STATE UNIVERSITY
Dayton, Ohio
Center for Teaching and Learning
http://www.wright.edu/dl

Wright State University was founded in 1964. It is accredited by North Central Association of Colleges and Schools. It first offered distance learning courses in 1995. In fall 2005, there were 1,616 students enrolled in distance learning courses. Institutionally administered financial aid is available to distance learners.

Services Distance learners have accessibility to academic advising, bookstore, e-mail services, library services.

Contact Terri Klaus, Associate Director of Center for Teaching and Learning and Distance Learning, Wright State University, 023 Library, 3640 Colonel Glenn Highway, Dayton, OH 45435. Telephone: 937-775-4965. Fax: 937-775-3152. E-mail: terri.klaus@wright.edu.

DEGREES AND AWARDS

BS Nursing–RN-BSN Completion Program

MS Human Factors Engineering; Nursing–Family Nurse Practitioner--First Master's; Nursing–Family Nurse Practitioner--Second Master's; Rehabilitation Counseling

COURSE SUBJECT AREAS OFFERED OUTSIDE OF DEGREE PROGRAMS

Undergraduate—biological and biomedical sciences related; biology; communication and media; economics; education; education (specific levels and methods); English; English composition; history; liberal arts and sciences, general studies and humanities; linguistic, comparative, and related language studies; mathematics; music; nursing; technical and business writing.

Graduate—communication and media; economics; educational/instructional media design; education related; geological and earth sciences/geosciences; nursing; technical and business writing.

Non-credit—economics; education related.

YORK COUNTY COMMUNITY COLLEGE
Wells, Maine
http://www.yccc.edu

York County Community College was founded in 1994. It is accredited by New England Association of Schools and Colleges. It first offered distance learning courses in 1999. In fall 2005, there were 300 students enrolled in distance learning courses. Institutionally administered financial aid is available to distance learners.

Services Distance learners have accessibility to academic advising, bookstore, campus computer network, e-mail services, library services.

Contact Fred Quistgard, Director of Admissions, York County Community College, 112 College Drive, Wells, ME 04090. Telephone: 207-646-9282 Ext. 311. Fax: 207-641-0837. E-mail: fquistgard@yccc.edu.

DEGREES AND AWARDS

Programs offered do not lead to a degree or other formal award.

COURSE SUBJECT AREAS OFFERED OUTSIDE OF DEGREE PROGRAMS

Undergraduate—accounting and related services; American literature (United States and Canadian); applied mathematics; business administration, management and operations; business/commerce; business/corporate communications; business, management, and marketing related; business operations support and assistant services; computer and information sciences; computer/information technology administration and management; computer programming; computer software and media applications; culinary arts and related services; English composition; hospitality administration; human development, family studies, and related services; management information systems; mathematics; psychology; sociology; technical and business writing.

YORK TECHNICAL COLLEGE
Rock Hill, South Carolina
Distance Learning Department
http://www.yorktech.com

York Technical College was founded in 1961. It is accredited by Southern Association of Colleges and Schools. It first offered distance learning courses in 1995. In fall 2005, there were 2,120 students enrolled in distance learning courses. Institutionally administered financial aid is available to distance learners.

Services Distance learners have accessibility to academic advising, bookstore, campus computer network, career placement assistance, e-mail services, library services, tutoring.

Contact Anita McBride, Department Manager, York Technical College, 452 South Anderson Road, Rock Hill, SC 29730. Telephone: 803-981-7044. Fax: 803-981-7193. E-mail: mcbride@yorktech.com.

DEGREES AND AWARDS

AAB Accounting–Associate of Business

COURSE SUBJECT AREAS OFFERED OUTSIDE OF DEGREE PROGRAMS

Undergraduate—accounting and related services; biological and physical sciences; business administration, management and operations; business/commerce; computer science; developmental and child psychology; economics; English; English composition; environmental/environmental health engineering; history; mathematics; nursing; philosophy; psychology; sociology.

Non-credit—computer and information sciences and support services related.

YORK UNIVERSITY
Toronto, Ontario, Canada
http://www.yorku.ca/

York University was founded in 1959. It is provincially chartered. It first offered distance learning courses in 1994. In fall 2005, there were 10,000 students enrolled in distance learning courses. Institutionally administered financial aid is available to distance learners.

Services Distance learners have accessibility to academic advising, bookstore, campus computer network, e-mail services, library services, tutoring.

Contact Ms. Amalia Syligardakis, Manager, e-Learning Services, York University, Office of Computing Technology and e-Learning Services, 4700 Keele Street, Room 2120, TEL Building, Toronto, ON M3J 1P3, Canada. Telephone: 416-736-2100 Ext. 30705. Fax: 416-736-5637. E-mail: amalias@yorku.ca.

DEGREES AND AWARDS

BBA Administrative Studies

COURSE SUBJECT AREAS OFFERED OUTSIDE OF DEGREE PROGRAMS

Undergraduate—accounting and related services; business administration, management and operations; business/corporate communications; business/managerial economics; communication and media; economics; history; human resources management; liberal arts and sciences, general studies and humanities; management sciences and quantitative methods; marketing; mathematics; nursing; philosophy; political science and government; psychology related; public administration and social service professions related; religious studies; social sciences; social work; sociology.

Non-credit—accounting and related services; air transportation; business administration, management and operations; computer software and media applications; mathematics and statistics related; social work.

YUBA COLLEGE
Marysville, California
Learning Resource Center
http://www.yubaonline.edu

Yuba College was founded in 1927. It is accredited by Western Association of Schools and Colleges. It first offered distance learning courses in 1975. In fall 2005, there were 1,877 students enrolled in distance learning courses. Institutionally administered financial aid is available to distance learners.

Services Distance learners have accessibility to academic advising, bookstore, campus computer network, career placement assistance, e-mail services, library services.

Contact Miss Jeanette O'Bryan, Distributive Education Support Specialist, Yuba College, 2088 North Beale Road, Marysville, CA 95901. Telephone: 530-741-6754. Fax: 530-741-6824. E-mail: jobryan@yccd.edu.

DEGREES AND AWARDS

Programs offered do not lead to a degree or other formal award.

COURSE SUBJECT AREAS OFFERED OUTSIDE OF DEGREE PROGRAMS

Undergraduate—accounting and computer science; agricultural business and management; agriculture and agriculture operations related; animal sciences; anthropology; applied mathematics; astronomy and astrophysics; behavioral sciences; biology; chemistry; communication and media; computer and information sciences and support services related; computer programming; computer systems networking and telecommunications; ecology, evolution, and population biology; economics; education related; education (specific subject areas); English composition; foods, nutrition, and related services; liberal arts and sciences, general studies and humanities; mathematics and computer science; music; personality psychology; plant sciences; psychology; psychology related; sociology; veterinary biomedical and clinical sciences.

In-Depth Descriptions

The following two-page descriptions were prepared for this book by the institutions. An institution's absence from this section does not constitute an editorial decision. Rather, in-depth descriptions were offered as an open forum for institutions to expand upon the information provided in the previous section of this book. The descriptions are arranged alphabetically by institution name.

ADAMS STATE COLLEGE

Extended Studies

Alamosa, Colorado

Adams State College (ASC), which was founded in 1921, is located in the San Luis Valley in south-central Colorado in the city of Alamosa. Alamosa, at an elevation of 7,500 feet above sea level, is surrounded by mountain ranges with peaks rising up to 14,000 feet above sea level. The student body is composed of approximately 2,500 individuals from various ethnic and racial backgrounds. Adams State College is accredited by the Higher Learning Commission of the North Central Association of Colleges and Schools. The School of Education is currently accepted as a candidate in the Teacher Education Accreditation Council (TEAC).

Distance Learning Program

Adams State College has been providing programs to off-campus students for more than twenty-five years. In the past year, more than 18,000 students took advantage of one of the options offered through Extended Studies.

The Distance Degree Program offers a Bachelor of Arts (B.A.) degree in business administration, interdisciplinary studies, and sociology; a Bachelor of Science (B.S.) degree in business administration; and the Associate of Arts (A.A.) and Associate of Science (A.S.) degrees.

Certificate programs are available in alternative dispute resolution (mediation), legal investigation, legal nurse consultant training, legal secretary studies, management information systems, paralegal studies, and victim advocacy. Students who are not interested in degree completion can enroll in more than 140 independent-study/correspondence courses in accounting, business, business finance, business management, business strategy, criminology, economics, education, English, geography, geology, history, management, marketing, math, psychology, social theory, social welfare, and sociology.

Delivery Media

A variety of delivery options are available to students for all the accounting, business administration, criminology, economics, education, English, geography, geology, history, management, sociology, and general education courses, including online delivery, print materials, and face-to-face instruction at various sites. Students enrolling in an online or independent-study (correspondence) course are provided with a syllabus explaining course requirements. In many cases, the student is able to print the syllabus from the ASC Web site. Students send completed course work directly to the instructor. Some courses require proctored examinations, while others have online examinations. Online and traditional tools are available for courses, such as e-mail, textbooks, and videotapes. All ASC instructors are available by telephone, fax, e-mail, and surface mail.

Programs of Study

The B.A. and B.S. degrees in business administration require 120 semester credits for graduation; 45 must be junior- or senior-level credits, and a minimum of 30 credits must be completed with ASC. B.A./B.S. degree requirements include 40 semester credits in general education and approximately 40 in electives and 40 in the major field (specific requirements subject to the academic major). A maximum of 90 semester credits can be transferred to ASC, of which a maximum of 60 may be from junior/community colleges. Admitted students must maintain active status by enrolling in at least one ASC course per semester.

A.A. and A.S. degree program requirements include 43 semester credits in general education and 17 in electives. Students must complete general education course work to satisfy requirements from the following eight areas: oral and written communication, human behavior and institutions, history and culture, and arts and literature (6 credits each); quantitative thinking (3 credits) and speech fundamentals (3 credits; speech is required for A.A. and A.S. degrees only); science foundations and issues (8 credits); and health and fitness (2 credits). For specific course titles that meet these requirements, students should visit the ASC Web site at http://exstudies.adams.edu/degree.html.

Transfer credit is accepted from accredited institutions recommended by the American Association of Collegiate Registrars and Admissions Officers. Credits from a nonaccredited institution may be petitioned for transfer after the student has completed at least 24 semester credits at ASC with a C (2.0 GPA) average or better. Students may petition the appropriate academic dean for approval of courses that are not accepted during the normal admission and transfer process.

Special Programs

Courses that have attracted the interests of many students include the popular certificate programs in paralegal studies, alternative dispute resolution (mediation), legal investigation, legal nurse consultant training, legal secretary studies, and victim advocacy.

More than 200 six-week, noncredit, online interactive courses are available to students who are not interested in a standard academic program but are seeking a short-term solution to a current need. These courses are designed to provide the student with new skills and knowledge or to improve current skills. The categories of courses include business management, computer and software applications, entrepreneur studies, health, Internet, personal enrichment, small business, and Web page design. For a complete listing, students should visit http://www.ed2go.com/adams/.

ASC offers a wide range of online and independent-study graduate courses that have been developed for teachers. Many schools and school districts allow these courses to be used for in-service training or recertification purposes. Customized graduate certificate programs are designed to meet the professional development needs of educators.

Student Services

Free unofficial transfer evaluations are offered to students who are interested in the degree program. The ASC adviser provides students with a free, preliminary, unofficial credit evaluation upon request. Students must provide copies of transcripts or grade reports showing previous college work. These "unofficial" documents are reviewed by the program adviser, entered on a degree advisement form, and returned to the student. Students have the opportunity to see how their previous college work might meet the ASC requirements. The unofficial evaluation is subject to change based on the outcome of the official admission evaluation and acceptance of transfer credits by the Admissions Office.

Degree-seeking students have access to ASC faculty members via mail, e-mail, or fax or by calling the Extended Studies Office toll-free at 800-548-6679. Books may be purchased from the ASC bookstore via telephone, mail, or fax. All pertinent forms are located on the Extended Studies Web site.

Credit Options

For the bachelor's degrees, students may transfer in a maximum of 90 semester credits to ASC. The remaining 30 semester credits must be completed with ASC. Only 60 credits from community colleges may be applied to the degree. For the associate degree, students may transfer in a maximum of 45 semester credits, with the remaining 15 credits completed at ASC.

ASC participates in the College-Level Examination Program (CLEP) (general or subject exams). Students who have performed satisfactorily in college-level courses before college entrance and have demonstrated a requisite achievement (minimum scores of 50th percentile) on tests of the College Board College-Level Examination Program may submit the results to ASC for consideration for college credit. The Records Office records the college credit based on determinations made by the appropriate school's department chair. The maximum credit on the general exams is 18 semester hours (in the areas of humanities, natural science, and social science). The semester hours of credit for each subject exam, as well as credit by examination in total, are determined by the appropriate school's dean.

Military and civilian training is also considered for credit. The chair of the academic department in which the degree is earned evaluates any military and civilian training and makes the decision as to how credit will be awarded. ASC uses the American Council on Education Guides for credit recommendations. Military service credit is processed when official documents or transcripts are received at ASC. Courses found in the American Council on Education Guide or on transcripts (CCAF, AARTS, SMART) can be evaluated. Locally conducted (base- or post-level) courses are generally not acceptable due to their unstructured and changing content.

Faculty

Approximately 65 percent of the faculty members in the Distance Degree Program have a Ph.D. and are full-time professors on campus at ASC. All professors have experience working with distance learners.

Admission

Transfer students with at least 12 transferable college credits are not required to submit ACT or SAT scores or their high school transcript but must submit the admission application, application fee, and official transcripts from all colleges previously attended. First-time freshman students must submit the program application fee, the application for admission, and high school transcripts with ACT or SAT scores. The Distance Degree Program application fee is $25. For admission and application information and details, students should visit http://exstudies.adams.edu/degree.html.

Tuition and Fees

Independent-study course tuition for undergraduate credit is $105 per semester hour; for graduate credit, it is $125 per semester hour. Tuition must be submitted with the registration for the course. Some courses may have additional fees for materials. For course details, applicants should see the specific course description at http://extudies.adams.edu/ind_study/independ.html.

Financial Aid

Currently, students admitted to the Distance Degree Program are eligible to apply for financial aid. Also, company-sponsored tuition and military tuition assistance programs may be used for ASC courses. Eligible military personnel should process DANTES applications through their education office.

Applying

Students can find course and degree application information, application and registration forms, and more answers to their questions by visiting the Extended Studies Web site.

CONTACT

Distance Degree Programs
Extended Studies
Adams State College
208 Edgemont Boulevard
Alamosa, Colorado 81102
Phone: 800-548-6679 (toll-free)
Fax: 719-587-7974
E-mail: ascexdeg@adams.edu
Web site: http://exstudies.adams.edu

AIU ONLINE—AMERICAN INTERCONTINENTAL UNIVERSITY

Accelerated Degrees

Hoffman Estates, Illinois

American InterContinental University (AIU) Online is one of the premier online universities in the United States. With a tradition of educating students for more than thirty years, AIU has created an online education environment that combines the most sophisticated in Internet technology with the tradition of excellent higher education. American InterContinental University is accredited by the Commission on Colleges of the Southern Association of Colleges and Schools to award associate, bachelor's, and master's degrees.

Distance Learning Program

AIU Online's virtual campus provides a rich, interactive education. AIU Online offers degrees with classrooms as close as any Internet-connected computer, so students have access to a complete campus experience 24 hours a day, seven days a week. An education from AIU Online provides students with an opportunity to continue their education and advance their careers without disrupting their current lifestyles and schedules.

Delivery Media

The Web-based degree programs delivered by AIU Online are specifically designed for the student who accesses the course from a home or work personal computer. Recommended PC specifications are provided to students at the time of enrollment.

Programs of Study

All AIU Online programs are accelerated, so students can make their move upward sooner. The associate and bachelor's degree programs can be completed in thirteen months. (The thirteen-month bachelor's degree is a 2+2 program and assumes that all associate-level requirements have been met through an associate degree or the equivalent.) A master's degree or M.B.A. can be completed in ten months.

Business: Today's increasingly complicated business environments demand that existing and future business professionals have a comprehensive knowledge of the economic climate in the modern workforce.

The business administration program includes many sought-after concentrations that students can choose from to tailor their business degree to a specific career interest. Business concentrations include accounting and finance, health-care management, human resource management, management, marketing, operations management, organizational psychology and development, and project management.

The Bachelor of Business Administration (B.B.A.) programs provide an in-depth study of business, management, and marketing and give students a strong foundation for continued studies should they wish to advance their business education in the future.

AIU Online's accelerated M.B.A. program helps ensure that a student is professionally up-to-date and prepared to meet the challenges of today's increasingly complicated business environments. An online education from AIU Online gives students the knowledge and understanding of the economic climate in the modern workplace.

Information Technology (IT): As the modern business world becomes increasingly dependent on computers, the demand for IT professionals may continue to grow. AIU Online's degree programs in information technology offer a real-world education and can help qualify a student to meet the demands.

The Bachelor of Information Technology (B.I.T.) provides students with the relevant, up-to-date knowledge to pursue exciting, in-demand IT careers. This curriculum focuses on the development of appropriate business and programming skills, the use of networks, education in data administration, and the completion of IT projects. Concentrations in computer systems, network administration, or programming empower students to self-direct their degree program in a specific area of interest

The Master of Information Technology (M.I.T.), with a concentration in Internet security, combines the technology and Internet security portions of the course work with key information management courses to help ensure success in the job market.

Visual Communications: AIU Online is one of the first universities to offer a Bachelor of Fine Arts in visual communication, with a concentration in digital design, completely online. This program is designed to educate and develop artistic and imaginative students who are interested in such careers as flash animators, Web designers, or computer-based training developers.

The accelerated Bachelor of Fine Arts in visual communication degree program can be completed in just thirteen months. All required graphics software is included in the cost of course materials, providing students with training in the latest design software necessary to pursue a chosen career upon completion of the degree program

Criminal Justice: The growing emphasis on homeland security has created an unprecedented demand for criminal justice and security professionals. This accelerated, thirteen-month program helps students prepare for such vital, in-demand careers as FBI officers, correction officers, security analysts, U.S. customs agents, and directors of security.

The Bachelor of Science in criminal justice provides students with a superb foundation in some of the most interesting aspects of the industry, including criminology, the causes of crime, and typologies and victims. Courses are taught by experts in the criminal justice field who bring their significant knowledge and expertise to each course.

Education: For students who have a passion for learning and inspiring others, AIU Online offers a Master of Education degree program. This program can provide the spark for an individual to advance a career as a teacher, corporate instructor, or military trainer. With a concentration in instructional technology, the Master of Education degree brings students to the forefront of modern education.

Health-Care Management: Health care is one of the fastest-growing fields. Whether a student is looking to start a new career in health-care management or upgrade an existing one, AIU Online's accelerated health-care management degree programs can help ensure he or she is prepared to meet the challenge in months, not years.

The thirteen-month B.B.A. in health-care management helps provide a solid foundation for those interested in a management position in health care, whether in a hospital, long-term care facility, insurance company, managed-care organization, pharmaceutical company, or one of the many other health care–related industries.

The ten-month M.B.A. in health-care management was designed to provide a unique, market-relevant combination of a comprehensive business education with real-world, health-care-focused deliverables. The M.B.A. in health-care management is designed to help turn managers into executives; to arm them with the knowledge, skills, and experience necessary to reach high-level success.

Marketing: Today's complicated business models demand qualified marketing professionals in the management, planning, implementation, and evaluation of marketing and advertising functions. AIU Online offers accelerated, career-focused bachelor's (B.B.A.) and master's (M.B.A.) degree programs for students interested in pursuing rewarding careers in the ever-changing, fast-paced marketing industry.

The B.B.A. in marketing is designed to deliver a solid foundation for business marketing professionals by combining a core education in business with a focus on topics relevant to various marketing careers. This degree can be completed in just thirteen months and provides the experience-based education that helps students qualify for a wide variety of challenging, interesting careers.

AIU Online's M.B.A. in marketing is a ten-month program that combines the specialized curriculum of an executive M.B.A. with a focused training in marketing management disciplines. The result is a program that provides the advanced knowledge, skills, and practical experience-based education necessary to qualify for top marketing positions.

Organizational Psychology and Development: As the career-focused society spends more and more time at the office, there is a growing need for knowledgeable professionals with a modern, up-to-date understanding of the principles of psychology as they apply to the workplace. AIU Online's accelerated degree programs in organizational psychology and development prepare graduates for career advancement in business or management, with specific emphasis on jobs requiring relevant knowledge of such issues as group dynamics, performance appraisal, training and development, and conflict management.

The thirteen-month B.B.A. in organizational psychology and development is designed to prepare business and management professionals to drive their careers forward with up-to-date knowledge and applicable, real-world, experience-based learning.

The M.B.A. in organizational psychology and development can be completed in just ten months. This real-world degree program is designed to be immediately applicable to issues facing today's modern workplaces. The experience-based curriculum focuses on preparing business and management professionals to achieve leadership roles within their organizations.

Student Services

To help ensure an overall high-quality educational experience and academic success, AIU Online provides a range of student support services, including admissions, academics, financial aid, career services, and technical support. All services are accessible through the University's virtual campus. Students also have access to their account information, degree plan, and personal information 24 hours a day through this secure Web site.

Credit Options

In addition to college credit earned at accredited postsecondary institutions, the following can be evaluated for academic advanced standing: CLEP Examination, Advanced Placement (AP) tests, Computer Competency Examination, extra-institutional credit/experiential learning, and DANTES/military credit.

Faculty

AIU Online provides experienced faculty members with advanced degrees, who bring their real-world experience and expertise to their students. All faculty members teaching online receive training and guidance in online delivery methods and pedagogy.

Admission

To be considered for admission to AIU Online, applicants must submit an application and a $50 application fee and fulfill all admission requirements for the program. Selection of students for admission into degree programs of study is based on an individual assessment of each applicant. Each applicant must submit proof of high school graduation or the equivalent and participate in an admissions interview arranged by admissions personnel. If the applicant's first language is not English or if the applicant graduated from a non-English-speaking university, a minimum TOEFL score of 500 (undergraduate) or 550 (graduate) or other acceptable proof of English proficiency must be submitted

Tuition and Fees

Tuition and fee schedules for programs of study are reviewed with students at the time of acceptance.

Financial Aid

AIU Online's Financial Aid Department is committed to providing financial aid to those who qualify. AIU Online participates in various federal, state, and private student financial assistance programs. These financial aid programs are designed to provide assistance to students who are currently enrolled or accepted for enrollment but whose financial resources are unable to meet the full cost of their education. In addition, alternative financing options are available to those who qualify.

Applying

To apply for admission, a prospective student should submit an online application at http://www.aiuonline.edu along with a $50 application fee and complete a personal telephone interview.

CONTACT

Richard N. Einstein
Vice President of Admissions
American InterContinental University Online
5550 Prairie Stone Parkway, Suite 400
Hoffman Estates, Illinois 60192
Phone: 877-701-3800 (toll-free)
E-mail: info@aiuonline.edu
Web site: http://www.aiuonline.edu

AMERICAN MILITARY UNIVERSITY

Distance Learning Programs

Charles Town, West Virginia

American Military University (AMU) is part of the American Public University System, and is a private institution of higher learning licensed by the West Virginia Higher Education Policy Commission. AMU is accredited by the Distance Education and Training Council (DETC) and is a member of the Servicemembers Opportunity Colleges (SOC). The University focuses on the educational needs of the military community and has developed a flexible distance learning model uniquely suited to the military student's lifestyle. Founded in 1993, the University System serves more than 12,000 students studying in 130 countries around the world. The University has continuously broadened its curricula, expanding to include management, business administration, information technology management, homeland security, national security, criminal justice, intelligence, security management, psychology, sports management, and many others in addition to its core military studies and history programs. The University's headquarters is located in Charles Town, West Virginia, with administrative offices in Manassas, Virginia.

Distance Learning Program

AMU is exclusively a distance learning institution. All courses are Web-based and accessible around the clock through the Electronic Campus from wherever students have Internet access. Students are led through the eight-week or sixteen-week courses via an online classroom with a qualified instructor.

Delivery Media

AMU delivers and supports its courses through its Electronic Campus, with classrooms served by Educator® courseware by Ucompass. Through these electronic classrooms, students communicate with professors and each other using LISTSERV, discussion boards, student lounge chat rooms, and e-mail. Through this system, students are able to interact with each other and with professors, submit assignments, receive feedback, and take examinations. Electronic communications are supplemented by phone consultations during professors' office hours, with classes restricted to 25 students to ensure adequate student-professor interaction.

Programs of Study

AMU offers more than 100 associate, bachelor's, and master's degree programs and certificates.

Graduate programs, consisting of 36 semester hours/twelve courses and a comprehensive final examination, thesis, or practicum project are offered in criminal justice, homeland security, intelligence, management (including public, logistics, and crisis), military studies (including air warfare and special operations), national security studies, political science, public administration, space studies, and transportation management.

Certificate programs, consisting of 15 semester hours/five courses, are offered in many specialties within the curriculum and in area studies, period studies, and both historical and contemporary study areas.

Undergraduate programs include the Associate of Arts in general studies, a 60-semester-hour program with 30 semester hours of specified general education courses and electives, and the Bachelor of Arts, a 120-122 semester-hour program that mirrors the associate degree's lower-division requirements and includes upper-division major requirements and electives. The bachelor's degree is offered in American studies, child development, criminal justice, English, family development, history, intelligence studies, interdisciplinary studies, management, marketing, military history (with American and world concentrations), military management, philosophy, political science, psychology, religious studies, and sociology.

Student Services

The Student Services department is staffed to assist students as needed by e-mail, phone, and even via online chat rooms. All students experience AMU's online orientation program that prepares them for distance learning, including navigating the electronic campus, using the classroom functions, and understanding transfer credit and tuition and financial aid options. Many Student Services' functions are available online, and it is easy for students to submit changes and check their status.

Credit Options

Credits may be earned through AMU by traditional courses, challenge examinations, and independent study. Courses may be audited without credit. AMU accepts transfer credit from accredited institutions, training and experience credit recommended by the American Council on Education, and credit by examinations (CLEP, DANTES, etc.).

Credit acceptance by program is as follows: associate degree, up to 45 semester hours; bachelor's degree, up to 90 semester hours; and graduate degree, up to 15 semester hours.

Faculty

AMU's faculty brings real-world experience and world-class credentials to the online learning experience. More than 300 adjunct faculty members, along with 50 full-time faculty members, work together to ensure AMU students achieve appropriate learning outcomes. All faculty members meet traditional accreditation standards with regard to degrees and professional preparedness.

Admission

Graduate students must possess an accredited baccalaureate degree. Undergraduate students must have a high school diploma or GED certificate. No examinations are required for admission.

Tuition and Fees

Tuition is $250 per semester hour for both graduate and undergraduate programs. There is no admission fee. All undergraduate students earning academic credit receive AMU's book grant, covering 100 percent of the costs of all textbooks. Transfer credit evaluations are subject to a one-time fee of $75, and all students who have attended other institutions of higher learning are required to submit a transfer evaluation by the end of their first semester at AMU. A graduation fee of $100 is assessed, which includes a framed and matted diploma.

Financial Aid

AMU accepts military tuition assistance, GI Bill and VA educational benefits, and corporate tuition assistance. Students may be eligible for Sallie Mae education loans, and AMU has an installment payment plan as well. AMU is committed to providing the military community with a quality, low-cost education, assisting the military community in achieving their educational goals.

Applying

The application process is easy and is completed online. There is no cost to apply for admission and applicants are conditionally admitted upon submission of the online application form. A student ID is issued, and applicants receive a password via e-mail, allowing them to log in to the electronic campus, complete their online orientation, and register for courses.

CONTACT

Admissions
American Military University
American Public University System
111 West Congress Street
Charles Town, West Virginia 25414
Phone: 877-468-6268, menu option 2 (toll-free)
E-mail: info@apus.edu
Web site: http://www.apus.edu/amu

Athabasca University
Canada's Open University

ATHABASCA UNIVERSITY

Quality Learning. Anywhere. Anytime.

Athabasca, Alberta, Canada

Athabasca University (AU) is a publicly funded university in the province of Alberta, Canada. It is accredited by both the Government of Alberta and the Middle States Commission on Higher Education in the U.S. Its accreditation by the Middle States Commission is the first time a Canadian university has been accredited by one of the regional accreditation boards in the United States.

AU is an open university, which means that its mission is to break down barriers that prevent people from pursuing university studies. By specializing in flexible online and distance learning, AU helps people continue their studies despite challenges, such as where they live, what their past education is, and commitments to careers and families. AU is committed to innovation, flexibility in learning, and excellence in teaching, research, and scholarship.

AU is a full member of the Association of Universities and Colleges of Canada, the Association of Commonwealth Universities, the International Council for Open and Distance Education, the Canadian Association for Distance Education, the Canadian Association for Graduate Studies, the Canadian Virtual University, the Circumpolar Universities Association, the Global University Alliance, and the Inter-American Distance Education Consortium.

Distance Learning Program

AU, Canada's largest online and distance education university, delivers courses and programs at both the undergraduate and graduate levels. Bachelor's degrees, master's degrees, and undergraduate and graduate university diplomas and certificates are offered. The flexibility of online and distance learning allows students to complete courses or programs on a full-time or part-time basis and to study when it is convenient for them. Students may also complete AU courses to satisfy their program requirements at other universities and colleges.

AU courses are accessed by more and more individuals each year. In 2004–05, the University served 32,000 students.

Delivery Media

AU uses a variety of learning methods, including multimedia online activities, print materials, e-mail, the Internet, CD-ROMs, CDs, DVDs, computer software, audio-conferencing, videoconferencing, TV, and radio. Any course might use a combination of these methods. Students have support from professors, tutors, advisers, and various other student services by e-mail and phone (toll-free in Canada and the United States).

Programs of Study

Graduate degree and diploma programs offered are the Master of Arts–Integrated Studies, Master of Business Administration (various majors), Master of Counselling, Master of Distance Education, Master of Health Studies, Master of Nursing, Master of Science–Information Systems, Advanced Graduate Diploma in Advanced Nursing Practice, Advanced Graduate Diploma in Distance Education (Technology), Graduate Diploma in Management, and Advanced Graduate Diploma in Project Management.

Undergraduate degrees offered are the Bachelor of Arts (three- or four-year, various majors); Bachelor of Commerce (four-year, general program or majors in accounting or e-commerce; post-diploma route available); Bachelor of General Studies (three-year, with designation in applied studies or arts and science); Bachelor of Health Administration (four-year, post-diploma route available); Bachelor of Human Resources and Labour Relations (four-year, post-diploma route available); Bachelor of Management (three- or four-year, general program or majors in human resources management or marketing; post-diploma route available); Bachelor of Nursing (four-year; post-RN or post-LPN; on-site at Mount Royal College); Bachelor of Professional Arts (four-year, various majors; post-diploma degree); Bachelor of Science (four-year, general program or majors in human science or computing and information systems; post-diploma route available).

University certificate programs are offered in accounting, administration, advanced accounting, career development, computers and management information systems, computing and information systems, counseling women, English language studies, French language proficiency, health development administration, human resources and labour relations, labour studies, and public administration.

University diploma programs in arts and inclusive education are also offered.

Special Programs

AU is a founding partner in Canadian Virtual University (CVU), an innovative partnership of Canada's leading universities in online and distance learning. Students can select from among 2,000 courses in the CVU catalogue and apply them to programs at any partner university. There are also fee savings for students who take courses from more than one partner university, and some courses are available in French as well as English. Students should visit CVU's Web site at http://www.cvu-uvc.ca for easy searching of courses and programs.

AU's many partnerships with various institutions and organizations provide a multitude of learning options for students. For more information, students should visit http://www.athabascau.ca/collab/collab.php.

Student Services

AU takes pride in providing exceptional service to students. Services, such as advising, counselling, registration support, help for students with disabilities, a long-distance library, and more are all available. The first point of contact is the Information Centre at 800-788-9041 (toll-free in Canada and the U.S.) or 780-675-6100 (international). Students can also visit http://www.askau.ca for a quick answer to most general questions.

Credit Options

AU grants credits for courses completed at other recognized postsecondary institutions. AU course credits are also eligible for transfer to programs at other higher education institutions worldwide.

Some of AU's programs are post-diploma degrees, which typically mean that if a student has completed a suitable college diploma, AU counts the diploma as the first two years or half of the degree.

Some students can apply for a prior learning assessment, which evaluates nonformal university-level learning, such as work experience, for credits toward an AU credential.

Faculty

As of March 31, 2005, AU employed 111 full-time academics, 148 part-time academics, and 276 part-time tutors. Courses are written and taught by these faculty members, most of whom have master's degrees or doctorates.

Admission

Undergraduate admission is year-round, and anyone 16 years or older is eligible for admission, regardless of previous educational experience, with or without a high school diploma. (Some programs and courses may have academic or geographic restrictions). Graduate programs typically require students to have a baccalaureate degree from a recognized postsecondary institution; additional admission requirements vary among programs. Students should consult AU's academic calendar or Web site for more information.

Tuition and Fees

Textbooks, course materials, and fees are included in the tuition fee. Until August 31, 2006, the cost for an undergraduate 3-credit course is Can$578 (in Alberta), Can$633 (rest of Canada), and Can$856 (international). Graduate program fees vary by program; students should consult the academic calendar or the graduate program itself for fee information.

Financial Aid

Financial assistance is available to full- and part-time students from Alberta Students Finance or the financial aid agency where a student resides. The amount varies according to need. In-province students can obtain a financial aid package from Athabasca University. Out-of-province students should contact their local financial aid agency.

AU students are automatically considered for many academic awards and scholarships without application unless specified otherwise. Students should visit http://www.athabascau.ca/registrar/studawrds.php for more information on AU student awards.

Applying

Admission to undergraduate programs is year-round, and many courses can be started on the first day of any month. To apply, students must complete and submit a General Application Form along with the application fee. Students may apply online at the Web site or submit a paper application form by fax or mail. Application forms are available in the academic calendar and on the Web site.

Graduate programs have application deadlines, which can be found in the academic calendar or the Web site.

CONTACT

Athabasca University Information Centre
1 University Drive
Athabasca, Alberta T9S 3A3
Canada
Phone: 780-675-6100 (international)
800-788-9041 (toll-free in Canada and the U.S.)
Fax: 780-675-6437
E-mail: inquire@athabascau.ca
Web site: http://www.athabascau.ca

AUBURN UNIVERSITY

Graduate Outreach Program

Auburn, Alabama

Auburn University was chartered in 1856 as the East Alabama Male College. In 1872, Auburn became a state institution—the first land-grant university in the South to be separate from a state university. Auburn University is Alabama's premier engineering and business institution. U.S. News & World Report's *"America's Best Colleges" ranks both Auburn's College of Business and its College of Engineering among the nation's top fifty programs at public institutions. Auburn's Graduate Outreach Program has been ranked by GetEducated.com's "Top 25 Best Buys" for Web-based distance learning graduate-degree programs. Auburn is dedicated to serving the state and the nation through instruction, research, and extension. Auburn University is accredited by the Commission on Colleges of the Southern Association of Colleges and Schools.*

The campus consists of more than 1,800 acres, with a student body of approximately 24,000. Auburn University, the largest school in the state of Alabama, is located in east-central Alabama. The city of Auburn has a population of about 40,000. Auburn is known for its small-town, friendly atmosphere and is often referred to as "the loveliest village on the Plain."

Distance Learning Program

In response to industry's request, Auburn's College of Engineering began offering courses to off-campus students through the Graduate Outreach Program in 1984. The Graduate Outreach Program allows professionals the opportunity to continue their education while maintaining full-time employment. The program serves more than 400 students in forty-eight states. The M.B.A. program is accredited by AACSB International–The Association to Advance Collegiate Schools of Business. The programs in the College of Engineering are accredited by the Accreditation Board of Engineering and Technology (ABET).

Note for international inquirers: Due to material distribution methods, the current distance learning program service area is limited to the U.S. and Canada and to U.S. military personnel with APO or FPO mailing addresses.

Delivery Media

The Graduate Outreach Program makes every effort to ensure that the off-campus students receive the same high-quality education as on-campus students. Live classes are recorded daily and distributed by streaming video and in DVD format. Professors establish telephone office hours and/or e-mail communication so that off-campus students may receive answers to any questions they may have. E-mail accounts are established for the Graduate Outreach Program students. Most faculty members also utilize the Internet to post handouts and class materials.

Programs of Study

The Graduate Outreach Program offers master's degrees in seven disciplines in engineering—aerospace engineering, chemical engineering, civil engineering, computer science and software engineering, industrial and systems engineering, materials engineering, and mechanical engineering—as well as the Master of Management Information Systems, Master of Accounting, and Master of Business Administration. These programs are all nonthesis and without residency requirements. Each candidate must pass an on-campus, comprehensive, final oral examination covering the program of study to graduate. The examination covers the major and minor subjects, including any research or special projects involved.

In the Master of Business Administration program, students may earn a concentration in either finance, health-care administration, human resource management, management information systems, management of technology, marketing, or operations management. The program consists of 36 to 42 semester hours of course work, including eight core courses and four electives. Applicants are required to complete a course in calculus and statistics prior to entering the program. Students with nonbusiness undergraduate degrees may be required to pass foundations exams in economics, finance, marketing, management, and accounting. Incoming students are also advised to have a working knowledge of word processing and spreadsheet software and an elementary understanding of database applications. M.B.A. students must visit the campus for five days during their final semester prior to graduating for on-campus presentations.

Nondegree professional development courses are available for those who need to meet job requirements or professional certification.

Special Programs

Career and job placement assistance is available through Auburn University's Career and Student Development Services. Accessibility to the R. B. Draughon Library is also available. A valid Auburn University student identification card is required to check out resources. The Division of University Computing provides University-wide computing and networking services to students. Computer accounts are free of charge to currently enrolled students.

Credit Options

Graduate credit taken in residence at another approved graduate school may be transferred to Auburn University but is not accepted until the student has completed at least 9 hours of work in the Graduate School at Auburn University. No prior commitment is made concerning whether transfer credit can be accepted. A student must earn at least 21 semester hours or half of the total hours required for a master's degree (whichever is greater) at Auburn University. No transfer credit is approved without two official transcripts. No course in which a grade lower than B was earned may be transferred.

Faculty

The Auburn University faculty consists of more than 1,200 members. Eighty percent of the faculty members hold a doctoral degree, and 88 percent hold a terminal degree in their field.

Admission

An applicant to the Graduate School must hold a bachelor's degree or its equivalent from an accredited college or university. The Graduate Record Examinations (GRE) is required for admission to the College of Engineering, and the Graduate Management Admission Test (GMAT) is required for admission to the M.B.A. program. Students whose native language is not English must submit scores of the Test of English as a Foreign Language (TOEFL) for admission to the M.B.A. program. Admission is based on the grade point average of university-level courses, GRE or GMAT scores, and recommendation letters from instructors and supervisors. Students can be informed by the Graduate Outreach Program on how they can enroll as off-campus students once they are accepted by the Graduate School.

Tuition and Fees

The Graduate Outreach Program fees are $525 per credit hour for engineering and $546 for business. Registration schedules and fee bills are mailed to the student prior to the beginning of each quarter.

Financial Aid

Military personnel who have been accepted into the Graduate School may apply for tuition aid through DANTES at their local education office. Many of the Graduate Outreach Program students receive tuition assistance through their employer's tuition reimbursement plan. The Auburn University Office of Student Financial Aid assists in the awarding of grants, loans, and scholarships for qualified full-time students.

Applying

To apply for admission, a prospective student must return a Graduate School application, an M.B.A. application (if applicable), a nonrefundable application fee of $25 for U.S. citizens or $50 for non-U.S. citizens, three letters of recommendation, GRE or GMAT scores, and two official transcripts of all undergraduate and subsequent course work from the respective institutions. Graduate School applicants may apply online at http://www.grad.auburn.edu. This ensures a quicker response in most cases.

CONTACT

Wanda Lambert
Graduate Outreach Program
202 Ramsay Hall
Auburn University
Auburn, Alabama 36849-5331
Phone: 888-844-5300 (toll-free)
Fax: 334-844-2502
E-mail: lambewf@eng.auburn.edu
Web site: http:// www.gop.auburn.edu

BAKER COLLEGE

Baker Online

Flint, Michigan

Baker College, founded in the true American tradition as a small business college in 1911, is a private, nonprofit, accredited, coeducational institution. The College has more than a dozen campuses and branch locations in the Midwest and has a total enrollment of more than 31,500 students. The College is uniquely designed for one purpose: to provide high-quality higher education that enables graduates to be successful throughout their challenging and rewarding careers. The College offers diploma, certificate, and associate, bachelor's, and master's degree programs in the fields of business, technical, and health service fields. Total commitment to the students' employment success in uniquely evident in all aspects of the College's operations.

Baker College is accredited by the Higher Learning Commission of the North Central Association of Colleges and Schools. Baker College is an equal opportunity/affirmative action institution.

Distance Learning Program

Baker Online offers the convenience of classroom accessibility 24 hours a day, seven days a week, from virtually anywhere in the world. It is not a self-paced program. Courses begin and end on specific dates and classwork is assigned deadlines, but as long as students have Internet access, they have access to their courses.

Delivery Media

Students are required to have a computer with the following minimum requirements: a Pentium III or higher system, Windows XP Professional or higher, a 56K (minimum) modem, Internet Explorer 5.5 or Netscape 4.7 or higher (AOL is not compatible), and Microsoft Office XP Professional. A CD-ROM drive and an Internet service provider are required. The virtual classroom is the common meeting area for all students taking classes online. Communication is accomplished by sending messages back and forth from the student's computer to the classroom computer. Each classroom has a unique name, and only students taking that class have access to the virtual classroom. This ensures privacy for all students.

Programs of Study

Baker Online offers the delivery of high-quality, respected courses and programs that enable a student to earn an associate, bachelor's, or master's degree at home, on the road, or anywhere in the world.

The Associate of Business Administration degree has been designed specifically for the online college environment, where students have a variety of choices in filling out the degree plan. The curriculum gives students a good background of business facts and knowledge upon which to build or enhance a career in business.

The Bachelor of Business Administration degree is a program designed for the working professional that combines core course work with independent research and experiential credit to provide a contemporary business degree for today's business environment. Each core course contains focused study in the content area accompanied by independent research.

The Master of Business Administration degree program seeks to combine the best of conventional academic training with the best of field-based learning. Most typical business disciplines are represented in the curriculum because the College believes that a successful manager must be conversant with different aspects of running any of today's organizations or companies. Students may also elect to focus their studies in one of the following areas: computer information systems, health-care management, human resource management, industrial management, integrated health care, international business, leadership studies, or marketing.

Special Programs

Baker Online offers undergraduate courses at all levels to support all of the campuses and their program offerings as a convenience for students who may have trouble commuting to a campus. Baker Online publishes a listing each quarter showing which classes will be offered.

Student Services

Every Baker College student is assigned an e-mail account on the BakerNet system. Through this system, students can communicate with each other and their instructors and with members of the graduate school staff. Students may also use their accounts to access the World Wide Web. They also have access to the Baker College Library System and FALCON, a consortium of libraries that supports an online catalog database of more than 500,000 holdings. Students also have access to InfoTrac periodical indexing databases, the UMI/ProQuest General Periodicals On-Disc full-article imaging station, Books-in-Print with Reviews, and all available Internet and World Wide Web resources.

Baker College offers a renowned Lifetime Employment Service, with access to thousands of career opportunities and employment databases, to all students. This service can be used for the rest of one's life.

Credit Options

Baker College recognizes the expediency of understandable and universally accepted standards related to transfer of academic credit. The College follows the Michigan Association of Collegiate Registrars and Admissions Officers Official Policies and recognizes the College-Level Examination Program (CLEP) or other standardized tests.

Faculty

The focus of Baker's faculty is somewhat different from that of traditional universities. Instead of placing an emphasis on empirical research, Baker values practitioner-oriented education. Faculty members remain continually active in their professions by consulting, conducting seminars, running their own businesses, writing, volunteering in their communities, and working with other organizations. The faculty-student ratio in distance education is 1:12.

Admission

Graduate program candidates must have a bachelor's degree from an accredited institution and a 2.5 or better GPA in their undergraduate work, be able to display appropriate communication skills, submit three letters of reference, submit a current resume, and have completed no less than three years of full-time work. Undergraduates must have graduated from high school, completed a GED program, or passed an Ability to Benefit assessment before entering.

Tuition and Fees

Undergraduate tuition for the 2005–06 school year was $175 per credit hour. Graduate tuition was $285 per credit hour. The cost of books ranged from $150 to $200 per quarter.

Financial Aid

Students who are accepted into Baker College may be considered for several forms of state, federal, and institutional financial aid. Students are requested to complete the Free Application for Federal Student Aid (FAFSA) and return it directly to the College.

Applying

Baker College uses a rolling admission process, so there are no deadlines for applications. Students are allowed to begin in any quarter. Once the Admissions Committee receives an application, applicants usually receive a decision in approximately four weeks. Once accepted, students participate in a three-week online orientation. They are not required to visit a campus at any time.

CONTACT

Chuck J. Gurden
Vice President for Admissions
Center for Graduate Studies
Baker Online
1116 West Bristol Road
Flint, Michigan 48507-9843
Phone: 810-766-4390
800-469-3165 (toll-free)
Fax: 810-766-4399
E-mail: adm-ol@baker.edu
Web site: http://www.bakercollegeonline.com

BELLEVUE UNIVERSITY

Online Programs

Bellevue, Nebraska

Bellevue University is one of Nebraska's largest fully accredited independent colleges. It is accredited by the Higher Learning Commission of the North Central Association of Colleges and Schools (30 North LaSalle Street, Suite 2400, Chicago, Illinois 60602-2504; telephone: 800-621-7440). Programs serve the needs of more than 5,900 students annually and cater to working adult students as well as traditional undergraduate students. Benefits include accelerated degree completion programs, online programs, an online library, and cooperative credit transfer agreements. Associate degrees are accepted in full, and credit is given for corporate and military training as well as life experience.

Distance Learning Program

Bellevue University is an information-age institution of higher learning with progressive options for online graduate and undergraduate degrees. Graduate and undergraduate programs, online, on campus, and in centers throughout the region, prepare students for an ever-changing environment.

Delivery Media

Online education is about taking classes and earning a degree entirely through the Internet. With Internet access, students go online to take classes, participate in discussions with professors and fellow students, conduct research at the online library, and interact with their online adviser. Online classes are small to give the Cyber-Active® Learning advantage that characterizes Bellevue University.

Programs of Study

Undergraduate programs are offered in an accelerated, cohort-based format. The program in business administration of technical studies emphasizes techniques, procedures, and methods for managing the technical functions of business. The business information systems program prepares students who do not have computer technology degrees or course work for management within information technology (IT) and positions with technical applications. The corrections administration and management program provides students the skills and knowledge necessary for the professional oversight of modern correctional programs. The program in criminal justice administration focuses on management and opportunities in the criminal justice system. The program is designed for individuals working in, or closely associated with, the criminal justice system. The health-care management program provides a systems perspective for those interested in pursuing management opportunities in health care. The program in management of health-care informatics is designed for students interested in the management of electronic records and information in the health-care arena. The program in Internet systems and software technology provides a comprehensive study of the information technology industry. Topics are included in an integrated format built around a common project management theme. The leadership program provides students the theoretical and practical preparation they need to assume positions of leadership in the professional ranks of organizations. The management program gives students a comprehensive background in the skills, methods, and theories that undergird all effective management. The management of human resources program covers methods and practices of the human resource management professional. The management information systems program emphasizes business knowledge and management skills for individuals working in the management information systems field. The security management program provides students with the theoretical and practical knowledge necessary for a career in the security field. The strengths-based management program focuses on management issues as they relate to the Gallup Organization's talent-based management principles. The marketing management program emphasizes the techniques and methods of managing and planning in marketing. The focus is on proven practices and application of theory. The logistics management program is designed for individuals interested in, or already working in, the field of logistics management and supply chain management.

The Master of Business Administration (M.B.A.) program covers the tools and methods required to run a business. The program requires 36 credit hours of course work. The schedule of course offerings permits an individual working full-time to complete all the requirements for the M.B.A. degree in eighteen months (two classes per term). Students who do not have an undergraduate degree in business generally take the Foundation (9 credits), the core (18 credits), and a concentration (9 credits) to complete the degree. M.B.A. concentrations are offered in accounting, advance programming, finance, health care, human resource management, interdisciplinary business, international management, management information systems, marketing, and supply chain management. The Master of Science in computer information systems program has strong elements of both business and computer/telecommunication subjects. Students with business or computer undergraduate preparation typically finish the program with 36 credits of graduate work. For students without a computer background, there are 9 additional prerequisite credits. The Master of Science in management of information systems was created for midlevel IT managers and future chief information officers who need to keep pace with the rapidly changing world of enterprise technology. The program requires 36 hours of course work. The Master in Health-Care Administration (M.H.A.) program provides clinical health-care providers with an opportunity to pursue in depth the various areas of planning, organizing, leading, and controlling as they provide administrative guidance to others within their health-related organization. Students in the Master of Arts in management program develop a working knowledge of the application of quantitative techniques, marketing analysis, human resource management, financial analysis, influencing behavior in organizations, and sensitivity to the legal environment in which operations occur. The Master of Arts in leadership program encourages individual thought, synthesis of group contribution, and assimilation of practical and theoretical teachings. Its mission is to combine leadership philosophy, derived from great leaders and their writings, with concepts and theoretical models of organizational leadership. The Master of Arts and the Master of Science in communication studies programs address competencies in the areas of critical thinking, research, professional and social skills, diversity and intercultural communication, applied theory, leadership, and emotional intelligence. The programs are designed to produce graduates who can bridge the modern workplace communication gap, meet internal training and development needs, and identify and utilize effective skills to address important communication issues inherent in all work environments. The Master of Science in security management prepares students to function effectively at the director level in a broad spectrum of homeland security and related occupations. The Master of Science in instructional design prepares students to be a master educator in the application of instructional technology for both online and traditional classrooms, emphasizing the integration of theory and practice.

Credit Options

Bellevue University grants credit for college-level learning that a student has obtained through sources other than college classes. Students may be granted credit for college-level learning acquired outside of a regionally accredited college setting. Procedures are in place to assess student learning from non-regionally accredited institutions, American Council on Education recommendations, corporate training or programs, CLEP/DANTES tests, and the Experiential Learning Assessment.

Faculty

The Bellevue University full-time and adjunct faculty consists of 398 full- and part-time members who teach students from freshman to graduate level. The student-faculty ratio is 15:1. For most classes and programs, Bellevue University employs adjunct faculty members who are professionals in their respective fields. Faculty members are screened to ensure each is current on issues and technology.

Admission

Online degree completion programs are offered in an accelerated format. To qualify for undergraduate programs, students must have at least 60 credit hours from an accredited institution or an associate degree. To qualify for graduate programs, students must have a baccalaureate degree from an accredited institution, a minimum 2.5 GPA over the course of the last two years of undergraduate work, two letters of recommendation, and a completed essay.

Tuition and Fees

Online undergraduate tuition for a 36-hour major program is $10,620; for the 9-hour Signature Series, it is $2655. Undergraduate fees include the nonrefundable application/assessment fee, $50; student fees, $150; and graduation fees, $75. The estimated total cost for an online undergraduate program is $13,550. This figure excludes the cost of books.

Tuition for the graduate online programs is as follows: the Master of Business Administration and the Master of Science in computer information systems, $340 per credit hour; the Master of Arts in leadership and the Master of Arts in management, $12,240 or $340 per credit hour (excluding books); and the Master in Health-Care Administration, $12,240. The application fee is $50 and the graduation fee is $75 for all online graduate programs. The general college fee is $45 per semester for the M.B.A. and the M.S. in computer information systems programs and $150 for the M.A. in management, the M.A. in leadership, and the Master in Health-Care Administration.

Financial Aid

Financial aid assists students with the costs of attending college. This assistance comes from the federal and state government, the institution, and private sources. Financial aid includes grants, scholarships, work-study programs, and student loans. Grants and scholarships do not have to be repaid.

Applying

Individuals interested in applying should transmit the application online or by mail, pay fees, and submit transcripts for evaluation. Admissions counselors work with students to complete the official admissions process. An educational degree plan is completed for each student, defining the requirements needed to achieve each student's degree goal.

CONTACT

Bellevue University
1000 Galvin Road South
Bellevue, Nebraska 68005
Phone: 402-293-2000
800-756-7920 (toll-free)
E-mail: info@bellevue.edu
Web site: http://www.bellevue.edu

BOSTON UNIVERSITY

Department of Manufacturing Engineering

Boston, Massachusetts

Boston University, the fourth-largest independent university in the United States, extends more than 70 acres from the historic Back Bay section of Boston, westward along the south bank of the Charles River. It traces its roots to a school founded by Methodist lay leaders in Vermont in 1839; it moved to Boston in 1867 to become the first American university to be modeled on the European system. Today, the University is home to more than 2,500 faculty members and over 28,000 students in seventeen schools and colleges who are enrolled in more than 250 degree programs.

The University is strongly committed to equality in opportunity. It was the first institution of higher education in Massachusetts to grant degrees to women, and it graduated the first African-American woman with an M.D. degree and the first woman with a Ph.D. degree. In addition, it takes a progressive approach to education, having introduced the first program in the country organized around a team method of instruction and numerous interdisciplinary programs that combine career goals and personal interests.

In recent years, the College of Engineering has succeeded in securing highly competitive grants from federal agencies and industrial sources, including a $14-million Whitaker Foundation Leadership Award in 2001, only the third such award made to a university. Total externally funded research and graduate student enrollment are at record-breaking highs, and more than 30 new faculty members have been appointed over the past five years in fields as diverse as photonics, nanotechnology, acoustics, and genomics.

Boston University is accredited by the New England Association of Schools and Colleges, Inc.

Distance Learning Program

The Manufacturing Engineering Distance Learning Program (DLP) at Boston University brings outstanding faculty members, relevant courses, and innovative research to working engineers via live videoconference and delayed video streaming. The DLP is designed for high-potential engineers with creativity, motivation, and a strong desire to achieve technical excellence. The program's unique content and synchronous delivery format enable students to immediately apply classroom learning to work-related challenges. Courses are continually redesigned to create competence in technical product leadership and to provide students with the total educational experience on which to build successful industrial and increasingly international careers.

Delivery Media

The program employs a VCON IP bridge and management software package so that students can participate in class from anywhere a high-speed Internet connection is available. Such connections can be made with VCON vPoint teleconferencing software on a fast PC with USB camera or with a slower PC and relatively inexpensive VCON ViGo hardware. This configuration permits class sessions to be recorded in RealVideo as they are conducted and then moved to the University's RealVideo server immediately after class.

Programs of Study

Students in the program focus their course work in one of three concentration areas: sensors and instruments, global product development, and lean supply chain design. Each concentration consists of 36 credit hours, of which at least 28 credits must be earned at Boston University and at least 20 credits are from technically oriented engineering courses. A cumulative GPA of at least 3.0 is required for all courses.

A dual-degree program leading to an M.S. degree in manufacturing engineering and an M.B.A. prepares recent graduates or practicing professionals who are committed to careers in industry for positions of technical leadership. The program requires completion of 80 credits, including 40 credits in the M.B.A. program (M.B.A. only available on campus), 36 credits in the M.S. program, and 4 credits from either program.

Student Services

The Office of Information Technology assists students in setting up their ACS accounts and obtaining their passwords for access to the online program. The Martin Luther King Jr. Center addresses the personal, educational, and career-development needs of students, including the Office of Career Services, which helps students obtain career and internship information and develop and implement career plans. The Educational Resource Center provides comprehensive support services and resources students need to ensure academic success, including peer tutoring.

Credit Options

Credits from graduate-level courses from other accredited engineering programs may be transferred with the recommendation of an academic adviser, department graduate associate chair, and the Associate Dean for Research and Graduate Programs. A grade of B or higher must have been earned from the course. No more than 8 credits may be transferred.

Faculty

There are 28 full-time faculty members in the department. Young professors, recently trained in new technologies and methods, focus on analysis, modeling, and theory. Senior faculty members, experienced in teaching, industry, and scholarly research, apply these concepts to the manufacturing process. In addition to teaching, many faculty members also participate in research projects at the University's research centers and labs.

Admission

While most students hold a bachelor's degree in an engineering-related discipline, some hold mathematics or science degrees. In some instances, the student already has an advanced degree but is returning to school to further his or her career or achieve personal goals. Students' backgrounds are looked at on an individual basis during the admissions process. Students are permitted to take three courses before being required to apply to the M.S. program.

Tuition and Fees

Tuition for part-time students is $985 per credit. Other expenses include a registration fee of $40 per semester and additional fees for textbooks and class materials. The Office of Student Accounting Services offers several deferred-payment plans.

Financial Aid

The is no financial aid available for part-time distance learning students.

Applying

Prospective students must submit the following to be considered for admission: a completed application, a $65 application fee, official records of all college work previously taken, two letters of recommendation, official GMAT or GRE scores sent directly from the testing center, a statement-of-purpose essay, and a current resume. There is a rolling admissions process.

CONTACT

Sarah Cowen, Distance Learning Administrator
Department of Manufacturing Engineering
College of Engineering
Boston University
15 Saint Mary's Street
Brookline, Massachusetts 02446
Phone: 617-353-2943
Fax: 617-353-5548
E-mail: scowen@bu.edu
Web site: http://www.bu.edu/mfg/dlp

BRENAU UNIVERSITY

Online College

Gainesville, Georgia

Brenau University, which was founded in 1878, is a historic, private, comprehensive university in Gainesville, Georgia. The University serves two populations: a coeducational population of adult and nontraditional students online, in the evenings and on weekends, and a single-gender population of women in traditional daytime classes at the picturesque north Georgia main campus.

Brenau University offers online classes for a population of students who are unable or unwilling to attend campus-based classes. Degree and certificate programs are offered entirely online, with a focus on collaborative learning. Evening and weekend classes serve a growing population of working adult men and women by offering degree and certificate programs and other classes in four locations across the state (Atlanta, Augusta, Gainesville, and Kings Bay). Daytime classes have provided a single-gender liberal arts education since the University's founding.

Brenau University is regionally accredited by the Southern Association of Colleges and Schools.

Distance Learning Program

Brenau's Online College provides high-quality educational experiences through the delivery of graduate and undergraduate programs utilizing the latest distance learning technology. Programs delivered in the online format are designed for working adult students, providing maximum flexibility without compromising learning outcomes or academic rigor.

Delivery Media

Online classes are delivered via the Internet. Common software programs are used to enhance the delivery of course materials. Dialogue among students, using an asynchronous bulletin board system, is central to the collaborative learning goal. Online students bring with them varied life and work experiences that, when shared with classmates, provide relevant applications of theory to real-world situations.

Programs of Study

Brenau University currently offers undergraduate degree programs entirely online in the areas of business, criminal justice, liberal studies, and nursing. Graduate degree programs are offered in business and education.

The Associate of Arts (A.A.) in liberal studies degree program is designed for the nontraditional, first-time college student or the student with very little college experience. This 60-hour degree program allows for maximum flexibility in scheduling and course selection and can be completed in as little as five semesters.

Brenau's RN-to-B.S.N. bridge program provides registered nurses the opportunity for career advancement by earning a bachelor's degree. An experienced and academically qualified faculty of registered nurses offers this 31-hour program. The clinical portion of this program may be completed in the student's local community, supervised by a Brenau nursing faculty member.

The Bachelor of Business Administration in management or marketing is a 120-hour degree program. These undergraduate business degree programs, which include courses in organizational behavior, ethics, and international business, can be completed in approximately four years.

The Bachelor of Science/Bachelor of Arts degree in criminal justice is a 120-hour degree program. This undergraduate degree program features courses in judicial process, law, management, and public administration/policy and can be completed in four years entirely online.

M.B.A. degrees in accounting, advanced management studies, business administration, and health-care management are available from the Department of Business Administration, which has a long history of offering M.B.A. programs. Students can reach their professional goals easily with Brenau's accelerated ten-course, 30-hour general M.B.A.; the thirteen-course, 39-hour M.B.A. in advanced management studies; the eleven-course, 33-hour M.B.A. in health-care management; or the twelve-course, 36-hour M.B.A. in accounting. Many states have adopted the 150-hour educational requirement to sit for the CPA exam. Brenau students meet this requirement by earning their M.B.A. degrees.

The M.Ed. degrees in early childhood education and middle grades education are available from the School of Education. The early childhood M.Ed., a long-standing degree offering at Brenau, is a twelve-course, 34- or 36-hour program, depending on the student's choice of a capstone activity (comprehensive exam or research project). The M.Ed. in middle grades education prepares professionals to teach children in grades four through eight. Students develop a variety of appropriate teaching methods and strategies that are specifically geared to the middle-grade learner. This program is an eleven-course, 34- or 36-hour degree program, depending on the student's choice of a capstone activity.

Special Programs

Brenau University's accelerated M.B.A. program in business administration is designed so that students may complete it in five semesters. Classes are small and offer students asynchronous discussion and work-related collaborative projects. These activities are designed to guarantee participation in online classes.

BA 500, the business administration department's intensive business foundations course that covers all undergraduate basics in the fields of statistics, management, accounting, and marketing, was designed for nonbusiness majors seeking to earn an M.B.A. Experienced faculty members from each of these fields collaborate to teach this unique 6-hour course.

Student Services

In addition to online application, advising, registration, and tuition payment, other student services include writing and math tutors, career services (job search and career selection), mental health counseling, and disability support services through the campus Learning Center. The Brenau Trustee Library catalog is available online using the popular Voyager software, and supplemental materials are offered via document delivery and interlibrary loan.

Credit Options

The residency requirement for undergraduate programs is 45 hours. For the nursing degree, 31 hours must be completed at Brenau University. Alternative credit options toward a Brenau University undergraduate degree (credit earned from advanced-placement exams, international baccalaureate programs, CLEP, military credit, experiential credit, or challenge exams) are limited to a total of 27 hours.

Brenau University may accept up to 6 hours of transfer credit from other regionally accredited institutions as part of a planned graduate program of study upon approval of the respective department chair.

Faculty

Classes are taught by professors who are trained and certified in online course delivery. Professors teaching in graduate programs have doctorates in their fields and corporate and/or practical experience.

Admission

Prospective students should submit a completed application, a $35 application fee, and transcripts from all institutions previously attended. Standardized test scores (GMAT, GRE, MAT, TOEFL) must be sent from testing services for graduate program applicants.

Tuition and Fees

Online tuition is $425 per hour ($75 technology fee per semester). Tuition rates are addressed prior to each academic year. Tuition is payable by check, money order, or credit card (Visa, MasterCard, and Discover). Brenau offers a military tuition discount.

Financial Aid

Online students who qualify are eligible for all need-based financial aid programs, including Pell Grants, other federal grants and loan programs, state-direct loans for students in nursing, and institutional grants. Program-specific funds are also available. The FAFSA financial aid application is available online.

A total of 1,831 (71 percent) Brenau University students received some type of financial aid this past academic year. The Office of Scholarship and Financial Assistance receives student loan applications (phone: 800-252-5119 Ext. 6152, toll-free).

Applying

The completed application, a $35 application fee, and official transcripts and test scores should be sent directly to the Office of Admissions, 500 Washington Street, SE, Gainesville, Georgia 30501. Military applicants should include a copy of a valid military I.D. or DD214. Online College representatives are available by phone at 800-252-5119 (toll-free) and e-mail.

CONTACT

Heather S. Gibbons, Ph.D.
Director of the Online College
Brenau University
500 Washington Street, SE
Gainesville, Georgia 30501
Phone: 770-718-5327
Fax: 770-718-5329
E-mail: online@brenau.edu
Web site: http://online.brenau.edu

BUENA VISTA UNIVERSITY

BVUOnline

Storm Lake, Iowa

*Founded in 1891, Buena Vista University (BVU) is a leading New American College, preparing students for successful careers as well as leadership and service in their communities. With approximately 1,300 undergraduate and graduate students on its main campus in Storm Lake, Iowa, plus an additional 1,500 students at fifteen branch sites throughout Iowa, BVU offers a balance between traditional liberal arts courses and innovative experiential-learning opportunities that require the practical application of knowledge. Long a leader in information technology, BVU is currently at the nation's forefront in providing "anytime, anywhere" online access with the launch of BVU*Online*, its new virtual campus.*

Distance Learning Program

BVU*Online,* the online campus of Buena Vista University, is committed to providing access to higher education to learners who, because of family and job responsibilities, need a great deal of flexibility in achieving their educational goals. Consistent with BVU's reputation for offering a technology-rich learning environment, the mission of BVU*Online* includes online delivery of a curriculum with the highest academic quality, an interactive and dynamic online learning environment, support services providing the highest level of convenience for students, and programs, courses, instructors, student support, and an online learning experience that is consistent with BVU's goal of education for service.

Delivery Media

BVU's e-learning platform, Angel, provides a full suite of online tools and features, including discussion areas, chat rooms, assignment drop-boxes, grade-books, and individual progress tools. Community areas enable students to interact with others outside of class, receive public announcements, and access the BVU*Online* calendar for important dates and information for their program. A complete student-orientation course provides details and tutorials on the e-learning platform's easy-to-use tools. A free demo of the course software is available at http://www.bvuonline.org/bvu/resource/aboutbvuonline/bvuonlinecoursedemo.aspx.

Programs of Study

BVU*Online* programs are accredited by the Higher Learning Commission of the North Central Association of Colleges and Schools. BVU*Online* offers students high-quality online programs and courses led by experienced faculty members. Students can earn a graduate degree completely online and complete course work anytime and anywhere it is convenient.

BVU*Online's* Master of Education (M.Ed.) program, offered in two tracks, provides a curriculum designed under the guidelines of the National Board of Professional Teaching Standards.

The Master of Education with a specialization in effective teaching and instructional leadership prepares teachers with the skills necessary to master, implement, and evaluate research-based effective teaching practice and provides the knowledge and skills necessary for data-driven leadership.

The Master of Education with a specialization in teaching English as a second language prepares teachers who work with English language learners with the knowledge of second-language acquisition, assessment procedures, skills, and techniques to more effectively address the academic and social challenges presented by an increasingly diverse population of students.

Special Programs

BVU*Online* enables students at all levels to take individual courses in a wide number of fields. For a complete listing of the available undergraduate and graduate courses, students should visit: http://www.bvuonline.org/bvu/resource/registration/coursedescriptions.aspx.

Student Services

Before enrolling in a BVU*Online* program, students receive academic advising by phone with a BVU counselor. Once enrolled, students have access to online registration tools, an online bookstore, state-of-the-art online library resources (40 searchable online databases) and reference help, 24/7 technical support (online and by phone), study guides, and access to career resources and the BVU Help Desk, which is available 24/7 online and by phone during business hours (8 a.m. to 5 p.m. Central time).

Credit Options

All credits earned through BVU*Online* are recorded on a Buena Vista University transcript and do not appear any differently than the on-campus courses. Graduate students may transfer up to 6 credit hours into the M.Ed. program if approved by the Graduate Office.

Faculty

Instructors in BVU*Online* programs hold advanced master's or doctoral degrees (in the graduate program) and also bring a wealth of practical experience to the online classroom. All BVU*Online* faculty members must complete the BVU*Online* instructor's certification program that emphasizes providing high-quality feedback to students in an online environment as well as facilitating courses. Faculty members have been specially trained to work with adult learners and online students, so they understand what it means to balance the demands of family, career, and education. Instructors interact with students via e-mail, on the phone, or in online chats and are eager to support each student's success.

Admission

Candidates for the graduate program must have a Bachelor of Arts or a Bachelor of Science degree from an accredited institution and a minimum 2.75 GPA in their undergraduate work. In addition to the application, candidates must submit a copy of a valid teaching certificate or license and three letters of recommendation (from a principal, a colleague, and a reference of choice).

Tuition and Fees

For 2005–06, graduate tuition is $350 per credit hour. Supplemental fees include a $50 application fee and an $80 technology fee that covers Microsoft Office Pro, SPSS, and Mathematica, which are provided to students upon their acceptance. The cost of books is not included.

Financial Aid

Students accepted into any of the BVU*Online* programs may be eligible for financial aid. Prospective students are encouraged to complete the Free Application for Federal Student Aid (FAFSA) at http://www.fafsa.ed.gov and release the information to Buena Vista University. The University's Title IV school code is 001847.

Applying

BVU*Online* courses are offered throughout the year in eight-week terms, beginning in late August. Students may enroll at the start of any term. Students should apply at least four weeks prior to the start of a new term to ensure that the admissions process is complete for the term start. For a calendar of term start dates, prospective students should visit http://www.bvuonline.org/bvu/resource/programs/calendar.aspx.

CONTACT

BVU*Online*
Buena Vista University
610 W. Fourth Street
Storm Lake, Iowa 50588
Phone: 712-749-1880
877-288-0423 (toll-free)
E-mail: bvuonline@bvu.edu
Web site: http://www.bvu.edu/online/petersons.jsp

CALIFORNIA INSTITUTE OF INTEGRAL STUDIES

Online Degree Programs

San Francisco, California

California Institute of Integral Studies (CIIS) in San Francisco is an accredited university offering an online M.A. in transformative leadership and an online Ph.D. in transformative studies in a unique learning community. Residential Ph.D., Psy.D., M.A., and B.A. completion degrees in psychology and the humanities are also offered. The Institute's commitment to the study and practice of multiple cultural and spiritual traditions and to their expression throughout the activities of the community promotes a stimulating learning environment with rigorous scholarship and a supportive community—including the online programs.

Distance Learning Program

The master's degree program in transformative leadership has been created for individuals who want to take the initiative and find ways to express their passion for making a contribution to the world. The program provides a context where they can prepare themselves in a community of like-minded individuals, exploring their own mission in life and developing the skills needed to make it a reality. The culminating capstone project grounds students' work in an action site, where they can apply their learning on a continuous basis.

The primary focus of the doctoral program in transformative studies is to develop thought-leaders who are committed to exploring leading-edge issues in innovative ways, combining scholarship, creativity, and self-inquiry. The program places great value in developing the ability to participate in scholarly discourse through publication and on the importance of viewing academic inquiry as an opportunity for personal and social transformation, while grounding transformative processes in academic depth, rigor, and imagination.

Current information about the programs and courses is available on the CIIS Web site, by telephone, or in person at CIIS in San Francisco.

Delivery Media

The M.A. and Ph.D. are offered as 36-semester-unit programs. The doctoral program also requires a dissertation. Both programs are offered in online format using community-based learning through CIIS's Web-based virtual campus, in which students, faculty members, and staff members interact.

Students from both online programs participate in weeklong intensives in a San Francisco Bay Area retreat setting. Intensives are held at the beginning of each semester. Distance students generally take all their courses on the virtual campus.

Student Services

The CIIS Library, Registrar's, Business Office, and Financial Aid Department are well prepared to support online students with their specific needs.

Faculty

CIIS programs attract a faculty of scholars who wish to act from a spiritual foundation while helping to improve the effectiveness and well-being of individuals, communities, and organizations. The online-degree faculty members bring practical experience and intellectual expertise relevant to transformation and change and the pedagogies appropriate for an online learning environment.

Admission

Individuals who wish to deepen their understanding and effectiveness as transformative change agents are welcome to apply. Typically, candidates have professional experience and are seeking to enhance their abilities through study, action, reflection, and scholarship.

Both master's and doctoral programs are also attractive to those wishing to make a career transition or looking to approach change differently in their current site of practice. The ideal candidate also is seeking a program that uses an integral pedagogy, one that honors body, mind, and spirit. And finally, those who require a program that caters to the working professionals find the virtual campus a convenient venue.

Tuition and Fees

For 2006–07, full-time tuition for the M.A. program, at 9 units per semester, is $6750 ($16,130 per year). For the Ph.D. program, at 9 units per semester, tuition is $8040 ($16,020 per year).

Financial Aid

Financial assistance through scholarships, loans, and grants is awarded on the basis of merit and/or need. A serious attempt is made to extend a personalized, concerned approach to student financial needs while complying with governmental and donor regulations. General financial aid programs include Federal Pell Grants, Federal Supplemental Educational Opportunity Grants (FSEOG), Institute scholarships, diversity scholarships, international scholarships, Veterans Administration Educational Benefits, Federal Family Education Loan Programs (FFELP), Federal Stafford Student Loans, and other loan and scholarship opportunities based on merit or need.

Applying

Applicants must meet the general admissions requirements of the Institute. In addition to official transcripts and an autobiographical statement, applicants must submit the following: two letters of recommendation, a critical writing essay, a resume, and a goal statement. Ph.D. applicants should include a statement telling how they will use the resources of the curriculum to advance a chosen inquiry.

Complete admission information and applications are available through the CIIS Web site or through the Admissions Office.

CONTACT

Admissions Counselor
California Institute of Integral Studies
1453 Mission Street
San Francisco, California 94103
Phone: 415-575-6150
Fax: 415-575-1264
E-mail: admissions@ciis.edu
Web site: http://www.ciis.edu

CALIFORNIA STATE UNIVERSITY, DOMINGUEZ HILLS

College of Extended and International Education

Carson, California

California State University, Dominguez Hills (CSUDH), is a national leader in distance learning, named by Forbes *magazine as one of the top cyber universities. The campus is located in the South Bay Area of Los Angeles. Founded in 1960, the University is one of twenty-three California State University (CSU) campuses and has the largest distance learning program in the CSU system. The University offered its first distance learning degree in 1974, and in 1995 offered one of the first online master's degree programs ever approved by the Western Association of Schools and Colleges.*

CSU Dominguez Hills continues to be in the forefront of distance learning technology and academic excellence, garnering numerous awards, including the Best Distance Learning Teacher from the U.S. Distance Learning Association, an Omni Intermedia Award, an Aegis Award, two Telly Awards, and a Top 100 Video Producer Award.

The CSU Dominguez Hills campus is located in the South Bay area of Los Angeles and is accredited by the Western Association of Schools and Colleges.

Distance Learning Program

The distance learning unit is part of the College of Extended and International Education, whose mission is to extend the resources of the University to better serve the educational needs of its communities. The University has more than 4,000 students enrolled in distance learning programs in all fifty states and more than sixty countries.

Delivery Media

All distance learning courses have a Web site, and participants can interact with faculty and staff members via e-mail, telephone, and correspondence. Courses are conducted via live Webcast, where students participate in a live, interactive educational environment, including video transmission of the lecture; via asynchronous Internet, where participants log in at their convenience to complete class assignments and engage in discussion groups with their peers; via television, where CSUDH broadcasts 24 hours a day on cable systems throughout southern California; and via correspondence.

Programs of Study

CSU Dominguez Hills currently offers ten degree and ten certificate programs via distance learning. There are no on-campus requirements for any CSUDH distance learning program. Programs include the following:

Master of Arts in Behavioral Science: Negotiation, Conflict Resolution, and Peacebuilding. Taught via asynchronous Internet, the program teaches participants valuable skills and knowledge that may be applied directly to police work, counseling, human resources management, labor relations, supervision, administration, alternative dispute resolution, arbitration, public policy, social work, teaching, intercultural and community conflicts, corporate contracts, and purchasing (telephone: 310-243-2162; e-mail: negotiation@csudh.edu; Web site: http://www.csudh.edu/negcon).

Master of Arts in the Humanities. Taught via correspondence, the degree offers an interdisciplinary approach to the disciplines of the humanities—history, literature, philosophy, music, and art—with emphasis on their interrelating effects and influences (telephone: 310-243-3190; e-mail: huxonline@csudh.edu; Web site: http://www.csudh.edu/hux).

Master of Business Administration. Taught via asynchronous Internet, the M.B.A. at CSUDH provides a solid qualification in business management with courses that are wide-ranging in content, covering the essential areas of knowledge and skills required in today's competitive business environment (telephone: 310-243-2714; e-mail: cnicholson@soma.csudh.edu; Web site: http://mbaonline.csudh.edu).

Master of Public Administration. Taught via asynchronous Internet, the program is designed to provide a high-quality graduate professional education for individuals entering or currently employed in public service and nonprofit professions (telephone: 310-243-2395; e-mail: mpaonline@soma.csudh.edu; Web site: http://mpaonline.csudh.edu).

Master of Science in Engineering Management (M.S.E.M.). Taught via asynchronous Internet, the M.S.E.M. is an interdisciplinary degree program designed to integrate the development of management and engineering skills focusing on problem solving in the synthesis of technical, financial, and organizational requirements for engineering projects in a rapidly changing environment. The program is currently offered jointly by California State University, Long Beach (for the engineering component), and CSU, Dominguez Hills (for business), and the degree is granted at CSU, Long Beach in the name of both institutions (telephone: 310-243-3165; e-mail: kpoertner@csudh.edu; Web site: http://csulb.edu/colleges/coe/).

Master of Science in Nursing and Bachelor of Science in Nursing. Taught via asynchronous Internet, the bachelor's completion program prepares graduates to function as leaders, managers, and resource people in a variety of health-care settings. The graduate program prepares professional nurses for advanced and specialized practice. Role emphasis options include clinical nurse specialist in gerontological nursing and nursing education (telephone: 310-243-3741; e-mail: eereg@csudh.edu; Web site: http://www.csudh.edu/msn or http://www.csudh.edu/bsn).

Master of Science in Quality Assurance and Bachelor of Science in Quality Assurance. Taught via asynchronous

Internet, the bachelor's program provides the academic environment and the requisite course of study to blend the basic sciences, technologies, management principles, quality concepts, and statistical tools needed to prepare professionals for careers in quality assurance and to serve working professionals seeking career enhancement. Master's degree students receive education in both the technical and administrative foundations of quality assurance, an interdisciplinary profession used in management in manufacturing, service, government, and health-care organizations (telephone: 310-243-3880; e-mail: msqa@csudh.edu; Web site: http://www.csudh.edu/msqa or http://www.csudh.edu/bsqa).

Bachelor of Science in Applied Studies. Taught via live broadcasts on the Web and cable television, as well as archived broadcasts and Web sites, the program enables students with associate degrees to complete their bachelor's degree entirely via distance learning. Eighteen courses representing a wide spectrum of management and liberal arts courses help students to become leaders in their profession and advance in their careers. (telephone: 866-278-6789; e-mail: appliedstudiestv@csudh.edu; Web site: http://www.appliedstudies.tv).

Quality Management, Quality Engineering, Quality Auditing, Reliability Engineering, and Software Quality Engineering Certificates of Completion. Taught via asynchronous Internet, the certificate completion programs in quality assurance allow professionals to gain certification in specialized areas of quality and prepare for American Society for Quality exams. Students who successfully complete three master's degree–level courses and the associated capstone course can earn a certificate of completion (telephone: 310-243-3880; e-mail: msqa@csudh.edu; Web site: http://www.csudh.edu/msqa).

Assistive Technology Certificate. Taught via asynchronous Internet, the program prepares individuals to comply with state and federal laws that require that school personnel be prepared to offer a full range of assistive technology services to disabled people. The program is useful to educational administrators, teachers, special education teachers, occupational and physical therapists, speech and language specialists, rehabilitation specialists, program specialists, resource specialists, and psychologists (telephone: 310-243-3741; e-mail: paul_richard@ocde.k12.ca.us; Web site: http://www.csudh.edu/at).

Community College Teaching Certificate. Taught via asynchronous Internet, the program is designed to enhance the skills and the employability of potential community college instructors (telephone: 310-243-2781; e-mail: dulloa@csudh.edu; Web site: http://www.csudh.edu/ccteaching).

Production and Inventory Control Certificate. Taught via asynchronous Internet, the program provides a broad education in the principles of production and inventory control. The program is taught by professionals currently employed in the field who are certified in production and inventory management (telephone: 310-243-3741; e-mail: smackay@csudh.edu; Web site: http://www.csudh.edu/lapicsonline).

Purchasing Certificate. Taught via asynchronous Internet, the program provides a broad education in the principles of procurement management and also helps students prepare for the Certified Purchasing Manager exam (telephone: 310-243-3741; e-mail: smackay@csudh.edu; Web site: http://www.csudh.edu/purchasingonline).

Technical Writing Certificate of Completion. The Technical Writing Certificate of Completion introduces students to the many aspects of contemporary technical writing practices and helps them develop the skills and confidence to communicate complex technical concepts simply and effectively (telephone: 310-243-3730; e-mail: bwald@lists.csudh.edu; Web site: http://www.csudh.edu/extension/technicalwriting.htm).

Special Programs

The Center for Training and Development at CSUDH works closely with the business community to develop custom-designed training programs to help meet the demands of the fast-paced workplace of the new millennium. Programs are delivered via distance learning, on-site, and on the CSUDH campus.

Student Services

Faculty members are available to students via e-mail, telephone, and mail. Student services available at a distance include academic advising, technical support, online tutoring, and access to the library and bookstore.

Credit Options

Depending on the specific program, students may transfer credit earned at other accredited colleges and universities. For more information, students should visit the CSUDH distance learning Web site.

Faculty

CSU Dominguez Hills has more than 100 faculty members teaching distance learning courses. Most of these faculty members have doctoral degrees in their chosen fields.

Admission

Admission requirements vary for each program. Students should consult the CSUDH distance learning Web site for specific program requirements.

Tuition and Fees

Tuition and fees vary for each program. For specific cost information, students should consult the CSUDH distance learning Web site.

Financial Aid

More than $30 million in financial aid is disbursed to CSUDH students each year. Approximately 68 percent of CSUDH students receive some form of financial assistance, and most financial aid programs are available to qualified distance learning students. For further information, students should visit the financial aid Web site (http://www.csudh.edu/fin_aid/default.htm).

Applying

Application processes vary for each program, and campus visits are not required for any program. Students should consult the CSUDH distance learning Web site for specific application information.

CONTACT

Registration Office
College of Extended and International Education
California State University, Dominguez Hills
1000 East Victoria Street
Carson, California 90747
Phone: 310-243-3741
877-GO-HILLS (toll-free)
Fax: 310-516-3971
E-mail: eereg@csudh.edu
Web site: http://dominguezonline.csudh.edu

CAPELLA UNIVERSITY

Online Learning

Minneapolis, Minnesota

Capella University is an online, accredited university that offers programs in business, information technology, education, human services, and psychology. Capella was founded in 1993 and today is a national leader in online education and is committed to providing academic excellence. For more information, students should visit http://www.capella.edu or call 888-CAPELLA (227-3552, toll-free).

Capella University is accredited by the Higher Learning Commission and a member of the North Central Association of Colleges and Schools, located at 30 North LaSalle Street, Suite 2400, Chicago, Illinois 60602-2504 (312-263-0456, http://www.ncahigherlearningcommission.org).

Distance Learning Program

The mission of Capella University is to extend access to high-quality bachelor's, master's, doctoral, and certificate programs to adults seeking to maximize their personal and professional potential. This mission is fulfilled through innovative programs that are responsive to the needs of adult learners. The programs include active, engaging, challenging, and relevant learning experiences. Capella offers thirteen degree programs, seventy-seven graduate and undergraduate specializations, and sixteen certificate programs. The online university currently serves more than 15,700 learners from all fifty states and sixty-three countries.

Delivery Media

As an online university, Capella provides active communication between faculty members and learners, primarily inside its online courseroom. In that framework, learners have e-mail access to faculty members and other learners as well as discussion boards where groups can interact and collaborate. As new technologies evolve and prove their instructional value, Capella investigates additional interactive tools.

Programs of Study

Capella University's programs are offered through five schools:

The School of Education offers the M.S. and Ph.D. degrees and post-master's certificates. Educators choose Capella to advance their careers and achieve personal and professional goals through the School of Education. The online education degrees and post-master's certificate programs in K–12, higher education, and continuing and adult education are designed to expand students' knowledge and improve their effectiveness in diverse educational settings. Graduates seek to improve their teaching practices and advance to leadership roles, such as superintendent, principal, academic dean, or dean of student affairs.

The School of Human Services offers the M.S. and Ph.D. degrees and post-graduate certificates, so students can follow their passion for social change. The programs prepare students for rewarding work in a variety of institutional, agency, community, and educational settings. Many graduates of the online master's degree program continue their advanced study and seek a Ph.D. in human services.

Capella University is one of the few online universities to offer Master of Science and Ph.D. programs with a specialization in criminal justice. The American Counseling Association's Council for Accreditation of Counseling and Related Educational Programs (CACREP) has accredited two of Capella's clinical counseling specializations: marital, couple, and family counseling/therapy and mental health counseling.

The Harold Abel School of Psychology offers the M.S., Ph.D., and Psy.D. degrees and specialist certificates. The school offers a range of academic and professionally oriented online psychology degree specializations. Students develop critical thinking skills to understand and apply key psychological principles in diverse work settings. They gain competencies and confidence through the advanced online psychology degree programs, which expand opportunities and help them achieve professional goals.

The School of Business and Technology offers the M.S., M.B.A., and Ph.D. degrees and postgraduate certificates. Business specializations provide a broad examination of core business functions and organizational management aspects that address issues critical to business professionals. They explore traditional business disciplines, such as finance, marketing, operations, strategy, and sales/CRM. For M.B.A. learners, this solid business foundation is supplemented by a core set of professional effectiveness courses that emphasize best practices for leading and managing others. The information technology master's degree explores the role of IT in today's business climate and examines the tools and systems used by leading organizations to solve business challenges. The curriculum reflects the skills associated with leading IT certifications, such as CCNA®, CCNP®, MCSE, CISSP®, and PMP.

The School of Undergraduate Studies offers the B.S. degree. Through relevant and practical course work, students gain knowledge and skills that can make an immediate impact in their career—even before they graduate. The programs help students master business fundamentals while developing skills and gaining knowledge in an area of interest. The online bachelor's degree programs enhance students' personal and professional effectiveness. Learners in the information technology bachelor's program benefit from a relevant curriculum that addresses essential information technology competencies in project management, information security, enterprise systems integration, application development, network architecture and design, systems design and programming, and graphics multimedia specializations. Capella's business program develops foundational knowledge and scholarship related to current issues in the specializations of accounting, business administration, finance, human resource management, management and leadership, and marketing.

Special Programs

Capella University has academic advisers who guide students personally throughout their education. Advisers help plan course work, develop a long-term educational plan, and understand the requirements for degree completion.

Capella has collaborated with the Sheridan Libraries at Johns Hopkins University to create the Capella University Library. A team of librarians is dedicated exclusively to working with Capella University learners and faculty and staff members. The library provides the full range of academic resources and services, including databases and online services, reference services, interlibrary loans, and training in research methodology.

Capella University's Writing Program fosters the connection between clear thinking and clear writing. Program faculty members have extensive writing and teaching experience and are eager to help students achieve a level of writing excellence that will advance their academic pursuits and life goals.

Effective, skilled career counselors can be essential allies during educational pursuits. Capella's Career Services staff members help students determine their strengths and focus energy in the right direction. Although job placement is not provided, throughout students' course work at Capella, Career Services professionals assist with career planning and development, one-to-one career guidance, job search assistance, and online resources.

Credit Options

Through the petition-review process, student's can apply to earn credit for the technical knowledge and skills they have gained from their real-world experience, training, certifications, and previous education. In addition, course work from both regionally accredited or internationally recognized institutions and military training and experience may transfer into Capella's degree programs. Earning credit for prior learning through the petition process or national testing program exams or by obtaining transfer credits can shorten the time required to complete a degree and reduce bottom-line tuition costs.

Faculty

Capella has 824 faculty members—121 core, full-time faculty members and faculty administrators as well as 703 adjunct faculty members. Capella faculty members live in forty-nine U.S. states and six foreign countries. Seventy-six percent of the faculty hold doctoral degrees.

Admission

Capella University was founded with a commitment to extend access to high-quality higher education. To achieve this goal, Capella admits applicants who have received the appropriate qualifying degree or course work from accredited institutions or programs and who have a qualifying grade point average. In addition, applicants must express educational goals that are appropriate for the program to which they have applied and must meet additional program-specific admission requirements.

Undergraduate learners entering the university with 23 or more quarter credits of successfully completed prior college/university course work and a cumulative college/university GPA of 2.0 or higher (on a 4.0 scale) are assumed to possess the writing and mathematical competency necessary to succeed in a Capella bachelor's degree program. Undergraduate learners without those criteria must demonstrate basic writing and mathematical competencies.

Tuition and Fees

The application fee is $75 ($175 for international applicants). Capella's tuition is based on the requirements of each school, so tuition can vary. For information about the tuition requirements of each school, students should visit http://www.capella.edu/inc/pdf/tuition_chart.pdf.

Financial Aid

Capella University offers assistance to learners who would like to secure educational funding to help finance their academic program. Sources for financial aid include federal aid, employer tuition reimbursement, military education benefits, and scholarships. More than three quarters (76 percent) of Capella learners receive some form of financial aid to support their education investment. For more information about financial aid, students should call the University.

Applying

Capella's eAdmissions process makes it easy to apply online (http://www.capella.edu). Admission requirements vary depending on the program and the school. The details of admission can be found in the catalog, available on request. For more information, students should call the University.

CONTACT

Capella University
225 South 6th Street, 9th Floor
Minneapolis, Minnesota 55402
Phone: 888-227-2736 (toll-free)
612-339-8650 (international)
Fax: 612-977-5060
E-mail: info@capella.edu
Web site: http://www.capella.edu

CMU
CENTRAL MICHIGAN UNIVERSITY

CENTRAL MICHIGAN UNIVERSITY

CMU Off-Campus Programs

Mount Pleasant, Michigan

Since its founding in 1892, Central Michigan University (CMU) has grown from a small teachers' college into a world-class Midwestern university offering more than 150 programs at the bachelor's level and nearly sixty programs at the master's, specialist's, and doctoral level. CMU is accredited by the North Central Association of Colleges and Schools. This accreditation includes all on- and off-campus programs. Central Michigan University is an institutional member of the Council for Adult and Experiential Learning; the Adult Education Association; the Alliance: An Association of Alternative Degree Programs for Adults; and the National Association of Institutions in Military Education.

Distance Learning Program

Programs are offered in a compressed format to help balance the demands of work, school, family, and other obligations. The compressed format does not mean easier courses. Distance learning courses are held to the same academic standards that on-campus courses must meet. To help insure success in the compressed format, procedures and support services are fast and accessible.

Delivery Media

Students have a choice of delivery formats: online, print-based learning packages, or classroom-based courses at more than sixty locations in North America.

Online courses use Web technology to involve the student in interactive learning. Students can interact with instructors and others through e-mail, chat sessions, and message forums. Student lecture materials and assignments are all online. Textbooks are still required.

Learning packages are print-based courses that use textbooks and study guides but may also include audio and videocassettes as well as the use of e-mail and Internet chat rooms to enrich the content.

Classes are also available in evening or weekend formats at locations throughout the United States, Canada, and Mexico. An up-to-date listing of locations is available at http://www.celmcmich.edu.

Programs of Study

CMU Off-Campus Programs offers undergraduate-, graduate-, and doctoral-level degree programs. Undergraduate program offerings are available at centers in Michigan and online through CMU's distance learning program. All bachelor's degrees are based on 124 semester hours of credit.

The Bachelor of Science degree with a major in administration is for students wishing to pursue an administrative career. The core courses provide a foundation in the concepts and applications critical to becoming a successful, effective administrator. Graduates of this program are prepared for careers as production supervisors, human resource administrators, and small business administrators. General education and elective courses allow students to acquire basic skills and learn to communicate with people in other disciplines and jobs and they provide an emphasis in liberal arts and natural or social sciences. A sampling of courses within the organizational administration concentration includes managerial economics, human resource management, and organizational behavior among other business topics.

The Bachelor of Science degree with an option in community development prepares students for work in the public sector or human services area. Graduates go on to careers in political office, the public health professions, directing community education, and more. Courses focus on the general theory and practice of community along with interaction of community institutions in a community setting. The community services concentration prepares students for employment at community agencies, for providing community services, and for work in non-profit organizations; many of the courses are focused in sociology. The public administration concentration is for those wishing to work in local, state, or federal government positions; many of the courses are centered on political science.

The Master of Science in Administration (M.S.A.) degree is a 36-semester-hour program that approaches administration and management from a broader perspective than other graduate degrees. This interdisciplinary program was developed to meet the needs of administrators in both the public and nonprofit sectors. M.S.A. concentrations are available at locations throughout North America, with two concentrations (general administration and information resource management) available completely online. Within the M.S.A. curriculum are core courses (about half of the degree) and concentration courses (the remaining half). The core courses provide students with quantitative analysis while the concentration courses allow them to tailor the program to their individual areas of interest. Among the concentrations offered, the general administration concentration gives an excellent foundation in management principals and is applicable to a wide variety of administrative settings. The health services concentration equips students to proactively meet the challenges faced in a health-care facility or in hospital administration. The concentration in human resource administration helps students develop their human resource management skills, focusing on the areas of labor relations, staffing, training, and organizational development. An information resource management concentration enables students to develop a comprehensive approach to the management of information systems in an organization to ensure that the chosen technology solution is the most appropriate one. The leadership concentration enhances abilities to think creatively, manage knowledge effectively, develop a vision, establish direction, and motivate staff. The public administration concentration prepares students for careers in public administration. Students get in-depth information on public policy-making and regulatory, budgetary, and personnel issues. Many of the courses are centered in political science.

The M.S. in Nutrition and Dietetics (M.S.N.D.) degree is designed to provide advanced training in human nutritional sciences for new and experienced professionals. Its objective is to enhance the graduate's knowledge base and expertise in the continually advancing field of nutrition and clinical dietetics. In addition, the program is designed to provide graduates with the quantitative and methodological knowledge necessary to better interpret the scientific literature to conduct their own nutritional research. This program is available completely online.

CMU's long-standing tradition of teacher excellence continues with its Master of Arts in Education degree (M.A.Ed.). This program is designed to provide knowledge and skills for individuals required to function effectively in various positions of educational leadership. The M.A.Ed. is a continuing education program for teachers; it presumes the individual is already trained and qualified in the technical aspects of her or his field. Concentrations available within the program are adult education (teaching in an adult education environment), community college (currently only available in Canada, this concentration is for effective teaching in a community college environment), and instructional (for K–12 curriculum and instruction), The M.A.Ed. degree is offered at select locations throughout the United States and Canada.

Special Programs

The Doctor of Health Administration (D.H.A.) is a 63-credit program that is cutting edge, academically sound, practice based, and flexible. Designed for leaders in the health-care field, the online format, combined with six weekend seminars, provides the ultimate combination of academic rigor and practical convenience.

Student Services

All services are available online and/or by a toll-free phone call. The service ranked highest by CMU's current students and graduates is the nationally recognized Off-Campus Library Services. Document delivery provides students with books, copies of journal articles, and other materials free of charge.

Credit Options

Credits earned through distance learning are recorded on Central Michigan University's transcripts in the same manner as credits earned in on-campus courses. These courses are part of the regular offerings of Central Michigan University. Relevant transfer credit and prior learning credits are also options.

Faculty

Faculty members are selected from the main campus in Mount Pleasant, Michigan; from other universities; and from the executive ranks of government, business, and industry. They enjoy the challenge of working with adult students and respect the knowledge and skills the students bring to the classroom. Approval of all faculty members is done by department chairpersons on the basis of their academic and professional qualifications.

Admission

Students must be admitted to CMU in order to take distance learning courses. The minimum requirement for admission to CMU undergraduate programs is a high school diploma or GED certificate. Undergraduate applicants must posses a GPA of 2.0 or higher. For those with GPAs lower than the required 2.0, conditional admission may be granted. One official transcript from all previously attended institutions should be provided to CMU.

Graduate applicants must have a baccalaureate or equivalent degree from an institution that has received regional accreditation or recognized standing at the time the student attended. Graduate applicants must have an overall grade point average of at least 2.7 in their bachelor's studies. Applicants whose GPA is between 2.3 and 2.7 may be considered for conditional admission. GMAT or GRE scores are not required.

D.H.A. applicants must have a master's degree of at least 27 semester hours or have earned a professional doctorate (such as M.D., D.O., J.D., or Pharm.D.) from a U.S. regionally accredited university.

Tuition and Fees

Tuition for the 2006–07 academic year is as follows: undergraduate, $286 per credit hour; graduate, $373 per credit hour; and D.H.A., $795 per credit hour. Military personnel (active duty and retired) and their dependents are eligible for a discounted tuition rate at both the undergraduate and graduate levels of $250/credit hour. This rate does not apply at the doctoral level. Proper identification is required to receive this lower discounted rate.

Additional fees include a $50 admission fee, $50 graduation fee, $100 prior learning application fee, and a $50 prior learning assessment fee (per credit hour).

Financial Aid

Financial aid is available to those students who qualify. Students interested in financial aid are encouraged to contact CMU for more information.

Applying

Students interested in taking classes through CMU Off-Campus Programs are encouraged to apply for admission to Central Michigan University. Admission applications can be downloaded from the Web site listed in the Contact section.

CONTACT

CMU Off-Campus Programs
Central Michigan University
Mount Pleasant, Michigan 48859
Phone: 877-268-4636 (toll-free)
Fax: 989-774-1822
E-mail: cmuoffcampus@cmich.edu
Web site: http://www.cmuoffcampus.com

CENTRAL MISSOURI STATE UNIVERSITY

Office of Extended Campus–Distance Learning Master of Science in Criminal Justice

Warrensburg, Missouri

Founded in 1871, Central Missouri State University is a state university offering approximately 150 areas of study to 11,100 undergraduate and graduate students. In 1996, Central Missouri State University was designated Missouri's lead institution for professional technology, an area long recognized as one of the University's greatest strengths. The new mission has expanded this commitment and means that Central will continue to integrate the latest technologies into every level of its comprehensive liberal arts curriculum. Central is committed to acquiring, disseminating, and utilizing technology to enhance the University's comprehensive educational mission. Central is accredited by the North Central Association of Colleges and Schools.

Distance Learning Program

Central's main Distance Learning Program provides undergraduate- and graduate-level courses through two-way interactive television and Web-based courses. The online program currently includes one doctoral degree, three master's degrees, and numerous graduate and undergraduate courses. From fall 1994 through spring 2004, Central provided instruction to more than 13,000 graduate, undergraduate, and high school students in a distance learning environment.

Institutional and financial information about Central Missouri State University may be accessed via the Web at http://www.cmsu.edu/rsearch/ir/toc.htm.

Delivery Media

Central uses a variety of technologies to deliver its distance learning courses. These include two-way, interactive television; broadcast television; and Internet technologies, including video and audio streaming. Central links to the Missouri Research and Educational Network (MOREnet) statewide backbone, which connects all of Missouri's public higher education institutions and several K–12 schools, to provide Internet-based and interactive television programming. Finally, Central's complement of six 2-way videoconferencing facilities, which are capable of ISDN, H.323, T.120, and audioconferencing, allow Central to provide distance learning content to anywhere in the world.

Programs of Study

The Master of Science in Criminal Justice program is designed to provide the requisite knowledge, skills, and abilities for those students who intend to enter and/or advance in the criminal justice fields of law enforcement, corrections, and juvenile justice or who seek leadership, professional specialization, research, or teaching positions in criminal justice. Course work emphasizes leading justice system issues, including legal aspects; organization, administration, management, and leadership; and information acquisition, analysis, and interpretation. Distance delivery of the Master of Science in Criminal Justice includes interactive television within the state of Missouri and complete online delivery of the degree program. Site-based programs are also held at various locations in Missouri.

The graduate with a Master of Science in Criminal Justice can use the knowledge and skills obtained in the program to articulate knowledge of the major issues facing the criminal justice system in the nation and world; conduct and present an independent research project; communicate and interact professionally in scholarly, academic settings; and delineate the ethical principles of human subject protection in social science research.

First offered in 1962, the program is one of the most respected criminal justice programs in the world. Among Central's criminal justice alumni are members of numerous police and corrections agencies, judges, attorneys, professors, and approximately 400 chief administrators in all parts of the world.

To be accepted into the program of study for the Master of Criminal Justice, a student must have an undergraduate degree in criminal justice or a related field and have earned a minimum grade point average of 2.75 on all undergraduate course work and 3.0 on all graduate course work. A student without a criminal justice degree may be required to complete up to 15 hours of background courses in criminal justice prior to taking graduate-level courses. The requirement to take background courses may be waived by the department's graduate coordinator based on previous courses taken and/or relevant professional experience. Students not meeting program admission requirements may request that the department's graduate committee admit them provisionally to the program. GRE scores are not required.

The 36-hour Master of Science in Criminal Justice program allows for 6 semester hours of departmentally approved electives under the thesis option and 12 hours under the nonthesis option.

Special Programs

Central's Distance Learning Program builds upon the existing curriculum offerings at Central as well as offerings that address special distance learning needs.

Central's distance learning students are eligible to participate in the same opportunities as on-campus students. These include study tours and internships in many disciplines.

The Office of Career Services reports a 93 percent placement rate for Central graduates within six months of graduation.

Student Services

A toll-free University number, 800-SAY-CMSU, allows access to offices involved with student services: extended campus-distance learning, admissions, academic advising, registrar, financial aid, revenue, accounts receivable, University housing, and the Graduate School. All students enrolled at Central are issued a mainframe Internet account. The HELP Desk is available to Central students needing technical computer assistance. Distance learning students receive individualized course information prior to the start of each semester as well as information regarding University resources available to them. Online library resources are available for distance learning and off-campus students. An online writing lab (OWL) provides writing assistance to distance learning students. A toll-free number provides ordering and delivery service for textbooks from the University Bookstore.

Credit Options

For entering graduate students, Central will accept up to 9 hours of transfer credits in graduate work.

Faculty

Faculty members at Central exemplify the goals of the institution as they balance personal attention with expertise in their respective fields. Approximately 74 percent of the 439 full-time faculty members hold doctoral degrees. The student-faculty ratio is 18:1.

The criminal justice faculty has a unique blend of academic credentials and field experience, with all members holding terminal degrees. In addition, 90 percent of the faculty members had significant experience with a criminal justice agency prior to joining the faculty of Central Missouri State University.

Admission

Individuals interested in pursuing a graduate degree at Central Missouri State University should contact the Graduate School for application information at 800-SAY-CMSU (toll-free) or visit the Web site at http://www.cmsu.edu/graduate. The Graduate School should receive all application materials at least three weeks prior to the beginning of the semester in which the student wishes to register.

All degree-seeking student applicants must submit a formal application for admission to the Graduate School and official transcripts of all undergraduate/graduate course work. If this is a student's first enrollment at Central, a $30 nonrefundable application fee is required (international students must remit $50). Admission to the Graduate School, which permits enrollment in classes, is not equivalent to admission for a particular program or degree.

Tuition and Fees

For 2005–06, graduate tuition was $242 per credit hour for Internet-based courses. Prospective students should note that tuition rates may be changed at any time by action of the Board of Governors.

Financial Aid

Central recognizes a student's continuing need for financial assistance. Federal grant and loan funds are available for eligible students who have been accepted for regular degree programs at Central. Application eligibility information may be obtained by contacting the Office of Financial Aid at 660-543-4040 or 800-SAY-CMSU (toll-free). Students who are veterans may also be considered for VA educational benefits to help with tuition costs.

The University participates in all federal student financial aid grant, loan, and employment programs. Visiting and non-degree-seeking students are not eligible to receive federal financial aid.

Applying

Graduate students should contact the Graduate School at 660-543-4621 or toll-free at 800-SAY-CMSU Ext. 3.

CONTACT

Dr. Betsy Kreisel
Faculty Graduate Coordinator
Central Missouri State University
Warrensburg, Missouri 64093
Phone: 660-543-8836
E-mail: kreisel@cmsu.edu
Web site: http://www.cmsu.edu/cj/index.html

Barbara Carder
Assistant Director for Distance Learning
Humphreys 410
Central Missouri State University
Warrensburg, Missouri 64093
Phone: 660-543-8480
800-SAY-CMSU Ext. 21 (toll-free)
Fax: 660-543-8333
E-mail: bcarder@cmsu.edu
Web site: http://www.cmsu.edu/cmsuonline

CENTRAL MISSOURI STATE UNIVERSITY

Office of Extended Campus–Distance Learning
Master of Science in Industrial Management

Warrensburg, Missouri

Founded in 1871, Central Missouri State University is a state university offering approximately 150 areas of study to 11,100 undergraduate and graduate students. In 1996, Central Missouri State University was designated Missouri's lead institution for professional applied science and technology programs, an area long recognized as one of the University's greatest strengths. The new mission has expanded this commitment and means that Central will continue to integrate the latest technologies into every level of its comprehensive liberal arts curriculum. Central is committed to acquiring, disseminating, and utilizing technology to enhance the University's comprehensive educational mission. Central is accredited by the North Central Association of Colleges and Schools.

Distance Learning Program

Central's main Distance Learning Program provides undergraduate- and graduate-level courses through two-way interactive television and Web-based courses. The online program currently includes one doctoral degree, three master's degrees, and numerous graduate and undergraduate courses. From fall 1994 through spring 2004, Central provided instruction to more than 13,000 graduate, undergraduate, and high school students in a distance learning environment.

Institutional and financial information about Central Missouri State University may be accessed via the Web at http://www.cmsu.edu/rsearch/ir/toc.htm.

Delivery Media

Central uses a variety of technologies to deliver its distance learning courses. These include two-way, interactive television; broadcast television; and Internet technologies, including video and audio streaming. Central links to the Missouri Research and Educational Network (MOREnet) statewide backbone, which connects all of Missouri's public higher education institutions and several K–12 schools, to provide Internet-based and interactive television programming. Finally, Central's complement of six 2-way videoconferencing facilities, which are capable of ISDN, H.323, T.120, and audioconferencing, allow Central to provide distance learning content to anywhere in the world.

Programs of Study

The Master of Science in Industrial Management is designed for students who are preparing for upward mobility in supervisory or management positions in business and industry, manufacturing, quality control or quality systems management, or related positions.

In a recent survey of graduates from this degree, the average response age was 40 years old, with a mean salary of $65,000 per year. Some occupational titles include vice president of operations, production manager, shift supervisor, quality systems manager, and plant manager.

Participants in the Master of Science in Industrial Management degree develop skills useful to business and industry. The program provides a balanced curriculum focusing on the human element of the workplace as well as a variety of industrial systems. Specific skills are developed in the fields of leadership, problem solving, and decision making.

The graduate with a Master of Science in Industrial Management degree can use the knowledge and skills obtained in the program to apply management skills and concepts to specific situations, plan and implement a project, analyze and develop a human relations strategy, demonstrate the ability to communicate effectively, explain and apply the basic concepts of an industrial economy, introduce and adapt technical expertise to a given process or product, and perform, interpret, and explain research.

The Master of Science in Industrial Management is a 33-credit-hour degree program. Complete online delivery of the program began in fall 2002. Students may enter the course cycle at the beginning of any semester. Courses are scheduled with the capability of completing the degree program in two calendar years, including one summer session. Degree information is available on the Web at http://www.cmsu/edu/mfgcont/indmnew.htm.

A strength of this program is the flexibility built into the cognate course work and culminating experience. The program allows several curricular paths leading to graduation and facilitates articulation to a cooperative doctoral program in technology management.

To be accepted into this program, a student shall have a minimum GPA of 2.6 in the undergraduate major. A student not meeting this requirement may petition the department for admittance on a conditional basis. GRE or GMAT scores are not required.

Special Programs

Central's Distance Learning Program builds upon the existing curriculum offerings at Central as well as offerings that address special distance learning needs.

Central's distance learning students are eligible to participate in the same opportunities as on-campus students. These include study tours and internships in many disciplines.

The Office of Career Services reports a 93 percent placement rate for Central graduates within six months of graduation.

Student Services

A toll-free University number, 800-SAY-CMSU, allows access to offices involved with student services: extended campus–distance learning, admissions, academic advising, registrar, financial aid, revenue, accounts receivable, University housing, and the Graduate School. All students enrolled at Central are issued a mainframe Internet account. The HELP Desk is available to Central students needing technical computer assistance. Distance learning students receive individualized course information prior to the start of each semester as well as information regarding University resources available to them. Online library resources are available for distance learning and off-campus students. An online writing lab (OWL) provides writing assistance to distance learning students. A toll-free number provides ordering and delivery service for textbooks from the University Bookstore.

Credit Options

For entering graduate students, Central will accept up to 9 hours of transfer credits in graduate work.

Faculty

Faculty members at Central exemplify the goals of the institution as they balance personal attention with expertise in their respective fields. Approximately 74 percent of the 439 full-time faculty members hold doctoral degrees. The student-faculty ratio is 18:1.

Admission

Individuals interested in pursuing a graduate degree at Central Missouri State University should contact the Graduate School for application information at 800-SAY-CMSU (toll-free) or visit the Web site at http://www.cmsu.edu/graduate. The Graduate School should receive all application materials at least three weeks prior to the beginning of the semester in which the student wishes to register.

All degree-seeking student applicants must submit a formal application for admission to the Graduate School and official transcripts of all undergraduate/graduate course work. If this is a student's first enrollment at Central, a $30 nonrefundable application fee is required (international students must remit $50). Admission to the Graduate School, which permits enrollment in classes, is not equivalent to admission for a particular program or degree.

Tuition and Fees

For 2005–06, graduate tuition was $242 per credit hour for Internet-based courses. Prospective students should note that tuition rates may be changed at any time by action of the Board of Governors.

Financial Aid

Central recognizes a student's continuing need for financial assistance. Federal grant and loan funds are available for eligible students who have been accepted for regular degree programs at Central. Application eligibility information may be obtained by contacting the Office of Financial Aid at 660-543-4040 or 800-SAY-CMSU (toll-free). Students who are veterans may also be considered for VA educational benefits to help with tuition costs.

The University participates in all federal student financial aid grant, loan, and employment programs. Visiting and non-degree-seeking students are not eligible to receive federal financial aid.

Applying

Graduate students should contact the Graduate School at 660-543-4621 or toll-free at 800-SAY-CMSU.

CONTACT

Dr. Ronald Woolsey
Faculty Coordinator
Central Missouri State University
Warrensburg, Missouri 64093
Phone: 660-543-4439
E-mail: woolsey@cmsu.edu
Web site: http://www.cmsu.edu/mfgcont

Barbara Carder
Assistant Director for Distance Learning
Humphreys 410
Central Missouri State University
Warrensburg, Missouri 64093
Phone: 660-543-8480
800-SAY-CMSU Ext. 21 (toll-free)
Fax: 660-540-8333
E-mail: bcarder@cmsu.edu
Web site: http://www.cmsu.edu/cmsuonline

CENTRAL MISSOURI STATE UNIVERSITY

Office of Extended Campus–Distance Learning
Department of Nursing

Warrensburg, Missouri

Founded in 1871, Central Missouri State University is a state university offering approximately 150 areas of study to 11,100 undergraduate and graduate students. In 1996, Central Missouri State University was designated Missouri's lead institution for professional technology, an area long recognized as one of the University's greatest strengths. The new mission has expanded this commitment and means that Central will continue to integrate the latest technologies into every level of its comprehensive liberal arts curriculum. Central is committed to acquiring, disseminating, and utilizing technology to enhance the University's comprehensive educational mission. Central is accredited by the North Central Association of Colleges and Schools.

Distance Learning Program

Central's main distance learning program provides undergraduate- and graduate-level courses through two-way interactive television and Web-based courses. The online program currently includes one doctoral degree, three master's degrees, and numerous graduate and undergraduate courses. From fall 1994 through spring 2004, Central provided instruction to more than 13,000 graduate, undergraduate, and high school students in a distance learning environment.

Institutional and financial information about Central Missouri State University may be accessed via the Web at http://www.cmsu.edu/rsearch/ir/toc.htm.

Delivery Media

Central uses a variety of technologies to deliver its distance learning courses. These include two-way, interactive television; broadcast television; and Internet technologies, including video and audio streaming. Central links to the Missouri Research and Educational Network (MOREnet) statewide backbone, which connects all of Missouri's public higher education institutions and several K–12 schools, to provide Internet-based and interactive television programming. Central's complement of six 2-way videoconferencing facilities, which are capable of ISDN, H.323, T.120, and audioconferencing, allow Central to provide distance learning content anywhere in the world.

Programs of Study

There are two degrees offered by the Department of Nursing primarily through distance learning technologies. The Bachelor of Science in Nursing is delivered through a combination of online courses, independent study, and one course on campus; a test-out option is available for the on-campus course. The Master of Science in Nursing degree is also delivered mostly online.

The Bachelor of Science in Nursing degree is designed for the registered nurse who wants to upgrade to a bachelor's degree. The bachelor's degree provides more flexibility and leads to more career opportunities in nursing than an RN license. Employment opportunities increase as the level of education increases. A baccalaureate degree provides many more options in the areas of public health, home health, nursing management, program planning, and health teaching. Registered nurses face increasingly complex demands that require a broad-based bachelor's degree preparation. Central's Bachelor of Science in Nursing includes general arts and science courses and an introduction to other disciplines in addition to the focus on nursing. The program enhances a nurse's ability to think critically, teaches more effective communication skills, and provides a deeper understanding of professional nursing.

The program features flexible scheduling that allows students to start any semester and set their own pace for completion. Full-time students can complete the course work in one year; part-time students can take up to four years to complete the program. The program allows the transfer of up to 64 credit hours of university studies and nursing prerequisites from other institutions. Students receive credit for courses completed within another accredited nursing program and for professional experience. Nursing faculty members understand the needs of working professionals who are students. The program is accredited by the Commission on Collegiate Nursing Education (CCNE). More information is available online in the undergraduate catalog at http://www.cmsu.edu/catalogs/.

The Master of Science in Nursing online degree program is designed for nurses with a baccalaureate degree who seek advanced practice as a specialist. Central, with more than forty years of experience providing high-quality nursing education, uses state-of-the-art technology to deliver the program. Students specialize in one of three professional tracks: family nurse practitioner, nurse informaticist, and nurse education.

There are many benefits for students earning a Master of Science in Nursing degree at Central. All professional tracks offer flexibility at an affordable cost. The online classes provide "anytime, anywhere" access, and the online format eliminates travel time and expense. Online classes expand the student's technical skills, increasing valuable workplace skills. Classes are student centered and user friendly, providing individual attention from the instructors. Earning this degree provides students with the foundation for advanced practice, specialty practice, and advanced study at the doctoral level. More information can be found in the graduate catalog online at http://www.cmsu.edu/catalogs/.

Special Programs

Central's Distance Learning Program builds upon the existing curriculum offerings at Central as well as offerings that address special distance learning needs. Central's distance learning students are eligible to participate in the same opportunities as on-campus students. These include study tours and internships in many disciplines. The Office of Career Services reports a 93 percent placement rate for Central graduates within six months of graduation.

Student Services

The toll-free University number allows access to offices involved with student services: extended campus–distance learning, admissions, academic advising, registrar, financial aid, revenue, accounts receivable, University housing, and the Graduate School. All students enrolled at Central are issued a mainframe Internet account. The help desk is available to Central students needing technical computer assistance. Distance learning students receive individualized course information prior to the start of each semester as well as information about University resources available to them. Online library resources are available for distance learning and off-campus students. An online writing lab (OWL) provides writing assistance to distance learning students. A toll-free number provides ordering and delivery service for textbooks from the University Bookstore.

Credit Options

For entering graduate students, Central accepts up to 9 hours of transfer credits in graduate work.

Faculty

Faculty members at Central exemplify the goals of the institution as they balance personal attention with expertise in their respective fields. Approximately 74 percent of the 439 full-time faculty members hold doctoral degrees. The student-faculty ratio is 18:1.

Admission

Students interested in pursuing an online degree through Central Missouri State University's Department of Nursing should contact the University at the address below. Applicants must be admitted to the University before enrolling in a nursing program. If this is a student's first enrollment at Central, a $30 nonrefundable application fee (international students, $50) must accompany the application and official transcripts of all undergraduate and graduate course work. Admission to the University or Graduate School is not equivalent to admission for a particular program or degree.

Tuition and Fees

For 2005–06, tuition for distance learning graduate course was $242 per credit hour. For distance learning undergraduate courses, tuition was $198 per credit hour. Prospective students should note that tuition rates may be changed at any time by action of the Board of Governors.

Financial Aid

Central recognizes a student's continuing need for financial assistance. Federal grant and loan funds are available for eligible students who have been accepted for regular degree programs at Central. Application eligibility information may be obtained by contacting the Office of Financial Aid at 660-543-4040 or at 800-SAY-CMSU (toll-free). Students who are veterans may also be considered for VA educational benefits to help with tuition costs. The University participates in all federal student financial aid grant, loan, and employment programs.

Applying

Students should contact the University at 660-543-4621 or at 800-SAY-CMSU (toll-free).

CONTACT

Barbara Carder
Assistant Director for Distance Learning
Office of Extended Campus
Humphreys 410
Central Missouri State University
Warrensburg, Missouri 64093
Phone: 660-543-8480
800-SAY-CMSU Ext. 21 (toll-free)
Fax: 660-543-8333
E-mail: bcarder@cmsu.edu
Web site: http://www.cmsu.edu/cmsuonline

CHAMPLAIN COLLEGE

Online Distance Learning Program
The Center for Online and Continuing Education

Burlington, Vermont

Since 1878, Champlain College has been dedicated to providing education that reflects the realities and needs of the contemporary workplace. It offers professional certificates, two- and four-year degree programs, and a master's program designed to provide sound professional training or updating for careers in today's complex world, as well as to provide broadening education in the humanities and general education. Champlain College is recognized as one of the leading career-building colleges in northern New England, and it has earned the respect of business, technical, and human services professions for its outstanding career-oriented education.

Distance Learning Program

Champlain College is a pioneer in the use of computer technologies in distance learning applications. Champlain College OnLine serves hundreds of students in the United States and internationally. Champlain offers complete degree and professional certificate programs that may be accessed online at any time of day.

Champlain College is an independent, nonprofit four- and two-year college. It is accredited by the New England Association of Schools and Colleges. It first offered distance learning courses in 1993, with more than eighty courses offered in 2004–05.

Delivery Media

Those who have access to a computer and the World Wide Web can access Champlain College OnLine. Once connected, students find messages posted from the instructor and classmates either in the course forum or in private e-mail. All communication occurs online and includes discussion comments from classmates, lectures, instructional material, and assignments. The material covered in Champlain College's online classes is the same as in traditional courses. New accelerated online courses allow students to complete their class in seven weeks.

Programs of Study

Champlain College offers an extensive array of traditionally delivered, career-oriented four- and two-year degrees and professional certificates. Through its distance learning program, the College offers Associate in Science (A.S.) degrees in accounting, business, computer and digital forensics, e-business management, global networks and telecommunications, international business, management, software development, and Web site development and management. Bachelor in Science (B.S.) degrees are offered in business, computer and digital forensics, e-business management, professional studies, software engineering, and Web site development and management, all of which are designed to complement associate degrees in career areas. Professional certificates are offered online in all of these career areas. A Master of Science (M.S.) degree is offered in managing innovation and information technology.

Professional certificates require successful completion of 12 to 24 credits. Associate degrees require completion of 60 credits, half of which must be taken through Champlain College. The bachelor's degree requires completion of 120 credits, at least 45 of which must be taken through Champlain. The master's degree consists of 36 credits. Students can also take individual undergraduate courses on a nonmatriculated basis.

Special Programs

The College has several expanding international programs that offer degree programs to students in India and the United Arab Emirates. These programs incorporate distance learning into the curriculum.

Corporate partnerships are also available for businesses that are interested in training employees. Since classes are available at any time, from anywhere the Internet can be accessed, distance learning allows businesses to offer high-quality training programs to employees—even when different shifts, different locations, and even different time zones are involved.

Student Services

Champlain College provides a number of services to adult learners. Distance learners receive academic advising from the Advising and Registration Center and the Career Planning Office, a full range of online library services, tutoring, and access to the computer Help Desk and an online bookstore.

Credit Options

Students may transfer credits earned through other accredited postsecondary institutions. Depending on the program selected, students may also transfer credit for life/work experience or credits from approved testing programs. Champlain accepts credit through approved portfolio assessment programs, CLEP, DANTES, and PONSI.

Faculty

Champlain's strength lies in its faculty. More than 120 full-time and part-time faculty members focus their primary energies on teaching. Faculty members have completed programs of advanced study, and many have doctoral or terminal degrees.

Admission

Admission requirements for degree programs include graduation from a recognized secondary school or possession of a high school equivalency certificate and submission of SAT or ACT scores. Students who have been out of high school for several years, who may not have taken all of the course work that is required for acceptance to a particular major, or who have not taken SAT or ACT tests, should speak with an admission counselor or academic adviser about how to apply. Admission to the certificate program requires submission of a high school transcript (or GED) and a current resume. Given the method of instructional delivery, online students should be self-motivated and possess effective reading and writing skills as well as basic computer skills. Master's degree candidates must possess a bachelor's degree and have at least two years of professional experience.

Tuition and Fees

In 2005–06, tuition for undergraduate programs was $420 per credit; most courses are 3 credits. The application fee was $40.

The tuition for the master's degree program was $505 per credit. The application fee was $50.

Textbooks may be purchased online through the bookstore. There are no additional fees.

Financial Aid

Payment and financial aid options depend on personal circumstances and whether students attend full- or part-time. The College participates in several federal financial aid programs, including Federal Pell Grant and Federal Stafford Student Loan, and state loan and grant programs.

Applying

Students may enroll for online undergraduate courses as nonmatriculating students by registering online or by mail, fax, or telephone. The College reviews applications for degree programs when they are received. A short, online orientation is required for all online students prior to gaining access to their courses.

CONTACT

R. J. Sweeney, Continuing Education Counselor
Center for Online and Continuing Education
Champlain College
163 South Willard Street
Burlington, Vermont 05402
Phone: 802-865-6449
888-545-3459 (toll-free)
Fax: 802-865-6447
E-mail: coce@champlain.edu
Web site: http://www.champlain.edu

CHARTER OAK STATE COLLEGE

New Britain, Connecticut

Charter Oak State College, one of America's leading distance learning colleges for adults, was established in 1973 by the Connecticut Legislature to provide an alternate way for adults to earn a college degree. Recognized as the College that offers "degrees without boundaries," Charter Oak responds to the degree-completion needs of adult learners. The College, which is regionally accredited by the New England Association of Schools and Colleges and is a Servicemembers Opportunity College, awards bachelor's and associate degrees.

Charter Oak's flexible degree programs are designed to assist adult learners in achieving their educational objectives as they continue to meet career, family, and financial obligations.

Students can combine, toward their Charter Oak degrees, credits earned–no matter how long ago—from regionally accredited colleges and universities, including Charter Oak, and from noncollegiate-sponsored instruction, standardized testing such as CLEP and Dantes, work or military experience, contract learning, and portfolio assessment.

Individualized professional advisement is a hallmark of Charter Oak State College. Each student benefits from one-on-one support from an academic counselor who specializes in the student's chosen field of study. Counselors, who are accessible via telephone, fax, e-mail, and the U.S. mail, work closely with each student to develop a plan of study.

Distance Learning Program

Charter Oak State College provides all of its services using distance technology. The College offers more than 130 online and video-based courses. Courses are fifteen, eight, and five weeks in duration. Students can elect to take Charter Oak courses or earn credits in other ways. Textbooks may be purchased electronically from a designated bookstore, and videotapes are rented through a mail-order service.

Programs of Study

Charter Oak State College offers four degrees in general studies: Associate in Arts, Associate in Science, Bachelor of Arts, and Bachelor of Science. To earn an associate degree, a student must complete at least 60 credits; a bachelor's degree requires at least 120 credits. The College accepts up to 90 community college credits toward a bachelor's degree.

A Charter Oak degree is more than an accumulation of the required number of credits. At least one half of the credits toward a degree must be earned in subjects traditionally included in the liberal arts and sciences—humanities, mathematics, natural sciences, and social sciences. Achievement in these areas demonstrates breadth of learning. To demonstrate depth of learning, students who pursue a baccalaureate degree must complete a concentration consisting of at least 36 credits.

A concentration plan, accompanied by an essay, must be submitted to the faculty for approval. Concentrations may be constructed in many areas, including applied arts, art history, the behavioral sciences, business, child study, communication, computer science, engineering studies, fire service administration, health-care administration, human services, individualized studies, languages, liberal studies, literature, music history, the natural sciences, organizational management and leadership, public safety administration, religious studies, the social sciences, and technology studies. As a graduation requirement, students must also submit an academic autobiography that provides them the opportunity to reflect on their educational experiences and demonstrate their writing ability and understanding of their degree program.

Special Programs

The College has evaluated a number of noncollegiate courses and programs for which it awards credit toward Charter Oak degree programs. Many health-care specialties from hospital-based programs are included, such as medical laboratory technician, nurse practitioner, physician assistant, radiologic technologist, registered nurse, and respiratory therapist or technician. Other evaluations include the Child Development Associate (CDA) credential; the FAA Airman Certificate; Famous Artists School in Westport, Connecticut; Institute of Children's Literature in West Redding, Connecticut; the National Opticianry Competency Examination; the Contact Lens Registry Examination; and several fire certifications, including Fire Marshal, Deputy Fire Marshal, Fire Inspector, Fire Fighter III, Fire Officer I or II, and Fire Service Instructor I or II.

Credit Options

Students can transfer credits from other regionally accredited colleges and universities. Age of credits is not a factor in most concentrations. There is no limit to the number of credits that can be earned using standardized examinations, prior learning—including ACE-evaluated military credits and ACE- and

PONSI-evaluated noncollegiate learning—and portfolio assessment

Faculty
Full-time faculty members, from public and independent institutions of higher education in Connecticut, serve as consulting examiners at Charter Oak. Distance learning faculty members come from all over the United States and possess appropriate degrees and/or experience.

Admission
Admission is open to any person 16 years or older, regardless of level of formal education, who is able to demonstrate college-level achievement. To be admitted, a student must have earned 9 college-level credits from acceptable sources of credit.

Tuition and Fees
All students pay a $60 application fee. Connecticut residents pay a first-year matriculation fee of $655 for an associate degree or $955 for a bachelor's degree. Nonresidents pay a first-year matriculation fee of $925 for an associate degree or $1245 for a bachelor's degree. Active-duty service members and their spouses pay in-state resident's rates for all Charter Oak fees and services. All students pay a graduation fee of $175. Tuition for video-based courses is $160 per credit for Connecticut residents and $227 per credit for nonresidents. There is a $30 registration fee for all students.

Financial Aid
Financial aid is available to eligible Charter Oak students from several sources, including federal, state, and institutional grants and loans. All students who wish to apply for aid must complete the Free Application for Federal Student Aid (FAFSA). The FAFSA may be completed online and can be accessed at http://www.fafsa.ed.gov. Charter Oak's forms can be accessed online at http://www.charteroak.edu/sfa. The Charter Oak State College school code is 032343.

Applying
Charter Oak reviews applications on a rolling basis; students may matriculate at anytime during the year.

CONTACT

Admissions Office
Charter Oak State College
55 Paul Manafort Drive
New Britain, Connecticut 06053-2150
Phone: 860-832-3855
Fax: 860-832-3999
Web site:
http://www.charteroak.edu

CITY UNIVERSITY

Distance Learning Option

Bellevue, Washington

City University was founded in 1973 on the philosophy that everyone should have access to high-quality higher education. The University upholds this philosophy by offering programs that are well designed, cost effective, and conveniently offered. The University's progressive approach to education has fueled its growth from a single classroom in downtown Seattle to one of the largest private universities in the state of Washington. It is a private, nonprofit institution and is accredited by the Northwest Commission on Colleges and Universities.

City University's programs cover a variety of academic fields, ranging from business management and technology to psychology and communications. The majority of faculty members actively work in the fields they teach. The combination of innovative program design and outstanding instruction makes City University an exceptional institution of higher learning.

Distance Learning Program

In keeping with its mission of providing convenient, accessible education, City University offers most of its degree programs through distance learning (DL), utilizing the World Wide Web. City University serves approximately 4,500 students annually through DL.

Delivery Media

City University delivers distance learning course work utilizing the Blackboard Course Management System. Delivered through asynchronous interaction on the World Wide Web, City University distance learning courses are designed for optimum learning anywhere, anytime. Highly qualified faculty members, who are working in the fields they teach, provide distance learning students with real-world application of course material. In addition, structured discussions provide students the opportunity to exchange in dialogue with peers without the need of traveling to a classroom.

Programs of Study

City University's undergraduate programs prepare students to compete in today's marketplace. Students may complete a Bachelor of Science (B.S.) or a Bachelor of Arts (B.A.) degree. Within these degrees, students may pursue one of several areas of study, including accounting, business administration, communications, computer systems, marketing, or psychology. Undergraduate courses are 5 credits each; 180 credits are required for completion of a B.S. degree, and students typically transfer the first two years of study.

City University's graduate business program prepares management professionals for leadership roles at local, national, and international levels. Students may pursue a Master of Business Administration (M.B.A.), a Master of Public Administration (M.P.A.), or a Master of Science in either project management or computer systems. Most graduate courses are worth 3 credits; total required credits range from 45 to 60. Students may also pursue a Master of Education (M.Ed.) in literacy. Total required credits for this program is 45.

Special Programs

City University has an "open-door" admissions policy for most programs. Students may begin course work at the start of any quarter once accepted to their program of study.

All of City University's programs are geared for adult students. From its student body to its faculty and staff, City University is a community of professionals. All who are associated with the University understand the needs of adult learners who are seeking high-quality education that applies to their individual lifestyle.

Student Services

Students may register online or by phone. Academic advising and assistance is available from a distance learning adviser by phone, fax, or e-mail. Students have full access to the library via the Internet and a toll-free phone number, and a mailing service for circulation of books and articles is available as well.

Credit Options

Students may transfer up to 90 approved lower-division and 45 approved upper-division credits from approved institutions for baccalaureate programs. The Prior Learning Experience Program lets students earn credits through documented experimental learning. Students may receive credit for the CLEP or other standardized tests. Graduate students may transfer up to 12 credits from approved programs.

Faculty

There are more than 250 faculty members included in the distance learning program. Faculty members have, at minimum, a master's degree and professional experience in the fields they teach.

Admission

Undergraduate programs are generally open to applicants over 18 years of age who hold a high school diploma or GED. Admission to graduate programs requires that students hold a baccalaureate degree from an accredited or otherwise recognized institution. Additional requirements apply to education programs. International students whose first language is not English are required to submit a TOEFL score of at least 540 for admission to undergraduate programs and 565 for graduate programs.

Tuition and Fees

For 2005–06, tuition was $233 per undergraduate credit hour and $398 per graduate credit hour. The tuition rate is the same for both in-class and distance learning study. Other fees may apply, depending on the specific course of study. Additional fees apply for certificate completion, graduation application, course registration, and various tests or examinations that the student may request. All initial applicants for certificate or degree programs pay a nonrefundable application fee of $80. Tuition and fees are subject to annual review on July 1.

Textbooks and other instructional materials are additional. While the number of required texts and other course materials vary with each course, textbooks typically cost between $100 and $150 each.

Financial Aid

For information, students should contact the Financial Aid Office at 800-426-5596 (toll-free).

Applying

DL students may enroll on a rolling admissions basis. Students must speak with an academic adviser to complete the initial enrollment. Students should then submit the application form, nonrefundable application fee, transcripts, and admission documents to the Office of Admissions.

CONTACT

Office of Admissions
City University
11900 NE First Street
Bellevue, Washington 98005
Phone: 425-737-1010
800-422-4898 (toll-free)
Fax: 425-709-5361
E-mail: info@cityu.edu
Web site: http://www.cityu.edu

COLORADO STATE UNIVERSITY

Continuing Education

Fort Collins, Colorado

Colorado State University has served the people of Colorado as the state's land-grant university since 1870. Today, the campus in Fort Collins is home to 25,000 students pursuing degrees at all levels in a wide range of subjects in the liberal arts, engineering, business, natural resources, agriculture, and the sciences. The University's instructional outreach activities go far beyond the campus and the state of Colorado.

Distance Learning Program

Colorado State University's distance education courses are designed to begin or to finish a degree, to explore new topics, to enrich life, and to give students an opportunity to develop a level of proficiency in professional development. Approximately 2,500 individuals from all over the country and overseas are enrolled in distance education courses from Colorado State University.

Delivery Media

Colorado State offers courses in online, print, and video formats. All courses are supported by Colorado State University faculty members. Students may contact course faculty members via telephone, fax, e-mail, or regular mail. Students should call Continuing Education or visit the Web site for contact information for an instructor.

Programs of Study

As an institution, Colorado State has been involved in distance education since 1967 and was one of the first schools to utilize technology in distance education.

Independent Study: Correspondence Study, Telecourses, and Online Courses removes the traditional boundaries of time and location for the distance learner. Through the use of a study guide, textbooks, videotapes, the Internet, and applicable reference materials, students have the opportunity to participate in an individualized mode of instruction offering a high degree of flexibility. Students interested in correspondence courses and telecourses may enroll at any time, set their own pace, and choose the most convenient time and place to study. Online courses are taught according to the regular University semester schedule.

Distance degrees offer working professionals the opportunity to earn credit from Colorado State without coming to campus. These are semester-based courses that use videotape, online, and mixed-media formats. Whether students are working on their degree or taking courses to stay current in their field, distance degrees offer the flexibility to pursue educational objectives as work schedules permit.

Courses are available in several disciplines, including agriculture, business, communication/public affairs, computer science, engineering, fire service, human resource development, statistics, and telecommunications. Distance degree students are located throughout the United States and Canada and at U.S. military APO and FPO addresses. At this time, only correspondence courses and online courses and degrees are available to overseas students. Thousands of motivated people have earned their degrees, and countless others have taken individual courses to enhance their skill base or keep current with the latest technology.

Special Programs

Colorado State also provides other distance education opportunities. These courses are open-entry/open-exit, meaning students may register at any time and take six months to complete the course. Many of the courses can be used for specific programs, such as Child Care Administration Certification or Seed Analyst Training.

The state of Colorado requires certification of all child-care center directors and substitute directors by the State Department of Human Services. Certification requires both experience working with young children and specific education. Colorado State University is proud to offer courses through distance education that may satisfy some of the educational requirements. Other states may have individual specific educational requirements. Students should contact the appropriate agency in their area for further information.

For instructors wanting to enhance their teaching, Colorado State offers a Postsecondary Teaching Certificate Program, consisting of three 3-credit courses: Models of Teaching, Communication and Classrooms, and Educators, Systems, and Change. In this program, new instructors acquire a practical overview of a range of effective teaching models, ideas for engaging students while addressing measurable learning objectives, and approaches to promote critical and creative thinking. Experienced instructors update and energize their teaching repertoires, connecting personal knowledge with established research on effective classroom practices. Students in the program can earn graduate credit for advanced course work in postsecondary education and apply the 9 credits toward a master's or doctoral degree.

An innovative Seed Analyst Training Program consisting of four distance learning (correspondence) courses has been developed by the National Seed Storage Laboratory and Colorado State University. The courses were prepared over a two-year period by University professors and other experts with the support of the Colorado seed industry. The four courses cover the basics of seed analyst training: 1) Seed Anatomy and Identification, 2) Seed Development and Metabolism, 3) Seed Purity Analysis, and 4) Seed Germination and Viability.

Counseling through the University Center for Advising and Student Achievement is offered to all those interested in continuing their learning. There is no fee for academic advising services. Students may schedule an appointment with an academic adviser by calling 970-491-7095. The Extended University Programs librarian is available to assist students with identifying and accessing library materials. Students should call 970-491-6952 to speak with the librarian.

Credit Options

All credits earned through distance education are recorded on a Colorado State University transcript. Distance education courses are the same as on-campus courses and are accredited by the same organizations as the University. A student currently enrolled in a degree program elsewhere is responsible for checking with the appropriate official at the degree-granting institution to make certain the course applies.

Faculty

Distance education faculty members must meet the same high standards any Colorado State University faculty member must meet. Most of the distance faculty members are faculty members within the department granting the course credit. Faculty members are available to answer questions and give feedback via telephone, fax, e-mail, or regular mail.

Admission

Anyone who has the interest, desire, background, and ability may register for distance learning courses. However, if prerequisites are listed for a course, they must be met. Registration in distance learning courses does not constitute admission to Colorado State University.

Tuition and Fees

Tuition for distance degrees for the 2005–06 academic year was $523 per credit (business courses), $520 per credit (weekly videotaped courses), or $403 per credit (online courses). Tuition for other distance education courses for the 2005–06 academic year was $198 per credit for undergraduate courses and $222 per credit for graduate courses. For current tuition information, students should visit the Web site.

Financial Aid

Colorado State University courses are approved for the DANTES program. Eligible military personnel should process DANTES applications through their education office. For information regarding veterans' benefits, students should contact the VA office at Colorado State University. With the exception of distance degrees, distance learning is not a degree-granting program and is therefore not eligible for federal grants. Students are encouraged to seek scholarship aid from organizations and local civic groups that may sponsor such study.

Applying

To complete a distance degree, admittance to the University is required. There is no application for distance education. Students should simply register for the course(s) of interest by mail or fax or online and pay the tuition. For more information about these and other distance courses from Colorado State University, or for registration information, students should contact the University.

CONTACT

Phone: 970-491-5288
877-491-4336 (toll-free)
Fax: 970-491-7885
E-mail: info@learn.colostate.edu
Web site: http://www.learn.colostate.edu

COLORADO STATE UNIVERSITY

College of Business, Distance M.B.A. Program

Fort Collins, Colorado

Colorado State University's College of Business offers a comprehensive M.B.A. program to professionals around the world who desire not only to learn the concepts and theories behind sound business practices but also to understand how to apply these ideas to their day-to-day operations. The Distance M.B.A. Program is offered through mixed-media DVD technology; students gain the benefit of the full lectures, student discussions, questions, and special topics presented by the guest speakers. Students are at a distance—not in isolation.

CSU strives to make all of its students feel part of the activities experienced on the main campus. The degree earned is not a diluted form of the on-campus degree but rather encompasses the same academic content and rigor as the on-campus M.B.A. program. Our distance M.B.A. students earn an M.B.A. from Colorado State University, not as an online or distance degree.

Accredited by AACSB International–The Association of Advance Collegiate Schools of Business more than thirty years ago, the Distance M.B.A. Program at Colorado State University was the first to earn this coveted accreditation and remains one of the only distance M.B.A. programs to be so accredited. The program strives to provide students with the knowledge, skills, and functional competencies they need to become effective decision makers and leaders in a business environment that is becoming more global, more competitive, and increasingly dynamic.

Distance Learning Program

Founded more than thirty years ago and one of the nation's oldest distance degree programs, the Distance M.B.A. Program delivers a high-quality education while providing students with the flexibility needed to earn their degrees. This program was the first distance M.B.A. program to earn the coveted AACSB International accreditation more than thirty years ago and remains one of the only distance/online M.B.A. programs with the prestigious accreditation. Program content is cross-functional and has a strong emphasis on leadership, entrepreneurship, and global issues. Nearly 2,000 professionals have earned their M.B.A. degrees through the CSU Distance M.B.A. Program.

Most individuals in the CSU Distance M.B.A. Program are working professionals, with an average of thirteen years of work experience. They are drawn from all fifty states, many provinces in Canada, and, increasingly, from around the world. Over the years, U.S. military personnel have been frequent participants in the program and continue to be heavy supporters of this flexible and convenient M.B.A. program. The average age of the distance students is 33; their average GMAT score is 610.

Delivery Media

Distance M.B.A. students are linked to each other and to the epicenter of the M.B.A. programs at CSU through a technologically advanced classroom and an online communications network. By virtue of the unique connectedness, all students come together as one class, even though they may be located across the country or in another part of the world.

The classroom lectures and discussions are recorded using a mixed-media DVD format for the distance M.B.A. students and are shipped the following day. The DVD format gives CSU's distance M.B.A. students a direct link to the classroom, the on-campus students, and the professors. In addition to lectures and discussions being delivered using the DVD technology, students also are part of the unique M.B.A. intranet for communication with professors, other students in the sections, and team members. The chat rooms and threaded discussions keep students engaged with others in the program, assignments, and group collaboration.

Program of Study

The Distance M.B.A. Program is designed to serve the needs of working professionals who need flexibility in schedule and location. There is no requirement to come to the campus during the course of the program; however, about 55 percent of the Distance M.B.A. Program graduates come to take part in commencement each year. The 36-credit program may be completed in as little as twenty-one months, or a student may take up to five years to complete the program; summer classes are required regardless of the time sequence selected. The College's M.B.A. adviser works with students throughout the program to match course offerings with professional and personal schedules. There is no thesis required in this program.

In this comprehensive and progressive M.B.A. degree program, students study the five major functional areas of a business and the interrelationship among those areas. Students are not only exposed to the concepts and theories of modern business practices but they also have the opportunity to apply those concepts and theories to their own companies/businesses or to others around them. This application-based course of study is lauded by CSU's students as immediately valuable in their day-to-day professional lives.

Student Services

A student in the Colorado State University Distance M.B.A. Program is afforded all the student-support services offered to those on campus. Each student is assigned to an M.B.A. adviser to help with course sequencing or special situations impacting program participation. In addition, each student has electronic access to the main CSU library's business databases and the library's reference materials, journals, and periodicals. Students can even sign up to receive books and articles directly from the library. In addition, each student has access to technical support and an operations assistant for the M.B.A. intranet.

Credit Options

The Distance M.B.A. Program is an offering of courses in a lock-step sequencing mode, so each class builds on the previous classes. Because of the lock-step sequencing of the program and because of the group collaboration, CSU does not accept transfer credits; however, there are no prerequisites for the program. For students who feel they could benefit from a refresher with accounting, finance, and statistics, an MBA Survival Kit is available through the bookstore. These self-paced CDs take students through the basics of each of these subject areas providing foundation knowledge and confidence.

Faculty

What differentiates CSU's Distance M.B.A. Program from other programs is the high quality of its faculty members, who not only teach the material but also demonstrate how to apply it to the business world. With the exception of a few extraordinary individuals with private-industry experience, the professors who teach in the M.B.A. program are full-time faculty members with Ph.D.'s in their disciplines. Their research efforts and work in their respective industries keep the faculty members in the forefront of what is happening in business today.

Admission

Admission to the Distance M.B.A. Program is predicated on an individual's performance at the undergraduate level; their professional experience, including management of projects or people; their GMAT scores; and their application materials. A balance of these four criteria is sought in the determination for admission. In special cases, petitions for GMAT waivers are considered.

Colorado State University seeks to balance each class with a representation of industries, years of experience, and a mix of undergraduate degree concentrations. In addition, attention is paid to provide a balance along gender lines and a rich mix of backgrounds. Applicants with all types of undergraduate backgrounds are encouraged to apply. The program does not have prerequisites.

Tuition and Fees

For the 2005–06 academic year, the tuition for the distance M.B.A. courses was $523 per credit hour. There is a small increase expected in the 2006–07 academic year. The $523 per-credit-hour cost includes the production of the course-delivery DVDs, shipping, the M.B.A. intranet, technical support, production assistance, and all other student services. Students are responsible for their own textbooks and course materials.

Financial Aid

Financial aid is available to qualified students admitted to the Distance M.B.A. Program who take at least 5 credits per semester. More information can be obtained at the Financial Aid Office; telephone: 800-491-4622 Ext. 7, (toll-free).

Applying

The application deadlines for the Distance M.B.A. Program are July 15 for the fall semester and December 8 for the spring semester. Applicants must submit a resume; a cover letter that reflects carefully considered reasons for pursuing a business degree at the master's level; GMAT scores (unless a petition for a waiver to the GMAT is submitted and approved); TOEFL scores (for international students); a completed data sheet for the College of Business; three references from individuals who know the applicant's work, each in a sealed envelope; two copies of official transcripts in sealed envelopes; a completed application (GS1 or GSF1); and a $50 application fee. To request an admissions packet, students should contact the College.

CONTACT

Rachel Stoll
Graduate Admission Coordinator
Colorado State University College of Business
1270 Campus Delivery
Fort Collins, Colorado 80523-1270
Phone: 800-491-4622 Ext. 1 (toll-free)
Fax: 970-491-3481
E-mail: rachel.stoll@colostate.edu
Web site: http://www.CSUM.B.A.com

COLORADO TECHNICAL UNIVERSITY

Colorado Technical University Online Accelerated Degrees

Colorado Springs, Colorado

Since 1965, Colorado Technical University has helped thousands of students achieve success in business, management, and technology careers. Academic programs are continually evaluated and updated for relevance and currency. Colorado Technical University is accredited by the Higher Learning Commission of the North Central Association of Colleges and Schools. For more information, students should visit the NCA Higher Learning Commission Web site.

Distance Learning Program

Colorado Technical University Online provides students with a high-quality education relevant to the needs and demands of the ever-evolving business and technical job markets. Colorado Tech Online offers innovative, career-relevant degree programs completely online, so students can learn anywhere, anytime, on any PC with Internet access. Each program's content is continually updated and instantly applicable.

Delivery Media

Colorado Tech Online offers one of the best online platforms available. All courses are taught in a multimedia format that provides a rich, dynamic, interactive classroom experience. The programs offer many opportunities for students to adapt their learning experiences to their own personal styles. Students who prefer to have a hard copy of notes can print the presentations. Students also control the pace of an instructor's presentation. Students participate in discussions with the instructors and other students. Since the participants are employed in a variety of interesting professions, students gain insightful knowledge and learn from each other's experiences.

Programs of Study

Colorado Tech Online offers accelerated bachelor's and master's degrees in a variety of career-relevant fields, including business, criminal justice, information technology, and marketing. The bachelor's degrees and master's degrees can be completed in fifteen months. (The fifteen-month bachelor's degree is a 2+2 program and assumes that all associate-level requirements have been met through an associate degree or the equivalent. Colorado Tech Online students with no previous college experience can complete this degree in about 2½ years.) All of Colorado Tech Online's degree programs incorporate professional certificates that students earn as they progress through the programs, without additional courses or added costs.

Colorado Tech Online is a registered educational provider of the Project Management Institute™ (PMI), the world's leading not-for-profit project management professional association. Select course content has been reviewed by PMI and found to be relevant to project management and consistent with the knowledge and process areas described in the *Guide to the Project Management Book of Knowledge*.

Business: Colorado Tech Online's School of Business can prepare versatile managers with the business and management skills they need to provide creative leadership vision, while solving modern business problems effectively and efficiently.

The Bachelor of Science in Business Administration (B.S.B.A.) degree programs emphasize practical competencies, creative leadership approaches, and the development of critical-thinking skills. Students can select from several career-relevant concentrations, including finance, human resource management, management, and project management.

The Master of Science in Management (M.S.M.) degree programs are designed to help provide immediate management applications, along with the knowledge and understanding of the critical skills necessary to analyze and solve various business problems. Available concentrations include business management and projec management.

The Master of Business Administration (M.B.A.), with a concentration in human resource management, was created to address the growing need for qualified, skilled HR professionals who have strong interpersonal skills and corporate operational expertise. This curriculum is designed to help prepare students to integrate HR functions into an organization's strategic plan. Topics of study include long-range planning approaches, development of leadership vision, downsizing strategies, international labor relations, and conflict resolution.

The Executive M.B.A. delivers immediate management applications, along with the knowledge and understanding of the critical skills necessary to analyze and solve various business problems. The emphasis is on real-world skills and knowledge that managers need to succeed in today's business world. This Executive M.B.A. program also incorporates information technology management and project management competencies.

Criminal Justice: The Colorado Tech Online School of Criminal Justice prepares students for a wide variety of careers in law enforcement, corrections, the court systems, and security by providing in-depth criminal justice knowledge in addition to strong business and management skills appropriate to the industry.

The Bachelor of Science in Criminal Justice (B.S.C.J.) offers students a component of forensic study not usually available at the undergraduate level. This degree program can help prepare students for positions such as police officer, deputy sheriff, fraud investigator, highway patrol officer, and more.

Information Technology: Information technology is a rapidly growing industry. Colorado Tech Online develops curricula to reflect current market conditions by incorporating relevant, up-to-date material into course content.

The Bachelor of Science in Business Administration (B.S.B.A.), with a concentration in information technology, gives students the technical skills and strong management skills they need to help position themselves for career advancement in this growing industry.

With the Bachelor of Science in Software Engineering (B.S.S.E.), students acquire a practical, real-world education from professors who are also computer science professionals. In addition to important undergraduate foundation studies, students learn computer programming languages, computer network systems operations, and software engineering skills.

The Master of Science in Management (M.S.M.) degree program includes two technology-related concentrations: information systems security and IT management. The M.S.M. in information systems security provides a strong foundation for students to help advance their technical skills to plan, manage, certify, and accredit an organization's security plan. The M.S.M. in IT management is designed as a broad-based IT management curriculum that provides an understanding of computer architecture, networking and telecommunication, database management, and business and financial management strategies.

Marketing: As the consumer marketplace continues to evolve into an increasingly complex environment, demand grows for professionals with the up-to-date knowledge and skills to drive it forward. The Colorado Tech Online School of Marketing was developed to help prepare marketing professionals who want to establish and advance successful careers.

The Bachelor of Science in Business Administration (B.S.B.A.), with a concentration in marketing, provides students with an understanding of the intricate relationships between organizations and their customers. Course content has been developed to emphasize current marketing trends and opportunities for success.

Student Services

Colorado Tech Online provides technical support 24/7 via an online help desk as well as a toll-free telephone number.

For research and curriculum support, Colorado Tech Online students have access to a full academic library completely online. The texts, journals, articles, and thousands of other resources are accessible whenever a student needs them.

The Career Services Department is staffed by skilled professionals who assist students with their career planning process. The department's full range of services includes career development strategies, job search strategies, interviewing tips, and resume and cover letter assistance.

Credit Options

Students with college credit or military experience may be eligible for the Colorado Tech Online Baccalaureate Degree Completion Program. If eligible, this program may reduce the time required to complete a degree program.

Faculty

Colorado Tech Online's faculty members have advanced degrees and are established professionals in their fields, giving students valuable opportunities to derive insights and real-world perspectives from their experiences. They bring situation-specific relevance to every course, so students receive an education they can apply in the real world. Colorado Tech Online also limits the number of students enrolled in each class to encourage interaction with, and personal attention from, professors.

Admission

To be considered for admission to Colorado Tech Online, applicants must submit an application and $50 application fee and fulfill all admission requirements for the program. Applicants are contacted to arrange for a personal telephone interview and for the necessary school transcripts to be submitted. TOEFL scores are required from nonnative speakers of English.

Tuition and Fees

Tuition amounts vary depending on the program. Students should call an Admissions Representative for more information.

Financial Aid

Financial aid is available for those who qualify.

CONTACT

Colorado Technical University Online
4435 North Chestnut Street, Suite E
Colorado Springs, Colorado 80907
Phone: 800-416-8904 (toll-free)
Web site: http://www.ctuonline.edu

CONNECTICUT STATE UNIVERSITY SYSTEM

OnlineCSU

Hartford, Connecticut

The Connecticut State University (CSU) System is the largest public university system in Connecticut, with more than 35,000 students and 150,000 alumni. OnlineCSU is the virtual classroom of the four Connecticut State Universities—Central Connecticut State University, Eastern Connecticut State University, Southern Connecticut State University, and Western Connecticut State University.

OnlineCSU supports CSU's mission to provide affordable and high-quality active learning opportunities that are geographically and technologically accessible. The collaborative efforts of the four universities provide a strong educational resource for students in Connecticut and around the world.

CSU institutions are fully accredited by the New England Association of Schools and Colleges, and all credits are generally transferable.

Distance Learning Program

More than 20,000 students have taken OnlineCSU's undergraduate and graduate courses and participated in its academic programs. OnlineCSU is not a university; degrees are conferred and credits are awarded by Central, Eastern, Southern, or Western Connecticut State University. Courses may be completed entirely online and do not require classroom attendance.

Delivery Media

Because OnlineCSU is an asynchronous learning environment, students and teachers do not need to log into the virtual classroom at the same time. The classroom is available 24 hours a day, seven days a week. Faculty members and students share documents and interact regularly through the WebCT learning platform, which utilizes chat rooms, threaded discussions, e-mail, and other tools to achieve learning objectives. Students taking online classes must have a computer running a Web browser, preferably Internet Explorer version 6.0 or higher; a connection to the Internet; and an e-mail account.

Programs of Study

Three graduate degrees, two certificate programs, and one bachelor's degree-completion program are available via OnlineCSU. They include a Master of Library Science (M.L.S.) offered by Southern Connecticut State University, a Master of Science (M.S.) in educational technology offered by Eastern Connecticut State University, and a Master of Science (M.S.) in data mining offered by Central Connecticut State University. The two certificates that are available include a certificate in data mining from Central and a sixth-year certificate in educational foundations from Southern. A RN-to-B.S.N. bachelor's degree-completion program is also available from Southern.

The M.L.S. degree is available from Southern's School of Communication, Information and Library Science. The program integrates library science, information science, and instructional technology. It offers preparation for careers in various types of libraries, including academic, public, special, and school libraries, and a range of alternative information science occupations. The 36-credit degree program is accredited by the American Library Association. The school media specialist studies concentration is also approved by the Connecticut Board of Education and offers Connecticut-certified teachers the opportunity to obtain cross-endorsement as a school media specialist.

The M.S. degree in educational technology from Eastern Connecticut State University is a 36-credit program that is designed to provide practical educational technology skills. To prepare students for success in a highly technological and rapidly changing world, the program integrates educational technology applications with the expertise of professional educators and teachers of grades pre-K–12. The program empowers graduates to meet and exceed outcomes standards in Connecticut and throughout the nation. The program is also unique because its curriculum is aligned with standards set by the International Society for Technology in Education.

The M.S. degree in data mining from Central Connecticut State University focuses on statistical methodology, machine learning, and business intelligence. Educated professionals with these skills are sought by industries seeking to improve products, marketing, sales, and customer service. Students gain hands-on experience with the Clementine data-mining software suite from SPSS, Inc., and other state-of-the-art programs to provide actionable results to real-world business problems. A certificate is also available.

The sixth-year certificate in educational foundations program explores the framework of education. This versatile 30-credit program examines the world in which today's educator must function from multicultural, American societal, legal, and moral perspectives.

The RN-to-B.S.N. bachelor's degree-completion program from Southern Connecticut State University is designed for professionals who already have completed the prerequisite course work and are seeking to further their knowledge of nursing. The program is accredited by the Commission of Collegiate Nursing Education. The completion program offers all seven required nursing courses online as well as supplemental general education courses. The B.S.N. degree requires a total of 125 credits, of which a maximum of 30 must be earned at Southern. Courses may be transferred in from any accredited community or four-year college.

Student Services

OnlineCSU offers a complete set of support services to its distance learners. This includes a 24-hour, seven-days-a-week, toll-free help desk to address technical issues and other questions. All OnlineCSU students are allowed full access to online library resources, a bookstore, tutoring, and more through MyOnlineCSU, the program's distance education portal. In addition, on-campus services such as advising, career counseling, and financial aid are available to OnlineCSU students.

Credit Options

Students should refer to the offering university for information about transferring credit, work or life experience evaluations, or admission test waivers. Classes generally are 3 credits each. Graduate programs require a minimum of 36 credits.

Faculty

All faculty members have extensive academic experience, with advanced degrees and practical experience in their disciplines. Before teaching online, faculty members receive pedagogical and tools training to prepare them for the online education experience. In addition, CSU faculty members do not use "canned" content, oftentimes having personally developed the course they teach.

Admission

Admission information and applications are available online. Students seeking information about the M.L.S., sixth-year, or RN-to-B.S.N. program can contact Southern at 888-500-SCSU (toll-free). For information about admittance to the educational technology program, students can call 860-465-5292. For information about data mining, students can call 860-832-2862. Most universities allow students to take up to three courses without formally applying to the university. Students should see the OnlineCSU Web site for details.

Tuition and Fees

Effective beginning with the summer 2005 semester, fees for Connecticut residents who are part-time students were $310 per credit for undergraduate courses and $390 per credit for graduate courses. Fees for out-of-state residents who are part-time students were $380 per credit for undergraduate courses and $480 per credit for graduate courses. Each registration also requires a $50 online registration fee. The M.L.S. and data-mining programs have alternate fee structures; students should visit the Web site at http://www.OnlineCSU.net/FinancialInfo for details.

During the regular academic terms of fall and spring, full-time Connecticut State University students must pay only the $50 online fee, as credits are billed as part of the student's full-time tuition. Full-time students taking classes during the winter and summer semesters are billed as part-time students, as is the case with on-campus classes.

Financial Aid

Students who receive financial aid may be able to apply all or part of this aid to OnlineCSU courses. Students who would like to apply for financial aid need to do so through their home university. Students at CSU institutions should refer to the corresponding university's Web site for specific information on financial aid policies and procedures.

Applying

Generally, students may take up to three courses without formally matriculating at one of the Connecticut State University institutions. To enroll in an online course, students can create a new student account and register via OnlineCSU's Web site. To formally apply to one of the four CSU institutions, students can download application forms from the OnlineCSU degree program pages or visit the Web site of the university offering the program.

CONTACT

OnlineCSU Student Services
Connecticut State University System Office
39 Woodland Street
Hartford, Connecticut 06105-2337
Phone: 860-493-0001
Fax: 860-493-0120
E-mail: onlineCSUso@so.ct.edu
Web site: http://www.OnlineCSU.net

CORBAN COLLEGE

Adult Studies Online Programs

Salem, Oregon

Corban College is an independent, Christian liberal arts college and is accredited by the Northwest Commission on Colleges and Universities. Its core purpose is to educate Christians who will make a difference in the world for Jesus Christ.

The College offered its first distance learning program in 1994, which developed into a uniquely online format in 1997. It now offers two online degree-completion programs for Christian students in the areas of management and communication and family studies.

Distance Learning Program

Corban's online degree-completion programs are specifically and conveniently formatted for the Christian student who has two years of college credit and desires a Christian college education but is unable to attend on-campus classes. With only a three-day residency orientation, the entirety of the sixteen-month program is completed from home via computer.

Delivery Media

Online course work requires an IBM-compatible computer system, Internet access, and completion of an initial orientation, which is held on campus. Complete precourse training is provided for all students via self-paced tutorials, hands-on workshops, and follow-up technical support. Course instruction is accomplished by utilizing facilitated discussion forums, live chat conferences, and collaborative project reports, which are supported by Internet course-management software, audio-video and keyboard conferencing programs, e-mail, and telephone.

Programs of Study

Corban offers two degree-completion programs entirely online. Individual online courses are also offered to assist students in completing general education requirements. The online degree-completion programs lead to a B.S. or B.A. degree. Students enrolling in the degree-completion program must have completed 60 semester hours of transferable credit. A total of 128 semester hours is required for the bachelor's degree.

Both online degree-completion programs in management and communication and family studies are excellent preparation for graduate study. The management and communication online degree-completion program is 41 semester hours in length. The curriculum is structured to develop leadership, analytical, and problem-solving skills with a Christian perspective. Course work provides expertise in management, organization development, and communication—three of the most important aspects of business and public administration. The family studies online degree-completion program is 44 semester hours in length. It uses an applied interdisciplinary approach, focusing on the study of family dynamics and the relationships between families and the society at large. The curriculum is integrated with biblical principles and is taught by Christian professionals. New optional tracks for these programs include mental health and strategic management.

Special Programs

Students are given the opportunity to earn college credit for prior learning through the Prior Learning Assessment program. Students learn how to identify, document, and describe appropriate prior learning experiences. Weekend classes are offered both online and on campus and are designed to meet general education requirements. The course offerings vary in length. Internships and research projects are required in the online degree-completion programs. They are generally completed within the workplace or in a related local business or agency.

Student Services

Online students enjoy complete access to the same College services as campus students via Web-based communication, fax, or telephone. In addition to academic advising and project mentoring, financial aid, the registrar's office, technical support, the campus bookstore, and library services are available. Online library resources include EBSCOhost, ERIC, Academic Universe, ProQuest Direct, and other comprehensive databases.

Credit Options

Qualifying college credit may be transferred, subject to the approval of the College registrar. Students may earn a maximum of 32 semester hours of credit through college-level exams (CLEP, DANTES) and 30 semester hours of credit through the Prior Learning Assessment program.

Admission

Enrollment in the online degree-completion program requires applicants to have a minimum of 60 semester hours of transferable college credit as well as profession of a personal faith in Jesus Christ.

Tuition and Fees

The 2006 tuition for the online degree-completion program is $15,158. Tuition includes all textbooks and graduation fees.

Financial Aid

Financial aid is available through federal and state financial aid programs. For further information, students should contact the financial aid office at 800-845-3005 (toll-free) or via e-mail at aid@corban.edu.

Applying

Applicants for online degree-completion programs must complete an application and submit transcripts, two references, an acceptable writing sample, and a profession of faith in Jesus Christ.

CONTACT

Adult Studies Online Program
Corban College
5000 Deer Park Drive, SE
Salem, Oregon 97301
Phone: 800-764-1383 (toll-free)
Fax: 503-375-7583
E-mail: asd@corban.edu
Web site: http://www.corban.edu

DEPAUL UNIVERSITY

School for New Learning
Center for Distance Education

Chicago, Illinois

DePaul University is nationally recognized for its innovative academic programs that enable students' personal and professional growth through applied learning and individual attention. With more than 23,000 students, it is the largest Catholic university in the United States. DePaul attracts students from all fifty U.S. states and sixty-five other countries, ensuring multiple perspectives.

The School for New Learning (SNL), established thirty years ago, is one of the eight schools and colleges of DePaul. SNL is a national leader in the design and delivery of competency-based learning for adults. In 1999, SNL was ranked by CAEL (the Council for Adult and Experiential Learning) as one of the six best institutions for serving adult learners in higher education. Choosing from among colleges and universities all across North America, CAEL called SNL a "cutting edge pioneer" and "truly innovative in the understanding of the need to improve education." DePaul University and the School for New Learning are fully accredited, which means that the degree earned is honored throughout the world.

Distance Learning Program

SNL's distance education program allows adult students age 24 and older to earn a Bachelor of Arts degree from DePaul University without ever visiting a campus. SNL provides excellent learning opportunities and individualized service to adult students.

Unique to SNL is its emphasis on experience. The degree is competency based, designed to honor adult experience and provide opportunities to earn academic credit through additional experience.

Delivery Media

The distance education program uses various platforms, such as the World Wide Web, CD-ROMs, and e-mail, for course work and for connecting students, faculty members, advisers, professional experts, and classmates.

Programs of Study

Students receive a Bachelor of Arts degree from DePaul University. Students individualize their study by designing a focus area relevant to their life and work goals. Approximately 60 percent of current SNL students graduate with a focus related to business, and other students study any area they choose.

The Bachelor of Arts degree consists of fifty requirements allocated across three areas: focus area, lifelong learning skills, and liberal arts. Students meet the requirements through DePaul courses, transfer courses, proficiency examinations, demonstration of prior learning, and independent study.

In order to ensure both academic quality and focus-area expertise, students work in a personalized committee format during their academic program. A committee consists of the student, a faculty mentor, and a professional adviser. The faculty mentor is a DePaul faculty member who works directly with the student throughout the program. The professional adviser is an expert in the field in which the student would like to focus. The student selects the professional adviser, with the help of the faculty mentor, to act as a guide to the student, particularly in the focus area.

Student Services

DePaul University offers students the following resources and services: admission, registration, identification cards, access to the library, career counseling, writing and math assistance, financial aid, academic advising, the bookstore, and more.

Students have continuing academic and administrative support throughout their academic programs. Advisers and counselors are available to serve students efficiently and effectively.

Credit Options

There is no maximum to the number of transfer credits accepted in the distance education program, although certain courses do not transfer. Courses with a grade of C- or better from accredited institutions are accepted for credit. Students may also transfer college-level learning from life and work experience into the program.

Faculty

The faculty members within the SNL community are dedicated to individualized, student-centered education in a collaborative environment. All have graduate degrees and experience in the fields in which they teach. The faculty members teach about what they know best.

Admission

Students must be 24 years old or older and proficient in the use of the English language and must have completed secondary education.

Students taking online courses are required to have access to a computer with an Internet connection and an e-mail account. Hardware and software requirements are a Pentium III computer with Win ME, Windows 2000, or XP Home or Professional Edition; at least 256 MB of RAM; a 20 GB hard drive; a 56 K baud modem or high-speed connection; a sound card; speakers; a CD-ROM drive; a 1024 x 728 pixels or better monitor; and a printer. Macintosh users must have OS 9.2.2 (or higher) with comparable features.

Tuition and Fees

Tuition and fees for the 2005–06 academic year are $384 per credit hour. The cost of textbooks varies from class to class.

Financial Aid

Financial aid opportunities are available to DePaul's SNL students. For more information, students should visit DePaul's financial aid Web site at http://www.depaul.edu/financial_aid/.

Applying

Applications for admission are accepted year-round. Students should visit SNL's Web site to request additional information about the program and an application for admission to be sent to them (this request can also be made by e-mail or telephone). Students can also apply online at www.snlonline.net.

CONTACT

School for New Learning
Center for Distance Education
DePaul University
25 East Jackson Boulevard
Chicago, Illinois 60604
Phone: 312-362-8821
866-SNL-FORU (toll-free)
Fax: 312-362-5053
E-mail: support@snlonline.net
Web site: http://www.snlonline.net

DEPAUL UNIVERSITY

School of Computer Science, Telecommunications, and Information Systems

Chicago, Illinois

DePaul University is nationally recognized for its innovative academic programs that enable students' personal and professional growth through applied learning and individual attention. With more than 23,000 students, it is the largest Catholic university in the United States. DePaul attracts students from all fifty states and sixty-five other countries, ensuring multiple perspectives.

The mission of the School of Computer Science, Telecommunications, and Information Systems (CTI) is to instill in its students an enthusiasm for their discipline, the knowledge necessary for its practice, an appreciation for the liberal arts, the values of a DePaul education, and a passion for lifelong learning.

Distance Learning Program

The School of Computer Science, Telecommunications and Information Systems—commonly known as DePaul CTI—takes an innovative approach to distance learning by offering distance learning courses in conjunction with courses that take place on campus. Using CTI's Course OnLine (COL) system, students view lectures online at their own convenience. The ability to convert the vital components of any live class into a course available on the Web allows CTI to offer nearly ninety online courses each quarter and nine entire degree programs online. Requirements are the same for distance learning and on-campus courses and degrees, so students are able to take a combination of online and on-campus courses to fit their needs.

Delivery Media

DePaul CTI's Course OnLine system allows registered students to view classroom lectures online. The COL system captures all of the important events in a class session: what the instructor says, points to, writes on the board, or displays on the projector. The parts are synchronized after class and posted to the Web for the remainder of the quarter. Distance learning students follow the assignment and exam schedule for the on-campus section of the course but have the flexibility of viewing the weekly lectures at a time that works best for them.

Course OnLine lectures are integrated into CTI's course-management system, which contains other important information, such as assignments, grades, course documents, announcements, instructor information, and links to external Web sites. In addition, courses take advantage of asynchronous communication tools, including threaded discussion groups and e-mail and the live interaction of online chat sessions. Distance learning students interact with other distance learning students as well as on-campus students.

Programs of Study

CTI offers the following nine degrees through distance learning: the M.A. in information technology; the M.S. in computer, information, and network security; the M.S. in computer science; the M.S. in distributed systems; the M.S. in e-commerce technology; the M.S. in information systems; the M.S. in instructional technology systems; the M.S. in software engineering; and the M.S. in telecommunication systems.

More information about each degree program is available on CTI's Web site at http://www.cti.depaul.edu/admissions/dl/dl_home.asp.

Student Services

DePaul University works hard to make services accessible to all of its students. Distance learning students can remotely access a number of vital University services, including online course registration, account payment, course grades and history, the help desk, degree planning, academic advising, course evaluations, faculty evaluation history, online exam scheduling, the library, career services, and the Graduate Student Association.

Credit Options

Generally, students who have experience with a subject that is required in the prerequisite phase may be able to avoid taking some of these courses. Students review their experience and education with a faculty adviser and may be given a course waiver or be able to take an equivalency exam.

Faculty

All distance learning courses are taught by the same distinguished CTI professors who teach on-campus courses. The School currently has 76 full-time and 120 part-time faculty members.

Admission

Applicants must possess a bachelor's degree from a regionally accredited institution or be in the final stage of completing the undergraduate degree. The primary criterion in determining eligibility is previous academic achievement. A prospective graduate student is expected to present a superior overall academic record, or at least a superior record in the last two years of undergraduate work.

Other factors, such as work experience and career progression, are also considered. There are no additional requirements for admission of distance learning students, and the intention to complete the program via distance learning is not considered in the admissions decision.

Tuition and Fees

The current costs are $551 per quarter hour or $2204 per 4-credit course. Costs are subject to change. All graduate CTI students are subject to the CTI graduate tuition rate for all graduate-level courses regardless of the courses taken. The average course is 4 credit hours. Additional fees may apply. There are no special costs for distance learning. However, distance learning students are responsible for any fees associated with taking exams at another college or university.

Financial Aid

Although CTI does not offer financial aid specifically for distance learning students, all graduate students may apply for financial aid through DePaul's Financial Aid Office Web site at http://www.depaul.edu/financial_aid or in person at one of two full-service offices in Chicago.

Applying

A $25 nonrefundable application fee is required and can be paid online by credit card after the application process. For more information and an online application, students should visit the school's Web site.

CONTACT

Marueen Garvey, Director of Admissions
School of CTI
DePaul University
243 South Wabash Avenue
Chicago, Illinois 60604
Phone: 312-362-8714
Fax: 312-362-5327
E-mail: distancelearning@cti.depaul.edu
Web site: http://www.cti.depaul.edu/admissions/news/home.asp

DEVRY UNIVERSITY
Online Center
Oakbrook Terrace, Illinois

Celebrating seventy-five years as one of the largest degree-granting, higher education systems in North America, DeVry University provides high-quality, career-oriented associate, bachelor's, and master's degree programs in technology, health-care technology, business, and management. Approximately 46,000 students are enrolled across eighty locations in twenty-three states and Canada. DeVry University is accredited by the Higher Learning Commission and is a member of the North Central Association of Colleges and Schools (NCA). DeVry University, a division of DeVry Inc. (NYSE: DV), is based in Oakbrook Terrace, Illinois. For more information about DeVry University, students should visit http://www.devry.edu.

Distance Learning Program
Distance learning, delivered through DeVry University's Online Center, integrates today's high-tech, Internet-based capabilities with DeVry's proven educational methodologies. The innovative "anytime, anywhere" educational delivery system extends the offering of DeVry programs to students who reside beyond the geographic reach of DeVry locations or whose schedules preclude their attending on site. The result is solid education enhanced by the latest in interactive information technology, which enables students to send messages and receive feedback from instructors as well as participate in various group and team activities with fellow online students. DeVry University Online has more than 6,500 enrolled undergraduate and graduate students.

Delivery Media
Typical distance learning technologies include the undergraduate site (http://www.devry.edu/online) and graduate site (http://online.keller.edu), which are accessible 24 hours a day, seven days a week. DeVry Online offers course syllabi and assignments; a virtual library and other Web-based resources; e-mail, threaded conversations, and chat rooms; text and course materials available through an online bookstore; CD-ROM companion disks; and study notes or instructor lectures for student review.

Programs of Study
DeVry University Online currently offers associate degree programs in accounting technology, health-information technology, and network systems administration. Bachelor degrees are available in business administration, computer information systems, game and simulation programming, information technology, network and communications management, and technical management. DeVry University's graduate-level programs include master's degrees in accounting and financial management, business administration, human resource management, information systems management, network and communications management, project management, and public administration. Graduate certificates are also available for students who wish to develop their expertise in these graduate-level programs without completing a degree or who wish to specialize in one of these areas within their degree program.

Undergraduate students must achieve a cumulative grade point average of at least 2.0 (on a 4.0 scale) and satisfactorily complete all curriculum requirements to graduate. Graduate students must achieve a cumulative grade point average of at least 3.0 as well as fulfill the graduation requirements for their specific programs.

Student Services
In addition to offering high-quality education online, DeVry is committed to providing online students with access to a full range of support services, including admission and registration information, academic advising, and financial aid information. DeVry University maintains an online library with full-text periodical databases and online short courses for self-instruction. DeVry Online staff members are available to assist students with administrative matters as well as with education-related issues. Students can complete all administrative details online, including purchasing books.

Faculty
Instructors for online courses are drawn from DeVry's faculty throughout North America as well as from leading organizations in business and technology, creating a systemwide student-faculty community. To ensure their effective delivery of course material as well as their ability to facilitate relevant and meaningful participation from all class members, faculty members teaching online courses complete specialized instruction to prepare them to teach via this medium. As a result, online students are provided with a comprehensive learning experience that enables them to master course content.

Admission
DeVry University's admission process is streamlined, so students learn quickly whether they have been accepted. Applicants must complete a personal

interview with an admissions representative and complete a written application. Applicants should visit DeVry University's Web site for further details (http://www.devry.edu).

For admission to undergraduate programs, specific requirements must be met regarding age, prior education, demonstrated proficiency in the basic and prerequisite skills needed for college-level work in the chosen field of study, and computer literacy. Each undergraduate applicant pays a $50 application fee.

For regular graduate admission, applicants must hold a baccalaureate degree from a U.S. regionally accredited institution (international applicants must hold a degree equivalent to a U.S. baccalaureate degree). Applicants who meet baccalaureate degree requirements and whose undergraduate cumulative grade point average is 2.7 or higher are eligible for admission. Applicants with a cumulative GPA below 2.7 must demonstrate quantitative and verbal skills proficiency in one of several possible standardized tests.

Tuition and Fees

For undergraduate online students attending 14 to 19 credit hours, standard tuition is $6530 per semester. For online students attending 1 to 13 credit hours, tuition is $480 per credit hour. Online students attending more than 19 credit hours are charged the standard tuition rate plus the per-credit-hour rate for each additional credit hour. All new students pay a $50 deposit, which is credited toward the first semester's tuition.

For graduate online students, tuition is $1950 per course. After acceptance into the graduate school, new students pay a $100 deposit, which is credited toward the first term's tuition.

Financial Aid

Federal Stafford Student Loan money is available to graduate students through the Federal Family Education Loan Program (FFELP). Undergraduate students who qualify can take advantage of the five major federal financial aid programs in which DeVry is eligible to participate. Undergraduate students may also qualify for state-funded programs and DeVry scholarships.

CONTACT

DeVry University
One Tower Lane
Oakbrook Terrace, Illinois 60181
Phone: 800-839-9009 (toll-free)
Web site: http://www.devry.edu/online
http://online.keller.edu

DREXEL UNIVERSITY

Drexel eLearning

Philadelphia, Pennsylvania

Founded in 1891, Drexel University is a leader in the integration of technology into academics. Fully accredited by the Middle States Association of Colleges and Secondary Schools, Drexel consists of eleven colleges and schools offering 161 degree programs to approximately 16,000 students. Drexel University has more than 90,000 alumni and 1,000 full-time faculty members. Known as Philadelphia's technological university, Drexel is among the top fifty private, nonprofit, national doctoral/research universities in the United States and is ranked by U.S. News & World Report *as one of "America's Best Colleges for 2006."*

Distance Learning Program

Drexel eLearning, a subsidiary of Drexel University, specializes in innovative, Internet-based distance education programs for working professionals in the United States and abroad. A pioneer in online education, Drexel has offered programs online since 1996. Using the same rigorous academic standards (admission criteria, curricula, accreditation, and exams), Drexel's online programs are taught by the same distinguished faculty members and lead to the same high-quality degree as those received on the campus.

Delivery Media

Drexel University's online courses require a student to have a personal computer with an Internet connection and use a Web browser to access the e-learning environment. Course instruction is delivered primarily asynchronously (i.e., where the teacher and learner are not physically at the same place at the same time). Instructional materials come in text, graphics, audio, and video formats and are available online 24/7. Students interact directly with each other and faculty members through e-mail, threaded discussions (online discussion boards), chat, and Web-based whiteboard facilities. All readings, assignments, quizzes, and exams are prespecified, monitored on a continuous basis, and submitted online.

Programs of Study

Drexel's online Bachelor of Science degree programs offered through the College of Nursing include RN-B.S.N. and RN-B.S.N.-M.S.N. programs, which focus on industry-current issues in nursing. In these programs, which are accredited by the National League for Nursing Accrediting Commission (NLNAC) and Commission on Collegiate Nursing Education (CCNE), students arrange to complete clinicals in their area. An RN license is required for admission to the programs. A B.S. in health services administration program is also available.

Bachelor of Science programs are also offered in business administration, communications and applied technology, computing technology, education, psychology, and general studies, with specializations in management and finance. The programs are designed for adult learners, who can transfer up to 135 out of 180 quarter credits.

Drexel's master's degree online programs offered through the College of Nursing include M.S.N. in contemporary nursing faculty, nursing leadership in health systems management, clinical trials research, acute care nurse practitioner (NP)*, adult psychiatric mental health (NP)*, completion program for NPs, and innovation and intra/entrepreneurship in advanced nursing practice. Programs are accredited by the National League for Nursing Accrediting Commission (NLNAC) and the CCNE and prepare nurses to move into managerial or leadership roles in their desired fields. Post-master's certificates are also available.

The M.B.A. Anywhere* program provides a broadly based management curriculum with available concentrations in marketing, finance, information systems strategy, engineering management, and entrepreneurship. This program optimizes the students' leadership potential in a twenty-four-month, part-time cohort format and is accredited by AACSB International, the highest accreditation for U.S. business schools.

Online master's degrees through Drexel's College of Engineering are available in engineering management, electrical engineering, software engineering, and computer science. Drexel University's College of Engineering is the third-largest private engineering college in the United States, with numerous faculty recognitions, highly ranked programs, and research accomplishments. Its curricula are accredited by the Accreditation Board for Engineering and Technology, Inc. (ABET), the leading authority on educational standards for the engineering and science professions.

Drexel, an internationally recognized center for education and research in all facets of information science and systems, also offers online M.S. degree programs in library and information science and in information systems. The M.S. program in library and information science is a top-ranked, ALA-accredited program that allows students to specialize in management of digital information or information/library services. The M.S. program in information systems features a wide range of courses that cover all stages of systems engineering as a life-cycle process.

Ranked as one of America's Best Graduate Schools for 2007 by *U.S. News & World Report,* Drexel's College of Education offers M.S. degrees in educational administration: collaborative leadership, global and international education, higher education, and the science of instruction.

The teacher certification program certifies students in elementary education or secondary education in the areas of biology, chemistry, physics, earth and space science, general science, environmental education, and/or mathematics. The certification program can be incorporated into the master's program or can be completed as a standalone program.

Add-on certificates available include instructional technology specialist, principal's certification, and teaching English as a second language. These programs incorporate current research on teaching and expose teachers to the latest developments in instructional technology.

Drexel's online M.S. in clinical research organization and management program allows students to earn the experience and knowledge necessary to conduct investigations in the increasingly complex and highly regulated clinical field. A five-course certificate of study is also available.

Programs accompanied by an * require on-campus attendance.

Special Programs

Undergraduate certificate programs are available in applied retail management and holistic health studies. Gradate nursing certificates are available in contemporary nursing faculty, nursing leadership in health systems management, clinical trials research, and innovation and intra/entrepreneurship in advanced nursing practice. Additional graduate certificates are available in epidemiology and biostatistics, healthcare informatics, engineering management, and toxicology and industrial hygiene.

Student Services

Online students have access to library facilities, career services, individual tutoring, learning resources, the writing center, 24/7 technical support, and more.

Credit Options

Students pursuing bachelor's degree programs may receive transfer credit for previous studies at an accredited college, CLEP exams, portfolio assessment, military training, Skillsoft, and more. The maximum number of transfer credits varies according to the student's program.

Faculty

Drexel has more than 1,000 full-time faculty members—90 percent of whom hold Ph.D.s. Many of them are distinguished authorities in their fields, including several members of the National Academies of Science and Engineering. Drexel's online programs are taught by the same distinguished faculty members who teach on campus.

Admission

All Drexel online programs run on ten-week quarters beginning in January, March, June, and September, with the exception of the M.S. and certificate in clinical research, which begin three times a year, in January, May, and August. Admissions requirements vary across programs. Students should visit the Web site for specific program information.

Tuition and Fees

Tuition rates vary across programs. Interested students should visit the Web site listed in the Contact section (http://www.drexel.com/petersons) for specific program rates. Students are required to purchase textbooks. There are no application fees.

Financial Aid

Students may apply for scholarships, loans, grants, federal and state aid, and more. Drexel is a Servicemember Opportunity College, welcoming adult students from the military who are using military aid or the Montgomery G.I. Bill benefits to cover their education costs. Deferred tuition payment plans are also available for students receiving reimbursement.

Applying

Application deadlines are typically six weeks before the start of classes. There is no application fee, and applications are accepted on a rolling basis. Students should visit the Web site for more information.

CONTACT

Drexel eLearning
Drexel University
3001 Market Street
One Drexel Plaza, Suite 300
Philadelphia, Pennsylvania 19104
Phone: 866-440-1949 (toll-free)
Fax: 215-895-0525
E-mail: info@drexel.com
Web site: http://www.drexel.com

EAST CAROLINA UNIVERSITY

Division of Continuing Studies

Greenville, North Carolina

Founded in 1907, East Carolina University (ECU) is the third-largest of the sixteen institutions in the University of North Carolina system and offers baccalaureate, master's, specialist, and doctoral degrees in the liberal arts and sciences and professional fields, including medicine. Fully accredited by the Southern Association of Colleges and Schools, the University's goal is to provide students with a rich and distinctive educational experience. ECU's commitment to providing outstanding off-campus educational opportunities is long-standing; the University offered its first distance education course in 1947. The Division of Continuing Studies provides a portal at http://www.options.ecu.edu to the resources of the University as well as assistance that allows adult learners to choose programs that fit their schedules and academic goals. East Carolina University is constantly evaluating and updating its distance learning programs to take advantage of the latest technology and is committed to meeting the evolving needs of the lifelong learner.

Distance Learning Program

East Carolina University's academic community has developed a diverse offering of distance learning programs in direct response to the needs of students. A number of fully online programs are currently available, with additional programs under development. ECU is committed to providing programs designed to meet the professional needs and demanding schedules of busy, working adults. For more information on the latest offerings, students should visit the Web site for the Division of Continuing Studies, which is listed in the Contact section of this description.

Delivery Media

East Carolina University's Web-based courses are faculty-member created Web sites that contain course materials and interactive tools. Most utilize the Blackboard Course Management System. Faculty members may employ a variety of communication tools within their courses, including threaded discussion groups, small-group work, asynchronous Web-based chats, and instant messaging. In addition, faculty members may elect to deliver essential components of their courses via audio and video streaming, by distribution of CDs, or by using desktop videoconferencing technologies.

Programs of Study

Graduate programs are offered in art education (M.A.Ed.), business administration (M.B.A.), business education (M.A.Ed.), criminal justice (M.S.), educational specialist/educational leadership (Ed.S.), English/technical and professional communications (M.A.), health education (M.A. or M.A.Ed.), instructional technology (M.A.Ed. or M.S.), library science (M.L.S.), music education* (M.M.), nursing/family nurse practitioner* (M.S.N.), nursing/neonatal nurse practitioner* (M.S.N.), nursing/nurse midwifery* (M.S.N.), nursing/nursing education (M.S.N.), nutrition and dietetics (M.S.), occupational safety (M.S.O.S.), psychology* (M.A.), science education (M.A.Ed.), special education (M.A.Ed.), speech-language pathology* (M.S.), technology systems/computer networking management (M.S.), technology systems/digital communications (M.S.), technology systems/distribution and logistics (M.S.), technology systems/information security (M.S.), technology systems/manufacturing (M.S.), technology systems/performance improvement (M.S.), and vocational education/information technologies (M.S.).

Undergraduate degree-completion programs are available in birth-kindergarten education (B.S.), communication (B.S.), general business (B.S.), health information management (B.S.), health services management (B.S.), hospitality management (B.S.), industrial technology (B.S.I.T.), information and computer technology (B.S.), information technologies (B.S.B.E.), and registered nurse/Bachelor of Science in Nursing (RN/B.S.N.).

Graduate certificates are offered in assistive technology, community college teaching, computer network professional, distance learning, information assurance, multicultural literature, performance improvement, professional communication, security studies, virtual reality in education and training, and Web site developer.

Post-master's nursing certificates can be earned in family nurse practitioner*, neonatal nurse practitioner*, nurse midwifery*, and nursing education.

Add-on teacher licensure programs are offered in driver's education, preschool*, and technology facilitator.

For the programs listed above, the * denotes programs for which some on-campus attendance is required.

Student Services

Distance learners at East Carolina University have access to library services, the campus network, e-mail accounts, the bookstore, registration, and academic advising at a distance. Academic advisers are available by phone, e-mail, fax, and in person to assist students with course selection.

Credit Options

Transfer credit is granted on academic course work within degree-specific limits, and no credit is granted on the basis of professional experience. CLEP course credit may also be available.

Faculty

ECU's approximately 1,300 full-time faculty members, the majority of whom hold terminal degrees, teach both the on-campus and distance-learning courses.

Admission

Before registering for a course, students must first apply and be admitted to ECU. Students may be admitted as degree-seeking or as nondegree/visiting students. Admission for students seeking a degree is based on their previous academic record and standardized test scores. In addition, graduate students are required to submit letters of recommendation.

Tuition and Fees

Undergraduate tuition and technology fees are $88 per semester hour for in-state residents and $443 per semester hour for out-of-state students. Graduate tuition and technology fees are $139 per semester hour for in-state residents and $645 per semester hour for out-of-state students. Graduate business-student tuition and technology fees are $199 per semester hour for in-state residents and $705 per semester hour for out-of-state students. Graduate students taking undergraduate courses are charged graduate tuition. Rates are projected and subject to change without prior written notice.

Financial Aid

Distance learning students are eligible to apply for financial aid and are encouraged to contact the Office of Financial Aid at 252-328-9379, faques@mail.ecu.edu, or via the Web at http://www.ecu.edu/financial/ for more information.

Applying

Prospective students must submit an application, accompanied by a fee of $60, for admission. Applications can also be obtained online from the Division of Continuing Studies at the Web site listed in the Contact section. While most programs accept students year-round, students are urged to apply early.

CONTACT

Carolyn Dunn
Division of Continuing Studies
404-E Self-Help Center
East Carolina University
Greenville, North Carolina 27858-4353
Phone: 252-328-9218
800-398-9275 (toll-free)
E-mail: options@ecu.edu
Web site: http://www.options.ecu.edu

EASTERN MICHIGAN UNIVERSITY

EMU-Online and Independent Learning

Ypsilanti, Michigan

Eastern Michigan University (EMU) is a public, comprehensive, metropolitan university that offers programs in the arts, sciences, and professions. Founded in 1849, the University comprises more than 24,000 students, who are served by 680 full-time faculty members as well as 1,200 staff members—on campus, off campus, and electronically. EMU offers undergraduate, graduate, specialist, doctoral, and certificate programs in its Colleges of Arts and Sciences, Business, Education, Health and Human Services, and Technology.

Eastern Michigan University continues to be the largest producer of educational personnel in the United States, including the largest producer of special education personnel, mathematics teachers, and science teachers, and is among the top ten producers of educational administrators. The University is fully accredited by the North Central Association of Colleges and Schools.

Eastern Michigan University's Continuing Education Office offers programs and courses online, at off-campus locations throughout the state, on weekends, in the evenings during the week, and in accelerated formats.

Distance Learning Program

EMU's Distance Education program offers students two convenient distance learning options. First, EMU's online courses allow students to attend class when it's convenient for their busy schedule—early in the morning, during the weekend, or even at 2 a.m. Whether students live just 5 or 500 miles from EMU's campus, they are able to learn conveniently, using a computer from their home, office, hotel room, military base, or "virtually" any other location in the world. Second, Independent Learning courses allow students to enroll anytime, learn at their own pace, avoid commuting and parking inconveniences, satisfy general education requirements, and submit course work via Internet, fax, or U.S. mail.

Delivery Media

Courses are delivered via World Wide Web, videotapes and DVDs, and print. Students may interact via e-mail, World Wide Web, mail, telephone, or fax.

Programs of Study

EMU-Online offers the Master of Arts in educational media and technology; Master of Science in engineering management; Master of Science in human nutrition; Master of Science in human nutrition through the Coordinated Program in Dietetics (CPD); Master of Science in quality; Bachelor of Science in dietetics (CPD); Bachelor of Science in technology management (degree-completion program); graduate certificate in educational media and technology; graduate certificate in geographic information systems (GIS) for educators; and graduate certificate in human resource management.

Special Programs

Prior Learning and Portfolio Development is offered to students seeking credit for prior learning through portfolio assessment. A free workshop helps students identify competencies and document experience to create a portfolio to present for assessment by faculty members in appropriate departments.

Student Services

Distance learners can complete their online education entirely via the Internet. Registration, book buying, discussions, homework assignments, library services, and exams are all available at the click of a computer mouse.

Credit Options

Students may transfer credits from another institution or may earn credits through examinations, portfolio assessment, military training, or business training.

Faculty

More than 200 faculty members from EMU's academic departments currently teach online, and Independent Learning courses at EMU.

Admission

Students may register by World Wide Web, mail, fax, and e-mail and in person.

Tuition and Fees

Out-of-state students can take EMU-Online courses at in-state tuition rates. In 2005–06, per-credit-hour rates for Michigan and Ohio residents were $182.10 for all levels (100–400) of undergraduate courses, $326.60 for lower-level (500–600) graduate courses, and $376 for upper-level (700–999) graduate courses.

A registration fee of $40 per semester and a general fee of $21 per credit hour are also assessed. Other fees include $110 for late registration, $10 per credit hour for technology, $27 for payment plan (for fall/winter only), $33 per month for late payments, and $20 for returned checks and declined charge cards. Program support fees also apply and vary by program. In addition to tuition and other applicable fees, online students are assessed an additional $40-per-credit-hour program fee. For specific continuing education program fees, candidates should visit http://www.emich.edu/controller/sbs/tutfee.htm.

All tuition and fees are subject to change by action of the EMU Board of Regents without prior notice and at any time.

Financial Aid

For financial aid information, students should visit http://www.emich.edu/finaid/ or call 734-487-0455.

Applying

For information on undergraduate admissions, prospective students should visit http://www.emich.edu/admissions or call 800-GO-TO-EMU (toll-free).

Each graduate program has its own requirements for admissions. Students should contact the graduate coordinator in their department of interest to determine which of these are required. For more information, students should call 800-GO-TO-EMU (toll-free).

CONTACT

EMU-Online and Independent Learning
Continuing Education
Eastern Michigan University
101 Boone Hall
Ypsilanti, Michigan 48197
Phone: 800-777-3521 (toll-free)
E-mail: distance.education@emich.edu
Web site: http://www.emuonline.edu
http://www.ce.emich.edu

EMBRY-RIDDLE AERONAUTICAL UNIVERSITY

Extended Campus

Daytona Beach, Florida

Embry-Riddle Aeronautical University is an independent, nonsectarian, nonprofit coeducational university with a history dating back to the early days of aviation. Embry-Riddle is accredited by the Commission on Colleges of the Southern Association of Colleges and Schools (1866 Southern Lane, Decatur, Georgia 30033-4097; Telephone: 404-679-4501) to award degrees at the associate, bachelor's, and master's levels. Residential campuses in Daytona Beach, Florida, and Prescott, Arizona, provide education in a traditional setting. The Extended Campus network of education centers throughout the United States and Europe and the distance learning program serve civilian and military working adults around the world. Embry-Riddle has served the public and private sectors of aviation through education for more than seventy years and is the only accredited not-for-profit university in the world totally oriented to aviation/aerospace. Alumni are employed in all facets of civilian and military aviation.

Distance Learning Program

Taking courses or completing a college degree in a traditional classroom environment doesn't work for everyone. Airline professionals have to deal with irregular schedules, and individuals serving in the military, civil service, or other industries spend significant amounts of time on the road. In addition, anyone juggling family life with a busy career knows there is not much time left over to go back to school.

For more than twenty years, Embry-Riddle has been offering Web-based courses and degree programs through its Distance Learning Enrollment Office. Today, the distance learning program encompasses a broad spectrum of classes and degrees offered entirely online, allowing students to take a course or two or earn their entire associate, bachelor's, or master's degree.

In terms of flexibility, Embry-Riddle's distance learning program allows students to complete assignments, join discussions, study, and ask questions. This dynamic educational method gives adult learners the flexibility and convenience of pursuing a degree via the Internet, regardless of their geographic location.

Through Embry-Riddle's commitment to innovative teaching and to learning excellence, convenience, and interaction, online learning through the Distance Learning Enrollment Office helps students realize personal and professional goals anywhere in the world.

With Embry-Riddle's, online learning program, students may be at home, but they are never on their own. Faculty members assigned to the Web-based classes are as accessible and supportive as they are in the classroom, and online learners develop a strong sense of community and camaraderie through online support groups, e-mail discussion forums, and an online help desk.

To discover more about the distance learning programs offered online or for enrollment information, prospective students may visit an Extended Campus Learning Center, visit the Distance Learning Enrollment Office Web site, or contact an adviser.

Delivery Media

The distance learning associate, bachelor's, and master's degree courses are delivered via the Internet. Each class is hosted on a private Embry-Riddle Web site, where students and professors interact by way of a bulletin board–type discussion forum. As a result, students are not required to log on to the Web site at specific times, but they may access their course work at a time of day that is most convenient to them. To participate in a distance learning class, students need access to a personal computer and the World Wide Web. Students who do not have access to the Web from home can usually gain access through their local library, military base education center, Embry-Riddle resident center or another public facility.

Programs of Study

At the graduate level, Embry-Riddle offers the Master of Aeronautical Science (M.A.S.) degree and the Master of Science in Management (M.S.M.) degree.

The M.A.S. degree, with specializations in aeronautics operations, education, human factors, management, safety, space operations management, or space studies, requires 36–39 semester hours of course work. The M.A.S. program enables aviation/aerospace professionals to master the application of concepts, methods, and tools used in the development, manufacture, and operation of aircraft and spacecraft as well as the public and business infrastructure that support them. The degree gives air traffic control personnel, aviation educators, flight crew members, flight operations specialists, and industry technical representatives an unequaled opportunity to enhance their knowledge and pursue additional opportunities. The special intricacies of aviation are woven into a strong, traditional management foundation and examined in greater detail through a wide variety of electives. M.A.S. core topics include air transportation, aircraft and space craft development, human factors in aviation/aerospace, and research methods and statistics. Specialization courses provide a strong knowledge base of subject material. The courses provide the student with skills needed in the professional arena. Electives and a graduate research project provide students with the ability to tailor their degrees, adding greater breadth and depth in aviation/aerospace–related intellectual pursuits.

The M.S.M. degree program is targeted for those students (or those organizations sponsoring students) who need and desire a focused management degree but are looking for a degree with a greater operational approach than a traditional M.B.A. The degree is a 36-semester-hour program, which comprises a strong management core of 24 semester hours and the opportunity for several different areas of concentration or specialization.

Undergraduate degree offerings include Associate in Science and Bachelor of Science degree programs in professional aeronautics, Associate in Science and Bachelor of Science degree programs in technical management, the Bachelor of Science degree in technical management–logistics, the Bachelor of Science in technical management–occupational safety and health, the Bachelor of Science degree in aviation maintenance management, and an Associate in Science degree in aircraft maintenance technology. The professional aeronautics degree program is designed specifically for students who work, have worked, or desire to work in aviation-related careers. For students with existing aviation-related knowledge and skills, the program recognizes those skills by awarding advanced-standing, prior-learning credit. The curriculum then builds upon those skills. The program also provides a path for those students new to aviation to acquire these skills through aviation-related courses. The Bachelor of Science in professional aeronautics requires 120 semester hours, and the Associate in Science in professional aeronautics requires 60 semester hours.

The Bachelor of Science degree in technical management is 120 semester hours, and the Associate in Science in technical management is 60 semester hours. In the technical management degree program, students learn how to apply specific management skills to their technical specialty. The degree program prepares students for supervisory and management positions in various segments of civilian and military aviation.

The Bachelor of Science degree in aviation maintenance management is 126 semester hours. In this degree program, students gain the management skills needed to effectively manage aviation maintenance. Students who already have their Airframe and Powerplant Maintenance Certificate gain a comprehensive business foundation that complements the FAA certification. Although the program is geared toward aviation and aerospace, its curriculum prepares graduates for success with companies in any industry.

The Associate in Science in aircraft maintenance technology program offers experienced maintenance technicians an opportunity to broaden their knowledge of aviation maintenance while gaining a solid foundation in the principles of management and communication. Students who enter the program holding an FAA Airframe & Powerplant Certificate are awarded 30 credit hours toward their degree. Others can earn their certificate as part of the overall curriculum. Students may also apply Associate in Science in aviation maintenance technology credits toward an Embry-Riddle bachelor's degree in aviation maintenance management or any of the other related degrees.

Through Embry-Riddle Aeronautical University's online learning department a student may choose to complete a certificate of completion to gain valuable academic knowledge to accompany their professional experience. Certificates of completion are offered in a variety of areas at both the undergraduate and graduate academic level.

Credit Options

Master's degree applicants may transfer up to 12 semester hours of credit into the University. Credit must be from a regionally accredited institution with a grade of B or better and awarded within seven years of application to Embry-Riddle. Courses must be applicable to the selected degree program. Undergraduate applicants may transfer credit from regionally accredited institutions with a letter grade of C or better. Advanced-standing credit may be awarded for prior learning achieved through postsecondary education, testing, and work or training experience.

Faculty

The faculty is a blend of traditionally prepared academicians and leaders with significant industry track records. Nearly all faculty members have doctoral or terminal degrees.

Admission

Admission to the master's degree program requires a bachelor's degree from a regionally accredited institution. Admission to the undergraduate programs is unique to each degree.

Tuition and Fees

Tuition for master's degree courses is $368 per credit hour for the 2006–07 academic year. Undergraduate tuition is $184 per credit hour. Textbook and shipping fees vary by course.

Financial Aid

Students accepted for admission may be considered for several forms of federal financial aid. There are three different federal programs available. Additional information is provided at the time of application. All Embry-Riddle degree programs have been approved by the U.S. Department of Veterans' Affairs (DVA) for enrollment of persons eligible to receive benefits from DVA.

Applying

Applications for admission are accepted continuously. There are six graduate online learning terms a year and eleven undergraduate online learning terms a year.

CONTACT

David A. Weagle, Senior Admissions Counselor
Sarah L. Ochs, Admissions Counselor
Distance Learning Enrollment Office
Embry-Riddle Aeronautical University
600 South Clyde Morris Boulevard
Daytona Beach, Florida 32114-3900
Phone: 800-359-3728 (toll-free)
Fax: 386-226-7627
E-mail: dleo.student.recruiter@erau.edu
Web site: http://www.erau.edu/ec/dleo

EXCELSIOR COLLEGE

Learning Services

Albany, New York

As a private institution with no residency requirement, Excelsior College—a recognized leader in distance education—has devoted itself to making college degrees more accessible to busy, working adults. The College accepts credits from a broad array of sources, including Excelsior College distance courses and Excelsior College Exams. As a result, many students find that most or all of their prior college-level credits transfer into their Excelsior College degree program.

Excelsior College offers undergraduate and graduate-level programs in liberal arts, business, and nursing and undergraduate degrees in technology. The College's self-paced degree programs are accessible worldwide, allowing students to complete their degrees from any location.

Excelsior College is accredited by the Commission on Higher Education of the Middle States Association of Colleges and Schools, 3624 Market Street, Philadelphia, Pennsylvania 19104; telephone: 215-662-5606. All of the College's academic programs are registered (i.e., approved) by the New York State Education Department, and its examinations are recognized by the American Council on Education, Center for Adult Learning and Educational Credentials, for the award of college-level credit.

The associate, baccalaureate, and master's degree programs in nursing are accredited by the National League for Nursing Accrediting Commission (NLNAC), 61 Broadway, New York, New York 10006; telephone 800-669-1656 (toll-free). The NLNAC is a specialized accrediting agency recognized by the U.S. Secretary of Education. The baccalaureate degree programs in electronics engineering technology and nuclear engineering technology are accredited by the Technology Accreditation Commission (TAC) of the Accreditation Board for Engineering and Technology (ABET) 111 Market Place, Baltimore, Maryland 21202; telephone: 410-347-7700. The TAC of ABET is a specialized accrediting agency recognized by the U.S. Secretary of Education.

Distance Learning Program

Excelsior College programs are designed to help busy adults pursue their degree at a distance through whatever combination of courses, exams, and training fits their situation. The College accepts credits from Excelsior College Courses and Excelsior College Examinations; classroom and distance courses from other accredited colleges and universities; other college-level proficiency examinations, such as CLEP and DANTES; and military and corporate training recognized for college credit by the American Council on Education (ACE), Center for Adult Learning and Educational Credentials, National Program on Noncollegiate Sponsored Instruction (PONSI), or training evaluated for college credit by Excelsior College.

Currently, the College has more than 27,000 students enrolled in its associate, baccalaureate, and master's degree programs and has more than 110,000 graduates worldwide.

Programs of Study

Excelsior College offers thirty-four degree programs through distinct schools in three major areas.

In the School of Business and Technology, twelve undergraduate business programs lead to degrees in such fields as accounting, finance, global business, management information systems, management of human resources, marketing, operations management, and risk management and insurance. The College also offers a Master of Business Administration (M.B.A.) program that can be completed entirely at a distance. The GMAT is not required. A dozen undergraduate technology degree programs educate students in fields such as computer technology, electronics engineering technology, electronics technology, information technology, nuclear engineering technology, and nuclear technology. The College awards college credit for approved industry training in several fields, including fossil fuel plant technology, information technology, and nuclear power.

Students in the School of Liberal Arts can earn associate or baccalaureate degrees in majors that include biology, chemistry, communication, criminal justice, economics, geography, geology, history, literature, mathematics, music, philosophy, physics, political science, psychology, sociology, or world language and literature. In addition, a liberal studies option provides flexibility for students to pursue a range of interests while focusing on a particular discipline. The School offers two associate and two baccalaureate degrees as well as a Master of Arts in liberal studies that can be earned entirely online. Master's students can now focus studies to match their interests and career goals by choosing one of five new tracks: Issues in Today's Society, Global Strategies, Educational Leadership, Natural Science and Society, and Self-Design. The Graduate Record Examinations (GRE) are not required.

The School of Nursing is one of the largest distance education nursing programs in the world. The nursing components of associate and bachelor's degree programs are made up of guided independent study and nationally recognized Excelsior College Examinations. Students can earn credit for General Education requirements through of wide variety of sources. Important curriculum changes allow RNs to receive at least 30 credits in nursing toward the Bachelor of Science in nursing for an associate degree or diploma program education validated by successful completion of the NCLEX-RN. Certificate programs for health-care professionals in nursing management and palliative care are offered online. Excelsior College offers an online Master of Science degree in nursing with a major in clinical systems management, an RN-M.S. in nursing program, and a program leading to an online graduate-level certificate in health-care informatics.

Special Programs

Through its Office of Military Education, Excelsior College has addressed educational needs of the members of the U.S. armed forces. The College awards credit for military training recognized for college credit by the American Council on Education. Four programs, including associate degrees in aviation, technical studies, and administrative/management studies, are specially designed to meet the needs of military personnel. DANTES-funded Excelsior College Examinations are free to all in active duty military, National Guard, and Reserve Component personnel. Special discounted fees and tuition are available to military personnel, military family members, veterans, and DoD civilians. Special partnerships allow active duty personnel to take Excelsior College distance courses that may be 100 percent covered by military tuition assistance. A college military deployment policy holds the status of deployed students without extension or penalty fees until their return.

Student Services

Excelsior College students draw on a team of experienced academic advisers who assist in the development of individualized degree completion plans.

Enrolled students can use Excelsior College Course Search, a searchable database of distance courses and examinations, to find credit sources to meet their degree requirements. It is the most comprehensive database of such offerings available today.

Students take advantage of a variety of online services through a customized Web user account, including paying bills online and viewing billing transactions, viewing transcript and graduation status, viewing course and exam registration status, and utilizing resources for career development, job hunting, resume writing, and other opportunities.

The Excelsior College Virtual Library gives students online access to millions of the world's most current and authoritative resources. The Electronic Peer Network (EPN) provides a Web-based community where students can join online study groups and buy and sell textbooks, among other things. For those who seek help as they study for Excelsior College Exams, the Online Writing and Online Tutoring Services connect students to experienced tutors and to select online practice exams.

Tuition and Fees

Undergraduate tuition for Excelsior College distance courses is $250 per credit hour. Excelsior College charges an $895 (associate programs) or $995 (baccalaureate programs) fee at enrollment, which covers a student's initial evaluation, academic advisement, and program planning services for one year; a $450 (associate) or $515 (baccalaureate) annual fee for each year after, which covers the ongoing evaluation of academic records submitted by a student; and a $465 to $490 (associate) or $495 (baccalaureate) fee for a final evaluation and verification of all academic records prior to program completion and graduation. Different fees and fee structures apply to military students, to students in the RN-M.S. in nursing, and graduate programs. Students can choose to pay their Excelsior College enrollment and annual service expenses through a special Payment Plan. Complete details can be found on the Excelsior College Web site.

Financial Aid

Excelsior College offers more than fifteen options for financing a degree, including ten scholarship and five private loan programs. Veterans Affairs educational benefits and New York State financial aid programs are also available. Excelsior College offers several flexible payment plan options that allow students to spread the cost of fees and tuition over several installments.

Applying

Students interested in the liberal arts and business and technology programs may enroll directly, but also have the option to submit an undergraduate application for admission as a pre-enrollment tool. They receive an unofficial, one-time review of prior learning that estimates the number of credits that may transfer. Enrollment online, by mail, or by fax is available.

Nursing students must first apply to the Excelsior College School of Nursing and, once accepted, can enroll in Excelsior College. The School of Nursing is open primarily to individuals with clinical experience, such as licensed practical nurses and registered nurses.

CONTACT

Admissions Office
Excelsior College
7 Columbia Circle
Albany, New York 12203
Phone: 518-464-8500 (press 2-7 at the prompt)
888-647-2388 (toll-free)
E-mail: leads@excelsior.edu
Web site: http://www.excelsior.edu

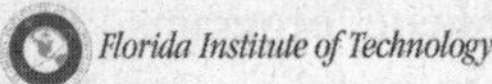

FLORIDA INSTITUTE OF TECHNOLOGY

School of Extended Studies–Virtual Campus

Melbourne, Florida

Florida Institute of Technology is an accredited, coeducational, and independently controlled and supported university. It is committed to the pursuit of excellence in teaching and research in the sciences, engineering, technology, management, and related disciplines as well as to providing the challenges that motivate students to reach their full academic and professional potential. Today, more than 4,700 students are enrolled, with more than 3,300 students on the Melbourne campus and the others at Florida Tech's off-campus graduate sites. All off-campus students and more than 1,000 on-campus students are enrolled in graduate programs. Florida Tech offers 140 degree programs in science and engineering, aviation, business, education, humanities, psychology, and communication. Doctoral degrees are offered in twenty disciplines, and more than sixty master's degrees are offered.

Distance Learning Program

University College consists of five divisions, including Distance Learning, Extended Studies, Florida Tech Consulting, Partnership Programs, and Applied Research. Extended Studies began in August 1972 as Off-Campus Programs, when 42 students enrolled in a master's degree program in electrical engineering at the Naval Air Test Center, Patuxent River, Maryland. From that modest beginning, the graduate programs have grown to more than 1,425 students per year enrolled in thirty degree programs. Since that beginning in 1972, nearly 16,000 Florida Tech master's degrees have been conferred on off-campus candidates representing the military services, federal and local government, and a wide variety of businesses and industries.

The mission of distance learning's Virtual Campus is to extend the opportunity to pursue high-quality educational studies to those who are unable to access traditional resident-based programs. The Virtual Campus offers complete degree programs and certificate programs in a distance learning environment, using today's advanced technology.

Delivery Media

With Blackboard as the learning management system, courses are offered via the Internet. Text information is supported by audio and video clips. Interaction between instructors and students is provided through e-mail, synchronous chats, and asynchronous threaded discussions.

Programs of Study

Degrees offered online include the Professional Master of Business Administration (P.M.B.A.), with concentrations in acquisition and contract management, e-business, human resource management, or information systems; the Master of Public Administration (M.P.A.); and the Master of Science (M.S.) in acquisition and contract management, computer information systems, human resources management, logistics management, management (with concentrations in acquisition and contract management, e-business, human resources management, information systems, logistics management, or transportation management), materiel acquisition management, systems management (with concentrations in information systems (through University Alliance) or operations research), project management (with concentrations in information systems or operations research), and operations research.

Programs require a set of core requirements and a set of electives, with some programs and courses requiring the completion of specific prerequisites prior to enrollment. All courses are 3 semester hours.

Additional details may be found at http://segs.fit.edu/academics/. Course prerequisites are available at http://www.fit.edu/catalog/.

Graduate certificate programs are offered online in the following areas of study: business management, contract management, e-business, human resources management, information systems, logistics, materiel acquisition management, program management, quality management, systems management, and transportation management. Each certificate program requires the completion of five 3-hour courses.

Recently added degree programs include an M.S. in space systems and an M.S. in space systems management. Details are available at http://segs.fit.edu/academics.

Student Services

Library service is provided via remote access to all internal holdings and electronic databases through http://www.lib.fit.edu. Access is provided to registered students via a personal identification number and password for certain restricted databases.

Recommendations for the purchase of computers and related equipment are available at http://ec.fit.edu/cdl/dlfaq.html.

Academic advising is provided through e-mail, fax, or telephone contact on a request basis.

Distance learning students are eligible to use the University's career placement services.

Credit Options

If the courses constitute a logical part of the student's program, up to a maximum of 12 semester hours of transfer credit from regionally accredited institutions may be transferred to Florida Tech (for one master's degree only). Transfer credit from foreign universities is considered on a case-by-case basis, subject to certain limitations.

Some courses presented by certain military schools, plus the resident courses of the U.S. Army Command and General Staff College, Ft. Leavenworth, Kansas, have been evaluated by Florida Tech, and specific courses have been found acceptable for transfer to designated degree programs without charge to the student. Information about the specific courses found acceptable and the Florida Tech equivalents is available from University College in Melbourne.

Faculty

Florida Tech is an organization that values and encourages intellectual curiosity and is committed to the pursuit of excellence in teaching and research. Virtual Campus courses are taught either by faculty members who hold doctorates or terminal degrees in their respective fields or by qualified adjunct faculty members. Each faculty member is devoted to building relationships with their students to motivate them to reach their full academic and professional potential.

Admission

Admission to graduate study is granted to highly qualified applicants. Successful applicants for the master's degree programs have received a bachelor's degree from a regionally accredited institution or its international equivalent. As a general rule, an undergraduate cumulative grade point average of at least 3.0 is required for regular admission. Individual academic units may have higher minimum standards.

Tuition and Fees

As of 2006–07, the per-credit-hour tuition rate is $455. There is no application fee for students applying to the Virtual Campus.

Financial Aid

As a general rule, a graduate student must be enrolled half-time (at least 5 credit hours per term) as a regular student in a degree program and must be a U.S. citizen or an eligible noncitizen to qualify for federal and/or state financial aid. Financial aid forms are available through the University's Office of Financial Aid.

Applying

Application information is available online at http://segs.fit.edu/admissions/apply.html. Applicants must sign and mail an affidavit attesting to the accuracy of the application to the University's Graduate Admission Office. Official transcripts are required from all colleges/universities attended.

CONTACT

University College
School of Extended Studies–Virtual Campus
Florida Institute of Technology
150 West University Boulevard
Melbourne, Florida 32901
Phone: 912-634-6336
888-225-2239 (toll-free in the U.S.)
Fax: 912-634-7783
E-mail: vgc@fit.edu
Web site: http://segs.fit.edu

FLORIDA STATE UNIVERSITY

Academic & Professional Program Services

Tallahassee, Florida

Since its founding more than 150 years ago, Florida State University (FSU) has been guided by its mission to meet the higher education needs of the people of Florida and the U.S. The University remains rooted in its tradition of encouraging critical inquiry, promoting lifelong learning, and responding to radical transformations within professions and society. University faculty members guide students in acquiring the knowledge and skills to learn efficiently and adapt quickly to new settings and challenges, long after earning their degree.

Distance Learning Program

Students learning from a distance receive the same high-quality education and degrees as those students who complete on-campus programs. No distinction is made on transcripts. Using the Internet and software designed specifically for online learning, students receive guidance from instructors, collaborate with classmates on projects, exchange ideas with course members, and contribute to online class discussions at any time of the day or night.

Most students currently enrolled in FSU's distance-degree programs maintain full-time careers. They attend to their online courses during non-work hours and without having to relocate to Tallahassee. Students may take proctored exams at an institution in their area.

Delivery Media

To provide distance students a comprehensive and easy-to-use online learning environment, FSU has partnered with an educational software corporation to create the leading product of its kind. Students "attend" class through course Web sites that deliver communication tools (including discussion boards, live chat, and e-mail) and course materials that are compatible with both PCs and Macs. FSU's online environment includes nearly every component of a face-to-face class, and some that are only possible via technology. Distance learning at FSU is accessible from anywhere an Internet connection is available.

Programs of Study

Bachelor's programs are available in computer science, interdisciplinary social science, nursing, and software engineering. Master's programs are available in adult education/human resource development, business administration, communication disorders, criminology/criminal justice, educational leadership, information studies, instructional systems, management information systems, mathematics education, nursing, physical education, risk management/insurance, science education, social work, and special education. Students pursuing these degrees online typically take one or two courses per semester and satisfy graduation requirements in two to four years.

Special Programs

Online certificate programs are available in adult education/human resource development, financial planning, instructional systems, museum studies, special education, and Webmaster.

Student Services

Florida State University has developed a team exclusively focused on supporting students in its distance-learning programs. Team members include lead faculty members, who are responsible for assuring course quality, mentors or graduate assistants, and distance-learning support staff. Mentors/graduate assistants are selected by FSU faculty members for their background and knowledge of the particular discipline as well as for their ability to guide and encourage a cohort of students. Mentors and graduate assistants are trained to provide each student with individualized tutorial guidance and attention in every course.

Credit Options

Students who have earned an Associate in Arts degree from a Florida public institution or completed at least 60 semester hours of transferable credit are eligible for admission to the University. Some programs may have additional admissions requirements. Master's degree programs are open to students who have earned a bachelor's degree and meet University graduate entrance and specific departmental requirements. Florida State University generally awards credit for classes that are offered at a comparable level and taken at regionally accredited community colleges, colleges, and universities in the U.S., and from fully recognized international institutions. After a student is admitted to the University, the Office of Admissions examines the student's transcripts to determine what credit will transfer toward a degree from FSU.

Faculty

Approximately 88 percent of the teaching faculty members hold doctorates or other terminal degrees. FSU has had five Nobel laureates on its faculty. The faculty currently includes five National Academy of Sciences elected members and two American Academy of Arts and Sciences fellows.

Admission

All applicants must submit official transcripts from each institution previously attended. Applicants for bachelor's degree programs with 60 or more transferable semester hours must have a 2.5 (out of 4.0) minimum GPA, unless they have earned an Associate in Arts degree from a Florida public institution and completed the University foreign language requirement. Individual departments may have additional requirements.

Master's degree program admission involves gaining acceptance by the department or school in which the applicant expects to study. While there are minimum University admission requirements, the departments can, and frequently do, set admission standards significantly higher than these minimums. Applicants should first determine departmental requirements.

Tuition and Fees

Tuition rates differ depending on whether a student is a Florida resident or an out-of-state resident, and an undergraduate or graduate student. Complete information is available through the Web site listed in the Contact section.

Financial Aid

Distance students may have access to many of the same types of financial aid as residential students. To qualify, students need to be enrolled for at least six hours per semester. Qualifying for financial aid is sometimes a lengthy process, and should be started at least two semesters in advance of the term for which financial aid is expected. FSU's Office of Financial Aid provides assistance in determining eligibility for financial aid. The academic coordinator for each distance-degree program can also answer questions about obtaining financial aid.

Applying

Applications may be submitted online and are accepted one year in advance of the start semester. The University deadline is July 1, but programs vary so applicants are encouraged to check the department Web sites. Notification typically takes four to six weeks from the time all necessary credentials are received. An initial orientation is required and available online. Students may register for courses online or by phone.

CONTACT

Academic & Professional Program Services
3500-C University Center
Florida State University
Tallahassee, Florida 32306-2550
Phone: 877-357-8283 (toll-free)
Fax: 850-644-5803
E-mail: inquiries@oddl.fsu.edu
Web site: http://learnonline.fsu.edu

FRANKLIN UNIVERSITY

The Virtu@l Campus™

Columbus, Ohio

Franklin University's primary objective is to provide services and programs for students who work full- or part-time. Franklin is focused on providing students with a supportive environment that allows achievement of goals and provides a practical education with immediate application in the workplace. Students learn from professionals who practice what they teach, are accessible, have a wealth of experience, and exhibit a true commitment to teaching and learning. Franklin University is an independent, nonprofit institution that celebrated its 100th anniversary in 2002. It has offered online courses since 1996 and currently offers twelve undergraduate majors as well as an Online Vantage M.B.A.™ Program through its Virtu@l Campus™. In 1998, the University unveiled the Community College Alliance (CCA) Program, which encourages community college graduates to obtain a bachelor's degree by combining on-site classes at their community colleges with online classes through Franklin. In addition, Franklin was chosen as one of the initial institutions partnering with the U.S. Army to offer online learning opportunities for soldiers through the eArmyU Program and has served more than 1,300 students to date through the Virtu@l Campus™.

Distance Learning Program

Franklin University has a total distance education enrollment of 4,813, an Online Vantage M.B.A.™ Program enrollment of 202, and an eArmyU enrollment of 818.

Delivery Media

Students in Franklin's Virtu@l Campus™ access courses, programs, and student services via the Internet. All of Franklin's Virtu@l Campus™ classes are designed to incorporate electronic communication tools that include chat rooms, bulletin boards, whiteboards, e-mail, and a grade book that can be accessed by students and faculty members online.

The Balanced Learning Format (BLF) course design and delivery format provides students with a wide range of offerings to meet their learning needs and busy schedules. With three-, six-, twelve-, and fifteen-week course lengths, new classes start every few weeks. The BLF allows students to anticipate consistent time commitments from week to week and from class to class. Franklin University uses a team of instructional designers, faculty members, and developers to create courses. This guarantees students consistent course outcomes, experiential learning, and consistent grading criteria.

Programs of Study

Franklin serves degree-seeking candidates, students who want to continue their education, and those who are interested in experiencing online learning. Franklin's Virtu@l Campus™ offers twelve undergraduate programs and one graduate degree program, the Vantage Master of Business Administration™ (M.B.A.). The Online Vantage M.B.A.™ Program, which includes eight focus areas, is a seventeen-month program consisting of six-week courses and two 3-day, high-intensity learning residencies. Admitted students can enter the M.B.A. program at multiple points along the academic calendar. The online graduate program enables students to continue their careers, balance family and social commitments, and still reach their educational goals.

Thirteen bachelor's degree completion majors are offered online: accounting, applied management, business administration, computer science, digital communication, financial management (available fall 2006), health-care management, human resources management, information technology, management, management information sciences (MIS), marketing, and public safety management.

Franklin University continually updates its programs and schedules to stay current with industry trends and the ever-changing job market.

Student Services

Through Franklin University's student-centered approach, each student is matched with a Student Services Associate (SSA) who, along with the course faculty members, becomes an important contact at the University. SSAs serve as both an initial and long-term resource, working from initial application through graduation.

The Community College Alliance (CCA) program is an educational alliance with more than 230 two-year colleges in thirty-one states. The CCA enables community college graduates, or those with equivalent credit, to earn a bachelor's degree from Franklin without leaving their community. Students complete their degrees through a combination of on-site courses at the community college and online courses through Franklin. For more information, students may visit the program's Web site at http://www.alliance.franklin.edu.

Credit Options

Franklin University has a credit transfer policy that is more student-friendly than those at most other institutions. More than 75 percent of Franklin students have transferred credit from other colleges and universities. Students also can earn credit outside the classroom through the College-Level

Examination Program (CLEP), Franklin University Proficiency Exams (FUPE), and Prior Learning Portfolios.

Faculty

Franklin faculty members enrich the virtual classroom with special talents and abilities drawn from successful careers in business, industry, government, and social service. Franklin University faculty members are working professionals who provide both excellence in teaching and real-world experience.

Admission

Admission to the Franklin M.B.A. program is based on the following selection criteria: a baccalaureate degree from a regionally accredited college or university, a minimum of four years of full-time work experience, a minimum cumulative undergraduate GPA of 2.75 on a 4.0 scale (GMAT scores are considered if the GPA is below 2.75), and a score of 550 (paper-based) or 213 (computer-based) or better on the Test of English as a Foreign Language (TOEFL).

To apply transfer credits from another institution, all official transcripts should be directly forwarded to Franklin University from the previous institution(s); however, a student can begin a distance learning course before the transcripts have been received.

Tuition and Fees

For the 2006–07 academic year, tuition for undergraduate online courses from Franklin University is $244 per credit hour for standard courses and $305 per credit hour for computer science, MIS, and information technology courses. For Online Vantage M.B.A.™ Program courses, tuition is $402 per credit hour.

Financial Aid

Franklin offers a variety of financial aid options, including a deferred-payment plan for students whose employers offer a tuition reimbursement program. More than 75 percent of Franklin students receive some type of financial assistance through grants, scholarships, loans, employer tuition reimbursement, and student employment. Franklin University awards approximately 250 scholarships every year to new and current students.

Applying

Anyone who is a graduate of an accredited high school or has passed the GED test is eligible for admission as a degree-seeking undergraduate student. Those seeking a bachelor's degree must complete an admission application and forward an official high school transcript or an official GED test score report to Franklin.

CONTACT

Franklin University Virtu@l Campus™
201 South Grant Avenue
Columbus, Ohio 43215
Phone: 877-341-6300 (toll-free)
E-mail: info@franklin.edu
Web site: http://www.franklin.edu

GEORGIA INSTITUTE OF TECHNOLOGY

Center for Distance Learning

Atlanta, Georgia

Founded in 1885, the Georgia Institute of Technology is the Southeast's largest technological institution. Georgia Tech is located on a 330-acre campus near downtown Atlanta—the financial, communications, and cultural hub of the Southeast. The Institute's mission is to be a leader among those few technological universities whose alumni, faculty, students, and staff define, expand, and communicate the frontiers of knowledge and innovation.

U.S. News & World Report *consistently lists Georgia Tech among the fifty best universities in the nation. Georgia Tech also makes their list of the top graduate engineering programs in the country. Eight of the engineering options were ranked in the top ten, with four in the top five.*

In addition to its high-quality undergraduate and graduate instructional programs, Tech has a world-class research program, with $314 million in new grants and contracts awarded during the 2004 fiscal year. This ranks Tech as the South's number one public institution in engineering research.

Distance Learning Program

Georgia Tech's Center for Distance Learning serves more than 500 distance learning students and is housed within a unit that reports directly to the provost. Georgia Tech is accredited by the Southern Association of Colleges and Schools. Engineering disciplines are accredited by the Accrediting Board for Engineering and Technology, Inc.

Delivery Media

Video cameras record instructor presentations and student-instructor interaction during regular Georgia Tech graduate classes. The videotapes, CDs or DVDs, and supporting materials are sent to off-campus students, who take courses without having to come to the campus. Selected courses are available at some locations via videoconferencing, satellite, and the Internet. Students enrolled in the program communicate with their Georgia Tech professor by telephone, fax, and/or e-mail. Students have access to the Georgia Tech Electronic Library and the computer system via a business or home computer and a modem. Access is also provided over the Internet. Every student is expected to high-quality computer with a printer and Internet access. (High-speed connection is highly recommended.)

Programs of Study

The Georgia Tech video-based distance delivery program provides high-quality graduate-level courses that can be applied to several master's degree programs. The School of Aerospace Engineering offers two master's degrees, the Master of Science in Aerospace Engineering (M.S.A.E.) and the Master of Science (M.S.). The M.S.A.E is generally referred to as a designated degree, while the M.S. is referred to as an undesignated degree. The difference between the two degree programs is that the designated degree program includes the completion of all academic course work required for a Bachelor of Science in Aerospace Engineering degree. The Master of Science in Electrical and Computer Engineering is offered with options in computer engineering, digital signal processing, power, and telecommunications; all options require 30 hours of course work. The M.S. and the Master of Science in Environmental Engineering (M.S.Env.E.) degrees are offered with concentrations in water quality, surface and subsurface systems, hazardous and solid waste, and air quality; all programs require 30 hours of course work or the equivalent. The Master of Science in Industrial Engineering is offered with specializations in automation, production and logistics systems, and statistical process control and quality assurance; it requires 30 hours of course work and students must hold an undergraduate degree from an ABET-accredited engineering curriculum. The Master of Science in Operations Research (M.S.O.R.) is a program for students who likely have a background in engineering, mathematics, the physical sciences, or computer science. The Master of Science in Mechanical Engineering is offered with specializations in thermal science and mechanical systems; it requires 30 hours of course work. The Master of Science in Medical Physics (M.S.M.P.) degree program is intended to prepare students with a bachelor's degree in science or engineering for productive careers as medical physicists. Students have the choice of a thesis or a nonthesis option in the medical physics curriculum. Both options include seven required courses (21 credit hours) and a clinical rotation (3 credit hours). The thesis option includes an additional 6 credit hours for the preparation of a thesis and the elective for a total of 33 credit hours.

New for the 2005–06 academic year is a Masters of Science degree in building construction and integrated facility management. The master's program requires 36 semester hours. Students can choose either the thesis option or the nonthesis option. The thesis option is 18 hours of required courses in addition to two elective courses and a master's thesis. The nonthesis option is 18 hours of required courses and 18 hours of professional electives. The course emphasis is on professional trends, environmental and safety concerns, planning and project management, real estate and facility maintenance and management, and financial topics.

Specific information on admission and degree requirements can be obtained by calling the academic coordinators for each area. Students should call the contact name for additional information.

Special Programs

Georgia Tech offers a series of graduate-level credit courses in mechanical engineering (ME) that enable qualified students around the world to earn a Georgia Tech master's degree in ME completely online. Georgia Tech also offers online graduate courses in electrical and industrial engineering that can be applied toward master's degrees in this discipline.

All Georgia Tech online graduate courses use state-of-the-art streaming audio and video technologies synchronized with slides, simulations, and other multimedia and make maximum use of the pedagogical advantages offered by Web-based courseware and instruction. Further information about these new online degree programs is available at the Georgia Tech Center for Distance Learning Web site at the address listed in the Contact section.

A Certificate in Manufacturing provides students with the fundamentals in support of education and research in manufacturing. Each student pursuing the certificate develops knowledge and skills in a particular discipline coupled with a general knowledge of the entire manufacturing enterprise and an ability to work well as a member of a team. The certificate emphasizes the philosophy that it is not possible to educate engineers, managers, or scientists in all aspects of manufacturing. Accordingly, the program is structured to broaden and enhance the education of students who are enrolled in traditional academic disciplines. The program encourages students to develop knowledge in multiple disciplines from class work and experiences in multidisciplinary team activities. Thus, the program balances technical depth with a broad exposure and comprehension of the realistic problems and solution methodologies that are faced by manufacturing industries every day. The Certificate in Manufacturing is obtained as part of a graduate degree program (M.S. or Ph.D.) from the Georgia Institute of Technology. Students must complete a graduate degree to obtain the certificate. The certificate program consists of a set of key courses that are fundamental to manufacturing, from which the students select 12 semester hours. Students are also required to attend seminars.

Credit Options

Students earn credit toward their degree by registering for and completing courses delivered by videotape. Requirements for each course are the same as for on-campus students enrolled in the course. A student may receive transfer credit of up to 6 hours for graduate-level courses (approved by the academic adviser) taken at an accredited institution in the United States or Canada and not used for credit toward another degree.

Faculty

There are 802 full-time faculty members at Georgia Tech. Of these, 93 percent hold doctoral degrees. Sixteen percent, or 125 faculty members, teach in the Distance Learning Program.

Admission

Admission requirements vary among the academic disciplines. To apply, individuals should contact the academic adviser or admissions office in the School to which he or she is applying.

Tuition and Fees

Tuition for in-state and out-of-state students for the 2005–06 academic year is $763 per credit hour. Fees are subject to change each year. Students are assessed a technology fee of $100 per semester; students must also purchase their own textbooks and software.

Financial Aid

There are financial aid programs available through Georgia Tech for distance learning students. Most employers have programs that will help students pay the course fees. The Department of Veterans Affairs has approved the Georgia Tech Video Program as independent study. Georgia Tech has a memorandum of understanding with DANTES and with the Air Force.

Applying

Application materials can be obtained from the School to which the student is applying. Applicants must submit an Application for Admission, three letters of recommendation, a biographical sketch, two official transcripts of all previous college work, and scores from the Graduate Record Examinations (GRE). Decisions are made by the individual Schools.

CONTACT

Student Support Services Manager
Center for Distance Learning
Georgia Institute of Technology
Atlanta, Georgia 30308-1031
Phone: 404-894-3378
Fax: 404-894-8924
Web site: http://www.cdl.gatech.edu/

GRANTHAM UNIVERSITY

The College of Engineering
The Mark Skousen School of Business
The College of Arts and Sciences

Kansas City, Missouri

Established in 1951, Grantham University, now with more than 8,300 active students, is a private institution that specializes in educating the working adult student. Grantham's mission is to level the playing field by making a high-quality college education available to adult learners, based on the combined academic and economic principles of accessibility, affordability, and academic accountability. Since 1951, Grantham has contributed to the formal education of thousands of working adults. Students from each of the fifty states and many countries around the world have discovered the benefits and convenience of the Grantham distance education model.

Grantham University has designed its degree programs to meet the needs of busy working adult students. Students can complete their course work at times and places that fit their busy schedules. The University's academic model is student centered, with online faculty support focused on academic accountability.

Grantham University is accredited by the Accrediting Commission of the Distance Education and Training Council, 1601 18th Street NW, Washington, D.C. 20009 (http://www.detc.org).

Distance Learning Program

Grantham University's degree programs are offered through distance education, or e-learning, formats. None of the programs requires on-campus or in-classroom attendance. Grantham students are not required to log on to the Internet on specific days or at specific times. Students enjoy self-paced, self-directed methods of study and course completion. This unique method of learning is advantageous for those students with full-time jobs or who have family or other commitments that do not allow them to participate in a regular classroom environment.

Other students who are attracted to the Grantham model are those who travel extensively or find that the nearest college or university may be hundreds of miles away. Grantham University also attracts thousands of military students who appreciate the benefit of being able to complete classes from anywhere in the world. These military students never have to worry about frequent deployments or transfers, because they can take their course work with them and complete it when and where it is convenient.

Grantham offers both undergraduate and graduate degree programs. All of Grantham University's degree programs include an emphasis on both theory and applications, and each program also incorporates general studies courses designed to help students learn to communicate clearly, formulate and analyze problems, and develop well-thought-out solutions.

Delivery Media

Grantham utilizes the latest technologies to deliver courses electronically to students worldwide. Students have access to course materials, announcements, e-mails, and grades through Grantham's online student information system. Online testing and grading provide students with immediate results to ensure they can work at their own pace. New students are required to take DE-100, a course designed to help them understand Grantham's distance education/e-learning method of course completion and to inform them of the wide array of services offered by Grantham.

Programs of Study

Associate and bachelor's degree programs are offered in business administration, computer engineering technology, computer science, criminal justice, electronics engineering technology, engineering management, general studies, interdisciplinary studies, information systems, and software engineering technology. Master of Business Administration and Master of Science degree programs are offered in information management technology, information management–project management, and information technology. General studies courses include English, economics, the humanities, social sciences, physical sciences, and business.

Each degree program is designed around a semester method of completion. A typical Grantham semester consists of four courses (12 credit hours minimum), and students have eight weeks to complete each course. Students may accelerate course completion based on study habits and time devoted to the material.

Students must complete 60 credit hours for an associate degree, of which, 15 credit hours must be completed with Grantham. The bachelor's programs require 120–125 credit hours, of which 30 credit hours must be completed with Grantham. The master's degree programs require 36 credit hours of which 27 credit hours must be completed with Grantham.

Credit Options

Grantham University makes every effort to apply college credit for military training and previous course work whenever possible. CLEP testing, DSST exams, and Grantham Challenge tests along with military and work-related training courses may be eligible for transfer credit. More information about transfer of credit is available on Grantham's Web site.

Faculty

Grantham's faculty, administration, and advisers consist of educators and business executives. Among them are Mr. D. Bruce Merrifield, former Assistant Secretary of Commerce under President Reagan and an endowed chair at the Wharton School of the University of Pennsylvania; Mr. Herbert I. London, founder, endowed chair, and former Dean of Students at New York University's Gallatin School of Individualized Study, and Dr. Mark Skousen, economist, financial adviser, author, and economics professor at Columbia University's Barnard College.

Admission

Students wishing to apply to Grantham must have earned a high school diploma or GED equivalent. Applicants with high school or previous education in another country and who do not reside in the United States, the United Kingdom, or Canada must demonstrate English-language proficiency. A minimum score of 500 on the Test of English as a Foreign Language (TOEFL) is required for admission.

Tuition and Fees

Grantham University's semester tuition rates include all courses, required textbooks, course guides, software, and postage for each semester (North America and APO/FPO only). Interested students should contact the Admissions Department or visit Grantham's Web site for current tuition rates and fees.

Tuition for students enrolling in individual courses totaling less than 13 credit hours is $335 per credit hour and includes books and software. Postage is included for APO/FPO and North American delivery addresses.

Financial Aid

Grantham University offers its students financing options through SLM Financial Corporation, a Sallie Mae company, and Education One, a Chase company. Prospective students who require financing for tuition and fees may e-mail contact Grantham's Admissions Department for more information about applying for these student loans.

Grantham University provides scholarships for active military service members, National Guard members, Reservists, veterans, military family members, and law enforcement professionals.

Applying

Students may apply to Grantham at any time. Grantham University offers continuous enrollment. Students may apply 24 hours a day, 365 days a year using the school's online enrollment services.

CONTACT

DeAnn Wandler
Director of Admissions
Grantham University
7200 Northwest 86th Street, Suite M
Kansas City, Missouri 64153
Phone: 800-955-2527 (toll-free)
Fax: 816-448-3796
E-mail: admissions@grantham.edu
Web site: http://www.grantham.edu

INDIANA STATE UNIVERSITY

Distance Learning Program

Terre Haute, Indiana

Indiana State University is a medium-sized, comprehensive university accredited by the North Central Association of Colleges and Schools. Founded in 1865, the University has grown to serve a student population that includes 11,000 students from all fifty states and sixty-one countries. International students comprise 4 percent of the student population.

Attention to and concern for the individual is reflected in the institution's offerings. Flexible and responsive programs are designed to facilitate student attainment of academic, vocational, and personal goals. Classes are designed to meet the needs of full-time and part-time students. Nondegree study is also available for those seeking personal growth, transferable credit, and enrichment through lifelong learning.

In addition to offering distance programs and courses, the University offers undergraduate and graduate programs in more than 100 areas of study on the Indiana State University campus in Terre Haute, Indiana.

Distance Learning Program

Indiana State University (ISU) has offered distance programs since 1969. Many programs can be completed entirely via distance learning; others require minimal campus visits. All distance programs are available in Indiana. Numerous programs and courses can be completed by out-of-state and international students. More than 1,000 students enroll in ISU distance learning courses each semester.

Delivery Media

Courses are offered via the Internet, videotapes, correspondence, and live television accessible at receive sites. Television courses offer live, two-way interaction among students and the instructor. Students enrolled in correspondence courses work independently, interacting with their instructors via written communications. Students in Internet courses and some videotape courses interact via e-mail and Internet chat rooms. Equipment requirements depend on course format and may include an Internet-connected computer, VCR, and audio cassette player.

Programs of Study

Students may complete individual undergraduate or graduate courses. Each semester, approximately 200 ISU courses are offered via distance learning, including professional development courses for teachers, principals, administrators, counselors, and other educational specialists.

In addition, eligible students may complete numerous undergraduate and graduate degrees and professional development programs.

Undergraduate degree programs include an Associate of Science in general aviation flight technology and bachelor's degree-completion programs in business administration, career and technical education, community health promotion, criminology, electronics technology, industrial technology, human resource development, industrial supervision, insurance and risk management, mechanical engineering technology, and nursing.

Undergraduate nondegree programs include basic and advanced certificate programs in corrections, law enforcement, and private security and a certificate in driver education.

Graduate degree programs include a doctoral program in technology management and master's programs in criminology, electronics and computer technology, health and safety, human resource development, nursing, and student affairs and higher education.

Graduate nondegree programs include certificate/licensure programs in driver education, library media services, public administration, middle/secondary teaching, school administration, teaching ESL or EFL, and visual impairment.

Special Programs

DegreeLink is a bachelor's degree-completion program that enables individuals to transfer previously earned credit to Indiana State University, and complete selected bachelor degrees via distance learning. Students may transfer credit earned from Ivy Tech Community College, Vincennes University, and other accredited institutions.

The Library Media Services Certification Program consists of 27 hours of library and media courses leading to graduate licensure/certification in library media services.

The Master of Science in nursing includes specializations in adult health, community health, family nurse practitioner, and nursing administration. All courses are offered via the Internet.

The Master of Science in electronics and computer technology program is a 32-semester-hour (minimum) program that includes a focus, or concentration, in instrumentation, systems, and automation.

The Ph.D. in technology management is offered through the College of Technology in cooperation with a consortium of four other universities. Course work includes a general technology core, a technical specialization, cognate studies, an internship, and a research core and dissertation.

Student Services

Indiana State University offers distance learners a comprehensive package of services, including online registration, academic advisement, a virtual bookstore, library services, technical support, and career counseling. The Office of Distance Support Services offers one-stop assistance to individuals interested in pursuing undergraduate and graduate courses and programs via distance learning.

Credit Options

Students earn credit by registering for and completing semester-based courses offered on campus or via distance learning. In addition, undergraduate students may opt to earn credit via year-based study. Selected programs enable undergraduates to earn credit for prior work experience, by examination, and through portfolios. Graduate students are eligible to transfer selected credit; each department determines the number of hours transferable.

Faculty

Distance courses are developed and taught by Indiana State University faculty members. Working with instructional designers and media specialists, faculty members transform on-campus courses to distance formats.

Admission

Admission requirements vary by program of study. For information, prospective students should contact the Office of Distance Support Services.

Tuition and Fees

Distance learners are eligible for fee waivers that equate to in-state fees. For details, students should visit the program's Web site.

Applying

Individuals may obtain undergraduate and graduate applications, information, and assistance by contacting the Office of Distance Support Services.

CONTACT

Melissa Hughes, Director
Office of Distance Support Services
Erickson Hall, Room 211
Indiana State University
Terre Haute, Indiana 47809
Phone: 888-237-8080 (toll-free)
Fax: 812-237-8540
E-mail: studentservices@indstate.edu
Web site: http://www.indstate.edu/distance

INDIANA UNIVERSITY

School of Continuing Studies

Bloomington, Indiana

Indiana University (IU) was established in 1820 in Bloomington, Indiana. There are now eight IU campuses located throughout the state of Indiana. Indiana University has more than 920 authorized degree programs. For fall semester 2004, the all-campus enrollment was 98,545 students (graduate and undergraduate).

Indiana University has offered University distance education courses since 1912 and high school distance education courses since 1925. It is accredited by the North Central Association of Colleges and Schools.

Distance Learning Program

The IU Independent Study Program (ISP) is one of the world's largest. It offers more than 195 undergraduate courses by correspondence, more than 100 high school courses by correspondence, and a growing inventory of undergraduate and high school online courses. Each year, it enrolls more than 15,000 students worldwide. The Independent Study Program has won fifty-four course awards from the University Continuing Education Association.

Delivery Media

The IU Independent Study Program courses use such technologies as the World Wide Web, e-mail, CD-ROMs, computer software, and audio cassettes and videotapes. Students may interact with their instructors by toll-free phone, e-mail, and the World Wide Web.

Programs of Study

Through the IU Independent Study Program, students can take individual courses, earn an Indiana University high school diploma, or complete all degree requirements leading to an IU Associate of Arts in General Studies (60 semester credit hours) or an IU Bachelor of General Studies (120 semester credit hours). Students may now earn both degrees online.

ISP courses are open to all students. In fact, many students at other educational institutions use ISP courses to fulfill degree or diploma requirements at their home institution.

Student Services

Students should visit the IU School of Continuing Studies Web site to find course information and enrollment forms. Students can contact the School 24 hours a day, seven days a week. They can enjoy a one-on-one relationship with their instructors either by phone or e-mail. Students enrolling in Independent Study Program courses receive a free IU e-mail account. Through the IU Bloomington Libraries Distance Education Services, students can obtain a library code for borrowing books; order books, articles, and other library materials to be delivered free of charge; get reference help; and learn how to search the library's catalog and databases.

Credit Options

Students can use a variety of options for earning credit toward their Associate of Arts in General Studies and their Bachelor of General Studies. Students who started their college education at another accredited college or university should be able to transfer a considerable number of credits to Indiana University. Other options include credit by examination, credit for self-acquired competency, and military service credit.

Students pursuing the Associate of Arts in General Studies must successfully complete at least 15 of the 60 required credit hours at Indiana University or through the IU Independent Study Program. Students pursuing the Bachelor of General Studies degree must successfully complete at least 30 of the 120 required credit hours at Indiana University or through the IU Independent Study Program.

Faculty

The 2005–06 ISP teaching faculty included 43 high school instructors and 135 University instructors.

Admission

Admission to Indiana University is not required for taking ISP courses. Students need only fill out a registration form for the desired courses.

Students wanting to earn an Associate of Arts in General Studies or a Bachelor of General Studies must submit an admission application to the General Studies Degree Program office. For more information, students should contact the General Studies Degree Program as listed below.

Tuition and Fees

Fees are the same for all students, regardless of where they live. The 2005–06 fee for University ISP courses was $132.15 per credit hour. The 2005–06 fee for high school ISP courses was $120 per 1-credit course and $60 per half-credit course. Students seeking admission to the General Studies Degree Program pay a $50 application fee ($65 for international students). Fees are subject to change.

Financial Aid

At this time, Indiana University is unable to administer federal or state financial aid for students pursuing degrees entirely through distance education, including those students enrolled in ISP courses.

Applying

There are no residency requirements for enrolling in Independent Study Program courses or applying to the General Studies Degree Program, and no on-campus meetings are required; these programs are open to students worldwide.

CONTACT

School of Continuing Studies
Owen Hall
Indiana University
790 East Kirkwood Avenue
Bloomington, Indiana 47405-7101
Phone: 812-855-2292
800-334-1011 (toll-free)
E-mail: scs@indiana.edu
Web site: http://scs.indiana.edu/guest/petersons_indepth.html

JONES COLLEGE

Distance Learning

Jacksonville, Florida

Founded in Jacksonville in 1918 by Annie Harper Jones, Jones College has been expanded and enriched to meet the needs of a student body pursuing relevant professional education. In 1947 the College was chartered by the State of Florida as a non-profit degree-granting institution. Under this charter, a Board of Trustees governs the College, and all income in excess of operating expenses is devoted to providing better equipment and educational facilities.

Jones College is a senior college accredited by the Accrediting Council for Independent Colleges and Schools (ACICS) to award Associate in Science and Bachelor of Science degrees. ACICS is listed as a nationally recognized accrediting agency by the United States Department of Education. Jones College is also recognized by the Council for Higher Education Accreditation. In addition, Jones College participates in Florida's statewide course numbering system, and all professors teaching in that system hold at least a master's degree.

The Arlington campus of Jones College is centrally located minutes away from downtown Jacksonville, suburban areas, and ocean beaches. The West campus is conveniently located on Edgewood Avenue South at Roosevelt Boulevard. In addition, Jones College maintains a Miami campus in Kendall.

Distance Learning Program

Jones College has an extensive distance learning program through which complete bachelor's and associate degrees may be earned in business administration or computer information systems. Details of all programs are contained in the Jones College catalog that is available at the College Web site.

Jones College distance learning classes, which are limited to a maximum of 20 students, are more self-paced than most on-campus classes. For each online class, students should set aside 11 hours per week for such aspects of learning as reading the text and online lessons, completing assignments, participating in chat sessions and threaded discussions, testing, and study and research.

Online classes are virtual classrooms that use Web sites and the Internet. Online classes require more work than on-campus classes, but students can work at the times that are most convenient to them.

The diploma earned in distance learning programs is identical to the diploma earned by students on campus. On a transcript, online classes are identical to on-campus classes.

Delivery Media

Jones College students can participate in online courses from almost anywhere on the globe. Online courses access course materials, announcements, and other information, plus a range of online activities that facilitate frequent student-teacher and student-student interaction. Faculty members and students interact via real-time electronic classrooms, online forums using threaded bulletin boards, real-time chat rooms, e-mail, and the Electronic Library. Students submit their assignments online in multimedia formats for review by faculty members. Students can find specific hardware the software requirements at http://www.jones.edu/dl/requirements.htm.

Programs of Study

The Associate in Science degree program with a business administration major is designed to provide a student with the basic business knowledge necessary to operate a small business; to assume an entry-level managerial, manager trainee, or marketing position; or to provide the student with the knowledge necessary to become promotable into an entry-level managerial position in an already established career field.

The Bachelor of Science degree program with a business administration major is designed to provide the student with the skills necessary to obtain an entry-level position in business administration or to provide a student with the knowledge necessary to become promotable into a managerial position in an already established career field. A core of essential business and general education courses supplements a broadly based sequence of business administration courses and an elective component that permits the student to effectuate an educational program which is consistent with the student's objective.

The Associate in Science degree program with a computer information systems major is designed to provide a student with the basic skills necessary to obtain entry-level employment as a junior programmer, programmer trainee, or other position in the computer information systems industry. The basic sequence of computer information systems courses is supplemented with general education and business offerings that help to ensure the student's productivity and mobility in the business environment.

The Bachelor of Science degree program with a computer information system major provides the combination of business administration course work coupled with computer information systems course work and is designed to provide the student with the skills necessary to obtain an entry level position as a computer programmer, systems analyst, or other position in computer information systems. A core of essential business and general education courses, and an elective component that permits the student to effectuate an educational program that is consistent with the student's objective supplements a comprehensive series of data processing courses.

The specific course requirements for the Associate in Science and Bachelor of Science degree programs can be found at the degree programs tab of the Jones College Web site.

Credit Options

A student must be actively enrolled in Jones College to be eligible to apply for credits through non-traditional means, and all such credits must be awarded prior to the beginning of the student's last semester in school. These nontraditional means include Credit by Examination (maximum of 15 hours), College Level Examination Program (CLEP) (25% of the credit hours for the degree program maximum), Advanced Placement, and non-collegiate training or experience, including military, industrial, or professional training or experience (21 credit hours maximum).

Faculty

Online classes are moderated by instructors who have the same qualifications as the on-campus instructors. In addition to having the approval of their department head and dean, all of the instructors have master's degrees, with at least 18 master's credits in the field that they teach. To become certified to teach distance learning courses, they also take and pass a distance learning course consisting of six online lessons, complete with assignments, tests, and a grade.

Admission

Graduation from high school with a standard diploma or its equivalent is a prerequisite for admission to Jones College. All applicants must have a preadmission interview conducted in person or by telephone.

Tuition and Fees

The tuition for all courses is $275 per semester hour, and there is a laboratory fee of $25 for each distance learning course taken.

Financial Aid

Financial assistance in the form of loans and grants is available to qualified students. Any qualified student may apply to attend Jones College regardless of personal financial circumstances. The college makes every possible effort to aid those students who need financial assistance. Students should apply for financial assistance at the same time they apply for admission to Jones College.

Applying

Students may apply on the Jones College Web site. They are notified of acceptance immediately after all application and financial aid requirements have been submitted. An online orientation is provided for all distance learning students.

CONTACT

For distance learning information, students should contact:

Thomas Clift, Director of Distance Learning
Phone: 800-331-0176 Ext 134 (toll-free)
E-mail: tclift@jones.edu

Correspondence should be sent to:

Jones College
5353 Arlington Expressway
Jacksonville, Florida 32211
Phone: 904-743-1122
800-331-0176 (toll-free)
Fax: 904-743-4446
E-mail: info@jones.edu
Web site: http://www.jones.edu

KANSAS STATE UNIVERSITY

Division of Continuing Education Distance Education

Manhattan, Kansas

Kansas State University (K-State) was founded on February 16, 1863, as a land-grant institution under the Morrill Act. Originally located on the grounds of the old Bluemont Central College, which was chartered in 1858, the University was moved to its present site in 1875.

The 664-acre campus is in Manhattan, 125 miles west of Kansas City, via Interstate 70, in the rolling Flint Hills of northeast Kansas. The Salina campus, 70 miles west of Manhattan, was established through a merger of the former Kansas College of Technology with the University. This was made possible by an enactment of the 1991 Kansas Legislature.

K-State is accredited by the North Central Association of Colleges and Schools (NCA). One of the six universities governed by the Kansas Board of Regents, Kansas State University continues to fulfill its historic educational mission in teaching, research, and public service.

Distance Learning Program

Kansas State University innovatively offers high-quality courses and degree programs to students who are not geographically located near the Manhattan campus. K-State utilizes cutting-edge technologies that enhance the learning environment and extend it far beyond the University's physical boundaries.

Adults across the country want to complete their education, advance their careers, or change their professions. Success requires dedication, self-direction, and perseverance on the part of the student. Distance education offered by K-State provides people with an opportunity to pursue these goals without leaving a current job or family. K-State offers bachelor's degrees, master's degrees, and certificate programs at a distance.

Delivery Media

K-State offers courses through a variety of delivery methods. Most courses follow regular K-State semester dates. Some courses require minimum computer system requirements. Kansas State University offers more than 250 courses per year through distance education. Courses are offered in a variety of subject areas, and students can take many of these without enrolling in a degree program.

Delivery methods include use of videotapes and audiotapes, the Web, listservs, e-mail, discussion rooms, guided study, desktop video, community-based outreach courses, independent study, and correspondence course work.

Programs of Study

K-State has been offering degree completion programs through distance education for more than thirty years. The goal of the Distance Education Degree Completion Programs is to help students complete the last two years of a Bachelor of Science degree. K-State staff is available to help students get started, stay directed, and earn a Bachelor of Science degree.

A student's requirements include a minimum of 30 K-State hours, with 20 of the last 30 hours earned from K-State. Students may transfer a maximum of 60 credit hours to K-State from other institutions. The average student completes a bachelor's degree in two to six years; the pace is up to the student.

Bachelor's degree completion programs are offered in animal sciences and industry, early childhood education, dietetics, food science and industry, general business, interdisciplinary social science, and technology management.

Master's degree programs offered include agribusiness, chemical engineering, civil engineering, electrical engineering, engineering management, food science, gerontology, industrial/organizational psychology, mechanical engineering, merchandising, personal financial planning, software engineering, and youth development.

Special Programs

Certificate/endorsement programs are also offered. These programs include an academic advising certificate, business administration graduate certificate, early childhood education credential and endorsement, engineering professional development hours, food science certificate program, gerontology graduate certificate, merchandising graduate certificate, occupational health certificate program, personal financial planning certificate program, and youth development graduate certificate.

K-State is a member of Service Members Opportunity College for the SOCAD-2 flexible-degree network. This network guarantees worldwide transfer of credit for military personnel who take courses from participating colleges and universities.

Student Services

Students in degree programs receive advising from the college offering the degree. The Division of Continuing Education also has Program Coordinators for each college, who can provide assistance.

Library services are available to students enrolled in degree completion programs. A K-State library services facilitator helps students access materials in the K-State library.

Financial aid is available for students seeking degrees. Scholarships are also available.

The technical support help desk can provide a variety of technical support services once a student is enrolled in a distance education course.

For information about all the student services, students should visit the Student Services Web site at http://www.dce.ksu.edu/studentservices.

Faculty

Kansas State University is an accredited institution offering credit courses through distance education. Distance education courses are taught by faculty members who teach K-State on-campus courses.

Admission

Each distance education degree program has specific admission requirements and procedures. Bachelor's degree completion programs require an application fee of $60. Admission information is available for each program at the Web address listed in the Contact section.

Tuition and Fees

Distance education tuition at K-State is the same for both in-state and out-of-state students. Tuition is the cost for an academic course and includes a per-credit-hour charge. It also includes additional tuition components. Tuition components include student services, TELENET 2 media fee, engineering equipment and maintenance, licensing, tape/Web media, and distance education support.

Financial Aid

Students may be eligible for financial aid for distance education courses if federal requirements are met, they are admitted and enrolled in a degree program in Kansas State University, and they are enrolled in a minimum of 6 credit hours of Kansas State University course work. Each student is assigned a financial aid adviser.

Scholarships are also available to students enrolled in degree programs.

Applying

The application process for each program varies. For complete information on a specific program, students can access the Web site listed below or contact the Division of Continuing Education at 785-532-5575 or at the toll-free number listed in the Contact section, or by e-mail at the address listed in the Contact section.

CONTACT

Division of Continuing Education
Kansas State University
13 College Court Building
Manhattan, Kansas 66506-6002
Phone: 785-532-5575
800-622-2KSU (toll-free)
Fax: 785-532-5637
E-mail: informationdce@ksu.edu
Web site: http://www.dce.ksu.edu/distance

KAPLAN UNIVERSITY

Fort Lauderdale, Florida

In a recent national study conducted by the independent consulting firm of R. W. Baird & Co., Kaplan University emerged as America's number 1-ranked online university, surpassing all for-profit institutions of higher learning for quality of education, benefits vs. cost, and student recommendation rate. Founded in 2000, the University provides innovative undergraduate, graduate, and continuing professional educational programs designed to offer working students the opportunity to launch, enhance, or change careers. Kaplan University is committed to general education, a student-centered service and support approach, and applied scholarship in a practical environment. It is accredited by the Higher Learning Commission (http://www.ncahigherlearningcommission.org) of the North Central Association of Colleges and Schools.

Distance Learning Program

As a distance learning institution, Kaplan University provides challenging academic programs developed and assessed by faculty members, staff members, and members of educational, professional, and business communities. These programs provide intensive and comprehensive instruction to more than 21,000 students, instilling the value of lifelong learning by stimulating intellectual curiosity, creative and critical thinking, and awareness of culture and diversity. The University plans and provides facilities and resources that respond to the needs of students and assists them in developing professional attitudes, values, skills, and strategies that foster success in their careers and in life.

Delivery Media

Kaplan University focuses on adding a human touch to the high technology of learning online. Faculty members are committed to providing students with personal attention and academic support when they need it. The flexibility and dynamic interaction of online education at Kaplan University also allow for innovative learning opportunities, including online quizzes with instant feedback, message boards for discussions and advice from professors, and interactive seminar sessions.

Programs of Study

Master's degrees are offered in business, criminal justice, and education, each averaging eighteen months to two years to complete (less with transfer credits).

Bachelor's degrees are awarded in business, criminal justice, education, information systems and technology, nursing and health care, and paralegal studies. Programs typically require 180 credits and four years to complete (less with transfer credits).

Associate degree programs are offered in the arts and sciences, business, criminal justice, information systems and technology, and paralegal studies. Each usually requires 90 credits and two years to finish.

Certificate programs in criminal justice and education may be completed in nine to fifteen months.

Continuing and professional studies programs in business, finance, and health care are self-paced.

Special Programs

Kaplan University offers a 15 percent tuition discount to active-duty service members and their immediate families, as well as discounts on other Kaplan, Inc., products, including educational test-preparation services. The University is a Servicemembers Opportunity College (SOC), part of an association of schools working together to help service members and their families enroll in college programs by simplifying credit transfers and reducing residency requirements.

Student Services

The University offers rich academic support through no-fee tutoring and online writing and mathematics labs, as well as a distinct virtual community made up of honor societies and professional associations. Kaplan University provides students a full complement of library services via the University of Alabama, whose entire library catalog is available online. Students can easily access a description of any item in the collection.

Credit Options

Kaplan University's policy is to transfer experiential and prior learning credit according to American Council on Education (ACE) guidelines. Students may also earn credit toward degrees through CLEP and DANTES examinations. These methods can greatly reduce the time it takes to earn a degree.

Faculty

Kaplan University programs are taught by practicing professionals. As of May 2006, the faculty comprises approximately 1,700 part-time and 170 full-time instructors. Nearly 45 percent have doctoral-level degrees.

Admission

Admissions advisers are trained to counsel and help students with all aspects of their educational and career goals, from selecting the program that is right for them to assisting them in securing financial aid. Prospective students can chat live with an admissions adviser online at http://www.kaplanuniversity.edu or speak with one at 866-527-5268 (toll-free), Monday to Thursday from 9 a.m. to noon (Eastern time) and Friday from 9 a.m. to 6 p.m. (Eastern time). For more information, students can also complete an online request form and receive a return call or e-mail within 24 hours.

Tuition and Fees

All undergraduate programs, the Master of Arts in Teaching and Learning, the Master of Education, the Iowa Teacher Intern Certificate, and the Professional Development for Teachers Program are $305 per credit, while the Master of Science in Criminal Justice is $350 per credit and the Master of Business Administration is $395 per credit. Books, when required, are included in the price of tuition for all undergraduate degree programs. Not all courses require textbooks; some use electronic instructional materials. All online students are required to pay an $85 technology fee per term (waived for the Professional Development for Teachers Program). For the M.B.A. program, the technology fee is prorated to $42.50 per six-week term. A minimum deposit of $95 is required at the time of enrollment and is credited toward tuition at the start of classes.

Financial Aid

Kaplan University actively assists students in securing financial support for their education. Sources include federal grants; federal, state, and private lending programs; and military financial aid. The University also awards scholarships to eligible undergraduate students.

CONTACT

Online Program Admissions
Kaplan University
6301 Kaplan University Avenue
Fort Lauderdale, Florida 33309
Phone: 866-527-5268 (toll-free)
954-515-4015 (international)
866-572-6026 (TYY-TDD; toll-free)
Fax: 888-887-6494 (toll-free)
E-mail: infoku@kaplan.edu
Web site: http://www.kaplan.edu

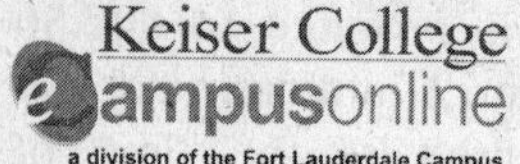

KEISER COLLEGE

Keiser College eCampus

Fort Lauderdale, Florida

For more than twenty-five years, Keiser College has provided high-quality career education and now offers degree programs online to prepare students for high-demand professions. Associate and bachelor's degrees are offered with a student-centered approach and curriculum that is in pace with technology and workforce demand trends.

Keiser College is accredited by the Commission on Colleges of the Southern Association of Colleges and Schools (1866 Southern Lane, Decatur, Georgia 30033-4097; telephone 404-679-4501) to award the associate and bachelor's degrees.

Keiser College eCampus offers degrees in fields that are in high demand and provides job placement assistance to all its students and alumni. The College researches trends for growing fields and tailors its curriculum to prepare students for entry into rewarding careers.

Distance Learning Program

Online learning is not impersonal at Keiser College eCampus. From admissions to faculty, Keiser College eCampus staff members are dedicated to superior student care accomplished through accessible staff and faculty members who foster a student-centered learning community, state-of-the-practice online classroom technology and user-friendly format to enhance learning, a one-class-at-a-time approach that allows busy students to focus on their education and develop the skills to excel, and extensive online resources that include information and access to all student services.

Delivery Media

Technical requirements are listed on the Web site at http://keisercollege.org/D1index.real?area=66.

Programs of Study

Keiser College eCampus is a fully online education campus. Students interact with their instructors and each other using advanced technology, from anywhere at anytime.

Bachelor's degrees online are offered in accounting, business administration (this program is also offered in Spanish), criminal justice, health services administration, management information systems (MIS), and in nursing (B.S.N.). Associate degrees online are offered in accounting, aquatics engineering, business administration, computer networking and security management, criminal justice, health services administration, homeland security, medical assistant studies, and paralegal studies.

All online students must log in at least three times a week and actively participate in class. Each student must maintain satisfactory progress. Students must maintain at least a C average or better during each grading period.

Student Services

Keiser College online programs are Web-based courses, designed by qualified faculty and staff members to create an interesting and interactive learning environment. Keiser's virtual classroom is comfortable, and courses can be taken easily by anyone with access to the World Wide Web. Lesson plans, assignments, and class schedules are posted online, while student-teacher interaction and student-student interaction also occur over the Internet. Scheduled discussions, e-mail messages, live chats, and real-time group discussions are a few of the opportunities for interacting during an online course.

Online students have access to all Keiser College resources, from the bookstore to on-campus libraries. In addition, online access to information and services includes application, enrollment and registration procedures, financial aid information, tuition and fee information, course schedules and outlines, course demonstrations, faculty information, and an e-mail directory. Online students also have access to online academic advising and technical support through e-mail or telephone.

Credit Options

Credit for courses or degrees completed at another institution by students enrolling at Keiser College are subject to approval by the Dean of Academic Affairs. These courses or degrees must be similar in content and duration to those offered in the program for which the student has applied. The Dean of Academic Affairs considers only official transcripts mailed directly to Keiser College. Students are responsible for having official transcripts sent to Keiser College from their transfer institutions. Keiser College requires that, as a minimum, the student must complete the last 25 percent of credits in a program of study at the College. All transfer students are informed in writing of any credits accepted as transferable. Preliminary notification is presented, in most cases, prior to enrollment, but in no case, later than the end of the transfer student's first semester.

Faculty

Keiser College has 95 online instructors, 20 of whom are full-time. Eighteen faculty members have doctoral degrees.

Admission

In order to be considered for enrollment at Keiser College, all applicants must supply verification of high school graduation (such as a transcript or diploma), verification of GED completion (GED scores or GED diploma), or proof of graduation from an international institution comparable to a U.S. secondary school.

Home schooled applicants who have a high school diploma are also considered for admission. Home schooled applicants should present their SAT or ACT scores with their application.

Students should make arrangements to take Keiser College's entrance examination (administered at the College) or provide results of their SAT or ACT exam. The College requirements for admission are a combined score of 800 on the SAT and a composite score of 17 on the ACT. In addition, students in Keiser College's medical programs must sign a Statement of Good Health prior to entrance into the program.

Keiser College is proud of the international character of its student body and welcomes students from other nations. All international students must be fluent in English before they enroll. Applicants must furnish proof that they can read, write, and speak English fluently. Keiser College has been approved by the United States Department of Immigration for students to pursue their studies at any of the College's nine campuses. The College can accept only F-1 visas based upon the student's program of study. International student applicants must meet the following requirements for admission to Keiser College: successful completion of a secondary school program that is equivalent to high school in the U.S., certification of financial ability to meet tuition and other necessary expenses or ability to qualify for financial aid as an eligible noncitizen, and the required minimum TOEFL score of 500 on the paper-based test or 225 on the computer-based test if the primary language is not English.

Applications for international students can be obtained through the Admissions Office. Students should apply at least two months prior to the start of the program.

Tuition and Fees

Costs for 2006–07 are $1379 per course, plus educational fees of $100 per month.

Financial Aid

Keiser College offers a number of financial aid programs to its students, including Federal Pell Grants, Federal Supplemental Educational Opportunity Grants (FSEOG), Keiser College Academic Scholarships, Federal Stafford Student Loans, Federal PLUS Loans, and Federal Perkins Loans.

Applying

Applications are accepted on an ongoing basis and can be accessed online at the College Web site at http://online.keisercollege.edu.

CONTACT

Susan Ziegelhofer
Vice President of Admissions
Keiser College eCampus
1500 Northwest 49th Street
Fort Lauderdale, Florida 33309
Phone: 954-351-4040
866-KEISER-1 (toll-free)
E-mail: admissions@keisercollege.edu
Web site: http://online.keisercollege.edu

LIBERTY UNIVERSITY

Distance Learning Program

Lynchburg, Virginia

Liberty University (LU) was founded in 1971 as a private, independent, Christian, comprehensive institution. Since then, Liberty has grown to an enrollment of more than 20,000 students through its various undergraduate and graduate divisions, the Liberty Baptist Theological Seminary, the Distance Learning Program, and the Liberty Bible Institute. Liberty University is accredited by the Commission on Colleges of the Southern Association of Colleges and Schools to award associate, baccalaureate, master's, and doctoral degrees.

Distance Learning Program

Liberty University offers students the opportunity to pursue an accredited college degree at a distance on the associate, baccalaureate, master's, and doctoral levels. The University assists students who are pursuing a degree with such services as transcript evaluation, a personal academic adviser, degree planning, online student services, online library, and career placement assistance. Flexible semesters allow course work to begin at the most convenient times for students. Courses start every three weeks, and students have 120 days to complete each course. The M.B.A. is offered completely online, and classes start eight times a year.

Delivery Media

Course lectures are presented online; through prerecorded VHS videocassettes or DVDs that students purchase along with the required print materials, such as books, workbooks, and study notes (all class materials are required to complete each class); and in on-campus intensives. Students in need of class assistance may contact the assigned academic adviser, a faculty member, and library services via phone, fax, e-mail, or regular mail. No residency is required for associate or baccalaureate degree programs. Graduate programs have minimal residency requirements offered in flexible formats.

Programs of Study

Liberty University's Distance Learning Program offers associate degrees in general studies and religion. Baccalaureate degrees are offered in business (accounting, finance, and management), multidisciplinary studies, psychology, and religion. Students may pursue a master's degree in professional counseling. A 30-credit-hour human relations track, a 48-credit-hour professional counseling certification track, and a 60-credit-hour marriage and family certification track are available. Other master's degrees include the Master of Arts in religion, the Master of Divinity, the Master of Business Administration, and the Master of Education (M.Ed.). The M.Ed. programs are approved by the Virginia Department of Education for the licensure of school personnel. The LU School of Education offers the Education Specialist (Ed.S.) and Doctor of Education (Ed.D.), with an emphasis in educational leadership. The Ph.D. in counseling is also offered by the College of Arts and Sciences.

Special Programs

Distance learners have access to online library and administrative services, the campus computer network, e-mail services, academic advising, tutoring, and career placement assistance.

Credit Options

Credit is given for courses completed at an accredited institution, provided the credit is appropriate to the curriculum chosen at Liberty University. Undergraduate students may also earn credit through standardized testing (CLEP, PEP, DANTES, and ICE), advanced placement, portfolio assessment, military training (ACE), and business training.

Faculty

There are 300 full-time and 188 part-time faculty members at Liberty University. Of the 300 full-time faculty members, 63 work specifically for the Distance Learning Program in either a full-time or part-time capacity. Faculty members who work with the Distance Learning Program hold a master's, doctorate, or other terminal degree in their field of specialty and are specially trained in order to ensure the highest-quality education possible for students.

Admission

An application with a $50 nonrefundable fee must be submitted prior to admittance. All official transcripts must be sent to the Office of Distance Learning Admissions to determine acceptance to a degree program and the evaluation of credit.

Tuition and Fees

For the 2005–06 academic year, tuition for the undergraduate programs was $250 per semester hour. Graduate tuition was as follows: $385 per semester hour for the M.A. in counseling; $375 per semester hour for the M.Ed., Ed.S., and Ed.D.; $395 per semester hour for the M.B.A.; and $225 per semester hour for the Master of Arts in religion and Master of Divinity programs. There is a $150 technology fee each semester of enrollment. Course materials are a separate charge and must be purchased by the student through the University's supplier, MBS Direct (telephone: 800-325-3252, toll-free).

Financial Aid

Liberty offers a full range of state (Virginia Tuition Assistance Grant), federal (Pell Grant), and school-sponsored financial assistance programs for those enrolled as matriculated students. Forms for state and federal aid can be obtained through the University's Web site or by calling the Office of Distance Learning Admissions. All students who apply for a Federal Stafford Student Loan must submit a Free Application for Federal Student Aid (FAFSA).

Applying

Distance learning students can apply for admission at any time of the year. Correspondence between the student and the University is conducted through the Office of Distance Learning Admissions. Applications are accepted by mail, by fax, or online.

CONTACT

Mr. Lee Beaumont
Director of Enrollment Management
Distance Learning Program
Liberty University
1971 University Boulevard
Lynchburg, Virginia 24502-2269
Phone: 800-424-9595 (toll-free)
Fax: 800-628-7977 (toll-free)
E-mail: dlpadmissions@liberty.edu
Web site: http://www.liberty.edu

LOCK HAVEN UNIVERSITY OF PENNSYLVANIA

eCampus Programs

Lock Haven, Pennsylvania

Lock Haven University of Pennsylvania (LHUP) encourages academic excellence. The University's educational programs are designed to develop the intellectual skills and talents of all students. Through formal and informal instruction, students are guided to achieve their full potential. Students gain a better self-understanding, a sense of individual and community responsibility, and knowledge of cultural diversity and the global community. The institution is accredited by the Middle States Association of Colleges and Schools, and distance education is included in the scope of the accreditation.

"This educational experience at LHUP has helped me to focus my goals and redefine them more clearly and has also given me the opportunity to achieve greater insight into this world. This has been the best experience of my life." Carolyne M. Timko, M.L.A.; Blossburg, Pennsylvania.

Distance Learning Program

Lock Haven University (LHUP) provides students with the opportunity to complete a full degree program (associate, bachelor's, or master's) or to complete individual courses either at a local education center or in the convenience of their homes.

Delivery Media

Lock Haven University offers distance learning programs via videoconferencing-based technologies or Web-based technologies to create a fully online experience. The videoconferencing sites are limited to sites contracting with the University. Web-based technologies include a full-featured course-management system, Web-casting of lectures, resource materials, threaded discussions, journaling, real-time chat discussions, document sharing, and other instructional methods that create active and engaged learning communities.

Programs of Study

LHUP offers associate degrees in criminal justice (online) and surgical technology (online) and a bachelor's degree in general studies (online). Students can complete some of their LHUP General Education requirements through the distance learning program as a nonmatriculating student. Four master's degree programs are also available. These include the Master of Education in Alternative Education program (online), Master of Education in Teaching and Learning program (online), Master of Liberal Arts (online), and Master of Health Science in Physician Assistant Studies program (distributed learning).

Noncredit certificates are available in business, construction technology (including International Code Council preparation courses for residential and commercial inspection), health care, Internet design and technical programs, networking and CompTIA certification prep, Microsoft certification prep, paralegal studies and legal secretary studies, and video game design and development. K–12 teachers can also take continuing education classes and receive Act 48 credit.

Special Programs

Lock Haven University encourages students to consider studying abroad. LHUP has a large and diverse international program, providing many opportunities for its students to study abroad for periods ranging from several weeks in a semester to a year or more. The University has direct exchange programs with institutions in Australia, China, Costa Rica, Croatia, England, Finland, France, Germany, Italy, Japan, Mexico, Poland, Russia, Scotland, Spain, and Ukraine. The University offers interested and qualified students an opportunity to participate in various internship programs that provide field experiences to supplement classroom learning.

Student Services

The course management system organizes information, services, and resources relevant to distance learners. Forms are available online to apply for admissions and/or register for courses. The Stevenson Library caters to online students, providing a catalog of resources and access to databases and full-text journals online.

Credit Options

The various subject examinations offered through the College Board's Advanced Placement (AP) program are approved and credit is awarded based on a test score of 3 or higher. With the exception of only one General Examination (English Composition) and four subject tests (Business Law, Educational Psychology, College Composition, and Freshman English) offered through the College Board's College-Level Examination Program (CLEP), degree credit may be earned by candidates who achieve a scaled score equivalent to the 50th percentile or higher using current national norms for each test. There is no limit to the number of courses for which CLEP or AP may award credit. A maximum of 6 graduate semester hours may be transferred and applied toward most graduate degrees.

Faculty

Of the 259 faculty members, 91 percent are full-time. Faculty members are noted for their diverse expertise, their interest in interdisciplinary study and their dedication to working with adult students. In addition to teaching, faculty members advise students, formulate program policy, and supervise independent study and capstone projects.

Admission

Admission requirements vary by program. Generally, undergraduates should have completed college-preparatory course work in high school, have a satisfactory command of the English language, and should have taken either the SAT or the ACT. In general, graduate students must have a baccalaureate degree from an accredited institution and a minimum GPA of 3.0.

Tuition and Fees

Tuition and fees are set by the Board of Governors of the Pennsylvania State System of Higher Education once a year.

For the 2005–06 academic year, undergraduate tuition was $204 per credit for Pennsylvania residents and $208 per credit for nonresidents; the distance education fee was 10 percent of the tuition. Graduate in-state tuition was $376 per credit, and out-of-state students paid $384 per credit. For graduate and undergraduate students, the tuition technology fee was $31 for residents and $47 for nonresidents.

For current information, students should check the Web site at http://www.lhup.edu/business/. The cost of noncredit courses and certificate programs may vary.

Financial Aid

Financial aid to meet the costs of attending LHUP is available from a variety of programs, including grants, loans, and scholarships. The majority of these programs provide funds based on computed financial need, but some non-need-based programs are also available. To apply for financial aid, students must complete the Free Application for Federal Student Aid (FAFSA). Pennsylvania residents should complete this form as provided by the Pennsylvania Higher Education Assistance Agency and any supplemental forms required for the Pennsylvania State Grant. Of all full-time matriculated undergraduates who enrolled in 2003, 77 percent of undergraduates had their financial need fully met.

Applying

Application procedures vary by program, and students should contact the distance education office for specific information. Applicants are required to submit the completed application, a $25 application fee, all high school transcripts, and official SAT or ACT scores. In addition, graduate programs require official transcripts of all undergraduate and graduate work; students applying to the Master of Education programs must also submit three letters of recommendation and a writing sample. International students must also submit TOEFL scores. All applications are processed on a rolling basis.

CONTACT

Dr. Ellen P. O'Hara-Mays, Executive Director
Learning Technology and Distance Education
Lock Haven University of Pennsylvania
Lock Haven, Pennsylvania 17745
Phone: 570-893-2072
877-268-4688 (toll-free)
Fax: 570-893-2638
E-mail: poharama@lhup.edu
Web site: http://www.lhup.edu/cde/

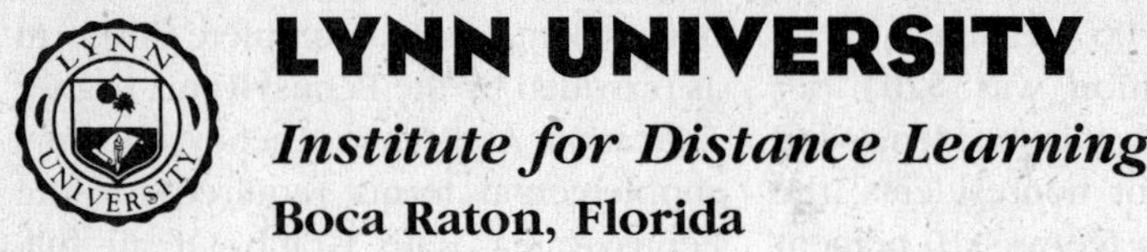

LYNN UNIVERSITY

Institute for Distance Learning

Boca Raton, Florida

Founded in 1962 and located in Boca Raton, Florida, Lynn University is a private coeducational institution whose primary purposes are education; the preservation, discovery, dissemination, and creative application of knowledge; and the preparation of its graduates with the academic foundation for lifelong learning. Service, scholarly activity that includes research, and ongoing professional development allow the faculty, in conjunction with the entire University community, to fulfill its purposes: facilitating student-centered learning and fostering the intellectual life of the University.

Distance Learning Program

Lynn University offers undergraduate, graduate, and doctoral degree programs to students who are unable to participate in a traditional classroom-based environment at the main campus. The aim of the University is to be a global institution for the twenty-first century, where learners can access higher learning opportunities, independent of time schedules and geographical limitations.

The Institute for Distance Learning (IDL) is designed for mature, self-directed learners, using technology and flexible delivery methods. IDL's design and delivery of all programs places a high value on the prior skills and knowledge that mature learners bring to their educational experience.

Lynn University is approved by the Commission on Colleges of the Southern Association of Colleges and Schools (SACS) (1866 Southern Lane, Decatur, Georgia 30033-4097; telephone: 404-679-4501) to offer complete distance learning degree programs via the Web.

Delivery Media

Internet technology encourages interactions between faculty members and students, students and other students, and students and resources (books, journals, electronic library services, and the Internet). Courses are delivered using Blackboard, a student-friendly platform that affords students the opportunity to complete assignments and engage in various discussions at convenient times and locations. Distance learning courses are delivered in an accelerated format, with six 8-week class terms per academic year. Students may begin their studies during any of the terms.

Programs of Study

The Ph.D. program in global leadership offers a specialization in corporate and organizational management. Other graduate degree programs are offered in administration, with specializations in criminal justice and in emergency planning and administration; business administration, with specializations in aviation management, financial valuation and investment management, hospitality management, international business, and marketing; and in educational leadership, with specializations in higher education administration, school administration, and school administration with ESOL endorsement.

Undergraduate degree programs include business administration, criminal justice administration, and psychology.

In addition, select undergraduate, graduate, and doctoral courses are available via the Web. Students can find the course schedule at http://www.lynn.edu/pm.

Credit Options

Most online courses are 3 credits each. Courses with labs are 4 credits. Courses offered with less than 3 credits are identified in the Academic Catalog, which can be found online at http://www.lynn.edu/lynnpm.

Lynn University accepts transfer credits from most other regionally accredited schools. Specific information about transfer credits may be found in the catalog. Credits earned in the online program are combined with credits earned on campus to complete a degree.

Faculty

The faculty members at Lynn University are highly qualified and committed to providing high-quality instruction and learning opportunities for self-directed learners. Along with excellent academic credentials, the faculty members are primarily practitioners in their fields of expertise, thus providing the theoretical context for the practical applications of the subject matter.

Admission

To enroll in an undergraduate degree program, students must have earned a high school diploma or GED. A student's credit hours are earned through instruction (distance learning or traditional classroom), transfer credits from an accredited college or university, military service course credits (DANTES), Florida Department of Law Enforcement (FDLE) or a similar state training facility, professional training or certification as recognized by the American Council on Education (ACE) or the College Level Examination Program (CLEP), and/or a student's professional experience or experiential learning.

Attendees of foreign schools are required to submit an International Transcript Evaluation and course equivalency report. International students whose first language is not English must submit a TOEFL score of at least 550 (213 on the computer-based test).

Graduate students must have earned a college diploma from a regionally accredited or internationally listed college or university. Applicants whose undergraduate grade point average (GPA) was less than 3.0 must also submit the appropriate entrance examination score from the GRE, GMAT, or MAT. All graduate degree program applicants must submit two recommendation letters, a resume, and a statement of professional goals. Other admission requirements vary by degree program and are outlined in the Academic Catalog.

In addition, online students enrolled in the Ph.D. program have a required campus residency of four on-campus immersions consisting of three to five days each and a fifth day for the defense of the dissertation. These immersions are associated with a program orientation and the research core: RES 700Q, RES 702Q, RES 704Q, RES 900Q, and RES 902 (dissertation defense). Students who are unable to meet this enrollment requirement may develop an alternative plan with their program coordinator.

Tuition and Fees

All new students pay a one-time nonrefundable $50 application fee. The tuition fees and registration fees follow the pricing established for the respective colleges and noncredit programs. For the 2006–07 academic year, the fees were as follows: undergraduate, $270 per credit hour; graduate, $525 per credit hour; and doctoral, $735 per credit hour. Noncredit tuition varies with the individual courses. There is a registration fee of $30 at the beginning of each term enrolled, and an experiential portfolio administration fee is $75 per credit hour. More information and specific details regarding fees are available in the Academic Catalog on the University's Web site.

Financial Aid

Financial aid is available to qualified Lynn students. For specific information, students should e-mail the Financial Aid Office at financialaid@lynn.edu or call the office at 561-237-7190.

Applying

Students may apply online or download a printable application at http://www.lynn.edu/lynnpm. To obtain an application by mail, students should call the Admissions Office at 800-888-LYNN (5966) (toll-free in the United States) or 561-237-7900 (outside the U.S.).

CONTACT

Mary L. Tebes, Ph.D.
Director, Institute for Distance Learning
Lynn University
3601 North Military Trail
Boca Raton, Florida 33431
Phone: 561-237-7902
Fax: 561-237-7537
E-mail: mtebes@lynn.edu
Web site: http://www.lynn.edu

Jennifer Lawless
Instructional Designer, Institute for Distance Learning
Lynn University
3601 North Military Trail
Boca Raton, Florida 33431
Phone: 561-237-7939
Fax: 561-237-7537
E-mail: jlawless@lynnedu
Web site: http://www.lynn.edu

MARIST COLLEGE

School of Management

Poughkeepsie, New York

Marist College is an independent, coeducational liberal arts and sciences institution located in Poughkeepsie, New York. Marist began offering graduate programs in 1972 and currently serves some 1,100 graduate students from all over the world. Marist has been listed among the finest colleges and universities in America by the Barron's Guide, The Princeton Review, *and* U.S. News & World Report.

Marist is registered by the New York State Education Department, Office of Higher Education and the Professions, and is accredited by the Middle States Association of Colleges and Schools. Its business programs are accredited by AACSB International–The Association to Advance Collegiate Schools of Business.

Distance Learning Program

Marist College was among the nation's front-runners in distance learning, offering working adults the unique opportunity to complete challenging graduate programs in business administration or public administration entirely on the Web. Professionals from as far away as Europe, India, and China currently count themselves as members of the Marist College family.

Marist's undergraduate and graduate degree programs in business are fully accredited by AACSB International–The Association to Advance Collegiate Schools of Business. AACSB International is the premier accrediting agency for baccalaureate, master's, and doctoral degree programs in business administration and accounting. It is devoted to the promotion and improvement of higher education in business administration and management. This accreditation places Marist among the top 30 percent of business programs in the country. Marist is proud to be among the 515 colleges, universities, and institutions of higher education worldwide accredited by AACSB International.

Marist's M.B.A. and M.P.A. programs provide an outstanding mix of quality, convenience, and flexibility. Students for whom regularly scheduled on-site classes are difficult may pursue equally challenging graduate course work at their convenience from anywhere in the world.

Delivery Media

Cutting-edge instructional technology enables students to interact extensively with their instructors and classmates. Communication is ongoing via e-mail, bulletin boards, group conference rooms, or private chat rooms.

A personal computer with a Pentium 166 processor, 32 megabytes of RAM, a 28.8K modem (56K recommended), and access to the World Wide Web via Internet Explorer (version 5.0 or higher) or Netscape (version 4.7 or higher) is essential. To ensure compatibility in reading attached files and sharing work with classmates, students also need Microsoft Office 97 or higher. Technical skills beyond familiarity with the basic Windows environment are not needed.

Programs of Study

Marist's online graduate programs in business administration and public administration are available to students worldwide. Candidates for either program must meet the admissions criteria required by that program and must have completed a baccalaureate degree from an accredited institution. International applicants must submit official TOEFL scores for admission.

Marist's M.B.A. is designed to cultivate managers who are capable of effective decision making in today's complex business environment. Emphasis is placed on the management process and the behavioral influences that significantly affect the success of modern organizations. Graduates of the program possess the strategic perspective that is necessary to identify opportunities and risks in a rapidly changing economic environment. Course requirements consist of a combination of foundation, core, and elective courses designed to develop the professional analytical, communication, and leadership skills needed to keep pace with the competitive demands of a global economy.

Marist's M.P.A. is designed to provide students with the knowledge and skills necessary for effective public-sector and not-for-profit program management.

The curriculum stresses the ethical, legal, and social context of administration. Graduates are proficient in understanding and developing positive organizational behavior and effectively utilizing a full range of management and administrative techniques to solve problems, address issues, and lead important programs.

Credit Options

The M.B.A. program requires a minimum of 30 credit hours, with a maximum of 51 credit hours, for the degree. Up to 21 credits of foundation courses may be waived, based on prior graduate or undergraduate study. Transfer credits are not applicable to foundation course work. Instead, particular foundation requirements are waived on the basis of prior study.

Transfer of credits into the M.B.A. or M.P.A. program requires the prior approval of the program director. Up to 6 graduate credits may be transferred from an AACSB International–accredited graduate program to satisfy graduate core and/or elective requirements. Criteria considered in awarding transfer credit include the grade received (must be B– or higher), the level of the course in the program at which it was taken, and the course content. Transfer credit is awarded for core courses only if the course is substantially equivalent to the Marist course requirement.

Faculty

The Marist College faculty comprises highly experienced, credentialed educators, many of whom are skilled professionals with practical hands-on experience in corporate, government, not-for-profit, and community settings. Faculty members regularly take part in research, publishing, and consulting and are frequently called upon by various organizations and institutions for their expertise in their given academic areas.

Admission

The M.B.A. and M.P.A. programs are concerned with the interest, aptitude, and capacity of a prospective student, as indicated in the applicant's previous academic record, achievement on the Graduate Management Admission Test (GMAT) or Graduate Record Examinations (GRE), and past professional achievement and growth. Each applicant's credentials are evaluated on an individual basis. Specific requirements for admission and completion vary by program. All applicants must submit a completed graduate application, the application fee, official transcripts for all prior undergraduate and graduate institutions attended, and a current resume. M.B.A. candidates must also submit two completed recommendation forms as well as responses to essay questions. A personal statement is required of M.P.A. candidates. The GMAT/GRE is waived for applicants who already hold a master's degree.

Tuition and Fees

Tuition for the 2005–06 academic year was $600 per credit, plus a $30 registration fee per semester and a one-time matriculation fee of $30. A $50 nonrefundable application fee is required at application.

Financial Aid

Marist College offers merit-based and need-based financial programs to assist students in meeting the cost of their graduate education. To be eligible, a student must be matriculated in a graduate program and maintain satisfactory academic progress each semester. Awards are made without reference to racial or ethnic origin, sex, age, religion, marital status, or disability. The process of applying for aid should begin in early summer for fall admittance and mid-fall for spring admittance.

Applying

Students wishing to pursue their M.B.A. or M.P.A. online should follow the same procedures as campus-based graduate students. All admissions documents should be sent directly to the Office of Graduate Admissions.

CONTACT

Graduate Admissions
School of Graduate and Continuing Education
Marist College
North Road
Poughkeepsie, New York 12601-1387
Phone: 845-575-3800
888-877-7900 (toll-free)
Fax: 845-575-3166
E-mail: graduate@marist.edu
Web site: http://www.marist.edu/management

MONTANA STATE UNIVERSITY-BILLINGS

MSU–B Online Program

Billings, Montana

Established in 1927, Montana State University-Billings provides excellent instructional and learning opportunities in the arts and sciences as well as in its professional programs in business, technology, human services, rehabilitation, and education. MSU-Billings is accredited by the Northwest Association of Schools and Colleges, and its various degree programs, including teacher education, are accredited by other individual organizations. The University offers a wide variety of preprofessional and certification programs and awards degrees at the associate, bachelor's, and master's levels to more than 4,000 students annually. For more information on Montana State University-Billings, prospective students should visit the University Web site.

Distance Learning Program

Through the Montana State University-Billings (MSU-B) Online University, established in 1998, MSU-Billings is pleased to offer students an opportunity to take college courses via the Internet as a way of overcoming barriers of time and place. The program ensures that students can achieve their personal, professional, and academic goals while not having to sacrifice the other things that are important in their lives. The program currently offers more than 130 individual online courses, including fifteen fully online degree programs, with more than 9,000 annual student enrollments.

Delivery Media

All MSU-B online classes are delivered entirely via the Internet, using the sophisticated eCollege online course delivery system. This system provides for complete course content hosting whereby all readings, assignments, multimedia tutorials, audio and video streaming media, and instructional documents are provided online. In addition to hosting course content, the delivery system provides access to a variety of cutting-edge online interaction tools, including centralized e-mail, Internet and course search tools, chat rooms, and threaded discussions, in addition to an online journal, calendar, Webliography, document sharing, exam manager, and gradebook features. Minimal hardware, software, and Internet connectivity requirements exist for all online classes.

Programs of Study

The MSU-Billings Online University currently offers fifteen fully online degree programs.

Online bachelor's degree programs are the Bachelor of Applied Science (B.A.S.), Bachelor of Arts (B.A.) in communication-mass communications, B.A. in communication-organizational communications, Bachelor of Science in Business Administration (B.S.B.A.), Bachelor of Science (B.S.) in education (*on-site requirements), Bachelor of Science (B.S.) in public relations, Bachelor of Science in Health Administration (B.S.H.A.) (*on-site enrichment available), and the Bachelor of Science in Liberal Studies (B.S.L.S.).

B.S.L.S. concentrations are available in health administration and organizational communication, health administration and public relations, management and mass communications, management and organizational communication, management and public relations, mass communications and public relations, organizational communications and accounting technology, organizational communications and human resource management, and organizational communication and public relations.

Online Associate of Applied Science (A.A.S.) and Associate of Science (A.S.) degree programs include Accounting Technology (A.A.S.), General Studies, Human Resource Management-General Applied Emphasis (A.S.), and Human Resource Management-College of Business Articulated Emphasis (A.S.).

Online graduate programs offered are Education-Interdisciplinary Studies (*on-site requirements), Post-Baccalaureate: Teacher Certification (*on-site requirements), Master of Health Administration (M.H.A.) (*on-site enrichment available), and Master of Science in Public Relations.

The B.S.L.S. degree completion program uses the same curriculum as the full four-year B.S.L.S. degree, but it allows students to transfer or substitute prior academic course work into the program while completing the thematic concentration. To complete the B.S.L.S. degree or the B.S.L.S. degree completion program, individuals must earn a minimum of 120 credits with a cumulative grade point average of 2.0 or better. In addition, all students must satisfy the general education requirements at MSU-Billings. MSU-Billings accepts transfer students with completed A.A. or A.S. degrees from other institutions as having fulfilled their MSU-Billings general education requirements, provided the A.A. or A.S. is comparable in total credit hours and content to the MSU-Billings general education requirements. Students should consult with an academic adviser for an evaluation of transfer credits. Students must complete a minimum of 30 credits through MSU-Billings.

The B.A. in communication degree program shares many of the same requirements as the B.S.L.S. degree program, but it allows students to complete a major core of courses in organizational communication, mass communication, or public relations. The degree is designed to educate students entering the fields of business and social service as managers, public relations personnel, trainers, human resource officers, and corporate communication staff members. The degree also provides students with an excellent preparation for graduate study in communication or law.

For more information on any of the online courses and degree programs, prospective students should visit the MSU–B Online University Web site at http://www.msubonline.org.

Special Programs

MSU–Billings offers individuals who have already earned an associate degree an opportunity to complete an interdisciplinary bachelor's degree through the new Health Career Pathways 2+2 Online Degree Completion Programs.

The Bachelor of Science in Liberal Studies degree in health-care management and in public relations and the Bachelor of Applied Science degree in health-care administration are fully online degree-completion programs that have been strategically designed to prepare graduates for success in leadership roles in health-care management, administration, and public relations. Some of the unique features of these programs include:

2+2 Transferability: Students seamlessly transfer after graduating from their two-year college to complete their bachelor's degree from MSU–Billings.

Affordability: Students can receive up to $2000 in scholarship support for the 2+2 online degree completion, and they may also qualify for federal financial aid through this unique program.

e-Learning: Students enjoy the freedom, flexibility, comfort, and convenience of e-Learning—with more time for work and family while completing the bachelor's degree entirely online through MSU–Billings' Online University.

Adult Learning Format: By enrolling in 6 credits per term in consecutive nine-week terms, students can complete their bachelor's degree within two years with only a part-time course workload.

Student Services

The MSU–B Online University provides online students with access to all student services offered to MSU–Billings on-site students, including admissions, degree planning and advising, financial aid, ordering books and supplies, fee payment, library, 24-hour HelpDesk technical support, and a number of other student support services. In addition, all students enrolling in an online class receive access to an online orientation course that is designed to help students learn how to use the course delivery system and to maximize their success and satisfaction in online learning.

Faculty

Most of the 120 faculty members who teach classes online for the MSU–B Online University are also full-time faculty members of Montana State University–Billings. In addition to teaching their online classes, these faculty members teach equivalent courses in traditional on-site classes. Eighty-six percent of the University's faculty members hold the highest degrees in their fields.

Admission

The requirements for admission to MSU–B are the same as those for individuals taking classes on-site. Online students should apply for admission and register for online courses through the MSU–B Online University Web site at http://www.msubonline.org.

Tuition and Fees

Tuition and fees for online classes are the same as for taking classes on-site, with an additional $40-per-credit nonrefundable fee that is assessed for all Internet courses. The exact rate of tuition and fees depends upon the number of credits taken and whether the student is a resident or nonresident of Montana. For a current schedule of tuition and fees, prospective students should visit the MSU–B Online University Web site at http://www.msubonline.org.

Financial Aid

Financial aid is awarded to more than 60 percent of the University population—including students taking courses online—in the form of grants, scholarships, tuition waivers, employment, and loans. For more information or to apply for financial aid, prospective students should visit the MSU–B Online University Web site at http://www.msubonline.org.

Applying

All students wishing to enroll in MSU–B Online courses or degree programs should do so by submitting an online application and registration form accessible from the MSU–Billings Online University Web site at http://www.msubonline.org.

CONTACT

Admissions Counselor
New Student Services
McMullen 101
Montana State University–Billings
1500 University Drive
Billings, Montana 59101
Phone: 406-896-5911
800-708-0068 Ext. 5911 (toll-free)
Fax: 406-657-2302
E-mail: inquiry@msubonline.org
Web site: http://www.msubonline.org
http://www.msubillings.edu

NAROPA UNIVERSITY

Boulder, Colorado

Naropa University is a private, nonprofit, nonsectarian, liberal arts institution dedicated to advancing contemplative education. This approach to learning integrates the best of Eastern and Western educational traditions, helping students know themselves more deeply and engage constructively with others. Accredited by the North Central Association of Colleges and Schools, the University comprises a four-year undergraduate college and graduate programs in the arts, education, environmental leadership, psychology, and religious studies, as well as study-abroad programs in Sikkim, North India, and Prague, Czech Republic.

Distance Learning Program

In addition to its many in-residence programs, Naropa offers four low-residency graduate degree programs: M.A. in contemplative education, M.A. in transpersonal psychology (MATP), M.A. in transpersonal psychology with a concentration in ecopsychology, and an M.F.A. in creative writing.

Delivery Media

Courses are offered from the heart of Naropa University's liberal arts curriculum. They are taught by experienced Naropa faculty members and translated and refined for delivery through state-of-the-art Internet technology. Naropa utilizes the latest interactive Internet technologies, with private, password-secure Web pages for the exclusive use of the students and instructors of each class. Communication tools include audio lectures, multimedia, chat rooms, threaded discussion groups, private online journals, written lectures, local assignments, and group projects in a dynamic online learning community. Enrolled students have access to 24/7 technical support.

Programs of Study

The Master of Arts in contemplative education is a two-year, professional-development degree for practicing teachers from all levels of instruction and for others interested in a nonsectarian, contemplative approach to teaching and learning. This low-residency, 36-credit degree program joins together the wisdom and skillful means of Eastern meditative traditions with Western holistic educational methods and insights. Based on the principles and practices of mindfulness and awareness primarily from Tibetan contemplative traditions, the curriculum offers a path of personal nourishment and effective pedagogy. The program begins in the summer with a three-week residential program, which is followed by two online courses in each of the fall and spring semesters. Online semesters apply contemplative approaches to each student's classroom, as well as extend academic studies of spiritual approaches to teaching, learning, and human emotional development. The second year repeats this sequence, except the Thesis Seminar is the only spring online course. The program is completed during the third summer conference with the thesis presentation. Summer retreats are typically held from late-June to mid-July in Colorado and focus on the contemplative transformation of the teacher. For further information, students should contact Richard Brown, Chair of the Contemplative Education Department (phone: 303-545-4765; e-mail: rbrown@naropa.edu.)

The low-residency Master of Arts in transpersonal psychology (MATP) is a two-year, 36-credit program that integrates intellectual rigor, contemplative practice, personal development, and applications of transpersonal psychology. The curriculum includes required courses on foundations, theories and applications of transpersonal psychology, and meditation practice. Two 1-week summer intensives on the campus provide community building and exploration of transpersonal practices and issues. The MATP program does not result in a clinical degree. Those who already have professional clinical or counseling training and credentials may use this degree to expand their understanding and practice. Prospective students should contact John Davis, the Director of the Master of Arts program in transpersonal psychology (phone: 303-245-4654; e-mail: jdavis@naropa.edu).

The Master of Arts in transpersonal psychology with a concentration in ecopsychology integrates psychology and ecology in the study of human/nature relationships. At Naropa University, contemplative practice and transpersonal psychology provide a foundation for this integration, and the result is a unique contemplative and transpersonal orientation. Following the general format of the MATP program, the low-residency ecopsychology program is a two-year, 38-credit program that begins in the summer. Students also attend a three-day intensive course in Boulder each winter. Course work integrates theory, experience, and contemplative practice in the study of ecopsychology, ecology, transpersonal psychology, and meditative practices. The ecopsychology concentration does not result in a clinical degree. Additional information is available from Jed Swift, the Director of the ecopsychology program (phone: 303-245-4837 or 614-921-1997; e-mail: jdavis@naropa.edu).

The Master of Fine Arts in creative writing is a low-residency, 49-credit degree program. Courses are taken online during the regular academic year, and 16 credit hours of the Summer Writing Program (spread out over two or three summers) are completed at Naropa University's Boulder campus. The curriculum balances online writing workshops and literature seminars. This reflects the department's conviction that creative writing, reading, and critical analysis must all be involved in a writer's growth. The contact person for the program is Junior Burke, Chair of the Department of Writing and Poetics and the Director of the M.F.A. in creative writing program (phone: 303-245-4820; e-mail: jrburke@naropa.edu).

Faculty

The Naropa University faculty is distinguished by a wealth of experience in the professional, artistic, and scholastic applications of their disciplines. In addition to the outstanding core faculty, an international community of scholars and artists is consistently drawn to Naropa because of its strong vision and leadership in education. The average class size is 13, and Naropa's student-teacher ratio is 12:1.

Admission

When making admissions decisions, Naropa considers inquisitiveness and engagement with the world as well as previous academic achievement. A student's statement of interest, interview, letters of recommendation, and supplemental application materials play important roles in the admissions process. GRE scores are not required.

Tuition and Fees

Beginning summer 2006, graduate tuition is $646 per credit hour, plus a registration fee ($120 for summer, $250 for fall, $250 for spring). In addition, technology fees are: 1 credit, $60; 1.5 credits, $75; 2 credits, $90; 2.5 credits, $105; 3 credits, $120; 4 credits, $150; and 5 credits, $180.

Financial Aid

Naropa University makes every attempt to assist students who do not have the financial resources to accomplish their educational objectives. Naropa offers institutional grants and scholarships, as well as all types of federal student aid, including subsidized and unsubsidized Federal Stafford Student Loans. Some financial aid for international students is available. Approximately 70 percent of Naropa's degree-seeking students receive financial assistance in the form of loans, student employment, scholarships, and grants. Naropa also offers Tuition Management Systems, which allows students to make monthly payments for tuition with no interest charges.

Applying

The suggested deadline for receiving completed applications for the summer and fall semesters is January 15, and for the spring semester, October 15. Any application received after the suggested deadline will be reviewed on a space-available basis.

CONTACT

Office of Admissions
Naropa University
2130 Arapahoe Avenue
Boulder, Colorado 80302
Phone: 303-546-3572
800-772-6951 (toll-free)
E-mail: admissions@naropa.edu
Web site: http:// www.naropa.edu

NEW JERSEY INSTITUTE OF TECHNOLOGY

Division of Continuing Professional Education eLearning—Extension Programs

Newark, New Jersey

Founded in 1881, New Jersey Institute of Technology (NJIT) is New Jersey's technological research university. An international leader in scientific and technological education, NJIT educates students to become frontrunners in the global marketplace. The university seeks students who are seriously committed to education and can bring energy, creativity, and a practical outlook to solving today's pressing problems. The degree programs are demanding, rewarding, and highly regarded by employers.

NJIT was designated America's "Tier 2" National Research University by U.S. News & World Report. *With more than 150 undergraduate and graduate courses, threaded discussion groups, lectures via CD-ROM, streaming videos, and more, NJIT course work is made available to students regardless of their geographic location. For the adult professional in particular, NJIT courses provide the flexibility and convenience needed to fit in with work, family, and community responsibilities. NJIT's customer-service orientation allows each student to receive the personal attention that is required for successful completion of a degree program or certificate.*

Distance Learning Program

Via eLearning, NJIT conducts full undergraduate and graduate degree programs, graduate certificates, and individual college courses using today's home electronics to provide the college experience. By virtue of the academic quality, focus, and advanced delivery format, NJIT helps adult men and women cross one bridge to knowledge acquisition leading to gainful employment.

Delivery Media

Faculty/student eLearning communities are created on a computer platform (e.g., WebCT) that is then used by the professor to present course material in streaming-video clips, animations, and online quizzes and as a forum for discussions anytime and in real time with and among students. Students may also use CD-ROMs or internally produced, standalone videotapes as sources of additional course content. These discussions occur through NJIT e-mail or the WebCT conferencing system. NJIT eLearning recommends that students own a 486 DX100 personal computer with 16 MB of memory, a VGA monitor, a 500 MB hard disk, and a 56k kpbs modem. NJIT's eLearning programs also use interactive television, satellite video distribution, streaming video, and CD-ROMs.

Programs of Study

With NJIT eLearning, students can obtain a Bachelor of Arts in Information Systems (B.A.I.S.), a Bachelor of Science in Computer Science (B.S.C.S.), and a Bachelor of Science in Information Technology (B.S.I.T.). The B.A.I.S. is a 129-credit program that enables students to apply computing and information systems principles to real problems in business and industry. B.A.I.S. graduates enter careers in accounting, environmental science, finance, manufacturing science, and marketing. The B.S. C.S. is a 134-credit program that equips students with the theoretical and practical elements of computer science. The core curriculum consists of 51 credits in computer science, while elective credit must be earned in engineering, mathematics, and science. The B.S.I.T. is a 127-credit program. The interdisciplinary field of information technology addresses the integration, design, deployment, and management of computing and telecommunications, as well as the development of technology infrastructures in organizations.

NJIT eLearning also offers Master of Science degrees in Computer Science (M.S.C.S.), Information Systems (M.S.I. S.), Engineering Management (M.S.E. M.), and Professional and Technical Communication (M.S.P.T.C.). Students seeking advanced training in artificial intelligence; graphics and image processing; software engineering; systems analysis, simulation, and modeling; or other subdisciplines may wish to enter the 30-credit M.S.C.S. program. The 36-credit M.S.I.S. allows participants to specialize in information systems analysis and design, software development, and software engineering methodology. Individuals with suitable technical qualifications who intend to assume a managerial role in the public or private sector may consider enrolling in the 30-credit M.S.E.M. program. The 30-credit M.S.P.T.C. program is designed to prepare students for careers in the field of technical communication. Students develop skills in communication theory, proposal writing, editing, graphics, multimedia, hypermedia, online publishing, and scientific writing.

The Institute also offers a Master of Business Administration (M.B.A.) in management of technology.

Special Programs

NJIT awards graduate certificates in six disciplines in their entirety via eLearning: information systems design, information systems implementation, practice of technical communications, project management, and telecommunications networking. Each certificate, worth 12 graduate credits, can be used as a springboard to advanced-degree study at NJIT or elsewhere. Consisting of four courses, each certificate is in a topic area considered by today's corporations to be employable "hot tracks" through the year 2006.

Credit Options

Students may be awarded transfer credit at the time of admission for courses that were completed at other institutions and are equivalent to courses offered by NJIT. A minimum grade of C must be earned in a course in order to receive transfer credit.

Faculty

Ninety-eight percent of NJIT's full-time faculty members hold the terminal degree in their field.

Admission

Admission policies for the NJIT eLearning programs follow the same admission criteria as do traditionally delivered NJIT academic programs. In general, admission on a nonmatriculated basis to an undergraduate course requires possession of a high school diploma or General Educational Development (GED) certificate. Admission as a nonmatriculated student to a graduate course requires possession, at minimum, of an undergraduate degree from an accredited college or university with a grade point average that meets NJIT academic department standards for regular admission as a Master of Science degree candidate. In general, an acceptable grade point average is no lower than 2.8 on a 4.0 scale.

Tuition and Fees

Undergraduate tuition is $300 per credit for New Jersey residents and $587 per credit for nonresidents. Graduate tuition is $561 per credit for New Jersey residents and $772 per credit for nonresidents. Graduate certificate students pay in-state tuition, regardless of location. The total for one eLearning course including fees is $1290 for an undergraduate course and $2092 for a graduate course. Tuition and fees are subject to change. For current tuition and fees, students should visit http://www.njit.edu/old/Registrar/.

Financial Aid

NJIT's Office of Financial Aid provides counseling and administers loans, scholarships, and grants to qualified students. Federal and state programs and private, industrial, and university resources are utilized to support the university's financial aid programs. For more information, students should visit http://www.njit.edu/old/finaid/page4.php.

Applying

Applications procedures vary depending on the program of enrollment and the applicant's status. First-time non-degree-seeking and graduate certificate students use the nonmatriculated application; continuing non-degree-seeking and graduate certificate students need only register for courses. For more information on the nonmatriculated process and application, students should visit http://cpe.njit.edu/GradCert/application.htm. Students may apply on a nonmatriculated basis by mail, by fax, or online.

Degree-seeking students and non-degree-seeking students with more than 9 graduate or 15 undergraduate credits should use the matriculated application. For the matriculated process and application, students should visit http://www.njit.edu/Admissions/. To apply for admission on a matriculated basis, students should contact the Office of Admissions at 973-596-3300 or 800-925-6548 (toll-free) to request a degree application or use the online matriculated application form on the admissions Web site.

CONTACT

Division of Continuing Professional Education
New Jersey Institute of Technology
University Heights, New Jersey 07102-1982
Phone: 973-596-3061
Fax: 973-596-3203
Web site: http://cpe.njit.edu

NORTHERN ARIZONA UNIVERSITY

Distance Learning

Flagstaff, Arizona

Established in 1899, Northern Arizona University (NAU) has maintained a tradition of excellence over the past century, through its commitment to providing quality academic programs, a wide range of majors, personalized services, and close faculty-student interaction. With thirty campus locations throughout Arizona and a growing number of online programs, NAU serves approximately 19,000 students from all fifty states and sixty-three countries. An integral part of NAU's mission, distance learning is recognized nationally and internationally for its outstanding programs in education, the health professions, the hospitality professions, forestry management, and more. Long-standing community partnerships, dedicated faculty and staff members, continued new-program development to meet market demand, powerful technology, and a philosophy of "expand on demand" create a unique, progressive learning environment.

Distance Learning Program

With more than twenty-five years of experience, NAU offers a growing number of programs in a range of venues, including Web-based learning opportunities. Convenient and comprehensive, this format provides students greater flexibility and options for earning a degree from an accredited university.

Delivery Media

NAU offers a variety of formats for distance learning students that includes the latest technological advances. Through NAU, video-conferencing connects rural and urban areas alike. DISH network, satellite broadcasting, and high-speed Internet access allow NAU to deploy the latest technology to deliver higher-education opportunities across traditional social and geographic boundaries. All delivery methods allow the instructors and students to interact via e-mail or online chat rooms. Textbooks and materials are available through the NAU bookstore.

Programs of Study

Dedicated to providing students with a high-quality education, NAU offers the same accredited degree via distance learning technology as the degree awarded on the NAU campus, holding all students and faculty members to the same standards of excellence. NAU currently offers the following programs: the Bachelor of Arts in Liberal Studies (B.A.I.L.S.) degree, with emphases in arts and letters, enterprise in society, parks and recreation management, and public agency service; the Bachelor of Applied Science (B.A.S.) degree in computer technology, early childhood education, health promotion, and public agency service; the Bachelor of Science (B.S.) degree in health promotion, hotel and restaurant management, and parks and recreation management; the Bachelor of Science in Education (B.S.Ed.) degree in career and technical education; the Bachelor of Science in Dental Hygiene (B.S.D.H.) degree-completion program; the Bachelor of Science in Nursing (B.S.N.) degree, an RN to B.S.N. program; the Master of Administration (M.Admin.) degree; the Master of Arts (M.A.) degree in applied communication; the Master of Arts in Teaching (M.A.T.) degree in mathematics; the Master of Education (M.Ed.) degree in career and technical education, educational technology, and elementary education; the Master of Engineering (M.Eng.) degree; endorsements in English as a second language, middle school, and reading; and certificates in educational technology, international tourism management, parks and recreation management, professional writing, public management, and restaurant management. Each of these programs of study was developed based on student needs.

Special Programs

A member of the Arizona Regents University, NAU works in conjunction with Arizona State University and the University of Arizona to offer students access to courses and degrees not offered by NAU. Students select a home campus through which they receive all services, including registration. Students may earn credit from all three institutions, which transfers to degree programs at any one of the three universities.

Western Governors University (WGU) is an online university offering Web-based classes from a variety of educational institutions in sixteen states, Guam, and Canada. NAU is a provider of classes for WGU. Students enrolled in these classes are considered non-degree-seeking for NAU purposes, though they may be earning a degree from WGU. Students pay 1½ times in-state tuition.

Student Services

NAU distance learning students are provided electronic access to academic records, enrollment, online research through Cline Library, and other online student services. Academic advising is available to distance students either online or through NAU's toll-free number. Students who do not have a computer and live in Arizona can complete their classes at one of the twenty-five NAU statewide computer labs.

Credit Options

To be eligible for financial aid, students must be admitted to a degree or certification program. Classes may be taken for audit or professional development credit; however, space may be limited due to for-credit student demand. Most classes are evaluated with a letter grade, but some classes are offered on a pass-fail basis. These classes are outlined in the current NAU undergraduate and graduate catalogs.

Faculty

All distance learning instructors are faculty members, 80 percent of whom hold a doctorate or other terminal degree in their field. All faculty members have continued involvement within their fields of expertise.

Admission

NAU has a rolling admissions policy.

Tuition and Fees

Nonresident students taking only Web or satellite courses are eligible for a special reduced tuition rate of 1½ times in-state tuition. The graduate degree- or certificate-seeking applicants pay a $50 admission fee. The non-degree-seeking or readmitting applicants pay a $25 admission fee. The undergraduate application fee is $25 for U.S. citizens and legal residents and $50 for international students. Some classes may have additional fees attached (students should see the online course catalog for those fees).

Financial Aid

NAU maintains an extensive financial assistance program. The amount of financial aid awarded to students is based upon their need as computed from the Free Application for Federal Student Aid (FAFSA). Students requiring financial aid or other benefits must comply with policies and deadlines.

Applying

Undergraduate applicants must provide transcripts from high school and all higher education institutions attended. Graduate applicants must hold a baccalaureate degree from an accredited institution and provide transcripts of college course work. Students should refer to the NAU catalog for specific program requirements.

CONTACT

Distance Learning
Northern Arizona University
P.O. Box 4117
Flagstaff, Arizona 86001-4117
Phone: 800-426-8315 (toll-free)
Fax: 928-523-1169
E-mail: distance.program@nau.edu
Web site: http://www.distance.nau.edu

NORTHWESTERN COLLEGE

Center for Distance Education

St. Paul, Minnesota

Northwestern College, which was founded in 1902, is an independent, Christian four-year college. It is accredited by the North Central Association of Colleges and Schools. It first offered distance learning courses in 1994. In 2003-04, the College offered forty-one courses at a distance and had almost 2,000 new distance enrollments.

Distance Learning Program

The Center for Distance Education (CDE) at Northwestern College is at the forefront of delivering high-quality, Christ-centered education in a flexible and convenient format. More than a correspondence school, the center utilizes the latest strategies in adult education and user-friendly technology to bring college courses to students. Since 1994, the CDE has enrolled more than 3,300 students and delivered more than 8,000 courses to students all over the world. With more than forty-five courses to choose from, students can take courses in Bible, English, history, math, science, speech, music, and physical fitness.

Delivery Media

The Center for Distance Education makes use of the most convenient delivery methods possible. Course media is determined by the content of the course but usually consists of printed study guides, video lectures, CD-ROMs, and textbooks. Some courses also require a computer with Internet access. Course work is submitted via postal mail or through the Internet. All courses host a Blackboard® course site that is used for interaction between students and instructors, although each course varies in the level of participation.

Programs of Study

The Center for Distance Education seeks to meet the educational needs of adult learners by offering Christ-centered curriculum. The center currently offers a Certificate of Bible, the INSIGHT program, a Bachelor of Arts in Global Studies, and dual-enrollment options for high school students.

The Certificate of Bible prepares students for Christian ministry through the completion of 30 credits. The program provides in-depth training in Bible study and develops credentials for ministry-related endeavors. All credits earned in the certificate program may be applied to a degree program at Northwestern.

The Associate in Arts and Bible is designed to prepare the graduate for transfer to an upper-level degree program at Northwestern or another institution. The degree is granted upon completion of 60 credits. Students should contact the Center for Distance Education for details. Students should also check the course requirements of the program and school where further study is planned.

The INSIGHT program is an on-site study in Pasadena, California, and Minneapolis, Minnesota, that is designed to provide first-year students with a comprehensive Christian worldview as a foundation for the major they eventually choose. The curriculum consists of four modules to be taken consecutively over the course of one year. Each INSIGHT module follows the unfolding of God's work through human developments, revealing His redemptive plan and consequently His glory. Each module is worth 8 semester credits, for a total of 32 lower-division college credits.

The Bachelor of Arts in Global Studies is designed for students who have previously completed two years of postsecondary course work and are serious about full-time ministry. The major is targeted at those preparing for or currently involved in missions endeavors. However, any Christian, whether at home or abroad, who desires to more fully understand God's evangelistic purposes benefits from this program.

Special Programs

The Post Secondary Enrollment Option (PSEO) is a program that is open to high school juniors and seniors who are public-, private-, or home-schooled and who are residents of the state of Minnesota. This program allows high school students to take courses through the Center for Distance Education and earn credit that applies to both high school and college. Credits earned under this program are applicable to degree programs at Northwestern or other institutions. The state of Minnesota finances the program.

The NextStep program offers college courses to qualified high school juniors and seniors anywhere. It is meant to be a stepping stone to their college career. These courses are offered at a discounted rate, and course materials are provided on a loan basis.

Student Services

The Center for Distance Education helps students achieve their educational goals without feeling like a number in someone's system. From enrollment through course completion, Student Services staff members provide caring, proactive service. The CDE processes course assignments, helps find mentors and exam proctors, and helps maintain contact with faculty members.

Northwestern College's Bernsten Library aids distance learners with research and resource acquisition for projects and papers. The CDE Web site and Course Management System contain independent-study tools and helpful resources to facilitate learning.

Free unofficial transfer evaluations are offered to students who are interested in a degree program. Students must provide copies of transcripts or grade reports showing previous college work. These documents are reviewed by the CDE Registrar, entered on a curriculum chart, and returned to the student. Students have the chance to see how previous college work meets the CDE's requirements.

Credit Options

Some students may transfer credits from another institution or may earn credits through examinations, portfolio assessment, life experience, or military training.

Faculty

Distance education faculty members are credentialed professionals who are highly qualified in their academic disciplines. More than 30 faculty members teach distance education courses. Of this group, 19 have earned doctoral degrees. The faculty members at Northwestern College care about each student's spiritual, intellectual, and emotional development as well as their academic development.

Admission

To qualify for a certificate or degree program, students must meet the admission requirements of Northwestern College. Students should contact the Center for Distance Education for specific requirements. Students not seeking to earn credits toward a degree or a certificate at Northwestern are allowed to take up to 16 credits without formal admission to the College. PSEO and NextStep applicants must be at least 16 years old, have suitable scores on a state-recognized benchmark exam or a letter of recommendation from a high school official, and demonstrate competence in college-level work.

Tuition and Fees

There is a one-time, nonrefundable $25 fee at the time of registration ($50 for the Bachelor of Arts in Global Studies degree). Tuition is $220 per semester credit. There is a required fee of $75 for each course's materials. Students enrolled in the Certificate of Bible and Bachelor of Arts in Global Studies programs receive a 10 percent tuition discount. Other discounts apply to groups, senior citizens, and full- or part-time Christian workers.

Financial Aid

Admitted students who register for at least 6 credit hours for a degree program in one semester may be eligible for financial aid. Northwestern College cooperates with the U.S. Department of Veterans Affairs when eligible admitted students request VA benefits for distance education courses. The College also works with the Defense Activity for Non-Traditional Education Support (DANTES). Students should contact the CDE for more information.

Applying

Information can be obtained either at the CDE Web site or by contacting the Center for Distance Education. Students may register for distance education by mail or fax, online, or in person. To register, students should complete a registration form either online or by mail, pay the nonrefundable processing fee, and contact the CDE to begin the registration process.

CONTACT

Center for Distance Education
Northwestern College
3003 Snelling Avenue North
Saint Paul, Minnesota 55113
Phone: 800-308-5495 (toll-free)
Fax: 651-631-5133
E-mail: distance@nwc.edu
Web site: http://www.distance.nwc.edu

NORTHWESTERN
UNIVERSITY

NORTHWESTERN UNIVERSITY

Communication Systems Strategy and Management Program

Evanston, Illinois

Northwestern University is an ambitious institution, striving for a level of preeminence achieved by only a handful of institutions in the world. Innovative teaching and pioneering research come together in a highly collaborative environment that transcends traditional academic boundaries.

Founded in 1851, Northwestern University is a private institution located in Evanston, Illinois, on the pristine shores of Lake Michigan, just 12 miles north of Chicago. Northwestern University currently has 11,600 students enrolled in seven schools on its Evanston campus.

The University has 2,250 full-time faculty members, including Nobel and Pulitzer Prize winners, MacArthur Fellowship recipients, and members of numerous honorary and professional societies. Northwestern has graduated more than 160,000 students—alumni who became leaders in business, government, law, science, education, medicine, media, and the performing arts. Northwestern is recognized both nationally and internationally for the quality of its educational programs at all levels.

Distance Learning Program

The School of Communication offers its Communication Systems Strategy and Management Program (Master of Science in Communication degree) in a blended learning environment to a cohort group of 30 midlevel to senior-level managers. This two-year program provides the advanced skills and expertise to effectively close the technology disconnect that occurs between an organization's technical experts and its nontechnical executive decision makers.

The distributed learning component gives students a real-time classroom experience via videoconferencing, the ability to work and learn in group projects with other students over a distance, and an outstanding environment of collaborative learning as compared to other remote classroom programs.

Students enrolled as distance learners interact with Evanston-based instructors and students in real time. All students, on campus or remote, work together on team assignments that allow them to learn from interactions with students employed in different companies.

Delivery Media

Distance learners are invited, but not required, to attend three on-campus instructional meetings during each year. In the first year, students participate in a new-student orientation at the beginning of the fall term and two weekend meetings at the beginning of the winter and spring terms. In the second year, students participate in the fall orientation, a weekend meeting at the beginning of the winter term, and a weekend during the spring term for Final Presentations.

The remainder of the program is delivered synchronously via DSL or cable teleconferencing. Students take two courses at a time, meeting one full day per week on alternating Fridays and Saturdays for thirty weeks per year. Classes meet from 9:30 a.m. to 12:30 p.m. and from 2 to 5 p.m. central time. There is no summer school.

Recorded Web-casts of all lectures are available for student review. The program creates a 24/7 conference bridge for all participants. This feature permits all learners, regardless of where they reside, to create virtual working groups.

Program of Study

The Communication Systems Strategy and Management Program focuses on business and management expertise, much like an M.B.A., but with the addition of an effective foundation of study in technology and system principles.

As the most effective organizations optimally align IT strategies with company business objectives, this program addresses the ever-increasing demands placed on the investment, productivity, and performance of these technologies and systems, including the development of products and services in both the traditional economy and the continually evolving Internet economy.

All students take the same courses in a lockstep sequence, with no electives or independent studies.

Student Services

The University offers library services online 24 hours a day, seven days a week.

Credit Options

All credits must be earned in the Communication Systems Strategy and Management Program (equivalent to 48 credit hours). No transfer credits are accepted.

Faculty

The faculty is made up of world-class Northwestern University professors. They possess extensive hands-on work experience as consultants to business and industry as well as government and private institutions.

As the program is interdisciplinary, it draws on faculty members not only from the nationally renowned School of Communication but also from Northwestern's McCormick School of Engineering and Applied Science, Kellogg

School of Management, Medill School of Journalism, and Northwestern University Information Technology department.

Admission

Applicants should have a minimum of six years of professional experience, an undergraduate degree from an accredited college or university, three letters of recommendation, and proficient written and oral English skills. Interviews are strongly recommended. Having an engineering degree or technical background is not required. GRE or GMAT scores are not required.

Tuition and Fees

The all-inclusive fee for the three-term 2006–07 academic year is $29,009 ($9670 per term). The fee covers tuition, the orientation session, books, the latest equipment and software for learning via videoconferencing, hotel accommodations, and meals for on-site meetings. Distance learners provide their own laptop computers and transportation to and from on-site meetings.

Students take two 10-week courses or one 10-week course and two 5-week courses per year. Each ten-week course is equivalent to 4 credit hours. Each five-week course is equivalent to 2 credit hours.

Financial Aid

Financial assistance is available to eligible students in the form of Federal Stafford Student Loans or private loans.

Applying

Applicants can download application materials from the Web site at http://www.communication.northwestern.edu/mscstrategy or may request materials via the methods listed in the Contact section.

CONTACT

Donna Weirich, Director
Communication Systems Strategy and Management Program
Northwestern University
2240 Campus Drive
Evanston, Illinois 60208
Phone: 847-491-3848
Fax: 847-467-1036
E-mail: jfinn@northwestern.edu
Web site: http://www.communication.northwestern.edu/mscstrategy

NOVA SOUTHEASTERN UNIVERSITY

Graduate School of Computer and Information Sciences

Fort Lauderdale, Florida

A major force in educational innovation, the Graduate School of Computer and Information Sciences (GSCIS) provides educational programs of distinction to prepare students for leadership roles in its disciplines. Its strengths include a distinguished faculty, a cutting-edge curriculum, and flexible online formats for its five M.S. and five Ph.D. programs and for its graduate certificate program in information security. All programs enable working professionals to earn their degrees without interrupting their careers. Online master's degree programs require no campus attendance and are available to part-time or full-time students worldwide. A unique online doctoral program requires only four weekends or two weeklong campus visits each year. The school has online students living in every state in the United States and in more than twenty-five countries. Ranked by Forbes *magazine as one of the nation's top twenty cyber universities and listed in the Princeton Review's* The Best Distance Learning Graduate Schools, *the School currently offers more than 300 online classes annually. A leader in online graduate education, the School began offering online programs in 1983 and created the first electronic classroom in 1985.*

In addition to its regional accreditation by the Commission on Colleges of the Southern Association of Colleges and Schools, Nova Southeastern University (NSU) has been designated a National Center for Academic Excellence in Information Assurance Education by the U.S. National Security Agency and the Department of Homeland Security. Its curriculum in information security has been certified by the NSA for compliance with CNSS standards. Collaborative programs include DANTES, the U.S. Army's eArmyU initiative, and the Southern Regional Education Board's Electronic Campus. The school has a chapter of Upsilon Pi Epsilon (UPE), the International Honor Society for the Computing and Information Disciplines, and a student chapter of the Institute of Electrical and Electronic Engineers (IEEE), the largest in Florida.

Located on a beautiful 300-acre campus in Fort Lauderdale, Florida, NSU has more than 25,000 students and is the largest independent institution of higher education in the southeast United States. The eighth-largest private university in the United States, it awards associate, bachelor's, master's, educational specialist, doctoral, and first-professional degrees in more than 90 disciplines. It has a college of arts and sciences, as well as schools of medicine, dentistry, pharmacy, allied health, optometry, law, computer and information sciences, psychology, education, business and entrepreneurship, oceanography, and humanities and social sciences.

Distance Learning Program

All of the school's graduate programs are offered in distance learning formats. Online master's programs require no on-campus classroom attendance. Students may complete the M.S. degree in twelve to eighteen months. Doctoral programs use one of two formats: cluster or institute. Cluster students attend four cluster meetings per year, held quarterly over an extended weekend (Friday, Saturday, and half-day Sunday) at the University. Cluster terms start in September and March. Cluster weekends take place in September, December, March, and June. Institute students attend a weeklong institute twice a year at the University. Institutes are held in mid-January and mid-July at the start of each five-month term. Clusters and institutes bring together students and faculty members for participation in courses, workshops, and dissertation counseling. Doctoral courses also have an online component. Between meetings, students complete assignments, research papers, and projects and participate in a range of online activities.

Delivery Media

Online students use the Web to access course materials, announcements, e-mail, distance library services, the Electronic Library, and other information and for interaction with faculty and fellow students. Online, interactive learning methods are used throughout the instructional sequence based on the use of WebCT as a course management system. Online activities facilitate frequent student-to-faculty and student-to-student interaction. They are supported by threaded discussion boards, white boards, chat rooms, and e-mail. In addition, WebCT enables students to submit assignments online in multimedia formats and to receive their professor's reviews of assignments online in the same formats.

Programs of Study

The School offers distance programs leading to the M.S. in computer information systems (including an optional specialization in information security), computer science, computing technology in education, information security, and management information systems (including optional specializations in information security and e-commerce); the Ph.D. in computer information systems (including an optional concentration in information security), computer science, computing technology in education, information science, and information systems, (including an optional concentration in information security); the Ed.D. in computing technology in education, and a graduate certificate in information security. The School's M.S. students may apply for early admission into the doctoral program, which provides the opportunity to earn the Ph.D. or Ed.D. in a shorter time. The M.S. requires 36 credit hours (thesis optional). Terms are twelve weeks long, and there are four terms each year. To earn the M.S. in twelve months, the student must enroll in three courses each term. To complete the M.S. in eighteen months, the student must enroll in two courses each term. Master's terms start in September, January, April, and July. Doctoral programs require 64 credits, including eight 3-credit courses, four 4-credit projects, and the dissertation. It may be completed in three years. The Ph.D. in computer information systems and computer science are offered only in cluster format. Doctoral programs in computing technology in education, information science, and information systems are offered in cluster and institute formats. Students attend clusters or institutes during their first two years of the program while completing course work.

Special Programs

All of the School's programs are offered through the Southern Regional Education Board's Electronic Campus and the U.S. Army's eArmyU program.

Credit Options

Up to 6 graduate credits from a regionally accredited institution may be transferred to one of the master's degree program. Courses proposed for transfer must have received grades of at least B. Credit is not awarded for life or work experience.

Faculty

GSCIS has 20 full-time and 10 part-time faculty members. All faculty members teaching at the graduate level have doctoral degrees.

Admission

The master's applicant must have an appropriate undergraduate degree with a GPA of at least 2.5 and a GPA of at least 3.0 in an appropriate major. The doctoral applicant must have a master's degree with an appropriate graduate major and a graduate GPA of at least 3.25. Degrees must be from regionally accredited institutions. All applicants must submit a summary of professional experience or score report of the GRE. English proficiency is a requirement for admission.

Tuition and Fees

Tuition is $425 per credit for master's students; for doctoral students, tuition is $500 per credit hour for coursework and $450 per credit hour for the dissertation.

Financial Aid

To qualify for financial assistance, a student must be admitted, must be a U.S. citizen or an eligible permanent resident, and must plan on registering for a minimum of 6 credit hours per term. A prospective student who requires financial assistance should apply for it while still a candidate for admission. For financial assistance information or application forms, students should call 800-806-3680 (toll-free).

Applying

Admission decisions are made on a rolling basis. To ensure evaluation for the desired starting term, reviewable applications must be received at least one month prior to the start of that term. The application fee is $50. Late applications that cannot be processed in time for the desired starting term are considered for the next term. Applicants may be granted provisional admission status pending completion of the application process. Admission forms, brochures, and the graduate catalog may be downloaded from the School's Web site. Master's terms start in September, January, April, and July. Doctoral cluster terms start in September and March. Doctoral institute terms start in January and July.

CONTACT

Graduate School of Computer and Information Sciences
Nova Southeastern University
Carl DeSantis Building, Fourth Floor
3301 College Avenue
Fort Lauderdale, Florida 33314-9918
Phone: 954-262-2000
800-986-2247 (toll-free)
E-mail: scisinfo@nova.edu
Web site: http://www.scis.nova.edu

OSU
Oregon State
UNIVERSITY
Extended Campus

OREGON STATE UNIVERSITY

Extended Campus

Corvallis, Oregon

Founded in 1868 and accredited by the Northwest Commission on Colleges and Universities, Oregon State University (OSU) is one of a select number of schools nationwide to receive the Carnegie Foundation's highest rating for education and research. A land-grant, sea-grant, and space-grant university, Oregon State serves the state of Oregon, the nation, and the world through its teaching, research, and outreach efforts. Today, OSU is the home of 19,236 students who are pursuing their degrees in one of more than 200 undergraduate and graduate academic degree programs. The American Productivity and Quality Center recently named Oregon State a top university for providing electronic services to students.

Distance Learning Program

During fall term 2005, more than 2,300 individuals throughout Oregon and the world were enrolled in Oregon State University courses off campus. Each year, through OSU Extended Campus (Ecampus), students have access to more than 400 distance and online courses in more than sixty subjects. Subject areas are as diverse as education, fisheries and wildlife, history, math, chemistry, and psychology. Courses are designed as part of bachelor's completion programs, undergraduate minors, certificate programs, and some graduate-level degrees and course work.

Delivery Media

Oregon State offers the majority of its distance courses via the Web, DVDs, videotapes, and streaming media. Courses often entail a combination of delivery methods, such as a video course with class interaction through an electronic listserv or Web site. Students communicate with instructors and administrative staff members via e-mail, phone, fax, or regular mail. Certain courses and programs are also delivered through face-to-face instruction or interactive television broadcasting (ITV) at statewide locations.

Programs of Study

Oregon State University is one of a handful of universities nationwide pioneering the field of online education. The majority of the more than 400 distance courses offered through Ecampus each year are delivered partially or entirely on the Web. The remainder of distance courses involve some online requirement, such as e-mail communication with faculty members or discussion board communication with peers.

Degree partnership programs are available through many Oregon community colleges; however, many students work with Ecampus Student Services staff to utilize past college experiences and to plan individual programs. Students can complete their degree from anywhere in the world by taking upper-division course work through OSU Extended Campus. Students may select from a Bachelor of Arts/Bachelor of Science (B.A./B.S.) in liberal studies (a preprofessional elementary education option is available statewide), a B.S. in environmental sciences, a B.S. in general agriculture, and a B.S. in natural resources. Students in bachelor's programs must accumulate a minimum of 180 quarter credit hours to graduate.

Undergraduate minors in anthropology, environmental sciences, fisheries and wildlife, natural resources, and political science are available worldwide. Minors usually include at least 27 quarter credit hours of study and can be pursued as part of a bachelor's program or added to a transcript after graduation.

OSU Ecampus also offers online graduate degrees in education, health physics, and radiation health physics. A graduate certificate in health management and policy is also offered, with four online courses and two weekend courses offered on-site at hospitals in Oregon. A professional certificate in geographic information science is also available online.

Special Programs

Web-based graduate-level course work in education is available through Ecampus for teachers, trainers, and other professional educators who wish to pursue an advanced degree or simply gain skills in advanced teaching strategies or teaching course work online. The School of Education offers an on-site/online program for those seeking to earn their Oregon Continuing Teaching License. The Master of Arts in Teaching (M.A.T.) in early childhood/elementary education and the ESOL bilingual endorsement programs are also delivered online and on-site. In these programs, students may enroll in Web courses and related practicums at a rate based on their individual needs, tailoring their education to meet both time and financial constraints. Students should visit the program's Web site for specific contact information on these and other graduate-level programs.

OSU's Professional Programs in Ecampus operates as an outreach to corporations, public agencies, organizations, and professionals seeking to upgrade their skill level and increase their employability and productivity. Professional Programs offers a variety of noncredit programs and individualized contract training in areas such as business, human resources management, and health-care leadership. Professional Programs also offers online short skill-building courses that fit the busy adult's lifestyle and pocketbook.

OSU Extended Campus offers OSU K–12 Online, a top-quality high school curriculum that is available to home-schooled students or high school students seeking courses that may not be available through their district. These online courses can be taken for elective credit and/or high school graduation completion.

Student Services

Oregon State makes it a priority to provide excellent student services to distance learners via e-mail, a toll-free phone number, and a comprehensive Web site that includes live chat, online forums, and a searchable knowledge base. Students have access to online library services, a toll-free hotline for computer consulting, online writing support, step-by-step assistance with procedures, and an online schedule of classes. Students can subscribe to *OSU E-News,* a free electronic newsletter that provides timely course and program information, student and faculty member profiles, and technical tips.

Credit Options

All credits earned through OSU distance or online education are recorded identically on the Oregon State University transcript as courses that were taken on campus. Each course falls under the same accreditation ratings of the individual department from which it originates. Transfer students enrolled in academic programs must have previous credits evaluated by an OSU adviser to ensure that program requirements are met. Forty-five of the last 75 credit hours for bachelor's completion programs must be from Oregon State University.

Faculty

Oregon State has more than 2,700 faculty members, with nearly 1,100 in the tenure system. Eighty-five percent of faculty members in professorial ranks have doctoral degrees. OSU distance education faculty members must adhere to the same quality standards as any faculty member teaching on campus.

Admission

Students taking distance or online courses to meet OSU degree requirements must be admitted to the University through the regular admission process and must meet the requirements for admission. Nondegree enrollment requires no formal admission and can be attained by contacting the Office of Admissions. For more information on regular or nondegree admission, students can visit the Office of Admissions Web site at http://oregonstate.edu/admissions.

Tuition and Fees

Tuition for undergraduate distance degree courses is $196 per quarter credit hour for most courses. Graduate-level courses are generally $381 per quarter credit, depending upon the program. Additional fees may be assessed for tape rental or other course materials. Students may check the Ecampus Web site for additional information.

Financial Aid

Distance learners are eligible for financial aid programs according to the same rules as on-campus students. Generally, to be considered, a student must be taking at least 6 quarter hours. Some scholarships are open to part-time distance learning students. Students can consult specific information on the Web site at http://oregonstate.edu/admin/finaid.

Applying

Online or distance learners seeking an OSU degree should apply through the regular application process. Some of the distance programs at the graduate level are cohort based and require admission prior to fall quarter. The undergraduate distance degree programs accept students year-round. It is recommended that students seek initial advising prior to the application process. Registration for individual courses generally requires no application other than to contact the registrar for admission as a nondegree or part-time student.

CONTACT

OSU Extended Campus
Attention: Student Services Center
4943 The Valley Library
Oregon State University
Corvallis, Oregon 97331-4504
Phone: 541-737-9204
800-667-1465 (toll-free)
Fax: 541-737-2734
E-mail: ecampus@oregonstate.edu
Web site: http://ecampus.oregonstate.edu

PACIFIC GRADUATE SCHOOL OF PSYCHOLOGY

Master of Science in Psychology

Palo Alto, California

Founded in 1975, the Pacific Graduate School of Psychology (PGSP) is committed to unifying the research-oriented scientific model with direct service-oriented training. PGSP is a diverse learning community, dedicated to the search for knowledge and its dissemination, forming a community of highly talented faculty members and graduate students working side by side to bring scientific rigor and theoretical knowledge to the analysis and practice of clinical psychology. A private institution, PGSP also offers the Ph.D. and Psy.D. in clinical psychology. The Ph.D. program has been APA-accredited since 1988. The Western Association of Schools and Colleges accredits PGSP's Master of Science (M.S.) in psychology distance-learning program.

Distance Learning Program

The M.S. in psychology distance-learning program has had participants from all over the United States as well as from Canada, Europe, Asia, Africa, and South America. About 30 students participated in the program in 2005–06. Evidence indicates that those enrolled in the distance-learning degree program perform as well as those taking on-campus courses.

Delivery Media

The program uses a number of techniques to accomplish its educational goals and partners with the educational technology company Docutek, which hosts the course materials. Many classes offer Microsoft PowerPoint presentations complete with lecture notes. Assigned readings are available on the Web in .PDF format, which students can easily read using the free Adobe Acrobat software. Some classes use threaded discussion groups, among other methods, to help students to discuss course material and ask questions. Students must have access to a computer as well as an Internet connection. High-speed Internet access, such as DSL or a cable modem, is strongly recommended.

Programs of Study

Classes begin in September and end in mid-June; students cannot enter the program once classes have started. The program consists of 39 units of course work, with no thesis requirement. Courses are taken over a two-year period during the regular academic year, and there are no summer classes. During most quarters, students take no more than two classes at a time. With one exception, most courses offered are the same as those taken by first-year graduate students enrolled in PGSP's residential Ph.D. program. Courses do not contain a clinical component. Student performance can be assessed through papers, exams, or both, depending on the instructor and the course. Tests are proctored by independent third parties. At the end of each course, students evaluate both the class and the instructor.

Special Programs

The distance-learning program was developed to provide students with the opportunity to demonstrate their ability to handle Ph.D.-level work at PGSP. Those who do well can transfer into the on-campus Ph.D. program. The doctoral program trains psychologists whose work is firmly grounded in theory and is informed by current research, who can function effectively as independent practitioners, and who can critically evaluate and perform research that contributes to the academic discipline of scientific psychology.

Students are strongly encouraged to attend an on-campus two-day orientation in September. This orientation gives students a chance to meet members of the faculty and administration, to be trained in the use of the Web-based library resources, and to spend some time getting to know each other. PGSP reimburses student attendees for one-half the cost of hotel accommodations and travel expenses so that everyone in the class can attend.

Student Services

Some classes use chat rooms to facilitate student-student and student-instructor communication. Chat times vary and instructors try to accommodate students from around the world.

Credit Options

Up to 6 units of prior graduate work that is not more than five years old can be transferred into the program. Students must submit a course description and supporting documentation. Credit is granted on a case-by-case basis.

Faculty

The PGSP faculty includes 15 full-time and approximately 12 part-time research and clinical teaching professors, drawn from the Bay Area's rich resource pool of active researchers and practitioners from a range of specializations. The faculty members are actively engaged in clinical practice and research; they provide the enthusiasm, knowledge, and insights of those actively working to find answers to central questions in the field of psychology. For the most part, full-time PGSP faculty members teach the distance-learning curriculum.

Admission

Applicants must have graduated from an accredited undergraduate institution. An applicant must submit the completed application, the $50 application fee, all official transcripts, three letters of reference, and an essay that outlines the goals and reasons for pursuing the Master of Science in psychology. For students coming from a nonpsychology background, there are four prerequisite courses that must be completed: developmental psychology, physiological psychology, personality or abnormal psychology, and statistics.

Tuition and Fees

In the 2005–06, academic year, tuition was $768 per unit, with 21 units in the first year. The technology fee is $257 per quarter. Tuition and fees totaled $16,899 for first-year students.

Financial Aid

Financial assistance is available to eligible PGSP students in the form of grants, fellowships, scholarships, loans (repayable with interest), and on-campus employment. U.S. citizens enrolled in the distance-learning program may be eligible for federal financial aid. For more information, students should contact the Financial Aid Office at 800-340-6986. Prospective students can also request financial aid information online at http://www.pgsp.edu/html/form-fin-aid-info.htm.

Applying

Although the application deadline is August 15, it is recommended that students apply in the spring or early summer. An online application form is available at http://www.pgsp.edu/html/form-application.html or students may request an application form from the Office of Admissions at 650-843-3419.

CONTACT

William Froming, Ph.D., Academic Vice President and Director
Distance Learning Program
Pacific Graduate School of Psychology
935 East Meadow Drive
Palo Alto, California 94303
Phone: 650-843-3530
800-818-6136 (toll-free)
Fax: 650-493-6147
E-mail: wfroming@pgsp.edu
Web site: http://www.pgsp.edu/html/prosp-dl-program.htm

PARK UNIVERSITY

College for Distance Learning

Parkville, Missouri

Park University was founded in 1875 and is accredited by the Higher Learning Commission of the North Central Association of Colleges and Schools. Park's College for Distance Learning offers Bachelor of Science (B.S.) and Master of Science (M.S.) degrees. Numerous undergraduate courses and degrees are offered through the Internet. Graduate programs in public affairs, education, and business administration are also offered.

Park University is a nonprofit entrepreneurial institution of learning that is devoted to providing access to academic excellence to prepare learners to think critically, communicate effectively, and engage in lifelong learning while serving a global community.

Distance Learning Program

Hectic schedules are the biggest reason most adults fail to complete their college education. With busy schedules, family responsibilities, and travel obligations, it is often impossible for many adults to attend regularly scheduled classes.

The Online learning environment at Park University allows course participants to go to class when and where their schedule permits. Commuting time disappears, travel conflicts no longer matter, and childcare issues disappear.

The Online learning programs offered by Park University represent more than thirty years of experience in extended learning—experience honed through operating forty-one satellite "campus centers" on military bases where course work needs to be compact and mobile. As a result of this experience, Park developed, and now offers, accelerated eight-week courses as well as standard sixteen-week offerings. Online courses, first developed in 1996, now number 200 different courses. Virtually all in-person courses that are taught at Park University are also taught Online, along with other unique course offerings that were developed specifically for Online delivery or a combination of on-ground activities with online interaction.

Surveys of Online students indicate a higher degree of satisfaction for the general learning experience. In traditional classroom settings, people are often treated according to others' preconceived perceptions of age, gender, ethnicity, and even income level. In Park University's Online learning program, students are judged only by the caliber of their thoughts and the quality of their contributions. This learning environment is active and student-centered. Some students find the online format particularly effective for certain types of courses. In fact, the level of interactivity is actually higher in Park University's Online courses. Online learning requires extensive work—including much reading and writing—but the majority of Online students actually learn better through the Online format than they do in traditional, face-to-face classes.

Delivery Media

Park University offers 200 Online courses at five entry points—terms— during each year. Most courses are in accelerated eight-week format. Some courses follow nine- and sixteen-week formats. All courses require minimum computer-system capabilities.

To ensure the highest degree of success, prospective Online students need a basic level of computer literacy. Learners will be asked to open and transfer files and have a working knowledge of the use of e-mail within a course environment. Online students will do well if they have access to a Windows-capable computer with at least a 56.6 kbps modem; Netscape Navigator, Internet Explorer, or an equivalent, reliable Internet browser. Students should not borrow someone else's account, use a public-access account (such as a public library terminal), or use a temporary free account when taking the Online courses.

Courses are offered in a variety of subject areas, and learners can take many courses without enrolling in a degree program.

Each undergraduate course is concluded with a proctored exam.

Program of Study

Park University has provided degree completion programs via distance learning for more than thirty years. The goal of Park's degree completion program is to provide students with the opportunity and assistance to enable them to complete the last two years of their undergraduate degrees. Current fields of study include the Bachelor of Science degree in computer information systems, criminal justice, human resources, management, marketing, and social psychology.

Graduate Online degree programs include the Master of Business Administration with an emphasis in entrepreneurship, health care/health services management, international business, or management of information services; Master of Public Affairs with an emphasis in government/business relations, health care, management of information services, nonprofit and community services management, and public management; and Master of Education with an emphasis in arts in teaching, educational administration, and special education.

Online learning is a dynamic, growing program at Park University. New courses continue to be developed on an on-going basis.

Special Programs

Online students have access to a bookstore and library and such services as registration, financial aid, and advising.

Credit Options

Park University Online courses are transferable to programs at other regionally accredited institutions. In turn, Park accepts credit from other regionally accredited institutions. Specifically, the University accepts up to 84 hours of course completion with a grade of C or better from two-year schools. Official transcripts from previous colleges or universities; official test reports or transcripts from CLEP, USAFI, or DANTES; and ACT/PEP documentation can accompany an application. Up to 24 hours of credit may be awarded for military service and for Validated Learning Equivalency.

Faculty

Park University has hundreds of Internet faculty instructors, all of whom have advanced degrees and have taught previously. In addition, each Online instructor has completed an intensive eight-week training program to develop the skills necessary for meeting the challenges of teaching Online. This course, which is taught Online, of course, enables instructors to learn firsthand the challenges of being an Online student.

Admission

Park's Online undergraduate programs are open to students who have earned a high school diploma, a GED certificate, or the equivalent; have a minimum 2.0 cumulative GPA in all previous college study; have completed the online Application for Admission; and have paid the application fee. To receive a degree from Park University, students must complete at least 30 semester hours through the University, with 12 hours in their major.

For admission to graduate programs, students must have a bachelor's degree from a regionally accredited U.S. institution of higher learning or four years of equivalent full-time college work from an accredited foreign institution. They must also have a 2.75 minimum GPA on a 4.0 scale. Individual programs may require appropriate entrance test scores, such as the GRE or GMAT. Although entrance test scores, by themselves, do not constitute the sole or final criterion for granting or denying admission to any student, each program that uses test scores will consider them, in combination with other criteria, as an essential part of the requirements for granting full admission.

Students are required to meet course and program standards to remain in the Online program.

Tuition and Fees

For the 2006–07 academic year, undergraduate Online tuition is $242 per credit hour, plus an Internet fee of $14 per credit hour. Graduate Online tuition is $336 per credit hour, with a $16 per credit hour Internet fee.

Financial Aid

Financial assistance may be awarded to full-time and part-time students who qualify.

Applying

Degree-seeking students must meet all admission standards for Park University and pay a one-time $25 application fee.

For more information, students should contact Park University at the telephone number listed below or visit the Web site at the address listed below.

CONTACT

Office of Admissions
Park University
8700 N.W. River Park Drive
Parkville, Missouri 64152-3795
Phone: 800-745-7275 (toll-free)
E-mail: admissions@park.edu
Web site: http://www.park.edu

PEIRCE COLLEGE

Peirce Online

Philadelphia, Pennsylvania

Founded in 1865, Peirce is a private, four-year, specialized institution providing practical, leading-edge curricula to primarily working adult learners. The College has been offering online programs since 2000 through Peirce Online.

Peirce is accredited by the Commission on Higher Education of the Middle States Association of Colleges and Schools and the Pennsylvania Department of Education to award bachelor's and associate degrees. The business administration program is accredited by the Association of Collegiate Business Schools and Programs (ACBSP). The American Bar Association (ABA) approves the paralegal studies program.

Distance Learning Program

Peirce Online offers students high-quality programs from an accredited college, the flexibility to fit higher education into their busy lifestyles, and the personalized attention from faculty and staff members needed to successfully complete their degrees.

Peirce Online courses are seven weeks in length, with new courses starting every month. Students can earn an associate degree in eighteen months and a bachelor's degree in thirty-six months.

Delivery Media

Peirce Online students must have access to the Internet and an e-mail account.

Courses and degree programs can be completed entirely online, with no residency requirement. While there are weekly deadlines, students complete course work at their own pace. As part of each course, students submit homework assignments, papers, and exams online and participate in asynchronous online discussions. Through the online courseware, students can join with classmates in threaded conversations, privately correspond with instructors, and review their progress with the online grade book.

Program of Study

Peirce College offers bachelor's and associate degrees in business administration, information technology, and paralegal studies. Degrees in business administration and information technology can be completed entirely online. A minimum of 61 credits is required for an associate degree and 121 credits for a bachelor's degree.

In business administration, students can choose from concentrations in accounting, business law, entrepreneurship/small business management, human resource management, management, marketing, or real estate management.

In information technology, students can select from concentrations in application programming with .NET technology, desktop applications for business, information security, networking, network security, or technology management.

In paralegal studies, students can complete most courses online. After taking four initial courses in a traditional classroom setting at Peirce's Philadelphia campus, or from other accredited paralegal programs, students can conveniently complete the remainder of their degree online.

Peirce maintains strong business community relationships and continually upgrades courses to reflect hiring trends. In all degree programs, students take general education core courses in English, communication, social sciences, mathematics, and science. Supervised cooperative education is available in all programs. Most of the bachelor's degree programs include a capstone course in the last term of the program.

Student Services

Peirce offers student services in an online format, including academic advising, workshops, and tutoring; career development counseling and workshops; and services for students with disabilities. Library services include an extensive collection of online databases incorporating full-text periodicals, e-books, industry and financial reports, legal research, and reference materials. All Peirce College students are welcome to request a free copy of Microsoft Office Professional.

Credit Options

Peirce College reserves the right, in its sole discretion, to allow students to earn 90 credits toward a bachelor's degree and 30 credits toward an associate degree through any combination of transfer credits, credit by examination, work experience, and portfolio assessment. Students wishing to receive a degree or certificate from Peirce must complete 15 credits in their concentration through courses offered by Peirce College.

Faculty

Peirce Online emphasizes personal attention from faculty and staff members. Small classes and convenient online courseware ensure that faculty members are readily available to offer professional guidance to individual students. Faculty members also serve as career and academic advisers.

Peirce College employs full-time and adjunct faculty members with diverse professional backgrounds. Most faculty members have advanced degrees and are practitioners in their field. Attorneys, certified public accountants, psychologists, market analysts, computer experts, health-care professionals, business managers, and other professionals are among the teaching staff members at Peirce.

Admission

In compliance with relevant federal, state, and local laws, the College does not unlawfully discriminate in its admissions decisions on the basis of age, sex, race, color, religion, creed, national origin, citizenship, disability, sexual orientation, marital status, veteran's status, military status, or membership in any other protected group.

Applicants for a degree program must submit the following official documents for consideration: a completed application for admission with application fee; an official transcript documenting high school graduation or a copy of the GED or state equivalency diploma and scores; official college transcripts for college transfer credit; and evaluation of transfer credits for final admission and acceptance into the College.

Complete admissions requirements are available in the Peirce *Student Handbook,* which is posted at the College Web site http://www.peirce.edu.

Tuition and Fees

For the 2005–06 academic year, tuition and fees were $392 per credit hour for day, evening, and online courses plus a $100 technology fee. Books and supplies average about $100 per course. Costs are subject to change.

Financial Aid

Financial assistance includes scholarships, grants, loans, and on-campus employment. Peirce College participates in most federal and state aid programs. Approximately 70 percent of students receive financial aid. Applicants for aid must submit the Free Application for Federal Student Aid (FAFSA).

Applying

The Peirce Online application process is convenient and flexible. When students apply to Peirce Online, they can register and begin their studies while transcripts and other documents are being processed. There is no long wait—the initial application should take only 15 minutes. The application/registration process can be completed online at http://www.peirceonline.net. There is a $50 fee due at time of application.

CONTACT

Online Programs
Peirce College
1420 Pine Street
Philadelphia, Pennsylvania 19102-4699
Phone: 888-GO-PEIRCE Ext. 9800 (toll-free)
Fax: 215-670-9101
E-mail: online@peirce.edu
Web site: http://www.peirce.edu
http://www.peirceonline.net (Online Learning)

PENNSYLVANIA COLLEGE OF TECHNOLOGY
An Affiliate of The Pennsylvania State University

Distance Learning

Williamsport, Pennsylvania

The mission of distance learning at the Pennsylvania College of Technology (Penn College)—a special mission affiliate of Penn State that is committed to applied technology education—is to provide educational opportunities, using a variety of media, as an alternative to traditional classroom-based learning. Distance learning courses are accessible to students both off and on campus and are intended to meet the needs of students who desire an alternative to traditional face-to-face courses due to work schedules, geographical distance from the campus, or other special needs.

Distance Learning Program

The Penn College distance learning program was founded on the central principle of providing excellence in instruction and appropriate educational opportunities to students. Serving approximately 450 students per semester, the College offers an average of forty-five distance courses per semester across a range of academic disciplines as well as five bachelor's degree-completion programs that are available entirely via distance learning.

Delivery Media

Penn College operates on the WebCT Campus Edition instructional platform. In addition, supported applications include Adobe Photoshop, Adobe Acrobat, Macromedia Director, Flash, Apple QuickTime, Windows Media Player, and Respondus. Certain discipline-specific software programs also are employed.

Programs of Study

The Bachelor of Science degree in residential construction technology and management allows students who have earned appropriate applied technology skills in their first two years to move into advanced course work related to residential construction and management. Course work includes basic management and accounting as well as advanced estimating and scheduling, residential building systems, cost control, codes compliance, construction law, purchasing, and energy management.

The Bachelor of Science degree in technology management allows students who enter with an associate degree in a technical/professional area to obtain a baccalaureate degree, with the last two years emphasizing the development of business management skills. Technical/professional associate degrees include those with a concentrated area of study in a technical/professional area.

The Bachelor of Science degree in applied health studies is a 127-credit major for individuals who are certified, licensed, or registered in a health-care profession or for students enrolled in the College's occupational therapy assistant studies, paramedic studies, or radiography majors who wish to earn a bachelor's degree. Students acquire the advanced-level core knowledge that guides all health-care practitioners. This degree allows the student to increase knowledge in management and administrative issues; assist in planning, problem solving, and evaluating health-care delivery methods and systems; and establish a more marketable, multiskilled background.

The baccalaureate-level dental hygiene program is designed to prepare licensed dental hygienists to contribute to the improvement of oral health in a rapidly changing health-care environment. This program enables hygienists to build upon their current knowledge base and assume positions of responsibility in a variety of alternate care settings as well as in positions created to meet future health-care needs.

The Bachelor of Science degree in automotive technology management is structured to meet the needs of the automotive service and manufacturing industries. The curriculum provides an in-depth study of technical skills, technical knowledge, and management skills as applied in the automotive industry. It emphasizes supervision and personnel management, financial analysis and accounting principles, sales promotion and marketing plan, problem-solving methods, and organization and planning techniques as well as communications and mathematics, which are essential for a management career.

Special Programs

The Office of Distance Learning assists in scheduling and determining each semester's class offerings in concert with the academic deans. Courses are offered on a regular and predictable basis to ensure academic progress and adequate course selection for those learning at a distance.

To accommodate the needs of distance learners, selected enrollments are restricted at the start of each semester scheduling period. Resident students also may enroll in distance courses on a space-available basis.

Student Services

Penn College distance learners have full student standing and are entitled to all the privileges and services of a Penn College student. The Financial Aid Office, Career Services, the Advisement Center, and the College Store all have a Web presence and respond to student inquiries via telephone or e-mail. Distance students may order textbooks via the Web site. The library catalog and other references, periodical abstracts, and full-text databases are available through the Penn College Library Web site. An electronic reserve system is provided for assigned readings and supplemental assignments. A College librarian is assigned to each distance learning course to address distance learning and library instruction needs.

Credit Options

Transfer credits, advanced placement, credit for military experience, professional certifications, and credit by exam may be considered during transcript review. Acceptance of credits varies by major.

Faculty

Approximately 55 faculty members teach distance learning courses; 92 percent are full-time faculty members.

Admission

Distance learners are accepted to Penn College and the academic department that houses their major. There is no separate admission process for distance learning students.

Tuition and Fees

Tuition and fee rates for 2005–06, including computer, lab, and activity fees, were $336 per credit hour for in-state students and $422 per credit hour for out-of-state students.

Financial Aid

As students in full standing, distance learners may be eligible for financial aid, including federal aid programs.

Applying

Students should submit an application for admission online at http://www.pct.edu/forms or contact the Office of Admissions at the College's toll-free number.

CONTACT

Paula Neal
Distance Learning Services Assistant
Pennsylvania College of Technology
One College Avenue
Williamsport, Pennsylvania 17701
Phone: 570-320-8019
800-367-9222 (toll-free)
Fax: 570-321-5559
E-mail: distancelearning@pct.edu
Web site: http://www.pct.edu/away

PRESCOTT COLLEGE

Adult Degree, Master of Arts, and Ph.D. Programs

Prescott, Arizona

Prescott College's mission is to educate students of diverse ages and backgrounds to understand, thrive in, and enhance the world community and environment. Prescott regards learning as a continuing process and strives to provide an education that enables students to live productive lives while achieving a balance between self-fulfillment and service to others. Students are encouraged to think critically and act ethically, with sensitivity to both the human community and the biosphere. The College's philosophy stresses experiential learning and self-direction within an interdisciplinary curriculum.

Prescott College is an independent liberal arts college that grants Bachelor of Arts (B.A.), Master of Arts (M.A.), and Ph.D. degrees. The College is accredited by the Higher Learning Commission of the North Central Association of Colleges and Schools. The teacher education program is approved by the Arizona State Board of Education and the Arizona State Directors of Teacher Education and Certification. The Association of Experiential Education also accredits the College.

Distance Learning Program

Students maintain their personal and professional lives while earning a degree. The program is self-designed, student-centered, and flexible. The programs require very limited residency. The College offers ongoing support from faculty members and other students.

Delivery Media

Students in the B.A. Adult Degree Program work with mentors (local professionals) in their home communities and core faculty members at Prescott College on an individualized course of study. Students are required to be in Arizona for two 3-day weekends during their program.

Faculty-chosen graduate advisers assist students in the Master of Arts Program in planning, executing, and evaluating their graduate study programs. All graduate students must attend two 3-day colloquia per semester.

Ph.D. Program students are guided by committees that consist of a core faculty member, 2 affiliate faculty members, and an external affiliate faculty member. Doctoral students attend thirty-seven days of residency over the course of the four-year program.

Programs of Study

B.A. students, working with faculty members, design degrees in areas such as environmental studies, human services, management, sustainable community development, and teacher education. Teacher education students may complete all courses leading to Arizona teaching credentials in elementary, secondary, or special education while earning their bachelor's degree. Students may also complete post-bachelor's teacher certification. Students in human services generally design concentrations in counseling psychology, human services, or psychology, depending on their career goals. Environmental studies students have earned competences in agroecology, environmental education, environmental resource stewardship, sustainable living, and many other areas. The sustainable community development program prepares students to plan and implement measures that build and strengthen communities. This includes studies in business, the environment, governments, social systems, and values. The Management Program combines traditional leadership theories and practices that are common in virtually any organization with innovative thinking. In addition, the curriculum focuses on the study of complex human factors involved in organizational decision making.

M.A. students may design programs in the five broadly defined programs of study listed below or in other areas of personal interest. The adventure education program provides students the opportunity to pursue studies that cover a range of outdoor and adventure-based programming applications. Areas of study may include community recreation, corrections, guiding and outfitting, school and college curricula, and therapeutic adventure. Counseling and psychology students may prepare for certification or licensure in professional counseling or marriage and family therapy or in a nonclinical, more theoretical, aspect of the field. Counseling and psychology students focus on specialties such as adventure-based counseling, child development, equine-assisted mental health, expressive arts therapies, forensic psychology, grief counseling, school guidance counseling, and somatic psychology. Education students seek degree concentrations with a wide variety of emphases, including bilingual, early childhood, elementary, environmental, experiential, secondary, and special education; curriculum design; English as a second language; literacy; pedagogy; and school renewal. Environmental studies graduates have completed programs in such diverse fields as agroecology, conservation biology, earth sciences, ecological design, ecological restoration, ecology, environmental education, environmental ethics and philosophy, environmental history, ethnobotany, marine studies, natural history, and natural resource management. The humanities program provides opportunities for students to develop programs within a wide range of interests. These range from cultural studies, philosophy and religious studies, and social sciences to the arts and business.

Ph.D. students design their own studies within the area of sustainability education. The four-year program consists of a year each of foundational courses, individually designed theory courses, practicum, and a doctoral dissertation.

Student Services

The B.A. program accepts transfer credits earned at regionally accredited institutions with a grade of C or higher. The B.A. program also offers credit for life experience to qualified students. Prescott College does not transfer credits into its graduate programs.

Admission

Application requirements are available in the program catalogs or online at Prescott's Web site. Applicants may apply online or use the application from the College's catalog. Students in Tucson and southern Arizona who are interested in the B.A. or M.A. programs should contact the Tucson office. All other geographic areas may work with the Prescott admissions office.

Tuition and Fees

Students should visit Prescott's Web site for current tuition and fee information.

Financial Aid

Students seeking any form of financial assistance are encouraged to speak with the Financial Aid Office. The financial aid process begins with filling out the Free Application for Federal Student Aid (FAFSA), which is available online at http://www.fafsa.ed.gov. The Prescott College school code is 013659.

CONTACT

Admissions Office
Prescott College
220 Grove Avenue
Prescott, Arizona 86301
Phone: 928-350-2100
877-350-2100, Option 1 (toll-free)
Fax: 928-776-5242
E-mail: admissions@prescott.edu
Web site: http://www.prescott.edu

Admissions
Prescott College Tucson Center
2233 East Speedway Boulevard
Tucson, Arizona 85719
Phone: 888-797-4680 (toll-free)
Fax: 520-319-1032

PURDUE UNIVERSITY
KRANNERT SCHOOL OF MANAGEMENT

PURDUE UNIVERSITY

Krannert Executive Education Programs

West Lafayette, Indiana

Purdue University, a state-supported land-grant university, was founded in 1869. It was named after its chief benefactor, John Purdue, and is known for its academic excellence and affordable education. The West Lafayette campus offers nearly 6,700 courses in the Schools of Agriculture, Management, Consumer and Family Sciences, Pharmacy, Nursing and Health Sciences, Education, Science, Engineering, Technology, Liberal Arts, and Veterinary Medicine. The goals of the University are symbolized in its emblem, the griffin, whose three-part shield represents education, research, and service. Purdue is accredited by the North Central Association of Colleges and Schools.

Distance Learning Program

The Krannert Executive Education Programs (KEEP) began its distance learning programs in 1983. The programs were developed specifically for midlevel managers or managers-to-be who are unable to attend classes on a full-time basis. The programs have unique scheduling that makes it possible for participants to be drawn from a wide geographical area. Six 2-week residencies spread across twenty-two months, from orientation to graduation, allow its participants to meet their educational goals while simultaneously fulfilling their job responsibilities. During the nineteen months the students are off campus, they utilize the Internet and World Wide Web, online discussion forums and chat rooms, and other electronic media to stay in touch with each other, the faculty, and Executive Education support staff. These internationally ranked programs are part of the Krannert Graduate School of Management and admit 55 students in each cohort.

Delivery Media

KEEP uses the World Wide Web and CDs to deliver its course materials to students. Current business cases provide a focal point for individual and group assignments in all courses and are easily available for download from course Web sites and the provided CD.

Students are expected to provide a modern, Microsoft Windows–based laptop with the current version of Microsoft Office Professional installed, beginning with the Program Orientation. The program provides all required software, including Office.

Students are expected to have access to the Internet via an Internet service provider that allows for the free exchange of Web-based materials. While not required, a broadband connection to the Internet is recommended. Use of Internet-based e-mail, course Web sites and online discussion forums, chat rooms, and other Internet-based communication technologies are regular components of the program. These collaboration tools enable students to maintain contact with faculty and staff members when at a distance from one another and to prepare their individual and group assignments.

Programs of Study

A Master of Business Administration (M.B.A.) is offered through two unique programs: the Executive Master of Business Administration (EMB) Program and the International Master in Management (IMM) Program.

The EMB Program begins each July with an orientation session where the participants are introduced to the course work, the instructors, and the KEEP information technology system. The courses have an applied policymaking orientation and make extensive use of case studies and other experiential material. The third module has an emphasis on international business and includes an international residency. Upon completion of the program, the M.B.A. degree is awarded by Purdue University.

The IMM Program is taught in conjunction with Tias Business School, Tilburg University, in the Netherlands; the CEU School of Business in Budapest, Hungary; and GISMA, the German International Graduate School of Management and Administration. It is structured like the EMB Program, but the residencies alternate among the campuses of the four collaborating institutions. Orientation initiates the program each February. Graduation yields two master's degrees: an M.B.A. degree from Purdue and an M.B.A. from Tias or CEU.

The EMB and IMM Programs are intensive and demanding, which is consistent with a graduate professional program in management. Serious preparation is expected, and academic standards are carefully maintained to ensure integrity of the earned degrees. As a result, however, the educational benefits are substantial, and the degrees earned are significant professional credentials.

Special Programs

Both the EMB and IMM Programs are open to executive students worldwide and are accredited by AACSB International–The Association to Advance Collegiate Schools of Business. Both national and international students are attracted to the program.

Student Services

Students may maintain contact with faculty, support staff, and KEEP administration members on a daily basis, if necessary. Other resources include online library services, tutoring, campus computer networks, e-mail services, academic advising, and online discussion forums and chat rooms.

Credit Options

The programs are cohort in nature; that is, all students in each class enter together, take a common set of courses, and graduate together. There are 48 total credits, 16 per module, that participants must complete within two years.

Faculty

Classes are taught by the senior faculty members of the Krannert School of Management at Purdue, the Tias Business School at Tilburg University, the CEU School of Business in Budapest, and experienced teachers from other U.S. and international programs. All faculty members have taught extensively in executive programs containing distance learning aspects, have substantial research and publication records, and have experience as consultants to corporations and government agencies.

Admission

Successful applicants are expected to have a completed baccalaureate degree with an average grade of B or better, a minimum of five years of work experience in positions of increasing professional responsibility, a current position of significant responsibility, and two supporting letters of recommendation. The GMAT is not a blanket requirement for admission but may be strongly recommended for some applicants. Any applicant whose first language is not English must have a minimum TOEFL score of 77. They must also meet the minimum required scores in each individual test section (writing, speaking, and listening).

Tuition and Fees

The total cost for each program is $60,000 ($20,000 for each of the three modules). The tuition covers books and course material, instructional costs, lodging, and most meals during the residencies. Tuition is due before the first residency of each program module. The EMB Program includes an international residency, for which there is an additional charge.

Financial Aid

EMBA loans offered through Purdue's financial aid office are available. Applications may be completed at a distance.

Applying

Candidates may apply online at any time. As admission to the program is on a rolling basis throughout the year until class capacity is reached, early application is recommended. Upon receipt of all necessary documents, the application is reviewed by the Program Admissions Committee and, upon approval, submitted to Purdue's Graduate School for the final decision. Typically, a candidate can expect word of his or her application status within two weeks of receipt of all application documentation.

CONTACT

JoAnn Whitford
Assistant Director, Executive M.B.A. Programs
Purdue University
425 West State Street
West Lafayette, Indiana 47907-2056
Phone: 765-494-7700
Fax: 765-494-0862
E-mail: keepinfo@krannert.purdue.edu
Web site: http://www2.mgmt.purdue.edu/info/degree

REGENT UNIVERSITY

Online Distance Learning Programs

Virginia Beach, Virginia

Regent University offers more than thirty bachelor's, master's, and doctoral degree programs from a Judeo-Christian worldview. Regent offers bachelor's degrees in the areas of communication, education, global business, organizational leadership and management, political science, psychology, and religious studies. Regent's graduate schools include the School of Business, School of Communication and the Arts, School of Divinity, School of Education, Robertson School of Government, School of Law, School of Leadership Studies, and School of Psychology and Counseling. Online programs are offered through all schools at Regent, except for the School of Law.

Since classes began in 1978, Regent University has grown to an enrollment of more than 5,000 students. In addition to the main campus in Virginia Beach, Regent also offers programs at its Washington, D.C., campus in Alexandria, Virginia, while also offering more than twenty degree programs online.

Regent University is accredited by the Commission on Colleges of the Southern Association of Colleges and Schools (1866 Southern Lane, Decatur, Georgia 30033-4097; telephone: 404-679-4501) to award the bachelor's, master's, and doctoral degrees. The School of Law is fully accredited by the American Bar Association. The School of Divinity is accredited by the Association of Theological Schools (ATS). The Council for Accreditation of Counseling and Related Educational Programs (CACREP), a specialized accrediting body recognized by the Council for Higher Education Accreditation (CHEA), has conferred accreditation to the following program areas of community counseling (M.A.) and school counseling (M.A.), which are offered by Regent University's School of Psychology and Counseling. The Committee on Accreditation of the American Psychological Association (750 First Street, NE, Washington, D.C. 20002-4242; telephone: 202-336-5979; fax: 202-336-5978) has conferred accreditation on the Regent University Doctoral Program in Clinical Psychology, which offers the Doctor of Psychology (Psy.D.) degree.

Distance Learning Program

Regent University serves more than 2,000 students via its distance learning programs in business, communication and the arts, divinity, education, government, leadership, and psychology and counseling. Each fully accredited program is taught from a Judeo-Christian perspective, allowing students to apply relevant ethical values to their professional pursuits within a scholarly framework. Regent's online classes allow students to connect with professors and other students in a global format that offers both flexibility and interactive learning, affording students the opportunity to maintain both their current residence and employment.

Delivery Media

BlackBoard® is Regent University's choice for distance learning via the Internet. With this powerful application, a student is able to access course material, chat with professors and other students, and submit course work and tests from anywhere in the world. Some materials, such as video and cassette tapes and multimedia CDs, may be sent to the student via postal services. Course previews in BlackBoard and detailed requirements can be found at http://www.regent.edu/distance.

Programs of Study

Online distance learning programs at Regent University include the Professional M.B.A., M.A. in Management, Certificate of Advanced Graduate Studies (C.A.G.S.) in Business, M.A. in Communication, M.A. in Journalism, Ph.D. in Communication, M.A. in Practical Theology, Master of Divinity (M.Div.) (concentration in practical theology), Master of Education (M.Ed.) (Christian school program, cross-categorical special education, educational leadership, individualized degree plan, master teacher/ESL, TESOL, TESOL/initial licensure with optional reading specialist endorsement, reading specialist), TESOL certificate, Doctor of Education (Ed.D.), Ph.D. in Education, M.A. in Government, Certificate of Graduate Studies (C.G.S.) in Public Policy, M.A. in Organizational Leadership, C.G.S. in Leadership (master's level), Ph.D. in Organizational Leadership, Doctor of Strategic Leadership (D.S.L.), C.A.G.S. in Leadership (doctoral level), M.A. in Human Services Counseling, and Ph.D. in Counselor Education and Supervision. Some programs require on-campus courses and/or residencies.

Regent University also offers six undergraduate degree programs online: the Bachelor of Arts (B.A.) in Communication, the B.A. in Religious Studies, the Bachelor of Science (B.S.) in Global Business, the B.S. in Organizational Leadership and Management, the B.S. in Political Science, and the B.S. in Psychology as well as several certificate options.

Credit Options

For all online master's-level distance programs, students may transfer a maximum of 25 percent of the total credits required for their chosen program except for programs that have articulation agreements with other schools. Articulation agreements may authorize transfer credit for up to 49 percent of the degree to be earned. Credits must have been earned at an approved institution (determined by Regent University and normally from regionally accredited institutions). Credits for courses with grades below B (C for the M.Div. program) are not accepted for transfer at the graduate level.

For all online bachelor's-level distance programs, students may transfer a maximum of 90 total credits from a regionally accredited institution toward their chosen program. Credit earned through approved entrance-level examinations (i.e. CLEP and Dantes), military credit, and credits from other institutions of higher learning that meet Regent University standards or with whom Regent has an articulation agreement, including institutions accredited via approved Council for Higher Education Accreditation (CHEA) listed accrediting bodies, such as TRACS, DETC, ACICS, and ACE are considered for transfer credit. Credits for courses with grades below C are not accepted for transfer at the bachelor's degree level.

Faculty

Regent online distance learning courses are taught by the same full- and part-time faculty members who teach on campus. Regent has a distinguished faculty of men and women of varying religious denominations and ethnic origins who are noted scholars hailing from such universities as Harvard, Duke, Johns Hopkins, and others. Regent provides opportunities for students to learn from people such as former U.S. Attorney General John Ashcroft and Admiral Vern Clark, Ret., now Regent University distinguished professors.

Admission

Student admission to Regent University undergraduate programs requires a completed high school diploma (or its equivalent); graduate programs require a completed four-year bachelor's degree for master's programs and a completed master's degree for doctoral programs from institutions that are regionally accredited. Exceptions may be considered on an individual basis.

While each Regent school maintains specific admissions criteria for its programs, the following are considered the norm: a minimum cumulative high school GPA of 2.5 (for undergraduate applicants only) and/or undergraduate GPA of 3.0 in the desired area of study, submission of test scores (SAT and/or ACT for undergraduate applicants or MAT, GMAT, or GRE for graduate applicants), maturity in spiritual and/or character qualities, and personal goals that are consistent with the mission and goals of Regent University.

International student admissions requirements also vary among Regent schools. Students should contact the school of their choice for specific information. Students should visit http://www.regent.edu/admissions for more information.

Tuition and Fees

Tuition varies by program, as do additional fees. The tuition costs for online distance learning programs for the 2006–07 academic year are as follows: bachelor's degree programs, $395 per credit hour, undergraduate certificate programs, $221 per credit hour, Executive M.B.A., $860 per credit hour; Professional M.B.A., M.A. in Management, and C.A.G.S. in Business, $645 per credit hour; M.A. in Communication, and M.A. in Journalism, $800 per credit hour; and Ph.D. in Communication, $850 per credit hour; M.A. in Practical Theology, $445 per credit hour; M.Div., $445 per credit hour; D.Min. in Divinity, $475; Ph.D. in Divinity, $575 per credit hour; M.Ed. and TESOL certificate, $525 per credit hour; Ed.D. and Ph.D. in Education, $670 per credit hour; C.A.G.S. in Education, $670; M.A. in Government and C.G.S. in Public Policy, $625 per credit hour; M.A. in Organizational Leadership and C.G.S. in Leadership, $525 per credit hour; Ph.D. in Organizational Leadership and C.G.S. in Leadership, $525 per credit hour; Ph.D. in Organizational Leadership, D.S.L., and C.A.G.S. in Organizational Leadership, $750 per credit hour; M.A. in Counseling, M.A. in Human Services Counseling, and C.A.G.S. in Counseling, $550 per credit hour; Ph.D. in Counselor Education and Supervision and the Doctor of Psychology (Psy.D.), $660 per credit hour; and J.D. in Law, $820 per credit hour.

Financial Aid

Students accepted for enrollment may apply for Federal Stafford Student Loans and a variety of school-specific scholarships and grants. Veterans' benefits may also apply.

Applying

Application deadlines and processes vary among schools. Students should contact the individual school for specific information.

CONTACT

Regent University
1000 Regent University Drive
Virginia Beach, Virginia 23464-9800
Phone: 800-373-5504 (toll-free)
E-mail: inquire@regent.edu
Web site: http://www.regent.edu

To contact online distance learning programs directly:

School of Business
Phone: 800-477-3642 (toll-free)
E-mail: bizschool@regent.edu
Web site: http://www.regent.edu/business

School of Communication and the Arts
Phone: 888-777-7729 (toll-free)
E-mail: comrep@regent.edu
Web site: http://www.regent.edu/communication

School of Divinity
Phone: 800-723-6162 (toll-free)
E-mail: divschool@regent.edu
Web site: http://www.regent.edu/divinity

School of Education
Phone: 888-713-1595 (toll-free)
E-mail: eduschool@regent.edu
Web site: http://www.regent.edu/education

School of Government
Phone: 888-800-7735 (toll-free)
E-mail: govschool@regent.edu
Web site: http://www.regent.edu/government

School of Leadership Studies
Phone: 757-226-3063
E-mail: leadercenter@regent.edu
Web site: http://www.regent.edu/leadership

School of Psychology and Counseling
Phone: 757-226-4121
E-mail: counschool@regent.edu
Web site: http://www.regent.edu/counseling

School of Undergraduate Studies
Phone: 800-210-0060 (toll-free)
E-mail: regentundergrad@regent.edu
Web site: http://www.regentundergrad.com

SCU

REGIONS UNIVERSITY

Distance Learning Programs

Montgomery, Alabama

Founded in 1967, Southern Christian University (SCU) is an independent, nonsectarian, coeducational institution dedicated to the spirit of its ideals and Christian heritage. All of SCU's programs are taught from a Christian perspective. SCU is the home of one of the nation's leading universities offering distance learning programs and services to adults nationally. Adding to the prestige of this University is its recent designation as a Distance Education Demonstration Program Institution by the U.S. Department of Education. One of fifteen initial participants in the nation, SCU is partnering with the U.S. Department of Education to serve as a national model that will help chart the future of distance learning. Accredited by the Southern Association of Colleges and Schools, SCU grants bachelor's, master's, and doctoral degrees—all available via a distance learning format.

Distance Learning Program

Regions University programs are designed with the adult learner in mind. Eighty percent of Region's students are employed while they are attending. Courses can be taken anywhere there is Internet access and at any time. Regions has enrolled thousands of students in distance learning courses throughout the United States and internationally.

Delivery Media

Utilizing state-of-the-art technologies, Region's distance learning programs are delivered to students over the Internet. Students participate via online discussion groups, testing, e-mail, and telephone. Some courses are streamed live over the Internet and can be viewed as the class is being taught or at the student's convenience. The flexibility of the programs ensures continuity for students in transit, such as military personnel, clergy, or salespeople who must move while still in school.

Programs of Study

Regions University programs are structured with the traditional program in mind. Distance education is approved by the Southern Association of Colleges and Schools and the U.S. Department of Education, ensuring that distance education students receive the same high-quality education as on-campus students. Faculty and student services for online students are available to distance learning students. Regions ensures that students have regular contact with faculty and staff members via e-mail and telephone. Residency is only required in certain programs. No residency is required for undergraduates. Undergraduate degrees are awarded in biblical studies, business administration, human development, human resource management, liberal studies, management communication, and public safety and human justice. These degrees promote biblical and Christian ministry skills, human development skills, knowledge in the arts, and management communication skills. Graduate degrees are awarded in counseling/family therapy, organizational leadership, and religious studies. These degrees prepare students for careers and professions that provide support and services for the well-being of individuals, families, or society; foster leadership, counseling, and family therapy skills; and develop knowledge and biblical and Christian ministry skills. The counseling degrees are designed to help prepare students for licensure. Doctoral degrees include family therapy and ministry. These degrees are advanced professional degrees for community organizations and church-related vocations, with a concentration designed to prepare participants to counsel families and individuals. Regions students are fully matriculated students of Regions University with full student privileges, rights, and responsibilities.

Special Programs

Regions University has developed fully accredited programs of study to help working adults obtain their bachelor's degree in a timely manner through the EXCEL program. This program allows undergraduates to receive credit for lifetime learning, enabling students to complete their degree at an accelerated rate. All undergraduate courses are 4 semester hours, rather than 3. A student only has to take three courses (12 semester hours) to be a full-time student and eligible for maximum financial aid benefits. Also, fewer courses are required for degree completion. Undergraduate students who enroll on a full-time basis enjoy a significant savings, receiving a scholarship equal to the tuition cost for 6 semester hours.

Regions University is one of only a few institutions participating in the expansion of eArmyU colleges and universities. eArmyU is the Army's popular e-learning virtual university, offering thousands of soldiers the opportunity to earn a college degree during their enlistment. With the flexibility of eArmyU, soldier-students are able to continue their education uninterrupted and complete their degrees in a timely manner while they serve.

Student Services

Regions University provides support for all aspects of the distance learning experience. ProQuest Religion Database and First Search library programs give students access to 65 online databases, including the Library of Congress. Students have access to the collections of 150 theological schools online. Personal academic advising is performed via phone or e-mail. Students also receive personal evaluations of their degree program.

Credit Options

Fulfillment of some degree requirements is possible by passing the CLEP/DANTES tests or Regents examinations and through credit for lifetime learning and credit for military experience.

Faculty

The instructional faculty members total 85. Seventy-six percent of the full-time faculty members hold doctoral degrees, 100 percent hold master's degrees, and 100 percent hold terminal degrees. Faculty members are specialized in their areas and have training in distance learning delivery.

Admission

There is a rolling admission plan. Admission requirements are verification of high school graduation or passage of the GED test for undergraduates and demonstrated proficiency in computer literacy. Ninety percent of applicants are accepted.

Tuition and Fees

The graduate tuition cost per semester hour is $485. Undergraduate tuition per semester hour is $400. Full-time undergraduates (students enrolling in at least 12 semester hours, or three courses) receive a scholarship equal to the tuition cost for 6 semester hours. A comprehensive fee of $400 per semester is required of all students.

Financial Aid

Aid from institutionally generated funds is provided on the basis of academic merit, financial need, or other criteria. A limited number of scholarships are available. Priority is given to early applicants. Federal funding available for undergraduates and graduates includes Pell and FSEOG grants for undergraduates, the Federal Work-Study Program, and FFEL subsidized and unsubsidized loans for undergraduates and graduates. Eighty percent of students receive financial aid.

Applying

Prospective students must submit a $50 nonrefundable fee along with the completed application for admission. During the first semester, graduate students must submit letters of recommendation, transcripts, and test scores.

CONTACT

Rick Johnson
Regions University
1200 Taylor Road
Montgomery, Alabama 36117
Phone: 800-351-4040 Ext. 7513 (toll-free)
E-mail: admissions@regionsuniveristy.edu
Web site: http://www.regionsuniversity.edu

SAINT JOSEPH'S COLLEGE

Division of Graduate and Professional Studies

Standish, Maine

Saint Joseph's College is a Roman Catholic, liberal arts college that nurtures intellectual, spiritual, and social growth in students of all faiths and all ages. Saint Joseph's was founded in 1912 by the Sisters of Mercy and chartered by the Maine Legislature in 1915. It is the Catholic college of Maine. Saint Joseph's grants degrees in fulfillment of the educational ideals of the Sisters of Mercy, founded by Mary Catherine McAuley in Dublin, Ireland, in 1831. The College's 350-acre campus is situated on the shore of Sebago Lake in Standish, Maine, a half hour from Portland, Maine's largest city, and 2 hours north of Boston. Approximately 1,000 young adults reside at the Collage's campus where they pursue their undergraduate studies.

In 1976, distance education was introduced at Saint Joseph's to serve the needs of nontraditional adult learners in the U.S. and abroad. The distance education program at Saint Joseph's College, the Division of Graduate and Professional Studies, is known for its quality education geared to working professionals and is one of the most established in the country. With three decades of experience of providing distance education to adult students, the College has the procedures and polices that work for busy professionals interested in furthering their education for career advancement and for personal growth.

Saint Joseph's College is accredited by the New England Association of Schools and Colleges to award baccalaureate and master's degrees. The nursing program is approved by the Maine State Board of Nursing, Augusta, Maine, and accredited by the Commission on Collegiate Nursing Education. The long-term-care administration program is accredited by the National Association of Boards of Examiners of Long-Term Care Administrators.

Distance Learning Program

Saint Joseph's College offers the adult learner an opportunity to integrate formal education in the liberal arts tradition with professional experience. The Graduate and Professional Studies Program provides academic options in a variety of disciplines leading to undergraduate and graduate certificates and to associate, baccalaureate, and graduate degrees. Students may also choose individual courses for personal goals and/or industry continuing-education requirements. Each option is designed to reflect the special nature of Saint Joseph's commitment to its students. Approximately 8,500 Saint Joseph's alumni have earned their degrees through the distance program.

Delivery Media

Distance education courses through the Division of Graduate and Professional Studies and the Department of Nursing are available online via the World Wide Web, using WebCT. This integrated online platform is a flexible learning system where students have access to course content, study tips, resources tailored to the individual course, and various communication tools. Instructors use asynchronous instruction, so students enjoy a highly flexible, accessible mode of education that allows them to complete their programs of study where they reside, completely on their individual schedules. Upon enrollment, students receive the necessary texts and materials for their courses, including course access instructions. (Some courses are available in a text format for students with limited Internet access. Interested students should contact the Admissions office for more information.) All online courses require a computer with Internet access. Faculty members assist each student with their studies through a combination of written feedback on assignments, telephone consultations, and e-mail. An academic adviser is assigned to work with each student from enrollment through graduation. Some undergraduate and graduate degree programs require attending the two-week summer program at the campus in Maine.

Programs of Study

Saint Joseph's College offers the following degree programs at the graduate level: a Master of Science in Education (33 credits) with specializations in teaching and learning and in administrative management, intended for teachers and/or administrators interested in initiating or enhancing a career in K–12 education, community college, or adult education; a master's degree in health-services administration (42 credits) for senior management roles in complex health-care organizations; a Master of Science in Nursing (39 credits), with specializations in nursing administration and in nursing education; and a Master of Business Administration (42 credits) with a specialization in quality leadership. Graduate certificates (18 credits) include programs in nursing and health-care education and in nursing administration and leadership.

At the undergraduate level, Saint Joseph's College offers the following degrees through distance learning: the Bachelor of Science (128 credits), offering majors in business administration, with specializations in banking through a joint venture with the Center for Financial Training, and in management; general studies (a degree-completion program for adult students transferring a minimum of 30 credits), with specializations in adult education and training, business administration, criminal justice, human services, information technology management, and psychology; health-care administration; long-term-care administration; professional arts (a degree completion program for licensed health-care professionals), with specializations in adult education and training, health-care administration, human services, information technology management, and psychology; and radiologic science (a postcertification baccalaureate degree for radiology technicians). A Bachelor of Arts (128 credits) is also available at the undergraduate level, with majors in liberal studies and adult religious education. In addition, a Bachelor of Science in Nursing (129 credits) is available for RNs; it can also be earned in the RN to M.S.N. program, a curriculum that allows students to more rapidly progress through the B.S.N. and M.S.N. requirements and earn both degrees. Students can also choose from eight majors within the Associate of Science degree (66 credits), including adult education and training, business administration, criminal justice, general studies, human services, information technology management, management, and psychology.

Undergraduate certificate programs (18 credits) are available in adult education and training, business administration, Christian tradition, health-care management, information technology management, and long-term-care administration. Students who would like to take individual courses at either the graduate or undergraduate level may enroll as continuing education students.

Special Programs

The Division of Graduate and Professional Studies has developed partnerships with numerous organizations and corporations to provide educational opportunities to their employees throughout the country at multiple locations. (For more information, students should visit http://www.sjcme.edu/partner.) Saint Joseph's College is also a member of Servicemembers Opportunity Colleges (SOC), which guarantees transfer of credit for military personnel completing courses from other SOC schools. The Division is also a member of eArmyU, the Navy College Program Distance Learning Partnership, and Troops to Teachers and assists active and nonactive military personnel in their educational pursuits.

Credit Options

The Graduate and Professional Studies Program acknowledges the value of certain formal learning and career-based experience. For most programs, the College follows the American Council on Education guidelines in granting transfer credit for courses of study from accredited colleges or universities with a grade of C or better; ACE/PONSI-approved credit; ACE-approved military training and experience credits; CEUs earned through professional seminars, workshops, internships, and in-service education classes as elective credit; and CLEP, ACT/PEP, and DANTES exams. The total number of credits that can be awarded varies depending on the program.

Faculty

Nearly 200 full-time and part-time faculty members serve students in the Graduate and Professional Studies Program. Many teach in the residential program at Saint Joseph's College as well as in distance education. Each online instructor is required to complete a comprehensive five-week online training program to develop and refine the necessary skills to teach in an online environment. All instructors excel in their fields and have substantial experience with nontraditional students. Students communicate with faculty members via e-mail, phone, fax, and/or regular postal mail.

Admission

Admission requirements vary by program of study. Prospective students should contact the Admissions Office for the Graduate and Professional Studies Program at 800-752-4723 (toll-free) with specific questions about admission requirements. Information can also be obtained from the Web site.

Tuition and Fees

For the 2005–06 academic year, tuition is $ 260 per credit hour ($780 per 3-credit course) at the undergraduate level. Graduate course tuition varies depending on the program, and ranges from $300 to $350 per credit hour ($900 to $1050 per 3-credit course). Application fees are $50 for degree programs and $25 for certificate programs and continuing education. A complete fee schedule is available at the College's Web site.

Financial Aid

Students may be eligible for the Federal Pell Grant and/or Federal Stafford Student Loan. Applying for financial aid is an individualized process requiring consultation and evaluation. For more information and assistance, students should call the Financial Aid Office at 800-752-1266 (toll-free).

Applying

Applicants for all programs and all courses are required to submit an application and a non-refundable application fee. Application fees are $50 for degree programs and $25 for certificate programs and continuing education. For many programs, students are accepted on a rolling-admissions basis and, therefore, can apply and begin their studies at any time during the year. Students may download the application forms online or apply online at the College's Web site. For further information, students may contact the Admissions Office.

CONTACT

Admissions Office
Division of Graduate and Professional Studies
Saint Joseph's College
278 Whites Bridge Road
Standish, Maine 04084-5263
Phone: 800-752-4723 (toll-free)
Fax: 207-892-7480
E-mail: info@sjcme.edu
Web site:
http://www.sjcme.edu/gps

ST. LOUIS COMMUNITY COLLEGE SYSTEM

Telelearning Services

St. Louis, Missouri

St. Louis Community College (SLCC) is a public coeducational college supported by local taxes, state funds, and student fees. Created by area voters in 1962, the College offers freshman- and sophomore-level career and college transfer, developmental, and continuing education programs at its three campuses, four education centers, and numerous other locations throughout the city of St. Louis and the county. Nearly 130,000 students enroll each year in credit and noncredit courses. The College also serves the business community with programs offering St. Louis area business stakeholders with performance improvement, consulting, and training services. St. Louis Community College and its campuses are accredited by the Higher Learning Commission of North Central Association of Colleges and Schools. The College is also a founding member of the League for Innovation in the Community College, serving on the League's Board of Directors and as a Board member of Project SAIL.

Distance Learning Program

The World Wide Web, videotapes, CD-ROMs, DVDs, e-mail, live interactive video, and streaming video are offered at St. Louis Community College in addition to face-to-face classroom instruction. Since 1973, St. Louis Community College has been offering distance education to students locally, nationally, and internationally. Approximately 5,000 students currently enroll in distance learning courseware through SLCC.

Delivery Media

Web-based courses and TeleWEB-courses: Course orientation and exams may be administered via the Web or held on campus or at instructor-approved sites, depending on the specific course. Assignments, announcements, projects, tutorials, e-mail, student discussion forums, essay submission and retrieval, operating instructions, bulletins, and library research are accomplished via asynchronous communication in distance learning courses.

Telecourses: Video lessons—televised, videocassette, or CD/DVD—accompany related readings and assignments, discussions, and examinations. When students need help, instructors are just a phone call or e-mail away. Special print materials (textbooks, study guides, and student manuals) have been prepared to accompany each course.

Interactive Television (ITV) classes enable students to participate in SLCC courses from multiple locations at the same time. High-end videoconferencing technology bridges distances and allows students and teachers to see and hear each other from remote locations. Students may participate in an SLCC course from different SLCC locations, area high schools, or other institutions.

Programs of Study

SLCC offers an Associate in Applied Science (A.A.S.) in hospitality studies and in information reporting technology as well as Certificate of Proficiency certificates in funeral directing, information reporting technology, and business administration.

Hospitality Studies Graduates of the Associate of Applied Science degree program are prepared to enter the hospitality industry at a supervisory level and perform management functions and duties. Students with a Certificate of Proficiency in hotel and restaurant management are prepared for entry-level positions such as front office management, guest services, bar and beverage management, and restaurant or facility management.

Funeral Directing This Certificate of Proficiency program prepares the student for licensure as a funeral director and entry-level employment in a funeral establishment. This is a nontechnical certificate, geared toward the business and public relations aspects of operating a funeral home. There are no courses in embalming. Graduates are eligible to take the licensing examinations for Missouri or any other states with similar licensing requirements.

Information Reporting Technology: CART and Captioning Reporting An Associate in Applied Science degree and a Certificate of Proficiency are offered through the Information Reporting Technology Program. Communication Access Realtime Translation (CART), also referred to as realtime captioning, is a word-for-word speech-to-text interpreting service for people who need communication access. For students who are fascinated with words and have good English skills, manual dexterity, keyboarding experience, and the ability to hear the spoken word, CART and captioning reporting may be the perfect career. This program prepares the student for entry-level positions in realtime captioning

Business Administration: This program, which offers a Certificate of Proficiency and a Certificate of Specialization, addresses the educational and occupational needs of several groups of people in the business field. Students can enroll in short-term, intensive training for job opportunities or they can complete specific undergraduate requirements toward an advanced degree in business.

Special Programs

St. Louis Community College offers an honors program; students are admitted based on their high school GPA and SAT or ACT scores. Students who earn 15 hours of honors credit receive the designation of Honors Program Scholar on their diplomas and transcripts.

In recognition of the importance of the United States' position within the international community, SLCC offers transcultural and international study. This includes semesters abroad and study tours. The International Education Office (314-539-5363) has additional information.

Student Services

Students have access to many student services via the Web at St. Louis Community College. Admission, registration, financial aid, library services, and a 24/7 HelpDesk are available for all students.

Credit Options

Students may be eligible for credit for academic knowledge gained outside the classroom. The number of credits earned through examination is limited by College policy that 15 of the final 25 semester hours toward the associate degree must be earned at St. Louis Community College. Students should have official transcripts mailed to the College and request an evaluation of previously earned credits at the campus admission/registration office.

Faculty

Faculty members specialize in teaching at the undergraduate level and hold advanced degrees—master's or doctoral—or advanced licensing degrees in technical fields. Career instructors have worked in business and industry and keep current with changes in their fields. Of the 570 faculty members, 32 percent are full-time.

Admission

St. Louis Community College has an open-admissions policy in keeping with its original purpose to provide a high-quality, low-cost education to area residents. Although admission to the College is not based on minimum academic qualifications, certain programs have required standards for admission and retention.

Tuition and Fees

Maintenance fees are $78 per credit hour for students in the SLCC service area, $103 per credit hour for out-of-district students, $138 per credit hour for out-of-state students, and $148 per credit hour for international students.

Financial Aid

St. Louis Community College provides a comprehensive financial aid program funded by federal, state, and private agencies. Aid awards fall into four categories—grants, scholarships, loans, and work. Although superior ability and talent are recognized through the College and other scholarship programs, most aid is awarded on the basis of financial need. Students are encouraged to apply for aid as early as possible (by April 1 for the fall semester). Students who wish to know more about their financial aid eligibility should contact the College's financial aid office.

Applying

Students can apply online, by mail or fax, or in person. Applicants must submit an official high school transcript or GED scores. International students must also submit TOEFL scores and certification of finances.

CONTACT

Daniel A. Bain, Ph.D., Director
Telelearning Services
St. Louis Community College System
300 South Broadway
St. Louis, Missouri 63102
Phone: 314-539-5056
Fax: 314-539-5125
E-mail: dbain@stlcc.edu
Web site: http://www.stlcc.edu/distance

SAINT MARY-OF-THE-WOODS COLLEGE

Distance Education Program

Saint Mary-of-the-Woods, Indiana

Founded in 1840, Saint Mary-of-the-Woods College (SMWC) is the nation's oldest Catholic liberal arts college for women and is accredited by the North Central Association of Colleges and Schools. The College offers the rich traditions of academic excellence and dedication to educating women personally and professionally for responsible roles in society. The diverse student community of 1,700 includes traditional resident students, commuters, and distance learners at both the undergraduate and graduate levels. The College also enrolls men in all adult and distance programs, including the Woods External Degree (WED) Program and all graduate programs. A hallmark of the College is an emphasis on personalized service.

The general studies curriculum required of all undergraduates is designed to develop the communication and analytical skills needed for success in college and in the professional world.

Distance Learning Program

Since 1973, the Woods External Degree (WED) Program has provided the College curriculum to contemporary adult women and men who juggle multiple responsibilities yet need or want a college degree. Now serving 1,200 students, this structured but flexible independent-study program is based on self-paced semesters ranging from five to twenty weeks. Semesters that begin with in-person appointments with instructors and faculty advisers, and a degree can be earned in one of more than thirty majors.

Delivery Media

Faculty members and students communicate by telephone, e-mail, and postal service. All full-time faculty members, some adjuncts, and many students have access to e-mail. All students must have access to computers with modems for communication, word processing, and research. Some courses use videotapes, audiotapes, or optional computer programs.

Programs of Study

The College is chartered to grant the Associate in Arts, Associate in Science, Bachelor of Arts, Bachelor of Science, and Master of Arts degrees.

Undergraduates complete the general studies curriculum, courses required for their chosen major, and additional electives to total 125 semester hours for a baccalaureate degree and 65 semester hours for an associate degree; a minimum of 30 hours must be earned at the College.

Associate majors available through WED are accounting, early childhood/child development, general business, gerontology, humanities, and paralegal studies. Baccalaureate majors include accounting, accounting information systems, business administration, computer information systems, digital media communications, E-commerce, education (preschool–grade 3/mild intervention, elementary, secondary, and special), English, gerontology, history/political science, human resource management, human services, humanities, journalism, marketing, mathematics, not-for-profit administration (several areas), paralegal studies, professional writing, psychology, social sciences (history concentration), and theology. Teacher licensure is also available for men and women who have already earned a bachelor's degree.

There are no geographical restrictions, except that education majors must reside within 200 miles of campus for faculty supervision of field experience and student teaching.

The Master of Arts in pastoral theology program is designed for persons who are or plan to be engaged in ministry and for those seeking personal enrichment in theological study.

The Master of Arts in earth literacy program is designed for persons who care for and advocate a sustainable and just earth community.

The Master of Arts in art therapy program emphasizes understanding and applying theories to art therapy, counseling, and psychopathology.

The Master of Arts in music therapy program is designed for professional music therapists who seek an advanced understanding of the therapeutic uses of music, especially as applied to psychotherapy and medicine. Master of Arts degrees require 36 to 40 credit hours.

Special Programs

SMWC offers several learning formats: traditional campus-based study, distance learning, and alternative format courses, a third format that combines independent study with intensive weekend seminars on campus. WED students may combine these formats in any semester of study; about 450 choose to enroll in weekend alternative format courses each year. However, all degrees offered through WED may be completed entirely through distance learning at home, with the exception of a few digital media communication courses, which must be taken via alternative format on campus on weekends.

Student Services

Full-time faculty members serve as academic advisers to the WED students in their departments, meeting each semester to monitor progress and plan subsequent semesters. A WED staff of 7 provides additional support, advocacy, registrarial assistance, and information, including a quarterly newsletter for distance learners. WED staff members also provide referrals to other campus services, such as career development (available by phone and in person) and library materials by mail.

Credit Options

Students may transfer credit earned at other accredited colleges and universities, although some credits may be too dated to meet the requirements. WED encourages students to earn credit for previous college-level learning through CLEP and DANTES, ACE/PONSI awards, and portfolio applications documenting other prior learning. At least 30 semester hours of course work must be earned under the direct supervision of SMWC faculty members to obtain a degree from SMWC.

Faculty

Fifty-seven full-time and 55 adjunct faculty members serve as instructors and academic advisers to WED students. Sixty percent of full-time faculty members have doctoral or other terminal degrees.

Admission

Applicants must have earned a high school diploma or GED certificate and demonstrate potential for success in a distance learning program. Academic history, employment and other life experience, writing skills, and stated goals are considered. Applicants for whom English is a second language must submit TOEFL scores. Applications and all documentation should be submitted at least thirty days prior to the planned enrollment date.

Tuition and Fees

For 2005–06, undergraduate tuition for the WED program is $342 per semester hour. Fees include a $30 application fee, a one-time fee of $80 for the initial on-campus residency (not including housing), an annual $70 technology fee, and modest materials fees for laboratory courses.

Financial Aid

Available financial aid includes Federal Pell Grants, student loans, and, for residents only, Indiana Higher Education Grants. The College awards small WED grants to eligible seniors and offers 10 percent tuition discounts through cooperating employers; this institutional aid totaled more than $63,000 in 2003–04. Finally, the WED staff maintains a directory of private grants and scholarships and encourages WED students to apply for them. Approximately 75 percent of WED students receive some form of aid.

Applying

Applications are reviewed when all materials are received; the evaluation process is usually completed within a month. Two-day orientation residencies are held on campus several times each year and conclude with enrollment in the initial semester.

CONTACT

Office of Distance Education Admission
Saint Mary-of-the-Woods College
Saint Mary-of-the-Woods, Indiana 47876
Phone: 812-535-5106
800-499-0373 (toll-free)
Fax: 812-535-5010
E-mail: wedadms@smwc.edu
Web site: http://www.smwc.edu

SALVE REGINA UNIVERSITY

Extension Study, eSalve

Newport, Rhode Island

Salve Regina is an independent, coeducational institution of higher learning that confers degrees in the arts and sciences. It teaches in the tradition of the Catholic Church and according to the Mission of the Sisters of Mercy, who continue as its sponsors. Salve Regina's Charter was amended in June 1991 to change its name to Salve Regina University. The University serves approximately 2,300 men and women from many states and other countries. Alumni number more than 14,000. Its 65-acre oceanfront campus in Newport's Ochre Point historic district includes thirty-nine new and adapted buildings.

The University, through teaching and research, prepares men and women for responsible lives by imparting and expanding knowledge, developing skills, and cultivating enduring values. Through liberal arts and professional programs, students develop their abilities for thinking clearly and creatively, enhance their capacity for sound judgment, and prepare for the challenge of learning throughout their lives. The graduate programs of Salve Regina University have two broad goals: to help the student realize his or her full potential and to prepare this student to help others do the same.

Salve Regina University is a fully accredited member of the New England Association of Schools and Colleges (NEASC). Inquiries about NEASC accreditation may be directed to the Vice President for Academic Affairs at Salve Regina or to the Commission on Institutions of Higher Education, NEASC, 209 Burlington Road, Bedford, Massachusetts 01730-1433 (telephone: 781-271-0022; e-mail: cihe@neasc.org).

Distance Learning Program

Salve Regina University's Office of Graduate Extension Study provides an alternative to traditional classroom learning by acknowledging the needs of students whose personal and professional circumstances make regular on-campus study difficult. Salve Regina University has been providing master's programs by extension for the past twenty years. Salve offers an M.B.A., an M.A. in international relations, an M.S. in management, and an M.A. in humanities, plus several concentrations and professional certificates online. The program of study completed online is the same as that completed by on-campus students.

Delivery Media

All courses are accessed through the World Wide Web. Once students register for a course, they are notified of their username and password. Online courses are offered in two formats: self-paced and interactive.

Online self-paced courses are usually available within two weeks of registration. The student has four months to complete each course. Course assignments are submitted through the assignment tool.

Online interactive courses have specific start and end dates. In these courses, students interact with other students and have the ability to participate in discussions with faculty members. Communication is asynchronous; there is no requirement for members of the class to be online at the same time. This interactive environment enriches course content, provides opportunity for discussion, and encourages the exchange of ideas.

Programs of Study

The Master of Business Administration program is designed to prepare graduates to successfully lead and manage organizations in a constantly changing environment. In both the for-profit and not-for-profit environments, today's executive is faced with myriad concerns ranging from ethical and human rights issues to globalization and environmental protection. The Salve Regina University Master of Business Administration curriculum provides the technical knowledge and skills to appreciate and address these and other critical contemporary issues. The program is directed toward developing leaders with a focus on ethics, organizational behavior, finance, economics, accounting, and strategic management. Social purpose and workplace humanization are underlying program values aligned with the University's mission. This degree program is accredited by the International Assembly for Collegiate Business Education (IACBE).

M.B.A. students may also choose concentrations in health-service administration, international business, international relations, management, or rehabilitation counseling.

The curriculum and content of the Master of Arts in international relations program is a reflection of the University's mission regarding justice and the increasing need to envision international political behavior in its framework. In its own capacity and within the University's mission, the international relations program promotes international and world politics. The program prepares graduates to be constructively critical of their immediate and broader political environment, whether in their place of work (government, education, the private sector, the media, or nongovernmental organizations) or simply as citizens of both their country and the world. The program's objective is to reinforce the vision of its graduates to view fellow human beings not only as representatives of national and social compartments but also as overlapping circles in a world community. In practical terms, this translates into global solidarity and the elimination of injustice everywhere. Graduates are able to produce creative and pragmatic solutions to problems and dilemmas confronting the world. The program accomplishes its objective by exposing the candidates in a systematic and comprehensive way to the realities of the political environment through a core of courses covering political thought, international relations, and comparative politics.

The M.A. in international relations also offers a concentration in justice and homeland security.

The Master of Arts in humanities is an interdisciplinary program that seeks to foster a broad understanding of the qualitative aspects of life and culture through a study of disciplines such as history, literature, philosophy, and religion. The course of study is intended for individuals who want to broaden their intellectual and cultural horizons. It also serves as excellent preparation for the Ph.D. degree in the humanities.

The Master of Science program in management offers a solid theoretical and practical management foundation and integrates information systems into the management role. In addition, the M.S. program offers a concentration in law enforcement leadership.

Special Programs

The certificate program in management is for students who already have a bachelor's degree and includes 15 hours of graduate credit. It offers opportunities for those who desire a graduate education without formal pursuit of a master's degree.

Credit Options

The master's degree programs are all twelve courses (36 credits). Students have up to five years to complete all of the requirements for the degree; however, at a rate of four courses per year, students are generally able to complete the degree in three years. Normally, only 40 percent of the total program credits are eligible to transfer into the graduate programs at Salve Regina University. The University, however, does recognize the unique situation of military members who are not located in one area long enough to obtain a graduate degree in the traditional manner. Accordingly, the University accepts up to 18 credits earned at military schools, colleges, or universities in accordance with the recommendations made by the American Council of Education (ACE) and with the University transfer policy regarding academic performance.

Faculty

The faculty members are a valued resource; many teach full-time on campus and others are adjunct faculty members who are successful professionals within their field. They come from leading doctoral, M.B.A., and law programs and represent a wide variety of backgrounds. Their superior teaching skills, academic training and research, and knowledge of practical application bring a wealth of experience to the curriculum.

Admission

Men and women with bachelor's degrees from accredited institutions of higher learning who are considered to have the ability to pursue graduate study and show a desire for personal development are admitted following a careful evaluation of their credentials, without regard to age, race, sex, creed, national or ethnic origin, or handicap.

Tuition and Fees

Tuition is $350 per credit hour for all Extension Study courses. All courses are 3 credit hours. Fees include application ($50), incomplete/delay of grade ($150), master's degree graduation ($175), and transcript ($5).

Financial Aid

Salve Regina University assists students in applying for loans through the Federal Family Educational Loan Programs, particularly the Federal Stafford Student Loans. These loans are available to all students and may be used to fund education at the University provided the student maintains continuous quantitative and qualitative progress. Benefit plans for veterans and active-duty service persons and employers' tuition-reimbursement plans are welcome.

Applying

The following must be submitted to the Graduate Admissions Office: an application form, a nonrefundable application fee, official transcripts from all accredited degree-granting institutions attended, two letters of recommendation, standardized test scores no more than five years old (GRE, MAT, GMAT, or LSAT), and a personal statement of intent of study. The TOEFL and official transcript evaluations are required of international students.

CONTACT

Maureen E. Moriarty, M.B.A., Director
Extension Study and Continuing Education
Salve Regina University
100 Ochre Point Avenue
Newport, Rhode Island 02840
Phone: 800-637-0002 (toll-free)
Fax: 401-341-2931
E-mail: graduate_studies@salve.edu
Web site: http://www.salve.edu/programs_esalve/ges_index.htm

SAVANNAH COLLEGE OF ART AND DESIGN

SCAD e-Learning Program

Savannah, Georgia

The Savannah College of Art and Design (SCAD) exists to prepare talented students for careers in the visual and performing arts, design, the building arts, and the history of art and architecture. SCAD is a private, coeducational institution with locations in Atlanta and Savannah, Georgia, and in Lacoste, France. Online programs are offered through SCAD e-Learning. SCAD e-Learning courses are custom-designed and taught by SCAD faculty members under the authority and accreditation of the Savannah College of Art and Design. SCAD is accredited by the Commission on Colleges of the Southern Association of Colleges and Schools (1866 Southern Lane, Decatur, Georgia 30033-4097; 404-679-4500) to award bachelor's and master's degrees. The Master of Architecture (M.Arch.) is accredited by the National Architectural Accrediting Board (NAAB). A balanced fine arts and liberal arts curriculum has attracted students from every state and from more than eighty countries, making SCAD one of the largest art and design colleges in the United States. Current enrollment is more than 7,300 students.

Distance Learning Program

The Savannah College of Art and Design offers degrees, certificates, and individual courses completely online via SCAD e-Learning. Students have the flexibility to further their education through an online delivery method to suit their locations, schedules, and preferences.

All courses are custom-designed and taught by SCAD faculty members and are offered for academic credit under the authority and accreditation of the Savannah College of Art and Design. SCAD is a member of the Sloan-C consortium of institutions committed to high-quality online education.

SCAD e-Learning programs include a certificate in digital publishing; graduate certificates in digital publishing management, historic preservation, and interactive design; Master of Arts degrees in broadcast design and motion graphics, digital photography, graphic design, historic preservation, illustration design, and interactive design and game development; and a Master of Fine Arts degree in graphic design.

Delivery Media

Courses are delivered via the Internet and are offered year-round; each is organized into 10 units, usually one per week. SCAD e-Learning courses are designed to run on a variety of computers and operating systems and may be accessed with a 56K modem connection or better.

SCAD e-Learning also provides a secure and user-friendly way for faculty members and students to communicate with one another. Throughout the courses, regular online discussions and live chat sessions with professors and peers, as well as assessments and feedback, help students maximize their SCAD e-Learning experience. Students have access to an extensive range of online services and resources and participate in an orientation course.

SCAD is a recognized leader in online course design, instructional technology, and online education. Instructional designers, instructional technologists, media designers, and e-services staff members work with faculty members to ensure that all courses are fully ADA-compliant and adhere to the same high standards as SCAD's on-site course offerings.

Courses adhere to a ten-week quarter with start and end dates, but they are not held at set times. Students are expected to complete course work according to a schedule that stipulates due dates, assessments, and discussions. SCAD e-Learning students are expected to participate in all assignments, examinations, and field trips or other activities. Attendance is determined by active login time and participation.

SCAD e-Learning students must possess basic computer skills and have regular access to appropriate hardware, software, and Internet connectivity. Specific technical requirements may be found on the SCAD e-Learning Web site at http://www.scad.edu/elearning.

Programs of Study

SCAD e-Learning programs include a certificate in digital publishing; graduate certificates in digital publishing management, historic preservation, and interactive design; Master of Arts degrees in broadcast design and motion graphics, digital photography, graphic design, historic preservation, illustration design, and interactive design and game development; and a Master of Fine Arts degree in graphic design.

Broadcast design and motion graphics students learn the skills that enable them to contribute wherever graphic content in motion is broadcast or communicated. The M.A. program combines critical approaches to spatial and material culture, project management, design methodology, research, communication, and design theory.

Digital photography students gain a thorough knowledge of the medium and the photographic applications of digital technology. In the M.A. program, students achieve a mastery of craft, technology, and aesthetics by exploring creative possibilities, developing a personal vision, and studying the history and criticism of the medium.

Programs in graphic design help prepare students for careers in a variety of fields, including publishing, education, advertising, and new media. These SCAD e-Learning programs prepare students to meet the demands of organizations and businesses with increasing in-house publishing needs. Students learn publishing and design fundamentals, including layout, graphic imaging, and typography. They are introduced to a variety of industry-standard computer applications that are used in the production and presentation of print and online media.

Through certificate programs, students learn to produce a broad range of materials, including newsletters, brochures, and Web sites. The undergraduate certificate features an emphasis on production, while the graduate certificate emphasizes management of content, design and development processes, and creative teams. The M.A. degree program is professionally oriented and allows a broad course of study; the M.F.A. includes a field or teaching internship and a thesis component.

The graduate certificate in historic preservation program is designed for individuals working in historic preservation or related fields and those with an interest in historic preservation who would like to expand their knowledge or prepare to enter or enhance their careers. The M.A. program includes courses in building assessment and preservation planning and requires a final project.

The graduate certificate and Master of Arts degree in interactive design and game development help prepare students for careers in interactive art and design, particularly with large design firms, advertising agencies, and product manufacturers, and in education. The method of course delivery is instructive, as students are educated in the electronically mediated environment in which they typically work or plan to work. Students are prepared for, or may enhance their careers in, interactive design, art direction, creative technology, exhibit design, and projection media.

All courses may be credited toward other applicable degree programs upon successful application and acceptance to the program.

Student Services

SCAD e-Learning provides a forum for students to participate in College events and discussions through Web casts, online forums, the College newspaper, and other digital-programming outlets.

New SCAD e-Learning students participate in an online orientation. Through the College's MySCAD Intranet, students may access comprehensive e-campus services, including online course registration, peer tutoring, career services, and Writing Center instruction. Students also may access SCAD's Jen Library online services.

Students are encouraged to communicate with their peers through course discussions, e-mail, quarterly online chats, and the e-Learning Club, which holds regular meetings online in real time. SCAD's Student Media Center allows students to connect through an Internet-based radio station, online forums, a student newspaper, and a student television production group.

Credit Options

Through SCAD e-Learning, the Savannah College of Art and Design offers students the option of taking courses without enrolling in a degree or certificate program. Depending on their admission status, students may take courses for credit. Students enrolled in degree programs may complete other online courses for elective credit. Course offerings change quarterly; students should consult the SCAD e-Learning Web site for an updated course list.

Faculty

A large and distinguished international faculty consists of professors with diverse professional and educational backgrounds. Faculty members hold terminal degrees or other outstanding credentials in their fields and emphasize learning through individual attention in a positively oriented environment.

Admission

Application and admission policies and procedures for SCAD e-Learning are the same as for all other undergraduate and graduate programs offered by the College. Qualified SCAD e-Learning students are eligible to receive scholarships, fellowships, and federal and state financial aid. For detailed information, prospective students should visit http://www.scad.edu/applynow.

Application requirements for graduate programs include the completed application form, a nonrefundable application fee of $50, an official transcript from each college or university attended, letters of recommendation, a statement of purpose, a portfolio, and a resume, if applicable. GRE scores are recommended but not required.

Tuition and Fees

Undergraduate tuition for 2006–07 is $2550 per 5-credit-hour course; graduate tuition is $2600 per 5-credit-hour course. All degree-seeking students pay a one-time, nonrefundable matriculation fee of $500. Non-degree-seeking students pay a tuition deposit of $200.

Financial Aid

Federal financial aid is available to degree-seeking students who are enrolled at least half-time (two classes). Aid programs offered by the state of Georgia are available to students who are enrolled full-time (three classes). Students are encouraged to check with their states for availability of state aid. Courses leading to a certificate or continuing education credits do not qualify for either federal or state financial aid.

Applying

To apply, learn about online programs offered by Savannah College of Art and Design, or to participate in the SCAD e-Learning self-assessment test, students should go online to http://www.scad.edu/scadelearning.

CONTACT

SCAD e-Learning
Savannah College of Art and Design
P.O. Box 2072
Savannah, Georgia 31402-2072
Phone: 912-525-5100
800-869-7223 (toll-free)
E-mail: admission@scad.edu
Web site: http://www.scad.edu/scadelearning/

SAYBROOK GRADUATE SCHOOL

Graduate Programs in Psychology, Human Science, and Organizational Systems

San Francisco, California

Founded in 1971, Saybrook Graduate School and Research Center has been a leader in distance learning for graduate education. Saybrook's Master of Arts (M.A.) and Doctorate in Philosophy (Ph.D.) degrees in psychology, organizational systems, and human science are accredited by the Western Association of Schools and Colleges (WASC). Saybrook was founded on the humanistic belief and emphasizes the study of and inquiry into the human experience. Programs are designed as a transformational process where students increase their knowledge and their capacity to make a difference. Saybrook believes that graduate education should prepare scholars and practitioners to take effective leadership roles in fostering the higher levels of individual and organizational awareness that are needed to realize the immense possibilities of the modern day. Students benefit from a teaching model whose premise is that students should have choices in what to study and how they want to learn.

Distance Learning Program

For more than thirty-five years, students have earned M.A. and Ph.D. degrees through Saybrook's distance learning model. This interactive learning environment blends unique and individualized one-on-one faculty mentoring, online academic courses, and residential conferences with intensive seminars and workshops with faculty members and students. With the School's one-on-one faculty mentoring format, students have the opportunity to develop their own curricula aligned with their personal and professional interests. Students who want to pursue a Ph.D. have the opportunity to transfer all credits from their master's degree, if the master's degree was earned at Saybrook.

Delivery Media

In Saybrook's virtual classroom, students who are enrolled in an online course begin and end the course together as a group. Saybrook requires students to use technology to perform research, send assignments, communicate regularly with faculty members, and connect with fellow students and administrators during their coursework. Consistent with the unique distance learning process, students are able to use many different learning methods: Web-based classrooms, e-mail, bulletin boards, residential conferences, faculty mentoring, and others to interact with faculty members and students.

Programs of Study

Students can earn M.A. and Ph.D. degrees in human science, organizational systems, and psychology. Each program emphasizes the study of and inquiry into understanding people in their entirety. Courses center on humanistic philosophical, scientific, social, and political contexts as well as practical, real world implications.

Students are eligible to take classes in any program Saybrook offers, although students have the option to focus their study by selecting a concentration from the following areas: consciousness and spirituality, humanistic and transpersonal psychology, integrative health studies, organizational systems, and social transformation.

The human science program explores the human experience in historical, contextual, cross-cultural, political, and spiritual terms. In particular, it addresses the ways in which self-reflection, art, music, poetry, drama, language, and imagery reveal the human state. Human science puts the person back into science and reopens the discussion between science, art, and philosophy. Students enter the human science program with an interest in how a person's outlook and perspective inform the theory and practice in their field.

The organizational systems (OS) program studies how to better understand organizations as systems, the ability to assess the need for change, and ways to implement productive changes for organizational and social systems. Students learn the theoretical and intervention skills necessary to bring about effective change. The OS program offers four optional focus areas: human systems inquiry and social systems design, leadership in the systems design of education, organization development and transformation, and sustainability and organizational systems. Note: Students earning a master's or doctoral degree in OS may not choose another concentration.

The psychology program is designed for a growing core of individuals with cutting-edge clinical interests and practices that embrace both individuals and culture. The program is designed for students planning for or engaged in careers in health, teaching, clinical work, community development, consultation, mediation and conflict resolution work, human resources, and counseling and guidance. Saybrook offers the coursework necessary to take the licensing exam for both the marriage and family therapy license and the psychologist license in most states. Please note that states' requirements could vary greatly and licensing grounds constantly shift, so students are encouraged to take the responsibility to check her or his state's licensing requirements.

Student Services

Saybrook's intent is to be responsive to student and institutional needs. As a distance learning graduate school, most administrative business can be conducted online. Students can find information at http://www.saybrook.edu/student_resources/ and students can e-mail or phone the appropriate department at any time.

Faculty

Students have the opportunity to work with an internationally recognized faculty of scholars and practitioners, all of which hold a doctoral degree in their field. In addition to teaching, faculty members have extensive experience as researchers, practitioners, consultants, authors, business people, and organizational leaders. They are committed to Saybrook's ideals and values and strongly support students' personal and scholarly growth.

Admission

All applicants seeking admission into a master's program must hold a bachelor's degree from a regionally accredited institution. The minimum expected grade point average (GPA) requirement is 3.0 from the last degree-granting institution; however, exceptions may be made with the approval of the Vice President of Academic Affairs.

Doctoral degree applicants must have an appropriate master's degree from a regionally accredited institution. Candidates wishing to pursue the doctoral degree but who lack a master's degree should apply to one of Saybrook's M.A. programs and, upon graduation from the master's program, apply for the Ph.D. program and transfer a maximum of 31 Saybrook credits toward Saybrook's Ph.D. degree.

Tuition and Fees

The annual tuition for the 2006–07 academic year is $16,800. The annual marriage and family therapy (MFT) tuition for the 2006-07 academic year is $15,800. Also required are fees of approximately $800 each for twice-a-year Residential Conferences (RCs). The fee covers the cost of registration, meals, conference materials, and meeting space, but does not include travel and lodging costs.

Financial Aid

U.S. citizens or eligible permanent residents may borrow up to $18,500 per year through the Federal Stafford Student Loan Program. Saybrook offers limited tuition assistance to qualified students.

Applying

It is strongly recommended that applications are completed at least three months before the proposed enrollment date. Priority is given to applications received by June 30 for a September enrollment. Applications received by December 15 have priority for March enrollment. Applications are reviewed on a case-by-case basis until the Residential Orientation for each term. The financial aid process should be initiated at least three months prior to the proposed enrollment date to guarantee timely disbursement of tuition funds.

An online admission fee of $50 is required for first- and second-degree candidates. An application fee is required every time an application is submitted for review.

CONTACT

Saybrook Graduate School and Research Center
747 Front Street, 3rd Floor
San Francisco, California 94111-1920
Phone: 415-433-9200
800-825-4480 (toll-free)
Fax: 415-433-9271
E-mail: admissions@saybrook.edu
Web site: http://www.saybrook.edu

SCHILLER INTERNATIONAL UNIVERSITY

M.B.A. Online Programs in Financial Planning, International Business, International Hotel and Tourism Management, and Management of Information Technology

Dunedin, Florida

Schiller International University (SIU), a leader in global education, with eight campuses in six countries, was founded in 1964. SIU is an independent, licensed, and accredited institution offering a curriculum of more than 300 courses in sixteen areas of study that leads to associate, bachelor's, and master's degrees. The mission of SIU is to prepare students, personally and professionally, for future leadership roles in an international setting. Schiller students have the unique opportunity of transferring among SIU's campuses without losing any credits while continuing their chosen program of study. SIU's campuses are in Dunedin, Florida; London, England; Paris, France; Strasbourg, France; Heidelberg, Germany; Engelberg, Switzerland; Leysin, Switzerland; and Madrid, Spain.

Schiller is a university where personal initiative is encouraged and where faculty members know students by name. The close attention paid to each individual student is one of the hallmarks of an SIU education. SIU is accredited by the Accrediting Council for Independent Colleges and Schools (ACICS) and is licensed by the Florida Commission for Independent Education. The accreditation and licensing applies to both traditional and online programs.

Distance Learning Program

Distance learning is a natural extension of the University's high-quality education, both on the undergraduate and graduate levels, for students from all over the world. This program has been developed in response to the needs of the adult learner in the Information Age. The creative use of modern education technology makes selected SIU programs available, anytime, anywhere, through the World Wide Web. Students may complete the entire M.B.A. program online, or online courses may be combined with one or more terms in residence at an SIU campus in the United States or in Europe. Online courses are usually limited to no more than 20 students per class.

Delivery Media

Online M.B.A.'s in international business, international hotel and tourism management, and management of information technology are available to all students who have access to a Pentium-based computer, a 28.8-Kbps (or faster) modem, the usual office software, and an Internet connection. All courses are Web-based and are delivered via the Internet, using the eCollege.com platform. Technical support is provided 24 hours a day, seven days a week, by eCollege.com's help desk. The course Web site contains a home page with the most essential information about the course, e-mail links to the instructor and other students taking the course, a discussion forum that allows instructor and students to communicate with the group as a whole, Web links, and glossaries. Each course utilizes a textbook, a study guide on CD-ROM, and the Web-based course materials, which also provide the medium of interaction. Although most interaction is asynchronous, chat rooms are available for student and faculty member use.

Programs of Study

Completion of an Online M.B.A. requires 45 credit hours. The curriculum for the international business degree concentrates on the more detailed aspects of international marketing, management, finance, and economics. For the concentrations in financial planning, international hotel and tourism management (IHTM), or management of information technology (MIT), students complete seven core M.B.A. courses, two elective courses, and six concentrated courses in either financial planning, IHTM, or MIT. Students whose undergraduate background does not include preparation in accounting/finance, economics, or statistics are required to take additional preparatory courses, which are available online. The degree requirements are designed to provide practical knowledge and training for future business executives. SIU M.B.A. programs promote a professional academic environment without borders in which world-class education is offered in worldwide classrooms online.

In addition to the Online M.B.A., selected courses on the undergraduate level are offered in a distance learning format. More information about all programs can be accessed from SIU's Web site.

Special Programs

SIU offers an Executive M.B.A. program, which combines online courses as well as evening, weekend, and accelerated summer courses at selected campuses. During specific semesters, several undergraduate- and graduate-level courses are available online in a variety of subjects, including accounting, business administration and management, business communications, computer/information technology administration and management, economics, English composition, history, hospitality services management, human resources management, international business, international relations and diplomacy, marketing management and research, mathematics, physical sciences, psychology, statistics, and tourism and travel services marketing operations.

Student Services

The University has developed a number of methods to assist students in distance learning programs. Each student receives a copy of SIU's publication, *A Guide to Distance Learning.* Specially trained faculty mentors are always available by e-mail for consultation, and the Web-based host for the courses offers technical assistance 24 hours a day. Students in the distance learning programs have access to the full range of support services, including the Library and Information Resource Network (LIRN) and NET Library, that are used by all Schiller students. Each online course has its own library of study aids and resources. Lecture notes, sample quizzes, assignment checks, and hyperlinks to other interesting sites are available for viewing and downloading.

Credit Options

For the master's program, students must earn at least 36 credit hours, and undergraduates must earn at least 33 credits at SIU. Credit may be awarded to students who receive appropriate scores in CLEP subject examinations. Students admitted to the Executive M.B.A. program at the Florida campus may earn up to 6 credits by portfolio.

Faculty

All virtual courses are taught by instructors with advanced degrees and extensive practical experience in their fields. The faculty members' ability to teach in both online and ground-based formats ensures consistency across the programs. All courses in the distance learning program are Web-based. An online course has learning objectives identical to those of a ground-delivered course, incorporating both asynchronous and the possibility of synchronous technology to facilitate learning. Each course has a syllabus describing the course content, assignments, and grading policy. The faculty members choose from many course-delivery technologies, including journals and e-mail for assignment submission and correspondence; and discussion forums and chat rooms for ongoing questions and answers. The instructor uses these technologies to enhance the learning experience.

Admission

Admission to the Online M.B.A. program requires completion of a B.B.A. degree or equivalent; a bachelor's degree or equivalent, with a major in business studies or economics, providing that core courses have been completed in economics, statistics, business law, marketing, management, and accounting; or a bachelor's degree or equivalent in a nonbusiness field, provided that course work in the areas listed above has been completed. Nonnative English speakers must provide scores of at least 550 (213 for the computerized test) on a TOEFL taken within the past two years. Test scores should be sent directly to the University.

A completed application form must be sent to the SIU Office of Admissions together with a $60 application fee, payable by check, credit card, or international money order. Applicants must also request that official transcripts of academic work be sent via airmail to the Office of Admissions. Applicants must submit transcripts of all college courses attended as well as proof of an earned degree. Undergraduate applicants must submit proof of high school graduation as well as TOEFL scores, if applicable. Original documents or certified copies must be submitted as well as a certified English translation of those documents not in English.

Tuition and Fees

Distance learning students pay the same tuition as on-campus students. Tuition for the 2006–07 academic year is $474 per graduate credit and $470 per undergraduate credit and is payable by check, credit card, or international money order. Tuition includes all instruction and faculty-produced materials. Students are responsible for the additional cost of textbooks, and information about online booksellers is provided. Room and board fees vary by campus. Students wishing to complete a portion of their degree in residence should contact the individual campus. Additional fees include a $60 application fee, a $90 graduation fee, and a late registration fee of $125, which is applicable only after classes commence.

Financial Aid

SIU participates in Title IV programs and is eligible to participate in the Veteran's Training Program. Both programs are for U.S. citizens and residents who qualify. Students should e-mail the Office of Financial Aid for further information.

Applying

Applications for admission are accepted year-round. Classes begin in September, January, and June. Students interested in online courses must complete two surveys, which are found on the distance learning page of the SIU Web site. Students can visit this site or contact the Office of Admissions for further information.

CONTACT

Office of Admissions
Schiller International University
453 Edgewater Drive
Dunedin, Florida 34698
Phone: 727-736-5082
800-336-4133 (toll-free in the U.S.)
Fax: 727-734-0359
E-mail: admissions@schiller.edu
financial_aid@schiller.edu
Web site: http://www.schiller.edu

SETON HALL UNIVERSITY

M.A. in Educational Leadership, Management, and Policy

South Orange, New Jersey

Founded in 1856, Seton Hall is a private coeducational Catholic institution—the nation's oldest diocesan institution of higher education. One of the region's most prestigious academic institutions and a recognized leader in online education, the University enrolls about 10,000 students.

Seton Hall University and its associated online programs are accredited by the National Council for Accreditation of Teacher Education (NCATE) and the Middle States Association of Colleges and Schools.

Distance Learning Program

SetonWorldWide, Seton Hall's online campus, provides learners with the opportunity to earn a Seton Hall University degree in an e-learning environment that allows the working professional to fit their education into their busy lifestyle.

Delivery Media

Learners access their online course rooms using an Internet connection—anytime, anywhere. This 24/7 access allows course study and interaction in a flexible user-friendly environment. The student-professor ratio is kept at 10:1 to ensure a timely response from the professor to each student.

Programs of Study

The M.A. in Education, Leadership, Management, and Policy (ELMP) program provides students with extensive knowledge of educational administration, including academic theories, skills, and techniques. This graduate degree concentration can lead to a supervisor certification with the New Jersey State Department of Education, and course work can be applied toward similar certification in other states. Students also train for the principal certification, which is built into this degree program.

The two-year program consists of eleven 3-credit courses and 6-credit principal internship for a total of 39 credits. All candidates take a comprehensive written examination at the end of the sixth semester.

The Department of Education Leadership, Management, and Policy holds two mandatory on-campus residency weekends. These weekend residencies usually begin in mid-July. Each weekend begins on Friday afternoon and runs through noon on Sunday. Residencies provide learning team members the opportunity to meet face-to-face, share experiences, continue discussions, provide feedback on program progress, and meet with instructors.

Special Programs

SetonWorldWide and Seton Hall University's College of Education and Human Services have teamed up to create an online supervisor's certificate program for teachers who have a master's degree but require additional credits to obtain the certificate. Successful completion of the 12-credit program enables students to be eligible for a supervisor of instruction position.

Student Services

Seton Hall provides online support and assistance throughout the program, and learners have access to Seton Hall University's extensive library resources.

Credit Options

Transfer credits are accepted on a selective, individual basis.

Faculty

All courses are taught by Seton Hall University faculty members with expertise in education, leadership, and management and policy as well as in online teaching and learning. There are 13 faculty members in the department.

Admission

Applicants must have a bachelor's degree from an accredited institution and at least a 3.0 GPA.

Tuition and Fees

The cost for the entire program is $21,000 and includes all fees and expenses, tuition, books and other materials, room and meals for the on-campus residencies, and graduation costs. Travel expenses to the residencies, the nonrefundable application fee, computer equipment, software, and Internet access are not included. Tuition for teachers in Catholic schools is $14,000, according to Seton Hall University policy.

Financial Aid

Most applicants who are American citizens are eligible for low-interest federal loans.

Applying

Interested students should apply online at http://www.setonworldwide.net, following the online instructions. A toll-free number and e-mail are available if questions arise. Applicants must submit the completed application, the nonrefundable $50 application fee, transcripts from all undergraduate institutions attended, a letter of intent that explains the reasons for applying to the program, a current resume, scores from the GRE or MAT, and three letters of recommendation from academic and/or professional references.

CONTACT

Mel Klein, Assistant Academic Director
Jubilee Hall, Room 357
Seton Hall University
400 South Orange Avenue
South Orange, New Jersey 07079
Phone: 888-738-6699 Ext. 2469
(toll-free)
Fax: 973-761-9325
E-mail: kleinmel@shu.edu

Al Galloway, Program Director
Jubilee Hall, Room 357
Seton Hall University
400 South Orange Avenue
South Orange, New Jersey 07079
Phone: 888-738-6699 Ext. 2469
(toll-free)
Fax: 973-761-9325
E-mail: gallowal@shu.edu
Web site:
http://www.setonworldwide.net

SETON HALL UNIVERSITY

M.A. in Strategic Communication and Leadership

South Orange, New Jersey

Founded in 1856, Seton Hall is a private coeducational Catholic institution—the nation's oldest diocesan institution of higher education in the United States. One of the region's most prestigious academic institutions and a recognized leader in online education, Seton Hall University enrolls approximately 10,000 undergraduate and graduate students. Seton Hall University is accredited by the Middle States Commission on Higher Education.

Distance Learning Program

SetonWorldWide, Seton Hall's online campus, provides learners with the opportunity to earn a Seton Hall University degree in an e-learning environment that allows the working professional to fit their education into their busy lifestyle.

Delivery Media

Learners access their online course rooms using an Internet connection—anytime, anywhere. This 24/7 access allows course study and interaction in a flexible user-friendly environment.

Programs of Study

A basic building block for success in today's highly competitive world is the manager who can lead and communicate effectively. Executives, managers, and military command personnel are increasingly expected to bring to their organizations these unique competencies. The Master of Arts in Strategic Communication and Leadership (MASCL) program has been designed to meet the needs of today's busy professional. Through a highly interactive curriculum that allows for significant discussion of strategies and solutions to current issues in effective leadership and communication, the program provides an opportunity to network and study with colleagues and experts in specialized disciplines. Using state-of-the-art online learning technologies, this rigorous program is aimed at helping the high-potential individual earn a Seton Hall University degree in a convenient format.

A serious program for the serious learner, MASCL requires 36 credits and takes eighteen months to complete. Students interact with a learning team of their peers (successful executives, managers, and professionals), experienced instructors, and other experts in an anytime, anyplace e-learning environment. Three on-campus weekend-long residencies, five 12-week modules, and an ongoing leadership and communication skills enhancement program combine to develop the superior abilities required for dynamic leadership. Faculty members mentor participants throughout the program to polish interpersonal, presentation, and writing skills.

The three on-site weekends—Orientation, Mid-Program Residency, and Final Residency—include sessions for students to practice their communication and leadership skills. Individual coaching is provided during all of the residencies. The Orientation Weekend prepares the learning team for the program. Students meet one another, faculty members, and administrators. They learn how to access and use the online learning technologies, and they make a presentation and receive feedback and coaching. At the Mid-Program residency, students give group and individual presentations, and they also take part in a mock press conference. During the Final Residency, students present their strategic-communication plan, with an emphasis on how they intend to communicate it to their organization's stakeholders. The weekend concludes with commencement exercises.

Student Services

Seton Hall provides online support and assistance throughout the program, and learners have access to Seton Hall University's extensive library resources.

Credit Options

All course waivers, including work experience, and transfer credits are subject to the review and approval of the program director.

Faculty

The Department of Communication faculty members combine practical experience with academic preparation. Each curricular area utilizes faculty members who have impressive professional records and those with doctoral degrees for a blend of the academic and practical.

Admission

Applicants should have a baccalaureate degree from an accredited college or university. The ideal candidate has significant experience in a corporate, military, governmental, association, or nonprofit organization. Candidates are ready for increased workplace responsibilities or a new executive position and seek to develop and enhance their leadership communication skills in preparation for these challenges and opportunities. They typically do not have the time to attend an on-campus program and seek a rigorous online program in communication, leadership, business strategy, and organizational development.

Tuition and Fees

The cost for the entire program is $27,500 and includes all fees and expenses, tuition, books and other materials, room and meals for the on-campus residencies, and graduation costs. Travel expenses to the on-campus residencies, the application fee, computer equipment, software, and Internet access are not included in this figure.

Financial Aid

Financial aid for graduate students is available in the form of a FFELP/ Stafford Loan, an alternative loan, or a personal loan. Another option available to students is a budget plan that divides tuition costs into monthly payments. Students are encouraged to check with their human resources departments to determine what educational assistance or tuition reimbursement programs may be available.

Applying

Students must submit the completed online application, the $50 nonrefundable application fee, official transcripts from all colleges and universities attended, two letters of recommendation (preferably one each from a present and a former supervisor), a current resume, a work sample in any medium that demonstrates the candidate's excellence in his or her field, and a short (about 500 words) essay that states the candidate's goals for engaging in the MASCL learning experience.

CONTACT

Regina Walker, Account Executive
Presidents Hall, Room 327
Seton Hall University
400 South Orange Avenue
South Orange, New Jersey 07079
Phone: 973-275-2419
Fax: 973-761-9325
E-mail: walkerre@shu.edu
Web site: http://www.setonworldwide.net

SETON HALL UNIVERSITY

Programs in Nursing

South Orange, New Jersey

Founded in 1856, Seton Hall is a private coeducational Catholic institution—the nation's oldest diocesan institution of higher education in the United States. One of the region's most prestigious academic institutions and a recognized leader in online education, the University enrolls about 10,000 students. Seton Hall University and its associated online programs are accredited by the Middle States Association of Colleges and Schools.

Distance Learning Program

SetonWorldWide, Seton Hall's online campus, offers degree programs and certificates designed for professionals who have demonstrated achievement in their respective fields and have the ability, desire, and dedication to accept the rigors of a fast-paced, challenging curriculum. Working professionals can benefit from "anytime, anywhere" education. As learning team members, students and faculty members have extensive interaction, and these relationships provide a rich and dynamic online learning experience. All SetonWorldWide degree program graduates receive an accredited Seton Hall University degree.

Delivery Media

Online learning takes advantage of different methods of presentation, but the educational objectives are the same as traditional, in-classroom learning at Seton Hall University. SetonWorldWide provides for student-teacher interaction through a discussion section for each unit, which poses questions and comments initiated by the instructor. Students then respond both to the instructor and to each other with answers that show critical thinking and synthesis of course content. E-mail is used for individual and small-group interactions. Instructors review student material submitted electronically, and students receive feedback via e-mail or telephone.

Programs of Study

The Bachelor of Science in Nursing (B.S.N.) program is designed for the busy RN who wants to balance career and personal commitments with a flexible educational program of study. The five-semester program offers the required 34 credits of nursing (nine courses) online, and students may complete their clinical requirements within their respective geographical locations.

The nationally ranked Master of Science in Nursing (M.S.N.)–Nurse Practitioner program provides highly interactive online multimedia programs in five clinical specialty areas: adult, gerontological, pediatric, women's health, and acute-care nurse practitioner. Students complete the didactic portion of the program online in their home or office at their convenience. The required clinical practice component is fulfilled within the students' geographical location. All nurse practitioner graduates are eligible to apply for advanced-practice certification.

The 33-credit M.S.N. in health systems administration is designed to prepare nurse managers, directors, and executives with the needed leadership skills demanded by today's complex health-care industry. Students become knowledgeable about the business and financial operations necessary to effectively manage large patient-care departments. Nurses looking to bring their career to a new level in management are ideal candidates.

Three on-campus weekend residencies enable students to meet their classmates and the faculty in person. On Orientation Weekend, students participate in hands-on training in accessing their online courses and resources, tour the Seton Hall campus, and meet other online learning teams. For the Mid-Program Weekend Residency, clinical assessment skills are refined and role development sessions are scheduled. The Final Residency Weekend is the culminating event of the program, with scheduled final student project presentations and graduation activities. The health systems administration students attend only the first and last weekend residencies.

Student Services

Students find everything they need online, including admission information, academic assistance, financial aid assistance, career guidance, and other services. The Help Desk's technical support staff has the knowledge and experience to help make every student's transition into the virtual classroom a smooth one. All SetonWorldWide participants have access to Seton Hall University library resources. During the orientation, students meet the librarians and technical staff members who provide assistance throughout the program. Students can use the library's ASK ME service to request and receive assistance from a fully qualified librarian.

Credit Options

Graduate credits earned recently at another accredited college or university may be accepted in partial satisfaction of graduate credit requirements. A total of 6 credits may be approved for transfer.

Faculty

The College of Nursing faculty includes distinguished educators and prolific researchers who bring real-world management perspectives to the learning environment. Students receive truly individualized personal attention as well as supportive career direction and guidance. The College has about 60 full- and part-time faculty members.

Admission

In addition to having a diploma or an associate degree from a nursing program, applicants to the B.S.N. program must have a minimum overall GPA of 3.0 and RN licensure. M.S.N. applicants must have graduated from an NLN- or CCNE-accredited baccalaureate program in nursing and have earned at least a B average in nursing courses and overall. GRE or MAT testing is required.

Tuition and Fees

The all-inclusive tuition includes all fees, except for the application fee and room and meals for the short on-campus residencies. Computer equipment, software, Internet access, and travel expenses to the residencies are not covered. The cost for tuition for the 2005–06 academic year was $717 per credit for undergraduate courses and $743 per credit for graduate courses.

Financial Aid

Almost 90 percent of the students who entered Seton Hall in 2005 received some form of financial aid, and 75 percent of these students received money directly from the University. The four types of financial aid include scholarships, grants and discounts, loans, and part-time jobs on campus. In addition, many working RNs use tuition remission through their places of employment. Specific nursing scholarships are available for nursing students during the clinical portion of the curriculum.

Applying

B.S.N. applicants must submit the completed application, the $45 nonrefundable application fee, all official high school and college transcripts, two letters of recommendation from academic and professional references, and a resume or curriculum vitae. M.S.N. applicants must submit the completed application, the $50 nonrefundable application fee, a typewritten statement of goals, a curriculum vitae or resume, all official college transcripts, two letters of recommendation, and scores from the Miller Analogies Test.

CONTACT

Mary Jo Bugel, Director of Recruitment
Schwartz Hall
Seton Hall University
400 South Orange Avenue
South Orange, New Jersey 07079
Phone: 973-275-9306
Fax: 973-761-9607
E-mail: nursing@shu.edu
Web site: http://www.setonworldwide.net

SETON HALL UNIVERSITY

Master of Healthcare Administration

South Orange, New Jersey

Founded in 1856, Seton Hall is a private coeducational Catholic institution—the oldest diocesan institution of higher education in the United States. One of the nation's most prestigious academic institutions and a recognized leader in online education, the University enrolls about 10,000 students.

Seton Hall University is accredited by the Middle States Commission on Higher Education. A member of the Association of University Programs in Health Administration (AUPHA), a national association of university-based educational programs dedicated to continuously improving the field of health management and practice, the Seton Hall University Master of Healthcare Administration Program is ranked seventh among AUPHA's survey of the nation's twenty-five largest M.H.A. programs in the nation.

Distance Learning Program

SetonWorldWide, Seton Hall's online campus, provides learners with the opportunity to earn a Seton Hall University degree in an e-learning environment that allows the working professional to fit their education into their busy lifestyle.

Delivery Media

Learners access their online course rooms using any Internet connection—anytime, anywhere. This 24/7 access allows course study and interaction in a flexible user-friendly environment.

Programs of Study

The Seton Hall University Online Master of Healthcare Administration (M.H.A.) and Online Certificate in Healthcare Administration programs prepare managers for leadership roles within the health-care industry. Providing a rigorous and thorough understanding of the health-care environment, the programs address "real-world" strategies and skills that help health-care managers make significant contributions to their organizations.

Using state-of-the-art learning technologies in a highly interactive learning environment, the program is designed around an applied-focused, rigorous curriculum. The 39-credit, twenty-three-month program consists of six competency areas: Understanding the Environment, Managing Change, Financial Competencies, Decision Making, Strategic Leadership, and Analysis as well as a capstone project. All course work is completed online. There are three required on-campus weekend residencies. Learners begin the program with an orientation residency, followed by a midprogram residency, and a final residency at the end of the program.

Special Programs

The 15-credit online Graduate Certificate Program in Healthcare Administration is designed for individuals who might wish to pursue a career in health-care administration, those who already have a graduate degree but need to develop specific management skills, or individuals who would like to enroll in a selected set of graduate health-care administration courses but choose not to commit to an entire graduate degree program.

Student Services

Seton Hall provides online support and assistance throughout the program, and learners have access to Seton Hall University's extensive library resources.

Credit Options

Learners enroll in a cohort class and follow a prescribed sequential course of study. In most cases previously earned academic course credits are not accepted toward fulfilling the degree requirements.

Faculty

The faculty is composed of full-time Seton Hall faculty members as well as experienced practitioners with extensive knowledge in their respective fields. The SetonWorldwide Online M.H.A. program faculty members provide an in-depth theoretical and real-world practice knowledge base.

Admission

Candidates should have a baccalaureate degree from an accredited college or university with an undergraduate GPA of at least 3.0 or equivalent and health-care managerial experience.

Tuition and Fees

The cost for the six-semester program is $29,500 and includes all fees and expenses, tuition, books and other materials, room and meals for the on-campus residencies, and graduation costs. Travel expenses to the residencies, the application fee, computer equipment, software, and Internet access are not included in this figure.

Financial Aid

Many learners fund their tuition through employer tuition-reimbursement benefits or through federal and private institutional loan programs. The University does not offer financial aid in the form of scholarships or grants for online M.H.A. students.

Applying

Application to the program can be submitted online. The application process includes submission of a completed online application, a $50 nonrefundable application fee, transcripts from all universities attended, a letter of intent, a current resume, and three letters of recommendation from academic or professional references. In addition, individuals who have graduated from a baccalaureate program within the last five years must submit test scores from the GRE (aptitude), GMAT, or LSAT.

CONTACT

James J. Howard, Ph.D., Program Director
SetonWorldWide Online Master of Healthcare Administration Program
Presidents Hall, Room 328
Seton Hall University
400 South Orange Avenue
South Orange, New Jersey 07079
Phone: 973-275-2559
Fax: 973-761-9325
E-mail: howardjj@shu.edu
Web site: http://www.setonworldwide.net

SETON HALL UNIVERSITY

M.A. in Counseling

South Orange, New Jersey

Founded in 1856, Seton Hall is a private coeducational Catholic institution—the nation's oldest diocesan institution of higher education in the United States. One of the region's most prestigious academic institutions and a recognized leader in online education, Seton Hall University enrolls approximately 10,000 undergraduate and graduate students. Seton Hall University is accredited by the Middle States Commission on Higher Education.

Distance Learning Program

SetonWorldWide, Seton Hall's online campus, provides learners with the opportunity to earn a Seton Hall University degree in an e-learning environment that allows the working professional to fit their education into their busy lifestyle.

Delivery Media

Learners access their online course rooms using an Internet connection—anytime, anywhere. This 24/7 access allows course study and interaction in a flexible user-friendly environment.

Programs of Study

Seton Hall University's online counseling degrees follow a predetermined set of courses and are designed to expertly train students of diverse backgrounds, providing them with a solid, general knowledge base and clinical preparation for advanced work in the mental-health field or in the field of school counseling. The program's primary goal is to provide students with a thorough grounding in the theories, skills, and models of interventions essential to function effectively as counselors in a variety of settings.

The 48-credit curriculum provides students with a thorough background in individual counseling and group counseling skills and theory; clinical practice and ethical, professional, and legal issues in counseling; social and cultural factors in counseling; human development across the life span; work, leisure, and career development theories and interventions; appraisal and assessment issues in counseling; the application of research methodology and statistics to understand mental-health issues; and the role and function of community mental-health agencies.

Seton Hall University's 48-credit online Master of Arts in School Counseling program prepares students for work in educational settings as school guidance counselors and may lead to certification as a school counselor in certain states. The program in school counseling emphasizes the development of competence, social consciousness, and reflection. Students are trained to work in ethnically, geographically, and socially diverse K–12 settings. This program promotes three major counseling functions within the context of school settings: prevention and intervention of personal and interpersonal concerns, fostering of optimal human development, and coordination of care services for students within school systems. Students begin the program learning the basics of counseling skills and foundational theories, and they end the program transitioning from a three-semester applied clinical experience.

Special Programs

A clinical experience is a part of the master's degree. Students receive individual counseling, guidance, and support from dedicated faculty members throughout this aspect of the program to ensure the most professional experience possible during the practicum and internship.

The program curriculum meets many state requirements for licensure. For students requiring an additional number of courses, Seton Hall University offers a 12-credit sequence of courses or a post-masters licensure program online.

Students who are completing the M.A. in Counseling program can also enroll in the 12-credit post-master's School Counselor Certificate program that meets many state requirements for certification as a school counselor in grades K–12, and they can enroll in a post-masters licensing sequence if additional courses are needed.

Student Services

Seton Hall provides online support and assistance throughout the program and learners have online access to Seton Hall University's extensive library resources.

Credit Options

This program is open only to those who are matriculating as new students. Transfer credits are accepted on a selective individual basis.

Faculty

The program uses Seton Hall University faculty members as well as qualified adjunct professors who are leading experts and practitioners in the field of counseling. Faculty members also engage in traditional classroom teaching and learning. Students have a variety of instructors, all highly qualified. All course facilitators meet requirements as instructors.

Admission

All applicants must have a bachelor's degree from an accredited college or university and submit three letters of recommendation, a personal statement, and a resume. GRE or MAT scores may be waived in individual cases.

Tuition and Fees

The total cost of the 48-credit program is $32,500. This includes all fees, except for the application fee, and all expenses, including books and other materials and room and meals for the short on-campus residencies. Computer equipment, software, Internet access, and travel expenses to the residencies are not covered.

Financial Aid

There are various options for financing a degree from Seton Hall University. In order to be eligible for financial aid, a student must be accepted into a degree program. Financial aid for graduate students is available in the form of a FFELP/Stafford Loan, an alternative loan, or a personal loan. Another option available to students is a budget plan that divides tuition costs into monthly payments. Students are encouraged to check with their human resources departments to determine what educational assistance or tuition reimbursement programs may be available.

To be considered for any federal, state or University financial aid programs administered by Seton Hall, students must fill out the Free Application for Federal Student Aid (FAFSA). This free form is used to determine a student's eligibility for all financial aid programs. The FAFSA application can be completed online at http://www.fafsa.ed.gov. The Seton Hall University school code for FAFSA is 002632.

Applying

Applicants must submit the completed online application, the $50 nonrefundable application fee, transcripts from all undergraduate or graduate institutions attended, GRE or MAT scores (may be waived in individual cases), TOEFL scores (if applicable), three letters of recommendation, a resume, and a personal statement.

CONTACT

Rosalie Maiorella, Program Administrator
Presidents Hall, Room 324
Seton Hall University
400 South Orange Avenue
South Orange, New Jersey 07079
Phone: 973-313-6239
Fax: 973-761-9325
E-mail: maiorero@shu.edu
Web site: http://www.setonworldwide.net

SKIDMORE COLLEGE

University Without Walls

Saratoga Springs, New York

University Without Walls (UWW) is the external degree program for adults at Skidmore College. UWW was in the vanguard in establishing a program for distance learners. The program began in 1971 as an experiment in nontraditional education jointly funded by the Ford Foundation and the U.S. Department of Education. When the funding for this experiment ended in 1975, Skidmore College took over the program as its own. Over the years, UWW has evolved to serve adult students pursuing baccalaureate degrees in a variety of liberal arts, performing arts, and preprofessional fields.

The UWW program is characterized by its flexibility and the high quality of education students receive. The unique advising system at UWW guarantees that each program meets the student's individual needs and the high standards of Skidmore College.

Distance Learning Program

UWW serves 280 full- and part-time baccalaureate students from as near as the city of Saratoga Springs and as far away as Europe, Africa, and Asia. The UWW program does not require its students to be in residence on campus. Student programs may include on-site UWW seminars, UWW online courses, independent study with Skidmore faculty members, courses at other accredited institutions, internships, and distance learning courses from major universities. Every program includes a final project in the area of the student's focus.

Delivery Media

With support from an Alfred P. Sloan Foundation grant, UWW is able to offer students the opportunity to earn a bachelor's degree entirely online. Students also take courses at other accredited institutions. Independent study takes place through telephone, mail, and e-mail communication. Students can work with their advisers to explore an individualized major or, through the Sloan Asynchronous Learning Network, complete their bachelor's degree entirely online in one of the following interdisciplinary concentrations: American History and Culture, Communication and the Arts, and Human Nature and Behavior.

Programs of Study

UWW offers Bachelor of Arts degrees in most traditional liberal arts fields, including American studies, anthropology, art history, biology, chemistry, classics, computer science, economics, English, French, geology, German, government, history, mathematics, philosophy, physics, political economy, psychology, religion, Russian, sociology, Spanish, and women's studies. Bachelor of Science degrees are available in art, business, dance, exercise science, human services, and theater. Students can also combine fields to create an interdisciplinary program, such as arts management, Asian studies, communications, environmental studies, health studies, human behavior, Latin American studies, management information systems, nonprofit management, organizational behavior, public administration, and religion and culture. Individually designed majors are welcomed.

All degrees are 120-credit programs. Programs are expected to include at least 12 credits in the humanities, 6 credits in history, 12 credits in the social sciences, and 9 credits in math or science, including laboratory experience. Professional programs must include at least 60 credits in the liberal arts. Courses taken prior to entry of UWW may be considered in satisfaction of these requirements.

Special Programs

UWW's flexibility allows many students to take advantage of unusual learning opportunities. Recent UWW students have studied abroad in Austria, Canada, Costa Rica, the Czech Republic, Germany, Ireland, Poland, Spain, Switzerland, and Thailand, among other locations. Business students often have the opportunity to include professional management and banking seminars in satisfaction of their degree requirements.

UWW students are often able to participate in programs sponsored by Skidmore College and the Office of Special Programs, including a summer study program in Florence, the New York State Writers Institute, the Skidmore Jazz Institute, the Summer Dance Workshop, and the Siti Summer Theater Workshop. UWW students are eligible for substantial discounts on courses offered by Skidmore Summer Academic Sessions and the Summer Six Art Program.

UWW business students are eligible to apply for 3/2 M.B.A. programs in cooperation with Rensselaer Polytechnic Institute in Troy and Rensselaer-Hartford.

Student Services

UWW is a small, personal program, and the staff members are happy to assist students in any way possible. Typical services include academic advising, registration assistance, financial aid counseling, and book-order assistance.

Local students also enjoy library privileges; career counseling, access to recreational facilities, access to computer labs, and an e-mail account. Some summer housing is available for special program participants.

Credit Options

UWW accepts transfer credit for courses completed with a grade of C or better. There is no limit to the number of credits transferred or the age of the work, provided that the course is appropriate to a liberal arts curriculum. Credit is also available for experiential learning. In addition, students may document knowledge through CLEP, ACT-PEP, DANTES, and Regents examinations. Many college-level courses offered through the military are accepted. Credit from international universities is usually accepted.

Faculty

There are approximately 200 full- and part-time members of the Skidmore faculty. Most participate as advisers and instructors in the UWW program. Ninety-three percent of the Skidmore faculty members have a terminal degree.

Admission

UWW considers any applicant able to succeed at demanding college-level work. However, the program works best for students who have had some college experience. Applicants must have a high school diploma or the equivalent.

Tuition and Fees

Students pay an initial enrollment fee of $4450; after the first year, an annual enrollment fee of $3750 is charged. Experiential credit review fee is $825. Independent study courses sponsored by Skidmore are $275 per credit hour. The final project fee is $800.

Financial Aid

Students are eligible for Federal Pell Grants, New York State TAP awards, and all federal loan programs. A small amount of scholarship assistance is available.

Applying

Application forms are available from UWW or can be downloaded from the UWW Web site. All students are required to attend a personal admissions interview on the Skidmore campus.

CONTACT

Kenneth Klotz, Acting Director
University Without Walls
Skidmore College
815 North Broadway
Saratoga Springs, New York 12866
Phone: 518-580-5450
866-310-6444 (toll-free)
Fax: 518-580-5449
E-mail: uww@skidmore.edu
Web site: http://www.skidmore.edu/uww

SOUTHERN METHODIST UNIVERSITY

School of Engineering

Dallas, Texas

Founded in 1911, SMU is a private, comprehensive university. SMU comprises six degree-granting schools: the School of Engineering, Dedman College of Humanities and Sciences, Meadows School of the Arts, the Edwin L. Cox School of Business, the Dedman School of Law, and Perkins School of Theology. Southern Methodist University is accredited by the Commission on Colleges of the Southern Association of Colleges and Schools.

For more than thirty years, the School of Engineering has been a national pioneer in offering distance education courses for graduate study. In 1964, the School of Engineering established one of the first two regional closed-circuit TV distance learning networks in the nation. In 1978, it instituted its own for-credit videotape program for students living outside the Dallas-Fort Worth area. Today, the program is delivered via DVD and students are enrolled nationally from coast to coast.

Distance Learning Program

The School of Engineering's distance learning program serves more than 600 graduate students. Master of Science degree programs are offered nationally via DVD. No campus attendance is required to complete the degree programs. Twenty M.S. degrees can be earned via DVD.

Delivery Media

Distance learning students are enrolled in classes that are given on the SMU campus. The lectures are recorded on DVD and sent once a week to the distance learning student. Distance learning students interact with their professors via phone, fax, e-mail, or the Internet. Many professors make course materials available to the student via the School of Engineering's Web site.

Programs of Study

Engineering schools have an obligation to be responsive to challenges and opportunities in a technological society. As a private university, SMU can respond quickly to engineering needs with high-quality academic programs.

The School of Engineering offers the following Master of Science degree programs via distance learning: civil engineering, computer engineering, computer science, electrical engineering, engineering management, environmental engineering, environmental science, environmental science (major in environmental systems management), environmental science (major in hazardous and waste materials management), facilities management, information engineering and management, manufacturing systems management, mechanical engineering, operations research, packaging of electronic and optical devices, security engineering, software engineering, systems engineering, and telecommunications.

The Master of Science degree requires 30–36 (depending on the program) semester credit hours for completion, with a minimum 3.0 grade point average on a 4.0 scale. Distance learning students may meet the credit requirement entirely by course work or have the option of preparing a thesis for 6 semester hours of credit.

Credit Options

Generally, up to 6 semester hours of graduate courses may be transferred from an institution approved by the School of Engineering's Graduate Division, provided that such course work was completed in the five years prior to matriculation, that the transferred courses carried graduate credit, that those courses were not used to meet the requirements of an undergraduate degree, and that grades of B– or higher were received in the courses to be transferred.

Faculty

Of the 45 full-time faculty members, 100 percent hold the doctorate or terminal professional degree in their fields. In addition, in the professional degree programs, the School of Engineering utilizes outstanding adjunct faculty members to bring into the classroom valuable experience from industry and government.

Admission

Admission to a Master of Science degree program requires the bachelor's degree appropriate to the program to which the student is applying, as well as a minimum grade point average of 3.0 (on a 4.0 scale) in previous undergraduate and graduate study. Scores on the Graduate Record Examinations (GRE) are required for the M.S. programs in civil engineering, computer engineering, computer science, electrical engineering, environmental engineering, environmental science, and mechanical engineering.

Tuition and Fees

Tuition for distance learning students is $930 per credit hour or $2790 for a 3-credit-hour course.

Financial Aid

Financial aid opportunities are available to distance learning students, including Federal Stafford Student Loans. SMU's distance learning programs are approved for Veterans Administration educational benefits.

Applying

Distance learning students must complete an application for admission to the Graduate Division of the School of Engineering and submit transcripts of all previous undergraduate and graduate work. Application deadline dates are as follows: for the fall semester, July 1; for the spring semester, November 15; and for the summer semester, April 15.

CONTACT

Jim Dees, Senior Director
Graduate Student Experience and Enrollment Management
School of Engineering
Southern Methodist University
P.O. Box 750335
Dallas, Texas 75275-0335
Phone: 214-768-1456
800-601-4040 (toll-free)
Fax: 214-768-3778
E-mail: jdees@engr.smu.edu
Web site: https://engr.smu.edu

SOUTHERN NEW HAMPSHIRE UNIVERSITY

SNHU Online

Manchester, New Hampshire

Southern New Hampshire University, founded in 1932, is a private, regional institution that is recognized for its solid academic programs and dedication to teaching. Southern New Hampshire University offers certificate and degree programs in business, community economic development, culinary arts, education, hospitality, and liberal arts, with degrees at the associate level through the doctoral level. Southern New Hampshire University is regionally and nationally accredited by the New England Association of Schools and Colleges, the Association of Collegiate Business Schools and Programs, the New England Postsecondary Education Commission, the New Hampshire State Department of Education for Teacher Certification, the American Culinary Federation Education Institute, and the North American Society for Sport Management.

Southern New Hampshire University's online program was established in 1996 and is one of New England's largest and fastest-growing programs. Southern New Hampshire University is a recognized leader in online learning and offers more than thirty undergraduate and graduate degree and certificate programs. SNHU Online reports more than 12,000 enrollments annually from all over the world.

Southern New Hampshire University is also approved for the education of veterans and the children of veterans and for the rehabilitation training of handicapped students. The program is listed in the Department of Education's Education Directory, Part 3, Higher Education®. *Staff and faculty members are dedicated to delivering high-quality academic and administrative support. Students have access to online applications, registration, academic advising, technical support, course work, tutoring, orientation, the bookstore, and the library.*

Distance Learning Program

Southern New Hampshire University's online program is recognized as a leader in online learning and Web-based education. Courses with SNHU Online are offered in six undergraduate terms (eight weeks in length) and four graduate terms (eleven weeks in length) each year. The residency requirement for undergraduate students, which may be satisfied by taking online courses, is 30 semester hours (ten classes) through Southern New Hampshire University, including 12 semester hours from the major for a bachelor's degree or 9 semester hours from the major for an associate degree. Each student's final 24 semester hours must be taken through Southern New Hampshire University. The final hours requirement is automatically waived for active military duty. The graduate program limits transfer credits to 6 semester hours, which must have been completed at an accredited institution within the last five years. In addition, the grade(s) earned must be a B or better.

Delivery Media

SNHU Online offers many advantages to students and faculty members. Classes are limited to 18 students, providing significant faculty-student interaction not found at many onsite-based class environments.

Blackboard Learning System is the learning management system for all online courses. In order to participate in Southern New Hampshire University's online courses, students must have a computer with Internet access. Courses with SNHU Online are not correspondence or CD-ROM–based. Instead, they are asynchronous, with no mandatory or set times that students are required to be online, and courses are self-paced—allowing students to complete their work at their own time and pace, within certain deadlines.

For the recommended technical specifications, a listing of personal characteristics that contribute to becoming a successful online student, or for additional information about SNHU Online, students should visit the SNHU Online Web site.

Programs of Study

Southern New Hampshire's online program provides students with a solid educational foundation through programs in business, hospitality, liberal arts, and tourism and culinary management. Undergraduate degree and certificate programs available online within the School of Business include accounting, accounting/finance, business administration, business studies, economics/finance, information technology, international business, management advisory services, marketing, and technical management. Online degree and certificate programs offered through the School of Liberal Arts include English language and literature, psychology, and social science. Graduate degree and certificate programs available online include Global M.B.A., M.Ed. in child development, Master of Science in business education, hospitality administration, and organizational leadership, and a graduate certificate in international business.

Southern New Hampshire University's online courses carry the same accreditation and provide the same semester hours toward a degree as classes taken through the day school or through any one of the University's Continuing Education centers. For an overview of degree requirements, prospective students should visit the SNHU Online Web site.

Credit Options

Students can transfer undergraduate credits earned at other accredited postsecondary institutions to Southern New Hampshire University and can also receive undergraduate credit by taking CLEP, DANTES, Regents College Examinations, institutional exams, military service training programs, ACE-certified career-related workshops and seminars, or other standardized tests. Southern New Hampshire University is designated as a Servicemembers Opportunity College (SOC, SOCNAV, and SOC-COAST)–approved and cooperating institution. As an SOC institution, Southern New Hampshire University awards credit for service-related education and for completion of an associate degree through the Community College of the Air Force.

A maximum of 90 semester hours may be transferred toward a bachelor's degree, and 30 semester hours may be applied to an associate degree. Academic advisers are available to conduct free transfer-credit evaluations. Prospective students should e-mail Southern New Hampshire University's advisers at advising@snhu.edu and fax transcripts to 603-645-9706.

Faculty

SNHU Online provides students with the opportunity to interact with highly qualified and specially trained instructors throughout the world who bring extensive work and life experiences into the classroom.

Admission

Applicants for undergraduate degree programs must have graduated from high school or passed the GED. Applicants for graduate programs require a bachelor's degree from an accredited institution. Official transcripts are required for admission.

International undergraduate applicants must have completed the equivalent of a U.S. secondary school. Students who have attended a recognized postsecondary institution may be eligible to receive transfer credits or exemptions. All applicants must submit a completed application and official or attested copies of academic records translated into English, including proof of graduation or completion of a program and proof of English proficiency. A minimum TOEFL score of 530 is required for undergraduate students. International graduate applicants must have completed the equivalent of a U.S. bachelor's degree and have a minimum TOEFL score of 550.

Tuition and Fees

The tuition for each SNHU Online undergraduate course is $750 and $1428 per 3-credit course. Tuition rates are subject to change. Some courses may require the purchase of specific software.

Financial Aid

Southern New Hampshire University accepts employer tuition reimbursement, federal and private loans, grants, VA Programs/Montgomery GI Bill, Navy College Fund (as part of the GI Bill), and scholarships. A federal financial aid application form is available online at http://www.fafsa.gov. Applicants may contact the University's financial aid office (telephone: 603-645-9645; e-mail: finaid@snhu.edu) to explore financial aid options.

Applying

Students may enroll in undergraduate classes on a rolling basis. Official acceptance is not necessary to begin undergraduate course work. All applicants (new and transfer students) must submit an application along with an official high school transcript or original copy of GED scores and, if applicable, official college transcripts. Graduate students who wish to enroll in course work only are limited to taking a maximum of two graduate courses (6 semester hours). Official or unofficial transcripts must be mailed or faxed to the SNHU Online office before a student may register for a graduate course, including course work only students. Applicants may register for course work by visiting the SNHU Online Web site and clicking on Apply and Register.

Southern New Hampshire University does not discriminate on the basis of race, color, national origin, citizenship, religion, marital status, age, sex, sexual orientation, or disability in admission to, access to, treatment in, or employment in its programs and activities.

CONTACT

SNHU Online
Southern New Hampshire University
2500 North River Road
Manchester, New Hampshire 03106-1045
Phone: 603-645-9766
866-860-0449 (toll-free)
Fax: 603-645-9706
E-mail: online@snhu.edu
Web site: http://www.snhu.edu/online

SOUTHERN POLYTECHNIC STATE UNIVERSITY

Extended University's Office of Distance Learning

Marietta, Georgia

At Southern Polytechnic State University, distance students are able to study the sciences, technologies, construction, quality and systems management, information technology, and technical communications in a unique and practical manner. They acquire an education that is career-based and balanced.

Since its founding in 1948, the University has earned an exceptional academic reputation. SPSU, Georgia's technology university, has approximately 4,000 students (traditional, nontraditional, and distance) from approximately thirty-five states and eighty-two countries.

Distance Learning Program

The Office of Distance Learning (ODL) provides administrative, marketing, and technical support for distance learning activities at Southern Polytechnic State University (SPSU). SPSU has offered distance learning options in a variety of formats since 1995. Current methods of distance delivery at SPSU include several Web applications and videoconferencing.

Delivery Media

Online students are required to have regular access to the Internet and a computer capable of running current versions of Web browsers as well as standard office and design applications. Students communicate with their professors and class members through discussions, chat, live classroom (voice chat), and e-mail. Assignments are completed using word processing, spreadsheet, and graphic software, such as Microsoft Word, Excel, and Photoshop. Other software may be required depending on the course.

Distance learning courses at SPSU use Vista, a Web-based course-management system from WebCT that is accessible through an Internet browser, such as Internet Explorer, Netscape, or Mozilla.

Programs of Study

SPSU offers the following degrees and certificates via distance learning: Master of Science (M.S.) in Quality Assurance (MSQA), Master of Science In Systems Engineering (MSSYE), Graduate Certificate in Technical Communication, Graduate Certificate in Informational Design and Communication (GCIDC), Graduate Certificate in Technical Communications (GCTC), Graduate Certificate in Content Development (GCCD), Graduate Certificate in Communications Management (GCCM), Graduate Certificate in Visual Communication and Graphics (GCVCG), and an undergraduate Certificate in Specialty Construction (SCC). Through two state consortia, SPSU also offers eCore, (University System of Georgia (USG) core-curriculum classes) and a Bachelor of Science degree in Information Technology (WebBSIT).

The M.S. in quality assurance has been offered at a distance since 1997 and was the first degree in quality assurance to be offered in the country as a distance program. The MSQA program is designed for anyone working in quality, training, and related disciplines and meets the needs of professionals who support total quality, continuous improvement, and process management within an organization.

The M.S. in systems engineering (MSSYE) is the first program of its kind in Georgia and joins an elite list of distance MSSYE programs in the country. The MSSYE helps professionals enhance the development of systems thinking and the ability to apply system-analysis techniques in a real-world environment. Participants learn to design, analyze, and manage the implementation of complex systems for business and technology.

Consisting of 20 credit hours or six graduate courses, the Graduate Certificate in Technical Communications (GCTC) is offered entirely in a Web-based learning environment that allows professionals already working in the field to update and expand their skills. For those new to the field, the program is an opportunity to learn desirable information design and communication skills that are sought by today's employers. This is the prerequisite for the other four certificate programs (18 hours each) also offered completely online.

The Specialty Construction Certificate (SCC) requires 19 semester hours and includes courses in building; mechanical, electrical, and plumbing loads; the estimating process; project management; and energy conservation.

The WebBSIT degree is offered in a consortium with four other schools in the University of Georgia System. This program of study provides a solid background in the technical, user-centric, and managerial skills required by today's information technology managers. Graduates can pursue careers in programming, systems design, database design, and e-commerce, among others.

eCore (Electronic Core Curriculum) is another USG-consortium effort that offers the first two years of core curriculum entirely online. eCore consists of online freshman- and sophomore-level courses designed, developed, taught, and supported by USG faculty and staff members. eCore courses comply with ADA standards to meet the needs of students with disabilities or special needs.

Student Services

The Office of Distant Learning's Web site at http://dl.spsu.edu provides links to all distance-learning student services available at SPSU, including admissions, registration, financial aid, career services, counseling services, the bookstore, and the Johnson Library's Resources for Distance Learners Web page (http://www.spsu.edu/library/Dl/dlguide.html).

The ODL web site also offers an online orientation to SPSU, a self-assessment test to determine how well a student's learning style is suited to distance learning, links and descriptions of the various degree and certificate programs, technical support, a self-directed Vista tutorial, and a Web form to request additional or more specific information about distance learning at Southern Polytechnic State University. Students can access this information on the Distance Learning Web site at http://dl.spsu.edu/.

Credit Options

In general, students can be awarded some transfer credit for course work already completed elsewhere. Distance learning M.S. students can choose the online graduate seminar class as the final course, which delves into special technical topics not normally covered in other courses. A technical semester project is required. Alternatively, distance learning students can choose to complete QA7503, a two-semester research methods project class, as their final course. This course requires two intensive full-day Saturday on-campus meetings, one in October and the other in March. At the second meeting, students present their completed research projects to faculty members and students.

Faculty

The faculty strives for excellence in teaching and service, providing a laboratory-centered and/or professionally oriented education that fosters problem solving, ethical awareness, and a desire for lifelong learning. All classes are taught by experienced, dedicated faculty members, not teaching assistants. At SPSU, teaching is the top criterion for promotion and tenure. All faculty members are required to have relevant work or research experience.

Admission

Incoming freshmen must have completed a minimum of 16 units in English, math, science, history, and foreign language and must have a minimum GPA of 2.5 and a minimum SAT score of 1000 (42 on the ACT).

Tuition and Fees

In 2006–07, undergraduate tuition is $189 per credit hour; graduate tuition is $227 per credit hour. Those enrolled in the WebBSIT program pay $290 per credit hour. The eCore program costs $144 per credit hour. All programs require the payment of a technology fee of $75 per semester.

Financial Aid

Each year, approximately 90 percent of undergraduate students receive aid, consisting of loans, scholarships, grants, and work-study assignments. Graduate students can receive aid through loans or a work-study program. Information about aid available to distance learners is available through the Office of Scholarships and Financial Aid.

Applying

Undergraduate applicants must submit the completed application form, a $20 nonrefundable application fee, all official high school and college transcripts, and official SAT or ACT scores. Graduate applicants must send in the completed application form, a $20 nonrefundable application fee, two copies of all official college transcripts, and three letters of reference. Applications may also be made online. The application deadlines for the summer, fall, and spring semesters are May 1, August 1, and December 1, respectively.

CONTACT

Office of Distance Learning
Southern Polytechnic State University
1100 South Marietta Parkway
Marietta, Georgia 30060-2896
Phone: 678-915-3713
Fax: 678-915-3576
Web site: http://dl.spsu.edu

Dawn Ramsey, Dean
Phone: 678-915-4287
E-mail: dramsey@spsu.edu

Stephen Rehberg, Instructional Designer
Phone: 678-915-3169
E-mail: srehberg@spsu.edu

Jennie Vitty-Rogers, eCore Coordinator
Phone: 678-915-4984
E-mail: jrogers4@spsu.edu

STATE UNIVERSITY OF NEW YORK EMPIRE STATE COLLEGE

Center for Distance Learning

Saratoga Springs, New York

Empire State College, of the State University of New York, is an internationally recognized innovator in adult education and a pioneer in distance learning. Since 1971, the College has served students who need alternatives to campus-based education because of work, family, or other responsibilities. Providing flexible degree programs at the associate, bachelor's, and master's levels, Empire State College features a number of student-focused study methods, such as one-to-one instruction, online courses, intensive mentoring by a faculty adviser, and undergraduate credit for college-level learning gained from life experience.

The College currently enrolls more than 16,000 students per year at thirty-five locations in New York State. Through its Center for Distance Learning (CDL), the College also serves students across the nation and around the world. Empire State College was the first public, nontraditional institution to receive regional accreditation by the Middle States Association of Colleges and Schools.

Distance Learning Program

More than 6,000 students are served annually by the College's Center for Distance Learning (CDL). Established in 1978, CDL now offers full degrees as well as individual courses entirely online. As a founding member of the SUNY Learning Network, the College was among the first in the State University of New York to offer online courses. It was also the first within the University to offer an entire degree (in business, management, and economics) online. Today, students may earn degrees online in all areas of study offered by the College. Through the Center for Graduate Programs, the College offers five Master of Arts degrees, including a Master of Arts in Teaching with online and on-site components. An M.B.A. is offered primarily via the World Wide Web.

Delivery Media

The Center for Distance Learning makes use of the latest distance learning technology on the World Wide Web. Empire State College's online courses can be accessed at any time of the day, allowing students and faculty members to share ideas and concepts at times that are convenient to them. In addition, all student services, such as registration, academic advising, career and library services, and peer support, are available on the Internet.

Programs of Study

The Center for Distance Learning offers both two- and four-year degrees: Associate in Arts, Associate in Science, Bachelor of Arts, Bachelor of Science, and Bachelor of Professional Studies. The College also offers five Master of Arts programs, with concentrations in business and policy studies, labor and policy studies, liberal studies, and social policy, in addition to an M.B.A. with online courses and a Master of Arts in Teaching.

One of the strengths of the Empire State College distance learning program is that students are assigned a faculty adviser, who guides them through all phases of their degree program, from academic planning to graduation. With their adviser, undergraduate students design individualized degree programs in any of eleven areas of study: the arts; business, management, and economics; community and human services; cultural studies; educational studies; historical studies; human development; interdisciplinary studies; labor studies; science, mathematics, and technology; and social theory, social structure, and change. Within these degree programs, a number of concentrations can be developed. Some examples of these are fire service administration, criminal justice, emergency management, health services administration, and information systems.

To earn an associate degree, a student must successfully complete 64 credits, with at least 24 earned through study with Empire State College. A bachelor's degree requires successful completion of 128 credits, with at least 32 being earned through the College.

Special Programs

The Center for Distance Learning is one of a select number of institutions of higher education to offer online degree programs to the United States Army, the United States Navy, the United States Coast Guard, and the Army National Guard. Through eArmyU, soldiers may take part in portable learning that suits the requirements of military life. The College also participates in the Navy College Program Distance Learning Partnership (NCPDLP) for sailors who need maximum flexibility in the ways they study. Many other organizations and corporations work with CDL to sponsor educational options for their employees, including a number of telecommunications companies and unions. A complete list is available at http://www.esc.edu/CDL.

In collaboration with nationally recognized online course provider Education To Go, Empire State College also offers a series of more than 250 noncredit online courses geared to adult learners in the workplace. The courses are available in a six-week, instructor-supported format.

Credit Options

Students can transfer credits earned at other regionally accredited institutions to Empire State College and can receive credit for college-level learning gained through work and life experience and through the College-Level Examination Program (CLEP), standardized tests, or individualized evaluation. A total of 40 prior learning credits may be granted in the associate degree program; 96 credits may be applied to a bachelor's degree program.

Faculty

There are 768 full- and part-time faculty members at Empire State College, including adjunct faculty. More than 90 percent of full-time faculty members and nearly half of part-time faculty members have doctoral or other terminal academic degrees.

Admission

There are two principal requirements for admission to Empire State College: possession of a high school diploma or its equivalent and the ability of the College to meet the applicant's educational needs and objectives.

Tuition and Fees

In 2004–05, undergraduate tuition was $181 per credit. A per-term telecommunications development and support fee of $75 was also charged, which provided access to electronic mail, computer conferencing, the Internet, and other information sources. Other fees also apply. Students should visit the College's Web site at http://www.esc.edu for further details

Financial Aid

More than $37 million in financial aid was awarded to Empire State College students in 2003–04, with more than 50 percent of the enrolled students receiving some form of financial assistance. General financial aid programs available through Empire State College include the Federal Pell Grant, Federal Supplemental Educational Opportunity Grant, Federal Perkins Loan, and the Federal Work-Study Program. New York State financial aid programs include the Tuition Assistance Program (TAP), Aid for Part-Time Study (APTS), and the SUNY Supplemental Tuition Award. The Empire State College Foundation awards more than $162,000 in scholarships and grants annually.

Applying

Empire State College reviews applications in order of date received, and students may apply online. The number of new students accepted depends on available space. There are five deadlines per year posted on the Web site (address listed below). Nonmatriculated students can take up to 16 credits without applying to the College.

CONTACT

Shelley Dixon
Center for Distance Learning
Empire State College
111 West Avenue
Saratoga Springs, New York 12866-6048
Phone: 800-847-3000 Ext. 2300 (toll-free)
Fax: 518-587-2660
E-mail: cdl@esc.edu
Web site: http://www.esc.edu/CDL

STATE UNIVERSITY OF NEW YORK AT OSWEGO

B.A. in Broadcasting and Mass Communication
B.S. in Vocational Teacher Preparation

Oswego, New York

The State University of New York at Oswego was founded in 1861 as the Oswego Normal School. The institution became Oswego State Teachers College and one of SUNY's charter members in 1948. While maintaining its high standards as a center for teacher education, the college began to broaden its academic perspective in 1962 when it became one of the colleges of arts and science of the State University of New York.

Today, Oswego is one of thirteen university colleges in the SUNY system. About 8,000 students enroll annually. Oswego offers more than 100 academic programs leading to bachelor's degrees, master's degrees, and certificates of advanced study. The college is accredited by the Middle States Association of Colleges and Schools and by the Commission on Higher Education. The School of Education is accredited by the National Council for Accreditation of Teacher Education.

Distance Learning Program

The Bachelor of Arts (B.A.) in broadcasting and mass communication and the Bachelor of Science (B.S.) in six majors in vocational teacher preparation (agricultural, business and marketing, family and consumer sciences, health careers, technical, and trade education) are available to students with two-year degrees in appropriate disciplines. Degrees in vocational teacher preparation are offered in the following areas: agriculture education, business education, family and consumer sciences, health occupations subjects education, technical subjects education, and trade subjects education. All required courses, cognates, and electives as well as courses in other disciplines to fulfill general education requirements are offered online. Students also have the opportunity to complete an economics minor online.

Delivery Media

All courses are taught via the World Wide Web in asynchronous mode through the SUNY Learning Network (SLN) (http://sln.suny.edu). Students are required to have reliable access to computers connected to the Internet. Courses use texts/reading materials and involve substantial writing assignments. Students may be required to arrange laboratory experiences with colleges or universities close to home with credits transferred to Oswego.

Students taking VTP 312 online must attend a one-week summer residency in Oswego.

Program of Study

Some required courses may be transferred into the program through substitution or through articulation agreements with two-year and four-year colleges. A transfer evaluation of credit assigns previously earned credits to the appropriate program and to general education and college requirements. Students must complete a total of 122 credit hours for broadcasting and 127 credit hours for vocational teacher preparation to graduate, with a minimum of 30 credit hours taken from SUNY Oswego. At least 60 hours must be from a four-year college. General education requirements also apply.

Specific requirements in the broadcasting major and the vocational teacher preparation major, including cognates and electives, are available at the Oswego State Web site. Students can find requirements for broadcasting at http://www.oswego.edu/ODP/ and for vocational teacher preparation at http://www.oswego.edu/vtp/.

Special Programs

Some degree program students may benefit from internship opportunities arranged through the Office of Experience-Based Education. Up to 15 hours of internship credit may be applied as electives both in the major and under the general studies curriculum. Past students have performed internships in network television, local and regional media, advertising, media research, and government. Such experiences often lead to job offers and referrals.

Student Services

Some of the campus services and resources that are available online include certain resources in Penfield Library, the Registrar's Office, Student Accounts, the Financial Aid Office, and the Career Services Center. The State University of New York at Oswego Web site is http://www.oswego.edu. Advisement options include e-mail and telephone consultation for all students.

Credit Options

Up to 62 transfer credits from a two-year school may be applied toward the broadcasting degree, and up to 67 transfer credits from a two-year school and 97 transfer credits from a four-year school may be applied toward the vocational teacher preparation degree. The College-Level Examination Program (CLEP) is offered and accepted. Up to 32 credits may be earned through CLEP, which is considered transfer credit.

Faculty

Approximately 40 full-time and 15 part-time faculty and professional staff members currently teach distance courses at SUNY Oswego. Of these, 70 percent have doctoral degrees. The student/teacher ratio is 20:1.

Admission

Applicants must submit official transcripts indicating that they have graduated with a two-year degree appropriate for their program. Students may enroll full-time or part-time and must become matriculated after completing 22 hours of study at Oswego.

Tuition and Fees

Part-time undergraduate tuition (in-state) is $181 per credit hour. Part-time undergraduate tuition (out-of-state) is $429 per credit hour. Full-time undergraduate tuition (in-state) is $2175 per semester. Full-time undergraduate tuition (out-of-state) is $5150 per semester.

Part-time fees (in-state and out-of-state) are $25.39 per credit hour.

Tuition and fee amounts are subject to change.

Financial Aid

Students should contact the Office of Financial Aid for information regarding income, credit hours, and other guidelines. In most instances, students must be enrolled in at least 6 credit hours to be eligible for financial aid.

Applying

A SUNY application needs to be submitted for both programs. Both programs have an additional application that must be obtained by contacting the applicable department. Students are notified in writing if and when they are accepted into the program. An orientation session is optional.

CONTACT

For information on broadcasting and mass communication:

Dr. Michael S. Ameigh, Assistant Provost and Coordinator, Online Degree Program
35A Lanigan Hall
Oswego, New York 13126
Phone: 315-312-3500
Fax: 315-312-3195
E-mail: ameigh@oswego.edu
Web site: http://www.oswego.edu/ODP/

For information on vocational teacher preparation:

Dr. Margaret Martin, Chair, Vocational Teacher Preparation Department
307 Park Hall
Oswego, New York 13126
Phone: 315-312-2480
Fax: 315-312-3062
E-mail: mmartin4@oswego.edu
Web site: http://www.oswego.edu/vtp/

STEVENS INSTITUTE OF TECHNOLOGY

Graduate School Distance Learning Programs

Hoboken, New Jersey

Stevens Institute of Technology, one of the world's premier technical universities, offers an array of Web-based distance learning graduate programs from WebCampus. Stevens is ranked among the top twenty-five schools with entrepreneurial programs. Optimize *magazine selected Stevens as one of the five schools that prepare technology managers. Stevens is one of only three schools accredited by the Project Management Institute. Stevens has won the Sloan Consortium's top award for best "institution-wide online teaching and learning programming" and the US Distance Learning Association's "21st Century Award for Best Practices is Distance Learning." Stevens offers thirteen master's degree programs and thirty-one graduate certificate programs in engineering, management, and science online..*

Students are instructed by noted faculty members who deliver the same superior courses taught on the main campus. Off-campus courses are conveniently offered at corporate sites. Many classes include a real-time Web conferencing component. Stevens is accredited by the Middle States Commission on Higher Education of the Middle States Association of Colleges and Schools. WebCampus is cosponsored by the Association of Computing Machinery (AMC), the Institute of Electrical and Electronics Engineers (IEEE), the American Society for Mechanical Engineers (ASME), the Society of Naval Architects and Marine Engineers (SNAME), the American Society of Civil Engineers (ASCE), and the National Exchange Carrier Association (NECA).

Distance Learning Program

Graduate certificates for professionals seeking advanced knowledge in science, engineering, and management are available online through WebCampus. In addition, a wide range of off-campus graduate degree programs in engineering, management, computer science, and mathematics, among other disciplines, are taught at corporate sites.

Delivery Media

Stevens has been at the forefront of distance learning for a number of years, offering instructor-led courses that take advantage of the benefits of Web conferencing and other net applications. WebCampus online graduate students use rich Web features such as real-time and recorded lectures, threaded discussions, chat, bulletin boards, e-mail, file sharing, whiteboards, and work groups for in-depth online participation. Students also have online library privileges, with instant search and retrieval of important databases such as the IEEE Electronic Library and Hoovers Company Records.

Programs of Study

Master's degree and certificate programs include biomedical engineering, construction management, cybersecurity, database systems, digital signal processing, engineering management, environmental engineering, financial engineering, human resource management, microelectronics, multimedia technology, networked information systems, pharmaceutical management, pharmaceutical manufacturing, photonics, professional communications, project management, software engineering, systems engineering, technology management, and telecommunications management.

Graduate certificate programs offer students the opportunity to focus on a specific area of study without having to complete a master's degree program. Credits earned toward a graduate certificate at Stevens may also be applied to a master's degree should students wish to continue their studies.

Off campus, at corporate and other sites, graduate students may enroll as part of company-sponsored programs, some of which are delivered using Web conferencing. Employees at some of the nation's most progressive and prominent companies, including Boeing, Johnson & Johnson, Con Ed, Verizon, and dozens of others, may take graduate certificate courses and master's degree courses in a number of disciplines at corporate sites. These include computer engineering, computer science, electrical engineering, management, mechanical engineering, project management, technology management, and telecommunications management.

For high school seniors who wish to get a head start on their college studies, Stevens created the Euclid Program of Online Courses. The Euclid Program covers the following areas: calculus and advanced math, computer science, and physics.

Student Services

Online learning graduate students access the entire range of Stevens' student services online, including faculty advising, books and materials ordering, admissions, registration, and financial aid. Graduate students also have instant online access to the school's digital library. A cyberlibrarian is available via e-mail and telephone to guide students in the use of electronic databases and other research tools and media. Technical and other help desk support services are also available online. Stevens' Student Information System allows distance learners to access course schedules, grades, account statements, and other documents entirely online.

Credit Options

All graduate courses are worth 3 credits. Most graduate certificates are awarded after students have completed four courses online, on campus, or both. To earn a master's degree in engineering and science, students are required to complete ten courses. Students must complete twelve courses for a master's degree in management.

Faculty

An impressive graduate faculty teaches courses at Stevens, providing the same superior instruction online and on and off campus. WebCampus faculty members are required to participate in teaching and learning colloquia, which are held periodically during each semester, in order to share their experiences and to demonstrate their online teaching capabilities. Faculty members who teach online are also trained in how to exploit the technological and pedagogical benefits of Web-based courseware applications.

Admission

To be admitted to an online learning program at Stevens, students are required to satisfy the same qualifications as those who wish to enroll in Stevens' conventional courses. Prospective graduate students need to have completed an undergraduate degree at an accredited institution. Applicants may either apply by mail or complete an application form online at https://apply.embark.com/grad/stevens/14/. There is no fee for submitting an application online. Two letters of recommendation are required. Applicants must also provide official transcripts in English for each college or university attended. Transcripts translated into English must be prepared by the school attended or by an official translator with a recognized seal. Applicants must provide official confirmation of the degree earned if it was awarded by a non-U.S. institution. The applicant's name, Social Security number, or date of birth must be on all submitted documents. All documents must be in English or have attested English translations.

Tuition and Fees

Each semester, students are required to pay nominal enrollment and technology fees. Tuition for management courses is $785 per credit hour. Tuition for engineering and science courses is $920 per credit hour. Other fees may apply for late enrollment and late payment, among other services.

Financial Aid

Stevens has a strong commitment to assisting and investing in talented students. The school offers a number of scholarships, many of which are made available through generous friends and successful alumni. Many graduate students receive tuition reimbursement from their companies. Members of the WebCampus cosponsoring professional societies receive a 10 percent discount upon successful completion of the course.

Applying

Before applying to the online or off-campus distance learning programs, it is recommended that students review the Graduate School Web site or Stevens' WebCampus site in order to obtain information, instructions, and online application forms.

CONTACT

Online programs:
Stevens Institute of Technology
Castle Point on Hudson
Hoboken, New Jersey 07030
Phone: 201-216-5092
800-494-4935 (toll-free)
Fax: 201-216-5011
E-mail: webcampus@stevens.edu
Web site: http://www.webcampus.stevens.edu

Off-campus programs:
Graduate Admissions
Stevens Institute of Technology
Castle Point on Hudson
Hoboken, New Jersey 07030
Phone: 201-216-5234
Fax: 201-216-5011
E-mail: thegradschool@stevens.edu
Web site: http://gradschool.stevens-tech.edu/home/

STRAYER UNIVERSITY

Strayer University Online

Newington, Virginia

Strayer University, founded in 1892, has more than 110 years of experience educating working adults. Currently, more than 27,000 students, most of whom work full-time, are enrolled at Strayer University. Undergraduate and graduate degrees are offered in technology and business-oriented programs. Strayer University has thirty-nine campuses located in Delaware, the District of Columbia, Florida, Georgia, Maryland, North Carolina, Pennsylvania, South Carolina, Tennessee, and Virginia and is accredited by the Middle States Commission on Higher Education. Strayer University is a subsidiary of Strayer Education, Inc., a publicly held corporation whose stock is traded on the NASDAQ market (STRA). Each year since 1998, Strayer Education has been recognized by Forbes *magazine as one of the "200 Best Small Companies in America."*

Distance Learning Program

Strayer University Online offers both real-time (synchronous) and time-independent (asynchronous) online courses.

Synchronous courses meet on the same day and time each week. Students and their professor are all online at the same time, engaging in a lively and interactive classroom environment. Students can access these courses from wherever they have access to the Internet but must attend the regularly scheduled class meetings.

Asynchronous courses are not held in real-time. Instead, students and faculty members log in throughout the week, downloading new course materials and uploading assignments and responses while maintaining a high level of interaction with classmates and the professor.

Delivery Media

The following is a list of the minimal hardware and software recommended for participation in Strayer University Online classes: a 300-MHz processor (Pentium II equivalent or higher) with Windows '98, Microsoft Office '97 Professional Edition (or more recent version), a 128-KB L2 Cache (laptop) or 512-KB L2 Cache (desktop), 64 MB of memory, a 4-GB hard drive, a 12.1-inch SVGA TFT display (laptop) or larger (desktop), a 1.44-MB floppy drive, 2 MB of video memory, a 24X (laptop) or 40X (desktop) CD-ROM drive, a 56-K PCMCIA modem with fax capability, a 10/100 Ethernet network card (laptop only), and an integrated microphone and speakers.

Programs of Study

Degree programs available online include the 54-credit Master of Business Administration (M.B.A.), Master of Education (M.Ed.), Master of Health Services Administration (M.H.S.A.), Master of Public Administration (M.P.A.), and Master of Science (M.S.) degrees in communications technology, information systems, management information systems, and professional accounting. Executive graduate certificate programs are offered in business administration, computer information systems, and professional accounting. Bachelor of Science (B.S.) programs (180 credits) in accounting, business administration, computer information systems, computer networking, database technology, economics, international business, and internetworking technology and Associate in Arts (A.A.) programs (90 credits) in accounting, acquisition and contract management, business administration, computer information systems, computer networking, database technology, economics, general studies, internetworking technology, and marketing are available.

There are also diploma programs in accounting, acquisition and contract management, computer information systems, internetworking technology, network security, and Web development. Undergraduate certificate programs are offered in accounting, business administration, and computer information systems.

Courses are taught on the quarter system, and each course provides 4.5 credit hours. Associate in Arts degree programs require twenty courses, or 90 hours, to complete. B.S. degrees require forty courses, or 180 hours. M.S. degrees require twelve courses, or 54 hours, to complete.

Each degree program has a business component and a major component. The undergraduate programs also have liberal arts/general studies and an elective component.

Student Services

Applications for federal financial aid and scholarships are available online. Students may register for classes through the Web site or by telephone. In addition, library resources, other learning resources, and career-development services are available online.

Credit Options

Students who have attended other educational institutions may receive transfer credit or advanced standing in Strayer University's degree and diploma programs. College credit may be awarded for CLEP and DANTES tests, certain training received in the military, or prior work/life learning demonstrated through portfolio preparation. The required number of credits taken in residence, online or on campus, is 36 for a master's degree, 54 for a bachelor's degree, 27 for an associate degree, and 31.5 for a diploma.

Faculty

Strayer University has more than 130 full-time and more than 926 part-time faculty members. Of these, more than 334 teach for Strayer University Online.

Admission

Students who apply to undergraduate degree programs must provide certification of high school graduation or the equivalent. For admission to graduate degree programs, students must have graduated from an accredited college or university with a baccalaureate degree.

Tuition and Fees

For the 2005 academic year, tuition for graduate courses is $362 per credit hour. Full-time undergraduate students (13.5 credits or more) pay $270 per credit hour, and part-time undergraduate students pay $285 per credit hour.

Financial Aid

Students may apply online for financial aid. The Free Application for Federal Student Aid (FAFSA) may be accessed on the Web at http://www.strayer.edu. Students may apply for the following grants, loans, and scholarships: Federal Pell Grant, Federal Supplemental Educational Opportunity Grant, Federal Perkins Loan, Federal Stafford Student Loan, Federal PLUS Loan, Federal Direct Loan Programs, Federal Work-Study Program, Strayer University Education Loan Program, and Strayer University Scholarships.

Applying

Applications are accepted on an ongoing basis and can be accessed online at http://www.strayer.edu. There is a $50 application fee.

CONTACT

Strayer University Online
P.O. Box 487
Newington, Virginia 22122
Phone: 866-344-3286 (toll-free)
Fax: 703-339-4948
E-mail: info@strayer.edu
Web site: http://www.strayer.edu

SULLIVAN UNIVERSITY

Master of Science in Dispute Resolution

Louisville, Kentucky

Sullivan University's educational mission has remained constant from its founding until the present: "the highest ideals and standards in preparing people for successful careers." Sullivan's commitment to career education has been sustained by the employment record of its graduates: 99.7 percent in 2002, 99.3 percent in 2001, 99.2 percent in 2000, and its lowest percentage, 97.8 percent in 1992.

Sullivan has unusual commitment to all graduates of its official degree, diploma, and certificate programs—graduates are allowed two free lifetime privileges: Graduate Employment Services (GES) and Lifetime Curricular Review (LCR). The GES staff members assist graduates in finding new employment, developing resumes, and participating in job fairs. The LCR allows graduates to reenroll in any class completed in their program to refresh their learning, although no grades are given nor attendance required or recorded.

Distance Learning Program

The methods and skills earned in the Master of Science in Dispute Resolution (M.S.D.R.) degree curriculum are of special usefulness for controlling lost capital due to grievances, complaints, and litigation in the workplace as well as for redirecting human and financial resources toward prevention of disputes, improvement of communication, and development of organizational mission. While the M.S.D.R. provides a strong career building block for students holding undergraduate degrees, it also expands employment applications for students holding professional credentials such as the CPA and the M.B.A., M.P.A., M.P.H., M.P.S.Y., M.S.W., and J.D. degrees. Executives, middle managers, and labor leaders apply knowledge and skills learned in the M.S.D.R. program to maintain and promote healthy workforce environments.

The Program Chair seeks to combine the following goals in all courses: predominance of classical bibliographic mastery in the subject areas—to provide students with long-term, firm theoretical foundations; mainstream workplace applications of theories taught—to enable students to graduate with real-world experiences useful to prospective employers or clients; rigorous academic and professional standards to ensure high-quality learning—to test students' readiness for graduation and employment; superior "best practices" in distance learning instructional design—to maximize the potential of the media and minimize inconvenience or frustration for students or their employment supervisors; and creative yet controlled uses of technology media—to enhance and accommodate learning for the majority of students in the U.S. and around the world, preventing encumbrances created by hardware or software requirements that would pose an unreasonable burden for most students.

Part of the M.S.D.R. program is the Mediation Practicums Module© (MPM). The MPM was created to enable students to transfer online learning into controlled, graduated, real-world dispute resolution experiences in their own workplaces. Certain specific practical interaction and professional skills must be demonstrated, critiqued, and developed in each M.S.D.R. student through professional evaluations in real time or personal observation. Sullivan employs a full-time MPM Director of Mediation Practicums who guides students and their evaluators to ensure the integrity of the student's experiential portfolio. When employers are too busy or unable to participate in the MPM, a network of practitioners in good standing with national dispute resolution organizations are recruited to assist in co-mediations, mentoring, and other educational experiences, either pro bono or for modest fees. In addition, unemployed students are placed in internships to fulfill the requirements of this portion of the program.

Delivery Media

Sullivan uses state-of-the-art technologies that include all standard distance learning methods and systems such as CD assist, videostreaming, and Web conferencing. Connected Learning. Network, a national leader in learning platforms for institutions of higher education, business, and industry, provides a premier media experience for students worldwide. All courses are asynchronous, permitting greater latitude for students in different time zones or continents to study together through common assignments. A 24/7, 365-day help-desk staff answers questions and resolves problems for students or faculty members.

Programs of Study

The M.S.D.R. degree is 100 percent online, is asynchronous, and exhibits complete continuity with Sullivan University's career education emphasis as reflected by its pedagogical structure. Five courses are core requirements and build a firm, centrist framework of theoretical understanding: Mediator Diagnostics and Skills© Conflict Theories, Dispute Resolution Methods, Organizational Conflict Management, and Family Conflict Mediation. Four courses are elective and may be drawn from major subject areas, each related to mainstream applications in U.S. and international settings: management, labor, EEO, law, education, health care, construction, legislative/public service, international, and religious. Three additional courses, the MPM courses, are nonelective and move theoretical learning into actual employment or organizational applications.

In addition to the M.S.D.R., Sullivan University also offers a Certificate in Dispute Resolution. The certificate program requires six courses for completion, half of the course load of the M.S.D.R. The certificate program is designed for students with specialized needs whose career applications do not require the broad career base offered by the M.S.D.R.

Special Programs

The Chair of the M.S.D.R. degree program actively seeks partnerships, alliances, and collaborations with governmental, public, and private sector organizations. These alliances enhance the quality of Sullivan's educational program and its outreach in the U.S. and world, provide value-added experiences for M.S.D.R. students, and, when possible, provide service to M.S.D.R. students' local employers, organizations, and communities.

Sullivan University is one of six academic partners with the Federal Mediation and Conciliation Service (FMCS) in Washington, D.C. (http://www.fmcs.gov). The FMCS has a revered reputation as a federal agency that functions superbly as a trusted neutral party to resolve major U.S. and international disputes. The M.S.D.R. degree program has been designed in consultation with FMCS staff members to ensure that M.S.D.R. graduates enter the workplace with methods and skills meeting or exceeding employment standards for federal and state agencies.

Student Services

The Sullivan University Library and Resource Center offers 43 searchable databases and portals accessible through the Internet that are available only to registered students. The entire card catalog is online, containing discipline-specific resources and monographs. Staff members are available via telephone at 800-844-1354 Ext. 308 (toll-free) Monday to Thursday 7 a.m. to 9:45 p.m., Friday to Saturday 8 to 4, and Sunday noon to 5, EST, U.S. holidays excepted. The Ask-A-Librarian e-mail reference service provides a 24-hour (or less) turnaround to questions on how to use resources, on the APA style, and on search strategies. Full interlibrary loan services are available to all students.

Credit Options

For information about credit options, students should contact the Financial Planning Office by telephone at 800-844-1354 Ext. 311 (toll-free) or by e-mail at cgeiser@sullivan.edu.

Faculty

The Chair of the M.S.D.R. degree program has a policy of employing only practitioner-experts as faculty members—those with terminal degrees and years of proven successful experience in the field being taught. Faculty profiles often include an array of publications, presentations at professional societies, training sessions offered around the U.S. and the world, and faculty member-owned corporations or sole proprietorships.

Admission

Students must meet criteria established by the Graduate School of Sullivan University. For current admission criteria, students should visit the Web site at http://www.sullivan.edu/louisville/admissions/index.htm or contact the Graduate Admissions Officer by e-mail at rhinson@sullivan.edu.

Tuition and Fees

All current tuition and fee information is available from the Graduate Admissions Officer by e-mail at the address listed in this description; it is also listed on the Web site at http://www.sullivan.edu/louisville/admissions/tuition.htm.

Financial Aid

Students in the M.S.D.R. degree program are eligible for two federal loan programs—Stafford Student Loans and Perkins Loans. In 2002–03, Sullivan awarded an estimated $37,048,460 in all forms of financial assistance to about 74 percent of students on all campuses. For more information about financial aid, students should contact the Financial Aid Office at cgeiser@sullivan.edu.

Applying

Students may complete an application online at http://www.sullivan.edu/louisville/admissions/application.htm. For further information, students can contact the University by e-mail at rhinson@sullivan.edu.

CONTACT

John D. Willis, Ph.D.
Chair, M.S.D.R. Degree Program
The Graduate School
Sullivan University
3101 Bardstown Road
Louisville, Kentucky 40205
E-mail: jwillis@sullivan.edu
Web site: http://www.sullivan.edu

SYRACUSE UNIVERSITY

School of Information Studies

Syracuse, New York

Syracuse University is a medium-sized, private, coeducational university with an international reputation. Founded in 1870, it is a comprehensive research university that has eleven degree-granting schools and colleges and several interdisciplinary and continuing education programs. The University's 640-acre, beautifully landscaped campus is situated among the hills of central New York State.

The School of Information Studies was the first information school in the nation. It is a leading center for innovative programs in information policy, information behavior, information management, information systems, information technology, and information services. The School has professional degree programs at the undergraduate and master's levels and a research degree at the doctoral level. The School's approach stands out from other institutions that offer computer science, management, information science, and related programs in that, as a starting point for integrating information and information technology into organizations, the focus is on users and their information needs.

Distance Learning Program

The distance learning programs offered by the School of Information Studies combine online courses with a brief on-campus residency. Distance learning students begin their first year in July with a seven- or nine-day required on-campus residency. During the fall and spring semesters, students take online courses. During the residencies, students are trained on the technology that allows them to complete their courses over the Internet, and they complete activities that are easier to accomplish face-to-face, e.g., hands-on labs and group activities. During these times, they also meet and bond with their cohort group and network with each other and faculty members.

Students in the distance learning programs come from across the United States and from several other countries. They range in age from their 20s through their 60s. Many are already working in the information field, but some are looking for a career change. The rich backgrounds of the students make each incoming class a dynamic group.

Delivery Media

The School of Information Studies uses a Web-based teaching and learning environment called WebCT. Each distance learning course has its own space within WebCT, which typically includes the syllabus, lectures, a forum for class discussions, and a place to submit assignments. Students are not required to be online at a specific time. They can log in and complete their assignments whenever it is convenient for them, as long as they meet course deadlines.

Programs of Study

Three graduate degrees are offered in the distance learning format: Master of Science in information management, in library and information science, and in telecommunications and network management. Graduate certificates of advanced study in information security management, information systems and telecommunications management, digital libraries, and school media are also offered.

The Master of Science in information management (IM) program is interdisciplinary in focus, combining expertise in the strategic management of information resources, organizational psychology, information economics, telecommunications policy, e-business, and information technology as well as data management and retrieval. New information and Internet-based technologies are revolutionizing the structure and operation of organizations to enable integrated business processes. Corporate profitability and effective delivery of public services are at stake. Staying competitive and productive in business and government demands a strategic response to the changes and innovations evolving from the computer, communications, and information processing industries. The IM program is ranked first in the nation by *U.S. News & World Report*.

The Master of Science in Library and Information Science (LIS) program educates students to be leaders in the ever-evolving library and information profession. The program focuses on twenty-first century librarianship within libraries, information centers, the information industry, and other venues. The LIS program is accredited by the American Library Association and is ranked third in the nation by *U.S. News & World Report*.

The Master of Science in telecommunications and network management (TNM) program combines an understanding of networking technologies with knowledge of their applications in organizations. The TNM degree is a selective 36-credit-hour program that provides students with the skills to design networks, make technology adoption and standards decisions, create cost models for new technology implementations, calculate return on investment, and understand the organizational and user implications of networking systems.

Student Services

All students are provided with free computer accounts and have access to the Syracuse University library and computer facilities. Online students have access to a help desk for technical problems. All distance students at Syracuse have access to a full range of online student services, including academic advising, financial aid, assistance, and registration.

During the summer semester, housing is available in Syracuse University residence halls. Students can stay in single or double rooms equipped with a microwave and refrigerator. Meal plans are not provided during the summer sessions, although dining halls and restaurants are within walking distance of campus.

Credit Options

On the graduate level, there is no provision for experiential credit. However, 6 credits may be transferred from other accredited graduate programs, with a grade of C or better.

Faculty

Members of the School of Information Studies faculty teach in both the online and on-campus formats. The faculty combines expertise in information systems, linguistics, computer science, business management, management information systems, library science, telecommunications, and communication. The faculty members are very active in research topics that reflect their diverse intellectual backgrounds and interests.

Admission

All applicants to graduate programs at Syracuse University must have a bachelor's degree from an accredited college or university. The School of Information Studies recommends that applicants have an undergraduate grade point average of 3.0 or better. However, in reviewing applications, all elements are weighed: references, educational record, test scores, honors, work experience, and the statement on academic plans.

Tuition and Fees

Distance learning students pay the same tuition rate as on-campus students. Tuition for the 2006–07 school year is $940 per credit. Tuition payment options for payment plans, company direct billing, and employer tuition deferrals are available for distance learning students.

Summer housing on campus costs approximately $100 to $150 per week. Students should also consider textbook, computer, Internet (if not already a subscriber to an Internet Service Provider), and travel expenses.

Financial Aid

Students must be U.S. citizens to qualify for need-based financial aid. The Financial Aid Office administers a variety of financial aid programs for distance learning students, including Federal Family Education Loan Programs, University College Grants, and Veterans' Education Benefit Programs. Merit-based scholarships are available through the School of Information Studies.

Applying

Students are encouraged to submit their applications by February 12 for priority admission to the distance learning program. Applications are accepted on a space-available basis through June 1. There are two application methods: online and paper. Use of the online application method is encouraged.

CONTACT

School of Information Studies
Syracuse University
343 Hinds Hall
Syracuse, New York 13244
Phone: 315-443-2911
Fax: 315-443-6886
E-mail: ist@syr.edu
Web site: http://www.ist.syr.edu

SYRACUSE UNIVERSITY

Martin J. Whitman School of Management, iMBA

Syracuse, New York

Founded in 1870, Syracuse University—a private, nonsectarian liberal arts institution—is one of the largest and most comprehensive independent universities in the nation. The University is one of only sixty American and Canadian universities chosen for membership in the prestigious Association of American Universities. Syracuse University enrolls more than 10,000 undergraduates and 4,800 graduate students for full-time and part-time study. The campus is located in the city of Syracuse, in an area of New York State known as upstate or central New York. Syracuse is less than half a day's drive away from New York City, Boston, Philadelphia, Toronto, and Montreal. The city is served by the Hancock International Airport, a mere 10-minute drive from downtown. Hancock Airport features daily nonstop flights to New York, Boston, Atlanta, Chicago, Philadelphia, Washington, D.C., and other business centers.

The Martin J. Whitman School of Management, in existence since 1919, has offered graduate programs since 1947. The School of Management has been continuously accredited by the premier accrediting body for business schools, AACSB International-The Association to Advance Collegiate Schools of Business, since 1921. The latest reaffirmation of accreditation was achieved by the School in April 2001. The Independent Study M.B.A. (iMBA) has been offered by the School of Management since 1977.

Distance Learning Program

The iMBA (Independent Study M.B.A.) program is a limited residency distance education program. It allows successful businesspeople, working around the world, to acquire a Master of Business Administration degree on a part-time basis while continuing to advance in their careers. The program enrolls students who reside in thirty-two states within the United States and ten other countries. The students' employers represent numerous prominent corporations and government agencies.

Delivery Media

Students meet on the Syracuse University campus three times each year for a weeklong residency at the beginning of the fall term in August, the spring term in January and the summer term in May. During these intensive weeks, students attend classes that serve to orient the students to the demands and expectations of the curriculum. Students also establish bonds and working relationships with faculty members and fellow students. At the conclusion of each residency, students return to their homes and workplaces with a clear understanding of the course requirements as well as access to the campus resources necessary for the successful completion of their courses. Final exams are taken on campus at the following residency.

Program of Study

The iMBA program emphasizes a broad, strategic-management view of business, leading to the Master of Business Administration in general management. The curriculum consists of eighteen courses for a total of 54 credits. There are twelve core courses and six electives in a student's program. Electives are drawn from accounting, entrepreneurship, finance, information systems, marketing, organizational management, and other areas.

Special Programs

Optional off-campus residencies are occasionally held in other cities, such as New York, London, and Shanghai. The programs held in these locations are identical in format to the on-campus residencies. Students take courses in the same manner and receive credit in the same manner as if they had attended a residency at Syracuse University.

Credit Options

A student who enters the program with no transfer credits completes 54 credits for the M.B.A. degree. The normal course load is two courses per trimester. Following this model, students typically finish the program within three years. However, the program is flexible, allowing students to skip a residency when necessary for personal or professional reasons.

The School accepts a maximum of 6 transfer credits, with a qualifying grade, if earned from an AACSB International-accredited school of business within five years of enrollment in the program.

Faculty

The faculty members who teach in the iMBA program include many of the same faculty members who teach in the School's full-time M.B.A. programs. However, during the residency weeks they are free of teaching obligations in other programs, so that they may concentrate their efforts on their iMBA students. This creates a strongly cohesive environment and provides a high degree of personal interaction in the program.

Admission

An applicant must have received a bachelor's degree or its equivalent from an accredited college or university to be considered for admission. Admission is competitive. Acceptance is based primarily upon potential for academic success and career achievement. Full-time work experience of at least three years is required for this program. A full description of the admissions policy is contained in the application instructions.

Tuition and Fees

Tuition in 2005–06 was $870 per credit. There is an annual tuition increase beginning with the summer residency. Textbooks average about $50 per credit. Housing and meal costs depend upon the accommodations chosen by the student, usually $70 to $120 per day. There is a $30 program fee for each residency.

Financial Aid

Most iMBA students hold full or partial sponsorship through their employer's tuition assistance program. Government or private loan programs are available for most students who are U.S. citizens or have a U.S. cosigner.

Applying

New students may begin the program at any of the three annual residencies. Applications are considered on a continuous year-round basis. The application should be completed at least six weeks prior to the intended first residency. Applicants must possess a minimum of five years of full-time work experience to be considered for admission. Graduate Management Admission Test (GMAT) scores are not required. Scores from the Test of English as a Foreign Language (TOEFL) are required of those for whom English is not the first language, unless the undergraduate degree was acquired in a program taught in English.

CONTACT

Paula C. O'Callaghan
Director, iMBA Program
315 Martin J. Whitman School of Management
721 University Avenue
Syracuse University
Syracuse, New York 13244-2130
Phone: 315-443-8384
Fax: 315-443-9517
E-mail: paula@syr.edu
Web site: http://whitman.syr.edu/imba

SYRACUSE UNIVERSITY

Undergraduate and Master of Social Science Degree Programs

Syracuse, New York

Founded in 1870, Syracuse University (SU) is a major private research university of 14,400 residential students and an additional 3,700 part-time adult students located in central New York State. Organized into twelve separate schools and colleges, each offering a variety of baccalaureate, master's, and doctoral degrees, Syracuse has excellent research facilities, including sophisticated computer networks and a library containing more than 2.8 million volumes. Syracuse is one of the select group of American and Canadian universities chosen for membership in the prestigious Association of American Universities. Syracuse has a long-standing commitment to adult education. The University's innovative distance education degree programs are a form of nontraditional education in which Syracuse was a pioneer. Offered through five of the University's academic units, SU's distance programs comprise one of the three oldest external degree programs in the United States. The programs have been active since 1966 and reflect the University's response to the demands for creative educational techniques and programs in a constantly changing society.

Distance Learning Program

Syracuse's distance education degree programs have a limited-residency structure: they combine short periods of intensive on-site instruction with longer periods of home study, during which students and faculty members communicate online. There are currently about 1,000 adults actively enrolled in twelve different degree programs through distance education, approximately one sixth of whom are international students or Americans living abroad. Syracuse degrees earned through distance study are the same as those earned by traditional Syracuse students in comparable campus programs and have the same accreditation.

Programs of Study

University College offers two undergraduate programs and a master's program by means of the limited-residency distance education format. Undergraduate degrees include an Associate of Arts in liberal arts, a Bachelor of Arts in liberal studies, and a certificate and a Bachelor of Professional Studies in organizational leadership. The associate degree is 60 credits. The bachelor's degrees are 120-credit programs. The certificate is 15 credits.

The graduate degree is a 30-credit Master of Social Science (M.S.Sc.) with an international relations emphasis. It offers an interdisciplinary, international, and multicultural approach to complex global issues. An internationally renowned faculty teaches courses for the degree from Syracuse University's Maxwell School of Citizenship and Public Affairs.

The degrees and the certificate are state and regionally accredited. Students may initially enroll on a nonmatriculated basis.

Special Programs

A number of online credit and noncredit courses are offered each semester. Detailed information on these is available at http://www.yesu.syr.edu/online.

Student Services

All distance education students are provided with free computer accounts and have access to the Syracuse University library and computer facilities. Online students have access to a help desk for technical problems. All distance students at Syracuse have access to a full range of online student services, including academic advising, financial aid, assistance, and registration.

Credit Options

The associate degree program accepts a maximum of 30 credits to be transferred from another postsecondary institution. The baccalaureate programs accept a maximum of 90 transfer credits, which may include 66 credits from a junior college. Transfer credit is granted for most courses in which a grade of C or better has been earned, provided courses are from an accredited college and fit the degree requirements. For credit to be accepted from an international institution of higher learning, the institution must be a recognized third-level institution.

A maximum of 30 credits gained through testing may be applied toward an undergraduate degree program. DANTES, CLEP, and Syracuse advanced credit exams may be used for this purpose. However, credit awarded through testing does not count toward the minimum number of credits that must be taken at Syracuse in order to earn a degree. On the graduate level, there is no provision for experiential credit. However, 6 credits may be taken in transfer from other accredited graduate programs, with a grade of C or better.

Faculty

Distance courses are taught by full-time Syracuse University faculty members, who participate in the distance education programs in addition to their full-time campus responsibilities.

Admission

Candidates for admission to the certificate, associate, and baccalaureate programs should have a high school diploma or its equivalent. Transfer students must have at least a 2.0 (C) average for the liberal studies program. Graduate applicants whose primary language is a language other than English must also take the TOEFL.

Applicants for all programs must submit official transcripts of prior academic work, three letters of recommendation, and a personal statement that accompanies the application form.

Tuition and Fees

For 2006–07, the undergraduate tuition rate is $520 per credit, and the graduate rate is $940 per credit. Additional expenses for room and board during the on-site residences vary depending upon the choice of facility, and book charges average $150 per course.

Financial Aid

Distance education students who are U.S. citizens are eligible for all the standard federal grants and loans available to part-time students. Selective institutional aid is available; detailed information is available upon request. Syracuse University awards more than $100,000 to distance education students each year. International students (non-U.S. citizens) are not eligible for financial aid.

Applying

Applicants should request application materials from the address below. The programs admit students on a continuous basis, and students can begin in the fall, spring, or summer terms. In-person interviews are not required, although they can be arranged upon request.

CONTACT

Marketing Department
Syracuse University/University College
700 University Avenue
Syracuse, New York 13244-2530
Phone: 315-443-3480
800-442-0501 (toll-free, U.S. only)
Fax: 315-443-4174
E-mail: distanceed@uc.syr.edu
Web site: http://www.yesu.syr.edu/distance

TAYLOR UNIVERSITY

Center for Lifelong Learning

Fort Wayne, Indiana

Taylor University is one of America's oldest evangelical Christian institutions. In 1846, it began as a women's college with the conviction that women as well as men should have an opportunity for higher education. In 1855, it became coeducational and, in 1938, it offered its first distance learning course.

Today, U.S. News & World Report *repeatedly ranks Taylor as one of America's best regional liberal arts colleges. The Templeton Foundation has named it one of the nation's top colleges for building character in students, and* Barron's *has listed it as a "best buy in college education."*

Taylor University's mission is to educate men and women for lifelong learning and for ministering the redemptive love of Jesus Christ. It is accredited by the Higher Learning Commission of the North Central Association of Colleges and Schools.

Distance Learning Program

The Center for Lifelong Learning is the virtual campus of Taylor University; it emphasizes the integration of faith and learning through distance education. The Center offers three Associate of Arts (A.A.) degrees, seven certificate programs, and more than 130 online courses from most academic disciplines. Annually, it enrolls more than 1,300 students.

Delivery Media

At the Taylor University Center for Lifelong Learning, the antiquated method of correspondence education has been replaced by the advantages of Internet technology and online learning. Rather than repackaging traditional classroom learning methods or simply creating digital versions of correspondence courses, Taylor has designed each course to ensure that it is learner-oriented and specifically designed for online, distance learning students. The eLearning platform brings together the elements that create the most valuable educational experience for the online distance learner—dynamic interaction and discussion with other students; close, continuous access to the instructor; and the convenience of having it all right at the student's fingertips.

Programs of Study

The 64-credit-hour A.A. degree in biblical studies is designed for individuals preparing for vocational or lay Christian ministry. The curriculum is designed to give the student a foundational understanding of the Bible, Christian theology, and the knowledge and skills required for serving in a church or parachurch setting. It consists of 43 credit hours of general education course work, 15 hours in the discipline, and 6 elective hours.

The 64-credit-hour A.A. degree in justice administration is designed for individuals currently serving in or seeking to enter criminal justice, courts, corrections, law enforcement, or juvenile justice. It consists of 43 credit hours of general education course work and 21 hours in the discipline. Students select a ministry or public policy concentration. The A.A. with a concentration in ministry is the only degree program in the nation from an accredited institution specifically designed to prepare the student for correctional ministry. The degree is designed for individuals currently serving in or seeking to enter corrections, outreach, or ministry to offenders and at-risk populations.

The 64-credit-hour A.A. degree in the liberal arts is for students who desire a breadth of knowledge. It consists of 43 credit hours of general education course work, 15 hours in the chosen discipline, and 6 elective hours. Students select an interdisciplinary, history, or social science concentration.

The seven certificate programs include the 24-credit-hour Certificate in Biblical and Cultural Leadership, which is designed to equip women and men with a thorough grounding of Biblical content, a systematic theological review, an opportunity for personal spiritual development, and a philosophical defense of the faith; the 24-credit-hour Biblical Studies Certificate, designed for busy pastors, church workers, and lay people who desire in-depth studies in the Bible; the 18-credit-hour Christian Worker Certification, designed for potential missionaries, pastors, and laypeople who desire a greater knowledge of the Bible and a better understanding of the professional challenges of ministry; the 18-credit-hour Justice and Ministry Certificate, specifically aimed at equipping individuals for correctional ministry; the 18-credit-hour Leadership Development Certificate, designed to equip current or potential leaders with the interpersonal skills and organizational abilities necessary for coping with business or ministry issues; the 18-credit-hour Certificate in Missions Studies, designed to assist those who desire to work in the mission field either as a full-time missionary or through frequent trips overseas for ministry purposes; and the 24-credit-hour Professional Writing Certificate, designed to strengthen students' abilities to write and communicate clearly in a style that is marketable to a contemporary audience.

Special Programs

All courses through the Taylor University Center for Lifelong Learning are competency-based, which means that students can complete the course as soon as the competencies are attained. The motivated student can progress at his or her own pace to ensure that the subject matter is understood well. Credit for each course is given when the expected learning results are documented and demonstrated.

Student Services

The Taylor University Center for Lifelong Learning staff is committed to providing qualified, efficient, and responsive service in a timely manner. Online registration facilitates course enrollments at any time of the day or night. Once enrolled, students become part of the Center's virtual campus, meeting the needs of today's Internet-savvy students. Within the virtual campus, students enjoy a relational, faith-based learning environment.

Credit Options

Students earn credits with the successful completion of courses. Up to 34 hours of transfer credit may be approved toward the 64-credit-hour A.A. degree programs. Only course work with a grade of C- or better is accepted.

To receive credit for work done at other accredited institutions, students should send their transcripts to the Taylor University Center for Lifelong Learning for review. CLEP, AP, and DANTES credit must meet Taylor's standards to be accepted as transfer credit.

Faculty

The faculty of the Taylor University Center for Lifelong Learning consists of more than 100 highly credentialed, dedicated Christians. These instructors, many of whom hold doctorates, are among the most qualified academic professionals in the field of Christian higher education.

Admission

Admission is open to all students registering for individual courses or beginning a certificate program. Degree-seeking students must meet certain minimum admission standards and complete an application, which includes a personal reference recommendation.

Tuition and Fees

All courses are $200 per credit hour. Other expenses may include textbooks, study guides, supplemental materials, and shipping and handling fees. Taylor's most current fee structure is maintained at its online registration center.

Financial Aid

Students who have been accepted into online degree programs and who will be registered for at least 6 credit hours in one term may apply for financial aid available through the University's Title IV agreement with the U.S. Department of Education.

The Department of Veterans Affairs has approved courses offered by the Taylor University Center for Lifelong Learning for those students entitled to receive veteran's educational benefits.

Applying

The Taylor University Center for Lifelong Learning offers open enrollment year-round through a secure, online registration process. Students may enroll online at any time in individual courses, certificate programs, or degree programs. Students seeking a degree must apply and be accepted. Secure, online registration is available at http://cll.taylor.edu/catalog. Students may also call toll-free at 800-845-3149. Students may also register and/or apply by fax, e-mail, mail, or in person.

CONTACT

Kevin Mahaffy, M.Min.
Director
Taylor University Center for Lifelong Learning
1025 West Rudisill Boulevard
Fort Wayne, Indiana 46807-2197
Phone: 260-744-8750
800-845-3149 (toll-free enrollment hotline)
Fax: 260-744-8796
E-mail: info@cll.taylor.edu
Web site: http://cll.taylor.edu

TEXAS STATE TECHNICAL COLLEGE WACO

Distance Learning

Waco, Texas

Texas State Technical College Waco (TSTC Waco) is a coeducational two-year institution of higher education offering associate degrees and certificates of completion in critical and emerging technical areas of study. Whether students want to add to existing skills or begin a new career, TSTC Waco can help them achieve their goals. The benefits of investing in a TSTC education are marketable skills, desirable job opportunities, and excellent starting salaries.

Founded in 1965, TSTC Waco is part of the only state-supported technical college system in Texas. Texas State Technical College Waco is accredited by the Commission on Colleges of the Southern Association of Colleges and Schools (1866 Southern Lane, Decatur, Georgia 30033-4097; telephone: 404-679-4501) to award Associate of Applied Science degrees and certificates of completion.

Distance Learning Program

Distance learning courses at Texas State Technical College Waco offer students flexibility in planning a course load that they can complete in their own homes and within their own schedules.

Delivery Media

TSTC Waco's distance education courses are delivered through Web-based Internet classes or interactive video. They mainly use Web pages, chatting software, discussion boards, telephone, and electronic mail. In order to take distance learning classes, students must have access to the Internet, an e-mail address, and a Web browser. Students must meet deadlines, complete assignments, and take scheduled tests. Some distance learning courses require proctored testing. Learning materials include textbooks, videos, other reading materials, group activities, and tests.

Programs of Study

In addition to its academic courses, TSTC Waco offers a variety of more than forty courses over the Internet in programs of study such as advertising, computer networking, computer science, design and print, media communication and information, network security, and Webmaster. The College also offers noncredit courses. Students should visit http://distance.tstc.edu/pjs/cs/dlcourses.cfm for a complete list of current courses offered through distance learning.

Special Programs

TSTC Waco provides many services for students with disabilities. Students should contact the Deaf-Disabled Student Services Office for information about specific services.

Student Services

TSTC distance learning students can take advantage of TSTC's many academic support services.

Library support is available to enrolled students through access to the TSTC library either in person at the campus or at http://walib.tstc.edu, where they can also access the EBSCO full-text periodical online database. In addition, there is a link to the library's reference and interlibrary loan services. For students who are Texas residents, there is a state program, TexShare that allows member libraries to give circulation privileges to patrons of member libraries. For more information about this program and participating schools, students should visit the Web site at http://www.texshare.edu.

The Counseling and Testing Center offers numerous services, including assessment and placement, career planning, personal counseling, transfer student counseling, academic counseling, and scholastic probation counseling. Counselors and faculty advisers can discuss the full range of programs and services offered and are available during the semester for continuing assessment and advisement.

The full-service campus bookstore is available to all distance learning students, and textbooks, ebooks, and other materials can be ordered online.

Credit Options

Upon application for admission, students must submit transcripts from all other postsecondary institutions. The amounts and types of credit transferable to TSTC depend on the student's intended degree program.

Faculty

In addition to their formal education, TSTC Waco faculty members have years of industry experience and bring to the classroom real-world skills. They bring from industry valuable knowledge and skills gained in their respective field. The TSTC student-faculty ratio is low, giving professors more one-on-one time with their students.

Admission

Admission is based on graduation from an accredited high school (or the equivalent) or college transfer. Individual programs may have additional specific requirements.

Tuition and Fees

TSTC students receive a valuable education at a reasonable price. The average investment to get an A.A.S. degree at TSTC is $5500. Students enrolled only in distance learning courses pay regular tuition plus a

$15-per-hour distance learning fee and all other fees except special use and student union fees.

Financial Aid

Even though an education at Texas State Technical College is reasonably priced, financial assistance is still available to all students. The variety of scholarships and aid available at each of the TSTC locations includes the Federal Pell Grant Program, the Federal Supplemental Educational Opportunity Grant Program, Federal and Texas Work-Study programs, TEXAS Grant Program, TEXAS II Grant Program, subsidized and unsubsidized Stafford Loans, and parent loans. For more information, students should contact the Financial Aid Office at http://www.waco.tstc or call 800-792-8784.

Applying

Applicants to the Distance Learning program must also be accepted as a student at the College. They should submit a completed Application for Admission, proof of residency (if claiming Texas residency), the Immunization Health History Form, and official high school transcript or GED certificate and all official college transcripts (if applicable) to the Admissions and Records Office. Upon acceptance to the College and the distance learning program, students contact the learning adviser for their technology major. The adviser then works with the student to determine the courses needed. Students may apply online at http://www.waco.tstc.edu.

CONTACT

Distance Learning Office
Texas State Technical College Waco
Administration Building
7th Street
Waco, Texas 76705
Phone: 254-867-3257
800-792-8784 (toll-free)
Fax: 254-867-3470
E-mail: lance.zimmerman@tstc.edu
sherry.pierc@tstc.edu
Web site: http://www.waco.tstc.edu

TEXAS TECH UNIVERSITY

Distance Learning

Lubbock, Texas

Texas Tech University (TTU), a state-supported comprehensive university, is accredited by the Commission on Colleges of the Southern Association of Colleges and Schools to award bachelor's, master's, and doctoral degrees. Created by legislative action in 1923, Texas Tech University is a four-year research university composed of ten colleges and two schools (Agricultural Sciences and Natural Resources, Architecture, Arts and Sciences, Business Administration, Education, Engineering, Honors, Human Sciences, Mass Communication, Visual and Performing Arts, the Graduate School, and the School of Law).

Committed to teaching and the advancement of knowledge, Texas Tech provides the highest standards of excellence in higher education, fosters intellectual and personal development, and stimulates meaningful research and service.

Distance Learning Program

Offering flexibility and convenience, programs provide high-quality course work comparable to traditional on-campus courses. Texas Tech University now offers twenty degree programs and eight certification programs at a distance.

Delivery Media

Courses are delivered via the World Wide Web by two-way interactive video; on audiotape, videotape, and CD-ROM; and by printed correspondence, depending on the course or degree program. E-mail, threaded discussions, chat rooms, and traditional communicative methods allow students to correspond with instructors and peers.

Programs of Study

The Bachelor of General Studies (B.G.S.) degree is offered by the College of Arts and Sciences through Extended Studies. A highly flexible program, the B.G.S. degree features three core areas of concentration (in lieu of a major) that are tailored to students' interests or professional goals. Each concentration area consists of courses that are consistent with the minor in various subject disciplines, e.g., English or psychology.

The College of Arts and Sciences offers two graduate-level degrees in technical communication through the Department of English. The Master of Arts in technical communication is a nonthesis program, and professionals in fields such as technical communication, human resources, consulting, software design, graphic design, engineering, and management find this degree to be invaluable for career advancement. The Ph.D. in technical communication and rhetoric (TCR) provides a broad approach to technical communication, offering classes in areas such as editing, design, rhetorical theory, online documentation, publications management, and usability testing.

The College of Visual and Performing Arts offers a Master of Art Education degree. This program supports practicing teachers with contemporary social theories and strategies that strengthen their classroom, studio practice, and research skills in relation to art and visual culture. Course work can be completed over the Internet and during the summers at TTU Center at Junction in Junction, Texas, or in Lubbock, Texas.

The College of Engineering offers four different Distance Learning master's degrees: the interdisciplinary Master of Engineering degree (M.En.), which allows students to take courses from a number of engineering fields while specializing in one area; the Master of Science in Systems and Engineering Management (M.S.S.E.M.) through industrial engineering; the Master of Science in Computer Science (M.S.C.S.); and the Master of Science in Software Engineering (M.S.S.E.) through computer science.

The College of Education also offers several degrees at a distance. The Master of Education (M.Ed.) in instructional technology is designed for K–12 educators and professional trainers who want to become online instructors, instructional designers, and managers of distance education programs. The Master of Education in special education has areas of emphasis in generic special education, educational diagnostician studies, autism, orientation and mobility, and vision. The Master of Education in language literacy education is designed to prepare teachers to provide reading and literacy leadership in their school districts. The Master of Education in educational leadership and principal professional certification preparation is a two-year, 45-hour cohort program leading to completion of the M.Ed. and preparation for midlevel management and school principal certification. This program is designed to accommodate working teachers who are interested in pursuing careers as elementary or secondary school principals in Texas.

The College of Human Sciences offers a Master of Science in restaurant/hotel and institutional management (RHIM) through the Department of Nutrition, Hospitality, and Retailing. This program is designed for industry professionals who work in management-level positions.

The College of Agricultural Sciences and Natural Resources (CASNR) offers several degrees at a distance. The Bachelor of Science in horticulture degree requires a minimum of 120 hours of undergraduate course work and focuses on the challenges and practices of genetics and breeding, propagation, biotechnology, production, management, handling and storage, marketing, and utilization of ornamental plants in the interior and exterior landscape. The Master of Science in horticulture is a terminal, 36-hour, nonthesis degree program that focuses on the art and science of cultivating edible and ornamental plants. The Master of Agriculture is a terminal, 36-hour, nonthesis degree program with four areas of emphasis (agronomy, horticulture, resource management, and agricultural education) designed to prepare students and professionals as leaders, managers, and executives in the agricultural sciences and natural resources areas. Because the degree is multidisciplinary, students are able to design a program to meet their unique career objectives. The Master of Science in crop science is a terminal, 36-hour, nonthesis degree program that includes the study of plant genetics, breeding, biotechnology, molecular biology, physiology, biochemistry, weed control, and crop management. In conjunction with Texas A&M University, Texas Tech University also offers a Doctor of Education (Ed.D.) in agricultural education through the Department of Agricultural Education and Communications. Targeted toward midcareer professionals in agricultural education, this program requires 64 semester hours and spans four years.

A Master of Science in human development and family studies, with an emphasis in gerontology, is offered through the College of Human Sciences and the Great Plains Interactive Distance Education Alliance (GPIDEA). The program is designed to prepare professionals who are either working directly with older people or involved in education and research that is related to the elderly.

The Graduate School offers a Master of Science in multidisciplinary science degree. This program is designed to meet the professional needs of K–12 science teachers and consists of graduate courses in the sciences, mathematics, and science education, culminating with the completion of a comprehensive portfolio project.

Special Programs

The College of Education offers seven certification preparation programs: Master Reading Teacher Certification Preparation Program, Post-baccalaureate Secondary Teacher Certification Preparation Program, Superintendent Professional Certification Program, Generic Special Education, Educational Diagnostician (Special Education), Visual Impairment (Special Education), and Orientation & Mobility (Special Education).

In addition, a Certificate in Gerontology is offered through the College of Human Sciences and the Great Plains Interactive Distance Education Alliance.

Student Services

College-assigned advisers provide information about accessing course materials online, register students for course work, disseminate course materials, and monitor students' progress through degree programs.

Credit Options

Distance learning college-credit courses or courses taken for continuing education credit are recorded on Texas Tech University transcripts. Distance learning course credits may be transferable to other institutions.

Faculty

Courses are taught by Texas Tech University faculty members or instructors who have been approved by the respective college. The majority of faculty members hold terminal degrees.

Admission

Prospective students should visit the University's Web site (http://www.ttu.edu) for detailed information about admission requirements.

Tuition and Fees

Tuition and fees vary from program to program.

Financial Aid

Distance learning students may be eligible for a variety of financial aid opportunities. Students should contact the Financial Aid Office at 806-742-3681 for more information.

Applying

Most degree programs require applications to be submitted by specific deadlines. Students should visit http://www.de.ttu.edu to obtain specific application procedures and deadlines for degree programs.

CONTACT

For specific information about degree programs, students should visit the Extended Studies Web site (http://www.de.ttu.edu). For general inquiries, students should contact:

Michele Moskos
Marketing Director
Division of Outreach & Extended Studies
Texas Tech University
Box 42191
Lubbock, Texas 79409-2191
Phone: 800-MY-COURSE (800-692-6877) Ext. 276 (toll-free)
E-mail: dldegrees.oes@ttu.edu
Web site: http://www.de.ttu.edu

THOMAS EDISON STATE COLLEGE

Trenton, New Jersey

Thomas Edison State College specializes in providing flexible, high-quality, collegiate learning opportunities for self-directed adults. One of New Jersey's twelve senior public institutions of higher education, the College offers fifteen associate, baccalaureate, and master's degrees in more than 100 areas of study. Students earn degrees through a wide variety of rigorous and high-quality academic methods that can by customized to meet their individual needs. Identified by Forbes *magazine as one of the top twenty colleges and universities in the nation in the use of technology to create learning opportunities for adults, Thomas Edison State College is a national leader in the assessment of adult learning and a pioneer in the use of educational technologies. Founded in 1972, Thomas Edison State College is regionally accredited by the Commission on Higher Education of the Middle States Association of Colleges and Schools.*

Distance Learning Program

Thomas Edison State College offers one of the most highly regarded, comprehensive distance learning programs in the United States. Adults may choose from more than 220 distance learning courses, including online classes. Students also take tests and submit portfolios to demonstrate and earn credit for college-level knowledge they already have and may transfer credits earned at other accredited institutions.

Delivery Media

Distance education courses are provided through several options, including Thomas Edison State College courses offered through the mail and online. Also available are online credit-by-examination e-Pack® courses, which allow students to prepare for a comprehensive final examination by taking a series of chapter quizzes delivered via the Internet.

Programs of Study

Thomas Edison State College offers fifteen associate, baccalaureate, and master's degrees in more than 100 areas of study. Undergraduate degrees offered include the Associate in Applied Science; Associate in Science in Management; Associate in Science in Applied Science and Technology; Associate in Arts; Associate in Science in Natural Science and Mathematics; Associate in Science in Public and Social Services; Bachelor of Arts; Bachelor of Science in Applied Science and Technology; Bachelor of Science in Business Administration; Bachelor of Science in Health Sciences, a joint-degree program with the University of Medicine and Dentistry of New Jersey (UMDNJ) School of Health Related Professions (SHRP); Bachelor of Science in Human Services; and Bachelor of Science in Nursing.

Each undergraduate degree requires work in general education, the area of study, and elective subjects. Students are encouraged to work in conjunction with one of the College's program advisers to develop an individual program plan.

In addition, the College offers three online master's programs. The Master of Science in Human Resources Management degree serves human resources professionals who wish to become strategic partners in their organizations. This program uses a cohort model and is designed to position human resources professionals as leaders within their organizations. The 36-semester-hour program provides practitioners with technical human resources skills in staffing, providing professional development, managing organizational culture, and measuring and rewarding performance. The Master of Science in Management degree program serves employed adults with professional experience in management. It integrates the theory and practice of management as it applies to diverse organizations. The College's Master of Arts in Liberal Studies degree program provides working professionals an opportunity to study the liberal arts from an applied perspective.

Special Programs

Thomas Edison State College's Military Degree Completion Program (MDCP) serves military personnel worldwide and was developed to accommodate the special needs of military personnel whose location, relocation, and time constraints make traditional college attendance difficult, if not impossible. The program allows students to engage in a degree program wherever they may be stationed and receive maximum credit for military training and education. Thomas Edison State College is a partner college for the Navy College Program Distance Learning Partnership and the Navy College Program Afloat College Education (NCPACE) and is a participant in the Army University Access Online (eArmyU) program.

The College's unique Degree Pathways Program allows community college students and graduates to complete a baccalaureate degree at home, in the workplace, or at their local two-year college. The Degree Pathways Program lets community college students and graduates make a smooth transition directly into a Thomas Edison State College baccalaureate program by transferring up to 80 credits toward the 120 credits needed for a baccalaureate degree. The program provides coordinated support in admissions, academic programming, advisement, registration, and the sharing of technologies. Students who have earned an associate degree within the past five years or are six months from completing an associate degree are eligible for the Degree Pathways Program. Students may continue to take classes and use technologies that are available at their community or county college as they move closer to the 80-credit limit of the 120 credits required for a baccalaureate degree.

Student Services

Academic advisement is provided to enrolled students by the College's Advisement Center, which assists students in integrating their learning style, background, and educational goals with the credit-earning methods and programs available. Students may access advisement through in-person appointments or through the Advisement Phone Center. They also have 24-hour access through fax and e-mail.

Credit Options

Students have the opportunity to earn degrees through traditional and nontraditional methods and use several convenient methods of meeting degree requirements, depending upon their individual learning styles and preferences. Once a student is enrolled in a specific degree program, an evaluator determines the number of credits the student has already earned and fits those into the degree program requirement.

Credit-earning options for nondegree students benefit individuals who would like to earn credit through examinations, prior learning assessment, and Thomas Edison State College courses. Students may do so by paying the appropriate fee for these programs. An application to the College is not required to take advantage of these nondegree, credit-earning options.

Credit Banking is for students who wish to document college-level learning and consolidate college-level work into a Thomas Edison State College transcript. Credits transcribed under the Credit Banking program may or may not apply to a degree program at Thomas Edison State College.

Thomas Edison State College grants credit for current professional licenses or certificates that have been approved for credit by ACE and the College's Academic Council. Students must submit notarized copies of their license or certificate and current renewal card, if appropriate, to receive credit. A list of licenses and certificates approved for credit may be found in the College's Undergraduate Prospectus.

Faculty

There are approximately 300 mentors at Thomas Edison State College. Drawn from other highly regarded colleges and universities, mentors provide many services, including assessment of prior knowledge and advisement.

Admission

Adults 21 years of age or older who are seeking an associate, baccalaureate, or master's degree and are high school graduates are eligible to become Thomas Edison State College students. Because Thomas Edison State College delivers high-quality education directly to students wherever they live or work, students may complete degree requirements at their convenience. There are two brief residency requirements for the organizational leadership professional focus area of the Master of Science in Management degree. A computer is required to complete graduate degrees and to take undergraduate online courses.

Tuition and Fees

Tuition is payment for all costs directly associated with the academic delivery of a Thomas Edison State College education. Fees are designated as payment for administrative services and for materials used by students for courses and other activities. Thomas Edison State College offers one annual tuition plan, the Comprehensive Tuition Plan, for students who want access to all components of the tuition package. For those students who have determined that their particular situation is one where only components of the Comprehensive Tuition Plan are required, the College offers the Enrolled Options Plan. A complete listing of tuition and fees is included in the College's information packet and is available by calling the Office of Admissions or by visiting the College Web site.

Financial Aid

Thomas Edison State College participates in a number of federal and state aid programs. Eligible students may receive Federal Pell Grants or federal education loans such as the Federal Stafford Student Loan (subsidized and unsubsidized). Eligible New Jersey residents may also tap a variety of state grant and loan programs. Students may use state aid to meet all or part of their college costs, provided they are taking at least 12 credits per semester. Detailed information about the financial aid process may be found in the financial aid packet, which is available from the Office of Financial Aid & Veterans' Affairs or on the College Web site. To receive this information, students should contact the office at 609-633-9658 or finaid@tesc.edu.

Applying

Students may apply to Thomas Edison State College by mail or fax or online at http://www.tesc.edu. The Office of Admissions assists potential applicants in determining whether Thomas Edison State College suits their particular academic goals.

CONTACT

Renee San Giacoma
Director of Admissions
Thomas Edison State College
101 West State Street
Trenton, New Jersey 08608-1176
Phone: 888-442-8372 (toll-free)
Fax: 609-984-8447
E-mail: info@tesc.edu
Web site: http://www.tesc.edu

TOURO UNIVERSITY INTERNATIONAL

Distance Learning Program

Cypress, California

Touro University International (TUI), located in southern California, is regionally accredited by the Commission for Senior Colleges and Universities of the Western Association of Schools and Colleges.

TUI offers affordable degree programs on the Internet, using the latest technology and innovative live interactive delivery methodology.

TUI is committed to sustaining the high quality of its pedagogical model, its faculty, and its support services. A worldwide university operating 24 hours a day, 365 days a year, TUI offers students an excellent learning experience accessed from their own homes, while allowing them to maintain their work and family responsibilities.

Distance Learning Program

TUI offers high-quality education utilizing online Internet instruction as its primary means of delivery. There is no residency requirement and no need for campus visits. The student-centered teaching model has two major elements: modular case-based learning and the cyber classroom. These essential elements are part of every module of every course.

Delivery Media

The cyber classroom approach includes the use of multimedia for academic transactions and interactive collaboration (live exchange with professors and peers). The multimedia approach includes audio and video on demand, Internet links, PowerPoint presentations, and live conferences among students and between professors and students. This allows students to work as a team with fellow students from around the world. Case-based learning provides real-world application to each topic.

Programs of Study

TUI consists of the College of Business Administration, the College of Education, the College of Health Sciences, and the College of Information Systems. The College of Business Administration offers three degree programs: the Bachelor of Science in Business Administration (120 semester credits), with concentrations in criminal justice, finance, general management, human resources information technology management, logistics, and degree completion specially designed for students with an A.A. or A.S. degree; the Master of Science in Business Administration (44 semester credits), with concentrations in conflict and negotiations management, criminal justice administration, entrepreneurship, finance, general management, human resource management, information technology management, international business, logistics management, public management, and strategic leadership; and the Doctor of Philosophy in Business Administration (44 semester credits of course work plus a research dissertation). The concentration depends on the candidate's specific research interests.

The College of Education offers two degree programs: the Master of Arts in Education (36 semester credits), with concentrations in teaching and instruction, educational leadership, higher education, and e-learning, and the Doctor of Philosophy in Educational Leadership (48 semester credits of course work plus a research dissertation), with specializations in K–12 leadership, higher education leadership, and e-learning leadership.

The College of Health Sciences offers three degree programs: the Bachelor of Science in Health Sciences (124 semester credits), with concentrations in health education, health-care management, and professional degree completion; the Master of Science in Health Sciences (40 semester credits), with specializations in clinical research administration, emergency and disaster management, health-care management, health-care informatics, health education, international health, law and expert witness studies, and public health, and graduate certificates in clinical research administration, emergency and disaster management, health-care administration, health informatics, law and expert witness studies, and quality assurance; and the Doctor of Philosophy in Health Sciences (44 semester credits in course work plus a research dissertation), with specializations in international health and educator/researcher/practitioner studies.

The College of Information Systems offers three degree programs: the Bachelor of Science in Computer Science (120 semester credits), the Bachelor of Science in Information Technology Management (120 semester credits), and the Master of Science in Information Technology Management (36 semester credits).

Student Services

Touro University International maintains five specific student services. Preadmission advisement assists students with enrollment procedures and any other student concerns. Preadmission English competency evaluation is provided for students whose first language is not English, who do not meet TUI's English competency requirements, or who feel that they do not possess adequate English skills. Post-admission advisement assists students with course selection and sequencing, developing good study habits, and other student concerns. Information technology assistance is provided to ensure that students have access to all information technology features of TUI courses. The Information Technology department also assists students with installation and configuration. Library resource assistance is provided via e-mail in the use of all cyber library holdings.

TUI provides financial assistance under three federal programs that are available to citizens and eligible noncitizens of the United States.

Faculty

All TUI faculty members hold doctoral degrees and have experience in their respective fields in addition to having sound academic teaching, research, and dissertation advisement records. Exceptional full-time faculty members teach nearly all TUI classes. The highest level of faculty expertise in each field is also available through guest lecturers and visiting faculty members via the cyber classroom delivery mode.

Admission

TUI offers four sessions per year, beginning in April, July, October, and January, with each session lasting twelve weeks. All TUI courses are valued at 4 semester credits. A full-time load is two courses per session, whereby students can earn 32 semester credits per year while continuing with family and work responsibilities.

The Office of Admissions assists potential students in determining their compatibility with the program based on past academic performance and educational goals. For specific details about each degree program, students may visit the Web site.

Tuition and Fees

TUI's tuition is one of the most affordable in the nation. Tuition is $250 per semester credit for B.S.-level courses, $300 per semester credit for M.S.-level courses, and $500 per semester credit for Ph.D.-level courses. Students may contact TUI registration for information about scholarships and financial aid.

Active-duty military, retired military, military dependents, and civilian military employees receive special tuition rates through TUI's DANTES agreement. Students should contact their base or post education officer or TUI for details.

Applying

Applications may be completed online at www.tourou.edu and are accepted year-round. A complete application package must be received by TUI two weeks prior to the start of the first session. TUI will respond within 24 business hours of receiving the complete package of application materials.

CONTACT

College of Business Administration
5665 Plaza Drive, 3rd Floor
Cypress, California 90630
Phone: 714-816-0366
800-375-9878 (toll-free)
Fax: 714-816-0367
E-mail: infocba@tourou.edu
Web site: http://www.tourou.edu

College of Education
5665 Plaza Drive, 3rd Floor
Cypress, California 90630
Phone: 714-226-9840
800-375-9878 (toll-free)
Fax: 714-226-9844
E-mail: infocoe@tourou.edu
Web site: http://www.tourou.edu
For program information:

College of Health Sciences
5665 Plaza Drive, 3rd Floor
Cypress, California 90630
Phone: 714-226-9840
800-375-9878 (toll-free)
Fax: 714-226-9844
E-mail: infochs@tourou.edu
Web site: http://www.tourou.edu

College of Information Systems
Cypress, California 90630
Phone: 714-816-0366
800-375-9878 (toll-free)
Fax: 714-816-0367
E-mail: infocis@tourou.edu
Web site: http://www.tourou.edu

UNITED STATES SPORTS ACADEMY

Continuing Education and Distance Learning

Daphne, Alabama

The United States Sports Academy (USSA) is a nonprofit, private graduate school designed to serve the nation and the world as a sport education resource, with programs of instruction, research, and service. Since 1972, the Academy has been addressing the need to provide high-quality, sport-specific programs. The Academy is accredited by the Commission on Colleges of the Southern Association of Colleges and Schools to award the Bachelor of Sports Science (B.S.S.) degree, Level III; Master of Sport Science degree (M.S.S.), Level III; and the Doctor of Sport Management degree (D.S.M.), Level V.

Distance Learning Program

Learning experiences and student requirements in distance learning are similar and equivalent to courses offered in the traditional on-campus setting. Courses are taught by an Academy faculty member, who is responsible for advising and facilitating the learning experience during the structured offering of distance learning. The vast majority of the Academy's students are using the distance learning system for part or their entire degree program.

The flexibility of the Academy's distance learning delivery system offers students the ability to pursue educational interests on their schedule and at their location. To experience the online option, prospective students should check out the free demo course at http://www.ussaonline.org and use the following information: Login: ussademo1 and Password: democourse.

Delivery Media

Distance learning students at USSA receive a code for the Web-based course and textbooks. The USSA library and its extensive reference database can be accessed through the USSA Web site. All students are required to have access to a computer and the Internet at the time they start the first course.

Programs of Study

Distance learning offers the student an opportunity to earn a master's degree or a doctoral degree through a Web-based environment, though there is a residency requirement for the doctoral degree.

The United States Sports Academy offers an upper-level Bachelor of Sport Science (B.S.S.) degree program in sports coaching and sports management. The program consists of the final 60 semester hours of the 120 hours required for the B.S.S. degree. The goal of the B.S.S. program is to provide needed education credentials to students interested in pursuing careers in the sport industry.

The Master of Sport Science degree is offered in the following majors: fitness management, sports coaching, sports management, sports medicine, and sports studies. Each major requires 33 semester hours of course work. The Academy offers dual majors in any two curriculums that range between 42 and 48 semester hours of course work.

The graduate program in fitness management examines issues in health and physical fitness, such as obesity. The fitness major is versatile in that it offers individuals opportunities to pursue careers in corporate, private, public, and not-for-profit organizations.

The graduate program in sports coaching is designed to prepare a student for leadership in the dynamic career of sports coaching. Program objectives are established to prepare each student for the multiplicity of demands involved in the control and operation of individual and team sports. The graduate curriculum is designed to prepare students for further study in sport at a higher level or develop and build their own concentration.

The graduate curriculum in sports management is designed to prepare each student for the increasing number of career leadership opportunities in the field of sport and recreational management. Program objectives prepare the student for a multiplicity of demand involved in the operation of sport programs at various levels. Sports management students are prepared for careers as sports facility managers, sport information directors, sport front office administrators, or sport community relations' directors.

The graduate program in sports medicine is designed to prepare students for prevention, management, and rehabilitation of athletic injuries with the multiplicity of demands involved with the successful operation of sports medicine programs at various levels. Upon graduation, successful students receive the United States Sports Academy's certification in sports medicine.

In the sports studies curriculum, students work with their adviser to select the courses from any major to build their own concentration. The courses are selected in accordance to the student's interest.

The Doctor of Sports Management, like the master's degree, is designed for the working professional. The 60 semester hours required to complete the degree may be earned through a combination of on-campus study and distance learning online, mentorship, and directed individualized study. The doctoral program is designed to prepare students to perform with a high degree of efficiency and proficiency in the sports industry, including sport education. There are three specialization areas: finance, marketing, and human resource management. There is also an emphasis in sports medicine for those already licensed or certified in the area. The curriculum is designed to enable students who are recent master's degree graduates, working professionals, sports enthusiasts, athletic administrators, and sports education instructors to achieve their personal, educational, and professional objectives in a sport-specific environment. The degree normally requires three to five years to complete.

Each course requires the student to complete online quizzes, assignments, a research paper, and a proctored final examination. A course is graded as follows: discussion, 10 percent; quizzes, 0 percent; written assignments, 20 percent; class paper, 35 percent; and the final exam, 35 percent.

All degree-seeking students must pass a written comprehensive examination in order to graduate. Students must have completed and passed all course work before taking this examination. Students at USSA have the option of a thesis, mentorship, or elective classes.

Special Programs

USSA has certification programs in several areas, including sports agency, sports coaching, and sports management. These programs are available to people of all educational backgrounds. The cost for the continuing education program is $150 per course, which is equivalent to 4 continuing education units (CEUs).

Credit Options

A student may transfer up to 15 (master's) and 24 (doctoral) semester hours from a regionally accredited graduate school as long as such courses are equivalent to courses offered in the Academy's undergraduate and graduate program, credit was earned in the past four calendar years, the student received a grade of B or better in the course(s), and the academic committee approves the transfer of credit. For more information, students should contact the Office of Student Services.

Faculty

The Academy has more than 30 faculty members. They are located both on-site and at various locations around the country. All faculty members have terminal degrees. The majority of them are specialized in a sport science.

Admission

Students who have completed at least 60 semester hours at another college or junior college or those who possess an associate degree from a community or junior college may be eligible to enroll immediately in the Bachelor of Sports Science program. The Academy has a different enrollment plan for those students who have 49 to 59 semester hours of credit from another institution.

For full-standing admission to the master's degree program, an applicant must be a graduate of a four-year regionally accredited undergraduate institution, with a cumulative grade point average of 2.5 or better, and obtain either a GRE score of at least 800, an MAT score of at least 27, or a GMAT score of at least 400. In the case in which the student's reported standardized test score (one of the three above) is below the stipulated score, students may still attain full standing by achieving a minimum 3.0 grade point average in their first 12 credits of course work.

Tuition and Fees

For online delivery, bachelor's degree courses are $250 per semester hour, master's degree courses are $425 per semester hour, and doctoral courses are $525 per semester hour. The cost does not include additional fees, textbooks, or shipping. International shipping is slightly higher. Prices are subject to change without notice, though current pricing can always be found on the Academy's Web site.

Financial Aid

USSA has a wide variety of financial aid programs available to qualified students. Students can obtain more information by visiting http://www.fafsa.gov.

Applying

A student applying for admission to the bachelor's degree program is required to submit the following items to the Office of Student Services: a completed application form accompanied by a $100 application fee (the fee is nonrefundable and constitutes part of the admission credentials), an official copy of all college transcripts, a written essay, a resume, and proof of insurance (residential students).

For the Master of Sports Science degree program, approval of applications from students currently enrolled in a bachelor's program are conditional based upon the successful completion of that degree prior to their commencement of study at the Academy. A student applying for admission to the master's degree program is required to submit the following to the Office of Student Services: a completed application form accompanied by a $50 application fee (the fee is nonrefundable and constitutes part of the admission credentials); an official copy of all college transcripts; three letters of recommendation; an official score report of the GRE, MAT, or GMAT results taken within the last five years; a written personal statement which describes the personal motivation or reasons for desiring a master's degree; and a resume or vita.

A student applying for admission to the doctoral degree program is required to submit the following to the Office of Student Services: a completed application form accompanied by a $100 application fee; an official copy of all college transcripts; three letters of recommendations; an official score report of the GRE (minimum 950), MAT (minimum 40) or GMAT (minimum 500) results within the last five years; a qualifying essay (not to exceed 3,000 words, in narrative form); and a resume or vita.

For further information, the complete catalogs of the United States Sports Academy can be viewed by visiting the Academy's home Web page at http://www.ussa.edu.

CONTACT

United States Sports Academy
1 Academy Drive
Daphne, Alabama 36526
Phone: 251-626-3303
800-223-2668 (toll-free)
Fax: 251-625-1035
E-mail: admissions@ussa.edu
Web site: http://www.ussa.edu

THE UNIVERSITY OF ALABAMA

College of Continuing Studies
Division of Academic Outreach
Tuscaloosa, Alabama

Founded in 1831, the University of Alabama has been selected repeatedly as one of the top fifty public universities in the country. By using technology and flexible formats, the Division of Academic Outreach provides diverse and convenient academic programs to students pursuing educational and personal development.

Distance Learning Program

The Division of Academic Outreach accommodates distance and adult learners who are limited by time, geography, work schedules, or personal obligations. Degrees and courses are available via the Internet, videotape, and videoconferencing.

Delivery Media

Academic Outreach delivers high school and college courses over the Internet directly to the student's computer. Students are instructed through a secure Internet site, and they interact with their professors and complete lessons through the online course-management system. Courses are offered either through a semester-based format or a six-month term format.

Through Independent Study, students may select their hours of study and work at their own pace to complete courses through written correspondence. With certain stipulations, the undergraduate courses may be used to complete a maximum of 25 percent of the work leading to the bachelor's degree. Nine of the last 18 hours required for a degree may be taken by written correspondence, provided that all residence requirements have been met.

Academic Outreach delivers undergraduate and graduate courses via videotape to students who cannot attend classes on campus. Courses are filmed as they occur, and videotapes are mailed to students the same week. Students take proctored exams at convenient locations. Video courses are semester based, with enrollment typically occurring during August, January, and May.

The Intercampus Interactive Telecommunication System (IITS) is a network of conference rooms connected to Vianet, a statewide videoconferencing network. Approximately 120 sites throughout Alabama are equipped with cameras, monitors, and other devices that allow teachers and students to interact as if they were in the same room. Courses are semester based, with enrollment typically occurring during August, January, and May.

Programs of Study

The University of Alabama offers the following programs through distance learning: B.S. in Commerce and Business Administration (general business), B.A. or B.S. in interdisciplinary studies (requires a three-day, on-campus orientation), B.S. in human environmental sciences (family financial planning and counseling), B.S. in human environmental sciences (general studies), B.S. in human environmental sciences (restaurant and hospitality management), B.S. in mechanical engineering (available in Dothan, Alabama), Bachelor of Science in Nursing (RN to B.S.N.), M.S. in operations management, M.S. in aerospace engineering, M.A. in health studies (health promotion), M.S. in human environmental sciences (food and nutrition), M.S. in human environmental sciences (general studies), M.S. in human environmental sciences (interactive technology), Master of Library and Information Sciences, M.S. in nursing case management, M.A. in rehabilitation counseling (Alabama only), Master of Law and Taxation, and Ed.S. in Counseling.

Special Programs

The External Degree Program is an interdisciplinary undergraduate distance learning program. Students may apply previously earned academic credits transferred from regionally accredited colleges or earned through national tests such as the College-Level Examination Program (CLEP), independent study, out-of-class learning contracts, correspondence studies, classroom work, and demonstrated prior learning toward a B.A. or a B.S. in interdisciplinary studies.

Applicants must have high school diplomas or minimum General Educational Development (GED) equivalency scores of 50, be 25 years of age or older, and have educational goals that are attainable through the program. As with most of the University's distance programs, applicants need not be Alabama residents.

Credit Options

Applicability of credit toward an undergraduate degree refers to the prerogative of the respective academic divisions to count specific credit toward a student's degree requirements. A maximum of 64 semester hours of two-year college credit may be applied toward graduation requirements. At the graduate level, a maximum of 12 semester hours of work taken as a nondegree student may be applied to the credit-hour requirements for a degree. Responsibility rests with the student to observe the limitations imposed on credit hours, course work, and transfer of credit. Procedures and forms are furnished upon request.

Faculty

Approximately 180 full-time and 10 part-time faculty members are involved in these programs. Of this group, 99 percent of the full-time faculty members and 90 percent of the part-time faculty members have doctoral or other terminal degrees.

Admission

Admission policies and procedures for degree programs and courses offered through Academic Outreach vary. Students are responsible for reading and understanding admissions polices and procedures for the degree program and courses they plan to enroll in. For more information, students should visit the Web site at http://BamaByDistance.ua.edu and click on the Prospective Student tab.

The Division of Academic Outreach provides services to assist students with the admission process, registration, advising and schedule building, and financial aid. Students should contact Nina Smith for assistance (telephone: 205-348-0089 or 800-452-5971 (toll-free); e-mail: nsmith@ccs.ua.edu or AOinfo@ccs.ua.edu).

Tuition and Fees

Tuition varies by program and format. Students should visit the Division of Academic Outreach Web site at http://BamaByDistance.ua.edu for current tuition rates.

Financial Aid

Loans are administered through the Office of Student Financial Services. Academic Outreach offers several scholarships for adult students each academic year. Applications are generally available in the fall semester, and the deadline is usually in early January.

Applying

Students may obtain information on admission and registration by contacting the Division of Academic Outreach.

CONTACT

Division of Academic Outreach
College of Continuing Studies
The University of Alabama
Box 870388
Tuscaloosa, Alabama 35487-0388
Phone: 205-348-0089
800-467-0227 (toll-free)
Fax: 205-348-0249
E-mail: AOinfo@ccs.ua.edu
Web site: http://www.BamaByDistance.ua.edu

UNIVERSITY OF ALASKA FAIRBANKS

Center for Distance Education and Independent Learning

Fairbanks, Alaska

In 1917, just fifteen years after the discovery of gold in the heart of the Alaskan wilderness, the Alaska Agricultural College and School of Mines was created by a special act of the Alaska Territorial Legislature. In 1922, the college opened with 6 faculty members and 6 students. Today, the University of Alaska Fairbanks (UAF), whose name was changed in 1931, continues to grow, both in size and stature. In addition to the main campus in Fairbanks, UAF has branch campuses in Bethel, Dillingham, Kotzebue, Nome, and the Interior/Aleutians. UAF is the state's land-, sea-, and space-grant institution. Its College of Rural and Community Development has the primary responsibility for Alaska Native education and study, and UAF remains the only university in Alaska that offers doctoral degrees. UAF's colleges and schools offer more than seventy fields of study and a wide variety of technical and vocational programs. All courses are approved and meet the accreditation standards of the Northwest Commission on Colleges and Universities. UAF is an Affirmative Action/Equal Opportunity employer and educational institution.

Distance Learning Program

UAF developed a Correspondence Study Program in the late 1950s, but the current Center for Distance Education and Independent Learning (CDE) was created in 1987. The Independent Learning Program offers more than 135 courses in nearly forty disciplines, with approximately 6,000 student enrollments throughout the world each year.

Independent Learning courses are open for enrollment any time of the year. Students have up to one year from the date of enrollment to finish course work. Extensions may be available, depending on the circumstances. Students are encouraged to use e-mail to submit lessons to circumvent delays in the standard mailing process.

CDE also supports close to 150 distance-delivered courses offered on a semester basis. CDE is part of the College of Rural and Community Development, with branch campuses in Bethel, Dillingham, Interior-Aleutians (Fairbanks), Kotzebue, and Nome, as well as participating with extended campuses of the University of Alaska Anchorage and University of Alaska Southeast.

Delivery Media

A wide range of media, including basic written materials, audiotapes, videotapes, CD-ROMS, e-mail, and the World Wide Web, is utilized to deliver instruction. Many courses are available online, most utilizing the Blackboard Learning System, and more are being developed regularly. Not all modes of delivery are available for every course, and students must have access to the appropriate equipment as specified in individual course descriptions. Most interaction between students and instructors is asynchronous in nature and may be via written communication, e-mail, or by phone interview.

Programs of Study

Approximately 135 independent learning courses can be used to fulfill degree program requirements within the University of Alaska's statewide system or at any other university that accepts the credits. The Center for Distance Education and Independent Learning is not a degree-granting organization. Future plans include delivery of certificates and degrees online.

Individual course requirements vary for Independent Learning courses and are detailed in the course description. Many courses list prerequisites, and it is up to the student to determine if he or she has fulfilled the requirements.

Special Programs

The Center for Distance Education and Independent Learning participates in the Defense Activity for Non-Traditional Education Support (DANTES) programs; information is available from base personnel or education officers. Veterans' educational benefits are also applicable. DANTES students must complete a UAF enrollment form as well as the DANTES forms.

People interested in being certified to teach in Alaska find courses available that fulfill teacher certificate and recertification requirements for the State of Alaska Department of Education. Students may choose among several courses that satisfy the Alaska studies and multicultural requirements.

Student Services

Students have access to the state library system and the UAF Rasmuson Library directly or through the Statewide Library Electronic Doorway (SLED). All students can obtain accounts on the University of Alaska computer network, which also gives access to the wider Internet and the World Wide Web. The UAF Writing Center offers free tutoring for student use. Papers are faxed to the center, and a telephone appointment is made between the tutor and the student. Students may not schedule more than one appointment per day. A toll-free UAF math hotline for problem solving and math help is also available for student use. Available hours may change each semester.

Credit Options

Since the Center for Distance Education and Independent Learning is not a degree-granting organization, there is no transfer of credit or credit for prior learning available.

Faculty

The Independent Learning Program includes approximately 90 faculty members, about half of whom are also full-time members of the UAF faculty and have terminal academic degrees. Adjunct faculty members and discipline professionals are hired to supplement the University's full-time faculty.

Admission

Students may enroll in individual courses any time during the year and have one year to complete the course. There are no admissions requirements or procedures, since the Center for Distance Education and Independent Learning is not a degree-granting organization.

Tuition and Fees

All students enrolled in UAF Independent Learning courses are charged the same tuition whether they are Alaska residents or not. Tuition for 100- to 200-level courses is $120 per credit, 300- to 400-level courses are $135 per credit, and 600-level courses are $268 per credit. There is an additional UA Network fee, which is assessed at 2 percent of tuition. The only other costs for courses are materials fees that vary by course and a $25 service fee per course. Students outside the U.S. must submit payment in U.S. dollars and are charged an extra $30 per course plus any additional shipping charges for the delivery of materials. (Actual costs of delivery are determined upon registration.)

Financial Aid

Alaska students who are full-time (enrolled in at least 12 credits per semester) and are taking independent learning courses on a semester basis are eligible for all the types of financial aid available to other students, including Federal Pell Grants, Federal Supplemental Educational Opportunity Grants, State Educational Incentive grants, Bureau of Indian Affairs grants, Federal Stafford Student Loans, and State of Alaska student loans. Students enrolled in regular yearlong courses are not eligible to receive financial aid.

Applying

No application is required of students taking Independent Learning courses. Completion of a UAF enrollment form and payment of fees are all that are required of students to take courses. Verification of enrollment and course materials are mailed to the students outside of the local Fairbanks area.

CONTACT

Curt Madison, Director
Center for Distance Education and Independent Learning
College of Rural and Community Development
P.O. Box 756700
University of Alaska Fairbanks
Fairbanks, Alaska 99775-6700
Phone: 907-474-5353
800-277-8060 (toll-free)
Fax: 907-474-5402
E-mail: distance@uaf.edu
Web site: http://distance.uaf.edu

UNIVERSITY OF ALBERTA

Master of Arts in Communications and Technology

Edmonton, Alberta, Canada

Opened in 1908 as a board-governed, public institution, the University of Alberta has grown to be one of Canada's foremost research-intensive universities. The University is located in Edmonton, the vibrant cosmopolitan capital of the province of Alberta.

The University of Alberta serves nearly 34,000 students in more than 200 undergraduate programs and 170 graduate programs. The University's pioneering spirit inspires faculty members and students to advance knowledge through research, to seek innovation in teaching and learning, and to find new ways to serve the people of Alberta and the world.

Distance Learning Program

The Master of Arts in Communications and Technology (MACT) program has attracted communication professionals from the world's leading organizations, including the United Nations, the Government of Canada, and Microsoft Corporation. Currently, students and graduates reside across Canada and the United States, and internationally.

The MACT is designed for individuals who seek to provide reflective and informed leadership in the management and use of information and communications technologies in their organizations and fields. Communication is examined across all contexts in the program: interpersonal, small group, public speaking, organizational, mass, and intercultural.

Delivery Media

MACT students use the Internet to access a course Web site, available within WebCT, that presents any required academic and administrative information. An electronic conferencing system is used for exchanging messages and distributing information during the term.

Students can access the course and do the work required for it whenever it is convenient for them—in the early morning, during their lunch hour, in the evening, or over the weekend. Chat sessions may be arranged at specified times, but these are optional and are not graded.

Since the MACT is a Web-based program, students are required to have a Pentium-generation computer that can sustain an Internet connection with a minimum speed of 56K, along with word-processing capabilities. WebCT is accessible using either a Mac or PC and with either a Netscape or Explorer browser. The faster the Internet connection and the more powerful the computer, the quicker a student is able to complete his or her work online.

Program of Study

The MACT requires the completion of seven core courses, three elective courses (offered by the University of Alberta or another recognized university), and a final applied research project.

Four of the core courses are completed during two Spring Institutes, held each May at the University of Alberta, with the remaining three core courses completed online during the fall and winter terms. Core courses are scheduled to permit completion of the degree by part-time study within two academic years.

Course work covers small-group and organizational communication; the theory, history, and practice of information and communications technologies; and the research skills associated with analyzing and evaluating these technologies, particularly as they are managed and used in the workplace.

Credit Options

Students may complete approved elective courses offered by other recognized universities. Credit for elective courses may be granted for course work previously completed. For more detailed information, prospective students should contact the program by e-mail or telephone.

Faculty

Professors associated with the program are engaged in disciplinary research connected to the theme of organizational uses of information and communication technologies. Students should visit the MACT Web site for detailed information about faculty members' publications, presentations, and research interests.

Admission

Admission to the program is competitive with up to 25 students being admitted each year. Admission requirements for the MACT are as follows: a four-year degree from a recognized university; a GPA of at least 3.0 (or equivalent) on a 4.0 scale; at least three years of relevant professional experience; three current and application-specific letters of reference; a letter of interest, which should state the applicant's academic or professional area of specialization, specifically how completion of the program would support the applicant's professional practice, and identifying a provisional topic for the final applied research project; where applicable, a TOEFL score of 600. For more information, students should contact the program by e-mail or telephone.

Tuition and Fees

The total cost for the MACT over a two-year period includes instructional and noninstructional fees for 36 credits of course work. In addition, a nonrefundable program fee of Can$3000 is due in each of the two years of study. A continuing program fee of Can$1000 is due in each additional year of study.

For international students, whether from the U.S. or another country, a 100 percent differential fee applies. Complete graduate fee information is available online at http://gradfile.fqsro.ualberta.ca/regfees/.

A Can$100 nonrefundable application fee is charged for each graduate studies application at the University of Alberta. Currently, the total cost for program texts is between Can$500 and $700.

Financial Aid

The MACT program does not offer any scholarships. For University of Alberta student award information, students should visit http://gradfile.fgsro.ualberta.ca.

Applying

The annual application deadline for the MACT program is December 15 each year. Applicants must complete an Application for Graduate Admission, which can be found at http://gradfile.fgsro.ualberta.ca/applyadmission/.

In addition to a completed Application for Graduate Admission, students must provide the following documents by December 15: official postsecondary transcripts; a statement of interest; three current and application-specific letters of reference; a TOEFL score of 600, where applicable; and a current curriculum vitae. All supporting documents should be sent directly to the Master of Arts in Communications and Technology Program office.

Students should visit the MACT Web site for further details. A decision regarding admission to the program is sent to applicants by mail in February.

CONTACT

Master of Arts in Communications and Technology
Faculty of Extension
University of Alberta
8303-112 Street
Edmonton, Alberta, Canada
T6G 2T4
Phone: 780-492-1501
E-mail: mact@ualberta.ca
Web site: http://www.extension.ualberta.ca/mact

UNIVERSITY OF COLORADO AT DENVER AND HEALTH SCIENCES CENTER

CU Online

Denver, Colorado

The University of Colorado at Denver and Health Sciences Center (UCDHSC) is one of three institutions in the University of Colorado system and the only public university in the Denver metropolitan area. The University of Colorado at Denver was founded in 1965 and is accredited by the North Central Association of Colleges and Schools.

Distance Learning Program

CU Online is the virtual campus of the University of Colorado at Denver and Health Sciences Center. Whether students are looking to take just a course or two or to complete a full degree program, CU Online provides the opportunity to complete courses without having to rearrange schedules, commute across town, find a place to park, or sit in a crowded classroom.

UCDHSC offers ten undergraduate and graduate degree programs and six certificate programs. Students can choose from more than 200 courses from both collegiate and professional development programs. CU Online connects them to diverse, virtual classrooms composed of international students and students from across the United States, including many Colorado locals.

Delivery Media

Professors use the latest technology in streaming audio and video and multimedia slide shows to present course materials. Live class discussions, guest speakers from across the country, Web conferencing, virtual animations, and simulations of course concepts are just a few ways faculty members deliver courses.

Programs of Study

Students can take courses in the liberal arts and sciences, arts and media, business, education, engineering, public affairs, and architecture and planning. Complete online degree programs include a B.A. in sociology, a B.A. in English writing, and master's degrees in business administration, early childhood education, eLearning and implementation, engineering (geographic information systems), finance, information and learning technologies, information systems, and public administration. Students can also complete short certificate and licensure programs, such as designing Web-based learning environments, early childhood special education, early literacy, international leadership and education, and nonprofit management. Students should check the Web site for the most recent updates. All of the courses may be applied to a degree program at the University of Colorado at Denver and Health Sciences Center or be transferred to a student's home institution, pending approval.

Special Programs

Hybrid-course offerings meet on campus only half as often as traditional courses, while students complete the remainder of the course online. Hybrid courses follow the same faculty governance policies as the established on-campus courses and have different fee structures than online courses. More information is available at http://www.cuonline.edu.

Student Services

Online student services and support allow students the advantages of a college campus—virtually. They can search the University catalog, register for courses, buy textbooks, receive guided advising, apply for financial aid, get tutoring, visit the library (which has online journals, online books, and subject guides) so they can achieve everything they strive for without missing the support or materials they need.

Credit Options

Credit, noncredit, and continuing and professional education courses are all available. Most online courses are measured through traditional letter grades. Some courses also offer the pass/fail option for students.

Faculty

Four out of five full-time faculty members hold doctoral degrees, and many have active rolls in their fields outside the classroom. CU Online faculty members are recognized scholars and researchers in their fields, with many years of teaching experience. Not only do they have real-world experience, but many are consultants, advisers, and partners with the leading organizations that hire CU Online graduates.

Admission

A smooth transition to the University of Colorado at Denver and Health Sciences Center is the University's goal. Students living in the state of Colorado must apply and be admitted as either a degree-seeking or a non-degree-seeking student. Students living outside of the state of Colorado do not need to be admitted to the University to take CU Online courses; however, if they wish to complete their degree through CU Online, they need to apply and be formally admitted to the University.

Tuition and Fees

Tuition rates vary between colleges and depending on residency status.

Most undergraduate courses cost approximately $201–$290 per credit hour for resident students. There is a $100 course fee that is added to each online course, a $7 fee for technology resources, and a $10 fee for the student information systems. Students should visit the CU Online Web site for current cost information.

Financial Aid

The University's firm belief that finances should never stand in the way of motivated, talented individuals keeps its strong financial aid programs alive. To be eligible for financial aid, students must be enrolled as degree-seeking students at the University of Colorado at Denver and Health Sciences Center. Students may contact the financial aid office for more information at 303-556-2886 or e-mail: finaid@carbon.cudenver.edu.

Applying

Students can apply to the University online or by paper application. Admission requirements vary by college and school. To find specific information about applying to the University of Colorado at Denver and Health Sciences Center, students may visit the CU Online Web site.

CONTACT

For more information about CU Online, students should contact:

CU Online, Campus Box 198
University of Colorado at Denver
and Health Sciences Center
P.O. Box 173364
Denver, Colorado 82017-3364
Phone: 303-556-6505
Fax: 303-556-6530
E-mail: inquiry@cuonline.edu
Web site: http://www.cuonline.edu/petersons

UNIVERSITY OF CONNECTICUT

Center for Continuing Studies

Storrs, Connecticut

Founded in 1881, the University of Connecticut (UConn) is categorized by the Carnegie Foundation among the Doctoral/Research Universities-Extensive, a distinction shared by fewer than 4 percent of America's higher education institutions that confer the widest number and range of degrees. UConn is the only public institution in New England with its own Schools of Law, Social Work, Medicine, and Dental Medicine. The University is accredited by the New England Association of Schools and Colleges.

The Center for Continuing Studies (CCS) offers a bachelor's degree program and two master's degree programs that are available online. The Center identifies, develops, and provides high-quality, research-based interdisciplinary, academic, professional, and enrichment programs as well as appropriate support services to diverse communities of learners in a fiscally responsible manner. Working with academic and student support units across the University, the Center for Continuing Studies provides a gateway linking the University with individuals as well as with corporate and public service sectors statewide, nationally, and internationally. CCS is dedicated to engaging learners in a lifelong academic partnership with the University of Connecticut.

Distance Learning Program

Based on educational demand and market research, the Center for Continuing Studies provides a variety of learning opportunities that utilize the most effective and efficient mode of delivery, given the course/program content and the intended learners. Individuals in CCS programs achieve relevant academic, professional, and technical competence and/or the personal enrichment they seek through a student-centered approach that reflects a high-quality education. Students may take individual courses or enroll in one of the online graduate or undergraduate degree or certificate programs. The asynchronous course format allows students to take courses from anywhere in the world. Faculty members are a key component of the online courses and programs and ensure that online students receive a high-quality education and personalized attention.

Delivery Media

All online courses are offered completely through the Internet using WebCT in a paced, asynchronous environment. The asynchronous format allows access to courses seven days a week, 24 hours a day, including holidays. Discussion and interactivity among the students and the instructor are a key component of all of the online courses. Much of this interactivity is accomplished using an asynchronous threaded discussion tool within the course. An e-mail system that is internal to the course is used for private communication. Some assignments have been designed for students working in groups. Online programs offered through the Center for Continuing Studies are geared toward working adults who need the flexibility to juggle work, family, and academic responsibilities. Courses are accessible using either a PC or a Macintosh. Prospective students are encouraged to review the list of frequently asked questions located at http://continuingstudies.uconn.edu/onlinecourses/faqs.html.

Programs of Study

The Center for Continuing Studies offers a Master of Professional Studies (M.P.S.) and a Bachelor of General Studies (B.G.S.). The online M.P.S. degree offers two fields of study: human resource management and humanitarian services administration. The M.P.S. degree is specifically designed for individuals and practitioners who are developing marketable skills to meet evolving workforce demands, seeking professional development or expanded promotional opportunities, or interested in changing careers. The M.P.S. requires 36 graduate-level credits, including 30 credits of course work and 6 credits of a capstone project toward the end of the program. The M.P.S. also includes an issues-based two-week on-site residency requirement.

The M.P.S. in human resource management is designed to meet the professional development needs of individuals who are currently working in the field of human resource management or who are interested in pursuing a career in human resource management. Interested individuals who do not have human resource management or supervisory experience are strongly encouraged to participate in an internship, which may be taken for course credit. Students may select a career track in either labor relations or personnel or may select a program combining electives from both tracks, depending upon their career interests.

The M.P.S. in humanitarian services administration is designed to meet the educational needs of individuals involved or interested in humanitarian assistance programs, whether in disaster relief or sustainability programs. Students develop theoretical and professional knowledge to operate and conduct humanitarian response missions with nongovernmental, governmental, and international organizations. Students can choose courses related to disaster relief or sustainability, or they may select courses from both areas, depending on their interests. A graduate certificate program (12 credits) is also available in humanitarian services administration.

The B.G.S. degree can be completed online. Two foci are offered: occupational and environmental safety and health and information technology. The B.G.S. program, established in 1977, is an interdisciplinary major designed for returning adults. A student needs at least 60 college credits or an associate degree from a regionally accredited college to be admitted to the program. B.G.S. students work one on one with the same academic adviser through graduation. The adviser and student work together to develop an academic program that suits the student's educational and career goals through an individualized major or by following a B.G.S. focus. B.G.S. alumnae have been accepted into graduate programs at Yale, Princeton, Columbia, MIT, Berkeley, and William and Mary in such fields as medicine, dentistry, law, ministry, and business.

The B.G.S. degree with a focus in occupational and environmental safety and health has served more than 450 students since its inception in 1995. The courses are designed for practitioners and nonpractitioners and provide students with marketable skills and knowledge that are relevant to a broad spectrum of industries and work environments. Students can also use the courses to prepare for the national Certified Safety Professional (CSP) examination, a prestigious designation in the occupational safety and health field.

The B.G.S. degree with a focus in information technology is geared toward preparing students for the variety of information technologies they will encounter in their career paths. This program provides immediate practical benefits and a solid foundation for corporate IT training programs and advanced study by taking a hands-on approach toward the understanding of IT. Courses generally fall under the areas of Web content development and Web system administration.

Undergraduate certificate programs are available in environmental health and safety, Himalayan studies, occupational safety and health, Web content development, and Web system administration. General education courses are also available online and may be taken individually or as part of an undergraduate degree program.

Students may enroll in a degree or certificate program, or they may take individual courses. Online noncredit programs are offered in health-care information technology and project management.

Special Programs

Students can take individual courses as nondegree students, allowing working adults to enroll in University of Connecticut undergraduate and graduate courses and earn academic credit without being formally admitted to a degree program. Nondegree study allows high school graduates of all ages to return to college at their own pace and gain the confidence they need to complete their education. If students later choose to apply for a degree program, it is likely that these credits can be applied toward their degree. Taking a course as a nondegree student at UConn is also a convenient way for students from other colleges and universities to take credit courses at UConn and then transfer the credits to their own university. Students in the online programs can take on-campus courses. If students are degree students, they need permission from their advisers. Nondegree students do not need to see an adviser before registering.

Student Services

All major student services are available to online students, including registration services, advising, bookstore ordering, library, e-mail, and tutoring. Technical support is available to all students in online courses.

Credit Options

Students in the B.G.S. program may transfer up to 90 credits that they have earned through other regionally accredited institutions.

Faculty

The Center for Continuing Studies employs full-time and adjunct faculty members. Faculty members who teach online are approved by the department and also teach on-campus courses. All full-time faculty members and all faculty members teaching in the graduate program have earned doctorates. Adjunct faculty members are accomplished practitioners and have the requisite educational experience to make them effective online instructors.

Admission

Applicants to the M.P.S. program must have completed a baccalaureate degree from a regionally accredited college or university. For further admission information for the M.P.S. program, students should visit http://continuingstudies.uconn.edu/mps/academicinfo.html. Applicants to the B.G.S. degree must have an associate degree from a regionally accredited college or university or must have completed at least 60 college credits from a regionally accredited college or university. For further admission information for the B.G.S. program, students should visit http://continuingstudies.uconn.edu/bgs/admissions.html. Students may register for individual courses without matriculating into a program, provided they meet specific course requirements. For course registration information, students should visit http://web.uconn.edu/ccsde/reg/reg.html

Tuition and Fees

Undergraduate course fees are $975 per 3-credit course. Graduate course fees are $1539 per 3-credit course. There is a $43 infrastructure maintenance fee for undergraduate and graduate courses. Course fees are calculated on a per-credit basis; current fees are subject to change. Students who enroll in the Center's online courses pay the same fees as in-state students. Students should visit the Web site listed below for current fees.

Financial Aid

Financial aid is available to online students who have matriculated into a degree program. For further information, students should contact the Office of Student Financial Aid Services at 860-486-2819 or visit the Web site at http://www.financialaid.uconn.edu.

Applying

Application to the M.P.S. degree program is available online at http://continuingstudies.uconn.edu/mps/academicinfo.html. Application to the B.G.S. degree program is available online at https://secure.uconn.edu/~wwwcce/regforms/admissionsapplication.html.

CONTACT

Dr. Judy Buffolino, Director
Distance Education Office
Center for Continuing Studies
University of Connecticut
One Bishop Circle, Unit 4056
Storrs, Connecticut 06269-4056
Phone: 860-486-1080
Fax: 860-486-0756
E-mail: ccsonline@uconn.edu
Web site: http://continuingstudies.uconn.edu/onlinecourses

UNIVERSITY OF DALLAS

Graduate School of Management Center for Distance Learning

Irving, Texas

The University of Dallas (UD) was founded in 1956 as in independent Catholic university dedicated to excellence in its educational programs.

The Graduate School of Management (GSM) is the largest Master of Business Administration-granting (M.B.A.) institution in the Southwest. GSM was founded in 1966 with a distinctive mission: to create a professionally sound M.B.A. program accessible to individuals who are already employed in business. More than 80 percent of GSM students work full-time. The student body is made up of Americans and international students representing more than sixty-five countries. The UD main campus is in Irving, adjacent to the thriving Las Colinas business community and near downtown Dallas and Dallas/Fort Worth International Airport.

The Commission on Colleges of the Southern Association of Colleges and Schools (SACS) accredits UD. In addition, UD is accredited by the International Assembly for Collegiate Business Education (IACBE) and the Association of Collegiate Business Schools and Programs (ACBSP).

Distance Learning Program

UD is committed to providing the kind of education, programming, and service that motivates and enables success. The online environment offers professionals the flexibility to maintain current schedules and perform to their fullest in a fast-paced educational program. The aspects of flexible course delivery help to create an environment conducive to an inflexible world.

The UD courses are available from any Internet connection worldwide at anytime. The learning model is designed to serve students with a program offering the greatest level of flexibility to participate in the online classroom. It allows participation whenever it is most convenient for the individual student while maintaining the highest educational standards. All courses are developed and taught by professors who have real-world business experience in addition to their academic qualifications. This allows students to learn tools and techniques proven in the changing business world.

In addition, the online program is an integral part of the academic environment at UD. Students can choose to complete all classes online or integrate online learning with the traditional classroom environment. Each method, online or traditional classroom, provides consistent, high-quality learning outcomes. This flexibility meets the needs of students living in the Dallas/Fort Worth area and students who are part of the global learning community.

GSM began its Internet-based M.B.A. program (IMBA) in 1997 with three courses and 30 students. Now GSM offers the entire M.B.A. core curriculum and thirteen concentrations online.

While taking an IMBA class, there is no requirement to come to the campus. However, many students take a blend of on-campus and Internet-based courses. Other students take their entire M.B.A. online. There is no distinction made on the transcript between classroom and IMBA courses.

Students are attracted to the GSM because it offers a comprehensive background in the general business disciplines, as well as industry-specific fields of knowledge, such as corporate finance, global business, health services, information assurance, interdisciplinary (custom curriculum), marketing, not-for-profit management, project management, sports and entertainment management, supply chain management, and telecommunications—all online.

Delivery Media

The virtual campus was created with the understanding that students need the ability to organize their class schedules without being confined to a certain time, campus, or even country. Students access the IMBA using a standard Internet connection and Web browser. The courses use an instructor-led, asynchronous method of teaching, which means that students and their professors do not have to be online at the same time. This allows flexibility for those students who travel or have other obligations. Classes fit into everyday life. However, both professors and students are expected to be online multiple times during the weekly sessions.

For additional information on the online delivery method or the IMBA, students should visit http://www.thedallasmba.com/imba.cfm.

Programs of Study

The University of Dallas offers Master of Business Administration (M.B.A.), Master of Management (M.M.), and Master of Science (M.S.) degree programs.

The University of Dallas Graduate School of Management (GSM) is a professional school whose primary purpose is to prepare its students to become competent, responsible practitioners in the profession of management. GSM's academic programs do not emphasize theoretical courses; instead, they offer highly pragmatic programs, both on-campus and online, that focus on the practical realities of managerial life and success. While scholarly writings on business topics are carefully examined in classes, the principal emphasis is on how to manage wisely and effectively.

Academic programs at GSM differ from those at more traditional management schools in three other ways: the faculty members have extensive business experience, and many professors are actively engaged in business pursuits; specialized M.B.A. concentrations provide detailed insights into the practical aspects of these fields; and project-driven courses give students hands-on experience with real problems in strategy and management. Since the 1960s, GSM has developed a distinct educational method in which student teams are assigned to actual consulting projects requested by a wide variety of local, national, and global firms. Students define client problems, analyze various solutions, and propose specific solutions to the client.

The Dallas M.B.A. program's practical approach makes it unique among graduate business schools and distinguishes its graduates from traditional M.B.A. students. The M.B.A. degree is offered online, with concentrations in accounting, corporate finance, financial services, global business, health services management, information assurance, information technology, information technology service management, market logistics, marketing management, not-for-profit management, project management, sports and entertainment management, supply chain management, and telecommunications management. An interdisciplinary option is also available. The M.B.A. program can be completed in three to four trimesters of full-time study. Part-time students normally take 2½ to 3½ years to complete the M.B.A. degree. However, students can complete the program at their desired pace. For more details, students should visit http://www.thedallasmba.com/programs.cfm.

The Master of Management (M.M.) degree (post-M.B.A.) and graduate certificates are also available online in any of the above concentrations. The M.M. degree provides profession-specific graduate education for those who already hold an M.B.A. from a regionally accredited U.S. college or university or the international equivalent. Adding an M.M. degree to an M.B.A. can strengthen an individual's academic credentials and help him or her stay ahead in today's and tomorrow's workplace. For more information, students should visit: http://www.thedallasmba.com/programs.cfm.

The Master of Science (M.S.) degree is a specialized graduate degree program for students who seek in-depth knowledge in a specific field. For more details, students should visit: http://www.thedallasmba.com.

Special Programs

GSM has partnerships with Fortune 500 corporations to provide classes to their employees through the Internet. Inquiries are welcomed from other organizations that may be interested in offering graduate business studies to their employees.

Student Services

The primary support structure is the IMBA professor. Class size is kept moderate, thus permitting professors and students to interact with one another.

At the Graduate School of Management there are talented individuals—all of whom have had personal experience with GSM programs—who provide customer support and service for prospective, current, and past students. Each enrollment manager specializes in one of the concentrations offered.

These professionals work for the students and are their advocates within the GSM community. Each enrollment manager stands ready to answer students' questions, address their unique concerns, and guide them through the application, admissions, and registration process—and beyond. Staff members in the Online Learning Department are available to address questions unique to distance learning. A help desk that operates 24 hours a day handles Web- and PC-based questions.

Credit Options

For the M.B.A. program, a maximum of four courses or 12 hours of transfer credits may be applied. A transfer course must be a 3-semester-hour (5-quarter-hour) graduate-level course from an accredited school. The transfer course must not be more than six years old. A grade of at least a B (3.0) is required. For further information, students can contact the GSM Admissions Office at the address below.

Faculty

GSM professors have business experience in addition to their academic qualifications. They have held positions ranging from entrepreneurs to senior-level executives in large companies. Full-time faculty members engage in consulting within their field, while adjunct professors hold jobs in their area of teaching, thus keeping the classes current and relevant.

Admission

Admission to the Dallas M.B.A. program is competitive. The program seeks highly motivated individuals demonstrating potential for management and leadership responsibility and possessing the intellectual ability, initiative, and creativity to excel in its programs as well as in the globally competitive marketplace.

Success in the Master of Business Administration program depends on a number of factors ranging from motivation to practical knowledge to academic ability. The primary purpose of the School's admission criteria and application process is to determine a prospective student's potential to successfully complete the requirements for the M.B.A. degree.

While an undergraduate degree is a prerequisite, no specific undergraduate major or concentration is required to pursue the Dallas M.B.A. program in any M.B.A. concentration.

Because the Graduate School of Management enrolls full-time, part-time, and international students, a variety of paths are available to individuals seeking admission.

Prospective students may apply for admission to the Graduate School of Management for any fall, fall II, spring, spring II, or summer II trimester, or intermester. For more information, students should go online to http://www.thedallasmba.com/admissions.cfm.

Tuition and Fees

Graduate tuition is $505 per credit hour in 2006–07 for residents and nonresidents.

Financial Aid

U.S. graduate students may obtain financial assistance through various loan programs. The University's Financial Aid Office (telephone: 972-721-5266; Web site: http://www.udallas.edu/admiss/gradaid.html) has information and application forms for loans.

Applying

Those interested are encouraged to contact GSM at the address in the Contact section or to visit the Web site for additional information. Students can apply online from anywhere in the world.

CONTACT

Office of Admissions
Graduate School of Management
University of Dallas
1845 East Northgate Drive
Irving, Texas 75062-4799
Phone: 972-721-5174
877-408-2335 (toll-free)
E-mail: admiss@gsm.udallas.edu
Web site:
http://www.thedallasmba.com

UNIVERSITY OF DELAWARE

UD Online/Distance Learning

Newark, Delaware

A private university with public support, the University of Delaware is a land-grant, sea-grant, space-grant, and urban-grant institution with a rich 250-year history. Its main campus is located in Newark, Delaware, a suburban community situated between Philadelphia and Baltimore. The University offers more than 100 undergraduate majors and more than seventy graduate degrees. The University has been fully accredited by the Middle States Association of Colleges and Schools since 1921. There are more than 21,000 students enrolled at the University as undergraduate, graduate, or continuing education students.

Distance Learning Program

The University's UD Online/Distance Learning system supports more than 3,700 registrations a year in a variety of undergraduate and graduate courses involving twenty-eight academic departments and six degree programs. UD Online offers a way for busy professionals to continue their education on a schedule tailored to their needs.

Delivery Media

More than 140 University of Delaware courses are available in videotape, CD-ROM, or Internet formats. Student-faculty interaction is maintained through e-mail, telephone office hours, and chat rooms.

Programs of Study

Students can use distance learning to pursue the following degree programs:

Associate in Arts (AA): The Associate in Arts curriculum includes a combination of general studies courses from the University's College of Arts and Sciences. For more information, students can visit http://www.continuingstudies.udel.edu/udonline/aa/.

Baccalaureate for the Registered Nurse (BRN): Nine of twelve required nursing courses are offered in distance learning format. Students are required to enroll in two 1-credit weekend courses held on the Newark, Delaware, campus. The BRN major requires 120 credits for program completion. For more information, students should visit http://www.udel.edu/nursing/RN_Education.htm.

Master of Science in Nursing (M.S.N.) with a concentration in health services administration, or Master of Science (M.S.) with a major in health services administration: The program is delivered entirely on the Internet except for a one-day seminar that takes place on the Newark, Delaware, campus. For students at a great distance, special accommodations may be made. For more information, students can visit http://www.udel.edu/nursing/graduate.html.

Master of Science in Nursing for the Registered Nurse (RN to M.S.N.): The program builds on basic nursing knowledge, enhancing nursing practice in an increasingly complex society. Recognizing the challenges of combining advanced education with professional and personal responsibilities, this program is structured to permit part-time study utilizing fall and spring semesters plus winter and summer sessions. The RN to M.S.N. program requires a total of 134 credits. For more information, students can visit http://www.udel.edu/nursing/RN_Education.htm.

Bachelor of Science in Hotel, Restaurant, and Institutional Management (HRIM): The specialized HRIM core courses, as well as most of the required liberal arts and business courses, are available in distance-learning format, except for a required one-week management institute held on the Newark, Delaware, campus. For more information, students can visit http://www.continuingstudies.udel.edu/udonline/hrim/.

Master of Engineering, Mechanical (M.E.M.): The 30-credit, nonthesis program is made up of five required courses and 15 credits of graduate electives. A popular concentration, available in distance format, is in composite materials. For more information, students should visit http://www.engr.udel.edu/outreach/MEM.html.

Master of Science in Electrical Engineering (M.S.E.E.): The program is a nonthesis master's program requiring 30 credits of graduate courses, including 6 credits (2 "foundation" courses) chosen from signal processing, devices and materials, or optics and electromagnetics (other options to be added), and 24 credits in advanced technical courses, with a maximum of 6 credits outside of the department. For more information, students can visit http://www.engr.udel.edu/outreach/MEM.html.

Special Programs

To pursue a graduate degree, engineering professionals may enroll in courses for professional development or may combine distance learning courses with campus courses. A graduate certificate program in composite materials is designed for engineering and science professionals who already possess a bachelor's degree. Students may access the program Web site at http://www.engr.udel.edu/outreach/composites-program.html. In addition, the Fundamentals of Engineering (FE) review course, providing intensive review of the FE exam topics, as well as a review course for the Professional Engineer (PE) licensing exam in environmental engineering, are available via videotape. The environmental PE review is also available on CD-ROM. Further information can be found online at http://www.engr.udel.edu/outreach/fe-video.html for the FE course and http://www.engr.udel.edu/outreach/PE-review.html for the PE course.

The University's dietetic internship is delivered entirely online with the exception of a one-week professional orientation that takes place on the Newark, Delaware, campus. Students complete internship rotations in their local areas. This program is accredited by the Commission on Accreditation for Dietetic Education of the American Dietetic Association. For more information, students can visit http://www.udel.edu/NTDT/internship/.

Credit Options

In order to be eligible for a University of Delaware degree, students must complete either the first 90 or the last 30 credits of the degree program with the University of Delaware. A credit-by-examination option allows students to demonstrate competence obtained through professional experience. Exam requirements are determined by each University academic department.

Faculty

Of the 998 full-time University faculty members, 87 percent hold the doctoral or terminal professional degree in their field. Approximately 10 percent of the faculty members participate in distance learning instruction.

Admission

An admissions committee considers all academic credentials, including high school and any previous college work. Students transferring from other schools are normally required to have at least a 2.5 grade point average to be considered for admission.

Tuition and Fees

Students registering as official UD Online/Distance Learning site participants pay $319 per credit hour (undergraduate) or $821 per credit hour (graduate). Delaware residents pay $276 per credit hour (undergraduate) or $368 per credit hour (graduate).

Financial Aid

The Financial Aid Office administers grants and scholarships, which do not have to be repaid; low-interest loans; and student employment. A need-based financial aid package may include one or more of the following: Federal Pell Grant, Federal Supplemental Educational Opportunity Grant, Federal Perkins Loan, and a Federal Direct Loan. The Federal Direct Parents Loan Program is also available. Delaware residents may also be eligible for need-based funding through General Fund Scholarships and Delaware Right to Education Scholarships. Students must be matriculated and carry at least 6 credit hours per semester.

Applying

A completed application consists of the Distance Learning Application for Admission, application fee, and official college and high school transcripts. Due dates for applications are no later than August 1 for fall admission and no later than December 1 for spring admission. BRN and RN to M.S.N. applicants need to provide a copy of their current nursing license.

CONTACT

Dr. Dayle Thorpe
Director of Academic and Professional Programs
UD Online/Distance Learning
214 John M. Clayton Hall
University of Delaware
Newark, Delaware 19716
Phone: 800-597-1444 (toll-free)
Fax: 302-831-3292
E-mail: ud-online@udel.edu
Web site: http://www.continuingstudies.udel.edu/udonline/

UNIVERSITY OF DENVER

University College

Denver, Colorado

The University of Denver (DU), the oldest independent university in the Rocky Mountain region, is a premier liberal arts university that was founded in 1864. In addition to its rich history, DU is known for its research and high-quality teaching. To augment the traditional undergraduate and graduate programs, this outstanding institution offers innovative graduate programs through its division for professional and continuing studies—University College. University College was founded in 1983. With more than forty national awards and many other distinctions from its peers, University College of the University of Denver is recognized as one of the very best providers of adult education in the nation. University College offered its first online master's degree program in 1996. Today, it offers master's degrees in ten different areas, more than thirty Certificates of Advanced Study, and numerous individual courses in a variety of subject areas. Starting in fall 2006, University College plans to offer a Bachelor of Arts Completion Program for students who have started their bachelor's degree, but for some reason have not finished. University College is accredited by the North Central Association of Colleges and Schools.

Distance Learning Program

The University College distance learning program provides the same premier, internationally recognized University of Denver program quality to students who, because of geographic location, work schedule, or personal commitments, would otherwise not have the opportunity to attend DU. The learning experience for the distance student goes beyond the traditional classroom by capitalizing on the advantages of distance learning technology. University College provides an anytime, anywhere support service as well as consistent high-quality instruction. University College has more than 600 students actively taking courses online from a wide list of states and countries.

Delivery Media

All of the University College distance learning bachelor's degrees, master's degrees, and Certificates of Advanced Study can be taken entirely online. A wide array of learning techniques is used to help students develop their knowledge, understanding, and problem-solving skills. University College has an entire team dedicated to utilizing emerging technologies and understanding individualized learning styles to enhance the educational experience. University College uses eCollege® as its courseware management tool. The system is interactive, allows students to work collaboratively in lively discussion boards and chat rooms, and promotes the exchange of ideas and the development of a learning community. This interaction includes extensive communication with faculty members over the Internet, virtual teams, individual and group assignments, online projects, and online papers and connects students to experts from around the world.

Programs of Study

The University College online programs offer master's degrees in ten different program areas and more than thirty graduate Certificates of Advanced Study. There are no on-campus requirements for any of the distance learning programs. The online master's degree programs require 54 quarter credit hours of study to be completed in five years or less. Typically, a program can be completed in 2½ years. Certificates are 18–24 quarter credit hours and typically take twelve to eighteen months to complete. A bachelor's degree is not required for a certificate, and certificate course credits may be applied toward a master's degree.

Professionals with at least one year of transferable undergraduate credits can now complete their degrees online and earn a Bachelor of Arts in communication arts, global studies, leadership and organization studies, public policy and social services, or science and technology in a program that provides a dynamic new experience. Designed with the input of business and civic leaders, the program focuses on developing the talents needed for success in the information age: effective communication, problem solving, creative thinking, multi-tasking, decision making, technology utilization, and teamwork. These talents are approached from an interdisciplinary perspective, providing the most balanced and well-rounded experience possible.

The Applied Communication master's degree program is designed to teach the real-time and practical knowledge and skills that provide the specific industry expertise required for career success in a wide range of communication professions. The program's curriculum emphasizes a balance of theory, principles, and practice combined with professional experience to generate focused outcomes that are not offered in generic communication degree programs. Concentrations are available online in alternative dispute resolution, organizational communication, public relations and marketing, and training and development.

The Computer Information Systems program is designed for computer professionals as well as for those planning a new career in the computer industry. This flexible program keeps current with today's changing technology and how it relates to new technologies, existing systems, and customers' needs. In addition to the master's degree program, five online certificate programs of advanced study are offered: computer information systems, database administration, distributed object-oriented analysis and design, information systems security, and Web design and development technologies.

The Environmental Policy and Management program provides a seamlessly blended graduate education that emphasizes ethical management, science-based environmental policies, and professional applications of technical knowledge. Six certificate programs of advanced study are offered in environmental, health, and safety management; environmental information management; environmental management; environmental policy; environmental project management; and natural resource management.

The Geographic Information Systems (GIS) program provides great job opportunities for those interested in managing physical facilities, providing services, analyzing markets, and managing information in public agencies or private organizations. The master's degree, designed in conjunction with DU's Department of Geography, allows students in the University College GIS certificate program to transfer up to 24 quarter hours from their certificate. The certificate program, also designed in conjunction with the DU's Department of Geography, offers working professionals the opportunity to acquire the background information and hands-on-expertise necessary to capitalize on the emerging technology.

The Human Resource Administration program offers a Master of Professional Studies (M.P.S.) in human resource administration. It provides a comprehensive examination of the HR profession and positions graduates for career advancement in a variety of organizational settings that include business, government, and not-for-profit organizations.

The Organizational Leadership program is a flexible management and leadership degree presenting both the analytic and interpersonal skills necessary to be an effective manager in a variety of enterprises. The degree is structured around a core of management and leadership courses. Students select from a wide range of specializations, such as project management, leadership, alternative dispute resolution, environmental policy and management, telecommunications, computer information systems, and others. Most of the concentrations offered in other University College degrees are potential concentrations in the M.P.S.

The Security Management degree is designed for business and organizational security management professionals. The program provides students with the latest skills for effectively leading and managing security operations and addressing personnel, property, facility, information, and business-continuity security. The program provides the management skills and technical knowledge required to function as a chief security officer, director of loss prevention, director of security, security consultant, investigator, firefighter, or police officer.

The Technology Management program is designed for those who understand the power of leveraging technology in business to create their own competitive advantage. Career opportunities are limitless for those who can create, manage, and use emerging technology. In addition, four certificate programs of advanced study are offered in electronic commerce, leadership, project management, and technology management.

The Telecommunications program fosters an integration of telecommunications technologies and effective management. In an industry driven by new technology, new applications, and an increasing demand for services, professionals need to maintain a current understanding of fundamental issues surrounding those technologies and the regulations which govern them. The telecommunications offerings at University College are designed to help students keep abreast of changes and take advantage of the opportunities change offers. Certificate programs of advanced study are offered in four areas: broadband, telecommunications management and policy, telecommunications networks, and telecommunications technology.

Student Services

University College is dedicated to providing complete student services online. This includes admissions, registration, student advising, online resources through the library, access to the bookstore, and an individualized career counselor. There is a complete support team for technical issues as well as student support and training for eCollege.

Credit Options

Students may be able to transfer credit earned at other accredited graduate colleges and universities. The credit hours for the certificates may apply toward the related master's degree.

Faculty

University College has 300 faculty members, all with advanced degrees, who are practicing professionals in the areas in which they teach. At any given time there are 20 to 30 faculty members teaching online. University College engages in advanced and continual training for its faculty members in the methods and application of distance learning.

Admission

Entrance examinations are not required. Students who are applying for admission to the master's degree programs must have a bachelor's degree from a regionally accredited institution and a minimum 3.0 undergraduate GPA. Applicants must also submit an essay, a career goal statement, and letters of recommendation.

Tuition and Fees

Tuition is $342 per credit hour for on-campus classes and $374 per credit hour for online classes. There is also a technology fee of $4 per credit hour.

Financial Aid

Some financial aid programs are available to assist University College students. The University of Denver's Office of Student Financial Services handles all financial aid applications (http://www.du.edu/sfs/).

Applying

To apply for admission to University College, students must complete a full application, including a degree plan. Registration is available on the University College Web site at http://www.universitycollege.du.edu/registernow/registerinstructions.asp# online. For more information or an application, students should visit the University College Web site.

CONTACT

Enrollment Manager
University College
University of Denver
2211 South Josephine
Denver, Colorado 80208
Phone: 303-871-3315
800-347-2042 (toll-free)
Fax: 303-871-3070
E-mail: ucolinfo@du.edu
Web site: http://www.universitycollege.du.edu

UNIVERSITY OF FLORIDA

College of Engineering UF EDGE (Electronic Delivery of Graduate Engineering)

Gainesville, Florida

The University of Florida (UF) is a major, public, comprehensive, land-grant, research university. Founded in 1853, it is the state's oldest, largest, and most comprehensive university, and it is among the nation's most academically diverse public universities. With more than 48,000 students, Florida is now the fourth-largest university in the nation. Florida has a 2,000-acre campus and more than 900 buildings (including 170 with classrooms and laboratories). The northeast corner of the campus is listed as a Historic District on the National Register of Historic Places.

UF is accredited by the Southern Association of Colleges and Schools (SACS; 1866 Southern Lane, Decatur, Georgia 30033-4097; telephone: 404-679-4501), and the College of Engineering is accredited by ABET.

Distance Learning Program

The College of Engineering distance learning program, the UF EDGE, serves more than 250 graduate students. UF EDGE programs have been delivered to practicing engineers in Florida and throughout the world since 1982. Master of Science degrees are offered via streaming video. No campus attendance is required to complete the degree programs.

Delivery Media

Distance learning students are enrolled in classes that are given on the UF campus. The lectures are recorded and are available via streaming video at the close of business on that same day at the course's WebCT Vista course site. Distance learning students interact with their professors via phone, fax, e-mail, or the Internet. Many professors make course materials available to their students via course Web sites.

Programs of Study

The College of Engineering offers the following Master of Science (M.S.) degree programs via distance learning: civil engineering; computer engineering/computer science; computer engineering/computer science, with a bioinformatics track; electrical and computer engineering, with a communications track; environmental engineering, with a specialization in water resources planning and management; environmental engineering, with a specialization in water, wastewater, and stormwater engineering; mechanical and aerospace engineering, with a specialization in fundamentals of thermal fluids transport; mechanical and aerospace engineering, with a specialization in solid mechanics; and material science engineering. The Master of Science degree requires 30 semester credit hours for completion, with a minimum 3.0 grade point average on a 4.0 scale. Distance learning students may meet the credit requirement entirely by course work.

Special Programs

The College of Engineering offers graduate certificate programs in the areas of environmental policy and management. Each certificate program requires the completion of three to five 3-semester-hour courses. The curriculum consists of required courses and two or more electives chosen from a specified list.

Student Services

Library service is provided via remote access to all internal holdings and to several electronic databases through http://www.uflib.ufl.edu. Access is provided to currently registered students via a personal identification number and password for certain restricted databases.

Academic advising is provided through e-mail, fax, and telephone contact on a request basis. Distance learning students are also eligible to use the University's career placement services.

Credit Options

Students earn credit toward their degree by registering for and completing courses delivered via distance learning. Requirements for each course are the same as for on-campus students enrolled in the course.

Only graduate-level work to the extent of 9 semester credits, earned with a grade of A, B+, or B, may be transferred from an institution approved by the Graduate School or 15 semester credits from postbaccalaureate work at the University of Florida. Credits transferred from other universities are applied toward meeting the degree requirement, but the grades earned are not computed in the student's grade point average. Acceptance of transfer of credit requires approval from the student's department and the Dean of the Graduate School.

Faculty

There are 2,685 full-time faculty members at the University, with 319 in the College of Engineering. In the College of Engineering, 126 faculty members (39 percent) have taught in the distance learning program.

Admission

Admission decisions are made by the individual departments based on GRE or Fundamentals of Engineering (FE) score, GPA, and letters of reference.

Tuition and Fees

Tuition and fees for the 2005–06 academic year are $300 per credit hour for in-state students and $961 per credit hour for out-of-state students. Achievement awards, which provide a discounted tuition of $500 per credit hour up to 30 credit hours, are available for highly qualified out-of-state students. Costs are subject to change each year. Students must purchase their own textbooks.

Financial Aid

As a general rule, a graduate student must be enrolled half-time (at least 5 semester hours per term) as a regular student in a degree program and must be a United States citizen or an eligible non-U.S. citizen to qualify for federal and/or state financial aid. Specific information is available through the Office of Student Financial Affairs. Although students may apply for Federal Direct Stafford/Ford Loans throughout the year, they must observe the deadlines set each semester for applying for loans for the following semester and should always apply as early as possible. Many employers have programs that can help students pay for courses.

Applying

Application materials can be obtained from the school to which the student is applying. For specific program information, prospective students should visit http://www.admissions.ufl.edu/grad/gradegreeprograms.html#engineering. Application information is available online through http://www.admissions.ufl.edu/start.html. Official transcripts are required from all colleges or universities attended. Admission decisions are made by the individual departments.

CONTACT

UF EDGE Registrar
College of Engineering
E-117, CSE
University of Florida
P.O. Box 116100
Gainesville, Florida 32611-6100
Phone: 352-392-9670
E-mail: ufedge@ufl.edu
Web site: http://ufedge.eng.ufl.edu

The University of Iowa

THE UNIVERSITY OF IOWA

Center for Credit Programs

Iowa City, Iowa

Established in 1847, the University of Iowa is a major national research university with a solid liberal arts foundation. Iowa was the first U.S. public university to admit men and women on an equal basis. It has won international recognition for its wealth of achievements in the arts, sciences, and humanities. A member of the select Association of American Universities, the University of Iowa maintains a balance between scholarly research and teaching. It places a strong emphasis on undergraduate, international, and interdisciplinary education. The University is accredited by the North Central Association of Colleges and Schools and other accrediting agencies.

Distance Learning Program

In cooperation with University of Iowa academic colleges and departments, the Center for Credit Programs (CCP) of the University of Iowa's Division of Continuing Education delivers University credit courses, both in Iowa City and off campus, to nontraditional and other part-time students who seek a college degree, career advancement, or self-improvement. The CCP supports some 20,000 enrollments annually, including some 3,000 Guided Independent Study (GIS) registrations. Distance education courses may use interactive and broadcast television (available only within Iowa), streaming video, or independent study and Web courses (available worldwide to English-speaking students). Approximately 120 GIS courses are available at both the undergraduate and graduate levels.

Delivery Media

University of Iowa distance education courses employ a variety of delivery media. Asynchronous independent study has been available for nine decades. All GIS courses are available on the Web in an eBook format. Printed study guides are available for a fee. Web courses provide students with numerous benefits: assignment submission/return by e-mail, online text ordering, instructional enhancements, access to library resources, and others. Streaming video/audio or CD-ROMs supplement some courses. Students interact with instructors via mail, fax, e-mail, or toll-free telephone. Within Iowa, degree program and other courses are offered via interactive video through the Iowa Communications Network (ICN), an advanced fiber-optic telecommunications network linking educational sites across the state. Semester-based Web courses also support these programs.

Programs of Study

The Bachelor of Liberal Studies (B.L.S.) external degree program provides an opportunity for students to complete a bachelor's degree from the University of Iowa without attending classes on campus or without ever visiting the campus. The B.L.S. degree has no specific major. Instead, students concentrate course work in three of five distribution areas (humanities, communications and arts, natural science and math, social sciences, or professional fields).

The B.L.S. degree is a flexible program offering convenient, self-paced work; advisers who work with students to create an individual plan of study; the diverse preparation a liberal arts degree provides; the flexibility to match education efforts with career goals; and an undergraduate degree awarded by a nationally recognized institution. More than 700 students have graduated from the program since it was established in 1977 by the Iowa Board of Regents, and hundreds of students are currently active. For more specific information, see the CCP Web site or call the toll-free number below.

Special Programs

The LionHawk program represents a formal partnership between Pennsylvania State University and the University of Iowa that allows students to earn both two- and four-year degrees without on-campus study. Students who complete Penn State's Extended Letters, Arts, and Sciences (ELAS) associate degree are ensured admission to the B.L.S. program. Upon admission to the B.L.S. program, all General Education Program requirements are considered satisfied except for the foreign language requirement.

Student Services

Students receive ongoing registration assistance, advising, library access, and other services. The CCP office hours are Monday–Friday, 8 a.m. to 5 p.m., Central Time.

Credit Options

Credit for B.L.S. degree requirements may be met in several ways, including University of Iowa campus, off-campus, or evening classes (available only in Iowa); transfer credit from other institutions (a minimum number of credits from the University of Iowa are required); and other methods. B.L.S. students primarily take GIS courses, which are available anywhere, are available for enrollment continuously, and allow for self-paced learning. GIS courses provide semester-hour credit. There is no limit on the number of GIS courses that may be applied toward the B.L.S. degree.

Faculty

All courses and instructors are approved by appropriate departmental and collegiate officers. Courses are taught by regular or adjunct faculty members or advanced graduate students.

Admission

Students applying for admission to the B.L.S. degree program may request an information packet by calling the CCP toll-free number. No special admission requirements are necessary to enroll in GIS courses. Enrollment in GIS courses does not constitute admission to the University of Iowa.

Tuition and Fees

Tuition for GIS and semester-based distance learning courses is the same as University of Iowa residential tuition. For 2005–06, tuition was $204 per semester hour for undergraduates and $318 per semester hour for graduates. GIS tuition is the same for both in-state and out-of-state students. Students should check with the CCP for new tuition rates after July 1, 2006.

Financial Aid

For information concerning the use of federal financial aid for GIS courses, University of Iowa degree-seeking students should contact the Office of Student Financial Aid (319-335-1450).

Applying

Students may enroll in GIS courses at any time. Enrollment forms may be found in the GIS catalog or on the CCP Web site. Students paying by credit card may enroll by phone. For information or enrollment in other CCP courses, students should call the toll-free number.

CONTACT

Center for Credit Programs
116 International Center
The University of Iowa
Iowa City, Iowa 52242-1802
Phone: 800-272-6430 (toll-free)
Fax: 319-335-2740
E-mail: credit-programs@uiowa.edu
Web site: http://www.continuetolearn.uiowa.edu/bls

UMUC

UNIVERSITY OF MARYLAND UNIVERSITY COLLEGE

Undergraduate and Graduate Online Programs

Adelphi, Maryland

Founded in 1947, University of Maryland University College (UMUC) is one of eleven degree-granting institutions in the University System of Maryland; its Graduate School of Management and Technology was founded in 1978. UMUC's principal mission is to serve nontraditional students by providing high-quality educational opportunities in Maryland and around the world.

Through its online programs, UMUC offers twenty-one bachelor's degree programs, twenty-four undergraduate certificates, nineteen master's degree programs, thirty-eight graduate certificates, and a Doctor of Management program.

UMUC is accredited by the Commission on Higher Education of the Middle States Association of Colleges and Schools, 3624 Market Street, Philadelphia, Pennsylvania 19104 (phone: 215-662-5606) and is certified by the State Council for Higher Education in Virginia.

Distance Learning Program

UMUC's online courses provide the same rigor, requirements, assignments, and tests as are available in a classroom environment. However, students are free to participate at times and from locations that are convenient to them. Online courses are highly structured and require students to log in several times a week and to participate actively in asynchronous full-class and small-group discussions and assignments.

Delivery Media

UMUC provides undergraduate and graduate degree programs via WebTycho, its proprietary online course delivery system. Students taking online classes via WebTycho require a computer running a Web browser such as Netscape Communicator (version 7.0 or higher) or Microsoft Internet Explorer (version 6.0 or higher), connection to the Internet, and an e-mail account.

Programs of Study

The School of Undergraduate Studies offers Bachelor of Arts (B.A.) and Bachelor of Science (B.S.) degree programs, with twenty-one majors and twenty-five minors available online. Majors include accounting, business administration, communication studies, computer and information science, computer studies, criminal justice, English, environmental management, finance, fire science, gerontology, global business and public policy, history, human resource management, humanities, information systems management, legal studies, management studies, marketing, psychology, and social science. In addition, UMUC offers twenty-four undergraduate certificate programs online.

The Graduate School of Management and Technology offers nineteen online master's degree programs, including the Global Master of Business Administration, the Master of Business Administration, the Master of International Management, the Master of Software Engineering, the Master of Education, and the Master of Distance Education. In addition, the Master of Science degree is available in the following areas: accounting and financial management, accounting and information technology, biotechnology studies, computer systems management, e-commerce, environmental management, financial management and information systems, health administration informatics, health-care administration, information technology, management, technology management, and telecommunications management. The Graduate School of Management and Technology also offers a Doctor of Management program (available with mandatory residencies at UMUC headquarters in Adelphi, Maryland), several dual-degree programs, and thirty-eight certificate programs.

Student Services

UMUC offers a complete range of support services online that allow students to apply for admission, obtain pre-entry advising, register, order books and materials, search for scholarships, apply for financial aid, and obtain ongoing academic advising. Most of these services are available through MyUMUC, the University's new online gateway to administrative and academic services and information.

UMUC students have access to a wealth of online library resources, including more than 140 Web databases with full-text articles and 24-hour assistance from expert library staff members. In addition, students who live outside of Maryland (but inside the continental United States) are eligible for home delivery of University System of Maryland library books. Through the University's Career Services, students can access online search tools, receive assistance with resume and interview preparation, and participate in online career development seminars.

Credit Options

UMUC offers undergraduate students a number of innovative options for earning credit, all of which are available at a distance. EXCEL Through Experiential Learning enables students to earn up to 30 credits for one semester's work toward an undergraduate degree for college-level learning gained from previous work or life experiences. Through Cooperative Education (Co-op), undergraduate students can earn academic credit in the workplace for new on-the-job learning.

Graduate students can transfer up to 6 semester hours of graduate credit (3 semester hours for the Master of Business Administration) to UMUC if the credit was earned at a regionally accredited institution and is relevant to the student's area of study, subject to approval by the Graduate School of Management and Technology.

Faculty

Before teaching online, UMUC faculty members must complete a five-week intensive training course and be certified. Of the more than 900 faculty members in the School of Undergraduate Studies, more than 50 percent have taught UMUC courses in distance formats. The undergraduate faculty is composed of full-time and part-time faculty members who work actively in the fields in which they teach. The Graduate School of Management and Technology's 60 full-time faculty members have terminal degrees that are relevant to the online degrees. They teach, are responsible for the design of the online curriculum, and provide leadership for the school's approximately 300 adjunct faculty members. More than 85 percent of those adjunct faculty members hold terminal degrees in their disciplines; all have years of practical experience in their fields.

Admission

Students who are applying for undergraduate admission must have graduated from a regionally accredited high school or have completed the General Educational Development (GED) exams with a total score of at least 2250 and no individual score less than 410. (If they completed the GED exam before January 2002, they must have a total score of at least 225 and no individual test score lower than 40.) To be granted regular admission status, students should also have maintained a cumulative grade point average (GPA) of at least 2.0 on all college-level work attempted at other colleges and universities.

Applicants to the Graduate School of Management and Technology must have a bachelor's degree from a regionally accredited college or university. Details are provided in the *Graduate School of Management and Technology Catalog* and the UMUC Web site. Test scores such as SAT, GMAT, or GRE are not required for admission to UMUC bachelor's or master's programs.

Tuition and Fees

Undergraduate tuition per credit is $230 for Maryland residents and $444 for nonresidents. The tuition for most graduate degree and certificate programs is $371 per credit for Maryland residents and $604 per credit for nonresidents. The tuition for the Master of Business Administration program is $635 per credit, regardless of residency. Executive program tuition varies by program and includes all fees, textbooks, and other materials. The tuition for the Doctor of Management program is $905 per credit. Books, certain course materials, and some fees are additional. Active-duty military personnel and their spouses are eligible for the in-state tuition for undergraduate and graduate courses. The undergraduate and graduate application fees are each $50. The Doctor of Management application fee is $100. For both undergraduate and graduate students, the late registration fee is $30. Tuition and fees are subject to change. Students are advised to consult the UMUC Web site for the most up-to-date information.

Financial Aid

UMUC offers a variety of financial aid programs to suit the needs of both undergraduate and graduate students. Students are eligible to apply for low-interest loans, state scholarship program funds, the Federal Work-Study Program, and UMUC grants and scholarships. Federal Direct Loans are available to students regardless of income. While UMUC handles most of the processes involved in delivering federal, state, and institutional funds, students are responsible for completing the Free Application for Federal Student Aid (FAFSA) and the UMUC Student Data Form and for adhering to deadlines. For more information and deadlines, students may contact UMUC by phone or e-mail or visit the Web site at http://www.umuc.edu/financialaid.

Applying

Students interested in applying to any of UMUC's online programs can find information from the points of contact or at the school's Web address. UMUC accepts and processes applications throughout the year.

CONTACT

University of Maryland University College
3501 University Boulevard East
Adelphi, Maryland 20783
Phone: 301-985-7000
800-888-UMUC (toll-free)
E-mail: umucinfo@umuc.edu
Web site: http://www.umuc.edu

UNIVERSITY OF MARYLAND, COLLEGE PARK

Online Studies

College Park, Maryland

The University of Maryland is the flagship institution among the University System of Maryland's eleven state public colleges and universities. Founded in 1856 as the original land-grant institution in Maryland, the University is the top public research institution in the mid-Atlantic region and one of the nation's best. Sixty-nine of its programs are ranked in the top twenty-five in the country, with fifty Maryland programs ranked in the top fifteen. The University of Maryland is accredited by the Middle States Association of Colleges and Schools and is a member of the Association of American Universities.

In 2000, the University of Maryland Office of Professional Studies introduced a University-wide online-learning strategy and launched its first program: Master of Life Sciences. The Web-based Master of Life Sciences is a content-rich, interdisciplinary program, with options in biology and chemistry, that focuses on the most current issues in modern science. Designed to enable practicing teachers to conveniently pursue an advanced degree, the program has attracted students worldwide. In 2003, the University launched an online Master of Engineering in fire protection program for practicing engineers working in fire safety anywhere in the world.

Distance Learning Program

The University of Maryland is dedicated to increasing the visibility and reputation of its high-quality professional and graduate programs, measured not only by advances in research but also by innovations in the delivery of programs to a worldwide audience. The University's online studies program provides the platform for conveniently delivering educational solutions to students anywhere, at any time.

Delivery Media

Courses are delivered asynchronously through the Internet using a range of technologies, including chat rooms, threaded discussions, and links to campus libraries and academic resources. Faculty members are available in person, through e-mail, and by prescribed phone appointments.

Programs of Study

Online Studies at the University of Maryland offers two completely Web-based graduate programs, a 30-credit Master of Life Sciences, a 30-credit Master of Engineering in fire protection, and a 12-credit graduate certificate in public health informatics.

The Master of Life Sciences provides in-depth knowledge of current research areas in the chemical, biological, biochemical, and biomedical sciences. Courses cover modern biology, modern molecular genetics, transmission genetics, human physiology, biodiversity and conservation biology, chemical ecology, principles of chemical biology, biochemistry, natural products chemistry, electrochemical cells, evolutionary biology and behavior, and experimental biology. Students may follow concentrations in chemistry or biology.

The Master of Engineering in fire protection is a graduate-level program in applied fire safety science and engineering. The curriculum supports the emerging international movement toward performance-based building approaches to building fire safety analysis and design. It provides students with an understanding of the physics and chemistry of fire necessary for predicting building system performance and analyzing failures. Course work covers fire risk assessment, fire dynamics, advanced fire modeling, smoke detection and management, toxicity evaluation and analysis, and structural fire protection.

In addition, students who qualify have the option of enrolling in individual online courses in fire protection without having to pursue a full master's degree. These "a la carte" courses are taught by the same renowned engineering faculty members who teach the degree programs, and students may apply credits earned toward the degree.

The graduate certificate in public health informatics offers online, graduate-level courses in applied health informatics. The curriculum supports the emerging international movement toward evidence-based approaches to health information management, including evaluation and integration of health information systems for health data collection, analysis, and presentation. It familiarizes students with the most recent technologies and computer applications in public health education and practice. The course work provides students with a thorough understanding of the theory and practice of health informatics in the real world. Additionally, students are required to demonstrate the ability to use scientific and population health principles to evaluate and implement health information systems for their organizations. They learn how to use qualitative and quantitative methods for conducting health surveillance activities and enhancing public health preparedness, as well as use computer models to measure and present health outcomes. There is no research component required and the courses can be completed entirely online in 10 weeks. This intensive program has been approved to award continuing education contact hours (CECHs) to meet requirements for health educators who are certified health education specialists through the Society for Public Health Education (SOPHE). The credits earned may also meet the degree requirements for the M.P.H. and Ph.D. degrees.

Student Services

Through Single Point of Contact (SPOC), listed in the Contact section, students may inquire about the programs, apply for admission, register, pay their bills, and purchase textbooks. Students also have access to equipment and software specifications needed for successful completion of course work, online library resources, and technical support.

Faculty

The Master of Life Sciences program has 11 full-time University of Maryland faculty members with doctoral degrees. The Master of Engineering program in fire protection and the graduate Certification in Public Health Informatics Program are taught by faculty members with outstanding teaching and research credentials.

Admission

The Master of Life Sciences program requires an undergraduate degree in biological science, chemistry, biochemistry, or science education; one year of teaching experience or the equivalent; letters of recommendation from a school principal and a science supervisor; and successful completion of a gateway review class, LFSC510 Concepts of Modern Biology or LFSC520 Concepts of Modern Chemistry, or acceptable performance on an admission exam based on LFSC510 or LFSC520.

The Master of Engineering in fire protection requires an earned bachelor's degree with a GPA of 3.0 or better in engineering or a related field from an accredited institution and courses in structural mechanics, differential equations, fluid mechanics, and heat transfer or equivalent. Applicants with an undergraduate GPA of less than 3.0 may be admitted on a provisional basis if they have demonstrated satisfactory performance in another graduate program and/or salutary work experience.

The graduate certificate in public health informatics is open to qualified applicants with an earned bachelor's degree, GPA of 3.0 or better, from an accredited institution. Applicants with foreign credentials must submit academic records in the original language with literal English translations. Allow at least three months for evaluation.

Tuition and Fees

The Master of Life Sciences program costs $361 per credit hour, and there are a $60-per-term technology/distance learning fee and an admission exam fee of $20.

The Master of Engineering in fire protection costs $700 per credit hour, and there is a $60-per-term technology/distance learning fee.

The graduate certificate in public health informatics costs $425 per credit hour. There is a $60-per-term technology/distance learning fee.

All tuition and fees are subject to change. All graduate students pay a one-time $60 application fee.

Financial Aid

Information regarding financial assistance may be obtained online at http://www.onlinestudies.umd.edu/financialaid.html.

CONTACT

Single Point of Contact (SPOC)
Mitchell Building, First Floor
University of Maryland
College Park, Maryland 20742-5231
Phone: 301-314-3572
877-989-SPOC (toll-free)
Fax: 301-314-1282
E-mail: onlinestudies@umd.edu
Web site: http://www.onlinestudies.umd.edu

UNIVERSITY OF MASSACHUSETTS AMHERST

Continuing and Professional Education

Hadley, Massachusetts

The University of Massachusetts Amherst (UMass Amherst) was founded in 1863 under the Land-Grant College Act of 1862 and is accredited by the New England Association of Schools and Colleges. UMass Amherst Continuing and Professional Education, founded in 1971, provides access to the academic resources of the University to students from the local, national, and international communities. Faculty members from the University teach both on-campus and online courses days, evenings, and weekends, allowing students to earn certificates and bachelor's and master's degrees and attend seminars and workshops in a wide range of subjects and majors.

Distance Learning Program

UMass Amherst Continuing and Professional Education, in partnership with the University's schools and colleges, began offering distance education courses in 1995. Online courses have the same rigorous academic requirements as on-campus courses.

Delivery Media

Continuing and Professional Education at UMass Amherst utilizes the Internet to deliver Web-based courses. Students interact with instructors via e-mail, threaded discussions, online office hours, telephone, fax, and mail.

Programs of Study

In addition to online credit courses in accounting, English, journalism, management, marketing, philosophy, psychology, sociology, and wildlife and fisheries conservation, seven online degree programs are offered.

The Master of Public Health (M.P.H.) degree program offers a broad-based, comprehensive, graduate-level public health curriculum designed for health professionals currently working in the field. Working health professionals may expand their knowledge base in public health, extend and sharpen their professional skills, broaden their perspective of public health problems, and prepare to assume greater professional responsibility.

The Master of Science in Nursing/Master of Public Health dual-degree program builds on previous nursing education and clinical experience and prepares graduates for leadership positions in public health. The 60-credit program includes 30 credits in nursing and 30 credits in public health; it integrates nursing science, public health science, administration, and leadership.

The RN-to-Bachelor of Science degree program is designed to meet the educational goals of Massachusetts registered nurses. Under faculty guidance, students provide nursing care to clients of all ages and develop skills in critical thinking, leadership, and research utilization.

The Professional M.B.A. program is an accelerated program for professionals who want to continue their education in the management field but cannot attend traditional classes because of full-time career commitments. The program is fully accredited by AACSB International–The Association to Advance Collegiate Schools of Business and is offered by the Isenberg School of Management.

The Bachelor of Business Administration degree program is geared toward individuals who are working full-time and need flexibility in completing the degree; the curriculum is delivered in an asynchronous format, allowing courses to be taken anytime and anywhere. The program is offered by the Isenberg School of Management and is accredited by AACSB International.

The Bachelor of Science degree in hospitality and tourism management is for working adults, both international and domestic, who are unable to pursue a residential degree program on the Amherst campus. The program integrates a variety of courses in the humanities and social and physical sciences, with a heavy concentration of business and hospitality/tourism courses.

A Bachelor of Science or Bachelor of Arts degree may be earned from UMass Amherst through the University Without Walls programs. Adult learners completing a degree can choose from among eight programs to find the one that best suits their educational goals and scheduling needs. Two of these programs are now online, with more planned for fall 2007. Weekends@UWW requires students attend the Amherst campus two weekends a month, with the balance of learning done online. Early Care and Education, a program for those interested in a concentration in education with a focus on pre-K children, is done entirely online. In all UWW programs, students have an opportunity to design an interdisciplinary major that matches their interests and incorporates appropriate courses. They can also receive credit for learning gained from life and work experiences.

Special Programs

The Certificate of Business Studies is a credit-based program intended for students who want to broaden their academic background with business courses without completing a bachelor's degree program. It is ideal for students who intend to pursue graduate-level work in business or for those who are looking to further their professional goals.

The Online Certificate in Hospitality and Tourism Management is a broadly based introductory program that is intended for individuals who wish to develop their practical managerial skills and gain a base for pursuing a career in the industry. It includes general management courses and introductory courses from each of the three areas of specialization within the hospitality and tourism management degree program.

The Online Certificate in Casino Management is designed to provide students with an opportunity to learn the casino industry business, learn about the legal and regulatory aspects of gaming, and recognize the relationship of the casino industry to the overall tourism environment.

The Online Certificate in Food Service Management is designed to prepare students to manage at a competent level of knowledge and skill in the food service industry and help students gain a deeper insight into food management areas for job enrichment, promotional consideration, or possible future positions.

Food Safety FIRST is an online training program for secondary science teachers who help with the implementation of active food safety education lessons in their classrooms. Learning activities encourage inquiry, experimentation, and theory. Emphasis is given to creating educational opportunities that encourage middle and high school students to describe, investigate, and explain phenomena and raise questions consistent with the National Science Education Standards.

The Certificate of Online Journalism Program equips students with skills in reporting, writing, and online research. The program welcomes students from any discipline who wish to gain an understanding of this exciting new area of journalism. It provides assessments of the current state of online journalism as well as the future of information technology.

The Criminal Justice Studies Certificate Program is designed to provide students with a solid foundation in the field of criminal justice and is intended to attract those planning or developing careers ranging from law enforcement to probation and from the courts to corrections.

The Basics in Exercise and Nutrition for Health and Human Performance Program is a collaboration between the Departments of Exercise Science and Nutrition and the School of Public Health and Health Services. It is designed to meet the needs of individuals with degrees in such fields as exercise physiology, nutrition, athletic training, and other health-related disciplines.

The Certificate of Individual Study in Arts Management is a valuable professional development opportunity for arts managers as well as people employed by nonprofit organizations or agencies. Courses teach strategic planning, board development, fund-raising, marketing, and arts programming and may also be taken for University of Massachusetts undergraduate credit.

Student Services

Academic advisers are available by phone, e-mail, and fax and in person to assist students in course selection and academic matters. Continuing and Professional Education has its own registration and business offices, which can provide assistance in registration, transcripts, financial aid, and billings.

Credit Options

Credits earned through distance education are University of Massachusetts Amherst credits and may be transferable to other colleges and universities.

Faculty

The distance education courses are taught by UMass Amherst faculty members who hold doctorates or terminal degrees in their respective fields or by qualified adjunct faculty members or graduate teaching assistants.

Admission

UMass Amherst Continuing and Professional Education allows any person with a high school diploma or its equivalent to register for courses. Some courses require prerequisite college-level work. Enrollment does not imply acceptance into a degree program. For both graduate and undergraduate degree programs, students must apply to the University of Massachusetts Amherst for admission.

Tuition and Fees

Fees vary depending on whether the course offered is noncredit or for credit and whether the level of that credit is undergraduate or graduate. Generally, a noncredit course costs from $195 to $350, while an undergraduate course costs from $240 to $400 per credit; graduate-level courses vary in cost from $270 to $670 per credit. All students, regardless of location, pay the same tuition.

Financial Aid

Availability of financial aid varies depending on course status and matriculation. Financial assistance may be available from employers, from The Education Resources Institute (TERI) Continuing Education loans, for eligible military personnel under the G.I. Bill, or from UMass Amherst financial aid (http://www.umass.edu/mfa).

Applying

Students can find information regarding application and registration procedures for degree programs and individual courses on the UMass Amherst Continuing and Professional Education's Web site.

CONTACT

Director, Continuing and Professional Education
University of Massachusetts Amherst
100 Venture Way, Suite 201
Hadley, Massachusetts 01035-9430
Phone: 413-545-2111
Fax: 413-545-3351
E-mail: info@contined.umass.edu
Web site: http://www.umassulearn.net

UNIVERSITY OF MINNESOTA

UNIVERSITY OF MINNESOTA, TWIN CITIES CAMPUS

Independent and Distance Learning, College of Continuing Education

Minneapolis, Minnesota

The University of Minnesota, with its four campuses, is one of the most comprehensive universities in the United States and ranks among the most prestigious. It is both a land-grant university with a strong tradition of education and public service and a major research institution. It was founded as a preparatory school in 1851 and was reorganized as a university in 1869, benefiting from the Morrill (or Land-Grant) Act of 1862.

The University of Minnesota has campuses in the Twin Cities (Minneapolis and St. Paul), Duluth, Morris, and Crookston, Minnesota. The Twin Cities campus, home of the College of Continuing Education, is a classic Big Ten campus with comprehensive academic programs offering unlimited opportunities for students and faculty.

Distance Learning Program

Independent and Distance Learning (IDL) offers outstanding University credit courses using mail and electronic technologies. In a recent year, the department received approximately 5,500 registrations from students throughout the United States and abroad. The 180 courses are fully accredited each year by approximately sixty different academic departments in fifteen colleges at the University. IDL is part of the College of Continuing Education (CCE), the division of the University of Minnesota that serves adult and part-time learners.

Delivery Media

Most courses are self-paced and available by mail for home study and postal mail assignment exchange with faculty members. Many faculty members provide the option of e-mail for lesson exchange. A continually growing number of courses are online and fully interactive. Most of the online courses are one semester (fifteen weeks) in length. All students who register for college credit with Independent and Distance Learning receive an e-mail and Internet account.

Programs of Study

Approximately 180 credit courses are offered in such varied subjects as applied business, child psychology, ecology, English literature and writing courses, foreign languages, management, math, and physics. Independent and Distance Learning courses are known for their high academic quality and variety of topics. No bachelor's degrees can be completed entirely through IDL. There is one professional master's degree available in paper science and engineering. There are two upper-level undergraduate certificates available online: applied business and paper science and engineering.

Student Services

The Continuing Education Information Center helps with finding information about specific courses, how to register, and financial aid.

University of Minnesota libraries fully support distance learners with reference services, research assistance, and home delivery of documents.

If students have a disability, Independent and Distance Learning coordinates efforts to provide accommodations that remove academic and physical barriers to earning credits. Such accommodations may include more time to complete exams or an alternate format for an exam, a separate testing room, audiotaping required materials, and taped rather than written comments from an instructor. Requests for such accommodations should be made well in advance of when they are needed so that necessary documentation may be obtained and accommodations facilitated.

Faculty

IDL has approximately 110 faculty members. Approximately 40 percent are University of Minnesota professors, 30 percent are graduate student teaching assistants, and 30 percent are adjunct faculty members, lecturers, or others. All professors and many adjunct faculty members hold doctorates or other terminal degrees, and all are approved by the relevant academic departments.

Admission

There are no admission requirements to register for courses through Independent and Distance Learning. Students who want to earn a certificate in applied business or paper science and engineering should go online to http://www.cce.umn.edu/certificates.

Tuition and Fees

Students who are not admitted to University of Minnesota certificate or degree programs qualify for in-state tuition rates, regardless of location. Tuition for 2006–07 is $291.85 per undergraduate semester credit. A University-wide fee of $48.75 per credit is assessed. An administrative fee of up to $247.50 per semester is assessed. Course study guides are included in the fee. Texts and other materials are purchased separately from the University of Minnesota Bookstore.

Financial Aid

Financial aid is limited. Eligibility requirements may vary, but most aid programs place restrictions on some types of IDL enrollment and require admission to a University of Minnesota, Twin Cities, degree program or eligible certificate program. Non-admitted students who reside in Minnesota may be eligible for College of Continuing Education grants or scholarships, which have more flexible eligibility criteria. Employer assistance may also be an option for some students.

Applying

No application is needed to register in individual courses. For information about applying for the online certificate programs in applied business or paper science and engineering, students can visit the Web site at http://www.cce.umn.edu/certificates.

CONTACT

College of Continuing Education Information Center
101 Wesbrook Hall
University of Minnesota
77 Pleasant Street, SE
Minneapolis, Minnesota 55455
Phone: 612-624-4000
800-234-6564 (toll-free)
Fax: 612-625-1511
E-mail: info@cce.umn.edu
Web site: http://www.cce.umn.edu/petersons

THE UNIVERSITY OF MONTANA-MISSOULA

Continuing Education, Educational Outreach

Missoula, Montana

The University of Montana-Missoula (UM-M), the main campus of the University of Montana System, founded in 1893, is a midsize, state-supported university located in Missoula, Montana, a small city of about 65,000 people located in the Rocky Mountain West. Approximately 10,500 undergraduate and 1,250 graduate students are enrolled, some of whom are taking courses through distance programs. UM-M is a Carnegie doctoral level-intensive university offering a variety of undergraduate and graduate degree programs through centers of excellence in its colleges and professional schools: Arts and Sciences, Business Administration, Education, Fine Arts, Forestry, Journalism, Law, Technology, and Pharmacy and Allied Health Sciences. The University of Montana-Missoula is governed by the Montana University System Board of Regents and accredited by the Northwest Association of Schools and Colleges (professional schools and departments are approved by specialized accrediting organizations). The University of Montana-Missoula ranks seventeenth in the nation and fifth among public universities in producing Rhodes scholars.

Distance Learning Program

For students who live throughout Montana, across the United States, or around the world or for students who are unable to attend class during the traditional school day, academic departments at the University of Montana-Missoula team with Continuing Education to offer programs through Extended Degree Programs and/or individual courses through UMOnline and Extended Courses. The University of Montana-Missoula serves a large, rural state and has a special commitment to the continued development of high-quality, affordable distance learning options.

Extended Degree Programs delivers programs via a combination of traditional classroom, videoconferencing, and UMOnline/Internet instruction. Classes typically meet during evenings or on weekends, with courses being offered each semester. Programs are open to qualified, regularly admitted UM-M students, and all aspects of the degrees are equivalent to those earned on campus. Although students are encouraged to pursue programs in their entirety, nondegree students may also register for individual courses with consent of the academic coordinator. For information about academic coordinators, logistics, costs, and schedules, students should contact Extended Degree Programs. Students are also advised to consult the University of Montana-Missoula's catalogs for complete program details and admission requirements.

UMOnline is the University of Montana-Missoula's online teaching and learning environment. Nearly 200 unique online courses have been offered. The mix of courses changes regularly, so students should check the UMOnline Web site for the current offerings. Every semester, a growing variety of regularly offered on-campus courses at the undergraduate and graduate levels are being added. Online course sections are open to qualified, regularly admitted UM-M students and are equivalent in every respect to those available on campus. Students taking online courses need not be seeking a degree.

Delivery Media

The University of Montana-Missoula delivers courses to distance students online over the Internet, via televised videoconferencing systems, or in person to locations throughout Montana.

Programs of Study

The Doctor of Education program is an external cohort program in educational leadership that meets on weekends on the Missoula campus.

The Master of Business Administration is offered via videoconference. This off-campus M.B.A. program is broadcast on a flexible evening schedule to classrooms in nine Montana cities.

The Master of Education in curriculum studies is delivered in partly online through UMOnline and partly in person in Butte, Montana, during evenings throughout the school year and via condensed daytime schedules during the summer. The degree is expected to be available soon delivered entirely through UMOnline.

The Master of Education in educational leadership is delivered throughout the year entirely over the Internet through UMOnline.

The Master of Public Administration is delivered year-round entirely over the Internet through UMOnline.

The Associate of Applied Science in surgical technology is offered through UMOnline, with clinical experiences in Butte and Billings, Montana. The UM-M College of Technology coordinates with UMOnline, other colleges of technology, and hospitals to bring the complete degree program to students in Butte and Billings.

Special Programs

The Library Media Endorsement Program is an online program intended for upper-division and graduate-level students who wish to receive endorsement in this field from the State of Montana Office of Public Instruction. The enhanced program is now offered jointly by UM–M and UM–Western.

The M.B.A. Foundation Program is an online program that prepares students for graduate studies in the UM–M Master of Business Administration degree program. The Foundation Program comprises a series of five courses offered through UMOnline over a one-year period.

Student Services

Distance learning students enjoy access to a wide variety of UM–M student services, including the Mansfield Library's distance education delivery services and UM–M's admission, academic advising, financial aid, registration, and career services. Select campus services are also available.

Credit Options

Courses are offered for undergraduate and graduate academic credit.

Faculty

Courses are developed and taught by UM–M faculty members.

Admission

Extended Degree Programs and UMOnline courses are available to qualified, regularly admitted UM–M students. Students may enroll in Extended Degree Programs, UMOnline, and on-campus course sections simultaneously or mix delivery modes over successive semesters.

Tuition and Fees

Depending upon the program, fees may be based on a state-support resident/nonresident model approved by the Montana University System Board of Regents or on a self-support model. The typical cost for a 3-credit UMOnline course is $495 for undergraduate courses or $555 for graduate courses.

Financial Aid

Students receiving any form of financial assistance are advised to check with the UM–M Financial Aid Office to determine coverage. Fee waivers and state fee matrix cost plateaus do not apply for self-supported courses.

CONTACT

Educational Outreach, Continuing Education
The University of Montana–Missoula
Missoula, Montana 59812
Phone: 406-243-2900
E-mail: edp@mso.umt.edu
Web site: http://www.montanaeducation.com

UNIVERSITY OF NEVADA, LAS VEGAS

Distance Education

Las Vegas, Nevada

The University of Nevada, Las Vegas (UNLV), has grown dramatically since its founding in 1957 and now enrolls more than 26,000 students. The campus is on 333 acres in urban Las Vegas, in a metropolitan area of more than 1.5 million. The University concentrates its resources on instructional and research programs that are student centered but responsive to the needs of the local, regional, national, and international communities. In addition to its educational offerings, the University plays a vital role in the economic development of the community and assumes a major role in identifying and solving many of the region's social and environmental problems. UNLV offers stimulating intellectual activities, diverse cultural and arts experiences, and exciting athletic competition, all of which invite community participation.

All programs are fully accredited by the Northwest Commission on Colleges and Universities. The University is a member of the American Association of State Colleges and Universities, the Council of Graduate Schools, the Western Association of Graduate Schools, the American Council on Education, and the Western College Association.

Distance Learning Program

Distance education (DE) at UNLV was started in 1996 to develop and deliver educational programs to southern Nevada's rapidly growing communities and as a result of Nevada's prior commitment to extended education and UNLV's desire to respond to community needs. Over time, an electronic network emerged, and online learning became a part of many of the regular course offerings.

The mission of the Office of Distance Education is to provide learning opportunities that are less restricted by time and place than are on-campus UNLV courses and programs. Through its network of distance education professionals, who use the latest in educational technology, students may work toward a college degree, enhance their professional standing, or enrich their understanding of the world. The office increases educational access for students unable to attend classes on campus, fully uses the resources of the University, and improves instruction by integrating technology into the curriculum. Distance education offers off-campus students the chance to complete their degrees in their own homes or at other computer-accessible locations.

There are currently more than 16,000 distance education students. UNLV's 74 percent retention rate is far above the national average of about 50 percent. More than 14 percent of UNLV courses now have an online component.

Delivery Media

Students need access to a computer capable of using Internet Explorer 6.0 or above to access the Internet. Las Vegas students without Internet access at home may use any one of UNLV's computer labs. All DE courses use WebCT, and 99 percent use streaming video. Lectures can be watched online with the RealPlayer plug-in.

Programs of Study

The University of Nevada, Las Vegas, offers a Bachelor of Arts (B.A.) in social science studies degree tailored to students seeking a wide range of knowledge applicable to a variety of careers. An interdisciplinary degree, it is designed to develop lifelong skills in critical and creative thinking, problem solving, effective communication, and intercultural understanding through an individualized course of study. Students acquire a broad, interdisciplinary understanding of many of the central issues addressed by research in the social sciences. They develop a critical awareness of the different methodologies used to answer questions about society, social interaction, and human subjectivity. Major areas of concentration in the social science program include anthropology, history, political science, and psychology. This program is intended primarily for students who have completed, or nearly completed, the equivalent of the first two years of college and are unable to complete a degree because they cannot attend classes on campus.

In 2005, UNLV began offering a Ph.D. in nursing education completely online through distance education. A highly competitive Master of Hospitality Administration is also offered through DE. Additional degrees are planned; students should check the UNLV DE Web site for the latest information.

UNLV offers more than 100 undergraduate and more than forty graduate classes online. Students should check the Web site to see which courses are available in a given semester.

Student Services

Support is available in a number of ways to students who are enrolled in distance classes. From student labs to online and telephone support, help is always available. The Student Computing Support Center is the central source of information for distance education course registration (except course listings) and all student WebCT information.

Leid Library makes every effort to ensure that off-campus students have access to all online electronic services provided to on-campus students, including the availability of databases, tutorials, and Internet links offered through the library Web site, as well as an expanding array of full-text information, reference by e-mail, and instructional assistance. Students can, if necessary, arrange to come to the campus to use the library at any time during its open hours (105 hours per week). Interlibrary loan and document-delivery services can be easily arranged. In addition, the library has classroom space designed to accommodate the instructional needs of the distance learner.

Credit Options

Most distance education courses, both undergraduate and graduate, are 3 credits. Those enrolling in the bachelor's degree in social science studies program should have the equivalent of about two years of college work completed.

Faculty

Many of the University's faculty members teach distance education courses. UNLV is committed to staffing the program with full-time tenure-track faculty members, and there are also some tenure-track faculty members from collaborating universities. Part-time faculty members can participate only if they have previously taught on campus. Of the University's 850 faculty members, 54 percent are full-time. Professors bring degrees and teaching experience from leading universities around the world. Faculty members are involved in important research for government and public service agencies and for scholarly books and journals, and many have won major awards.

Admission

Information on admission to the bachelor's degree program is available from the Office of Distance Education.

Tuition and Fees

Tuition for Nevada residents is $113 per credit for undergraduate courses and $151 per credit for graduate courses, which includes the $15 per credit DE fee. In addition to these costs, nonresidents must pay $136.50 per credit for 6 or fewer credits ($4734 per semester for 7 or more credits) for undergraduate classes and $150 per credit for 6 or fewer credits ($4734 per semester for 7 or more credits) for graduate work. Out-of-state students should contact the Office of Distance Education to find out about special tuition rates. Fees vary.

Financial Aid

UNLV offers more than $70 million each year to students who apply for scholarships, grants, student loans, part-time work, or veterans' benefits. Funds come from federal, state, and private sources. Financial assistance can be used to help cover the costs of registration, fees, tuition, and books. To apply for federal, state, and institutional financial aid, students must complete the Free Application for Federal Student Aid (FAFSA).

Applying

Students already enrolled at UNLV can register for classes online. Other students must first fill out a non-admitted student information form, which lets them use UNLV's registration system. Nevada residents must also fill out a residency form. More information is available from the Distance Education Office.

CONTACT

Alonda Allen
Program Manager of Distance Education
University of Nevada, Las Vegas
4505 Maryland Parkway, Box 451038
Las Vegas, Nevada 89154
Phone: 702-895-2918 or 0334
Fax: 702-895-3647
E-mail: alonda.allen@unlv.edu
Web site: http://distance-ed.unlv.edu

THE UNIVERSITY OF NORTH CAROLINA AT CHAPEL HILL

The William and Ida Friday Center for Continuing Education

Chapel Hill, North Carolina

As the nation's first state university, the University of North Carolina (UNC) at Chapel Hill was chartered in 1789 and opened to students in 1795. UNC–Chapel Hill was the only public university to award degrees to students in the eighteenth century. Today, there are more than 3,100 faculty members and 27,000 students at UNC. Carolina's academic offerings span a broad range of fields, including seventy-one bachelor's, 110 master's, and seventy-seven doctoral degree programs as well as professional degrees in dentistry, medicine, pharmacy, and law. Distance learning has been available since 1913. The University is accredited by the Southern Association of Colleges and Schools.

Distance Learning Program

The Friday Center for Continuing Education offers a variety of credit programs for part-time students. Carolina Courses Online and Self-paced Courses are college-level distance courses that enable students to earn college credit without having to be admitted to UNC or travel to the campus. The Friday Center administers courses from eight institutions of the University of North Carolina: Appalachian State University, East Carolina University, Elizabeth City State University, North Carolina State University, UNC–Chapel Hill, UNC–Greensboro, Western Carolina University, and Winston-Salem State University. Approximately 5,000 students enroll in distance education courses through the Friday Center each year.

Delivery Media

The Self-paced Courses program offers correspondence and online courses. Students enrolled in print-based Self-paced Courses receive a printed course manual that contains all lessons, assignments, and instructions. Students enrolled in online Self-paced Courses receive information on how to access the Web pages containing this information.

Students work through the course at their own pace. Each course has an instructor who grades assignments and answers questions. The minimum completion time for a Self-paced Course is twelve weeks, and students have nine months to complete the course. Students may take two courses at a time. More than 140 Self-paced Courses are available, and most courses are offered for credit at the undergraduate college level.

The Carolina Courses Online program follows the UNC calendar. Students enrolled in a Carolina Courses Online course receive information on how to access the Web pages that contain all lessons, assignments, and instructions. They communicate with classmates and their instructor via e-mail and discussion forums and are encouraged to use the vast resources available through the Internet as they complete their course work. More than seventy Carolina Courses Online courses are available, and most courses are offered for credit at the undergraduate college level.

Programs of Study

The Friday Center offers a variety of courses in more than thirty subjects, including accounting, African and Afro-American studies, art, biology, business, chemistry, classics, criminal justice, communication studies, drama, economics, education, English, environmental sciences, French, geography, geology, history, hospitality management, Italian, journalism, Latin, law, mathematics, music, nursing, nutrition, philosophy, physics, political science, psychology, recreation administration, religious studies, Russian, sociology, Spanish, and statistics. Credit earned in courses offered through the Friday Center can be applied toward degree requirements at UNC–Chapel Hill and other institutions.

Special Programs

Credit courses offered by the Friday Center may be used for teacher license renewal at the discretion of the local district. Students should visit the Friday Center Web site listed in the Contact section for more information.

Student Services

Friday Center staff members are available to answer questions, provide academic advising, and process enrollments. Online library services are available through the UNC–Chapel Hill library system.

Credit Options

Most courses are offered for credit at the undergraduate college level. Credit earned in these courses may be applied toward a degree, if the course is applicable to the requirements of the particular degree program.

Faculty

Faculty members are appointed by the department or school offering the course. Approximately 120 faculty members teach in the program at any given time.

Admission
Carolina Courses Online and Self-paced Courses are open to anyone who wishes to enroll; there are no admission requirements.

Tuition and Fees
Tuition must be paid in full at the time of enrollment. The 2006 tuition is $108 per credit hour for North Carolina residents and $220 per credit hour for nonresidents. Most courses are 3 credit hours. Tuition and other charges are subject to change without notice. Textbooks must be purchased separately.

Financial Aid
Financial aid may be available through VA benefits, vocational rehabilitation grants, local education agencies, and Defense Activity for Non-Traditional Education Support (DANTES).

Applying
Enrollments in Self-paced Courses are accepted at any time by mail, fax, in person, or online. Carolina Courses Online enrollments must be received by specified deadlines. Students should visit the Friday Center Web site for more information.

CONTACT
Student Services Manager
CB #1020
University of North Carolina at Chapel Hill
Chapel Hill, North Carolina 27599-1020
Phone: 919-962-1134
800-862-5669 (toll-free)
Fax: 919-962-5549
E-mail: ceinfo@unc.edu
Web site: http://fridaycenter.unc.edu

The University of Oklahoma OUTREACH

THE UNIVERSITY OF OKLAHOMA

University Outreach
College of Continuing Education
College of Liberal Studies

Norman, Oklahoma

The University of Oklahoma's (OU) College of Continuing Education (CCE) is a lifelong learning organization dedicated to helping individuals, businesses, groups, and communities transform themselves through knowledge. Formally organized in 1913, CCE is the outreach arm of the University of Oklahoma. Nationally recognized for its pioneering efforts in continuing education, CCE extends the educational resources of the University through more than thirty different program formats, including undergraduate and graduate degree programs, correspondence and other distance programs, and on- and off-campus courses as well as through a wide variety of programs conducted under the auspices of federal and state grants and contracts. On the Norman campus, adult and other learners attend programs at the Oklahoma Center for Continuing Education, one of eleven W. K. Kellogg Foundation–funded, University-based residential conference centers in the world. Annually, CCE offers some 2,000 courses and activities to more than 250,000 nontraditional learners in Oklahoma and in locations all over the world.

The mission of the College of Liberal Studies is to provide the highest-quality interdisciplinary education to nontraditional undergraduate and graduate students through innovative delivery formats. By combining independent study with weekend classes or brief seminars on campus or Internet-guided study, adult students can earn a Bachelor of Liberal Studies or Master of Liberal Studies degree. The College of Liberal Studies is a fully accredited, academic division of the University of Oklahoma.

Distance Learning Program

In carrying out its mission to help nontraditional learners transform themselves through knowledge, CCE offers a variety of credit and noncredit distance learning courses and programs within the state of Oklahoma and beyond. Each year, CCE extends the educational resources of the University of Oklahoma through more than thirty different program formats. Annually, CCE offers some 2,000 courses and activities to more than 250,000 nontraditional learners in Oklahoma and worldwide.

Delivery Media

Courses are delivered via television, videotapes, videoconferencing, interactive television, audiotapes, audioconferencing, computer software, CD-ROM, computer conferencing, World Wide Web, e-mail, and print. Students and faculty members may meet in person or interact via videoconferencing, audioconferencing, mail, telephone, fax, e-mail, interactive television, or World Wide Web. The following equipment may be required: audiocassette player, fax machine, television, cable television, videocassette player, computer, modem, Internet access, e-mail, and CD-ROM.

Programs of Study

A variety of programs are available in various distance formats. Independent study courses (credit and noncredit)—some of which are offered online—are available in the following subjects: anthropology, astronomy, business administration, business communication, chemistry, Chinese, classical culture, communication, drama, economics, education, engineering, English, finance, French, geography, geology, German, Greek, health and sport sciences, history, human relations, journalism and mass communication, Latin, library and information studies, management, marketing, mathematics, modern languages, music, philosophy, political science, psychology, Russian, sociology, and Spanish. Master's degree programs in the following areas are presented on-site at military and civilian locations around the world: communication, economics, human relations (including a human resource development emphasis and a community services emphasis), public administration, and social work. In addition, a doctorate in organizational leadership is available at some overseas sites. (These programs combine on-site course delivery with online and correspondence study.) In addition, students in Oklahoma have access to telecourses and OneNet courses.

Special Programs

CCE offers a number of distance learning special programs. Among these are the DHS/SATTRN (Satellite Training Network) programs held for Oklahoma Department of Human Services and other state employees. CCE's Independent Study Department works closely with the DANTES program and the Navy College PACE program. In addition, this department offers a number of noncredit writing courses and more than seventy-five high school courses, many of them available online.

Student Services

Students enrolled in CCE's Advanced Programs have access to the facilities and resources of OU's Norman-based library. Advanced Programs students order all their textbooks online through Follett, and Independent Study offers students a complete array of bookstore services.

Credit Options

CCE's Independent Study Department provides students various options to earn credit through testing. Among these are the College-Level Examination Program (CLEP), DANTES, and institutionally developed advanced-standing examinations.

Faculty

The faculty for distance programs includes regular University of Oklahoma faculty members, adjunct faculty members, and instructors with special appointments. All are experienced and highly qualified instructional professionals who are knowledgeable about the needs, concerns, and capabilities of distance education students.

Admission

Admission to the University of Oklahoma is necessary for credit courses other than those offered through Independent Study. Independent Study students need not be first admitted to OU. To participate in graduate programs, admission to OU's Graduate College is required. For more information, prospective students should use the information listed in the Contact section.

Tuition and Fees

Tuition and fees vary based on the chosen program. Prospective students are encouraged to inquire about the costs associated with the program in which they are interested. Expenses relating to continuing education courses taken to maintain and improve professional skills may be tax deductible (Treas. Reg. 1.162-5, Coughlin v. Commissioner, 203f.2d 307). A tax adviser can make this determination based on the particular facts relating to one's professional situation. All tuition and fees at the University of Oklahoma are subject to changes made by the State Regents for Higher Education.

Financial Aid

Financial aid is available for many of the semester-based programs offered through CCE. Financial aid is not available to Independent Study students. Each program has different eligibility requirements. Interested students are encouraged to use the contact information below. They will then be put in touch with the appropriate CCE department that can fully answer their financial aid questions.

Applying

Distance learners interested in credit and noncredit programs may enroll by telephone (800-522-0772 Ext. 2248) or by fax (405-325-7164). Prospective students should use the contact information below to determine the appropriate telephone number.

CONTACT

Larry Hayes
College of Continuing Education
The University of Oklahoma
1700 Asp Avenue
Norman, Oklahoma 73072-6400
Phone: 405-325-4414
Fax: 405-325-7196
E-mail: lhayes@ou.edu
Web site: http://www.outreach.ou.edu

UNIVERSITY OF PHOENIX

Online Campus

Phoenix, Arizona

Founded in 1976, University of Phoenix is now the largest accredited private university in the United States. The University is accredited by the Higher Learning Commission and is a member of the North Central Association (312-263-0456; http://www.ncahigherlearningcommission.org). University of Phoenix serves thousands of students every year with more than 20,000 highly qualified instructors at over 180 campuses and through Internet delivery worldwide.

High academic standards, commitment to quality, and programs designed specifically to address the needs of today's marketplace have earned University of Phoenix a reputation for leadership in both the academic and business communities. A distinguishing blend of proven academic models and innovative instructional delivery systems, combined with a focus on excellent service to students, has pioneered the University's phenomenal growth. The mission of University of Phoenix is to provide access to higher education opportunities that enable students to develop the knowledge and skills necessary to achieve their professional goals, improve the productivity of their organizations, and provide leadership and service to their communities.

Distance Learning Program

The online learning format utilizes computer communications to link faculty members and students from around the world into interactive forums. Class size is limited to 20 for maximum interaction. Course work is completed entirely online for the convenience of working students who find it difficult or impossible to attend classes at fixed times and places.

Delivery Media

Once enrolled in an online degree program, students are required to log on at least four days each week to participate in class discussions focused on the topics they are studying. All interaction among students and instructors is completed through e-mails and online forums, while assignments are completed offline. This balance of both online and offline interaction is referred to as asynchronous communication.

Programs of Study

The Bachelor of Science (B.S.) and Bachelor of Science in Business (B.S.B.) degree programs require 120 credits (124 in Kansas) for degree completion. The Associate of Arts (A.A.) degree consists of 60 credits and has a specialization in general studies.

The Bachelor of Science (B.S.) degree programs feature specializations in criminal justice administration, elementary education (Arizona residents only), health administration, health administration/health information systems, health administration/long-term care, human services management, information technology, information technology/visual communication, management, nursing, and organizational security and management.

The Bachelor of Science in Business (B.S.B.) degree programs feature specializations in accounting, administration, communications, e-Business, finance, global business management, hospitality management, information systems, integrated supply chain and operations management, management, marketing, public administration, and retail management.

The Master of Arts in Education (M.A.Ed.) degree programs consist of a number of specializations and vary in the number of credit hours required. The specializations are administration and supervision, curriculum and instruction, curriculum and Instruction/adult education, curriculum and instruction/ESL, early childhood education, elementary education, secondary education, and special education.

The Master of Business Administration (M.B.A.) degree program features specializations consisting of varying credit hours. In addition to the M.B.A., the following specializations are available: accounting, global management, health care management, human resources management, marketing, and technology management.

The Master of Health Administration (M.H.A.) degree program prepares leaders who can effectively respond to the dynamic and ever-changing health-care industry.

The Master of Information Systems (M.I.S.) degree focuses on technology theory and its application in real-world business opportunities and challenges.

The Master of Management (M.M.) degree features specializations in human resource management and public administration management. Credit hours can vary between the M.M. degree and the M.M. degree with the specialization.

Master of Science in Nursing (M.S.N.) degree programs feature a number of specializations. In addition, bridge programs are available for students who hold a degree in another subject other than nursing. The specializations include nursing/health-care education, integrative health care, M.B.A./health-care management, and Master of Health Administration.

Doctoral degree programs are available with a number of specializations.

They include the following: Doctor of Business Administration, Doctor of Education in Educational Leadership, Doctor of Education in Educational Leadership with a Specialization in Curriculum and Instruction, Doctor of Health Administration, Doctor of Management in Organizational Leadership, and Doctor of Management in Organizational Leadership with a Specialization in Information Systems.

For more information on the programs, including program descriptions, prospective students should visit the Web site at http://www.uopxonline.com/programs.asp.

Credit Options

Through the University of Phoenix's Prior Learning Assessment Center (PLAC) or through a number of national testing programs (such as CLEP, DANTES, and Excelsior) that test students for college-level knowledge, students may be able to earn a number of credits depending on University policy and individual program requirements.

Faculty

All faculty members have both academic credentials and demonstrated success in the fields they teach. The University recruits only those who are working in their area of expertise—bringing practical, real-world experience to the students they teach. In addition, all faculty members undergo extensive training in online instruction, and all participate in periodic evaluations that include a peer-review component.

Admission

For graduate applicants, an undergraduate degree from a regionally accredited college or university, with a minimum cumulative GPA of 2.5 (3.0 for prior graduate work) is required. Students must also be currently employed or have access to an organization where they can apply concepts they have learned. Undergraduate applicants must have a high school diploma or its equivalent, be at least 18 years old, and be currently employed or have access to an organizational environment. Students must complete the University-proctored Comprehensive Cognitive Assessment.

For international applicants and those whose primary language is not English, a minimum score of 213 on the computer-based TOEFL; 750 on the TOEIC; 6.5 on the IELTS; or 550 on the Berlitz Online English Proficiency Exam within the last two years is required.

Admission requirements may vary depending on state and program requirements. Prospective students should contact the University for a complete list of admission requirements.

Tuition and Fees

Graduate business tuition is $612 per credit; graduate nursing and graduate education tuition is $485 per credit. Undergraduate business tuition is $494 per credit; undergraduate nursing tuition is $430 per credit. Doctoral programs are $692 per credit. Additional costs include an application fee of $45 and a graduation fee of $65. A resource fee ($75 for undergraduate courses and $95 for graduate courses) is required to access online readings and texts. Textbook costs vary by course.

Applying

Unless students are relying on foreign transcripts for admission, all that is needed to begin the first course is to complete an application, enrollment agreement, and disclosure form. While students are in their first three classes, academic counselors work with them to complete transcript requests, the Comprehensive Cognitive Assessment, and any other items necessary for formal registration.

CONTACT

Enrollment Department
University of Phoenix Online
3157 East Elwood Street
Phoenix, Arizona 85034
Phone: 800-833-0287 (toll-free in the U.S.)
Fax: 602-387-6440
Web site: http://www.uopx.com/petersons

THE UNIVERSITY OF TEXAS SYSTEM

UT TeleCampus (UTTC)–Online Courses and Degrees

Austin, Texas

The University of Texas (UT) System offers online degree programs and courses via the award-winning UT TeleCampus (UTTC). The UT TeleCampus is the central support center for online learning within UT System institutions. Students can access virtual classrooms, links to University services and offices, a UT TeleCampus digital library, and many other service features. Launched in May 1998, the UT TeleCampus gives students the assurance of accredited universities, expert faculty members, and quality online education, along with the support services students need to succeed. The UT TeleCampus has received numerous national and regional awards since its development. All UT academic institutions participating in UT TeleCampus-based programs are SACS (Southern Association of Colleges and Schools) accredited. To learn more about online degrees or courses, prospective students should visit the UTTC Web site or contact Student Services.

Distance Learning Program

UT TeleCampus-based programs and courses are composed of the same rigorous content found on-site at UT's fifteen institutions. From application to graduation, students face the same general expectations and receive the same high-quality courses on site or online. Online courses follow a semester schedule, allowing flexibility during the week for study and participation in Web-based group discussions. An online syllabus identifies when tests and projects are due.

The majority of the courses offered through the UT TeleCampus can be taken entirely online. Students can learn from anywhere in the world with access to the Internet.

Delivery Media

The UT TeleCampus uses Internet technologies for course delivery and student support via the World Wide Web. Courses may also utilize additional distance education tools, including CDs, audiotapes and videotapes, streaming video and audio, e-mail, discussion groups, and chat rooms.

Programs of Study

The UT TeleCampus offers online master's degrees, bachelor's degree-completion programs, and various graduate, undergraduate and professional development courses and certificate programs.

The M.B.A. in general management is a 48-hour program that received the 2001 U.S. Distance Learning Association's Excellence in Distance Learning Programming award.

The Master of Public Administration is a 36-hour nonthesis program designed to provide students with the skills needed for effective public leadership.

The Master of Science in human resource development is a 36-hour nonthesis program ideal for corporate trainers, HR directors, and administrators in education as well as others with an interest in technology for human resource development. Certification programs in office education, trade and industrial, and health science technology are available with this degree plan.

Designed for individuals with significant ability in a science discipline as well as a serious commitment to teaching, the online Master of Arts in teaching science education prepares educators in research and pedagogy focused on science content.

Physical educators, athletics directors, wellness trainers, and coaches can earn their master's degree in kinesiology online from their choice of four UT institutions. This 36-hour program received the 2002 U.S. Distance Learning Association's Excellence in Distance Learning Programming award.

The 36-hour M.Ed. in educational technology is designed for teachers, technology coordinators, administrators, and corporate trainers who want to excel at integrating technology into their curriculum.

The 36-hour M.Ed. in curriculum and instruction with a literacy emphasis includes a Master Reading Teacher (MRT) certification program, a reading specialist certification program, and a four-course English as a second language (ESL) endorsement program. Certificate and endorsement course work can also be taken separately.

A bilingual Master of Fine Arts in creative writing program is offered to prepare writers for the publishing marketplace and teaching and editing careers in both the United States and Latin America.

A four-course superintendent certification program, UTOPS, prepares candidates for superintendent certification in Texas.

An alternative teacher certification program (ATCP) is available to individuals with bachelor's degrees in areas other than education wanting to become fully-certified teachers.

A postprofessional certificate program, Improved Training of Physical Therapists in Early Intervention Settings (IMPRINTS), prepares physical therapists to provide services to infants and toddlers with disabilities.

Online nursing programs include an RN to B.S.N. program, which offers the five required nursing courses for registered nurse students to complete their B.S. in nursing degree, and a graduate certificate in nursing education, a three-course program designed for registered nurses interested in pursuing the role of a nurse educator.

A bachelor's degree completion program in criminology and criminal justice is available entirely online. The program consists of 66 hours of upper-level course work.

A bachelor's completion program in applied technology health services technology is offered for graduates of Associate of Applied Science degrees in the allied health and nursing fields.

Other areas of academic study include most general undergraduate curriculum required in Texas, an undergraduate track in management information systems, a chess in education program, a blood bank technology program, and border studies and border administration certificates.

Special Programs

The UT TeleCampus also facilitates the delivery of professional development training in a wide range of topics, including paralegal, blood bank technology, and border studies certificates. Interested students should visit the UTTC Web site and follow the links to PDO (Professional Development Online) to view the catalog.

Student Services

The UT TeleCampus was designed with the online student in mind. It provides all of the services students need to succeed, including technical support available 24/7, an extensive digital library, and free online academic support that provides students with tutorials and writing labs. In addition, department liaisons are available at each campus to aid online students with questions about the library, registration, financial aid, and veteran's affairs.

Credit Options

Transfer credit toward online courses and programs is generally the same as comparable on-site programs. Students should contact the program advisers listed on the UT TeleCampus Web site for specifics.

Faculty

The same expert faculty members who teach on-campus courses at the University of Texas campuses teach online academic courses offered through the UT TeleCampus. Courses are designed and developed by these faculty members, with production support and faculty development provided by the institutions and the UT TeleCampus.

Admission

Admission criteria and processes for online offerings are generally the same as on-site courses. It is advisable to start the initial application process at least 90 days prior to the beginning of a semester.

Tuition and Fees

The amount of tuition and fees charged by each UT System institution varies and is based on residency status. Students should access the UT TeleCampus Web site for links to campus tuition and fee information.

Financial Aid

Financial aid opportunities are available for students enrolled in UT TeleCampus courses.

Applying

Prospective students need to apply and be admitted to the UT System institution offering their course or degree program. Depending on the program of interest, different institutions participate.

CONTACT

Student Services
UT TeleCampus
The University of Texas System
702 Colorado Street, Suite 4.100
Austin, Texas 78701
Phone: 888-TEXAS-16 (toll-free)
Fax: 512-499-4715
E-mail: telecampus@utsystem.edu
Web site: http://www.telecampus.utsystem.edu

THE UNIVERSITY OF THE INCARNATE WORD

Universe Online

San Antonio, Texas

The University of the Incarnate Word (UIW) was founded in 1881 as an outgrowth of the original mission of the Sisters of Charity of the Incarnate Word who settled in San Antonio, Texas, in 1869. The school maintains the mission of the founders by providing quality educational opportunities to all students, developing graduates who are concerned and enlightened citizens. UIW is accredited by a variety of regional and national associations, but most notably by the regional accrediting body of the Commission on Colleges of the Southern Association of Colleges and Schools. Through its College of Professional Studies, UIW is nationally accredited by the Association of Collegiate Business Schools and Programs. Universe Online is accredited by the Association of Accredited Online Programs International.

Distance Learning Program

Universe Online is a natural extension of the mission and the entrepreneurial nature of UIW. By utilizing personal computers and asynchronous instruction, the program addresses the changing needs of adult learners. Maintaining the quality for which it is known, UIW allows students to complete a degree program totally online.

Delivery Media

Students accepted into the program use computer-conferencing software that allows for asynchronous interaction, in an eight-week-term format. Students interact throughout the week in both private and group discussions. Students are required to have an Internet service provider (ISP) to connect and upload/download assignments.

Programs of Study

Universe Online offers a variety of undergraduate degree programs and graduate programs.

Associate of Arts degrees are currently available in the fields of business, information systems, and liberal arts.

The Bachelor of Business Administration (B.B.A.) prepares the student for today's changing business climate. The required core and choice of specialization prepare students for positions of leadership in the business world. Areas of specialization include accounting, marketing, management, international business, and information systems.

Two new degrees have been developed specifically for the student with transfer credit that doesn't fit the major requirements but is still a valuable addition to their degree program. The Bachelor of Arts in organizational development and the Bachelor of Arts in human resources combine courses relevant to today's business world and the specialty with the opportunity for students to include transfer work or a minor.

The Bachelor of Arts degrees in applied administration and organizational administration are designed for the person who has an associate's degree in a specialized field or up to 60 credits of concentration area. Both degrees build a degree around the specialized field.

The Master of Business Administration (M.B.A.) degree program seeks to develop in each student a broad understanding of how the elements and processes of business organizations relate to one another and to the external environment. Degree requirements are designed to develop students' proficiency and confidence in all of the functional areas of business. Students can elect the general or international focus.

The Master of Arts in Administration (M.A.A.) degree program provides participants with the knowledge and skills required for managers, administrators, and supervisors to function more effectively in all types of organizations, plus the specialized managerial expertise needed for management positions within or related to the organizational development profession. Concentrations are communication arts, organizational development, and urban administration.

Students must complete both the course work in their major field of study and the University's general studies core as required in all courses. A minimum of 128 credits of course work is required to graduate in all undergraduate programs. All classes, including graduate classes, are 3 credits (semester hours). Students must complete 36 semester hours to graduate from the graduate programs.

Student Services

All students at UIW, including Universe Online students, have a wide variety of student service options. Online students have access to academic and financial aid advising, library and bookstore services, and online admission application and registration. In addition, students have access to career planning services.

Credit Options

Universe Online welcomes transfer students. UIW accepts all transfer work, requiring students to complete a minimum of 45 credit hours to receive the UIW degree.

Upon acceptance as a degree-seeking student at the University, a student must obtain prior written approval to transfer any additional credits from other institutions.

Faculty

Given the stringent requirements of national/regional accreditation, faculty members must meet a very exacting set of requirements; this has led to a high-quality educational program delivered by highly credentialed and dedicated faculty members.

Admission

Undergraduate students must possess a high school diploma or its equivalent. Students having previous college work must have a 2.5 GPA or better. Students must have worked for three years prior to application, in or outside of the home. Students who have not completed English composition I and II and college algebra must take these courses early in their program of study and may be tested for level.

International student transcripts and course descriptions must be translated.

Tuition and Fees

Undergraduate tuition is $360 per credit and graduate tuition is $545 per credit. There is a one-time transcript fee of $30. There are no other fees assessed.

Financial Aid

Financial aid and payment plans are available for all qualified students. Military benefits, as well as employer reimbursement benefits, may be used for online courses.

Applying

To apply for admission, students can fill out an application for admission through the Web site listed below. In order to be considered for admission, students must fill out an application online at the school Web site and submit official high school or postsecondary school transcripts from all institutions attended. Students are notified of application decisions via e-mail and U.S. mail.

CONTACT

Universe Online
University of the Incarnate Word
CPO #324
4301 Broadway
San Antonio, Texas 78209
Phone: 877-827-2702 (toll-free)
Fax: 210-829-2756
E-mail: virtual@uiwtx.edu
Web site: http://www.uiw.edu/online

THE UNIVERSITY OF TOLEDO

THE UNIVERSITY OF TOLEDO

Division of Distance and eLearning

Toledo, Ohio

Established in 1872, the University of Toledo (UT) has a diverse enrollment of more than 19,000 students representing nearly ninety countries. Located in the heart of Toledo in northwest Ohio, the University plays an important role in the region. Faculty members participate in research, are involved in the community, and are committed to teaching. Eight colleges—Arts and Sciences, Business, Education, Engineering, Health and Human Services, Pharmacy, Law, and University College—offer a variety of certificate, associate, bachelor's, master's, and doctoral degree programs. UT is regionally accredited by the Higher Learning Commission and a member of the North Central Association of Colleges and Schools and is authorized to offer degrees online. UT is recognized as a leader in distance education in Ohio.

Distance Learning Program

The Division of Distance and eLearning was established in June 1995 to meet the distance learning mission of the University of Toledo (UT). The Division provides greater access to educational opportunities for learners in Ohio and worldwide. The University is the leader in distance learning among Ohio's four-year public universities and colleges, offering more than 800 courses online.

Delivery Media

Student-faculty interaction is accomplished through e-mail, chat room discussions, bulletin board postings, CD-ROM, and phone. Most courses are offered via the Internet in an asynchronous environment. Students are responsible for having access to a computer and Internet service provider.

Programs of Study

The Division of Distance and eLearning at the University of Toledo provides a flexible environment to fit its students' busy lifestyles for a variety of undergraduate and graduate degree and certificate programs as well as an array of individual courses. The Division works with colleges throughout the University to offer courses taught by leading UT faculty members. Programs offered online are also offered in the traditional on-campus setting. Programs and courses are available in business, communications, counseling, education, engineering, English, health information, humanities, liberal studies, mathematics, natural sciences, and social sciences.

Accounting Technology Certificate Program: This program provides participants with the skills necessary to prepare financial statements and record business transactions and offers a foundation in the current technology pertaining to the profession. Students may apply the completed courses toward an associate degree.

Business Management Technology Certificate Program: This 24-credit program, which can be completed in one year, consists of eight courses: business principles, workplace communication and presentation, organizational behavior, workplace management, human resource development, managing in a global economy, managing diversity in the workplace, and marketing principles. Students can apply the completed courses to an associate degree.

Computer Software Specialist Certificate Program: This program gives students the necessary skills to organize and perform activities related to the office environment and stresses the importance of software knowledge and such professional certifications as Microsoft Officer User Specialist (MOUS). Graduates are prepared to sit for the Microsoft certification examination. Credits may be applied to an associate degree.

Diversity Management Certificate Program: Participants in this program learn how to create a bias-free workplace, develop diversity training for all types of organizations, and set up mentorship programs and diversity councils. Students may apply the completed courses toward an associate degree.

Information Services and Support Certificate Program: This certificate prepares students for careers as software and hardware support professionals, operating-systems experts, information technologists, and computer technicians. Credits may be applied to an associate degree.

Marketing and Sales Technology Certificate Program: This program prepares students for careers in new product development, merchandising, advertising, and wholesale/retail trade management.

Programming and Software Development Certificate Program: This certificate prepares students to work in the computer industry as programmers, software developers, data managers, and information system designers. Credits may be applied to an associate degree.

Associate Degree in Accounting Technology Program: The Business Technology Department offers this degree. Students receive a well-rounded education in all areas of accounting, including payroll, accounts receivable/payable, purchasing, and taxation, and are prepared for careers in the public and private sectors. Students may apply the earned credits toward a bachelor's degree.

Associate Degree in Business Management Technology Program: This two-year, 65-credit program explores aspects of human resources, computer technology, marketing, accounting, and workplace diversity. Upon completion, students may apply to a bachelor's degree program.

Associate Degree in Business Management Technology Program—Fast-Track Option: This degree can be completed in fifteen months or less. Students become part of a cohort group, which provides a supportive, interactive distance-learning experience. Courses are presented in either eight- or sixteen-week sessions.

Associate Degree in Computer Software Specialist Program: Students in this program obtain skills necessary to organize and perform activities related to the office environment. The program stresses the importance of software knowledge and such professional certifications as Microsoft Officer User Specialist (MOUS), and its highly marketable graduates are prepared to sit for the Microsoft certification examination. Credits may be applied to a bachelor's degree.

Associate Degree in Programming and Software Development Program: This program prepares students to work in the computer industry as programmers, software developers, data managers, and information system designers. Credits may be applied to a bachelor's degree.

Associate Degree in Information Services and Support Program: This degree program prepares students for careers as software and hardware support professionals, operating-systems experts, information technologists, and computer technicians. Credits may be applied to a bachelor's degree.

Associate Degree in Interdisciplinary Technical Studies Program: This program allows students to individualize a program to meet their unique interests and career goals. Students work closely with an academic adviser and faculty members to develop their programs. Credits may be applied to a bachelor's degree. Depending on the courses selected, the entire program can be completed online.

Associate Degree in Marketing and Sales Technology Program: This two-year program enables students to develop the business skills necessary to recognize changes in the marketplace and technology; students can specialize in the process of bringing raw materials from the producer to the final customer. Credits may be applied to a bachelor's degree.

Bachelor of Arts in Liberal Studies Program: This program is for students who have no college credits or wish to utilize previously earned credits from a regionally accredited institution and seek a liberal arts degree. Students complete topical seminars in humanities, natural sciences, and social sciences along with an individualized component of traditional courses. Students may qualify for experiential credit via portfolio or credit through CLEP testing.

Bachelor of Science in Engineering Technology Program: This program leads to a B.S. degree by providing the last two years of the program's computer science and engineering technology curriculum, focusing on aspects of computer networking and Web-based programming. Applicants must have an associate degree in electrical engineering technology or a closely related field. UT partners with several Ohio community colleges that provide the first two years of the curriculum.

Bachelor of Science in Health Information Management Program: Health Information Management (HIM) professionals play a critical role in maintaining, collecting, and analyzing data that health-care providers need to deliver high-quality health care. Students who have an associate degree in health-information technology or a closely related field may apply those credits to this degree. The program is accredited by the Commission on Accreditation for Health Informatics and Information Management Education (CAHIM). Graduates are eligible to sit for the national certification examination to become registered health administrators (RHIA).

Master of Liberal Studies Program: This flexible, customized program is offered by the College of Arts and Sciences. Students complete seminars in humanities, natural and social sciences, and visual and performing arts and a master's thesis. Admission to the program is open year-round. A minimum 2.7 undergraduate GPA is required. Applicants with a lower GPA can enroll provisionally and must take the GRE.

Master of Science in Engineering Program: This part-time program, with a concentration in engineering practice, integrates engineering, business, and elective courses. The program is designed for students who hold a bachelor's degree in engineering, engineering technology, or a closely related area. A cross-disciplinary program, it combines study in business management and engineering and presents an alternative to a traditional business management or technical M.S. degree. M.S.E. students typically have a background in engineering, science, or technology and seek to further their career development with a degree that builds management skills while sharpening their technical capabilities.

Student Services

The Division of Distance and eLearning provides comprehensive student services by experienced professionals and offers a wide range of services to enable students to become involved participants in the online-learning process. Students are encouraged to contact Distance and eLearning student-service professionals for assistance. Students have access to a number of services through the Division's Web site, including online applications, applications for financial aid, registration, academic advising, software information, and access to the UT Bookstore, Career Services, UT's online library, and the eWriting Center. The University is a member of the OhioLINK consortium, which provides students online access to library resources from Ohio's university and college libraries. Technical support is available days, evenings, and weekends to all online students. The University has been awarded the designation of meeting Best Practices in Student Services by the Ohio Learning Network.

Credit Options

College credits earned through distance learning courses are recorded on a University of Toledo transcript in the same manner as credits earned in on-campus courses. There is no special designation on the transcript. Students who have attended a regionally accredited college or university may be able to transfer those credits. Online courses are equivalent in content to the on-campus courses. Students should contact the Division of Distance and eLearning for further information. The University is regionally accredited by the Higher Learning Commission of the North Central Association of Schools and Colleges and is authorized to offer degrees online.

Admission

All distance learners must be admitted to the University and meet the same requirements as traditional students. Special-status admission is available for nondegree students.

Tuition and Fees

Tuition and fees for online courses are the same as for on-campus courses. Tuition rates vary depending on residency status. A one-time $25 matriculation fee is charged at the time of registration. Scholarships are available for both in-state and out-of-state students. Prospective students should visit the Distance and eLearning Web site for additional information.

Applying

Prospective students should submit an official application along with the $40 admission fee, an official high school transcript, GED scores, or official transcripts from all previous colleges or universities. Applications are available online or by mail.

CONTACT

Janet Green, Assistant Director for Marketing and Enrollment Management
Division of Distance and eLearning
The University of Toledo
401 Jefferson Avenue
Toledo, Ohio 43604-1005
Phone: 866-886-5336 (toll-free)
Fax: 419-321-5147
E-mail: utdl@utoledo.edu
Web site: http://www.dl.utoledo.edu

UNIVERSITY OF TULSA

MBA Online
Online Master of Taxation (MTAX)

Tulsa, Oklahoma

The University of Tulsa is a private institution that was founded in 1894 in Indian Territory. The College of Business Administration was established in 1935 and is fully accredited by AACSB International–The Association to Advance Collegiate Schools of Business at both the graduate and undergraduate levels. As faculty members in the College of Business have sought to provide programs that are on the leading edge of technology, they have acted on the need to address new ways of delivering advanced education. The MBA Online and an online Master of Taxation (MTAX) are their response to professionals whose schedules do not permit regular classroom attendance. Interaction between student and professor is emphasized and encouraged in the MBA Online and MTAX programs. Graduates of the MBA Online program receive the fully accredited University of Tulsa M.B.A. degree. Graduates of the MTAX program receive the fully accredited Master of Taxation degree. The MTAX program prepares students to become successful, integral members of the business team, and the MBA Online program prepares graduates to be the effective leaders businesses have come to expect from the University of Tulsa.

Distance Learning Program

The MBA Online and MTAX programs make graduate business education accessible to the motivated professional who wishes to earn an M.B.A. or graduate tax degree but whose schedule does not permit regular classroom attendance. Students in classes of no more than 25 people enjoy more options for interaction with their professors and classmates than ever before.

Delivery Media

The technology-based online programs require students to have a computer with Internet access; Win98 SE, Win2K, or WinXP; Office 2K or Office XP; Netscape or Internet Explorer; speakers; and a sound card. All courses have been developed utilizing WebCT. Students are able to access chat rooms, e-mail, online forums, and bulletin boards. To access a sample course, interested individuals may visit the MBA Online Web site at http://www.imba.utulsa.edu or the MTAX Web site at http://bus.cba.utulsa.edu/mtax.

Programs of Study

The University of Tulsa has designed a successful M.B.A. curriculum that can be delivered online. This part-time program consists of two courses per term, three terms per year, in which students can complete their degree in only two years, depending on their undergraduate degree and grades. Those applying for this program must have at least two years of working experience following completion of their baccalaureate degree. Students earn a high-quality M.B.A. from the University of Tulsa, which is internationally recognized and accredited by AACSB International.

Interactivity is a key component of the MBA Online program. Chat rooms, e-mail, electronic bulletin boards, and online forums provide a powerful arena for discussion, analysis, and collaboration. Students also have access to an online library. Students come to the campus for two 2-day sessions during the course of the program to meet with their professors and classmates, receive orientation materials, and participate in various workshops and seminars.

Building on the successes of the MBA Online program, the University of Tulsa now offers a two-year Internet-based Master of Taxation program. This 30-hour specialized program consists of two courses per term, three terms per year, with no on-campus requirement. The program offers high-potential professional employees currently holding a bachelor's degree the opportunity to earn a Master of Taxation in as little as two years from an institution that is accredited by AACSB International while continuing to meet the demands of the workplace. (Students can choose to complete the degree in more than two years.) Because the specifics of tax code vary from year to year, the curriculum focus is on big-picture issues with enduring applicability.

Interactivity is also a key component of the MTAX program. The virtual classroom includes application-sharing software, CD-ROM multimedia courseware, audio/video, electronic bulletin boards, e-mail, an online library, and lecture resources with direct links to other course materials. The entire program is taught online; no campus time is required.

Students are able to complete a high-quality degree in an extremely flexible format without the need to miss work in order to attend regular classes. Course materials are available anytime and anywhere. Course work can be completed at home, at work, or while away on business or personal travel.

Student Services

All students in the online programs receive training in the use of WebCT, the software in which all of the distance education courses reside. Students have an e-mail address within WebCT for communicating directly with classmates and faculty members. In addition, all students enrolled at the University of Tulsa are assigned a universal e-mail account. With the establishment of a University e-mail account, students may access McFarlin Library electronically. Both part-time and full-time students and alumni of the University of Tulsa may utilize Career Services.

Credit Options

University policy allows for transfer of up to 6 credit hours at the master's level. Any such graduate credit must have been earned at an AACSB-accredited graduate school and have been completed within the last six years. The Graduate Program Director is responsible for determining the applicability of transfer work to the student's program, subject to final approval by the faculty and the Dean of Research and Graduate Studies.

Faculty

All faculty members who teach in the MBA Online program have obtained a Ph.D. and/or a J.D. All faculty members who teach in the MTAX program have advanced degrees and extensive professional experience.

Admission

Enrollment in the MBA Online is limited to the fall term, with the exception of foundation courses, which are offered year-round. Students must have a baccalaureate degree in any field (a business degree is not required), two years of work experience, preferably a 3.0 or better GPA, an acceptable GMAT score, three letters of reference, and a resume.

Enrollment in the MTAX program is offered for the fall, spring, and summer terms. Students must have a baccalaureate degree in any field (a business degree is not required), preferably a 3.0 or better GPA, an acceptable GMAT or LSAT score, three letters of reference, and a resume.

Tuition and Fees

Tuition for the MBA Online and MTAX degrees is $674 per credit hour. There are no additional fees except for books.

Financial Aid

Students are eligible to apply for Federal Stafford Student Loans (subsidized and unsubsidized) as well as other funded loans. Graduate students can normally apply year-round for these loans. Students who are residents of the state of Oklahoma may apply for an Oklahoma Tuition Aid Grant. The annual deadline for these grants is March 1. Students receiving reimbursement from their employers may arrange to defer tuition to match their employer's reimbursement policy. For more information on available financial aid, students should visit http://www.utulsa.edu/financialaid.

Applying

For more detailed information on the MBA Online program or to apply online, students should visit http://www.imba.utulsa.edu. For more information on the MTAX program or to apply online, students should visit http://bus.cba.utulsa.edu/mtax.

CONTACT

Graduate Business Programs, Bah 217
University of Tulsa
600 South College Avenue
Tulsa, Oklahoma 74104-3189
Phone: 918-631-2242
Fax: 918-631-2142
E-mail: graduate-business@utulsa.edu
Web site: http://www.imba.utulsa.edu

UNIVERSITY OF WASHINGTON

UW Extension

Seattle, Washington

Founded in 1861, the University of Washington (UW) is one of the oldest state-supported institutions of higher education on the Pacific coast. The University comprises three campuses: the Seattle campus, which is made up of seventeen schools and colleges offering educational opportunities to students ranging from first-year undergraduates through doctoral-level candidates; the Bothell campus; and the Tacoma campus.

The primary mission of the University of Washington is the preservation, advancement, and dissemination of knowledge. UW advances new knowledge through many forms of research, inquiry, and discussion. Accreditation is by the Northwest Association of Schools and Colleges.

Distance Learning Program

The University of Washington offers twelve degree programs, twenty-five certificate programs, and hundreds of courses online, making it one of the leading public institutions in the online field. The UW online program has been rated among the top ten online learning education offerings available through U.S. universities. Distance learning courses at UW are developed by a team of online learning designers working with UW faculty members and academic departments. They create courses that are academically rigorous, suitable for a distance format, and convenient. Several courses have won the prestigious Helen Williams Award for Excellence in Collegiate Independent Study from the well-respected American Association for Collegiate Independent Study (AACIS) as well as awards from the University Continuing Education Association (UCEA). The distance learning program at UW has 4,074 students enrolled.

Delivery Media

Most programs rely on the Internet and e-mail to access instruction and to communicate with teachers and fellow students. Some classes start and finish at set times; others enable students to start according to their own schedule. Students can contact their instructors at any time with questions about the courses. Many courses use online discussion, and some courses incorporate chats into their curriculum.

Programs of Study

UW offers a Master in Strategic Planning for Critical Infrastructures degree program that was developed in partnership with the Washington National Guard for leaders who are responsible for ensuring the reliability and security of critical infrastructures and emergency services. This program was developed for officials in public and private infrastructure, emergency management, and homeland security.

Master's degrees in engineering are available through UW's Education at a Distance for Growth and Excellence (UW/EDGE), with five areas of specialization: aeronautics and astronautics, aerospace engineering, manufacturing engineering, materials science and engineering, and mechanical engineering.

The master's in construction engineering is designed for professionals in the heavy construction industry, combining courses in construction management and civil engineering.

The Master of Library and Information Science degree was established to meet the high demand for library and information professionals. Delivery of instruction is primarily Internet-based, with on-campus three-day residencies at the beginning of each quarter.

Twenty-five certificate programs are offered, with each requiring three to nine intensive courses. Certificate programs include Brain Research in Education, Business Foundations, C++ Programming, Construction Management, Curriculum Integration in Action, Data Resource Management, E-learning Design and Development, Facility Management, Gerontology, Heavy Construction Project Management, Infrastructure Construction, Internet Programming, Java 2 Programming, Object-Oriented Analysis and Design Using UML, Paralegal Studies, Project Management, Quantitative Construction Management, School Library Media Professional, Site Planning, Web Administration, Web Consultant for Small Business, Web Technology Essentials, and Writers' Program: Literary Fiction Writing and Nonfiction Writing.

More than 200 courses are available in architecture and urban planning, arts and sciences, business and management, computing, engineering and technology, education, health sciences, languages, and library and information science. The OpenUW program at the UW offers twelve free noncredit classes.

Student Services

Academic advising is available via e-mail and telephone and, for those who are able to come to the campus, in person. Advisers can answer questions about prerequisites and course content. Students enrolled in online learning courses receive student numbers and have library checkout privileges at UW libraries. Distance learning students living outside the Seattle area may request specific library materials by mail. Technical support for courses is provided. Textbooks may be ordered online.

Credit Options

Credit earned by taking a distance learning course can be applied to an undergraduate degree or can help students prepare for UW admission. Online learning credits are not considered residence credits. It is not possible to earn an undergraduate degree from the University of Washington through online learning alone. However, nine master's degrees may be completed solely through online learning.

Faculty

Most UW online learning courses are designed and taught by faculty members who teach the same courses on the UW campus. The instructors are familiar with student questions and needs. With the help of instructional designers, they have developed the appropriate methods and materials, interactive strategies, and online activities to help students achieve the course objectives in a distance learning format.

Admission

It is not necessary to be admitted to the University of Washington before taking distance learning courses. (There are prerequisites for some courses, and TOEFL scores are required for international students.) Certificate and graduate degree programs have an application process.

Tuition and Fees

All registrants pay a nonrefundable $30 registration fee. Fees for credit courses through distance learning are $176 per credit for undergraduate students and $387 per credit for Tier 1 graduate and graduate courses. Prices for graduate instruction vary by degree program.

Financial Aid

UW distance learning students are ineligible for the University's financial aid programs in most cases. For information about alternative funding, students should visit http://www.outreach.washington.edu/extinfo/loan_sources.asp.

Applying

Prospective students can register online for courses. Application forms for certificates and degree programs can be downloaded.

CONTACT

University of Washington Online Learning
4311 11th Avenue, NE
Seattle, Washington 98105-4608
Phone: 206-897-8936
800-506-1338 (toll-free)
E-mail: uwonline@extn.washington.edu
Web site: http://www.onlinelearning.washington.edu

UNIVERSITY OF WISCONSIN–SUPERIOR

Distance Learning Center

Superior, Wisconsin

The Distance Learning Center (formerly known as the Extended Degree Program) at the University of Wisconsin-Superior (UW-Superior) was established in 1978. UW-Superior is part of the highly acclaimed University of Wisconsin System.

The Distance Learning Program is a nationwide program with one tuition for all students. It is accredited by the North Central Association of Colleges and Schools and serves adults who do not have access to a four-year institution because of where they live or because of career and/or family responsibilities.

UW-Superior recognizes that adults are dedicated to achieving educational goals but must also address other priorities. By enrolling in UW-Superior's Distance Learning Program, students can obtain a degree without having to come to the campus. The individually designed major is designed by the student to fit his or her career goals and educational needs. Elementary education is an option for the student who wants to teach in Wisconsin. Communications is the third major offered by the Distance Learning Center.

Distance Learning Program

The Distance Learning Program is a semester-based program. The three enrollment periods include fall, spring, and summer. Each class is taught by a UW-Superior faculty member to ensure that students are receiving the best instruction possible, with an up-to-date curriculum. At any given time, more than 200 students are enrolled in the program. Advisers work closely with students as they complete their degrees.

Delivery Media

Courses are delivered in both online and print-based formats. Access to the Desire 2 Learn software is provided through the UW-Superior network system. Students are encouraged to utilize e-mail and message boards while enrolled in the online courses. Print-based course materials can be mailed or faxed to the Distance Learning Office.

Programs of Study

The Distance Learning Program offers three bachelor's degree options: communications, elementary education, and the individually designed major.

The communications degree is the newest major offered. Students work with faculty members who specialize in improving communications. It not only allows students to dig deeper into the communications discipline but also gives students a wide range of communication venues to explore—interpersonal, conflict, persuasion, organizational, and intercultural communication.

The individualized major allows students to plan a major using both past and new learning experiences. It is designed by students to meet their educational and career goals. Examples of individualized majors include human services, child development, and health management.

The elementary education degree at a distance has been in existence for more than twenty-five years. It provides preparation for Wisconsin licensure for birth through ages 11–12 or ages 6 through 12–13. UW-Superior's Teacher Education Department has an excellent reputation for quality and innovation.

Credit Options

Credit for prior learning is made possible through credit by exam, credit for military service, and credit for non-university programs. Students also have the option to petition for technical college credit and to seek credit through portfolio development.

Admission

Students seeking admission to the Distance Learning Program can apply online at the University's Web site (http://www.uwsuper.edu). They can also request admission information via e-mail.

Tuition and Fees

All distance learning students pay the same tuition regardless of residency. An additional course fee is charged for each course.

Financial Aid

Financial aid is available to distance learning students.

CONTACT

Distance Learning Program
Erlanson Hall, Room 105
University of Wisconsin–Superior
Belknap and Catlin Avenues
Superior, Wisconsin 54880
Phone: 877-528-6597 (toll-free)
E-mail: dlc@uwsuper.edu
Web site: http://www.uwsuper.edu/distancelearning

UNIVERSITY OF WYOMING
New Thinking

THE UNIVERSITY OF WYOMING

Outreach School

Laramie, Wyoming

The University of Wyoming (UW), a land-grant university founded in 1886, is accredited by the Higher Learning Commission and is a member of the North Central Association of Colleges and Schools. The University of Wyoming was the first university west of the Missouri River to offer correspondence courses. In its outreach mission, the University of Wyoming is guided by the following vision: the state of Wyoming is the campus of the University of Wyoming. The University has one faculty and staff, one student body, and one set of academic programs. Teaching, research, and service are the missions of the University, regardless of location. The University recognizes that its "one student body" is composed of a wide variety of students whose needs differ.

Distance Learning Program

The UW Outreach School delivers the University's distance learning programs. The mission of the Outreach School is to extend the University of Wyoming's educational programs and services to people in the state of Wyoming and beyond. The School delivers more than 300 courses and complete degree and certificate programs to approximately 3,500 students per semester.

Delivery Media

The Outreach School launched Online UW, the University of Wyoming's virtual campus, in the spring of 1999 in cooperation with eCollege. In addition, the School delivers programs via correspondence study, audio-teleconference, and videoconferencing.

For more information, students can access the Online UW Web site at http://online.uwyo.edu. For a list of audio, videoconferencing, and correspondence study courses, students should visit the Web site listed at the end of this description. All correspondence study courses, a limited number of audio-teleconference courses, and all Online UW courses are available to students outside the state of Wyoming.

Programs of Study

Degrees, certificates, and endorsements are available to students through distance education. Certificate programs include land surveying (offered nationwide through audio-teleconference with videotaped lectures), real estate (available online), and family and consumer sciences/early childhood program director's certificate (available online). Endorsement programs include early childhood birth to 5 (available through online, audio teleconferencing, and on-site) and the Wyoming reading endorsement literacy program (statewide). Graduate programs include an Executive M.B.A. (available online); an M.S. in education, with a specialization in instructional technology (available online); an M.S. in kinesiology and health (statewide, some courses nationwide); an M.S. in nursing, with an advanced practice in rural health/nurse educator option (online); an M.S.W. in social work (statewide); and an M.S. in speech-language pathology (available nationwide through audio-teleconference with videotaped lectures). Other available distance degrees are bachelor's degrees in business administration and family and consumer science (online); criminal justice, psychology, and social science (statewide, some courses nationwide); an RN/B.S.N. completion program (online); an M.P.A. (available through audio-teleconference and videoconferencing statewide); and master's degrees in education, with specialization options in special education, adult and postsecondary education, and teaching and learning (statewide, some courses nationwide).

Special Programs

The University of Wyoming's Internet campus, Online UW, currently offers more than ninety courses and nine degrees completely online. Courses are available worldwide via http://online.uwyo.edu. Online courses are available in the areas of adult learning, astronomy, biochemistry, business administration, child development, directing preschool and day-care programs, economics, education, engineering, family and consumer sciences, human resources management, instructional technology, nutrition, physics, psychology, real estate, religion, and statistics.

Student Services

All student services (such as admission, enrollment, tuition payment, grade reporting, financial aid, bookstore, and library outreach) are available through the UW Outreach School. The library outreach service is available at http://www.lib.uwyo.edu. Students can purchase textbooks and course packets online at the University Bookstore at http://www.uwyobookstore.com.

Credit Options

Students may transfer courses from accredited institutions of higher education to the University of Wyoming. Credit is also available through AP, CLEP, portfolio assessment, and departmental examinations. Degrees require a minimum of 48 hours of upper-division credit, with a minimum of 30 credits from the University of Wyoming. Most degree programs require 120–124 credits for graduation.

Faculty

The majority of those who teach at the Outreach School are full-time faculty members at the University of Wyoming. A limited number of adjunct faculty members, who are approved by the academic departments, offer distance learning courses. In any given semester, approximately 75 regular full-time faculty members and 15 part-time adjunct faculty members teach distance learning courses for the Outreach School. The programs offered via distance learning are the same as the programs offered on the main University campus in Laramie, Wyoming.

Admission

Students not seeking University of Wyoming degrees may enroll in distance learning courses without being admitted to the University. Students can apply a maximum of 12 credit hours toward the requirements for a UW undergraduate degree prior to admission to the University. Degree-seeking students should apply at the admissions office. Undergraduate admission generally requires completion of at least 13 high school units in a precollege curriculum, a cumulative high school grade point average of at least 2.75, and an ACT score of at least 20 or an SAT score of at least 960. Conditional admission is available for adult learners who do not meet these criteria. Graduate programs require a Graduate Record Examinations (GRE) combined verbal and quantitative score of at least 900. The University offers GRE testing through the University of Wyoming Testing Center. For more information, students can visit the Web site at http://www.uwyo.edu/ucc/utc/.

Students not seeking University of Wyoming graduate degrees that have baccalaureate degrees and are enrolled in graduate course must file a Graduate Enrichment Application and pay a fee if they plan to use course work for a graduate program at a later date. Up to 12 hours of course work taken during the graduate enrichment status may be used for a graduate program. Degree-seeking students may reserve up to 6 hours of graduate-level course work for graduate credit if it is taken within twelve months prior to completing a baccalaureate degree or during the last semester prior to completing a baccalaureate degree. To do this, students must complete the Request to Reserve Coursework for Graduate Credit form. Students can visit the Graduate School Web site at http://www.uwyo.edu/uwgrad/petitions@instructions.asp to download a copy of the form. Enrichment or certification-seeking students who enroll in graduate courses do not need to complete a Graduate Enrichment Application. Courses taken without graduate enrichment status cannot be used in a graduate program of study. Students must file a Graduate Enrichment Application and pay the fee if they plan to use the course work for a graduate degree.

Tuition and Fees

All outreach students are charged tuition at an in-state rate. Undergraduate tuition for outreach courses is $92 per credit hour, with an $11-per-credit-hour delivery fee or a $40-per-credit-hour delivery fee for Online UW courses. Graduate tuition for outreach courses is $155 per credit hour, with an $11-per-credit-hour delivery fee or a $40-per-credit-hour delivery fee for Online UW courses. Tuition for the Executive M.B.A. program is $500 per credit hour plus a $40-per-credit-hour delivery fee, and tuition for the land surveying program is $192 per credit hour.

Financial Aid

All forms of federal financial aid and other scholarship aid are available to Outreach students. The Outreach School also has a number of scholarships available to Outreach students. Information describing available aid and award criteria is available from the Office of Student Financial Aid, Department 3335, University of Wyoming, 1000 East University Avenue, Laramie, Wyoming 82071.

Applying

Non-degree-seeking students may apply through the Division of Outreach Credit Programs. Degree-seeking students should apply through the Admissions Office (telephone: 800-DIAL-WYO (toll-free) or 307-766-2287; Web site: http://www.uwyo.edu) or Graduate Admissions (telephone: 307-766-2287; Web site: http://www.uwyo.edu/uwgrad).

CONTACT

Outreach School
Division of Outreach Credit Programs
Department 3274
University of Wyoming
1000 East University Avenue
Laramie, Wyoming 82071
Phone: 307-766-4300
800-448-7801 (toll-free)
Fax: 307-766-4048
E-mail: occ@uwyo.edu
Web site: http://outreach.uwyo.edu/ocp

UPPER IOWA UNIVERSITY

Extended University

Fayette, Iowa

Upper Iowa University (UIU) was established in 1857 and has since become the largest private university in the state of Iowa. Unlike some of the newer schools offering distance learning programs, UIU has a beautiful residential campus on 90 acres with eight academic buildings and three residence halls. Upper Iowa also has seventeen sports teams, known as the Peacocks, who compete in the NCAA Division II. As a nonprofit, rapidly growing, four-year liberal arts institution of higher learning, UIU offers a wide range of high-quality degree programs to nearly 6,000 students worldwide. UIU provides educational opportunities to the global community, focusing on the future while preserving the traditions of the past. Upper Iowa University is accredited by the Higher Learning Commission and is a member of the North Central Association of Colleges and Schools (Web site: http://www.ncahigherlearningcommission.org; telephone: 312-263-0456).

Distance Learning Program

The Extended University's distance learning programs are offered through two primary modes of delivery. Its External Degree program offers Associate of Arts and Bachelor of Science degree programs with seventeen majors through independent study/correspondence, and its Online program currently offers a Bachelor of Science (B.S.) with seven business majors, criminal justice, emergency and disaster management, health-services administration, interdisciplinary studies, public administration, a Master of Business Administration (M.B.A.) and a Master of Public Administration (M.P.A.). Courses offered through both External Degree and Online formats meet the same standards as courses offered through the residential University in Fayette, Iowa. The External Degree program, which began in 1972, has been successfully delivered to more than 10,000 learners. Upper Iowa's External Degree program was one of the first and most successful in the United States. Both the External Degree and Online programs continue to be vital components in serving both civilian and military learners worldwide.

Delivery Media

In the External Degree program, students communicate with instructors via e-mail, fax, and regular mail. Classes are self-paced with no minimum completion time. Upper Iowa's Online program is noted for its e-mail–like feel. Online students log on (via the Internet) just long enough to send and receive materials, anytime, anywhere, day or night. Most work is accomplished off-line, or through asynchronous communication. Online students may also communicate with their instructors through course software, e-mail, fax, or phone.

Programs of Study

Upper Iowa University has a long history of offering high-quality degree programs through distance learning.

In the External Degree program, associate and bachelor's degree programs are available in a wide range of academic areas, including accounting, business administration, criminal justice, emergency and disaster management, finance, health-services administration, human resources management, human services, interdisciplinary studies, management, marketing, psychology, public administration (general, law enforcement, or fire science), social science, and technology and information management.

Upper Iowa's Online program offers a Bachelor of Science degree with fifteen majors to choose from: accounting, business administration, criminal justice, emergency and disaster management, finance, health-services administration, human resources management, human services, interdisciplinary studies, management, marketing, psychology, public administration (general, law enforcement, or fire science), and technology and information management.

The M.B.A. offers six areas of emphasis: accounting, corporate finance management, global business, human resources management, organizational development, and quality management.

The M.P.A. offers four areas of emphasis: health and human services, homeland security, justice administration, and public personnel management. The course work focuses on the theories and skills that are the foundation for tomorrow's organizations, including organizational design, total quality management, self-managed teams, employee empowerment, change management, facilitation skills, high-performance work systems, and more.

Special Programs

Each summer, the External Degree program sponsors the Institute for Experiential Learning (IEXL) for undergraduate students. During an intensive weeklong session held on the Fayette campus, students have the opportunity to earn 3 semester hours of undergraduate credit while visiting the residential campus and networking with other learners from around the world.

Student Services

External Degree and Online students are provided with one-on-one academic advising via U.S. mail, e-mail, telephone, fax communication, and through use of a special software/courseware package (for Online program students). In addition to local university libraries, undergraduate and graduate students and faculty members have access to the Henderson Wilder Library holdings through Upper Iowa University's Web site.

Credit Options

Full credit is given to students for college-level courses completed at regionally accredited colleges and universities. Students can transfer a maximum of 45 semester hours for an associate degree, 90 semester hours for a bachelor's degree, and 12 semester hours for a master's degree. Other sources of credit include the American Council on Education (ACE), the College-Level Examination Program (CLEP), Defense Activity for Nontraditional Education support (DANTES) subject exams, and experiential learning.

Faculty

Upper Iowa University's distance learning program has more than 100 adjunct faculty members, many of whom have doctoral or terminal degrees. Faculty members are experienced in the areas in which they teach.

Admission

Admission criteria for undergraduate degrees include graduation from an accredited public or private high school or completion of the GED test or its equivalent. For the graduate program, prospective students must hold an undergraduate degree from a regionally accredited college or university. More information regarding grade point requirements, TOEFL scores for international students, and transfer credit is available upon request or on the UIU Web site.

Tuition and Fees

Associate- and baccalaureate-level tuition for courses taken through External Degree (independent study/correspondence) or at off-campus learning centers (classroom) for 2005–06 was $651 per 3-semester-credit course. Undergraduate and graduate online (Internet-based) courses were $807 and $999, respectively, per 3-semester-credit course.

Financial Aid

Financial aid in the form of Federal Stafford Student Loans, Federal Pell Grants, Iowa Tuition Grants (Iowa residents only), Veterans Assistance, and Military Tuition Assistance is available. Recently, a total of $273,420 in financial aid was disbursed to 21 percent of Upper Iowa University's distance learning students.

Applying

Students may enroll in UIU distance learning programs at any time. In the External Degree program, students may start courses at any time. In the Online program, eight-week terms begin six times a year. Students should send official transcripts (including CLEP, DANTES, or DD-214), GRE/GMAT score reports (if required), and a completed Application for Admission form (available online or by contacting the school via telephone or e-mail) directly to Upper Iowa University.

CONTACT

Extended University
Upper Iowa University
605 Washington Street
P.O. Box 1857
Fayette, Iowa 52142-1857
Phone: 877-366-0581 (toll-free)
Fax: 563-425-5771
E-mail: moreinfo@uiu.edu
Web site: http://www.uiu.edu

UTAH STATE UNIVERSITY

Independent and Distance Education

Logan, Utah

Utah State University (USU) was founded in 1888 as part of the public educational system of Utah and operates under the constitution and laws of the state. It belongs to the family of institutions known as land-grant universities, which had their origin in 1862. USU is governed by the State Board of Regents and accredited by Northwest Association of Accredited Schools.

USU integrates teaching, research, extension, and service to meet its unique role as Utah's land-grant university.

Distance Learning Program

USU Extension Services is an integral part of USU's outreach mission. Extension's Independent and Distance Education division provides educational opportunities for time- and place-bound students who are not able to come to the campus to attend classes.

Independent and Distance Education offers several bachelor's and master's degree programs via interactive broadcast and a master's degree over the Internet. Many other interactive broadcast, Internet-based, and independent-study CD-ROM courses are offered.

USU is one of the leading institutions in the United States for its off-campus programs.

Delivery Media

Independent and Distance Education is made up of three program delivery units: interactive broadcast (satellite, video teleconferencing), online, and independent study.

Interactive broadcast degree programs are offered at USU education centers and are only available to Utah students. Online courses are designed for access any time of the day or night. Online students submit assignments electronically and interact with their instructors and classmates via e-mail and online discussions.

Students who register for independent study courses receive a CD-ROM or printed course outline at registration. Independent study students mail in assignments, take proctored examinations, and may contact their instructors by phone or e-mail.

Programs of Study

Independent and Distance Education offers several interactive broadcast degrees to students in Utah. An online Master of Science degree in English with a specialization in technical writing is available to students anywhere.

The graduate technical writing degree program is designed mainly to help practicing professional writers advance their careers, and most students in the program are employed full-time as writers in nonacademic workplaces. Some students in the program may be considering careers that involve both practicing and teaching technical writing, but the program is oriented toward educating the practicing specialist and does not focus on pedagogical issues.

Student Services

Student services available to distance learners include access to the University bookstore, Library Support System for Distance Learners, and the Academic Resource Center. For more information on student services available to distance learners, prospective students should visit the Web site at http://extension.usu.edu.

Credit Options

Credit earned through USU Independent and Distance Education is measured in semester units and is transferable to most colleges and universities in the U.S. Students who plan to transfer credit should make arrangements with the transfer institution prior to registration.

Faculty

The majority of Independent and Distance Education instructors are USU faculty members; many are leading researchers in their field. Independent and Distance Education faculty members recognize that the needs of individuals are of major importance; programs have been established to give students optimal individual attention.

Admission

Non-degree-seeking students do not need to be admitted to enroll in Independent and Distance Education courses. Degree-seeking students must apply for admission. Admission requirements are program specific and may be obtained by contacting the Admissions Office at 435-797-1079.

Prospective students may complete an application for admission online at http://www.usu.edu/admissions.

Tuition and Fees

For tuition and fee information, prospective students should visit the Web site at http://extension.usu.edu.

Financial Aid

Financial aid is available for distance education students. Utah State University participates in the following financial aid programs: Federal Pell Grants, Federal Supplemental Educational Opportunity Grants (FSEOG), LEAAP Grants, Federal Perkins Loans, Federal Work-Study, Federal Stafford Loans, Plus Loans, scholarships, and emergency loans. For more information, prospective students should contact the financial aid office at 435-797-0173 or visit the Web site at http://www.usu.edu/finaid/.

Applying

Students working toward any of the degree programs offered through Independent and Distance Education must be admitted to the University. Prospective students may complete an application for admission online at http://www.usu.edu/admissions or request a printed application by contacting the Admissions Office at 435-797-1129 or toll-free at 800-488-8108.

CONTACT

Independent and Distance Education
5055 Old Main Hill
Utah State University
Logan, Utah 84322-3080
Phone: 800-233-2137 (toll-free)
Fax: 435-797-1399
E-mail: enroll@ext.usu.edu
Web site: http://extension.usu.edu

VIRGINIA POLYTECHNIC INSTITUTE AND STATE UNIVERSITY

Institute for Distance and Distributed Learning

Blacksburg, Virginia

Virginia Polytechnic Institute and State University is a public land-grant university serving the Commonwealth of Virginia, the nation, and the world community. The discovery and dissemination of new knowledge are central to its mission. Through its focus on teaching and learning, research, and outreach, the University creates, conveys, and applies knowledge to expand personal growth and opportunity, advance social and community development, foster economic competitiveness, and improve the quality of life. Founded in 1872, Virginia Tech typically ranks in the nation's top fifty research universities, offering 170 degree programs to Virginia's largest full-time student population (more than 25,000 total enrollments).

The University's growing reputation for excellence includes national recognition as a leader in distance and distributed learning. Virginia Tech is helping to meet the changing needs of undergraduate and graduate students with online and distance-delivered master's degree programs, certificates, and licensures as well as noncredit offerings for personal and professional growth. Innovative use of technology is transforming the educational process, while making it more accessible and learner-centered. Virginia Tech is fully accredited by the Commission on Colleges of the Southern Association of Colleges and Schools.

Distance Learning Program

As part of the Office of the University Provost and Vice President for Academic Affairs, Virginia Tech's Institute for Distance and Distributed Learning (IDDL) provides leadership, coordination, management, and support to the distance and distributed learning (eLearning) activities of Virginia Tech. Through these activities, Virginia Tech extends its campus to communities throughout the world and provides an open campus environment that allows individuals to engage in learning at anytime and from anywhere. In addition, Virginia Tech shares the practical application of the University's knowledge and expertise in support of economic development, increases the University's access to the world and the world's access to the University, and researches new teaching and learning environments through the application of technology.

More than 12,000 annual enrollments are accounted for in over 500 courses and twenty-one master's degree programs, certificates, and licensures. Virginia Tech actively participates in the Electronic Campus of Virginia and collaboratively delivers courses and degree programs at a distance with other Virginia colleges and universities through the Commonwealth Graduate Engineering Program and Virginia Consortium of Engineering and Science Universities. Virginia Tech also participates in the Southern Region Electronic Campus and the Natural Resources Distance Learning Consortium.

Programs of Study

Virginia Tech offers certificate programs in business information systems, communications, computer engineering, decision support systems, natural resources, networking, and software development.

Licensure is available in career and technical education.

Programs leading to a Master of Arts degree are available in instructional technology and political science.

The Master of Science can be earned in career and technical education, civil and environmental engineering, civil infrastructure engineering, computer engineering, electrical and computer engineering, engineering administration, health promotion, ocean engineering, and systems engineering.

The Master of Business Administration and the Master of Information Technology are also awarded.

A wide variety of credit and noncredit courses is also offered through distance learning in the areas of accounting, architecture, art, biology, black studies, building construction, business, communications, computer science, economics, education, engineering, English, entomology, finance, geography, history, hotel management, horticulture, information science, landscape architecture, management, marketing, math, music, philosophy, physics, psychology, science and technology, sociology, Spanish, statistics, women's studies, and more.

Student Services

Recognizing the diverse needs of distance learners, Virginia Tech employs a holistic approach to distance learning in which the student's total educational experience is considered. This approach provides learners with accessible learning resources, support services, and interactive technologies in addition to renowned faculty members who create and teach the wide array of distance and distributed learning courses. Through cross-University collaboration, Virginia Tech works to create accessible online support services that include academic program information, the admissions process, preadmissions advising, enrollment services, an orientation to distance learning, a distance learning compatibility self-test, course delivery format descriptions, technical requirements, degree requirements, program of study descriptions, library resources and services, bookstore services, academic advising, tutoring, writing center, study skills, an online wellness resource center, services for students with disabilities, career services, technical help, and FAQ.

Credit Options

Distance learners can transfer credits earned at other accredited postsecondary institutions to Virginia Tech following the established University policies. Students admitted to the University who have been certified by the Virginia Community College System or Richard Bland College as completing the transfer module are deemed to have completed the University core curriculum components and receive 35 total credits for the module.

Faculty

The faculty is the foundation of Virginia Tech's distance learning programs and assures its academic excellence. The same faculty members, including some of the most highly honored faculty at the University, who teach traditional classroom-based campus courses also teach distance learning courses. Currently, 85 percent of Virginia Tech's academic teaching departments are involved in teaching distance learning courses.

Admission

To become undergraduate or graduate degree candidates at Virginia Tech, students must apply formally for admission. Students' records at Virginia Tech and all other colleges and universities attended are reviewed within the context of current admission policies. Virginia Tech allows qualified students at other Virginia universities and colleges to enroll in its courses as non-degree-seeking or Commonwealth Campus students. For more information on undergraduate admission, students should visit the IDDL Web site http://www.iddl.vt.edu; those interested in graduate programs should visit http://www.grads.vt.edu.

Tuition and Fees

For the latest information, students should visit http://www.bursar.vt.edu.

Financial Aid

Virginia Tech is a direct lending institution and awards financial aid from federally funded and state-funded programs as well as privately funded sources. Financial aid sources include the Federal Direct Stafford Loan, Federal Perkins Loan, Federal Direct PLUS Loan, Federal Pell Grant, Federal Work-Study, Virginia Guaranteed Assistance program, Commonwealth Award, and the College Scholarship Assistance Program.

Applying

Students applying for undergraduate admission can access current information at http://www.admiss.vt.edu. Students applying for graduate admission can access current information at http://www.grads.vt.edu. Students can register for Internet-based courses at http://www.vto.vt.edu.

There is a nonrefundable fee ($40 undergraduate, $45 graduate) for non-Virginia Tech, non-program-bound undergraduate students.

CONTACT

Angie Starr
eLearner Support Specialist
Institute for Distance and Distributed Learning
Virginia Tech (0445)
Blacksburg, Virginia 24061
Phone: 540-231-1264
Fax: 540-231-2079
E-mail: vto@vt.edu
Web site: http://www.iddl.vt.edu
http://www.vto.vt.edu (online catalog)

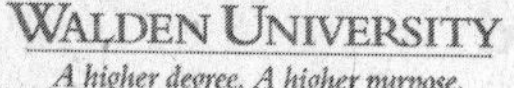

WALDEN UNIVERSITY

Graduate Distance Education

Minneapolis, Minnesota

Walden University's online doctoral, master's, and bachelor's programs are designed to help students achieve their goals—personal enrichment and professional advancement—and make a difference in the lives of others. Walden's degree programs combine high-quality curricula, expert faculty members, and innovative distance-delivery models to offer highly applied, rigorous programs that allow adult learners to pursue advanced degrees while maintaining their personal and professional commitments.

Founded in 1970, Walden University offers master's and doctoral degrees in education, health and human services, management, psychology, and public policy and administration as well as master's programs in engineering and IT and bachelor's completion programs in business. Walden University is accredited by the Higher Learning Commission and is a member of the North Central Association (http://www.ncahlc.org/; telephone: 312-263-0456).

Distance Learning Program

With a global network of peers and faculty mentors, Walden's students collaborate with a diverse range of professionals to gain the critical insights and skills that are highly relevant to the work they do every day.

Delivery Media

Students and faculty members exchange ideas and collaborate with their colleagues through e-mail, online courses, study teams, and, in some programs, face-to-face residency sessions. Individual mentoring, online courses, and progress based on demonstrations of knowledge are among the components of Walden's delivery system. Students who enroll in a Walden program should be comfortable using a personal computer, a word processor, and e-mail.

Programs of Study

The Ph.D. in applied management and decision sciences program offers an interdisciplinary approach that prepares students to advance the knowledge and practice of management and leadership. Students can complete a general program or specialize in accounting, engineering management, finance, information systems management, knowledge management, leadership and organizational change, learning management, or operations research.

The Ph.D. in education program produces leaders who can address the nation's most pressing educational challenges. Options include general and self-designed programs and specializations in adult education leadership, community college leadership, early childhood education, educational technology, higher education, K–12 educational leadership, and special education.

The Ph.D. in health services program prepares students to serve at the forefront of the design and delivery of cutting-edge private and public health services. General study is available, as are a self-designed specialization and specializations in community health, health and human behavior, health management and policy, and health promotion and education.

The Ph.D. in human services program prepares students to serve at the forefront of the design and delivery of cutting-edge public services and to excel within a diverse service-delivery system. Students may design a specialization or specialize in clinical social work, counseling, criminal justice, family studies and intervention strategies, human services administration, or social policy analysis and planning.

The Ph.D. in public health program focuses on seeking solutions to significant public health problems and applying and integrating new knowledge into public health research and practice settings. Specializations are available in community health promotion and education and in epidemiology.

The Ph.D. in psychology program prepares psychology professionals to fully excel in today's health-care settings, private practices, and global industries. Specializations include clinical psychology, counseling psychology, general psychology (with tracks in educational psychology and in research and evaluation), health psychology, organizational psychology, and school psychology. The clinical, counseling, and school psychology specializations are designed to meet the academic licensure requirements of most state psychology boards.

The Ph.D. in public policy and administration program prepares students to meet the challenges of governance and effective service delivery. Specializations include criminal justice, health services, homeland security policy and coordination, international nongovernmental organizations, knowledge management, nonprofit management and leadership, public management and leadership, public policy, and public safety management.

The Doctor of Education (Ed.D.) program has specializations in teacher leadership and in administrator leadership for teaching and learning. Both are designed for K–12 educators who want to continue their practice while assuming leadership roles in their schools and communities.

The Master of Business Administration (M.B.A.) offers students new insights and comprehensive cross-discipline skills to meet the complex issues and challenges of the global economy. Students may choose a general program or select from several specializations: e-business, finance, global business, health services, human resource management, knowledge/learning management, management of technology, marketing, nonprofit management, and risk management/insurance.

The Master of Public Administration (M.P.A.) program prepares public/nonprofit professionals to excel in today's complex, politicized, inter-sector environment. Students may choose a general program or specialize in a variety of areas, including criminal justice, health services, homeland security policy and coordination, international nongovernmental organizations, knowledge management, nonprofit management and leadership, public management and leadership, public policy, and public safety management.

The course-based online M.S. in psychology program includes a specialization in industrial/organizational psychology.

Through a mix of research, fieldwork, and courses taught by national experts, the M.S. in mental health counseling program prepares students to address and treat behavioral disorders knowledgeably, ethically, and with respect for diversity.

The M.S. in education program develops scholar-practitioners among educators serving students in K–12 classrooms. The program offers specializations in curriculum, instruction, and assessment (grades K–12); educational leadership; elementary reading and literacy (grades K–6); elementary reading and mathematics (grades K–6); integrating technology in the classroom (grades 3–12); literacy and learning in the content areas (grades 6–12); mathematics (grades K–5); mathematics (grades 6–8); middle level education (grades 5–8); and science (grades K–8).

The M.S. in public health program prepares students to lead communities in the development of population-based assessment techniques and intervention strategies to improve health-care access and service delivery.

The Master of Public Health (M.P.H.) program is practice-oriented, designed to prepare students who have little or no experience in community health to work with communities to map their assets and needs. Graduates are able to develop and evaluate culturally relevant interventions to promote public health.

The M.S. in nursing program is based on the American Association of Colleges of Nursing (AACN) Essentials of Master's Education and American Nurses Association's (ANA) Scope and Standards for Nurse Administrators. It offers specializations in education and in leadership and management, and is accredited by the Commission on Collegiate Nursing Education (CCNE).

The High-Tech M.B.A. is designed to propel technology professionals into positions of leadership at today's highly competitive technology-based businesses. Specializations include business process management, emerging technologies, engineering innovation, global product management, information strategies, and technical project management.

The M.S. in computer engineering program prepares students to work in the dynamic and rapidly expanding field of digital technology. Specializations include computer systems, digital systems, networks, and secure computing.

In the M.S. in computer science program, students develop an advanced body of knowledge in the design, analysis, and implementation of algorithmic processes that transform raw data into valuable information. Specializations are offered in algorithms and complexity, artificial intelligence, computer systems, data management, networks, secure computing, simulation and game design, and Web applications.

The M.S. in electrical engineering program provides students with a technical background for analysis, design, development, operation, or research on electrical or electronic systems. Specializations include communications, integrated circuits, and microelectronics and semiconductors. Several concentrations are available for each specialization.

The M.S. in engineering management program, designed with industry input, provides a broad technical management educational experience.

In the M.S. in software engineering program, students become experts in the latest software development theories and the fundamental engineering principles that support progressive software design. Specializations include secure computing, simulation and game design, software development, software management, software systems engineering, and software testing and reliability.

The M.S. in systems engineering program provides the necessary processes and tools to define and validate system requirements, develop effective designs, and ensure those designs are safe and meet customer requirements. Specializations include business process engineering, resource optimization engineering, systems engineering, systems engineering management, and systems quality and reliability.

Student Services

Student services include academic advising, course management, financial aid, technical assistance, orientation programming, disability services, tutoring, and a writing center. Walden University's partnership with the Indiana University Bloomington library provides reference, search, catalog, and distribution services.

Credit Options

Transfer of credit from other institutions is permitted in most programs. Applicants can request an informal transfer of credit evaluation prior to admission. Official notification of credits accepted for transfer may be issued at admission or once required documents are received.

Faculty

Walden attracts esteemed scholars, researchers, and distinguished professionals as faculty members. The distance-delivery model allows students to fully benefit from the diverse talents and experiences of the finest faculty members, regardless of where they reside. Some are deans or faculty members at major universities, while others are corporate executives, educators, clinicians, or military leaders. All faculty members are credible subject experts who demonstrate vast experience and a profound commitment to adult learners.

Admission

Walden University has a long-standing commitment to providing educational opportunities to a diverse population of learners. Walden's admission process focuses on selecting learners who can benefit from a distributed educational or online learning approach and who, with the benefit of a Walden education, are most likely to contribute to their current or future academic or professional fields and communities. Admission requirements vary by program and major. To learn more, students should contact a Walden enrollment adviser.

Tuition and Fees

Tuition and fees vary by program.

Financial Aid

Walden offers students a variety of options to assist in funding their educational expenses. Most Walden students receive some form of financial assistance. Available options include federal programs, veterans' education benefits, and institutional fellowships. Tuition reductions are also available for group/spousal enrollment. Walden can also assist students in securing private scholarships, employer tuition benefits, and loans from private lenders.

Applying

Submission of a completed and signed application, a $50 application fee, and a personal/professional statement of purpose is required. Applicants must also send a resume, official transcripts from the institution that conferred the bachelor's or master's degree, and, in health and human services, two required recommendation forms. Students can also apply online.

CONTACT

Walden University
155 Fifth Avenue South
Minneapolis, Minnesota 55401
Phone: 866-492-5336 (toll-free)
E-mail: info@waldenu.edu
Web site: http://www.waldenu.edu

WASHINGTON STATE UNIVERSITY

WSU Center for Distance and Professional Education

Pullman, Washington

Washington State University (WSU), the state's land-grant institution, is dedicated to the preparation of students for productive lives and professional careers, to basic and applied research, and to the dissemination of knowledge. Founded in 1890, the University is a statewide institution with a main campus in Pullman, three branch campuses, ten community learning centers, and numerous Cooperative Extension and research facilities throughout the state. WSU is accredited by the Northwest Association of Schools and Colleges. In addition, the University is an acknowledged leader in developing and delivering distance education programs. Since 1992, WSU's Office of Distance Degree Programs (DDP) has served students in Washington and across the nation and continues to expand online credit and noncredit options as the Center for Distance and Professional Education (CDPE). The University's undergraduate core curriculum, including world civilization courses and expanded writing requirements, is nationally recognized. Money *magazine has called WSU a "public ivy" and rated the honors program as one of the nation's best.*

Distance Learning Program

WSU's Center for Distance and Professional Education offers degree-completion programs leading to a Bachelor of Arts (B. A.) in business administration (with majors in management information systems (MIS) or management and operations), criminal justice, human development, humanities, or social sciences; a Bachelor of Science (B.S) in Nursing (B.S.N.); and a Master of Science (M.S.) in agriculture. Formal minors in aging, business administration, criminal justice, English, history, human development, management information systems, psychology, and sociology are also available. The undergraduate degree programs are designed primarily for students who have completed the equivalent of the first two years of college. They are delivered directly to students' homes through a variety of distance learning technologies, primarily the Internet. They are the same degrees offered on three WSU campuses; requirements are the same, but students can complete their degrees without attending WSU in person.

CDPE also offers two online credit certificate programs, Graduate Online Instructional Design Certificate and Profession Writing Certificate, as well as two online noncredit certificate programs, Volunteer Management Certificate Program (VMCP) and Telework Certificate Program.

Delivery Media

Courses are delivered primarily by the Internet, and most have Web and e-mail requirements. Courses also incorporate media (DVDs, CDs, videotapes), lab kits, library resources, and print materials.

Programs of Study

WSU's B.A. in social sciences is a liberal arts degree that offers students multiple options and emphases in the social sciences and provides a broad background applicable to a variety of careers. It emphasizes an interdisciplinary approach with possible major and/or minor concentrations in anthropology, criminal justice, history, human development, political science, psychology, sociology, and women's studies.

WSU's B.A. in criminal justice prepares students for positions in the criminal justice system, other government agencies, and the private sector. A completion degree, the distance B.A. in criminal justice offers a policy-focused curriculum, providing students with a broad exposure in the social sciences that is preferred by government and private agencies.

A B.A. in human development is also available with an asynchronous distance format from WSU. The human development degree is especially effective for individuals who work in child- or elder-care programs or in direct service roles with a variety of special-needs clients. The degree program includes an internship component supervised by a WSU faculty member.

The B.A. in business administration with a major in management and operations is designed to provide a broad foundation for employment in the world of business, either at a large corporation or in the student's own business. A set curriculum, fully accredited by AACSB International–The Association to Advance Collegiate Schools of Business, leads students through courses in finance, management, information systems, marketing, international business, business law, and economics.

Within the B.A. in business administration, WSU now offers an MIS major. This major, available entirely in an online, asynchronous format, is designed to enable graduates to enter the working world as systems analysts, systems project managers, or Web masters. The set curriculum, also fully accredited by AACSB International–The Association to Advance Collegiate Schools of Business, takes students through computer hardware issues, software applications, and networking protocol. Graduates are employed with the nation's top corporations and consulting firms as well as in numerous international settings.

The B.A. in humanities is a broad-based, interdisciplinary liberal arts degree program. It is configured in the same manner as the social sciences program. There is not a set list of required courses for students to take. Working with an academic adviser, each student develops a program of study that best meets his or her educational goals. The focus of the program is on developing skills in communication, writing, problem solving, and critical thinking, with a focus on the humanities.

A B.S. in Nursing degree program is available for registered nurses. The Intercollegiate College of Nursing/WSU College of Nursing offer nine theory courses using Web-based software and two clinical courses, which, in some circumstances, may be taken close to home. Out-of-state students may be required to complete the two clinical courses in Washington, which are scheduled based on negotiations between the student and faculty. RNs work with B.S.N.-prepared preceptors; nursing faculty members supervise the course. RN students must meet specific criteria prior to application to this program.

Emphasis of the M.S. in agriculture program is on the agricultural professional, practitioner, and educator. The program is designed for students, at a distance and on campus, who wish to prepare for or further their careers in agriculture without having to relocate or interfere with their current employment. A maximum number of electives are permitted to enable the student to concentrate in one or two fields, or otherwise tailor the curriculum to fit their particular needs. Students may choose between a thesis or nonthesis program.

The online Graduate Certificate in Instructional Design is designed for working professionals, educators, Web designers, and corporate trainers to strengthen their traditional face-to-face education and training skills and improve their ability to work in alternative learning environments. The 12-credit graduate program incorporates constructivist learning design, educational technology and media, and leadership in courses conducted in an online environment.

WSU's Professional Writing Certificate allows students to develop a base of skills and knowledge of effective communication (including editorial and technical skills and the broader skills of analysis and synthesis) useful in the professional world. The certificate requires completion of 15 credits (made up of five courses taken in a specific order), with a grade of B (3.0) or better in each course.

To earn a bachelor's degree, WSU generally requires the completion of at least 120 semester credits, 40 at the upper-division level. At least 30 of the 120 credits must be taken through WSU. The 120 credits must include courses that meet WSU general education requirements. Graduate credit programs require admission to the WSU Graduate School.

Nearly 200 courses are available to the students. Courses are also available from the National Universities Degree Consortium (NUDC), a group of eight land-grant and state universities formed to address the needs of adult and part-time learners.

The online Volunteer Management Certificate Program (http://capps.wsu.edu/vmcp/) and the online noncredit Telework Certificate Program (http://capps.wsu.edu/telework/) provide noncredit professional education options. These programs have requirements different from the credit and degree programs; students should visit their Web pages for details.

Student Services

Academic advising is available to all prospective and currently enrolled degree-seeking students through toll-free telephone or e-mail. The WSU Office of Admissions prepares an official evaluation of a student's transcript when he or she is admitted to the University. A DDP adviser assists DDP students in developing a study plan based on the program options and University requirements. A student services coordinator is available to help students with logistical details.

Students register online or with support from DDP student services. DVDs, CDs, videotapes, lab kits, and other supplementary materials are available through the DDP office. Students may order textbooks and course guides from the WSU Students Book Corporation online or via the toll-free telephone number.

All DDP students have access to the WSU libraries. The DDP librarian is available via toll-free telephone to assist students with database searches, checking out materials, and copying.

The ASWSU-DDP Career Counselor is available to WSU DDP students to discuss career-related concerns. These may range from developing a school-to-career identity to providing assistance and resources to find satisfying work or a graduate school program.

Credit Options

Undergraduate students may transfer to WSU a maximum of 60 semester credits of lower-division credit and up to 30 credits from other four-year institutions. The exact number of transfer credits accepted by WSU may vary depending upon an individual's choice of degree.

WSU recognizes there are alternative ways students may gain knowledge and credit. The University has developed a method of accepting credit by examination, including Advanced Placement (AP), College-Level Examination Program (CLEP), DANTES, and American Council on Education (ACE). Interested students should check with their advisers for details.

Faculty

There are 1,111 full-time and 218 part-time instructional faculty members in the Washington State University system. Eighty-one percent have terminal academic degrees.

Admission

Admission to the Center for Distance and Professional Education Distance degree programs requires at least 27 semester or 40 quarter credits of transferable college course work from an accredited community or four-year college, with at least a 2.0 cumulative GPA.

Tuition and Fees

In 2005–06, undergraduate tuition (semester-based) was $275 per semester credit for Washington residents and $402 per semester credit for nonresidents. DVD, CD, and videotape rental charges vary by course. Correspondence (flexible enrollment) course tuition is $220 per credit. Payment options for full-time students are available as well.

Financial Aid

A financial aid adviser is available to all DDP students. WSU students receive aid from all federal programs, such as the Federal Pell Grants and Federal Supplemental Educational Opportunity Grants (FSEOG) and the Federal Perkins, Federal Stafford Student, and Federal PLUS Loans. Washington residents are eligible for institutional and state need grants. In 2004–05, WSU awarded approximately $190 million in financial aid. Approximately 61 percent of all WSU students receive financial aid.

Applying

WSU degree-seeking students must be admitted to the University. Admission requires that a student submit an admissions form, have official copies of transcript(s) sent directly from the postsecondary institution(s) attended, and pay the $50 undergraduate application fee. Graduate requirements differ, so students should visit http://www.gradsch.wsu.edu/howtoapply.htm. for information on WSU Graduate School admission requirements.

CONTACT

Student Support Services
Center for Distance and Professional Education
Van Doren 104
Washington State University
P.O. Box 645220
Pullman, Washington 99164-5220
Phone: 509-335-3557
800-222-4978 (toll-free)
Fax: 509-335-4850
E-mail: distance@wsu.edu
Web site:
http://www.distance.wsu.edu

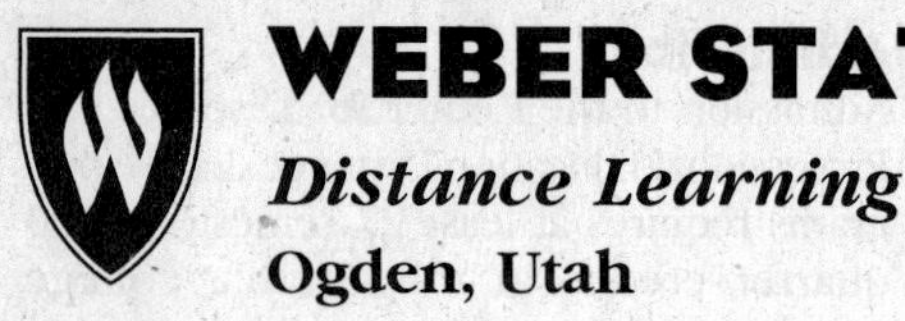

WEBER STATE UNIVERSITY

Distance Learning

Ogden, Utah

Weber State University (WSU) provides lifelong opportunities for diverse learners on and off campus. It offers degrees through seven colleges and forty departments via distance learning options, including online and independent study courses. Students may earn their Associate of Science in general studies or receive specialized training in health professions, criminal justice, and manufacturing. WSU's academic programs prepare students for immediate employment or further study and equip them with liberal education concepts and skills to support their lifelong learning.

WSU serves as Utah's premier public undergraduate university. The institution was founded in 1889, became a state junior college in 1933, and added upper-division courses and began bachelor's degree programs in 1959. On January 1, 1991, Weber State further expanded its offerings and was granted university status.

Weber State University is accredited by the Northwest Association of Schools and Colleges. In addition, professional agencies such as the Commission on Accreditation for Allied Health Education Programs and the Association of University Programs in Health Administration accredit specific disciplines.

Distance Learning Program

The WSU Distance Learning Program serves students who cannot attend college classes in person. During the 2005–06 academic year, more than 20,000 students enrolled in print- and Internet-based courses. Students use distance learning to earn general education credits, as well as degrees and professional credentials in manufacturing, criminal justice, and health science areas.

Delivery Media

Students follow study guides, read textbooks, view videotapes, hear cassettes, and/or participate in online courses. They interact with other students, instructors, and advisers by using mail, telephone, e-mail, and online discussion groups. Exams are delivered online or through the mail and are administered by approved proctors. Access to a videocassette/DVD player, audiocassette player, word processor, or a computer with browser software and an Internet service provider may be required.

Programs of Study

The WSU Distance Learning degree program evolved from a commitment to providing education for health-care professionals and other working adults regardless of location. Combining independent study with Internet courses, a bachelor's degree requires 120 semester hours (40 upper-division, 30 through WSU) with a minimum GPA of at least a 2.0 (or C).

Bachelor's degrees are available in clinical laboratory science, diagnostic medical sonography (medical-vascular), health information management, health promotion, health services administration, nuclear medicine, radiation therapy, and radiologic science (emphases in advanced radiography, cardiovascular-interventional technology, computed tomography, magnetic resonance imaging, mammography, and quality management).

Associate of Science degrees are available in health information technology and respiratory therapy. An Associate of Applied Science degree is also available in clinical laboratory science.

The associate degree in general studies serves the needs of students who want to individualize the first two years of their academic programs, students who want to obtain a broad liberal education, and students who want to lay broad foundations for continued higher education.

The Weber State University Distance Learning Associate of Science degree program in criminal justice and the professional certificate programs in production and inventory management are designed for professionals whose work and travel schedules and remote locations make it difficult for them to participate in classroom course work.

Law enforcement and security professionals can register online with the Utah Electronic College (UEC) and take courses through Weber State University or one of its six collaborating institutions, completing their training on their home or work computers.

Weber State University works in partnership with the 70,000-member APICS (The Association for Operations Management) to offer its certification program through WSU Online for people who work in production and resource management.

WSU certificate programs include health information technology, health-care coding and classification, and radiologic sciences. Radiologic sciences classes can be used toward continuing education units (CEU).

Special Programs

WSU Online, the award-winning extension of the University on the Internet, allows students to take online courses, use online support services, and participate in online discussions and activities with faculty and staff members and other students. WSU Online makes it possible for students with busy schedules and/or long commutes to take advantage of the convenience of online courses with support services and interpersonal experiences that are essential to their success. For current course listings and additional information, students can visit the WSU Web site at http://wsuonline.weber.edu.

Courses from a wide range of academic disciplines are available through Weber State University's independent study program, allowing students to complete their course work at their convenience. Each year, more than 2,000 students enroll in these Internet or print-based courses and take advantage of this self-paced, individualized mode of study.

Student Services

WSU recognizes that most of its students have work, family, and other responsibilities that limit their participation in traditional classroom college courses; therefore, convenience is a major factor in the design of the Distance Learning Program.

Students receive guidance from distance learning staff and faculty members. Degree-seeking students are assigned academic advisers who review transcripts and past learning experiences. This information is used to design individualized programs of study.

Students may access Stewart Library's catalog, interlibrary loan, reference help, document delivery, and other services electronically at http://library.weber.edu. Textbooks can be purchased directly from the WSU bookstore, by telephone (800-848-7770 Ext. 6352), or online (http://bookstore.weber.edu) for a small handling charge.

Credit Options

WSU may grant credit for active military, National Guard, or reserve experience; 38 or more credits to registered radiographers; a maximum of 45 credits to diploma nursing school graduates; and varying credits to registered respiratory therapy technicians and graduates of accredited therapy/specialty programs. Official transcripts should be sent directly from universities and colleges attended. WSU also recognizes College-Level Examination Program (CLEP) credits.

Faculty

WSU Distance Learning currently employs 200 full-time university faculty members and 50 adjunct faculty members. Nearly all faculty members hold terminal degrees in their respective fields.

Admission

Degree-seeking Distance Learning applicants must meet WSU admission requirements. The programs in health professions require separate applications and information specific to their academic areas. Students not seeking to complete a degree at WSU may be eligible for simplified, nonmatriculated admission.

Tuition and Fees

Distance Learning tuition averages $147 per semester hour. Additional materials may include course study guides ($3-$40) and audiotape, videotape, or DVD deposits of $60 to $100, with a $40 refund upon their return.

Tuition fees for online courses are $177 per semester hour for non-Utah residents. Utah residents pay regular on-campus tuition and fees. All fees are subject to change. Students can consult the current catalog or visit the Web site at http://www.weber.edu/distancelearning/ for more information.

Financial Aid

Eligible students may apply for federal financial aid such as Pell Grants, Supplemental Educational Opportunity Grants (SEOG), Perkins Loans, and Stafford Student Loans. Students can contact the office of financial aid toll-free at 800-848-7770 Ext. 7569.

Veterans may also be considered for VA educational benefits (office of Veteran Affairs telephone: 800-848-7770 Ext. 6039, toll-free). Health professions degree programs are approved by DANTES.

Applying

Students should apply online at http://weber.edu/admissions/ and send an individual program application (if required); official transcripts from previous colleges; and an application fee of $30 (may be paid online by credit card) to the contact address. Distance Learning students need not attend an orientation.

CONTACT

Office of Distance Learning
Weber State University
4005 University Circle
Ogden, Utah 84408-4005
Phone: 801-626-6600
800-848-7770 Ext. 6600 (toll-free)
Fax: 801-626-8035
E-mail: dist-learn@weber.edu
Web site: http://wsuonline.weber.edu
http://weber.edu/distancelearning

WESTWOOD COLLEGE–DENVER NORTH ONLINE PROGRAMS

Westwood College Online

Denver, Colorado

Westwood College has been providing accelerated career-focused education since 1953. In addition to online degree programs, Westwood College currently operates fourteen Technology campuses and three Aviation Technology campuses with locations in California, Colorado, Georgia, Illinois, and Texas.

Westwood's accelerated programs enable a student to complete an associate degree in as little as seventeen months, or a bachelor's degree in thirty-four months, allowing that student to enter or advance in a chosen field in less time.

Online degree programs are offered through Westwood College–Denver North Online Programs and are accredited by the Accrediting Commission of Career Schools and Colleges of Technology (ACCSCT).

Distance Learning Program

Westwood College started offering online degree programs in May 2002. Westwood College Online is an excellent option for students who are outside of the metro areas served by Westwood campuses or students whose work or family obligations do not allow time to attend scheduled classes on campus.

Delivery Media

The online courses are instructor-led, not self-paced. Assignments are due weekly. The online courses may include the use of threaded discussions simulating in-class discussion and interaction; group projects; student-to-student, student-to-instructor, and instructor-to-student e-mails, chat rooms, short online audio and video lectures, and graphical demonstrations of concepts.

Programs of Study

Currently, Westwood offers ten bachelor's degree programs and three associate degree programs though distance learning. Students should check the Web site for up-to-date listings.

The Bachelor of Science (B.S.) in animation (183 quarter credit hours) equips students with the skills necessary to enter the field of animation. This program covers topics such as the laws of human motion, physics, and psychology as applied to 2-D and 3-D characters, life drawing and rendering techniques, and the application of audio and video to an animation project.

The Bachelor of Science in Business Administration with a concentration in accounting (180 quarter credit hours) equips students with the business and financial skills necessary to advance in the field of accounting. In addition, the combination of management and general education courses in the program helps students apply skills in general management, critical thinking, logic, communication, and problem solving to workplace challenges. This program also includes critical courses that cover such topics as cost accounting, financial accounting, auditing, and financial reporting.

The Bachelor of Science in Business Administration with a concentration in marketing and sales (180 quarter credit hours) equips students with the business skills necessary to advance in the field of marketing and sales. In addition, the combination of management and general education courses in the program helps students apply skills in general management, critical thinking, logic, communication, and problem solving to workplace challenges. This program also includes critical marketing and sales courses that cover such topics as consumer behavior, marketing research, professional selling, and Internet marketing and sales.

The Bachelor of Science in computer network management program (180 quarter credit hours) is designed to provide students with the advanced networking skills required to design, install, configure, and maintain enterprise-wide networks.

The Bachelor of Science in criminal justice (183 quarter credit hours) equips students academically and professionally by developing a knowledge base, social awareness, and technological skills for an entry-level position in today's criminal justice environment.

The Bachelor of Science in e-business management program (181.5 quarter credit hours) is designed to integrate technology, business, and employability skills to prepare students for entry-level jobs in the burgeoning field of e-business.

The Bachelor of Science in visual communications program (183 quarter credit hours) is designed to prepare students with the design, marketing, and technical skills necessary to advance in the field of visual communications.

The Bachelor of Science in Web design and multimedia (183 quarter credit hours) equips students with Web design, e-commerce, scripting, and authoring skills necessary to advance in the field of Web design.

The Game Software Development Bachelor Program (193.5 quarter credit hours) is designed to provide students with the ability to apply core knowledge of software engineering to employment settings through a curriculum that emphasizes game and interactive software development. In addition, general education courses assist students in applying critical thinking, logic, communication, and problem-solving skills in managing challenges that occur in a game development environment.

The Information Systems Security Bachelor Program (180 quarter credit hours) is designed to provide students with the advanced security skills required to implement e-business security solutions and policies, identify security threats and develop countermeasures using firewall systems and attack recognition technologies, and manage the deployment of security solutions.

The Associate of Applied Science (A.A.S.) in computer network engineering program (108 quarter credit hours) is designed to provide students with the skills required to design, install, configure, and maintain enterprise-wide networks.

The Associate of Applied Science in graphic design and multimedia program (90 quarter credit hours) prepares students for entry-level jobs in the graphic design and multimedia industry. Students learn to create effective designs that communicate visually in both print and multimedia environments.

The Associate of Applied Science in software engineering program (91.5 quarter credit hours) provides students with the skills required to design and implement computer software.

Special Programs

Alumni retraining is a special program at Westwood. All Westwood alumni are entitled to tuition-free graduate retraining in the program they completed at Westwood. Graduates are able to audit classes to update their skills as curriculum changes in their field of study. Charges for books and student fees may apply.

Student Services

Westwood distance learning students receive online access to the same student services that are provided to on-campus students. With its academic advising, Westwood is dedicated to helping students remove obstacles to success. There are several programs that provide students with the opportunity to solve problems, share ideas, and set goals with members of the college staff. Westwood has a free tutoring program that provides online help. There is a full research library that is available online to students 24 hours a day, seven days a week. Distance learning students also have access to technical assistance 24 hours a day, 7 days a week.

The primary objective of the Career Development Services Office is to help students achieve their career goals. At Westwood, successful job-placement assistance begins long before graduation. In fact, Westwood's unique approach to career planning and job-placement assistance begins at registration and continues beyond graduation.

Credit Options

There are four ways to achieve advanced academic standing at Westwood College: with transfer credits from accredited colleges or universities, through articulation agreements with selected high schools and colleges, through Westwood College Proficiency Exams, and through Advanced Placement (AP) exams, College Level Examination Program (CLEP) exams, or nationally recognized certification exams.

Faculty

Westwood Online's faculty is composed of full-time and part-time instructors from Westwood's fourteen technology campuses, plus additional experts in the individual field of study.

Admission

Each applicant must demonstrate proficiency in basic college-level skills as evidenced by attaining passing scores on any of the following examinations: For the ACT, the applicant must have a composite score of at least 17 on both the English and the Mathematics sections of the exam. For the SAT, the applicant must have a score of at least 460 on both the Mathematics and Verbal sections of the exam. For the Accuplacer Computerized Placement Tests, applicants must have passing scores on at least three of the following four exams: Reading Comprehension, Sentence Skills, Arithmetic, and Elementary Algebra.

Tuition and Fees

The standard tuition fee is $3729 per term plus a $30 online fee per credit hour. Lab charges, tool kits, and books are additional and vary with the program of study.

Financial Aid

Tuition assistance is available for those who qualify. In order to help guide applicants through the tuition assistance application process, Westwood provides a step-by-step guide as well as links to all of the forms that can be filled out online.

Applying

To qualify for admission, students must submit an application fee of $25 and a registration fee of $75, provide proof of a high school diploma or GED completion, and provide passing test scores from college-level exams outlined in the Admission section.

CONTACT

Westwood College Online
Westwood College–Denver
North–Online Programs
7350 North Broadway
Denver, Colorado 80221
Phone: 888-996-6546 (toll-free)
Fax: 303-426-1832
E-mail: wolinternet@westwood.edu
Web site:
http://www.westwoodonline.edu

Consortium In-Depth Descriptions

The organizations listed in this section represent consortia of institutions offering Distance Learning programs. Each consortia has been formed so that an expanded set of distance learning options can be offered beyond the resources available through any single member institution.

The following consortia do not have a central application process and/or do not directly award credits and degrees. The application process, credits, or conferred degrees are awarded through one of the member institutions. Further, consortia generally are not directly granted accreditation; rather, credits and degrees reflect the accreditation of the awarding institution. The reader should obtain specific information directly from the consortia itself.

THE ARIZONA UNIVERSITIES NETWORK

Arizona Board of Regents

Flagstaff, Arizona

The Arizona Universities Network (AZUN), through the vision of the Arizona Board of Regents, is the gateway to Arizona's premier public institutions of higher education. Through AZUN, students can earn a fully accredited, online undergraduate degree, graduate degree, or professional certification from one of Arizona's three distinguished universities, each with a proven track record of more than a century of excellence.

AZUN offers online programs through Arizona State University (ASU), Northern Arizona University (NAU), and the University of Arizona (UA).

Distance Learning Program

AZUN is a consortium of Arizona's three universities: Arizona State University, Northern Arizona University, and The University of Arizona. Students can earn an online degree from one institution and take classes from all three.

Fifteen hundred online classes and fifty-three degrees allow students to design a course of study that fits busy work schedules and lifestyles. The distance courses engage students in activities that take them beyond their computer screens. AZUN students learn skills in real-world settings to advance their professional careers and facilitate networking, a key to career fulfillment.

Delivery Media

Most online classes are Web based; the class lectures and assignments are delivered through the Internet. Instructors work with designers and technicians at the three universities to adapt the classes to the Web format. When students sign up for a Web class they get the URL (the Internet site) of the class. Information on the Web site tells students how to progress through the class and what is expected.

Programs of Study

Only reputable, experienced faculty members from ASU, NAU, and UA teach classes offered through AZUN.

All three participating AZUN universities are accredited by the North Central Association of Colleges and Schools (NCA).

Undergraduate programs leading to a Bachelor of Arts degree are offered in arts and letters, enterprise in society, humanities, parks and recreation management, and public agency service. The Bachelor of Applied Science is offered in computer technology, early childhood education, health sciences, and public agency service. Bachelor of Science degrees are offered in dental hygiene, education–career and technical education, health sciences–community health, hotel and restaurant management, and parks and recreation management. A Bachelor of Science in Nursing (B.S.N.) is also offered.

On the graduate level, master's programs include Master of Administration (M.Admin.); Master of Arts (M.A.) in applied communication, English (emphases in literacy, professional writing, and technology), and information resources and library science; Master of Arts in Teaching (M.A.T.) (mathematics); Master of Business Administration (M.B.A.); Master of Education (M.Ed.) in career and technical education, early childhood educational, elementary education–continuing professional emphasis, technology education; Master of Engineering (M.Eng.); Master of Science in Engineering (M.S.E.) in electrical engineering, executive embedded systems, materials science engineering, semiconductor processing and manufacturing; Master of Science Nursing (M.S.N.); Master of Science in optical sciences and in technology.

Programs at the graduate level also include the Doctorate of Nursing (Ph.D.).

Certificates are available in educational technology, international tourism management, parks and recreation management, professional writing, public management, restaurant management, and speech-language pathology assistant studies.

Postbaccalaureate certificates are offered in case management and in multimedia writing and technical communication. SOLISTC Secondary Mathematics and Science Teacher Certification is also offered.

The Statistics-Six Sigma Black Belt Program graduate certificate is offered, as well as professional graduate certification in optical science. The College of Architecture and Environmental Design offers an Interdisciplinary Graduate Certificate Program in transportation systems.

Two endorsements are available through AZUN: English as a second language and reading.

Student Services

AZUN students have access to services from each of the three participating universities: Arizona State University, Northern Arizona University, and the University of Arizona. These services include, but are not limited to, academic advising, technical assistance, online textbook purchase, online course grades, computer labs, online libraries, and online tutoring services.

Faculty

AZUN provides access to world-class instruction from three premier universities. The distance courses allow easy access to responsive professors and staff who are familiar with the challenges of managing a schedule that includes work, study, and family.

Admission

All AZUN programs require admittance to one of the three participating institutions.

Tuition and Fees

AZUN offers competitive, affordable tuition rates through its three participating universities. Tuition rates of the home campus apply.

There are program or class fees, depending on the degree and/or class. Textbooks may be purchased online through the bookstores of the participating universities.

Financial Aid

Financial aid is available through the participating universities.

A variety of scholarships are available to help fund AZUN programs. Each university offers assistance to help students apply for scholarships.

Applying

Prospective students can begin the online application process immediately by completing and submitting the form available at http://www.azun.net. An adviser will contact the prospective student with the information needed to continue.

CONTACT

For answers to general questions, students should contact:

AZUN Service Center
Phone: 800-685-8120 (toll-free)
E-mail: azun.help@nau.edu
Web site: http://www.azun.net

Students can contact AZUN Campus Coordinators:

Jennifer Fleege
Arizona State University
Phone: 480-965-6176
E-mail: azun@asu.edu

Pam Torbico
Northern Arizona University
Phone: 928-523-6694
E-mail: azun@nau.edu

Robin Allen
The University of Arizona
Phone: 520-626-1339
E-mail: azun@email.arizona.edu

FLORIDA DISTANCE LEARNING CONSORTIUM

Florida's Online Presence for K–20 Education

Tallahassee, Florida

The Florida Distance Learning Consortium (FDLC) was established by the State Board of Community Colleges in 1996. In 2003, it completed a merger with the Florida Virtual Campus and expanded its mission to provide coordination in the development, delivery, marketing, and acquisition of distance learning instruction and its infrastructure across the K-20 system.

FDLC provides an online catalog of distance learning courses and degree programs at http://www.distancelearn.org. The catalog lists thousands of courses and more than 230 degree and certificate programs in many disciplines offered by Florida's eleven state universities, twenty-eight community colleges, and some of Florida's private colleges and universities. Each institution is fully accredited by the Southern Association of Colleges and Schools. More than 290,000 students are currently taking courses or earning a degree at a distance from participating institutions at the associate, baccalaureate, and graduate levels.

Distance Learning Program

FDLC provides information about distance learning opportunities at Florida institutions. The programs and courses listed on the Consortium's Web site meet the same academic standards of those found on-site at participating institutions. Students can generally study, take classes, and complete entire degree programs at any time and from any place.

The electronic catalog provides information about distance learning programs offered and lists thousands of distance learning courses in several different subject areas. Students can search the database by institution, term/semester, delivery method, subject/discipline, keywords, or course prefix and/or number. Once a student has located a course of interest, clicking on the college offering the course links the student to that institution and allows them to enroll. Each institution enters its own course information; therefore, the catalog reflects only those courses currently entered by each institution.

Delivery Media

Participating institutions select the delivery methods and have their own distance learning policies and procedures. Courses and programs are taught in a variety of delivery formats including the Internet, real-time two-way television conference, audio tapes or audio conferencing, printed materials through a correspondence or independent-study program, videos that can be viewed on a local TV channel or checked out of the library, or through a combination of these technologies.

The predominant delivery method is through the Internet, and courses are offered in real time or asynchronously. Internet courses require students to have access to a computer, a modem with an Internet connection, a World Wide Web browser, and e-mail. Two-way television courses include live audio and visual communication between multiple parties and locations using video and computer technology and satellite transmission. Audio courses are presented through audiotapes or through audio conferencing. Print courses use instructor-student print-based communication and are exchanged by postal service. Telecourses take advantage of public educational broadcast channels for distribution. Videotape courses can be checked out from the library and viewed by attaching a VCR to a television. Multimode courses incorporate a variety of technologies, such as the Internet, CD-ROM, video, TV, and print materials.

Programs of Study

The individual colleges and universities grant the degrees offered through FDLC. Students need to work with their home campus to ensure that they fulfill the requirements of the degree program. Each institution is fully accredited by the Southern Association of Colleges and Schools. Appropriate national organizations accredit the academic programs. Currently, more than 160 associate, bachelor's, master's, and a few doctoral degrees are offered. In addition, more than seventy special or certificate programs are listed in the online catalog. Participating institutions regularly add degree programs.

Student Services

To better assist students in searching the catalog, the Consortium's Web site has a "personal assistant" function that allows students to save course searches as well as searches for the specific classes of interest to them; it also enables students to receive information from a selected college or university as a way to help them get started. Each institution provides its own student support services. The distancelearn.org Web site provides links to student support services, such as admissions, financial aid, registration, and academic advising for each institution.

Credit Options

Credits can be earned as a combination of on-campus and distance learning courses or, for many programs, credit can be completed entirely at a distance. Each institution determines the number of credits required to complete the degree programs offered. Credits are typically transferable, but students should check with their home institution before taking a course.

Faculty

The same faculty members who teach on-campus courses at the institutions often design and teach the distance learning courses as well. Participating institutions determine who teaches each course and provide ongoing training and support to both the face-to-face and distance learning faculty members. The percentage of faculty members who have doctoral or advanced degrees varies among the participating institutions.

Admission

Participating institutions have their own admission requirements and make admission decisions to accept students into a program. Admission criteria are the same as those for on-campus courses. Students may be able to complete the entire application for admission online for many of the participating institutions.

Tuition and Fees

Each college or university determines tuition and fees for the courses and programs it offers. Some institutions also charge supplemental fees for particular classes or, in some cases, there is an additional fee to take a course at a distance.

Financial Aid

Financial aid opportunities are available for students enrolled in distance learning courses. Students should apply for financial aid through the college or university offering the courses.

Applying

Application procedures for distance learning offerings are the same as those for on-campus courses. Application requirements vary among the participating institutions. FDLC's Web site provides links to each institution's academic calendar, which includes application deadlines and other important dates for students to note during the application process. Students can often complete the application for admission online.

CONTACT

Florida Distance Learning Consortium
1753 West Paul Dirac Drive
Tallahassee, Florida 32310-3708

Phone: 850-922-3359
Fax: 850-922-3109
E-mail: info@distancelearn.org
Web site: http://www.distancelearn.org

MINNESOTA STATE COLLEGES AND UNIVERSITIES

Minnesota Online

St. Paul, Minnesota

Minnesota Online provides access to all online educational opportunities available from the Minnesota State Colleges and Universities (MnSCU)system. As one of the largest higher education consortia in the United States, the system consists of twenty-five 2-year colleges and seven state universities.

All online degrees are accredited by the Higher Learning Commission. Minnesota Online also offers a variety of planning tools, online services to help prospective students with financial aid and other needs, contact guides, and live and online support to answer students' education questions.

Distance Learning Program

Minnesota Online offers 3,500 credit and noncredit courses and more than 100 degree, certificate, and diploma programs completely or predominantly online. Courses are designed and taught by faculty members from the Minnesota State Colleges and Universities system. Minnesota Online currently is serving more than 30,000 online students.

Delivery Media

Students participating in the Minnesota Online courses need a computer with a sound card and speakers, at least 128MB RAM (256MB or greater recommended), and an Internet connection with a minimum 56K modem (broadband DSL or cable-modem is strongly recommended). Technical specifications often vary from course to course and from school to school. The minimum requirements for those using a Microsoft Windows computer are Windows 2000, ME, NT, XP (or higher) and Microsoft Internet Explorer 6.0 or higher or Mozilla.Org FireFox 1.0 or higher or Netscape 7.0 or higher. Minimum requirements for Macintosh users are MacOS 9 or OS X (or higher) and Apple Safari 1.2 or higher or Mozilla.Org FireFox 1.0 or higher or Netscape 7.0 or higher. Students are urged to research the computer requirements before registering for any online course.

Programs of Study

Minnesota Online offers undergraduate and graduate awards in more than 100 programs available from the Minnesota State Colleges and Universities system. The awards currently offered are associate, bachelor's, and master's degrees; undergraduate and graduate certificates; and diplomas. Continuing education courses are also available.

Specific programs are offered in the following areas: agriculture, food, and natural resources; architecture and construction; arts, AV technology, and communications; business, management, and administration; education and training; finance; government and public administration; health science; hospitality and tourism; human services; information technology; law, public safety, and security; manufacturing; marketing, sales, and service; science, technology, engineering, and mathematics; and transportation, distribution, and logistics.

Special Programs

The Minnesota Online Corporate Division works with corporations to provide planning, assessment, and course/degree program design and delivery to corporate employees. Education and training can be tailored to meet the company's specific needs and are delivered via the corporate university intranet or via the Internet.

eFolio Minnesota, offered through Minnesota Online, is a multimedia electronic portfolio available to all Minnesota residents, including students enrolled in Minnesota schools, educators, and other professionals. eFolio is a fun and easy-to-use Web-based tool that enables users to digitally document and share their education, career, and personal interests.

The ITeach Center, offered through Minnesota Online, provides a number of ways for faculty and staff members to learn, interact with their peers, and share knowledge. The sections of this interactive guide include Resources and Tools, Educational Opportunities, Online Teaching, and an Interactive Community.

Minnesota Online is a member of MERLOT (Multimedia Educational Resource for Learning and Online Teaching), a free and open resource designed primarily for faculty members and students in higher education. MERLOT.org provides links to online-learning materials along with annotations, such as peer reviews and assignments. Faculty members and students can browse the collection or search for materials. In addition, members may add materials, comments, and assignments to MERLOT.

Student Services

Minnesota Online recently was awarded the WCET Outstanding Work Award (WOW) for outstanding eStudent services. Services include advising, career services, disability services, electronic portfolio, financial aid, libraries, and test proctoring.

Faculty

Courses and programs offered through Minnesota Online are taught by faculty members from the thirty-two institutions that make up the Minnesota State Colleges and Universities system. Faculty members interact with students in the online setting as well as through traditional channels.

Admission

Before students can register for the courses listed on Minnesota Online, they must be admitted to a participating college or university. For a list of these schools, students should visit http://www.mnonline.org/visitor/members.htm.

Admission is handled directly by the individual campus that is offering the course(s). To find the admission contact for the specific MnSCU institution, students should use the selector tool on the admissions page of Minnesota Online at http://mnonline.org/student/admissions.htm.

Tuition and Fees

Tuition and fee information can be obtained from the individual institutions represented by Minnesota Online. Students with prior educational experience can go online to learn more about transfer and course equivalency opportunities at http://www.mnonline.org/student/transfer.htm or http://www.mnonline.org/student/courseequiv.htm.

Financial Aid

Money from federal, state, college, and private programs comes in the form of grants, loans, scholarships, or college work-study programs. About two thirds of students attending Minnesota State Colleges and Universities receive financial aid. Grants are awarded by the state and federal governments based on established criteria. Scholarships are awarded for academic and other achievements (music, athletics, etc.), financial need, or special interests or talent. There are many opportunities for this type of funding.

For more information, prospective students should visit the financial aid section of the Minnesota Online Web site at http://www.mnonline.org/student/finaid.htm.

Applying

The universal application form, which can be found online at http://www.mnonline.org/student/appform.htm, may be used to apply to any MnSCU institution, including state universities, community colleges, technical colleges, and comprehensive community and technical colleges.

CONTACT

Minnesota Online Support Center
Minnesota Online
Minnesota State Colleges and Universities
Phone: 651-556-0596
800-456-8519 (toll-free)
E-mail: mnscuonline@custhelp.com
Web site: http://www.minnesotaonline.org

SREB'S ELECTRONIC CAMPUS

Atlanta, Georgia

In February 2004, the Southern Regional Education Board (SREB) launched a more robust Electronic Campus, recreating it as a regional "learning network for the South" with improved levels of function. The expanded Electronic Campus Web site (http://www.ElectronicCampus.org) now provides more regional information, online services, and connectivity to colleges and universities across the sixteen SREB member states, and builds on and adds significant levels of "functionality" to the original Electronic Campus. While the learning network serves all learners, it is targeted at the unique needs of adult and e-learners to help them get the education they need to meet the demands of the twenty-first-century workforce. The Electronic Campus helps them find courses and degrees, secure career information and guidance, locate financial aid, and complete the admission process online. It is now a simpler, friendlier one-stop Web site for all learners.

SREB's original Electronic Campus functioned as an "electronic marketplace" of courses and programs from hundreds of participating colleges and universities from the sixteen member states. Established in 1998, the Electronic Campus has grown from 104 courses to more than 9,000 courses and over 450 degree programs from colleges and universities throughout the South. New courses and programs are added continually.

The Southern Regional Education Board, the nation's first interstate compact for education, was created in 1948 at the request of Southern business, education, and governmental leaders. It is designed to help leaders in government and education work together to advance education and thus improve the social and economic life of the region. SREB's member states are Alabama, Arkansas, Delaware, Florida, Georgia, Kentucky, Louisiana, Maryland, Mississippi, North Carolina, Oklahoma, South Carolina, Tennessee, Texas, Virginia, and West Virginia.

Distance Learning Program

The Electronic Campus provides detailed common and comparable information about distance learning courses and programs offered by participating colleges and universities. The goal is to provide enhanced educational opportunities for adult e-learners as well as traditional and nontraditional students by removing many of the barriers that have long hindered access to higher education.

Delivery Media

Courses and programs are available in a variety of delivery formats. The predominant delivery method is the World Wide Web. Courses and programs are available via the Web in both synchronous and asynchronous modes. Other delivery formats are videotapes, satellite, CD-ROMs, compressed video, and open broadcast. Information on the delivery formats for each course and program is available on the Electronic Campus Web site at the address listed in the Contact section.

Programs of Study

The Electronic Campus provides access to more than 450 academic programs from regionally accredited public and private colleges and universities. Programs are available in a variety of disciplines and majors at the associate, bachelor's, master's, and doctoral levels. Certificate programs at various levels are also available. More than 9,000 credit courses at the undergraduate and graduate levels, all offered electronically, are available and fully searchable on the site.

All courses and programs available at the Electronic Campus meet SREB's Principles of Good Practice and have undergone a review at the institutional, state, and regional levels. The Principles are the quality cornerstone of the Electronic Campus. Institutions offering courses and programs must meet a variety of requirements: the course or program must provide appropriate interaction between faculty members and students and among students, high-quality faculty members must provide appropriate supervision of the program or course that is offered electronically, and academic standards for all programs or courses offered electronically must be the same as those for other courses or programs delivered at the institution from which they originate.

Special Programs

The expanded Electronic Campus also offers specialized portals to help individuals meet their professional development needs in specific career areas. The first is the Teacher Center (http://TheTeacherCenter.org), a new site that links teachers, administrators, counselors, librarians, teacher aides, and aspiring teachers to a comprehensive set of services. These educators can search for and enroll in online courses and programs that are offered at the undergraduate and graduate level and that provide either college credit or continuing education units. The portal also provides information about financial aid; information about the federal No Child Left Behind Act and each state's requirements for highly qualified teachers; information about each SREB state's licensure, certification, and alternative routes to teaching; and numerous other online services.

The Academic Common Market/ Electronic Campus program enables a student in the SREB states to get a waiver of out-of-state tuition if certain conditions are met. Those conditions include the following: no public college or university in a student's home state (state of residence) offers a degree program in the chosen field of study; the program is available in another SREB state participating in the Academic Common Market; the program is available through distance learning; the home state adopts/accepts the program for its residents; the student meets admissions requirements; and the student can be certified as a resident in their home state to participate. Several degree programs are now available through the Academic Common Market/ Electronic Campus.

Faculty

Many of the SREB region's most respected professors teach courses and programs on the Electronic Campus. The faculty members respond to students' questions online and often list times that they can be reached by telephone in their campus offices. Students often say communication with online professors is as effective as or even more effective than in a classroom setting.

Admission

Each college or university handles admission to its degree programs offered on the Electronic Campus. Students can access this information directly from its Web site. Many institutions allow potential students to complete the application for admission online with just a few mouse clicks. Students who wish to enroll in a specific course may be able to do so without formal application and admission. The enrollment procedure and requirements for all colleges and universities participating in the Electronic Campus are outlined on its Web site.

Tuition and Fees

Each college or university offering courses and programs sets its tuition and fees. Tuition and fee charges are available at the Electronic Campus site.

A growing number of colleges and universities participating in the Electronic Campus are offering courses at a single or "electronic rate." These rates apply to students enrolling in courses irrespective of their residence. These courses are clearly marked to help more students gain access and afford these learning opportunities.

Financial Aid

Participating colleges and universities coordinate financial aid. Specific information on financial aid is available from the institutions. General information is available on the Electronic Campus site.

Applying

Anyone with Internet access may search courses and programs available through the Electronic Campus. There is no charge for accessing or using the services available at the site. A simple registration can be completed when visiting. Creating an account (registration) allows users to use (and reuse) data to complete online applications, save searches, establish e-mail and personal calendars, and take advantage of other services described at the Electronic Campus.

CONTACT

Mary Agnes Larson
Associate Director, Electronic Campus
Southern Regional Education Board
592 10th Street, NW
Atlanta, Georgia 30318-5776
Phone: 404-875-9211
Fax: 404-872-1477
E-mail: electroniccampus@sreb.org
Web site: http://www.ElectronicCampus.org

Indexes

INSTITUTIONS OFFERING DEGREE AND CERTIFICATE PROGRAMS

ACADEMIC ADVISING

Kansas State University (GC)

ACCOUNTANCY

Auburn University (M)
National University (B)

ACCOUNTANT

Lake Superior College (A)

ACCOUNTING

Ashworth College (A)
Athabasca University (B,UC)
Blackhawk Technical College (A)
Brenau University (M)
Bryant and Stratton Online (A)
Caldwell College (B)
Capella University (M)
Champlain College (A,B,UC)
City University (B,UC)
Colorado Technical University (M)
Darton College (A)
Davenport University Online (A)
Excelsior College (B)
Florida Atlantic University (M)
Franklin Pierce College (UC)
Franklin University (A,B)
Indiana Business College (A)
Indiana Wesleyan University (A)
Keiser College (A)
Lenoir Community College (A)
Liberty University (M,A,B)
Madison Area Technical College (A)
Mercy College (A)
Minnesota School of Business–Richfield (A,B)
Mountain Empire Community College (A)
Myers University (B)
Northwest Missouri State University (B)
Randolph Community College (A)
Saint Leo University (B)
Saint Mary-of-the-Woods College (A,B)
Seminole Community College (A)
Shoreline Community College (UC)
Southern New Hampshire University (A,B,UC)
Southwestern College (B)
Stanly Community College (A)
Strayer University (A,B,UC)
Thomas Edison State College (A,B)
University of Alaska Southeast (B)
University of Dallas (GC,M)
The University of Maine at Augusta (B)
University of Maryland University College (GC,B)
University of Phoenix Online Campus (M,A)
Upper Iowa University (B)
Mount Saint Vincent University (UC)

ACCOUNTING (ASB)

Penn Foster Career School (A)

ACCOUNTING (BACHELOR COMPLETION)

Indiana Wesleyan University (B)

ACCOUNTING AND FINANCE

New England College of Finance (GC)

ACCOUNTING AND FINANCE CONCENTRATION (10-MONTH PROGRAM)

American InterContinental University Online (M)

ACCOUNTING AND FINANCE CONCENTRATION (COMPLETION PROGRAM)

American InterContinental University Online (B)

ACCOUNTING AND FINANCIAL MANAGEMENT

DeVry University Online (M)
University of Maryland University College (M)

ACCOUNTING AND INFORMATION TECHNOLOGY

University of Maryland University College (GC,M)

ACCOUNTING APPLICATIONS

Seminole Community College (UC)

ACCOUNTING CLERK

Shoreline Community College (UC)

ACCOUNTING EMPHASIS

Community College of Southern Nevada (A)

ACCOUNTING INFORMATION MANAGEMENT–INTERNAL AUDITING SPECIALTY

Davenport University Online (B)

ACCOUNTING INFORMATION MANAGEMENT–MANAGEMENT ACCOUNTING SPECIALTY

Davenport University Online (B)

ACCOUNTING INFORMATION SYSTEMS

Saint Mary-of-the-Woods College (B)

ACCOUNTING NYS CPA TRACK

Excelsior College (B)

ACCOUNTING SPECIALTY

Davenport University Online (M)

ACCOUNTING TECHNICIAN

Minot State University–Bottineau Campus (A)
University of Alaska Southeast (UC)

ACCOUNTING TECHNOLOGY

DeVry University Online (A)
Montana State University–Billings (A)
The University of Toledo (A,UC)

ACCOUNTING–ASSOCIATE OF BUSINESS

York Technical College (A)

ACCOUNTING–BSACC

Colorado Technical University (B)

ACCOUNTING–FINANCIAL ACCOUNTING

Rasmussen College Eden Prarie (A)

ACCOUNTING–HEALTHCARE ACCOUNTING AND FINANCIAL MANAGEMENT

Indiana University System (UC)

ACCOUNTING–INTERNAL AUDITING SPECIALTY

Davenport University Online (B)

ACCOUNTING, ADVANCED

Athabasca University (UC)
Champlain College (UC)
College of Southern Maryland (UC)

ACCOUNTING, BASIC
College of Southern Maryland (UC)

ACCOUNTING, FINANCE, INFORMATION SYSTEMS, MARKETING
Old Dominion University (B)

ACCOUNTING/FINANCE
Southern New Hampshire University (B)

ACCOUNTS RECEIVABLE/ PAYABLE CLERK
Shoreline Community College (UC)

ACQUISITION AND CONTRACT MANAGEMENT
Florida Institute of Technology (M)
Strayer University (A,B,UC)

ACQUISITION AND CONTRACTING CONCENTRATION OR PROJECT MANAGEMENT CONCENTRATION
American Graduate University (M)

ACQUISITION MANAGEMENT
University of Management and Technology (M,UC)

ACQUISITION MANAGEMENT–MASTER OF ACQUISITION MANAGEMENT
American Graduate University (M)

ADDICTION COUNSELING (CPAC)
Bethany University (UC)

ADDICTION STUDIES
Bethany University (B)
The Pennsylvania State University University Park Campus
University of Cincinnati (B)

ADMINISTRATION
Athabasca University (UC)
Northern Arizona University
University of Michigan–Flint (B)

ADMINISTRATION OF JUSTICE
Arizona Western College (A)
Salve Regina University (M)
Thomas Edison State College (A,B)

ADMINISTRATION OF JUSTICE AND SECURITY
University of Phoenix Online Campus (M)

ADMINISTRATION–BUILDING CODE ADMINISTRATION
Central Michigan University (B)

ADMINISTRATION–COMMUNICATION ARTS
University of the Incarnate Word (M)

ADMINISTRATION–GENERAL ADMINISTRATION CONCENTRATION
Central Michigan University (M)

ADMINISTRATION–HEALTH SERVICES ADMINISTRATION CONCENTRATION
Central Michigan University (M)

ADMINISTRATION–HUMAN RESOURCE ADMINISTRATION
Central Michigan University (M)

ADMINISTRATION–INFORMATION RESOURCE MANAGEMENT CONCENTRATION
Central Michigan University (M)

ADMINISTRATION–LEADERSHIP CONCENTRATION
Central Michigan University (M)

ADMINISTRATION–ORGANIZATIONAL ADMINISTRATION
Central Michigan University (B)

ADMINISTRATION–PUBLIC ADMINISTRATION CONCENTRATION
Central Michigan University (M)

ADMINISTRATIVE ASSISTANT
Indiana Business College (A)
Madison Area Technical College (A)
Minot State University–Bottineau Campus (A)
North Dakota State College of Science (A)

ADMINISTRATIVE COMMUNICATIONS–LIBERAL STUDIES
Washburn University (B)

ADMINISTRATIVE OFFICE MANAGEMENT
Thomas Edison State College (A,B)

ADMINISTRATIVE OFFICE SUPPORT
University of Alaska Southeast (UC)

ADMINISTRATIVE OFFICE TECHNOLOGY–EXECUTIVE OFFICE ADMINISTRATION SPECIALTY
Davenport University Online (A)

ADMINISTRATIVE OFFICE TECHNOLOGY–OFFICE SOFTWARE SPECIALIST
Vincennes University (UC)

ADMINISTRATIVE PRINCIPAL PROGRAM
California University of Pennsylvania (M)

ADMINISTRATIVE PRINCIPALS PROGRAM
California University of Pennsylvania (UC)

ADMINISTRATIVE SERVICES CERTIFICATE
National University (UC)

ADMINISTRATIVE STUDIES
Missouri State University (M)
St. John's University (B)
Thomas Edison State College (A)
York University (B)

ADMINISTRATIVE SUPPORT
Rappahannock Community College (UC)

ADMINISTRATIVE SUPPORT TECHNOLOGY
Mountain Empire Community College (A)

ADMINISTRATIVE SUPPORT TECHNOLOGY MEDICAL OFFICE SPECIALIST
Mountain Empire Community College (A)

ADMINISTRATIVE/MANAGEMENT STUDIES
Excelsior College (A)

ADMINISTRATOR LEADERSHIP FOR TEACHING AND LEARNING
Walden University (D)

ADULT DEVELOPMENT AND AGING SERVICES
The Pennsylvania State University University Park Campus (UC)

ADULT EDUCATION

Brock University (UC)
Buffalo State College, State University of New York (GC,M)
Indiana University System (M)
Northwestern State University of Louisiana (M)
Oregon State University (M)
The Pennsylvania State University University Park Campus (M)

ADULT EDUCATION (BED IN ADULT EDUCATION)

Brock University (B)

ADULT EDUCATION AND TRAINING

Saint Joseph's College of Maine (A,UC)

ADULT LEARNING

University of Calgary (UC)

ADULT LEARNING AND DEVELOPMENT

Cleveland State University (GC,M)

ADULT LIBERAL STUDIES

The University of Toledo (B)

ADULT NURSE PRACTITIONER

Clarkson College (M,)

ADULT RELIGIOUS EDUCATION

Saint Joseph's College of Maine (B)

ADULT, CONTINUING, AND LITERACY EDUCATION

National-Louis University (M)

ADVANCED PROGRAMS

University of Oklahoma (D,M)

ADVENTURE EDUCATION

Prescott College (M,B)

ADVERTISING

Academy of Art University (M,A,B)
University of Maryland University College (GC)

ADVERTISING AND PUBLIC RELATIONS

Seminole Community College (A)

ADVERTISING DESIGN

Syracuse University (M)

ADVERTISING MANAGEMENT

Thomas Edison State College (B)

AERONAUTICAL SCIENCE

Embry-Riddle Aeronautical University, Extended Campus (M)

AERONAUTICS AND ASTRONAUTICS

Stanford University (M)
University of Washington (M)

AEROSPACE

The University of Tennessee (M)

AEROSPACE ENGINEERING

Auburn University (M)
Georgia Institute of Technology (M)
North Carolina State University (M)
The University of Alabama (M)
University of Colorado at Boulder (M)
The University of Texas at Arlington (M)
University of Washington (M)

AEROSPACE STUDIES

American Military University (B)
American Public University (B)

AFRICAN AMERICAN MINISTRY LEADERSHIP MODULE

Defiance College (UC)

AFRICAN AND AFRICAN AMERICAN STUDIES

American Military University (B)
American Public University (B)

AGRIBUSINESS

Kansas State University (M)

AGRICULTURAL AND EXTENSION EDUCATION

The University of Tennessee (M)

AGRICULTURAL AND EXTENSION EDUCATOR

New Mexico State University (M)

AGRICULTURAL AND LIFE SCIENCES

Virginia Polytechnic Institute and State University (M)

AGRICULTURAL BUSINESS ECONOMICS

West Texas A&M University (M)

AGRICULTURAL EDUCATION

Texas Tech University (D)
Colorado State University (M)

AGRICULTURAL EDUCATION AND COMMUNICATION

University of Florida (M)

AGRICULTURAL OPERATIONS MANAGEMENT

The University of Tennessee at Martin (M)

AGRICULTURAL TEACHER EDUCATION

North Carolina State University (M)

AGRICULTURAL, FOOD AND LIFE SCIENCES NON-THESIS (FOOD SAFETY EMPHASIS)

University of Arkansas (M)

AGRICULTURE

Iowa State University of Science and Technology (M)
Texas Tech University (M)
University of Nebraska–Lincoln (M)
Washington State University (M)

AGRICULTURE, GENERAL

Oregon State University (B)

AGRONOMY

Iowa State University of Science and Technology (M)

AIR TRAFFIC CONTROL

Thomas Edison State College (A,B)

AIRCRAFT MAINTENANCE TECHNOLOGY

Embry-Riddle Aeronautical University, Extended Campus (A)

ALLIED HEALTH

California College for Health Sciences (A)
National University (B)

ALLIED HEALTH LEADERSHIP–BS COMPLETION PROGRAM

East Tennessee State University (B)

ALPS INTERNATIONAL EDUCATIONAL LEADERSHIP PROGRAM

University of Colorado at Denver and Health Sciences Center—Downtown Denver Campus (UC)

ALTERNATIVE DISPUTE RESOLUTION–CERTIFICATE OF ADVANCED STUDY

University of Denver (UC)

ALTERNATIVE EDUCATION

Lock Haven University of Pennsylvania (M)

ALTERNATIVE ENERGY SYSTEMS

Prescott College (M)

ALTERNATIVE TEACHING

Virginia Polytechnic Institute and State University (UC)

AMERICAN SIGN LANGUAGE–ENGLISH INTERPRETATION

University of Northern Colorado (B)

AMERICAN STUDIES

Columbia College (B)
Skidmore College (B)

ANALYTICAL CHEMISTRY

Illinois Institute of Technology (M)

ANALYTICAL METHOD DEVELOPMENT

Illinois Institute of Technology (GC)

ANALYTICAL SPECTROSCOPY

Illinois Institute of Technology (GC)

ANGLICAN STUDIES

Trinity Episcopal School for Ministry (UC)

ANIMAL SCIENCE AND INDUSTRY

Kansas State University (B)

ANIMATION

Westwood Online (B)

ANIMATION AND VISUAL EFFECTS

Academy of Art University (M,A,B)

ANTHROPOLOGY

Darton College (A)
Prescott College (M)
Thomas Edison State College (B)
University of North Texas (M)
Skidmore College (B)

ANTHROPOLOGY (3 YEAR)

Athabasca University (B)

ANTHROPOLOGY (4 YEAR)

Athabasca University (B)

ANTHROPOLOGY PRE-MAJOR

Seminole Community College (A)

ANTITHROMBOSIS THERAPY MANAGEMENT PROGRAM

University of Illinois at Chicago (UC)

APOSTOLIC CATECHETICAL DIPLOMA

The Catholic Distance University (UC)

APPAREL AND MERCHANDISING

Colorado State University (M,UC)

APPLIED ARTS AND SCIENCES (BAAS)

University of the Incarnate Word (B)

APPLIED BEHAVIOR ANALYSIS FOR SPECIAL EDUCATION

The Pennsylvania State University University Park Campus (GC)

APPLIED BUSINESS

University of Minnesota, Twin Cities Campus (UC)

APPLIED COMMUNICATION

Northern Arizona University (M)

APPLIED COMMUNICATION–MASTER OF PROFESSIONAL STUDIES IN APPLIED COMMUNICATION

University of Denver (M)

APPLIED COMPUTER SCIENCE

Northwest Missouri State University (M)

APPLIED ELECTRONIC STUDIES

Thomas Edison State College (A)

APPLIED HEALTH STUDIES

Pennsylvania College of Technology (B)
Thomas Edison State College (A)

APPLIED HEALTH–BACHELOR OF APPLIED HEALTH ONLINE

University of Minnesota, Crookston (B)

APPLIED INFORMATION TECHNOLOGY, TELECOMMUNICATIONS DEGREE

Pace University (A)

APPLIED MANAGEMENT

Franklin University (B)

APPLIED MANAGEMENT AND DECISION SCIENCES–ACCOUNTING

Walden University (D)

APPLIED MANAGEMENT AND DECISION SCIENCES–ENGINEERING MANAGEMENT

Walden University (D)

APPLIED MANAGEMENT AND DECISION SCIENCES–FINANCE

Walden University (D)

APPLIED MANAGEMENT AND DECISION SCIENCES–INFORMATION SYSTEMS MANAGEMENT

Walden University (D)

APPLIED MANAGEMENT AND DECISION SCIENCES–KNOWLEDGE MANAGEMENT

Walden University (D)

APPLIED MANAGEMENT AND DECISION SCIENCES–LEADERSHIP AND ORGANIZATIONAL CHANGE

Walden University (D)

APPLIED MANAGEMENT AND DECISION SCIENCES–LEARNING MANAGEMENT

Walden University (D)

APPLIED MANAGEMENT AND DECISION SCIENCES–OPERATIONS RESEARCH

Walden University (D)

APPLIED MANAGEMENT AND DECISION SCIENCES–SELF-DESIGNED

Walden University (D)

APPLIED MANAGEMENT AND DECISION SCIENCES, GENERAL

Walden University (D)

APPLIED PROFESSIONAL STUDIES
Bethany University (B)

APPLIED RETAIL MANAGEMENT
Drexel University (UC)

APPLIED SCIENCE
Big Sandy Community and Technical College (A)
Central Texas College (A)
Pueblo Community College (A)

APPLIED SCIENCE–ASSOCIATE IN APPLIED SCIENCE
Central Carolina Community College (UC)

APPLIED SCIENCE–BACHELOR OF APPLIED SCIENCE
East Tennessee State University (B)
The University of Maine at Augusta (B)

APPLIED STATISTICAL STRATEGIES
The University of Tennessee (GC)

APPLIED STATISTICS
Rochester Institute of Technology (M)

APPLIED STATISTICS AND DATA ANALYSIS
Colorado State University (UC)

APPLIED STUDIES
Abilene Christian University (UC)
Athabasca University (B)
California State University, Dominguez Hills (B)

APPLIED TECHNOLOGY
Central Texas College (A)
Granite State College (B)

APPLIED TECHNOLOGY AND PERFORMANCE IMPROVEMENT
University of North Texas (B)

APPLIED TECHNOLOGY, TRAINING, AND DEVELOPMENT
University of North Texas (M)

AQUACULTURE
Kentucky State University (M)

ARCHITECTURAL DESIGN
Thomas Edison State College (A,B)

ARCHITECTURAL DRAFTING AND ESTIMATING TECHNOLOGY
North Dakota State College of Science (A)

ARCHITECTURAL STUDIES
University of Missouri–Columbia (D)

ARCHITECTURE
University of Nebraska–Lincoln (M)

ART
Darton College (A)
Northwestern State University of Louisiana (M)
Prescott College (B)
Thomas Edison State College (B)

ART (STUDIO)
Skidmore College (B)

ART EDUCATION
East Carolina University (M)
Mansfield University of Pennsylvania (M)
Texas Tech University (M)

ART HISTORY
Mansfield University of Pennsylvania (B)
Prescott College (M)
Skidmore College (B)

ART THERAPY
Prescott College (M)
Saint Mary-of-the-Woods College (M)

ARTIFICIAL INTELLIGENCE
Stanford University (GC)

ARTS
Athabasca University (UC)
Big Sandy Community and Technical College (A)
Jackson Community College (A)
Lurleen B. Wallace Community College (A)
Spartanburg Technical College (A)
Wilkes Community College (A)

ARTS (GENERAL)
Colorado Christian University (A)

ARTS AND LITERATURE–CERTIFICATE OF ADVANCED STUDY
University of Denver (UC)

ARTS AND SCIENCE
Athabasca University (B)

ARTS AND SCIENCE DEGREE PROGRAM
Southwest Virginia Community College (A)

ARTS AND SCIENCE–APPLIED ARTS AND SCIENCE
Rochester Institute of Technology (B)

ARTS AND SCIENCES
Clarion University of Pennsylvania (A)
College of Southern Maryland (A)

ARTS AND SCIENCES DEGREE FOR TRANSFER
John Tyler Community College (A)

ARTS AND SCIENCES–APPLIED SCIENCE AND TECHNOLOGY
College of Southern Maryland (A)

ARTS AND SCIENCES–ARTS AND HUMANITIES
College of Southern Maryland (A)

ARTS AND SCIENCES–SOCIAL SCIENCES
College of Southern Maryland (A)

ARTS MANAGEMENT
Prescott College (M)
University of Massachusetts Amherst (UC)

ASIAN STUDIES
American Military University (B)
American Public University (B)
Skidmore College (B)

ASSISTIVE TECHNOLOGY
California State University, Dominguez Hills (UC)
East Carolina University (GC)

ASSISTIVE TECHNOLOGY SPECIALIZATION
Bowling Green State University (M)

AT-RISK YOUTH SPECIALIZATION
Central Texas College (A)

ATHLETIC COACHING
West Virginia University (M)

ATMOSPHERIC AND ENVIRONMENTAL SCIENCE AND ENGINEERING
Stevens Institute of Technology (GC)

AUDIOLOGY

University of Florida (D)

AUTISM

Texas Tech University (GC)
The Pennsylvania State University University Park Campus (UC)

AUTISTIC SPECTRUM DISORDERS

University of North Dakota (GC)

AUTOMOTIVE ENGINEERING

University of Michigan (M)

AUTOMOTIVE SYSTEMS ENGINEERING

University of Michigan–Dearborn (M)

AUTOMOTIVE TECHNOLOGY MANAGEMENT

Pennsylvania College of Technology (B)

AVIATION (BACCALAUREATE DEGREE TRANSFER)

Utah Valley State College (A)

AVIATION FLIGHT TECHNOLOGY

Thomas Edison State College (A,B)

AVIATION FLIGHT TECHNOLOGY, GENERAL

Indiana State University (A)

AVIATION JOB READY DEGREE

Utah Valley State College (A)

AVIATION MAINTENANCE MANAGEMENT

Embry-Riddle Aeronautical University, Extended Campus (B)
St. Cloud State University (B)

AVIATION MAINTENANCE TECHNOLOGY

Thomas Edison State College (A,B)

AVIATION MANAGEMENT

Schoolcraft College (A,UC)

AVIATION PROFESSIONAL PILOT

Utah Valley State College (B)

AVIATION SCIENCE

Utah Valley State College (B)

AVIATION STUDIES

Excelsior College (A)

BACHELOR OF ARTS COMPLETION PROGRAM

University of Denver (B)

BACHELORS DEGREE IN MULTILINGUAL EDUCATION

Northern Arizona University

BAILS ARTS AND LETTERS

Northern Arizona University (B)

BAILS CRIMINAL JUSTICE

Northern Arizona University (B)

BAILS ENTERPRISE IN SOCIETY

Northern Arizona University (B)

BAILS ENVIRONMENTAL SCIENCES

Northern Arizona University (B)

BAILS LEARNING AND PEDAGOGY

Northern Arizona University (B)

BAILS MATHEMATICS/ STATISTICS

Northern Arizona University (B)

BAILS ORGANIZATIONAL COMMUNICATION

Northern Arizona University (B)

BAILS PARKS AND RECREATION MANAGEMENT

Northern Arizona University (B)

BAILS PSYCHOLOGY

Northern Arizona University (B)

BAILS SOCIOLOGY

Northern Arizona University (B)

BANKING

Mercy College (M,A)
Strayer University (B)
Thomas Edison State College (A,B)

BANKING STUDIES

New England College of Finance (GC)

BEHAVIOR ANALYSIS

St. Cloud State University (M)
University of North Texas (GC)

BEHAVIORAL INTERVENTION IN AUTISM

University of Massachusetts Lowell (GC)

BEHAVIORAL LEADERSHIP AND MANAGEMENT

Regions University (M)

BEHAVIORAL SCIENCE

Lynn University (B)
Mercy College (B)

BEHAVIORAL SCIENCE–SUBSTANCE ABUSE CERTIFICATE

Vincennes University (UC)

BEHAVIORAL SCIENCES

Vincennes University (A)

BIBLE

Briercrest Distance Learning (UC)
Northwestern College (UC)
Southwestern Assemblies of God University (A)

BIBLE STUDIES–ONE YEAR BIBLE CERTIFICATE

Eugene Bible College (UC)

BIBLICAL AND CULTURAL LEADERSHIP

Taylor University (UC)

BIBLICAL AND THEOLOGICAL STUDIES

Bethany University (B)

BIBLICAL STUDIES

The Baptist College of Florida (B)
Colorado Christian University (UC)
Dallas Baptist University (B)
Hope International University (A,UC)
Life Pacific College (A)
Moody Bible Institute (A,B,UC)
Northwestern College (A,B)
Regent University (M)
Regions University (D,M,B)
Taylor University (A,UC)
Temple Baptist Seminary (UC)
Tennessee Temple University (A,B)

BIBLICAL STUDIES–OVER 20 CONCENTRATIONS AVAILABLE

Temple Baptist Seminary (M)

BILINGUAL EDUCATION

Prescott College (M)

BILINGUAL EDUCATION ENDORSEMENT
Northern Arizona University (UC)

BILINGUAL/MULTICULTURAL EDUCATION
Northern Arizona University (M)

BIOCHEMISTRY
Illinois Institute of Technology (M)

BIODESIGN
Stanford University (GC)

BIOETHICS
Cleveland State University (GC,UC)

BIOINFORMATICS
Stanford University (GC)
University of Illinois at Chicago (UC)
University of Maryland University College (GC)

BIOLOGICAL AND AGRICULTURAL ENGINEERING
North Carolina State University (GC)

BIOLOGICAL SCIENCE
Darton College (A)

BIOLOGY
Illinois Institute of Technology (M)
Skidmore College (B)
Thomas Edison State College (A,B)
University of Nebraska at Kearney (M)

BIOMEDICAL ELECTRONICS
Thomas Edison State College (A,B)

BIOMEDICAL ENGINEERING
Columbia University (M)

BIOMEDICAL INFORMATICS
Stanford University (M)

BIOMEDICAL QUALITY SYSTEMS
San Diego State University (M)

BIOMEDICAL WRITING
University of the Sciences in Philadelphia (M)

BIOMETRIC SECURITY
Davenport University Online (B)

BIOPROCESS MANUFACTURING TECHNOLOGY
Central Carolina Community College (UC)

BIOSCIENCE MANAGEMENT
George Mason University (M)

BIOTECHNOLOGY
Illinois Institute of Technology (M)

BIOTECHNOLOGY MANAGEMENT
University of Maryland University College (GC)

BIOTECHNOLOGY STUDIES
University of Maryland University College (M)

BIOTERRORISM PREPAREDNESS
The Pennsylvania State University University Park Campus (GC)

BLOOD BANK TECHNOLOGY
The University of Texas System (UC)

BLOOD BANK TECHNOLOGY SPECIALIST CAMPUS CERTIFICATE
University of Illinois at Chicago (UC)

BOOKKEEPING
Minot State University–Bottineau Campus (UC)

BOOKKEEPING–PARAPROFESSIONAL ACCOUNTING PROGRAM
Bellevue Community College (UC)

BOOKKEEPING–PROFESSIONAL BOOKKEEPER
Lake Superior College (UC)

BOOKKEEPING/ACCOUNTING
Rappahannock Community College (UC)

BORDER ADMINISTRATION
The University of Texas System (UC)

BORDER STUDIES
The University of Texas System (UC)

BRAIN RESEARCH IN EDUCATION
University of Washington (UC)

BRANCH MANAGEMENT
New England College of Finance (GC)

BRIDGE DOCTOR OF PHYSICAL THERAPY
Simmons College (D)

BROADBAND–CERTIFICATE OF ADVANCED STUDY
University of Denver (UC)

BROADCAST ENGINEERING
Cleveland Institute of Electronics (UC)

BS—BACHELOR OF INTERDISCIPLINARY STUDIES (CONCENTRATION IN INTEGRATIVE STUDIES)
Winston-Salem State University (B)

BUILDING A SUSTAINABLE WORLD
Saybrook Graduate School and Research Center (GC)

BUILDING CODE ENFORCEMENT
Red Rocks Community College (A)

BUILDING CONSTRUCTION
Georgia Institute of Technology (M)

BUSINESS
Andrew Jackson University (A)
Ashford University (A)
Caldwell College (B)
California College for Health Sciences (A)
Champlain College (A,B,UC)
Colorado State University (UC)
Community College of Southern Nevada (A)
Dallas County Community College District (A)
Drexel University (M)
Excelsior College (M,A)
Indiana Wesleyan University (A)
Judson College (B)
Kaplan University (B)
Keiser College (A)
Lansing Community College (A)
Liberty University (A,B)
Lynn University (B)
Mercy College (A)
New York Institute of Technology (M)
Prescott College (B)
Pueblo Community College (A)
Red Rocks Community College (A)
St. John's University (A)
Salve Regina University (B)
Southwestern Assemblies of God University (B)
University of Phoenix Online Campus (A)
University of the Incarnate Word (A)
Utah State University (B)

BUSINESS (ABUS)
Coconino Community College (A)

BUSINESS (TRANSFER FRAMEWORK)–AA TO BS

Big Sandy Community and Technical College (A)

BUSINESS ACCOUNTING

California College for Health Sciences (A,B)

BUSINESS ADMINISTRATION

Acadia University (UC)
Adams State College (B)
Adirondack Community College (A)
American Military University (M,B)
American Public University (M,B)
Arizona Western College (A)
Athabasca University (M)
Auburn University (M)
Baker College of Flint (M,A,B)
Ball State University (M)
Bellevue University (M,B)
Berkeley College (A,B)
California National University for Advanced Studies (M,B)
Capitol College (M)
Cayuga County Community College (A)
Central New Mexico Community College (A)
Chadron State College (M)
Champlain College (M)
Clarion University of Pennsylvania (M)
College of Southern Maryland (A)
College of The Albemarle (A)
Colorado Christian University (M,B)
Colorado State University (M)
Columbia College (A,B)
The Community College of Baltimore County (A)
Community College of Denver (A,UC)
Concordia University Wisconsin (M)
County College of Morris (A)
Culver-Stockton College (B)
Dallas Baptist University (B)
Darton College (A)
Des Moines Area Community College (A)
DeVry University Online (M,B)
Drexel University (M,B)
East Carolina University (M,B)
Eastern New Mexico University (M,B)
Eastern Oregon University (B)
Eastern Wyoming College (A)
Edmonds Community College (A)
Florida Gulf Coast University (M)
Florida State University (M)
Franklin University (A,B)
Georgia Southern University (M,B)
Grantham University (M,A,B)
Harford Community College (A)
Indiana Business College (A)
Indiana State University (B)
Indiana Tech (A,B)
Indiana Wesleyan University (M)
Jackson Community College (A,UC)
Jacksonville State University (M)
Jefferson Community College (A)
Jones College (A,B)
Kansas State University (GC)
Kaplan University (M)
Keiser College (A,B)
Lake Superior College (A)
Lehigh University (M)
Lenoir Community College (A)
LeTourneau University (M)
Liberty University (M)
Limestone College (A)
Lynn University (M)
Marist College (M)
Marylhurst University (M)
Mayville State University (B)
Memorial University of Newfoundland (B,UC)
Mercy College (M,B)
Metropolitan State University (B)
Midstate College (B)
Minnesota School of Business–Richfield (M,A,B)
Mississippi State University (M)
Missouri State University (M)
Monroe Community College (A)
Montana State University–Billings (B)
Montgomery Community College (A)
Mountain Empire Community College (A)
Mount Saint Vincent University (B)
Mount Wachusett Community College (A)
National University (M,B)
New England College of Finance (A)
New Mexico State University (B)
New York Institute of Technology (B)
Northern Virginia Community College (A)
The Ohio State University (M)
Oral Roberts University (M,B)
Park University (M)
Patrick Henry Community College (A)
The Pennsylvania State University University Park Campus (A)
Pfeiffer University (M)
Randolph Community College (A)
Raritan Valley Community College (A)
Regent University (M)
St. Cloud State University (M)
Saint Joseph's College of Maine (A,B,UC)
Saint Leo University (A,B)
Saint Mary-of-the-Woods College (B)
Salve Regina University (M)
Shippensburg University of Pennsylvania (M)
Sinclair Community College (A)
Southeast Community College, Beatrice Campus (A)
Southeast Community College, Lincoln Campus (A)
Southeast Community College, Milford Campus (A)
Southern Arkansas University Tech (A)
Southern New Hampshire University (A,B)
Southern Oregon University (B)
Southwestern Assemblies of God University (A)
Southwestern College (M,B)
Stanly Community College (A)
State University of New York Empire State College (M)
Stephens College (B)
Strayer University (M,,A,UC)
Syracuse University (M)
Taft College (A)
Taylor University (B)
Texas Woman's University (M)
Touro University International (D,M,B)
Troy University (M)
University of Alaska Southeast (M,A)
University of Colorado at Colorado Springs (M)
University of Colorado at Denver and Health Sciences Center—Downtown Denver Campus (M)
The University of Findlay (M)
University of Florida (M,B)
University of Hawaii–West Oahu (B)
University of Houston–Victoria (M)
University of Illinois at Springfield (B)
University of La Verne (M)
The University of Maine at Augusta (A)
University of Management and Technology (A)
University of Maryland University College (M,B)
University of Massachusetts Amherst (B)
University of Michigan–Flint (M)
University of Nebraska–Lincoln (M)
University of North Dakota (M)
University of Phoenix Online Campus (D,M)
University of St. Francis (M)
The University of Tennessee at Martin (M)
The University of Texas at Tyler (M)
The University of Texas of the Permian Basin (M)
University of the Incarnate Word (B)
University of Wisconsin–Platteville (B)
University of Wisconsin–Platteville (B)
University of Wyoming (M,B)
Upper Iowa University (B)
Vance-Granville Community College (A)
Vincennes University (A)
Virginia Polytechnic Institute and State University (M)
Washington State University (B)
Webster University (M)
Western Piedmont Community College (A)
West Texas A&M University (M)
West Virginia University (M)
Westwood Online (M)
Wilkes Community College (A)
Ashworth College (M)

BUSINESS ADMINISTRATION (BACHELOR COMPLETION)

Indiana Wesleyan University (B)

BUSINESS ADMINISTRATION (BACHELOR OF APPLIED SCIENCE)

Mayville State University (B)

BUSINESS ADMINISTRATION (IMBA)

The Pennsylvania State University University Park Campus (M)

BUSINESS ADMINISTRATION (INFORMATION SYSTEMS/ TECHNOLOGY EMPHASIS)

City University (B)

BUSINESS ADMINISTRATION (MARKETING EMPHASIS)

City University (B)

BUSINESS ADMINISTRATION (OFF CAMPUS MBA)

The University of Montana (M)

BUSINESS ADMINISTRATION (PROJECT MANAGEMENT EMPHASIS)

City University (B)

BUSINESS ADMINISTRATION AND BUSINESS EDUCATION CONCENTRATIONS

Parkland College (A)

BUSINESS ADMINISTRATION AND LIBERAL ARTS; HUMANITIES AND SOCIAL SCIENCE

Clinton Community College (A)

BUSINESS ADMINISTRATION AND MANAGEMENT

Alaska Pacific University (B)
Hope International University (B)
The University of Texas System (M)

BUSINESS ADMINISTRATION AND MANAGEMENT–NONPROFIT EMPHASIS

Alaska Pacific University (B)

BUSINESS ADMINISTRATION BUSINESS LAW

Peirce College (UC)

BUSINESS ADMINISTRATION CAREER

Middlesex Community College (A)

BUSINESS ADMINISTRATION COMPLETION–FINANCE

Walden University (B)

BUSINESS ADMINISTRATION COMPLETION–HUMAN RESOURCE MANAGEMENT

Walden University (B)

BUSINESS ADMINISTRATION COMPLETION–INFORMATION SYSTEMS

Walden University (B)

BUSINESS ADMINISTRATION COMPLETION–MANAGEMENT

Walden University (B)

BUSINESS ADMINISTRATION COMPLETION–MARKETING

Walden University (B)

BUSINESS ADMINISTRATION COMPLETION, GENERAL

Walden University (B)

BUSINESS ADMINISTRATION IN AVIATION

Embry-Riddle Aeronautical University (M)

BUSINESS ADMINISTRATION OF TECHNICAL STUDIES

Bellevue University (B)

BUSINESS ADMINISTRATION TRANSFER

Anne Arundel Community College (A)
Middlesex Community College (A)

BUSINESS ADMINISTRATION–ACCELERATED FOUNDATION COURSE PROGRAM

Missouri State University (M)

BUSINESS ADMINISTRATION–ACCELERATED ONLINE BACHELORS OF BUSINESS ADMINISTRATION

LeTourneau University (B)

BUSINESS ADMINISTRATION–ACCOUNTING

Limestone College (B)

BUSINESS ADMINISTRATION–ACCOUNTING CONCENTRATION

Peirce College (A,B)
Westwood Online (B)

BUSINESS ADMINISTRATION–APPLIED MANAGEMENT

Tompkins Cortland Community College (A)

BUSINESS ADMINISTRATION–BUSINESS LAW CONCENTRATION

Peirce College (A,B)

BUSINESS ADMINISTRATION–COMPUTER PROGRAMMING

Limestone College (B)

BUSINESS ADMINISTRATION–COMPUTER SOFTWARE APPLICATIONS

Limestone College (B)

BUSINESS ADMINISTRATION–DISTANCE MBA PROGRAM

Colorado State University (M)

BUSINESS ADMINISTRATION–E-COMMERCE EMPHASIS (BULGARIA)

City University (B)

BUSINESS ADMINISTRATION–E. MBA

Pace University (M)

BUSINESS ADMINISTRATION–ECONOMIC CRIME AND FRAUD MANAGEMENT

Utica College (M)

BUSINESS ADMINISTRATION–ENTREPRENEURSHIP/SMALL BUSINESS MANAGEMENT CONCENTRATION

Peirce College (A,B)

BUSINESS ADMINISTRATION–EXECUTIVE BUSINESS ADMINISTRATION

University of North Alabama (M)

BUSINESS ADMINISTRATION–EXECUTIVE MASTER OF BUSINESS ADMINISTRATION

Colorado Technical University (M)
Purdue University (M)

BUSINESS ADMINISTRATION–GENERAL BUSINESS

Limestone College (B)

BUSINESS ADMINISTRATION–GENERAL MANAGEMENT EMPHASIS

City University (B)

BUSINESS ADMINISTRATION–GLOBAL MBA

Southern New Hampshire University (M)

BUSINESS ADMINISTRATION–GLOBAL MBA ONLINE

The University of Texas at Dallas (M)

BUSINESS ADMINISTRATION–HUMAN RESOURCE EMPHASIS

City University (B)

BUSINESS ADMINISTRATION–HUMAN RESOURCE MANAGEMENT CONCENTRATION
Peirce College (A,B)

BUSINESS ADMINISTRATION–INDIVIDUALIZED STUDY EMPHASIS
City University (B)

BUSINESS ADMINISTRATION–MANAGEMENT
Limestone College (B)

BUSINESS ADMINISTRATION–MANAGEMENT CONCENTRATION
Peirce College (A,B)

BUSINESS ADMINISTRATION–MANAGEMENT EMPHASIS
Community College of Denver (A)

BUSINESS ADMINISTRATION–MARKETING AND SALES CONCENTRATION
Westwood Online (B)

BUSINESS ADMINISTRATION–MARKETING CONCENTRATION
Peirce College (A,B)

BUSINESS ADMINISTRATION–MASTER OF BUSINESS ADMINISTRATION WITH CONCENTRATION
Saint Leo University (M)

BUSINESS ADMINISTRATION–ONLINE MASTERS OF BUSINESS ADMINISTRATION
University of Wisconsin–Whitewater (M)

BUSINESS ADMINISTRATION–ONLINE MBA
Franklin University (M)

BUSINESS ADMINISTRATION–ONLINE MBA PROGRAM
University of North Alabama (M)

BUSINESS ADMINISTRATION–ONLINE PROFESSIONAL MBA PROGRAM (UMASS AMHERST DEGREE)
University of Massachusetts Amherst (M)

BUSINESS ADMINISTRATION–PROFESSIONAL ACCOUNTANCY
Utica College (M)

BUSINESS ADMINISTRATION–REAL ESTATE MANAGEMENT CONCENTRATION
Peirce College (B)

BUSINESS ADMINISTRATION–TECHNICAL MANAGEMENT
College of Southern Maryland (A)

BUSINESS ADMINISTRATION, ENTREPRENEURSHIP
Community College of Denver (UC)

BUSINESS ADMINISTRATION, GENERAL
Walden University (M)

BUSINESS ADMINISTRATION, INTERNATIONAL BUSINESS
Community College of Denver (UC)

BUSINESS ADMINISTRATION/ ACCOUNTING
Kaplan University (A)

BUSINESS ADMINISTRATION/ GENERAL BUSINESS
Regions University (B)

BUSINESS ADMINISTRATION/ HEALTH ADMINISTRATION
Pfeiffer University (M)

BUSINESS ADMINISTRATION/ HEALTH CARE MANAGEMENT
University of Phoenix Online Campus (M)

BUSINESS ADMINISTRATION/ INFORMATION COMMUNICATION
Regions University (B)

BUSINESS ADMINISTRATION/ INFORMATION SYSTEMS MANAGEMENT
Regions University (B)

BUSINESS ADMINISTRATION/ MANAGEMENT
Chadron State College (B)
Kaplan University (A)

BUSINESS ADMINISTRATION/ MANAGEMENT INFORMATION SYSTEMS
Chadron State College (B)

BUSINESS ADMINISTRATION/ MARKETING
Chadron State College (B)
University of Phoenix Online Campus (M)

BUSINESS ADMINISTRATION/ ORGANIZATIONAL CHANGE AND LEADERSHIP
Pfeiffer University (M)

BUSINESS ADMINISTRATIONS
Ashford University (M)

BUSINESS AND ECONOMICS
Eastern Oregon University (B)

BUSINESS AND LEADERSHIP
Marylhurst University (B)

BUSINESS AND MANAGEMENT
Skidmore College (B)

BUSINESS AND ORGANIZATIONAL SECURITY MANAGEMENT
Webster University (M)

BUSINESS AND TECHNOLOGY
Columbia University (UC)

BUSINESS ASPECTS OF PUBLISHING
Pace University (GC)

BUSINESS COMPLETION
Presentation College (B)

BUSINESS COMPLETION PROGRAM, GENERAL
Missouri State University (B)

BUSINESS COMPUTER SPECIALIST OPTION
Darton College (A)

BUSINESS CONCENTRATION
American InterContinental University Online (A)

BUSINESS EDUCATION

Darton College (A)
East Carolina University (M)
Edmonds Community College (A)
Southern New Hampshire University (M)

BUSINESS ENGLISH ONLINE

University of Illinois at Chicago (UC)

BUSINESS ESSENTIALS

Regent University (GC)

BUSINESS FINANCE

California College for Health Sciences (A,B)

BUSINESS FOUNDATIONS

University of Washington (UC)

BUSINESS GENERALIST EMPHASIS

Community College of Denver (A)

BUSINESS HOSPITALITY MANAGEMENT

University of Phoenix Online Campus (B)

BUSINESS IN GENERAL BUSINESS

California College for Health Sciences (A)

BUSINESS INFORMATION SYSTEMS

Bellevue University (B)
Utah State University (M)

BUSINESS INFORMATION SYSTEMS (BACHELOR COMPLETION)

Indiana Wesleyan University (B)

BUSINESS INFORMATION TECHNOLOGY

Edmonds Community College (A)

BUSINESS INTELLIGENCE ANALYST

Bellevue Community College (UC)

BUSINESS INTELLIGENCE DEVELOPER

Bellevue Community College (UC)

BUSINESS MANAGEMENT

Anne Arundel Community College (A)
Bramson ORT College (A)
Burlington County College (A)
California College for Health Sciences (B)
Central Texas College (A)
Columbus State Community College (A)
Dawson Community College (A)
Edmonds Community College (A)
Malone College (B)
Northern Virginia Community College (A)
Northwest Missouri State University (B)
Parkland College (A)
The Pennsylvania State University University Park Campus (UC)
The University of Findlay (B)

BUSINESS MANAGEMENT CONCENTRATION

Colorado Technical University (M)

BUSINESS MANAGEMENT TECHNOLOGY

The University of Toledo (A,UC)

BUSINESS MANAGEMENT TECHNOLOGY–FASTTRACK OPTION

The University of Toledo (A)

BUSINESS MANAGEMENT–ASB

Penn Foster Career School (A)

BUSINESS MANAGEMENT–EBUSINESS EMPHASIS

North Dakota State College of Science (A)

BUSINESS MANAGEMENT–FINANCE OPTION ASB

Penn Foster Career School (A)

BUSINESS MANAGEMENT–MARKETING OPTION ASB

Penn Foster Career School (A)

BUSINESS MANAGEMENT–PUBLIC MANAGEMENT SPECIALIZATION

Northern Virginia Community College (A)

BUSINESS MANAGEMENT, ACCOUNTING

Rasmussen College Eden Prarie (A)

BUSINESS MANAGEMENT, BANKING AND FINANCE

Rasmussen College Eden Prarie (A)

BUSINESS MANAGEMENT, BUSINESS ADMINISTRATION

Rasmussen College Eden Prarie (A)

BUSINESS MANAGEMENT, CHILD CARE

Rasmussen College Eden Prarie (A)

BUSINESS MANAGEMENT, HUMAN RESOURCES

Rasmussen College Eden Prarie (A)

BUSINESS MANAGEMENT, INTERNET MARKETING

Rasmussen College Eden Prarie (A)

BUSINESS MANAGEMENT, SALES AND MARKETING

Rasmussen College Eden Prarie (A)

BUSINESS MARKETING

California College for Health Sciences (A,B)

BUSINESS ONLINE

Bryant and Stratton Online (A)
University of Minnesota, Crookston (B)

BUSINESS OPERATIONS–ACCOUNTING

International Institute of the Americas (A)

BUSINESS OPERATIONS–BUSINESS TECHNOLOGY

International Institute of the Americas (A)
International Institute of the Americas (A)

BUSINESS PROFESSIONAL STUDIES

Davenport University Online (B)

BUSINESS QUALITY MANAGEMENT

Southwestern College (B)

BUSINESS SECURITY AND ASSURANCE

Kaplan University (B)

BUSINESS SOFTWARE APPLICATIONS SPECIALIST

Madison Area Technical College (UC)

BUSINESS SOFTWARE SPECIALIST–BUSINESS TECHNOLOGY SYSTEMS

Bellevue Community College (UC)

BUSINESS STRATEGY

Northwestern University (M)

BUSINESS STUDIES

Granite State College (A)
Southern New Hampshire University (B)
University of Massachusetts Amherst (UC)

BUSINESS TECHNOLOGY

Motlow State Community College (A)
West Virginia University at Parkersburg (A)

BUSINESS TECHNOLOGY MANAGEMENT–MASTER OF SCIENCE IN BUSINESS TECHNOLOGY MANAGEMENT

Coleman College (M)

BUSINESS–APPLIED BUSINESS

Davenport University Online (B)

BUSINESS–ASSOCIATE IN BUSINESS, MAJOR IN GENERAL BUSINESS

Piedmont Technical College (A)

BUSINESS–ASSOCIATE IN BUSINESS, MAJOR IN OFFICE SYSTEMS TECHNOLOGY

Piedmont Technical College (A)

BUSINESS–BACHELOR OF SCIENCE IN BUSINESS

Murray State University (B)

BUSINESS–BUSINESS ADMINISTRATION

Erie Community College (A)

BUSINESS–BUSINESS ADMINISTRATION (TRANSFER OPTION)

Erie Community College (A)

BUSINESS–ENTREPRENEURSHIP

Andrew Jackson University (B)

BUSINESS–FASHION MERCHANDISING

Westwood Online (B)

BUSINESS–FOUNDATIONS OF BUSINESS

University of Massachusetts Lowell (GC)

BUSINESS–GENERAL BUSINESS CONCENTRATION

Andrew Jackson University (B)

BUSINESS–MANAGEMENT/ LEADERSHIP CONCENTRATION

Andrew Jackson University (B)

BUSINESS–OFFICE MANAGEMENT

Erie Community College (A)

BUSINESS–SALES CONCENTRATION

Andrew Jackson University (B)

BUSINESS–SALES MANAGEMENT

Andrew Jackson University (B)

BUSINESS, GENERAL

Berkeley College-New York City Campus (B)
Berkeley College-Westchester Campus (B)
California College for Health Sciences (B)
Capella University (M)
Chadron State College (B)
Excelsior College (B)
Kansas State University (B)
New Mexico State University–Carlsbad (B)
Saint Mary-of-the-Woods College (A)
Seminole Community College (A)
Southwestern Assemblies of God University (A)
Taft College (A)
University of Alaska Southeast (B)
University of Houston–Victoria (B)
Upper Iowa University (A)

BUSINESS, HUMANITIES, SOCIAL SCIENCES

Columbia Basin College (A)

BUSINESS, MANAGEMENT, AND COMMUNICATION

Corban College (B)

BUSINESS, MANAGEMENT, AND ECONOMICS

State University of New York Empire State College (A,B)

BUSINESS,GENERAL

Schoolcraft College (A)

BUSINESS/ACCOUNTING

Capella University (B)
Kaplan University (B)
University of Phoenix Online Campus (B)

BUSINESS/BUSINESS ADMINISTRATION

Capella University (B)
University of Phoenix Online Campus (B)

BUSINESS/COMMUNICATION

University of Phoenix Online Campus (B)

BUSINESS/E-BUSINESS

University of Phoenix Online Campus (B)

BUSINESS/FINANCE

Capella University (B)
Kaplan University (B)
University of Phoenix Online Campus (B)

BUSINESS/GLOBAL MANAGEMENT

University of Phoenix Online Campus (B)

BUSINESS/HUMAN RESOURCE MANAGEMENT

Capella University (B)

BUSINESS/INTEGRATED SUPPLY CHAIN AND OPERATIONS MANAGEMENT

University of Phoenix Online Campus (B)

BUSINESS/MANAGEMENT

University of Phoenix Online Campus (B)

BUSINESS/MANAGEMENT AND LEADERSHIP

Capella University (B)

BUSINESS/MANAGEMENT OF INFORMATION SYSTEMS

Kaplan University (B)

BUSINESS/MARKETING

University of Phoenix Online Campus (B)
Capella University (B)

BUSINESS/PUBLIC ADMINISTRATION

University of Phoenix Online Campus (B)

BUSINESS/RETAIL MANAGEMENT

University of Phoenix Online Campus (B)

CANADIAN STUDIES

Western Kentucky University (UC)

CANADIAN STUDIES (3 YEAR)

Athabasca University (B)

CANADIAN STUDIES (4 YEAR)

Athabasca University (B)

CARDIOVASCULAR BIOENGINEERING

Stanford University (GC)

CAREER AND TECHNICAL EDUCATION

Ball State University (M)
Indiana State University (B)

Northern Arizona University (M)
University of South Florida (M)
University of Wisconsin–Stout (M,B)
Virginia Polytechnic Institute and State University (M,UC)

CAREER AND TECHNICAL EDUCATION (BS ED.)

Northern Arizona University (B)

CAREER AND TECHNICAL EDUCATION (CTE)

University of West Florida (M)

CAREER AND TECHNICAL STUDIES EDUCATION SPECIALIZATION

University of West Florida (B)

CAREER DEVELOPMENT

Athabasca University (UC)
Memorial University of Newfoundland (UC)

CAREER STUDIES CERTIFICATE–ACCOUNTING

Mountain Empire Community College (UC)

CAREER STUDIES CERTIFICATE–CHILD DEVELOPMENT

Mountain Empire Community College (UC)

CAREER STUDIES CERTIFICATE–COMPUTER SOFTWARE SPECIALIST

Mountain Empire Community College (UC)

CAREER STUDIES CERTIFICATE–GEOGRAPHICAL INFORMATION SYSTEMS

Mountain Empire Community College (UC)

CAREER STUDIES CERTIFICATE–HEALTH INFORMATION TECHNOLOGY

Mountain Empire Community College (UC)

CAREER STUDIES CERTIFICATE–LEGAL OFFICE ASSISTING

Mountain Empire Community College (UC)

CAREER STUDIES CERTIFICATE–MEDICAL RECORDS CLERK

Mountain Empire Community College (UC)

CAREER STUDIES CERTIFICATE–MEDICAL TRANSCRIPTIONIST

Mountain Empire Community College (UC)

CAREER STUDIES CERTIFICATE–OFFICE AUTOMATION SPECIALIST

Mountain Empire Community College (UC)

CAREER STUDIES CERTIFICATE–PERSONAL COMPUTING FOR HOME AND OFFICE

Mountain Empire Community College (UC)

CAREER STUDIES CERTIFICATE–POLYSOMNOGRAPHY

Mountain Empire Community College (UC)

CAREER STUDIES CERTIFICATE–WASTEWATER PLANT OPERATOR

Mountain Empire Community College (UC)

CAREER STUDIES CERTIFICATE–WATER PLANT OPERATOR

Mountain Empire Community College (UC)

CAREER STUDIES CERTIFICATE–WORD PROCESSING

Mountain Empire Community College (UC)

CAREER STUDIES–ALLIED HEALTH

Patrick Henry Community College (UC)

CAREER STUDIES–MANAGEMENT ASSISTANT

Patrick Henry Community College (UC)

CAREER STUDIES–MEDICAL TRANSCRIPTIONIST

Patrick Henry Community College (UC)

CAREER STUDIES–OFFICE ASSISTING

Patrick Henry Community College (UC)

CAREER STUDIES–WELLNESS

Patrick Henry Community College (UC)

CASE MANAGEMENT

Kaplan University (UC)

CASE MANAGEMENT FOR AGING CLIENTS

Lewis and Clark Community College (UC)

CASINO MANAGEMENT

University of Massachusetts Amherst (UC)

CATECHIST CERTIFICATE, ADVANCED

The Catholic Distance University (UC)

CELL BIOLOGY

Illinois Institute of Technology (M)

CERTIFIED INFORMATION SYSTEMS SECURITY PROFESSIONAL (CISSP)

Peirce College (UC)

CERTIFIED NUTRITIONIST

American Health Sciences University (GC)

CFP CERTIFIED FINANCIAL PLANNING

University of Dallas (GC,M)

CHARACTERIZATION OF ORGANIC AND INORGANIC MATERIALS

Illinois Institute of Technology (GC)

CHEMICAL DEPENDENCY SPECIALIZATION

Central Texas College (A)

CHEMICAL DEPENDENCY STUDIES COUNSELING

Tompkins Cortland Community College (A)

CHEMICAL ENGINEERING

Auburn University (M)
Columbia University (M)
Illinois Institute of Technology (M)
Kansas State University (M)
Lehigh University (M)
North Carolina State University (M)
University of North Dakota (B)

CHEMISTRY

Lehigh University (M)
Skidmore College (B)

CHESS IN EDUCATION ONLINE

The University of Texas System (UC)

CHILD AND FAMILY DEVELOPMENT–EARLY INTERVENTION

The University of North Carolina at Charlotte (GC)

CHILD AND FAMILY STUDIES

University of Southern Mississippi (M)

CHILD CARE ADMINISTRATION TRAINING
Colorado State University (UC)

CHILD CARE–BIRTH TO FIVE CARE
Western Washington University (UC)

CHILD DEVELOPMENT
American Military University (B)
American Public University (B)
Concordia University, St. Paul (B)
Southern New Hampshire University (M)

CHILD DEVELOPMENT ASSOCIATE
University of Alaska Southeast (UC)

CHILD DEVELOPMENT SERVICES
Thomas Edison State College (A,B)

CHILDREN'S LITERATURE
The Pennsylvania State University University Park Campus (GC)

CHILDREN'S MENTAL HEALTH
University of South Florida (GC)

CHILDREN, YOUTH, AND FAMILY SERVICES
The Pennsylvania State University University Park Campus (UC)

CHRISTIAN CARE AND COUNSELING
Oral Roberts University (B)

CHRISTIAN EDUCATION
Dallas Baptist University (M)
Union Theological Seminary and Presbyterian School of Christian Education (M)

CHRISTIAN LEADERSHIP
Liberty University (M)

CHRISTIAN MINISTRIES
Anderson University (M)
Crown College (A)
Dallas Baptist University (B)

CHRISTIAN MINISTRY
Crown College (B)
Hope International University (A,B,UC)
Master's College and Seminary (UC)
Regions University (D)

CHRISTIAN OUTREACH
Concordia University, St. Paul (M)

CHRISTIAN SCHOOL ADMINISTRATION
Oral Roberts University (M)

CHRISTIAN SCHOOL ADMINISTRATION (PK–12)
Oral Roberts University (D)

CHRISTIAN SCHOOL CURRICULUM
Oral Roberts University (M)

CHRISTIAN SCHOOL POSTSECONDARY ADMINISTRATION
Oral Roberts University (M)

CHRISTIAN SCHOOL PROGRAM
Regent University (M)

CHRISTIAN STUDIES
Briercrest Distance Learning (A,B)
Luther Rice University (M)

CHRISTIAN STUDIES, BASIC
Trinity Episcopal School for Ministry (UC)

CHRISTIAN TRADITION
Saint Joseph's College of Maine (B,UC)

CHRISTIAN WORKER
Taylor University (UC)

CHROMATOGRAPHY
Illinois Institute of Technology (GC)

CHURCH EDUCATION
Defiance College (UC)

CHURCH LEADERSHIP
Bethany University (B)

CHURCH MINISTRIES
Luther Rice University (D)
Oral Roberts University (B)
Southwestern Assemblies of God University (B)

CINEMA ARTS
Regent University (M)

CIVIL AND CONSTRUCTION ENGINEERING TECHNOLOGY
Thomas Edison State College (A)

CIVIL AND ENVIRONMENTAL ENGINEERING
Virginia Polytechnic Institute and State University (M)

CIVIL ENGINEERING
Auburn University (M)
Colorado State University (M)
Columbia University (M,UC)
Georgia Institute of Technology (M)
Kansas State University (M)
North Carolina State University (M)
Southern Methodist University (M)
University of Florida (M)
University of Florida (M)
University of North Dakota (B)
The University of Texas at Arlington (M)

CIVIL ENGINEERING TECHNOLOGY
Old Dominion University (B)
Penn Foster Career School (A)
Thomas Edison State College (B)

CIVIL ENGINEERING–CONSTRUCTION ENGINEERING AND MANAGEMENT
Columbia University (M)

CIVIL INFRASTRUCTURE ENGINEERING
Virginia Polytechnic Institute and State University (M)

CLASSICAL CIVILIZATION
University of Florida (D)

CLASSICS
Skidmore College (B)

CLASSROOM TECHNOLOGY
Wilkes University (M)

CLERICAL ASSISTANT
Mountain Empire Community College (UC)

CLERICAL STUDIES
Patrick Henry Community College (UC)

CLINICAL GENETICS
Simmons College (GC)

CLINICAL INFORMATICS
Stanford University (GC)

CLINICAL INFORMATION SYSTEMS MANAGEMENT
Stephens College (M)

CLINICAL INVESTIGATION
Boston University (GC)
Boston University (GC)
MGH Institute of Health Professions (GC)
University of South Florida (GC)

CLINICAL INVESTIGATIONS
MGH Institute of Health Professions (M)

CLINICAL LAB SCIENCE
Thomas Edison State College (A,B)

CLINICAL LABORATORY SCIENCE
University of Cincinnati (B)

CLINICAL LABORATORY SCIENCE (LATERAL ENTRY)
Winston-Salem State University (B)

CLINICAL LABORATORY SCIENCES
Weber State University (B)

CLINICAL LABORATORY SCIENCES (ADVANCED AND CATEGORICAL)
Rosalind Franklin University of Medicine and Science (M)

CLINICAL LABORATORY SCIENCES (ENTRY-LEVEL)
Rosalind Franklin University of Medicine and Science (M)

CLINICAL LABORATORY TECHNICIAN
Weber State University (A)

CLINICAL NURSE SPECIALIST
East Carolina University (M)

CLINICAL NUTRITION
University of Medicine and Dentistry of New Jersey (M)

CLINICAL NUTRITION (DCN)
University of Medicine and Dentistry of New Jersey (D)

CLINICAL NUTRITION/NUTRITION EDUCATION
Rosalind Franklin University of Medicine and Science (M)

CLINICAL PATHOLOGY
University of Massachusetts Lowell (GC)

CLINICAL PSYCHOLOGY
Fielding Graduate University (D)

CLINICAL RESEARCH ORGANIZATION AND MANAGEMENT
Drexel University (M)

CLINICAL TRIALS
Drexel University (M,UC)

COACHING–NATIONAL COACHING CERTIFICATION
United States Sports Academy (UC)

COACHING–NEW YORK STATE COACHING CERTIFICATION
Monroe Community College (UC)

COLLABORATIVE EDUCATIONAL LEADERSHIP
Fielding Graduate University (M)

COLLABORATIVE TEACHER AND EARLY CHILDHOOD EDUCATION
Auburn University (M)

COLLEGE STUDENT PERSONNEL
Arkansas Tech University (M)

COLLEGE TRANSFER
Caldwell Community College and Technical Institute (A)
Randolph Community College (A)

COLLEGE TRANSFER DEGREE
Central Piedmont Community College (A)

COLLEGE/UNIVERSITY TRANSFER
Wake Technical Community College (A)

COMMERCE AND BUSINESS ADMINISTRATION (GENERAL BUSINESS)
The University of Alabama (B)

COMMERCIAL LENDING
New England College of Finance (GC)

COMMUNICATION
Andrew Jackson University (A)
Regent University (M)
Utah Valley State College (A)

COMMUNICATION DISORDERS
Western Kentucky University (M)

COMMUNICATION DISORDERS AND SCIENCE–CEUS IN COMMUNICATION DISORDERS AND SCIENCE
California State University, Northridge (GC)

COMMUNICATION DISORDERS AND SCIENCES
California State University, Northridge (M)

COMMUNICATION STUDIES
Athabasca University (B)
University of Maryland University College (B)

COMMUNICATION STUDIES–PROFESSIONAL COMMUNICATION STUDIES
Pace University (B)

COMMUNICATION–PROFESSIONAL COMMUNICATION
East Carolina University (GC)

COMMUNICATION/ORGANIZATIONAL COMMUNICATIONS/MASS COMMUNICATION/PUBLIC RELATIONS
Montana State University–Billings (B)

COMMUNICATION/PUBLIC RELATIONS/JOURNALISM CONCENTRATION
East Carolina University (B)

COMMUNICATIONS
Andrew Jackson University (B)
Indiana Wesleyan University (UC)
Prescott College (B)
Regent University (B)
State University of New York at Oswego (B)
Thomas Edison State College (B)

COMMUNICATIONS AND APPLIED TECHNOLOGY
Drexel University (B)

COMMUNICATIONS AND TECHNOLOGY
University of Alberta (M)

COMMUNICATIONS MANAGEMENT
Southern Polytechnic State University (GC)
Syracuse University (M)

COMMUNICATIONS STUDIES

The Pennsylvania State University University Park Campus (UC)

COMMUNICATIONS TECHNOLOGY

Strayer University (M)

COMMUNICATIVE DISORDERS

Eastern New Mexico University (M)

COMMUNICATIVE DISORDERS AND DEAF EDUCATION (POST BACHELOR'S)

Utah State University (B)

COMMUNITY AND ECONOMIC DEVELOPMENT

The Pennsylvania State University University Park Campus

COMMUNITY AND HUMAN SERVICES

State University of New York Empire State College (A,B)

COMMUNITY AND REGIONAL PLANNING

Iowa State University of Science and Technology (M)

COMMUNITY CHANGE AND CIVIC LEADERSHIP

Antioch University McGregor (M)

COMMUNITY COLLEGE EDUCATION

University of Central Florida (GC)

COMMUNITY COLLEGE LEADERSHIP

Mississippi State University (D,M)

COMMUNITY COLLEGE MANAGEMENT

Antioch University McGregor (M)

COMMUNITY COLLEGE TEACHING

California State University, Dominguez Hills (UC)
North Carolina State University (GC)

COMMUNITY COUNSELING

St. Mary's University of San Antonio (M)

COMMUNITY DEVELOPMENT

Fort Hays State University (UC)

COMMUNITY DEVELOPMENT, COMMUNITY SERVICES MAJOR

Central Michigan University (B)

COMMUNITY DEVELOPMENT, HEALTH SCIENCES MAJOR

Central Michigan University (B)

COMMUNITY DEVELOPMENT, PUBLIC ADMINISTRATION MAJOR

Central Michigan University (B)

COMMUNITY HEALTH

Old Dominion University (M)
Walden University (M)

COMMUNITY HEALTH AND DEVELOPMENT

Saybrook Graduate School and Research Center (GC)

COMMUNITY HEALTH PROMOTION

Indiana State University (B)

COMMUNITY LEADERSHIP

Duquesne University (M)

COMMUNITY MENTAL HEALTH

New York Institute of Technology (B)

COMMUNITY PSYCHOLOGY

St. Cloud State University (B)

COMMUNITY REHABILITATION

University of Calgary (B)
Vincennes University (UC)

COMMUNITY SERVICES

Thomas Edison State College (A,B)

COMMUNITY STUDIES

Cape Breton University (B)

COMMUNITY SUPPORTS FOR PEOPLE WITH DISABILITIES

South Central College (A,UC)

COMMUNITY WELLNESS ADVOCATE

University of Alaska Southeast (UC)

COMMUNITY, MEDIA, AND TECHNOLOGY

University of Massachusetts Boston (UC)

COMMUNITY-BASED DEVELOPMENT

Colorado State University (UC)

COMPLETER PROGRAM IN COMMUNITY STUDIES

University of Massachusetts Boston (B)

COMPLETION PROGRAM

American InterContinental University Online (A)

COMPUTATIONAL FLUID DYNAMICS

The University of Tennessee (GC)

COMPUTER AND DIGITAL FORENSICS

Champlain College (B,UC)

COMPUTER AND INFORMATION SCIENCE

University of Maryland University College (B)

COMPUTER AND NETWORK SECURITY TECHNOLOGIES

Illinois Institute of Technology (GC)

COMPUTER APPLICATIONS

University of Alaska Southeast (UC)

COMPUTER APPLICATIONS FOR THE OFFICE

Erie Community College (UC)

COMPUTER ARCHITECTURE

Stanford University (GC)

COMPUTER ARTS/NEW MEDIA

Academy of Art University (M,A,B)

COMPUTER EDUCATION AND COGNITIVE SYSTEMS

University of North Texas (M)

COMPUTER ENGINEERING

Illinois Institute of Technology (GC,M)
Iowa State University of Science and Technology (M)
Southern Methodist University (M)
University of Florida (M)
University of Michigan–Dearborn (M)
University of Wisconsin–Madison (M)

Virginia Polytechnic Institute and State University (GC,M)
Walden University (M)

COMPUTER ENGINEERING (BIOINFORMATICS TRACK)

University of Florida (M)

COMPUTER ENGINEERING (GENERAL TRACK)

University of Florida (M)

COMPUTER ENGINEERING TECHNOLOGY

Grantham University (A,B)

COMPUTER ENGINEERING–BIOINFORMATICS

University of Florida (M)

COMPUTER GAME DEVELOPMENT

Edmonds Community College (UC)

COMPUTER GRAPHICS

Stevens Institute of Technology (GC)

COMPUTER HARDWARE AND VLSI DESIGN

Stanford University (GC)

COMPUTER INFORMATION AND OFFICE SYSTEMS

University of Alaska Southeast (A,UC)

COMPUTER INFORMATION MANAGEMENT

Ashworth College (A)

COMPUTER INFORMATION SYSTEMS

Bellevue University (M)
Caldwell College (B)
Champlain College (B)
The College of St. Scholastica (M,UC)
Darton College (A)
DeVry University Online (B)
Ivy Tech Community College–Bloomington (A)
Ivy Tech Community College–Central Indiana (A)
Ivy Tech Community College–Columbus (A)
Ivy Tech Community College–East Central (A)
Ivy Tech Community College–Kokomo (A)
Ivy Tech Community College–Lafayette (A)
Ivy Tech Community College–North Central (A)
Ivy Tech Community College–Northeast (A)
Ivy Tech Community College–Northwest (A)
Ivy Tech Community College–Southeast (A)
Ivy Tech Community College–Southern Indiana (A)
Ivy Tech Community College–Southwest (A)
Ivy Tech Community College–Wabash Valley (A)
Ivy Tech Community College–Whitewater (A)
Jamestown Community College (A)
Jones College (A,B)
Kaplan University (A)
Mercy College (B)
Missouri State University (M)
Moberly Area Community College (A)
Mount Wachusett Community College (A)
Nova Southeastern University (D,M)
Prescott College (B)
Saint Leo University (B)
Saint Mary-of-the-Woods College (B)
Strayer University (A,B,UC)
Thomas Edison State College (B,A)

COMPUTER INFORMATION SYSTEMS (BACHELOR OF APPLIED SCIENCE)

Mayville State University (B)

COMPUTER INFORMATION SYSTEMS–CERTIFICATE OF ADVANCED STUDY

University of Denver (UC)

COMPUTER INFORMATION SYSTEMS–DATABASE MANAGEMENT SPECIALTY (BAS)

Davenport University Online (B)

COMPUTER INFORMATION SYSTEMS–MASTER OF APPLIED SCIENCE IN COMPUTER INFORMATION SYSTEMS

University of Denver (M)

COMPUTER INFORMATION SYSTEMS–MASTER OF SCIENCE IN COMPUTER INFORMATION SYSTEMS

Boston University (M)

COMPUTER INFORMATION SYSTEMS–WEB DESIGN

North Dakota State College of Science (UC)

COMPUTER INFORMATION SYSTEMS/JAVA

Kaplan University (A)

COMPUTER INFORMATION SYSTEMS/NETWORKING

Kaplan University (A)

COMPUTER INFORMATION SYSTEMS/PROGRAMMING

Kaplan University (A)

COMPUTER INFORMATION SYSTEMS/WEB DEVELOPMENT

Kaplan University (A)

COMPUTER INFORMATION SYSTEMS/WIRELESS NETWORKING

Kaplan University (A)

COMPUTER INFORMATION TECHNOLOGY

Franklin Pierce College (B)
Western Kentucky University (B)

COMPUTER INFORMATION TECHNOLOGY AND SYSTEMS MANAGEMENT

Cleveland Institute of Electronics (A)

COMPUTER LANGUAGES AND OPERATING SYSTEMS

Stanford University (GC)

COMPUTER NETWORK ENGINEERING

Westwood Online (A)

COMPUTER NETWORK MANAGEMENT

Westwood Online (B)

COMPUTER NETWORK PROFESSIONAL

East Carolina University (GC)

COMPUTER NETWORKING

George Mason University (GC)
Strayer University (A,B)

COMPUTER NETWORKING AND SECURITY MANAGEMENT

Keiser College (A)

COMPUTER OPERATIONS TECHNOLOGY

Southwestern College (B)

COMPUTER PROGRAMMER/ANALYST

Lansing Community College (UC)

COMPUTER PROGRAMMING

Cleveland Institute of Electronics (UC)
College of Southern Maryland (A)
Seminole Community College (UC)
North Carolina State University (UC)

COMPUTER PROGRAMMING (POST-BACCALAUREATE)

Winston-Salem State University (UC)

COMPUTER PROGRAMMING AND ANALYSIS

Seminole Community College (A)

COMPUTER PROGRAMMING AND ANALYSIS (C++ PROGRAMMING SPECIALIZATION)

Seminole Community College (A)

COMPUTER PROGRAMMING AND ANALYSIS VISUAL BASIC PROGRAMMING SPECIALIZATION

Seminole Community College (A)

COMPUTER PROGRAMMING TECHNOLOGY

Southwestern College (B)

COMPUTER PROGRAMMING–C PROGRAMMING

University of Washington (UC)

COMPUTER PROGRAMMING–C++ PROGRAMMING

City University (GC)
University of Washington (UC)

COMPUTER PROGRAMMING–JAVA 2 PROGRAMMING

University of Washington (UC)

COMPUTER RELATED CRIME INVESTIGATIONS

St. Petersburg College (UC)

COMPUTER SCIENCE

Acadia University (UC)
Boston University (M)
California National University for Advanced Studies (B)
California State University, Chico (M,B)
Capitol College (M)
Colorado State University (M)
Columbia University (GC,M)
DePaul University (M)
Drexel University (M)
Franklin University (A,B)
George Mason University (M)
Grantham University (A,B)
Illinois Institute of Technology (M)
Jamestown Community College (A)
Mercy College (B)
National University (M)
North Carolina State University (M)
Northwest Missouri State University (B)
Nova Southeastern University (D,M)
Old Dominion University (B)
Skidmore College (B)
Southern Methodist University (M)
Stanford University (M)
Texas Tech University (M)
Thomas Edison State College (A,B)
Touro University International (B)
University of Colorado at Boulder (M)
University of Illinois at Springfield (M,B)
University of Management and Technology (M,A,B)
Utah State University (M,B)
Walden University (M)

COMPUTER SCIENCE AND ENGINEERING

Auburn University (M)
The University of Texas at Arlington (M)

COMPUTER SCIENCE AND ENGINEERING TECHNOLOGY

The University of Toledo (A,B)

COMPUTER SCIENCE COMPUTER AND INFORMATION SYSTEMS SECURITY

Limestone College (B)

COMPUTER SCIENCE INFORMATION TECHNOLOGY

Limestone College (B)

COMPUTER SCIENCE INTERNET MANAGEMENT

Limestone College (A)

COMPUTER SCIENCE INTERNET MANAGEMENT–DATABASE

Limestone College (B)

COMPUTER SCIENCE INTERNET MANAGEMENT–E-COMMERCE

Limestone College (B)

COMPUTER SCIENCE INTERNET MANAGEMENT–OPERATIONS MANAGEMENT

Limestone College (B)

COMPUTER SCIENCE INTERNET MANAGEMENT–WEB DEVELOPMENT

Limestone College (B)

COMPUTER SCIENCE INTERNET MANAGEMENT, GENERAL

Limestone College (B)

COMPUTER SCIENCE MANAGEMENT INFORMATION SYSTEMS

Limestone College (A)

COMPUTER SCIENCE PROGRAMMING

Limestone College (A,B)

COMPUTER SCIENCE TECHNOLOGY

Thomas Edison State College (A,B)

COMPUTER SCIENCE WITH CYBERSECURITY CONCENTRATION

Stevens Institute of Technology (M)

COMPUTER SCIENCE–A+ CERTIFICATION AND COMPUTER TECHNOLOGY

Cleveland Institute of Electronics (UC)

COMPUTER SCIENCE–APPLIED COMPUTER SCIENCE

Columbus State University (M)

COMPUTER SCIENCE–APPLIED COMPUTER SCIENCE ASB

Penn Foster Career School (A)

COMPUTER SCIENCE–APPLIED COMPUTER STUDIES

Thomas Edison State College (A)

COMPUTER SCIENCE–CISCO CERTIFIED NETWORK ASSOCIATE PREPARATION, ACCELERATED

Fort Hays State University (UC)

COMPUTER SCIENCE–CISCO CERTIFIED NETWORK ASSOCIATE PREPARATION, MILITARY

Fort Hays State University (UC)

COMPUTER SCIENCE–CISCO NETWORK ASSOCIATE

Indiana Business College (A)

COMPUTER SCIENCE–FOUNDATIONS IN COMPUTER SCIENCE

Stanford University (GC)

COMPUTER SCIENCE–INFORMATION SYSTEMS

Austin Peay State University (B)
University of Management and Technology (B)

COMPUTER SCIENCE–INFORMATION TECHNOLOGY

Central Texas College (A)
University of Management and Technology (B)

COMPUTER SCIENCE–MASTER OF COMPUTER SCIENCE

University of Illinois at Urbana–Champaign (M)

COMPUTER SCIENCE–MICROSOFT CERTIFIED SYSTEMS ADMINISTRATOR

Seminole Community College (UC)

COMPUTER SCIENCE–MICROSOFT CERTIFIED SYSTEMS ENGINEER

Seminole Community College (UC)

COMPUTER SCIENCE–SOFTWARE ENGINEERING

University of Management and Technology (B)

COMPUTER SCIENCE/TELECOM MANAGEMENT WITH CONCENTRATION IN SECURITY

Stevens Institute of Technology (M)

COMPUTER SECURITY

University of Illinois at Urbana–Champaign (GC)

COMPUTER SKILLS FOR MANAGERS

College of Southern Maryland (UC)

COMPUTER SOFTWARE

Excelsior College (A)

COMPUTER SOFTWARE SPECIALIST

The University of Toledo (A,UC)

COMPUTER STUDIES

University of Maryland University College (B)

COMPUTER SYSTEMS (NETWORKING/ TELECOMMUNICATIONS EMPHASIS)

City University (B)

COMPUTER SYSTEMS (PROGRAMMING IN C++ EMPHASIS)

City University (B)

COMPUTER SYSTEMS (WEB DESIGN EMPHASIS)

City University (B)

COMPUTER SYSTEMS MANAGEMENT

University of Maryland University College (M)

COMPUTER SYSTEMS–C++ PROGRAMMING EMPHASIS

City University (M)

COMPUTER SYSTEMS–DATABASE TECHNOLOGY EMPHASIS

City University (B)

COMPUTER SYSTEMS–INDIVIDUALIZED STUDY EMPHASIS

City University (M,B)

COMPUTER SYSTEMS–INFORMATION TECHNOLOGY SECURITY EMPHASIS

City University (B)

COMPUTER SYSTEMS–TECHNOLOGY MANAGEMENT EMPHASIS

City University (M)

COMPUTER SYSTEMS–WEB DEVELOPMENT EMPHASIS

City University (M)

COMPUTER SYSTEMS–WEB LANGUAGES EMPHASIS

City University (B)

COMPUTER SYSTEMS–WEB PROGRAMMING IN E-COMMERCE EMPHASIS

City University (M)

COMPUTER TECHNOLOGY

Excelsior College (B)

COMPUTER TECHNOLOGY (BAS)

Northern Arizona University (B)

COMPUTER, INFORMATION, AND NETWORK SECURITY

DePaul University (M)

COMPUTER/TECHNOLOGY

Cleveland State University (UC)

COMPUTERS AND MANAGEMENT INFORMATION SYSTEMS

Athabasca University (UC)

COMPUTING AND INFORMATION SYSTEMS

Athabasca University (B,UC)

COMPUTING AND INFORMATION SYSTEMS–POST-DIPLOMA

Athabasca University (B)

COMPUTING AND INFORMATION TECHNOLOGY

Community College of Southern Nevada (A)
Granite State College (UC)

COMPUTING SKILLS, BASIC

University of Alaska Southeast (UC)

COMPUTING TECHNOLOGY

Drexel University (B)

COMPUTING TECHNOLOGY IN EDUCATION

Nova Southeastern University (D,M)

COMPUTING–DOCTOR OF PROFESSIONAL STUDIES IN COMPUTING

Pace University (UC)

CONCENTRATION IN COMMUNITY COLLEGE LEADERSHIP

Oregon State University (D)

CONFLICT RESOLUTION
Antioch University McGregor (M)
Kansas State University (GC)
The University of North Carolina at Greensboro (M,UC)

CONFLICT RESOLUTION AND RECONCILIATION
Abilene Christian University (M)

CONSTRUCTION
Thomas Edison State College (B)

CONSTRUCTION ENGINEERING
National University (B)
University of Washington (M)

CONSTRUCTION MANAGEMENT
East Carolina University (M)
University of Washington (UC)

CONSTRUCTION PROJECT MANAGEMENT
University of Florida (GC)

CONSTRUCTION SCIENCE AND MANAGEMENT
Clemson University (M)

CONSTRUCTION TECHNOLOGY
University of Southern Mississippi (B)

CONSTRUCTION TECHNOLOGY–CONSTRUCTION ELECTRICIAN EMPHASIS
Red Rocks Community College (A)

CONSTRUCTION TECHNOLOGY–POWER TECHNOLOGY EMPHASIS
Red Rocks Community College (A)

CONSUMER AND FAMILY SCIENCES WITH CHILD STUDIES EMPHASIS
Western Kentucky University (B)

CONTEMPLATIVE EDUCATION
Naropa University (M)

CONTEMPORARY COMMUNICATIONS
University of Massachusetts Lowell (UC)

CONTENT DEVELOPMENT
Southern Polytechnic State University (GC)

CONTINUING TEACHING LICENSURE
Oregon State University (UC)

CONTRACT MANAGEMENT–MASTER OF CONTRACT MANAGEMENT
American Graduate University (M)

CONTROL AND SYSTEM ENGINEERING
Stanford University (GC)

CONTROL SYSTEMS
Illinois Institute of Technology (GC)

CORPORATE COMMUNICATION
Austin Peay State University (M)

CORPORATE COMMUNICATIONS
Mercy College (B)

CORPORATE FINANCE
University of Dallas (GC,M)

CORPORATE MANAGEMENT
Myers University (B)

CORRECTIONAL ADMINISTRATION AND MANAGEMENT
Bellevue University (B)

CORRECTIONAL OFFICER
Lansing Community College (UC)

CORRECTIONAL SERVICES
Mountain Empire Community College (A)

CORRECTIONS
Indiana State University (UC)

CORRECTIONS PRE-CERTIFICATION
Tunxis Community College (UC)

COUNSELING
Athabasca University (M)
Liberty University (D)
Mercy College (M)
Northern Arizona University (M)
Seton Hall University (M)
University of North Dakota (M)

COUNSELING AND PSYCHOLOGY
Prescott College (M)

COUNSELING EDUCATION AND SUPERVISION
Regent University (D)

COUNSELING PSYCHOLOGY
Memorial University of Newfoundland (M)

COUNSELING PSYCHOLOGY/HUMAN SERVICES
Prescott College (B)

COUNSELING–FAMILY THERAPY TRACK
University of Massachusetts Boston (M)

COUNSELING–MENTAL HEALTH COUNSELING TRACK
University of Massachusetts Boston (M)

COUNSELING–REHABILITATION COUNSELING TRACK
University of Massachusetts Boston (M)

COUNSELING–SCHOOL COUNSELING, ADVANCED
The University of North Carolina at Greensboro (GC)

COUNSELING–SCHOOL GUIDANCE COUNSELING
Prescott College (M)

COUNSELING–SCHOOL GUIDANCE TRACK
University of Massachusetts Boston (M)

COUNSELING/HUMAN RELATIONS
Northern Arizona University (M)

COUNSELING/SCHOOL COUNSELING
Northern Arizona University (M)

COUNSELLING
Athabasca University

COUNSELLING WOMEN
Athabasca University (UC)

COUNSELOR EDUCATION
The University of Alabama

COURT REPORTING AND CAPTIONING
Lenoir Community College (A)

CREATIVE STUDIES

Buffalo State College, State University of New York (M)

CREATIVE WRITING

Naropa University (M)
National University (M)
Prescott College (B)
Wilkes University (M)

CREATIVE WRITING–BILINGUAL

The University of Texas System (M)

CREATIVITY STUDIES

Saybrook Graduate School and Research Center (GC)

CREATIVITY, CHANGE LEADERSHIP, AND CREATIVE PROBLEM SOLVING

Buffalo State College, State University of New York (GC)

CRIME SCENE TECHNOLOGY

St. Petersburg College (A,UC)

CRIMINAL JUSTICE

American Military University (M)
American Public University (M,B)
Andrew Jackson University (M,A,B)
Ashworth College (M,A)
Athabasca University (B)
Bismarck State College (A)
Boston University (M)
Boston University (M)
Brenau University (B)
Caldwell College (B)
Central Missouri State University (M)
Central Texas College (A)
Clovis Community College (A)
College of The Albemarle (A)
College of the Southwest (B)
Columbia College (A,B)
Concordia University, St. Paul (B)
Darton College (A)
Drury University (A)
East Carolina University (M)
Eastern Wyoming College (A)
Excelsior College (B)
Florida Gulf Coast University (B)
Franklin Pierce College (A,B)
Grantham University (A,B)
Indiana Business College (A)
Indiana Wesleyan University (A,UC)
Jefferson Community College (A)
Judson College (B)
Kaplan University (M,A,B)
Keiser College (A,B)
Liberty University (A,B)
Limestone College (B)
Lock Haven University of Pennsylvania (A)
Lynn University (B)
Mercy College (B)
Monroe Community College (A)
Montgomery Community College (A)
New Mexico State University (M)
New York Institute of Technology (B)
Northern Arizona University (B)
Northwestern State University of Louisiana (A,B)
Old Dominion University (B)
Ouachita Technical College (A)
Peninsula College (A)
Penn Foster Career School (A)
The Pennsylvania State University University Park Campus (B)
Prescott College (B)
Randolph Community College (A)
St. John's University (A,B)
Saint Joseph's College of Maine (A)
Saint Leo University (GC,M,B)
Southwestern College (B)
Thomas Edison State College (B)
Troy University (M)
Tunxis Community College (A)
University of Central Florida (M)
University of Cincinnati (M)
University of Florida (UC)
University of Great Falls (B)
University of Maryland University College (B)
University of Massachusetts Lowell (M)
University of Phoenix Online Campus (A)
The University of Texas of the Permian Basin (B)
University of Wisconsin–Platteville (GC)
University of Wisconsin–Platteville (GC)
University of Wisconsin–Platteville (M)
University of Wisconsin–Platteville (M)
University of Wyoming (B)
Upper Iowa University (B)
Utah Valley State College (A)
Washburn University (B)
Washington State University (B)
Weber State University (A)
West Virginia University at Parkersburg (A)
Westwood Online (B)
American Military University (B)
Rasmussen College Eden Prarie (A)

CRIMINAL JUSTICE (13-MONTH PROGRAM)

American InterContinental University Online (B)

CRIMINAL JUSTICE (BACHELOR COMPLETION)

Indiana Wesleyan University (B)

CRIMINAL JUSTICE (BSCJ)

Colorado Technical University (B)

CRIMINAL JUSTICE (COMPLETION DEGREE)

The University of Texas System (B)

CRIMINAL JUSTICE (POLICE SCIENCE)

Adirondack Community College (A)

CRIMINAL JUSTICE ADMINISTRATION

Bellevue University (B)
Lynn University (M)
Myers University (B)
National University (B)
Park University (B)
Taft College (A)
The University of Findlay (B)
University of Great Falls (M)
University of Phoenix Online Campus (B)

CRIMINAL JUSTICE ADMINISTRATION (MSA)

University of West Florida (M)

CRIMINAL JUSTICE ADMINISTRATION CONCENTRATION

American InterContinental University Online (A)

CRIMINAL JUSTICE ECONOMIC CRIME INVESTIGATION

Utica College (B)

CRIMINAL JUSTICE STUDIES

St. Cloud State University (M,B)

CRIMINAL JUSTICE TECHNOLOGY

Stanly Community College (A)

CRIMINAL JUSTICE–BACHELOR OF CRIMINAL JUSTICE

New Mexico State University–Carlsbad (B)

CRIMINAL JUSTICE–COMPUTER SCIENCE

Grantham University (A,B)

CRIMINAL JUSTICE–HOMELAND SECURITY

Grantham University (A,B)

CRIMINAL JUSTICE–MASTER OF CRIMINAL JUSTICE

New Mexico State University–Carlsbad (M)

CRIMINAL JUSTICE–POLICE

Cayuga County Community College (A)

CRIMINAL JUSTICE, CORRECTIONS

Solano Community College (A)

CRIMINAL JUSTICE, LAW ENFORCEMENT

Lansing Community College (A)
Solano Community College (A)

CRIMINAL JUSTICE/ CORRECTIONS

Kaplan University (A,B)

CRIMINAL JUSTICE/CRIME ANALYSIS

Kaplan University (B)

CRIMINAL JUSTICE/CRIME SCENE INVESTIGATION

Kaplan University (B)

CRIMINAL JUSTICE/FORENSIC PSYCHOLOGY

Kaplan University (B)

CRIMINAL JUSTICE/FRAUD EXAMINATION AND INVESTIGATION

Kaplan University (B)

CRIMINAL JUSTICE/GLOBAL ISSUES IN CRIMINAL JUSTICE

Kaplan University (M)

CRIMINAL JUSTICE/HOMELAND SECURITY

Austin Peay State University (B)

CRIMINAL JUSTICE/LAW

Kaplan University (M)

CRIMINAL JUSTICE/LAW ENFORCEMENT

Kaplan University (A,B)

CRIMINAL JUSTICE/LEADERSHIP AND EXECUTIVE MANAGEMENT

Kaplan University (M)

CRIMINAL JUSTICE/POLICING

Kaplan University (M)

CRIMINAL JUSTICE/PRIVATE SECURITY

Kaplan University (A,B)

CRIMINAL JUSTICES STUDIES

University of Massachusetts Amherst (UC)

CRIMINOLOGY

Indiana State University (M,B)
Memorial University of Newfoundland (UC)
University of La Verne (B)

CRIMINOLOGY AND CRIMINAL JUSTICE

Florida State University (M)
Southern Oregon University (B)

CRIMINOLOGY AND CRIMINAL JUSTICE (COMPLETION DEGREE)

The University of Texas at Arlington (B)

CRITICAL AND CREATIVE THINKING (FOCUS ON CREATIVITY AT WORK)

University of Massachusetts Boston (GC)

CRITICAL CARE (ADVANCED TECHNICAL CERTIFICATION)

St. Petersburg College (UC)

CROP SCIENCE

Texas Tech University (M)

CROSS CULTURAL TEACHING

National University (M)

CROSS DISCIPLINARY PROFESSIONAL STUDIES

Rochester Institute of Technology (M)

CROSS-CATEGORICAL SPECIAL EDUCATION

Regent University (M)

CULTURAL AND REGIONAL STUDIES

Prescott College (B)

CULTURAL STUDIES

Prescott College (M)
State University of New York Empire State College (A,B)

CULTURE OF U.S. BUSINESS

University of Illinois at Chicago (UC)

CURRENT ENERGY ISSUES

Illinois Institute of Technology (GC)

CURRICULUM & INSTRUCTION

Stephens College (M)

CURRICULUM AND INSTRUCTION

Black Hills State University (GC)
The College of St. Scholastica (M)
Concordia University Wisconsin (M)
New Mexico State University–Carlsbad (M)
North Carolina State University (M)
University of Florida (M,)
University of Massachusetts Lowell (M)
The University of North Carolina at Greensboro (M)

CURRICULUM AND INSTRUCTION (FOR HEALTH CARE PROFESSIONALS)

University of Cincinnati (M)

CURRICULUM AND INSTRUCTION (FOR LICENSED K-12 TEACHERS)

Capella University (M)

CURRICULUM AND INSTRUCTION CONCENTRATION (10-MONTH PROGRAM)

American InterContinental University Online (M)

CURRICULUM AND INSTRUCTION TEACHER LEADERSHIP

The Pennsylvania State University University Park Campus (M)

CURRICULUM AND INSTRUCTION–ADULT EDUCATION

University of Phoenix Online Campus (M)

CURRICULUM AND INSTRUCTION–CHILDREN'S LITERATURE

The Pennsylvania State University University Park Campus (M)

CURRICULUM AND INSTRUCTION–EDUCATIONAL LEADERSHIP

University of Colorado at Colorado Springs (M)

CURRICULUM AND INSTRUCTION–EFFECTIVE TEACHING AND INSTRUCTIONAL LEADERSHIP EMPHASIS

Buena Vista University (M)

CURRICULUM AND INSTRUCTION–HEALTH PROMOTION EMPHASIS

Virginia Polytechnic Institute and State University (M)

CURRICULUM AND INSTRUCTION–LEARNING TECHNOLOGIES EMPHASIS

New Mexico State University (D)

CURRICULUM AND INSTRUCTION–LITERACY EMPHASIS

The University of Texas System (M)

CURRICULUM AND INSTRUCTION–SCIENCE EDUCATION CONCENTRATION

University of Massachusetts Lowell (M)

CURRICULUM AND INSTRUCTION–TEACHING ENGLISH AS A SECOND LANGUAGE EMPHASIS

Buena Vista University (M)

CURRICULUM AND INSTRUCTION/ READING

The University of Texas at Arlington (M)

CURRICULUM INTEGRATION IN ACTION

University of Washington (UC)

CURRICULUM STUDIES

The University of Montana (M)

CURRICULUM STUDIES IN LEARNING AND TECHNOLOGY

Acadia University (M)

CURRICULUM TEACHING AND LEARNING STUDIES

Memorial University of Newfoundland (M)

CUSTOMER RELATIONS

The University of Montana (UC)

CUSTOMIZED EMPHASIS

Stephens College (M)

CYBER SECURITY

Stevens Institute of Technology (GC)

CYBERSECURITY AND INFORMATION ASSURANCE

Utica College (B)

CYTOTECHNOLOGY

Thomas Edison State College (B)

DANCE

Skidmore College (B)

DANCE EDUCATION

The University of North Carolina at Greensboro (M)

DATA MINING

Connecticut State University System (M)
New Jersey Institute of Technology (GC)

DATA MINING AND APPLICATIONS (STATISTICS)

Stanford University (GC)

DATA RESOURCE MANAGEMENT

University of Washington (UC)

DATA/TELECOMMUNICATIONS

University of Massachusetts Lowell (UC)

DATABASE ADMINISTRATION–CERTIFICATE OF ADVANCED STUDY

University of Denver (UC)

DATABASE MANAGEMENT

University of Washington (UC)

DATABASE SYSTEMS

Stevens Institute of Technology (GC)

DATABASE TECHNOLOGY

Strayer University (A,B)

DATABASES

Stanford University (GC)

DEAF AND HARD OF HEARING

Texas Tech University (GC)

DEAF EDUCATION

Texas Woman's University (M)

DECISION ANALYSIS

Stanford University (GC)

DECISION SUPPORT SYSTEMS

Webster University (GC)

DEGREE COMPLETION

Duquesne University (B)

DEGREE COMPLETION AND BACHELOR'S DEGREE COMPLETION PROGRAM

Boston University (B)

DEGREE COMPLETION–EXECUTIVE UNDERGRADUATE DEGREE COMPLETION

Boston University (B)

DENTAL ASSISTING

Monroe Community College (UC)

DENTAL HYGIENE

Pennsylvania College of Technology (B)
St. Petersburg College (B)
Thomas Edison State College (B)

DENTAL HYGIENE COMPLETION PROGRAM

Northern Arizona University (B)

DENTAL HYGIENE ONLINE (DEGREE COMPLETION PROGRAM)

University of Bridgeport (B)

DENTAL HYGIENE–BS COMPLETION PROGRAM

East Tennessee State University (B)

DENTAL HYGIENE–DEGREE COMPLETION IN DENTAL HYGIENE

Oregon Institute of Technology (B)

DENTISTRY–PRE-DENTISTRY

Darton College (A)

DESIGN FOR CUSTOMER VALUE AND MARKET SUCCESS

Stanford University (GC)

DESIGNING AND IMPLEMENTING WEB-BASED LEARNING ENVIRONMENTS

University of Colorado at Denver and Health Sciences Center—Downtown Denver Campus (UC)

DIAGNOSTIC MEDICAL SONOGRAPHY

Darton College (A)
Jackson Community College (A,UC)

DIAGNOSTIC MEDICAL SONOGRAPHY ECHOCARDIOGRAPHY

Jackson Community College (A,UC)

DIETARY MANAGEMENT

Auburn University (UC)

DIETETIC FOOD SYSTEMS MANAGEMENT, DIETETIC TECHNICIAN EMPHASIS
The Pennsylvania State University University Park Campus (A)

DIETETIC FOOD SYSTEMS MANAGEMENT, SCHOOL FOOD SERVICE EMPHASIS
The Pennsylvania State University University Park Campus (A)

DIETETICS
Eastern Michigan University (B)
Kansas State University (B)
University of Northern Colorado (UC)

DIETETICS (DEGREE COMPLETION/DIDACTIC PROGRAM IN DIETETICS)
University of Northern Colorado (B)

DIFFERENTIATED LEARNING
Concordia University, St. Paul (M)

DIGITAL CINEMA
National University (M)

DIGITAL COMMUNICATION
Franklin University (B)
Stanford University (GC)

DIGITAL LIBRARIES
Syracuse University (GC)
Syracuse University (GC)

DIGITAL MEDIA COMMUNICATION
Saint Mary-of-the-Woods College (B)

DIGITAL MUSIC EDUCATION
University of South Florida (GC)

DIGITAL PUBLISHING
Savannah College of Art and Design (GC,UC)

DIGITAL SIGNAL PROCESSING
Stevens Institute of Technology (GC)

DIRECT MARKETING
Mercy College (M)

DIRECT TRANSFER
Everett Community College (A)

DISASTER AND EMERGENCY MANAGEMENT
Park University (M)
Rochester Institute of Technology (UC)

DISASTER MANAGEMENT
University of South Florida (GC)

DISASTER MEDICINE AND MANAGEMENT
Philadelphia University (M)

DISASTER READINESS
The Pennsylvania State University University Park Campus (GC)

DISCIPLESHIP COUNSELING
Luther Rice University (M)

DISCIPLESHIP/CHRISTIAN EDUCATION STUDIES
Temple Baptist Seminary (UC)

DISCOVERY TEACHER TRAINING
Mississippi State University (UC)

DISPUTE RESOLUTION
Sullivan University (UC)

DISPUTE RESOLUTION, CONFLICT MANAGEMENT
Sullivan University (M)

DISTANCE EDUCATION
Athabasca University (M)
Indiana University System (UC)
The Pennsylvania State University University Park Campus
University of Maryland University College (M)
University of Wisconsin–Madison (UC)

DISTANCE EDUCATION (TECHNOLOGY)
Athabasca University (GC)

DISTANCE LEARNING
East Carolina University (GC)

DISTANCE LEARNING DESIGN AND DEVELOPMENT
University of Washington (UC)

DISTANCE MBA PROGRAM
Colorado State University (M)

DISTRIBUTED OBJECT-ORIENTED ANALYSIS AND DESIGN–CERTIFICATE OF ADVANCED STUDY
University of Denver (UC)

DIVERSITY MANAGEMENT
The University of Toledo (UC)

DIVINITY
The Baptist College of Florida (A)
Liberty University (M)
Oral Roberts University (M)

DIVINITY–MASTER OF DIVINITY–ENGLISH BIBLE TRACK WITH OVER 20 CONCENTRATIONS AVAILABLE
Temple Baptist Seminary (M)

DOCTORAL COMPLETION PROGRAM
Saybrook Graduate School and Research Center (D)

DOMESTIC VIOLENCE PREVENTION
University of Massachusetts Lowell (GC)

DRIVER EDUCATION INSTRUCTOR
Indiana State University (UC)

DUAL DEGREE
Walden University (M,M)

DUAL IMPAIRMENTS
Texas Tech University (GC)

DUKE ENVIRONMENTAL LEADERSHIP MASTER OF ENVIRONMENTAL MANAGEMENT
Duke University (M)

E-BUSINESS
Bellevue University (B)
Dallas Baptist University (M,UC)
Lansing Community College (A,UC)

E-BUSINESS
Regent University (GC)

E-BUSINESS
Rochester Institute of Technology (UC)
Strayer University (B)

E-BUSINESS

Walden University (M)

E-BUSINESS MANAGEMENT

The Community College of Baltimore County (A)
Westwood Online (B)

E-BUSINESS SOFTWARE (DATABASE TRACK)

Seminole Community College (UC)

E-BUSINESS SOFTWARE (WEB DESIGN TRACK)

Seminole Community College (UC)

E-BUSINESS TECHNOLOGY

The Community College of Baltimore County (A)

E-BUSINESS TECHNOLOGY (MICROSOFT TRACK)

Seminole Community College (UC)

E-BUSINESS TECHNOLOGY (SECURITY SPECIALIZATION)

Seminole Community College (A)

E-BUSINESS TECHNOLOGY (SOFTWARE SPECIALIZATION)

Seminole Community College (A)

E-BUSINESS TECHNOLOGY (TECHNOLOGY SPECIALIZATION)

Seminole Community College (A)

E-COMMERCE

Athabasca University (B)
Columbus State Community College (GC)
University of Maryland University College (M)
University of North Texas (UC)

E-COMMERCE TECHNOLOGY

DePaul University (M)

E-COMMERCE WEB DEVELOPMENT

Fort Hays State University (UC)

E-LEARNING

Roosevelt University (GC)
University of Calgary (UC)

E-LEARNING PROFESSIONAL DEVELOPMENT

University of Central Florida (GC)

EARLY CHILD DEVELOPMENT

Bethany University (A,B)

EARLY CHILDHOOD

Concordia University, St. Paul (M)
Southeast Community College, Beatrice Campus (A)
Southeast Community College, Lincoln Campus (A)
Southeast Community College, Milford Campus (A)

EARLY CHILDHOOD (BAS)

Northern Arizona University (B)

EARLY CHILDHOOD (BIRTH TO FIVE)

University of Wyoming (UC)

EARLY CHILDHOOD ASSOCIATE

Stanly Community College (A)

EARLY CHILDHOOD ASSOCIATE–ADMINISTRATION

Vance-Granville Community College (UC)

EARLY CHILDHOOD ASSOCIATE–GENERAL EDUCATION

Vance-Granville Community College (UC)

EARLY CHILDHOOD DEVELOPMENT

J. Sargeant Reynolds Community College (A)
National University (B)

EARLY CHILDHOOD EDUCATION

Arkansas Tech University (A,B)
Ashworth College (A)
Brenau University (M)
California College for Health Sciences (A)
Casper College (A)
Clarion University of Pennsylvania (A)
Haywood Community College (A)
Ivy Tech Community College–Bloomington (A)
Ivy Tech Community College–Central Indiana (A)
Ivy Tech Community College–Columbus (A)
Ivy Tech Community College–East Central (A)
Ivy Tech Community College–Kokomo (A)
Ivy Tech Community College–Lafayette (A)
Ivy Tech Community College–North Central (A)
Ivy Tech Community College–Northeast (A)
Ivy Tech Community College–Northwest (A)
Ivy Tech Community College–Southeast (A)
Ivy Tech Community College–Southern Indiana (A)
Ivy Tech Community College–Southwest (A)
Ivy Tech Community College–Wabash Valley (A)
Ivy Tech Community College–Whitewater (A)
Mayville State University (B)
Northern Arizona University (M)
Oral Roberts University (M)
Penn Foster Career School (A)
Southern Oregon University (B)
Southwestern Assemblies of God University (A)
Southwestern Oregon Community College (A)
Taft College (A)
University of Alaska Southeast (M,A,UC)
University of Cincinnati (A,B)
University of Colorado at Denver and Health Sciences Center—Downtown Denver Campus (M)
University of Missouri–Columbia (M)
University of North Dakota (M)

EARLY CHILDHOOD EDUCATION ADMINISTRATION CREDENTIAL

Kansas State University (UC)

EARLY CHILDHOOD EDUCATION ASSISTANT

San Joaquin Delta College (UC)

EARLY CHILDHOOD EDUCATION ASSOCIATE

Mayville State University (A)

EARLY CHILDHOOD EDUCATION, ELEMENTARY EDUCATION, SECONDARY EDUCATION, SPECIAL EDUCATION, AND MASS COMMUNICATION (INTEGRATED) CONCENTRATIONS

Parkland College (A)

EARLY CHILDHOOD EDUCATION, GROUP/LEADER/CHILD DEVELOPMENT ASSOCIATE–INFANT/TODDLER

Community College of Denver (UC)

EARLY CHILDHOOD EDUCATION, GROUP/LEADER/CHILD DEVELOPMENT ASSOCIATE–PRESCHOOL

Community College of Denver (UC)

EARLY CHILDHOOD INTERVENTION

Auburn University (M)

EARLY CHILDHOOD LITERACY

Wilkes University (M)

EARLY CHILDHOOD PROGRAM

Pueblo Community College (UC)

EARLY CHILDHOOD SPECIAL EDUCATION

National University (UC)
University of Missouri–Columbia (M)

EARLY CHILDHOOD SPECIAL EDUCATION, GENERALIST

University of Colorado at Denver and Health Sciences Center—Downtown Denver Campus (UC)

EARLY CHILDHOOD/CHILD DEVELOPMENT

Saint Mary-of-the-Woods College (A)

EARLY CHILDHOOD/ ELEMENTARY EDUCATION

Oregon State University (M)

EARLY CHILDOOD ASSOCIATE–SPECIAL NEEDS

Vance-Granville Community College (UC)

EARLY LITERACY CERTIFICATE PROGRAM

University of Colorado at Denver and Health Sciences Center—Downtown Denver Campus (UC)

EARTH AND ENVIRONMENTAL ENGINEERING

Columbia University (M)

EARTH LITERACY

Saint Mary-of-the-Woods College (M)

ECOLOGY

Prescott College (M)

ECOMMERCE

Franklin Pierce College (GC)

ECONOMIC CRIME MANAGEMENT

Utica College (M)

ECONOMICS

Community College of Denver (A)
Darton College (A)
Skidmore College (B)
Strayer University (A,B)
Thomas Edison State College (B)
University of Illinois at Springfield (B)
University of Waterloo (B)

ECONOMICS (BUSINESS TRACK)

Seminole Community College (A)

ECONOMICS (LIBERAL ARTS TRACK)

Seminole Community College (A)

ECONOMICS/FINANCE

Southern New Hampshire University (B)

EDUCATION

Arizona Western College (A)
Briar Cliff University (M)
Buena Vista University (M)
Casper College (A)
Central Michigan University (M)
Chatham College (M)
College of the Humanities and Sciences, Harrison Middleton University (M)
Concordia University (M)
Drexel University (B)
Eastern New Mexico University (B)
Fort Hays State University (M)
Indiana Wesleyan University (M)
Judson College (B)
Liberty University (D,M)
Mount Saint Vincent University (M)
New Mexico State University (M)
Oregon State University (M)
Prescott College (M,B)
Saint Joseph's College of Maine (M)
Southwestern Assemblies of God University (M,A,B)
Strayer University (M)
Touro University International (M)
University of Maryland University College (M)
University of Phoenix Online Campus (B)
The University of Tennessee at Martin (M)
University of Wisconsin–Stout (M)
Utah State University (D)

EDUCATION (K-8)

Alaska Pacific University (A,B)

EDUCATION ADMINISTRATION

Concordia University Wisconsin (M)
Laura and Alvin Siegal College of Judaic Studies (M)

EDUCATION AND HUMAN RESOURCE STUDIES (ADULT EDUCATION AND TRAINING–AET)

Colorado State University (M)

EDUCATION AND HUMAN RESOURCE STUDIES (ORGANIZATIONAL PERFORMANCE AND CHANGE-OPC)

Colorado State University (M)

EDUCATION AND TRAINING MANAGEMENT SUBSPECIALTY/ HUMAN PERFORMANCE TECHNOLOGY

University of West Florida (M)

EDUCATION AND TRAINING MANAGEMENT SUBSPECIALTY/ INSTRUCTIONAL TECHNOLOGY

University of West Florida (M)

EDUCATION COUNSELING

Cape Breton University (M)
Concordia University Wisconsin (M)

EDUCATION DOCTORATE

Regent University (D)

EDUCATION LEADERSHIP

San Diego State University (M)
University of North Dakota (M)

EDUCATION LEADERSHIP (MSA)

University of West Florida (M)

EDUCATION LEADERSHIP, MANAGEMENT, AND POLICY (ELMP)

Seton Hall University (M)

EDUCATION SPECIALIST

Liberty University

EDUCATION SPECIALIST–SCHOOL SUPERINTENDENT

University of Nebraska at Kearney

EDUCATION TECHNOLOGY

Cape Breton University (M)

EDUCATION–6-12 ALTERNATIVE CERTIFICATION

Marquette University (UC)

EDUCATION–ACADEMICALLY AND INTELLECTUALLY GIFTED

The University of North Carolina at Charlotte (GC)

EDUCATION–ADAPTING CURRICULUM FRAMEWORKS FOR ALL LEARNERS

University of Massachusetts Boston (GC)

EDUCATION–ADMINISTRATION AND SUPERVISION SPECIALIZATION

University of Phoenix Online Campus (M)

EDUCATION–ADULT AND POST-SECONDARY EDUCATION

University of Wyoming (M)

EDUCATION–ADULT EDUCATION LEADERSHIP

Walden University (D)

EDUCATION–ALTERNATIVE TEACHER

The University of Texas System (UC)

EDUCATION–BIRTH TO KINDERGARTEN EDUCATION (LATERAL ENTRY/ CERTIFICATION)

Winston-Salem State University (B)

EDUCATION–BIRTH-KINDERGARTEN EDUCATION

East Carolina University (B)

EDUCATION–BIRTH-KINDERGARTEN TEACHER LICENSURE

The University of North Carolina at Greensboro (B)

EDUCATION–COMMUNITY COLLEGE LEADERSHIP

Walden University (D)

EDUCATION–COMPREHENSIVE MASTERS IN EDUCATION

University of West Florida (M)

EDUCATION–COMPUTER EDUCATION

University of Phoenix Online Campus (M)

EDUCATION–CURRICULUM AND INSTRUCTION

University of Phoenix Online Campus (M)

EDUCATION–CURRICULUM, INSTRUCTION, AND ASSESSMENT (GRADES K–12)

Walden University (M)

EDUCATION–EARLY CHILDHOOD EDUCATION

Walden University (D)

EDUCATION–EARLY CHILDHOOD EDUCATION SPECIALIZATION

University of Phoenix Online Campus (M)

EDUCATION–EDUCATIONAL LEADERSHIP

Walden University (M)

EDUCATION–EDUCATIONAL TECHNOLOGY

Walden University (D)

EDUCATION–ELEMENTARY EDUCATION LICENSURE

New Mexico State University–Carlsbad (B)

EDUCATION–ELEMENTARY OR SECONDARY TEACHER EDUCATION

University of Phoenix Online Campus (M)

EDUCATION–ELEMENTARY READING AND LITERACY (GRADES K–6)

Walden University (M)

EDUCATION–ELEMENTARY READING AND MATHEMATICS (GRADES K–6)

Walden University (M)

EDUCATION–GRADUATE INTERN TEACHING CERTIFICATE

Drexel University (UC)

EDUCATION–GRADUATE TEACHER EDUCATION

Newman University (M)

EDUCATION–HIGHER EDUCATION

Walden University (D)

EDUCATION–INSTRUCTIONAL LEADERSHIP

Marquette University (M)

EDUCATION–INSTRUCTIONAL TECHNOLOGY

University of Wyoming (M)

EDUCATION–INTEGRATING TECHNOLOGY IN THE CLASSROOM (GRADES 3–12)

Walden University (M)

EDUCATION–K-12 EDUCATIONAL LEADERSHIP

Walden University (D)

EDUCATION–KINDERGARTEN-ELEMENTARY EDUCATION

Saint Mary-of-the-Woods College (B)

EDUCATION–LEVEL I EDUCATION SPECIALIST CREDENTIAL: MILD/ MOD

National University (UC)

EDUCATION–LITERACY AND LEARNING IN THE CONTENT AREAS (GRADES 6–12)

Walden University (M)

EDUCATION–MASTER OF ARTS IN TEACHING BLENDED

Saint Leo University (M)

EDUCATION–MASTER OF EDUCATION

University of Calgary (M)

EDUCATION–MASTER OF EDUCATION--EXCEPTIONAL STUDENT EDUCATION CONCENTRATION

Saint Leo University (M)

EDUCATION–MASTER READING TEACHER

The University of Texas System (UC)

EDUCATION–MATHEMATICS (GRADES 6–8)

Walden University (M)

EDUCATION–MATHEMATICS (GRADES K–5)

Walden University (M)

EDUCATION–MIDDLE AND SECONDARY EDUCATION (TEACHER LICENSURE)

The University of North Carolina at Charlotte (UC)

EDUCATION–MIDDLE GRADES

The University of North Carolina at Charlotte (M)

EDUCATION–MIDDLE LEVEL EDUCATION (GRADES 5–8)

Walden University (M)

EDUCATION–MIDDLE SCHOOL/ HIGH SCHOOL SPECIAL EDUCATION

Saint Mary-of-the-Woods College (B)

EDUCATION–MIDDLE/SECONDARY TEACHING

Indiana State University (UC)

EDUCATION–MISSOURI VISUAL IMPAIRMENT CERTIFICATION TRAINING PROGRAM

Missouri State University (UC)

EDUCATION–POST-BACCALAUREATE DIPLOMA IN EDUCATION PROGRAM

University of Manitoba (GC)

EDUCATION–POST-BACHELOR'S TEACHING CERTIFICATE

Drexel University (UC)

EDUCATION–POSTSECONDARY SCHOOL ADMINISTRATION

Oral Roberts University (D)

EDUCATION–PRE-K THROUGH 6

Old Dominion University (M)

EDUCATION–PRESCHOOL-GRADE 3 EDUCATION/MILD INTERVENTION

Saint Mary-of-the-Woods College (B)

EDUCATION–SCIENCE (GRADES K–8)

Walden University (M)

EDUCATION–SECONDARY EDUCATION

Judson College (B)
Southern Oregon University (M)
University of North Texas (M)

EDUCATION–SELF-DESIGNED

Walden University (D)

EDUCATION–SIXTH YEAR IN EDUCATIONAL FOUNDATIONS

Connecticut State University System (UC)

EDUCATION–SPECIAL EDUCATION

University of Wyoming (M)
Walden University (D)

EDUCATION–SPECIAL EDUCATION SPECIALIZATION

University of Phoenix Online Campus (M)

EDUCATION–SUSTAINABILITY EDUCATION

Prescott College (D)

EDUCATION–TEACHER PREPARATION

Old Dominion University (B)

EDUCATION–TEACHING AND LEARNING

University of Wyoming (M)

EDUCATION–TED MULTIPLE OR SINGLE SUBJECT TEACHING CREDENTIAL

National University (UC)

EDUCATION, GENERAL

Gadsden State Community College (A)
Ouachita Technical College (A)
Park University (M)
University of Alaska Southeast (A)
Walden University (D)

EDUCATION, GENERAL TRANSFER

Northwestern Michigan College (A)

EDUCATION/CURRICULUM AND INSTRUCTION

Capella University (D)

EDUCATION/ESL

University of Phoenix Online Campus (M)

EDUCATION/INSTRUCTIONAL DESIGN FOR ONLINE LEARNING

Capella University (D)

EDUCATION/K-12 STUDIES IN EDUCATION

Capella University (D)

EDUCATION/LEADERSHIP FOR HIGHER EDUCATION

Capella University (D)

EDUCATION/LEADERSHIP IN EDUCATIONAL ADMINISTRATION

Capella University (D)

EDUCATION/POSTSECONDARY AND ADULT EDUCATION

Capella University (D)

EDUCATION/PROFESSIONAL STUDIES IN EDUCATION

Capella University (D)

EDUCATION/TRAINING AND PERFORMANCE IMPROVEMENT

Capella University (D)

EDUCATIONAL ADMINISTRATION

California State University, Northridge (M)
Fort Hays State University (M)
Marygrove College (M)
New Mexico State University (M)
Prescott College (M)
St. Cloud State University (M)
Skidmore College (B)
University of Massachusetts Lowell (M)
University of Nebraska–Lincoln (D,M,UC)
University of North Texas (M)
University of South Alabama (UC)

EDUCATIONAL ADMINISTRATION (EDUCATIONAL LEADERSHIP)

New Mexico State University (D)

EDUCATIONAL ADMINISTRATION AND ADMINISTRATIVE SERVICES

National University (M)

EDUCATIONAL ADMINISTRATION AND COUNSELING

College of the Southwest (M)

EDUCATIONAL ADMINISTRATION AND SUPERVISION

Ball State University (M)
St. John's University (M)
University of North Texas (M)

EDUCATIONAL ADMINISTRATION–COLLABORATIVE LEADERSHIP

Drexel University (M)

EDUCATIONAL ADMINISTRATION–SCHOOL ADMINISTRATION

The University of North Carolina at Greensboro (M)

EDUCATIONAL ADMINISTRATION–SCHOOL ADMINISTRATION (MSA)

The University of North Carolina at Charlotte (M)

EDUCATIONAL ADMINISTRATION–SCHOOL DISTRICT ADMINISTRATOR

St. John's University (GC)

EDUCATIONAL ADMINISTRATIVE LICENSURE

New Mexico State University (UC)
New Mexico State University–Carlsbad (UC)

EDUCATIONAL AND INSTRUCTIONAL TECHNOLOGY

National University (M)

EDUCATIONAL ASSESSMENT AND EVALUATION CONCENTRATION (10-MONTH PROGRAM)

American InterContinental University Online (M)

EDUCATIONAL DIAGNOSTICIAN

College of the Southwest (M)
Texas Tech University (UC)

EDUCATIONAL LEADERSHIP

Clemson University (D)
Crown College (M)
Dallas Baptist University (M)
LeTourneau University (M)
Northern Arizona University (D,M)
Regent University (M)
Touro University International (D)
University of Cincinnati (M)
University of Missouri–Columbia (M)
The University of Montana (M)
University of North Dakota (D)
University of Phoenix Online Campus (D)
University of South Alabama (M)

EDUCATIONAL LEADERSHIP (WEEKEND COHORT PROGRAM)

The University of Montana (D)

EDUCATIONAL LEADERSHIP AND CHANGE

Fielding Graduate University (D)

EDUCATIONAL LEADERSHIP AND INSTRUCTION

Northwestern State University of Louisiana (GC)

EDUCATIONAL LEADERSHIP AND PRINCIPAL PROFESSIONAL CERTIFICATION PREPARATION

Texas Tech University (M)

EDUCATIONAL LEADERSHIP STUDIES

Memorial University of Newfoundland (M)

EDUCATIONAL LEADERSHIP, CURRICULUM AND INSTRUCTION SPECIALIZATION

University of Phoenix Online Campus (D)

EDUCATIONAL LEADERSHIP/ ADMINISTRATION

Florida State University (M)

EDUCATIONAL MANAGEMENT AND DEVELOPMENT

New Mexico State University–Carlsbad (M)

EDUCATIONAL MEDIA

University of Central Florida (GC)

EDUCATIONAL MEDIA (LIBRARY MEDIA)

University of South Alabama (M,UC)

EDUCATIONAL MEDIA AND SCHOOL LIBRARY MEDIA ENDORSEMENT

University of Northern Colorado (M)

EDUCATIONAL MEDIA AND TECHNOLOGY

The College of St. Scholastica (M)
Eastern Michigan University (GC,M)

EDUCATIONAL MEDIA GRADUATE ENDORSEMENT

University of Nebraska at Kearney (UC)

EDUCATIONAL PSYCHOLOGY

University of North Texas (M)

EDUCATIONAL PSYCHOLOGY (INFORMATION TECHNOLOGY EMPHASIS)

University of Nevada, Reno (M)

EDUCATIONAL STUDIES

State University of New York Empire State College (A,B)
University of Nebraska–Lincoln (D)

EDUCATIONAL TECHNOLOGY

Azusa Pacific University (M)
Boise State University (M)
Boise State University (M)
Chadron State College (M)
Cleveland State University (M)
Connecticut State University System (M)
Dakota State University (M)
National University (M)
New Jersey City University (M)
Northern Arizona University (M,UC)
Northwestern Connecticut Community College (A)
Northwestern State University of Louisiana (M)
Pepperdine University (D,M)
San Diego State University (M)
University of Alaska Southeast (M,UC)
University of Nebraska–Lincoln (GC)
University of Northern Colorado (M)
The University of Texas System (M)
Western Michigan University (M)

EDUCATIONAL TECHNOLOGY AND MULTIDISCIPLINARY STUDIES

Webster University (M)

EDUCATIONAL TECHNOLOGY EMPHASIS

Boise State University (M)

EDUCATIONAL TECHNOLOGY INTEGRATION

The Pennsylvania State University University Park Campus

EDUCATIONAL TECHNOLOGY PRODUCTION

University of Florida (GC)

EDUCATIONAL TECHNOLOGY–MASTER OF EDUCATIONAL TECHNOLOGY

The University of British Columbia (M)

ELEARNING DESIGN AND IMPLEMENTATION

University of Colorado at Denver and Health Sciences Center—Downtown Denver Campus (M)

ELECTRIC POWER TECHNOLOGY

Bismarck State College (A,UC)

ELECTRIC TRANSMISSION SYSTEM TECHNOLOGY

Bismarck State College (A,UC)

ELECTRICAL AND COMPUTER ENGINEERING

Illinois Institute of Technology (M)
University of Colorado at Boulder (M)
University of Florida (M)
University of Florida (M)
Virginia Polytechnic Institute and State University (M)

ELECTRICAL AND COMPUTER ENGINEERING (TELECOMMUNICATIONS)

Colorado State University (M)

ELECTRICAL ENGINEERING

Arizona State University (M)
Capitol College (M)
Clemson University (M)
Columbia University (GC,M)
Drexel University (M)

Georgia Institute of Technology (M)
Illinois Institute of Technology (M)
Iowa State University of Science and Technology (M)
Kansas State University (M)
Southern Methodist University (M)
Stanford University (M)
University of Delaware (M)
University of Maryland, College Park (M)
University of North Dakota (B)
University of South Florida (M)
The University of Texas at Arlington (M)
University of Washington (M)
University of Wisconsin–Madison (M)

ELECTRICAL ENGINEERING (MSEE)

University of South Florida (M)

ELECTRICAL ENGINEERING TECHNOLOGY

Old Dominion University (B)
The University of North Carolina at Charlotte (B)

ELECTRICAL ENGINEERING TECHNOLOGY AST

Penn Foster Career School (A)

ELECTRICAL ENGINEERING–COMMUNICATIONS TRACK

Walden University (M)

ELECTRICAL ENGINEERING–INTIGRATED CIRCUITS TRACK

Walden University (M)

ELECTRICAL ENGINEERING–MICROELECTRONIC AND SEMICONDUCTOR ENGINEERING

Walden University (M)

ELECTRICAL TECHNOLOGY

Thomas Edison State College (A,B)

ELECTRICAL/MECHANICAL ENGINEERING TECHNOLOGY

Rochester Institute of Technology (B)

ELECTROMAGNETICS TECHNOLOGY CAMPUS CERTIFICATE

University of Illinois at Chicago (UC)

ELECTRONIC BUSINESS

National University (M)

ELECTRONIC CIRCUITS

Stanford University (GC)

ELECTRONIC DEVICES AND TECHNOLOGY

Stanford University (GC)

ELECTRONIC ENGINEERING TECHNOLOGY

Cleveland Institute of Electronics (A)
Thomas Edison State College (A,B)

ELECTRONICS AND COMPUTER TECHNOLOGY

Indiana State University (M)

ELECTRONICS ENGINEERING

Cleveland Institute of Electronics (UC)

ELECTRONICS ENGINEERING TECHNOLOGY

Excelsior College (B)
Grantham University (A,B)

ELECTRONICS TECHNOLOGY

Excelsior College (A)
Indiana State University (B)

ELECTRONICS TECHNOLOGY AND ADVANCED TROUBLESHOOTING

Cleveland Institute of Electronics (UC)

ELECTRONICS TECHNOLOGY AST

Penn Foster Career School (A)

ELECTRONICS TECHNOLOGY WITH DIGITAL MICROPROCESSOR LAB

Cleveland Institute of Electronics (UC)

ELECTRONICS TECHNOLOGY WITH FCC LICENSE PREPARATION

Cleveland Institute of Electronics (UC)

ELECTRONICS TECHNOLOGY WITH LABORATORY

Cleveland Institute of Electronics (UC)

ELECTRONICS, ADVANCED

Illinois Institute of Technology (GC)

ELEMENTARY EDUCATION

Ball State University (M)
Coconino Community College (A)
Community College of Denver (A)
Fort Hays State University (B)
Mississippi State University (B)
Missouri State University (M,B)
New Mexico State University (B)
Northern Arizona University (M)
Prescott College (B)
University of Alaska Southeast (M,UC)
The University of North Carolina at Charlotte (M,B)
University of North Dakota (M)
University of Wisconsin–Superior (B)

ELEMENTARY EDUCATION (BS ED.)

Northern Arizona University (B)

ELEMENTARY EDUCATION (POST-BACCALAUREATE CERTIFICATION)

Stephen F. Austin State University (UC)

ELEMENTARY EDUCATION EMPHASIS

Community College of Southern Nevada (A)

ELEMENTARY EDUCATION POSTDEGREE

Northern Arizona University (UC)

ELEMENTARY EDUCATION WITH CERTIFICATION

Oral Roberts University (B)

ELEMENTARY EDUCATION/READING

University of Arkansas (M)

ELEMENTARY LICENSURE (POST BA)

New Mexico State University (UC)

ELEMENTARY OR SECONDARY EDUCATION

Marshall University (M)
Utah State University (M)

ELEMENTARY/SPECIAL EDUCATION, DUAL MAJOR

University of West Florida (B)

ELEMENTS OF COMPUTER SCIENCE

Stevens Institute of Technology (GC)

ELEMENTS OF HEALTH CARE LEADERSHIP

Rochester Institute of Technology (GC)

EMBA

Western Kentucky University (M)

EMBEDDED AND REAL-TIME SYSTEMS PROGRAMMING

University of Washington (UC)

EMBEDDED SYSTEMS

Arizona State University (M)

EMERGENCY ADMINISTRATION AND MANAGEMENT

Arkansas Tech University (B)
St. Petersburg College (A,UC)

EMERGENCY AND DISASTER MANAGEMENT

American Military University (M,B)
American Public University (M,B)
Upper Iowa University (B,UC)

EMERGENCY DISASTER MANAGEMENT

Thomas Edison State College (A,B)

EMERGENCY MANAGEMENT

Jacksonville State University (GC,M)
New Jersey Institute of Technology (GC)

EMERGENCY MANAGEMENT (PUBLIC SAFETY COMMUNICATIONS MINOR)

Jacksonville State University (B)

EMERGENCY MANAGEMENT ADMINISTRATION

West Texas A&M University (B)

EMERGENCY MANAGEMENT AND PLANNING

Red Rocks Community College (A)

EMERGENCY MANAGEMENT–HOMELAND SECURITY MINOR

Jacksonville State University (B)

EMERGENCY MANAGEMENT/HOMELAND SECURITY

Western Washington University (UC)

EMERGENCY PREPAREDNESS AND CONTINUITY PLANNING

University of Illinois at Chicago (UC)

EMERGENCY PREPAREDNESS TECHNOLOGY

Caldwell Community College and Technical Institute (A)

EMERGING NETWORK TECHNOLOGIES

Franklin Pierce College (GC)

ENERGY MANAGEMENT

New York Institute of Technology (M)

ENERGY RESOURCES MANAGEMENT AND POLICY

University of Maryland University College (GC)

ENGINEERING

California National University for Advanced Studies (M,B)
Eastern Michigan University (M)
Northern Arizona University (M)
Texas Tech University (M)
University of Illinois at Chicago (M)
The University of Toledo (M)
University of Virginia (M)
University of Wisconsin–Platteville (M)
University of Wisconsin–Platteville (M)

ENGINEERING ADMINISTRATION

Virginia Polytechnic Institute and State University (M)

ENGINEERING AND MANAGEMENT SYSTEMS

Columbia University (M)

ENGINEERING GRAPHICS

Thomas Edison State College (A,B)

ENGINEERING LAW AND MANAGEMENT CAMPUS CERTIFICATE

University of Illinois at Chicago (UC)

ENGINEERING MANAGEMENT

California National University for Advanced Studies (M)
California State University, Northridge (M)
Drexel University (GC,M)
Grantham University (A,B)
Kansas State University (M)
Kettering University (M)
National University (M)
New Jersey Institute of Technology (M)
Old Dominion University (M)
Southern Methodist University (M)
The University of Alabama in Huntsville (M)
University of Colorado at Boulder (GC,M)
University of Colorado at Colorado Springs (M)
University of Massachusetts Amherst (M)
University of Michigan–Dearborn (M)
University of Nebraska–Lincoln (M)
University of South Florida (M)
The University of Tennessee (GC,M)
University of Wisconsin–Platteville (UC)
Walden University (M)

ENGINEERING MANAGEMENT (MSEM)

University of South Florida (M)

ENGINEERING MECHANICS–MATHEMATICAL FOUNDATIONS AND APPLICATIONS

Stanford University (GC)

ENGINEERING ONLINE

North Carolina State University (M)

ENGINEERING TECHNOLOGY

University of Central Florida (B)

ENGINEERING TECHNOLOGY INSTRUCTIONAL SUPPORT

University of West Florida (B)

ENGINEERING TECHNOLOGY MANAGEMENT

University of South Florida (GC)

ENGINEERING TECHNOLOGY, GENERAL

Old Dominion University (B)

ENGINEERING–ARIZONA TRI-UNIVERSITY MASTER OF ENGINEERING PROGRAM

Arizona State University (M)

ENGINEERING–COMPUTATIONAL AND MATHEMATICAL ENGINEERING

Stanford University (M)

ENGINEERING–ELECTRICAL AND COMPUTER ENGINEERING CONCENTRATION

Kettering University (M)

ENGINEERING–MANUFACTURING ENGINEERING CONCENTRATION

Kettering University (M)

ENGINEERING–MECHANICAL DESIGN CONCENTRATION

Kettering University (M)

ENGLISH

American Military University (B)
American Public University (B)
Caldwell College (B)
Darton College (A)
Drury University (A)
Eastern New Mexico University (M)

Judson College (B)
Mercy College (B)
National University (M,B)
Northern Arizona University (M)
Saint Mary-of-the-Woods College (B)
Skidmore College (B)
Southwestern Assemblies of God University (A,B)
Thomas Edison State College (B)
University of Illinois at Springfield (B)
University of Maryland University College (B)
University of Waterloo (B)

ENGLISH (3 YEAR)

Athabasca University (B)

ENGLISH (4 YEAR)

Athabasca University (B)

ENGLISH AS A SECOND LANGUAGE

Murray State University (UC)
Northern Arizona University (UC)

ENGLISH AS A SECOND LANGUAGE (ESL)

The University of Texas System (UC)

ENGLISH AS A SECOND LANGUAGE EDUCATION PROGRAM

University of Colorado at Colorado Springs (M)

ENGLISH EMPHASIS

Community College of Southern Nevada (A)

ENGLISH LANGUAGE AND LITERATURE

Southern New Hampshire University (B)

ENGLISH LANGUAGE LEARNER/ ENGLISH AS A SECOND LANGUAGE

University of North Dakota (UC)

ENGLISH LANGUAGE STUDIES

Athabasca University (UC)

ENGLISH LANGUAGE TEACHING

The New School (UC)

ENGLISH LITERATURE

Mercy College (M)

ENGLISH–PROFESSIONAL AND TECHNICAL COMMUNICATION CONCENTRATION

East Carolina University (M)

ENGLISH–SINGLE SUBJECT PREPARATION IN ENGLISH

National University (B)

ENGLISH–WRITING

University of Colorado at Denver and Health Sciences Center—Downtown Denver Campus (B)

ENGLISH/LITERATURE EMPHASIS

Community College of Denver (A)

ENGLISH/TECHNICAL WRITING SPECIALIZATION ONLINE

Utah State University (M)

ENROLLMENT MANAGEMENT

Capella University (M)

ENTERPRISE SYSTEMS ARCHITECTURE

New Jersey Institute of Technology (GC)

ENTOMOLOGY

University of Florida (M)
University of Nebraska–Lincoln (M)

ENTREPRENEURSHIP

Kaplan University (M)
Regent University (GC)
University of South Florida (GC)
University of South Florida (GC)

ENTREPRENEURSHIP CONCENTRATION

Andrew Jackson University (M)

ENVIONMENTAL HEALTH AND SAFETY MANAGEMENT

Mercy College (B)

ENVIRONMENTAL MANAGEMENT

University of Maryland University College (M)

ENVIRONMENTAL AND OCCUPATIONAL SAFETY AND HEALTH FOCUS

University of Connecticut (B)

ENVIRONMENTAL AND TECHNOLOGICAL STUDIES

St. Cloud State University (M)

ENVIRONMENTAL AND WATER RESOURCES ENGINEERING

University of Illinois at Urbana–Champaign (GC)

ENVIRONMENTAL EDUCATION

Prescott College (M)

ENVIRONMENTAL ENGINEERING

Georgia Institute of Technology (M)
Illinois Institute of Technology (M)
Southern Methodist University (M)
The University of Tennessee (M)
Worcester Polytechnic Institute (GC,M)
Iowa State University of Science and Technology (GC)

ENVIRONMENTAL ENGINEERING–WATER RESOURCES PLANNING AND MANAGEMENT TRACK

University of Florida (M)

ENVIRONMENTAL ENGINEERING–WATER, WASTEWATER, AND STORMWATER ENGINEERING

University of Florida (M)

ENVIRONMENTAL HEALTH AND SAFETY

University of Connecticut (UC)

ENVIRONMENTAL HEALTH AND SAFETY MANAGEMENT

Rochester Institute of Technology (M)

ENVIRONMENTAL HEALTH INFORMATICS CAMPUS CERTIFICATE

University of Illinois at Chicago (UC)

ENVIRONMENTAL INFORMATION MANAGEMENT–CERTIFICATE OF ADVANCED STUDY

University of Denver (UC)

ENVIRONMENTAL MANAGEMENT

University of Calgary (UC)
University of Maryland University College (B,GC)

ENVIRONMENTAL MANAGEMENT–CERTIFICATE OF ADVANCED STUDY

University of Denver (UC)

ENVIRONMENTAL POLICY AND MANAGEMENT
American Military University (M)
American Public University (M)

ENVIRONMENTAL POLICY AND MANAGEMENT–MASTER OF APPLIED SCIENCE IN ENVIRONMENTAL POLICY AND MANAGEMENT
University of Denver (M)

ENVIRONMENTAL POLICY MANAGEMENT
University of Florida (GC)

ENVIRONMENTAL POLICY–CERTIFICATE OF ADVANCED STUDY
University of Denver (UC)

ENVIRONMENTAL PROJECT MANAGEMENT–CERTIFICATE OF ADVANCED STUDY
University of Denver (UC)

ENVIRONMENTAL SCIENCE
Cape Breton University (B)
Southern Methodist University (M)

ENVIRONMENTAL SCIENCE (ENVIRONMENTAL SYSTEMS MANAGEMENT MAJOR)
Southern Methodist University (M)

ENVIRONMENTAL SCIENCE (HAZARDOUS AND WASTE MATERIALS MANAGEMENT MAJOR)
Southern Methodist University (M)

ENVIRONMENTAL SCIENCE AND MANAGEMENT
Duquesne University (M)

ENVIRONMENTAL SCIENCES
Northern Arizona University (B)
Oregon State University (B)
Thomas Edison State College (A,B)

ENVIRONMENTAL STUDIES
American Military University (B)
American Public University (B)
Columbia College (A)
Prescott College (M,B)
Skidmore College (B)
Thomas Edison State College (B)

ENVIRONMENTAL STUDIES IN CONSERVATION BIOLOGY
Green Mountain College (M)

ENVIRONMENTAL STUDIES MANAGEMENT
Drury University (A)

ENVIRONMENTAL STUDIES–NATURAL RESOURCES AND SUSTAINABLE DEVELOPMENT CONCENTRATION
University of Illinois at Springfield (M)

ENVIRONMENTAL TECHNOLOGY
University of Alaska Southeast (A,UC)

ENVIRONMENTAL TECHNOLOGY MANAGEMENT
Arizona State University (M)
Arizona State University at the Polytechnic Campus (M)

ENVIRONMENTAL, HEALTH, AND SAFETY MANAGEMENT–CERTIFICATE OF ADVANCED STUDY
University of Denver (UC)

ENVIRONMENTAL, SAFETY, AND HEALTH MANAGEMENT
The University of Findlay (M,B)

ENVORONMENTAL TECHNOLOGY
University of Alaska Southeast (UC)

EPIDEMIOLOGY AND BIOSTATISTICS
Drexel University (UC)

EQUINE ASSISTED MENTAL HEALTH
Prescott College (M)

ERGONOMICS (BASIC AND ADVANCED)
Colorado State University (UC)

ESOL/BILINGUAL EDUCATION
Oregon State University (UC)

ESR ACCESS
Earlham School of Religion (M)

ESSENTIAL SKILLS FOR THE WORKPLACE
Granite State College (UC)

EVANGELISM AND CHURCH GROWTH
Liberty University (M)

EXCEPTIONAL EDUCATION
University of Central Florida (M)
Western Kentucky University (M)

EXCEPTIONAL NEEDS WITH MILD INTERVENTIONS (SPECIAL ED)
Indiana Wesleyan University (UC)

EXECUTIVE COACHING
Kaplan University (UC)

EXECUTIVE EMERGENCY MANAGEMENT OFFICER
University of Florida (UC)

EXECUTIVE EMS OFFICER
University of Florida (UC)

EXECUTIVE FIRE OFFICER
University of Florida (UC)

EXECUTIVE MASTER OF BUSINESS ADMINISTRATION (SPANISH VERSION)
National University (M)

EXERCISE SCIENCE
Skidmore College (B)

EXERCISE SCIENCE AND HEALTH PROMOTION–PERFORMANCE ENHANCEMENT AND INJURY PREVENTION
California University of Pennsylvania (M)

EXERCISE SCIENCE AND HEALTH PROMOTION–SPORTS PSYCHOLOGY
California University of Pennsylvania (M)

EXERCISE SCIENCE AND HEALTH PROMOTION–WELLNESS AND FITNESS
California University of Pennsylvania (M)

EXERCISE SCIENCE AND HEALTH PROMOTION-REHABILITATION SCIENCES

California University of Pennsylvania (M)

EXPRESSIVE ARTS FOR HEALING AND SOCIAL CHANGE

Saybrook Graduate School and Research Center (GC)

FACILITIES MANAGEMENT

Southern Methodist University (M)

FACILITY MANAGEMENT

University of Washington (UC)

FAMILY AND CONSUMER SCIENCES

Iowa State University of Science and Technology (M)
University of Nebraska–Lincoln (M)

FAMILY AND CONSUMER SCIENCES (EARLY CHILDHOOD PROGRAM DIRECTOR'S CERTIFICATE)

University of Wyoming (UC)

FAMILY AND CONSUMER SCIENCES (FAMILY AND COMMUNITY SERVICES OPTION)

University of Wyoming (B)

FAMILY AND CONSUMER SCIENCES (PROFESSIONAL CHILD DEVELOPMENT OPTION)

University of Wyoming (B)

FAMILY AND FINANCIAL PLANNING

Montana State University (M)

FAMILY AND HUMAN DEVELOPMENT

Utah State University (M)

FAMILY DEVELOPMENT

American Military University (B)
American Public University (B)

FAMILY FINANCIAL PLANNING

Iowa State University of Science and Technology (GC)
North Dakota State University (GC,M)

FAMILY LIFE EDUCATION

Concordia University, St. Paul (B)

FAMILY LIFE STUDIES AND HUMAN SEXUALITY

Laurentian University (UC)

FAMILY LITERACY

The Pennsylvania State University University Park Campus (UC)

FAMILY NURSE PRACTITIONER

Clarkson College (M,)
University of Missouri–Columbia (M)

FAMILY STUDIES

Texas Woman's University (M)

FAMILY SUPPORT STUDIES/ HUMAN DEVELOPMENT

Edmonds Community College (A)

FAMILY THERAPY

Regions University (D)

FASHION

Academy of Art University (M,A,B)

FCSEE OR AST SPECIALIZATION

Utah State University (M)

FICTION WRITING

University of Washington (UC)

FILM AND CINEMA STUDIES

Prescott College (M)

FINANCE

Ashworth College (A)
Capella University (M)
Colorado Technical University (M)
Dallas Baptist University (M)
Excelsior College (B)
Kaplan University (M)
Myers University (B)
New Jersey City University (M)
Regent University (GC)
Strayer University (B)
Thomas Edison State College (A,B)
University of Colorado at Denver and Health Sciences Center—Downtown Denver Campus (M)
University of Maryland University College (B)
Upper Iowa University (B)
Walden University (M)

FINANCE CONCENTRATION

Andrew Jackson University (M)
Colorado Technical University (B)

FINANCE–METHODS IN FINANCE

Columbia University (M)

FINANCIAL ACCOUNTING

Champlain College (UC)

FINANCIAL CRIME INVESTIGATION CERTIFICATE PROGRAM

Utica College (UC)

FINANCIAL CRIME INVESTIGATION CERTIFICATE PROGRAM

Utica College

FINANCIAL ECONOMICS

Caldwell College (B)

FINANCIAL ENGINEERING

Columbia University (UC)
Stevens Institute of Technology (GC)

FINANCIAL MANAGEMENT

City University (GC)

FINANCIAL MANAGEMENT AND INFORMATION SYSTEMS

University of Maryland University College (M)

FINANCIAL MANAGEMENT IN ORGANIZATIONS

University of Maryland University College (GC)

FINANCIAL PLANNING

Kaplan University (UC)
Schiller International University (M)

FINANCIAL PLANNING–FAMILY FINANCIAL PLANNING

University of Nebraska–Lincoln (GC)

FINANCIAL SERVICES

Nipissing University (B)

FINANCIAL SERVICES STUDIES

New England College of Finance (GC)

FINE ART

Academy of Art University (M,A,B)

FIRE AND EMERGENCY SERVICES

University of Florida (B)

FIRE AND EMERGENCY SERVICES ADMINISTRATION (FESA)

Colorado State University (UC)

FIRE INSPECTOR I
St. Petersburg College (UC)

FIRE INSPECTOR II
St. Petersburg College (UC)

FIRE INVESTIGATOR I
St. Petersburg College (UC)

FIRE INVESTIGATOR II
St. Petersburg College (UC)

FIRE OFFICER I
St. Petersburg College (UC)

FIRE OFFICER II
St. Petersburg College (UC)

FIRE PROTECTION
Middlesex Community College (A)

FIRE PROTECTION ENGINEERING
Worcester Polytechnic Institute (GC,M)

FIRE PROTECTION SCIENCE
Thomas Edison State College (A,B)

FIRE SCIENCE
Cogswell Polytechnical College (B)
Prescott College (M)
University of Maryland University College (B)
The University of North Carolina at Charlotte (B)

FIRE SCIENCE ADMINISTRATION
Columbia College (A)

FIRE SCIENCE MANAGEMENT
American Military University (B)
American Public University (B)
Red Rocks Community College (A)

FIRE SCIENCE TECHNOLOGY
University of Cincinnati (A,B)

FIRE SCIENCE/FIRE ADMINISTRATOR
Midland College (A)

FIRE SERVICES ADMINISTRATION
Eastern Oregon University (B)

FITNESS AND WELLNESS SERVICES
Thomas Edison State College (A)

FITNESS MANAGEMENT
United States Sports Academy (M)

FOLKLORE ET ETHNOLOGIE DE L'AMERIQUE FRANCAISE
Laurentian University (B,UC)

FOOD AND NUTRITION
Bowling Green State University (GC)

FOOD PROTECTION
North Dakota State University (GC)

FOOD SCIENCE
Kansas State University (GC,M,UC)

FOOD SCIENCE AND INDUSTRY
Kansas State University (B)

FOOD SCIENCE, NUTRITION, AND HEALTH PROMOTION
Mississippi State University (M)

FOOD SERVICE AND LODGING MANAGEMENT
Iowa State University of Science and Technology (D)

FOOD SERVICE MANAGEMENT
University of Massachusetts Amherst (UC)

FOOD SERVICE TRAINING PROGRAM
Southeast Community College, Beatrice Campus (UC)
Southeast Community College, Lincoln Campus (UC)
Southeast Community College, Milford Campus (UC)

FOREIGN LANGUAGE
Auburn University (M)
Caldwell College (B)
Darton College (A)
Thomas Edison State College (B)

FOREIGN LANGUAGES
Prescott College (M)

FOREIGN LANGUAGES AND LITERATURE
Skidmore College (B)

FORENSIC ACCOUNTING
Davenport University Online (UC)
Myers University (B)
New England College of Finance (GC)

FORENSIC CRIMINOLOGY
University of Massachusetts Lowell (GC)

FORENSIC DEATH INVESTIGATION
University of Florida (GC)

FORENSIC DNA AND SEROLOGY
University of Florida (GC)

FORENSIC DRUG CHEMISTRY
University of Florida (GC)

FORENSIC SCIENCE
Darton College (A)

FORENSIC SCIENCE–FORENSIC ANALYSIS TRACK
University of Central Florida (M)

FORENSIC SCIENCE–FORENSIC BIOCHEMISTRY TRACK
University of Central Florida (M)

FORENSIC SCIENCES–MASTER OF FORENSIC SCIENCES
National University (M)

FORENSIC STUDIES
The University of Montana (UC)

FORENSIC TOXICOLOGY
University of Florida (GC)

FORESTRY
Thomas Edison State College (A,B)

FOUNDATIONS FOR HUMAN RESOURCE MANAGEMENT
University of Maryland University College (GC)

FOUNDATIONS OF NETWORK DESIGN
Champlain College (UC)

FRENCH
Skidmore College (B)

FRENCH (3 YEAR)
Athabasca University (B)

FRENCH (4 YEAR)
Athabasca University (B)

FRENCH LANGUAGE PROFICIENCY

Athabasca University (UC)

FUNERAL SERVICE EDUCATION

Vincennes University (A)

FUNERAL SERVICES

St. Petersburg College (A)

GAME AND SIMULATION PROGRAMMING

DeVry University Online (B)

GAME ART AND DESIGN

Westwood Online (B)

GAME SOFTWARE DEVELOPMENT

Westwood Online (B)

GAS ENGINEERING

Illinois Institute of Technology (M)

GAY AND LESBIAN STUDIES

Prescott College (M)

GENDER STUDIES

Prescott College (M)

GENERAL DEGREE STUDIES–3-YEAR GENERAL DEGREE

University of Manitoba (B)

GENERAL EDUCATION REQUIREMENTS

Adams State College (A)

GENERAL MANAGEMENT

City University (GC)
Thomas Edison State College (B)

GENERAL MINISTRIES

Bethany University (B)

GENERAL PROGRAM

Ball State University (A)
North Idaho College (A)
Pulaski Technical College (A)
St. Louis Community College System (A)
St. Petersburg College (A)
Seattle Central Community College (A)
Triton College (A)
University of the Incarnate Word (M)
Walden University (M)
Western Wyoming Community College (A)

GENERAL STUDIES

American Military University (A)
American Public University (A)
Anne Arundel Community College (A)
Ball State University (B)
Bellevue Community College (A)
Bethany University (A)
Black Hills State University (A)
Butler County Community College (A)
Cape Fear Community College (A)
Central Carolina Community College (A)
Central Texas College (A)
Charter Oak State College (A,B,UC)
City University (A,B)
College of Southern Maryland (A,UC)
Columbia College (A,B)
Columbus State Community College (A)
The Community College of Baltimore County (A)
Community College of Southern Nevada (A)
Copiah-Lincoln Community College (A)
Dallas County Community College District (A)
Darton College (A)
Dawson Community College (A)
Drury University (A,B)
Everett Community College (A)
Fort Hays State University (A,B)
Franklin Pierce College (A,B)
Gadsden State Community College (A)
Granite State College (A)
Grantham University (A,B)
Harford Community College (A)
Indiana Tech (A)
Indiana University System (A)
Indiana Wesleyan University (A,B)
Ivy Tech Community College–Bloomington (A)
Ivy Tech Community College–Central Indiana (A)
Ivy Tech Community College–Columbus (A)
Ivy Tech Community College–East Central (A)
Ivy Tech Community College–Kokomo (A)
Ivy Tech Community College–Lafayette (A)
Ivy Tech Community College–North Central (A)
Ivy Tech Community College–Northeast (A)
Ivy Tech Community College–Northwest (A)
Ivy Tech Community College–Southeast (A)
Ivy Tech Community College–Southern Indiana (A)
Ivy Tech Community College–Southwest (A)
Ivy Tech Community College–Wabash Valley (A)
Ivy Tech Community College–Whitewater (A)
Jackson Community College (A)
Johnson County Community College (A)
Lansing Community College (A)
Liberty University (A)
Marshall University (A)
Mountain Empire Community College (A)
Mount Wachusett Community College (A)
Northern Virginia Community College (A)
North Seattle Community College (A)
Northwestern State University of Louisiana (A)
Palm Beach Community College (A)
Parkland College (A)
Patrick Henry Community College (A)
Pueblo Community College (A)
Rappahannock Community College (A)
Reading Area Community College (A)
Saint Joseph's College of Maine (A,B)
Seminole Community College (A)
Southwestern Assemblies of God University (A)
Southwest Virginia Community College (A)
Strayer University (A)
Texas Tech University (B)
Texas Woman's University (B)
Three Rivers Community College (A)
University of Alaska Southeast (B)
University of Management and Technology (A,B)
University of North Dakota (B)
University of Phoenix Online Campus (A)
Utah State University (A)
Utah Valley State College (A)
Vance-Granville Community College (A)
Vincennes University (A)
Weber State University (A)
Western Oklahoma State College (A)
West Shore Community College (A)
West Texas A&M University (B)

GENERAL STUDIES (SECONDARY EDUCATION)

University of North Dakota (M)

GENERAL STUDIES DEGREE PROGRAM

Indiana University System (B)

GENERAL STUDIES PROGRAM

Concordia University, St. Paul (A)

GENERAL STUDIES SURGICAL TECHNOLOGY DEGREE COMPLETION

Vincennes University (A)

GENERAL STUDIES WITH CRIMINAL JUSTICE SEQUENCE

University of Maine at Fort Kent (A)

GENERAL STUDIES–ASSOCIATE OF ARTS

National University (A)

GENERAL STUDIES–BACHELOR OF GENERAL STUDIES

East Tennessee State University (B)

GENERAL STUDIES–BUSINESS STUDIES

Vincennes University (A)

GENERAL STUDIES–CUSTOMIZED CERTIFICATE

Vincennes University (UC)

GENERAL STUDIES–FINANCE SPECIALIZATION

Drexel University (B)

GENERAL STUDIES–MANAGEMENT SPECIALIZATION

Drexel University (B)

GENERAL STUDIES–ONLINE BACHELOR OF GENERAL STUDIES COMPLETION PROGRAM

University of Missouri–Columbia (B)

GENERAL STUDIES, NON-MAJOR

University of Waterloo (B)

GENERAL STUDIES/LIBERAL ARTS

Tunxis Community College (A)

GENERALIST

Community College of Denver (A)

GEOGRAPHIC INFORMATION SCIENCE

Northwest Missouri State University (M)

GEOGRAPHIC INFORMATION SCIENCES

Oregon State University (UC)

GEOGRAPHIC INFORMATION SYSTEMS

Columbus State Community College (GC)
Eastern Michigan University (GC)
North Carolina State University (GC)
The Pennsylvania State University University Park Campus (M,)

GEOGRAPHIC INFORMATION SYSTEMS (GIS)

University of Colorado at Denver and Health Sciences Center—Downtown Denver Campus (M)

GEOGRAPHIC INFORMATION SYSTEMS–CERTIFICATE OF ADVANCED STUDY

University of Denver (UC)

GEOGRAPHIC INFORMATIONS SYSTEMS (GIS)

Fort Hays State University (UC)

GEOGRAPHY

University of Manitoba (B)

GEOSCIENCES, BROADCAST METEOROLOGY

Mississippi State University (B)

GEOSCIENCES, OPERATIONAL METEOROLOGY

Mississippi State University (B)

GEOSCIENCES, TEACHERS IN GEOSCIENCE

Mississippi State University (M)

GERIATRIC CARE MANAGEMENT

Kaplan University (UC)
University of Florida (UC,GC)

GERIATRIC RECREATIONAL THERAPY

Florida Gulf Coast University (M)

GERIATRIC REHABILITATION AND WELLNESS

Sacred Heart University (M)

GERMAN

Skidmore College (B)

GERONTOLOGICAL NURSE PRACTITIONER

University of Missouri–Columbia (M)

GERONTOLOGY

Florida Atlantic University (UC)
Iowa State University of Science and Technology (GC)
Kansas State University (M)
Laurentian University (B,UC)
Mount Saint Vincent University (UC)
North Dakota State University (GC,M)
Saint Mary-of-the-Woods College (A,B,UC)
Texas Tech University (GC)
Thomas Edison State College (A,B)
University of Washington (UC)

GERONTOLOGY–APPLIED GERONTOLOGY

University of North Texas (GC,M)

GERONTOLOGY–MANAGEMENT OF AGING SERVICES TRACK

University of Massachusetts Boston (GC,M)

GERONTOLOGY–MASTER OF ARTS IN GERONTOLOGY (MAG)

Chatham College

GIFTED AND TALENTED

Murray State University (UC)

GIFTED AND TALENTED EDUCATION

University of North Texas (UC)

GIFTED AND TALENTED GRADUATE TEACHING ENDORSEMENT

Western Kentucky University (UC)

GIFTED EDUCATION

Northern Arizona University (UC)
University of Central Florida (GC)
University of Missouri–Columbia (M)
University of North Texas (GC)
University of South Florida (GC,M)

GIFTED EDUCATION ENDORSEMENT

Bowling Green State University (GC)

GIFTED GRADUATE ENDORSEMENT

University of Nebraska at Kearney (UC)

GLOBAL AND INTERNATIONAL EDUCATION

Drexel University (M)

GLOBAL BUSINESS

Excelsior College (B)
Regent University (B)
University of Dallas (GC,M)
Walden University (M)

GLOBAL BUSINESS AND PUBLIC POLICY

University of Maryland University College (B)

GLOBAL BUSINESS MANAGEMENT

Bellevue University (B)

GLOBAL COMMERCE–MBA CERTIFICATE IN GLOBAL COMMERCE

Webster University (GC)

GLOBAL LOGISTICS

Lenoir Community College (A)

GLOBAL LOGISTICS AND FINANCE

Champlain College (UC)

GLOBAL MANAGEMENT

University of Phoenix Online Campus (M)

GLOBAL MASTER OF BUSINESS ADMINISTRATION FOR LATIN AMERICAN MANAGERS

Thunderbird, The Garvin School of International Management (M)

GLOBAL MASTER OF BUSINESS ADMINISTRATION ON-DEMAND

Thunderbird, The Garvin School of International Management (M)

GLOBAL MBA

University of Houston–Victoria (M)

GLOBAL STUDIES

National University (B)

GOVERNANCE, LAW, AND MANAGEMENT

Athabasca University (B)

GOVERNMENT

Regent University (M)
Skidmore College (B)

GOVERNMENT CONTRACTING

Webster University (GC)

GOVERNMENT–BUSINESS RELATIONS

Park University (M)

GOVERNMENTAL SERVICES

Darton College (A)

GRADUATE CERTIFICATE IN PUBLIC HEALTH INFORMATICS

University of Maryland, College Park (GC)

GRADUATE TEACHING LICENSURE

The College of St. Scholastica (M,UC)

GRANT PROPOSAL WRITING AND PROGRAM EVALUATION

Fort Hays State University (UC)

GRAPHIC DESIGN

Academy of Art University (M,A,B)
Mohawk Valley Community College (A)
Savannah College of Art and Design (M)

GRAPHIC DESIGN AND MULTIMEDIA

Westwood Online (A)

GRAPHIC INFORMATION TECHNOLOGY

Arizona State University (M)
Arizona State University at the Polytechnic Campus (M)

GREENHOUSE TECHNOLOGY

Minot State University–Bottineau Campus (UC)

GROUNDS WORKER SKILLS, BASIC

Minot State University–Bottineau Campus (UC)

GUIDANCE AND CONTROL (AERONAUTICS AND ASTRONAUTICS)

Stanford University (GC)

HACCP/FOOD SAFETY MANAGERS

North Carolina State University (UC)

HAZARDOUS WASTE ENGINEERING

Illinois Institute of Technology (GC)

HEALTH

Chatham College (M)

HEALTH ADMINISTRATION

Athabasca University (B)
Montana State University–Billings (M)
Pfeiffer University (M)
University of North Dakota (GC)
University of Phoenix Online Campus (A,B)
University of Southern Indiana (M)

HEALTH ADMINISTRATION INFORMATICS

University of Maryland University College (M)

HEALTH ADMINISTRATION POST-DIPLOMA

Athabasca University (B)

HEALTH ADMINISTRATION–DOCTOR OF HEALTH ADMINISTRATION (DHA)

University of Phoenix Online Campus (D)

HEALTH ADMINISTRATION–MASTER OF HEALTH ADMINISTRATION

University of Phoenix Online Campus (M)

HEALTH ADMINISTRATION/HEALTH INFORMATION SYSTEMS

University of Phoenix Online Campus (B)

HEALTH ADMINISTRATION/LONG-TERM CARE

University of Phoenix Online Campus (B)

HEALTH ADMINISTRATIVE SERVICES

Weber State University (B)

HEALTH AND HUMAN PERFORMANCE

Fort Hays State University (M)
Northwestern State University of Louisiana (M)

HEALTH AND NUTRITION COUNSELING

Thomas Edison State College (B)

HEALTH AND PHYSICAL EDUCATION (EXERCISE SCIENCE)

Darton College (A)

HEALTH AND PHYSICAL EDUCATION (RECREATION)

Darton College (A)

HEALTH AND PHYSICAL EDUCATION (SPORTS MANAGEMENT)

Darton College (A)

HEALTH AND PHYSICAL EDUCATION (TEACHER ED OPTION)

Darton College (A)

HEALTH AND SAFETY

Indiana State University (M)

HEALTH ARTS

University of St. Francis (B)

HEALTH CARE

California College for Health Sciences (M)

HEALTH CARE ADMINISTRATION

Bellevue University (M,B)
California College for Health Sciences (M)
Saint Joseph's College of Maine (B)
University of Maryland University College (GC,M)

HEALTH CARE ADMINISTRATION (MSA)

University of West Florida (M)

HEALTH CARE BUSINESS LEADERSHIP

Clarkson College (M)

HEALTH CARE BUSINESS–HEALTH INFORMATION MANAGEMENT MAJOR

Clarkson College (B)

HEALTH CARE BUSINESS–INFORMATICS MAJOR

Clarkson College (B)

HEALTH CARE BUSINESS–MANAGEMENT MAJOR

Clarkson College (B)

HEALTH CARE CODING AND CLASSIFICATION

Weber State University (UC)

HEALTH CARE LEADERSHIP

University of St. Francis (B)

HEALTH CARE MANAGEMENT

Capella University (M)
Franklin University (B)
Saint Joseph's College of Maine (UC)

HEALTH CARE MANAGEMENT CONCENTRATION

Colorado Technical University (M,B)

HEALTH CARE MANAGEMENT SPECIALTY

Davenport University Online (M)

HEALTH CARE MANAGEMENT, ADVANCED

Saint Joseph's College of Maine (UC)

HEALTH CARE RISK MANAGEMENT

University of Florida (GC)

HEALTH CARE/HEALTH SERVICES MANAGEMENT

Park University (M)

HEALTH DEVELOPMENT ADMINISTRATION

Athabasca University (UC)

HEALTH EDUCATION

East Carolina University (M)

HEALTH INFORMATICS

University of Illinois at Chicago

HEALTH INFORMATICS (EXECUTIVE PROGRAM)

University of Missouri–Columbia (M)

HEALTH INFORMATION ADMINISTRATION

Stephens College (B,UC)

HEALTH INFORMATION ADMINISTRATION DEGREE COMPLETION PROGRAM

Dakota State University (B)

HEALTH INFORMATION MANAGEMENT

Ashworth College (A)
Clarkson College (A)
The College of St. Scholastica (M)
Darton College (A)
East Carolina University (B)
University of Alaska Southeast (A)
University of Cincinnati (B)
The University of Toledo (B)
Vincennes University (A)

HEALTH INFORMATION MANAGEMENT CODING SPECIALIST

University of Alaska Southeast (UC)

HEALTH INFORMATION MANAGEMENT DEGREE COMPLETION

The College of St. Scholastica (B)

HEALTH INFORMATION MANAGEMENT TECHNOLOGY

Quinebaug Valley Community College (UC)

HEALTH INFORMATION MANAGEMENT–FOUNDATIONS

Clarkson College (UC)

HEALTH INFORMATION MANAGEMENT–HIM

Clarkson College (UC)

HEALTH INFORMATION RESOURCES

Rochester Institute of Technology (GC)

HEALTH INFORMATION TECHNICIAN

North Dakota State College of Science (A)

HEALTH INFORMATION TECHNICIAN (RECORDS MANAGEMENT/CODING)

Rasmussen College Eden Prarie (A)

HEALTH INFORMATION TECHNOLOGY

Dakota State University (A)
Darton College (A)
Davenport University Online (A)
DeVry University Online (A)
Edgecombe Community College (A)
Passaic County Community College (A)
Penn Foster Career School (A)
Weber State University (A)

HEALTH INFORMATION–MASTER OF HEALTH INFORMATION (MHIM)

Louisiana Tech University (M)

HEALTH MANAGEMENT AND POLICY

Oregon State University (GC)

HEALTH PHYSICS

Illinois Institute of Technology (M)

HEALTH PRACTICE MANAGEMENT

Franklin Pierce College (GC)

HEALTH PROFESSIONS AND RELATED SCIENCES

University of Southern Indiana (B)

HEALTH PROFESSIONS EDUCATION

Simmons College (GC)
University of Illinois at Chicago (M)

HEALTH PROMOTION

Northern Arizona University (B)
Weber State University (B)

HEALTH PROMOTION (BAS)

Northern Arizona University (B)

HEALTH SCIENCE

Cleveland State University (M)
Florida Gulf Coast University (M,B)
Mercy College (B)
University of St. Augustine for Health Sciences (D)

HEALTH SCIENCE TECHNOLOGY TEACHER

The University of Texas System (UC)

HEALTH SCIENCE–MASTER OF HEALTH SCIENCE (MHSC)

University of St. Augustine for Health Sciences (M)

HEALTH SCIENCES

Excelsior College (B)
Old Dominion University (B)
Touro University International (D,M,B)
University of Medicine and Dentistry of New Jersey (D,M,B)

HEALTH SCIENCES–MASTER OF HEALTH SCIENCES

Chatham College (M)

HEALTH SERVICE ADMINISTRATION

Austin Peay State University (M)
Keiser College (A)

HEALTH SERVICES

Thomas Edison State College (B)
Walden University (M)

HEALTH SERVICES ADMINISTRATION

Alaska Pacific University (B)
Berkeley College (A)
Davenport University Online (B)
Saint Joseph's College of Maine (M)
Strayer University (M)
Thomas Edison State College (B)
University of Central Florida (B)
University of Delaware (M)
University of St. Francis (M)
Upper Iowa University (B)

HEALTH SERVICES ADMINISTRATION AND NURSING DUAL DEGREE

Saint Joseph's College of Maine (M)

HEALTH SERVICES ADMINISTRATION/HEALTH SERVICES ADMINISTRATION AND MEDICAL IMAGING

Washburn University (B)

HEALTH SERVICES COMMUNITY HEALTH

California College for Health Sciences (M)

HEALTH SERVICES EDUCATION

Thomas Edison State College (B)

HEALTH SERVICES MANAGEMENT

California College for Health Sciences (B)
East Carolina University (B)
Mercy College (M)
Myers University (B)
University of Dallas (GC,M)

HEALTH SERVICES MANAGEMENT (EXECUTIVE PROGRAM)

University of Missouri–Columbia (M)

HEALTH SERVICES MANAGEMENT CONCENTRATION

Andrew Jackson University (M)

HEALTH SERVICES TECHNOLOGY (BAT)

The University of Texas System (B)

HEALTH SERVICES WELLNESS PROMOTION

California College for Health Sciences (M)

HEALTH SERVICES–COMMUNITY HEALTH

Walden University (D)

HEALTH SERVICES–HEALTH AND HUMAN BEHAVIOR

Walden University (D)

HEALTH SERVICES–HEALTH MANAGEMENT AND POLICY

Walden University (D)

HEALTH SERVICES–HEALTH PROMOTION AND EDUCATION

Walden University (D)

HEALTH SERVICES–SELF-DESIGNED

Walden University (D)

HEALTH SERVICES, GENERAL

Walden University (D)

HEALTH STUDIES

Texas Woman's University (M,B)

HEALTH STUDIES–HEALTH PROMOTION

The University of Alabama (M)

HEALTH STUDIES–MASTER OF HEALTH STUDIES

Athabasca University (M)

HEALTH SYSTEMS

University of Medicine and Dentistry of New Jersey (M)

HEALTH SYSTEMS ADMINISTRATION

Rochester Institute of Technology (M,UC)

HEALTH SYSTEMS FINANCE

Rochester Institute of Technology (GC)

HEALTH TECHNOLOGY MANAGEMENT–MEDICAL ASSISTANT

International Institute of the Americas (A)

HEALTH TECHNOLOGY MANAGEMENT–PATIENT CARE TECHNICIAN

International Institute of the Americas (A)

HEALTH, PHYSICAL EDUCATION, AND RECREATION

Utah State University (M)

HEALTH/TEACHER EDUCATION

East Carolina University (M)

HEALTHCARE ADMINISTRATION

Central Michigan University (D)
Seton Hall University (M)

HEALTHCARE ADMINISTRATION CONCENTRATION

American InterContinental University Online (A)

HEALTHCARE INFORMATICS

The College of St. Scholastica (UC)
Drexel University (UC)

HEALTHCARE MANAGEMENT

Brenau University (M)
Rosalind Franklin University of Medicine and Science (GC,M)

HEALTHCARE MANAGEMENT CONCENTRATION (10-MONTH PROGRAM)

American InterContinental University Online (M)

HEALTHCARE MANAGEMENT CONCENTRATION (COMPLETION PROGRAM)

American InterContinental University Online (B)

HEALTHCARE PRIVACY

University of Alaska Southeast (UC)

HEARING HEALTHCARE

Arkansas State University–Mountain Home (A)

HEAVY CONSTRUCTION PROJECT MANAGEMENT

University of Washington (UC)

HEBREW LANGUAGE AND LITERATURE

Laura and Alvin Siegal College of Judaic Studies (M)

HIGH-TECH–TECHNICAL MBA

Walden University (M)

HIGHER EDUCATION

Dallas Baptist University (M)
Drexel University (M)
University of North Dakota (D)

HIGHER EDUCATION ADMINISTRATION

Prescott College (M)

HISTOLOGIC TECHNOLOGY

Darton College (A)

HISTOLOGY

Darton College (UC)

HISTORIC PRESERVATION

Savannah College of Art and Design (GC,M)

HISTORICAL STUDIES

State University of New York Empire State College (A,B)

HISTORY

American Military University (M,B)
American Public University (M,B)
Caldwell College (B)
Columbia College (B)
Darton College (A)
Drury University (A)
Judson College (B)
Mercy College (B)
National University (B)
Prescott College (B)
Skidmore College (B)
Southwestern Assemblies of God University (B)
Thomas Edison State College (B)
University of Illinois at Springfield (B)
University of Maryland University College (B)

HISTORY (3 YEAR)

Athabasca University (B)

HISTORY (4 YEAR)

Athabasca University (B)

HISTORY AND POLITICAL STUDIES

Saint Mary-of-the-Woods College (B)

HISTORY EMPHASIS

Community College of Denver (A)

HISTORY, LIBERAL ARTS AND SCIENCES, MASS COMMUNICATIONS (ADVERTISING/PUBLIC RELATIONS; JOURNALISM), POLITICAL SCIENCE, AND PSYCHOLOGY CONCENTRATIONS

Parkland College (A)

HIT–MEDICAL CODING

North Dakota State College of Science (UC)

HOMELAND SECURITY

American Military University (M,B)
American Public University (M,B)
Keiser College (A)
Schoolcraft College (A)
University of South Florida (GC)
University of South Florida (GC)

HOMELAND SECURITY AND SAFETY ENGINEERING

National University (M)

HOMELAND SECURITY IN PUBLIC HEALTH PREPAREDNESS

The Pennsylvania State University University Park Campus (M)

HOMELAND SECURITY LEADERSHIP

University of Connecticut (M)

HOMELAND SECURITY MANAGEMENT

University of Maryland University College (GC)

HOMELAND SECURITY, POLICY, AND COORDINATION

Walden University (M)

HORTICULTURE

Texas Tech University (M,B)
Thomas Edison State College (A,B)

HORTICULTURE SCIENCE

North Carolina State University (GC)

HOSPITAL HEALTH CARE ADMINISTRATION

Thomas Edison State College (A,B)

HOSPITALITY ADMINISTRATION

Southern New Hampshire University (M)

HOSPITALITY AND TOURISM MANAGEMENT

Strayer University (B)
University of Massachusetts Amherst (B,UC)
University of Wisconsin–Stout (M)

HOSPITALITY MANAGEMENT

American Military University (B)
American Public University (B)
Central Texas College (A)
East Carolina University (B)
Excelsior College (B)
New York Institute of Technology (B)
The Pennsylvania State University University Park Campus (UC)
University of North Texas (GC,M)

HOSPITALITY MANAGEMENT (ASB)

Penn Foster Career School (A)

HOTEL AND RESTAURANT MANAGEMENT

Northern Arizona University (B)
Tompkins Cortland Community College (A)
Auburn University (M)

HOTEL, RESTAURANT AND TOURISM MANAGEMENT

New Mexico State University (B)

HOTEL, RESTAURANT, AND INSTITUTIONAL MANAGEMENT

The Pennsylvania State University University Park Campus (A,UC)
University of Delaware (B)
University of Minnesota, Crookston (UC)

HOTEL/MOTEL/RESTAURANT MANAGEMENT

Thomas Edison State College (A,B)

HUMAN AND COMMUNITY SERVICES–BACHELOR OF HUMAN AND COMMUNITY SERVICES

New Mexico State University (B)
New Mexico State University–Carlsbad (B)

HUMAN AND ORGANIZATIONAL DEVELOPMENT

Fielding Graduate University (D)

HUMAN BEHAVIOR

National University (M)

HUMAN DEVELOPMENT

Hope International University (B)
Regions University (B)
State University of New York Empire State College (A,B)
Washington State University (B)

HUMAN DEVELOPMENT AND FAMILY STUDIES

Colorado State University (B)
The Pennsylvania State University University Park Campus (A)

HUMAN DEVELOPMENT AND FAMILY STUDIES (GERONTOLOGY EMPHASIS)

Texas Tech University (M)

HUMAN ENVIRONMENTAL SCIENCES–FOOD AND NUTRITION

The University of Alabama (M)

HUMAN ENVIRONMENTAL SCIENCES–GENERAL STUDIES OPTION

The University of Alabama (B)

HUMAN ENVIRONMENTAL SCIENCES–INTERACTIVE TECHNOLOGY

The University of Alabama (M)

HUMAN ENVIRONMENTAL SCIENCES–RESTAURANT AND HOSPITALITY MANAGEMENT

The University of Alabama (B)

HUMAN FACTORS ENGINEERING

Wright State University (M)

HUMAN NUTRITION

Eastern Michigan University (M)
University of Bridgeport (M)

HUMAN PERFORMANCE TECHNOLOGY (MSA)

University of West Florida (M)

HUMAN RELATIONS AND BUSINESS

Amberton University (M)

HUMAN RESOURCE ADMINISTRATION–CERTIFICATE OF ADVANCED STUDY

University of Denver (UC)

HUMAN RESOURCE ADMINISTRATION–MASTER OF PROFESSIONAL STUDIES IN HUMAN RESOURCE ADMINISTRATION

University of Denver (M)

HUMAN RESOURCE DEVELOPMENT

Buffalo State College, State University of New York (GC)
Clemson University (M)
Dakota County Technical College (UC)
Florida State University (M)
Indiana State University (M,B)
Limestone College (B)
Rochester Institute of Technology (GC)
Southwestern College (B)
University of Arkansas (B)
The University of Texas System (M)

HUMAN RESOURCE LEADERSHIP

Regions University (B)

HUMAN RESOURCE MANAGEMENT

Ashworth College (A)
Boston University (M)
Champlain College (UC)
Dallas Baptist University (M)
Davenport University Online (B)
DeVry University Online (M)
Eastern Michigan University (GC)
Fort Hays State University (UC)
Franklin Pierce College (GC)
Mercy College (M)
Myers University (B)
Regent University (GC)
Saint Mary-of-the-Woods College (B)
Stony Brook University, State University of New York (GC)
Strayer University (B)
Thomas Edison State College (A)
Troy University (M)
University of Calgary (UC)
University of Connecticut (M)
University of Maryland University College (B)
University of Phoenix Online Campus (M)
University of Wisconsin–Platteville (UC)
University of Wisconsin–Platteville (UC)
Walden University (M)

HUMAN RESOURCE MANAGEMENT AND ORGANIZATIONAL DEVELOPMENT

National University (M)

HUMAN RESOURCE MANAGEMENT CONCENTRATION

Andrew Jackson University (M)
Colorado Technical University (M,B)

HUMAN RESOURCE MANAGEMENT CONCENTRATION (10-MONTH PROGRAM)

American InterContinental University Online (M)

HUMAN RESOURCE MANAGEMENT CONCENTRATION (COMPLETION PROGRAM)

American InterContinental University Online (B)

HUMAN RESOURCE MANAGEMENT PRACTICE

California National University for Advanced Studies (UC)

HUMAN RESOURCE MANAGEMENT SPECIALTY

Davenport University Online (M)

HUMAN RESOURCES

California National University for Advanced Studies (M)
Indiana Business College (A)
Indiana Tech (B)
The Pennsylvania State University University Park Campus (UC)
University of the Incarnate Word (B)

HUMAN RESOURCES AND LABOUR RELATIONS

Athabasca University (B,UC)

HUMAN RESOURCES CONCENTRATION

American InterContinental University Online (A)

HUMAN RESOURCES MANAGEMENT

Briar Cliff University (GC)
Davenport University Online (UC)
Florida Institute of Technology (M)
Southern New Hampshire University (UC)
Stevens Institute of Technology (GC)
Thomas Edison State College (M,B)

Upper Iowa University (B,UC)
Kaplan University (M)

HUMAN RESOURCES MANAGEMENT/MARKETING (3 YEAR)

Athabasca University (B)

HUMAN RESOURCES MANAGEMENT/MARKETING (4 YEAR)

Athabasca University (B)

HUMAN SCIENCE

Athabasca University (B)
Saybrook Graduate School and Research Center (D,M)

HUMAN SCIENCE–POST-DIPLOMA

Athabasca University (B)

HUMAN SERVICES

Alaska Pacific University (B)
Athabasca University (B)
Bismarck State College (A)
Columbia College (A)
Dawson Community College (A)
Franklin Pierce College (A,B,UC)
Indiana Wesleyan University (UC)
Ivy Tech Community College–Bloomington (A)
Ivy Tech Community College–Central Indiana (A)
Ivy Tech Community College–Columbus (A)
Ivy Tech Community College–East Central (A)
Ivy Tech Community College–Kokomo (A)
Ivy Tech Community College–Lafayette (A)
Ivy Tech Community College–North Central (A)
Ivy Tech Community College–Northeast (A)
Ivy Tech Community College–Northwest (A)
Ivy Tech Community College–Southeast (A)
Ivy Tech Community College–Southern Indiana (A)
Ivy Tech Community College–Southwest (A)
Ivy Tech Community College–Wabash Valley (A)
Ivy Tech Community College–Whitewater (A)
Liberty University (M)
Mount Wachusett Community College (A)
Saint Joseph's College of Maine (A)
Saint Mary-of-the-Woods College (B)
Upper Iowa University (B)
Washburn University (B)
Western Washington University (B)

HUMAN SERVICES ADMINISTRATION–MASTER OF HUMAN SERVICES ADMINISTRATION

University of Great Falls (M)

HUMAN SERVICES COUNSELING

Old Dominion University (B)
Regent University (M)
Southwestern Assemblies of God University (M)

HUMAN SERVICES SHORT-TERM CERTIFICATE

Sinclair Community College (UC)

HUMAN SERVICES–CLINICAL SOCIAL WORK

Walden University (D)

HUMAN SERVICES–COUNSELING

Walden University (D)

HUMAN SERVICES–CRIMINAL JUSTICE

Walden University (D)

HUMAN SERVICES–CRIMINAL JUSTICE LEADERSHIP

Concordia University, St. Paul (M)

HUMAN SERVICES–FAMILY LIFE EDUCATION

Concordia University, St. Paul (M)

HUMAN SERVICES–FAMILY STUDIES AND INTERVENTION STRATEGIES

Walden University (D)

HUMAN SERVICES–HUMAN SERVICES ADMINISTRATION

Walden University (D)

HUMAN SERVICES–SELF-DESIGNED

Walden University (D)

HUMAN SERVICES–SOCIAL POLICY ANALYSIS AND PLANNING

Walden University (D)

HUMAN SERVICES–SOCIAL SERVICES ADMINISTRATION CONCENTRATION

University of Illinois at Springfield (M)

HUMAN SERVICES, GENERAL

Walden University (D)

HUMAN SERVICES/COUNSELING STUDIES

Capella University (D,M)

HUMAN SERVICES/CRIMINAL JUSTICE

Capella University (D,M)

HUMAN SERVICES/GENERAL HUMAN SERVICES

Capella University (D,M)

HUMAN SERVICES/HEALTH CARE ADMINISTRATION

Capella University (D,M)

HUMAN SERVICES/MANAGEMENT

University of Phoenix Online Campus (B)

HUMAN SERVICES/MANAGEMENT OF NONPROFIT AGENCIES

Capella University (D,M)

HUMAN SERVICES/MARITAL, COUPLE, AND FAMILY COUNSELING/THERAPY (CACREP ACCREDITED)

Capella University (M)

HUMAN SERVICES/MENTAL HEALTH COUNSELING

Capella University (M)

HUMAN SERVICES/SOCIAL AND COMMUNITY SERVICES

Capella University (D,M)

HUMANE LEADERSHIP

Duquesne University (B)

HUMANITARIAN ASSISTANCE

University of South Florida (GC)

HUMANITARIAN SERVICES ADMINISTRATION

University of Connecticut (M)

HUMANITIES

American Military University (M)
American Public University (M)
California State University, Dominguez Hills (M)
College of the Humanities and Sciences, Harrison Middleton University (A,B)
County College of Morris (A)
Prescott College (M,B)
Saint Mary-of-the-Woods College (A,B)
Salve Regina University (M)
Thomas Edison State College (B)
University of Maryland University College (B)
University of Pittsburgh (B)
University of Waterloo (B)

Washington State University (B)

HUMANITIES (3 YEAR)

Athabasca University (B)

HUMANITIES (4 YEAR)

Athabasca University (B)

HUMANITIES OPTION

Passaic County Community College (A)

HUMANITIES/PHILOSOPHY EMPHASIS

Community College of Denver (A)

ILLUSTRATION

Academy of Art University (M,A,B)
Syracuse University (M)

IMAGINATIVE LITERATURE

College of the Humanities and Sciences, Harrison Middleton University (M)

IMAGING SCIENCE

Rochester Institute of Technology (M)

IMBA

Syracuse University (M)

INCLUSIVE EDUCATION

Athabasca University (UC)

INDEPENDENT BUSINESS MANAGEMENT

Parkland College (UC)

INDEPENDENT STUDIES–BACHELOR OF INDEPENDENT STUDIES/GENERAL STUDIES

Murray State University (B)

INDIVIDUAL STUDIES

Jamestown Community College (GC,A)
Jefferson Community College (A)

INDIVIDUALIZED DEGREE PROGRAM

Regent University (M)

INDIVIDUALIZED LIBERAL AND PROFESSIONAL STUDIES (VARIOUS SELF-DESIGNED TOPICS)

Antioch University McGregor (M)

INDIVIDUALIZED MAJOR

University of Wisconsin–Superior (B)

INDIVIDUALIZED STUDIES

Governors State University (B)
Metropolitan State University (B)
Skidmore College (B)

INDIVIDUALLY DESIGNED FOCUS AREA

DePaul University (B)

INDOOR AIR QUALITY

Illinois Institute of Technology (GC)

INDUSTRIAL AND SYSTEMS ENGINEERING

Auburn University (M)
Georgia Institute of Technology (M)
The University of Alabama in Huntsville (D)

INDUSTRIAL DESIGN

Academy of Art University (M,A,B)

INDUSTRIAL ELECTRONICS WITH PLC TECHNOLOGY

Cleveland Institute of Electronics (UC)

INDUSTRIAL ENGINEERING

Columbia University (UC)
Iowa State University of Science and Technology (M)
Mississippi State University (M)
New Mexico State University (M)
The University of Alabama in Huntsville (M)
The University of Texas at Arlington (M)

INDUSTRIAL ENGINEERING AND OPERATIONS RESEARCH

Columbia University (GC)

INDUSTRIAL ENGINEERING TECHNOLOGY AST

Penn Foster Career School (A)

INDUSTRIAL ENGINEERING–MASTER OF SCIENCE IN INDUSTRIAL ENGINEERING

New Mexico State University (M)

INDUSTRIAL ENVIRONMENTAL MANAGEMENT

Rochester Institute of Technology (UC)

INDUSTRIAL FACILITIES

Illinois Institute of Technology (M)

INDUSTRIAL FACILITIES DEGREE COMPLETION

Illinois Institute of Technology (B)

INDUSTRIAL HYGIENE

Montana Tech of The University of Montana (M)

INDUSTRIAL LOGISTICS

Illinois Institute of Technology (M)

INDUSTRIAL LOGISTICS DEGREE COMPLETION

Illinois Institute of Technology (B)

INDUSTRIAL MANAGEMENT

Central Missouri State University (M)
Myers University (B)

INDUSTRIAL SUPERVISION

Indiana State University (B)

INDUSTRIAL TECHNOLOGY

East Carolina University (B)
Indiana State University (B)

INDUSTRIAL TECHNOLOGY–BACHELOR OF APPLIED SCIENCE IN INDUSTRIAL TECHNOLOGY (TWO-YEAR COMPLETION)

Missouri State University (B)

INDUSTRIAL/ORGANIZATIONAL PSYCHOLOGY

Kansas State University (M)

INFORMATION AND COMMUNICATION TECHNOLOGY–BACHELOR OF INFORMATION AND COMMUNICATION TECHNOLOGY

New Mexico State University (B)

INFORMATION AND COMPUTER SECURITY

Davenport University Online (A,B,UC)

INFORMATION AND LEARNING TECHNOLOGIES, SCHOOL LIBRARY

University of Colorado at Denver and Health Sciences Center—Downtown Denver Campus (M)

INFORMATION AND SYSTEMS ENGINEERING (MS OR MENG)

Lehigh University (M)

INFORMATION AND TECHNOLOGY MANAGEMENT

Concordia University, St. Paul (B)

INFORMATION AND TELECOMMUNICATION SYSTEMS MANAGEMENT

Capitol College (M)

INFORMATION ASSURANCE

Capitol College (M)
East Carolina University (GC)
Iowa State University of Science and Technology (UC)
University of Dallas (GC,M)

INFORMATION ASSURANCE AND COMPUTER SECURITY

Dakota State University (M)

INFORMATION COMMUNICATION TECHNOLOGY–BACHELOR OF INFORMATION COMMUNICATION TECHNOLOGY

New Mexico State University–Carlsbad (B)

INFORMATION ENGINEERING AND MANAGEMENT

Southern Methodist University (M)

INFORMATION MANAGEMENT

Grantham University (M)
Syracuse University (M)
Syracuse University (M)

INFORMATION MANAGEMENT FOR MANAGERS

New Jersey Institute of Technology (GC)

INFORMATION MANAGEMENT TECHNOLOGY

Grantham University (M)

INFORMATION MANAGEMENT–APPLIED INFORMATION MANAGEMENT

University of Oregon (M)

INFORMATION MANAGEMENT–PROJECT MANAGEMENT

Grantham University (M)

INFORMATION NETWORKING AND TELECOMMUNICATIONS (COMPUTER NETWORKING AND TELECOMMUNICATIONS CONCENTRATION)

Fort Hays State University (B)

INFORMATION NETWORKING AND TELECOMMUNICATIONS (WEB DEVELOPMENT CONCENTRATION)

Fort Hays State University (B)

INFORMATION PROCESSING SPECIALIST

Bismarck State College (UC)

INFORMATION REPORTING TECHNOLOGY

St. Louis Community College System (A)

INFORMATION RESOURCES MANAGEMENT

University of Maryland University College (GC)

INFORMATION SCIENCE AND TECHNOLOGY

Colorado State University (UC)
The Pennsylvania State University University Park Campus (UC)

INFORMATION SCIENCES

University of North Texas (M)
The University of Tennessee (M)

INFORMATION SCIENCES AND TECHNOLOGY

The Pennsylvania State University University Park Campus (A)

INFORMATION SECURITY

Champlain College (UC)
James Madison University (M)
Nova Southeastern University (M)

INFORMATION SECURITY MANAGEMENT

Syracuse University (GC)
Syracuse University (GC)

INFORMATION SECURITY–CERTIFICATE OF ADVANCED STUDY

University of Denver (UC)

INFORMATION SERVICES AND SUPPORT

The University of Toledo (A,UC)

INFORMATION SERVICES TECHNOLOGY

College of Southern Maryland (A,UC)

INFORMATION SERVICES TECHNOLOGY–WEB DEVELOPER

College of Southern Maryland (A)

INFORMATION STUDIES

Florida State University (M)

INFORMATION SYSTEMS

Athabasca University (M)
City University (GC)
Columbia University (UC)
Dakota State University (M)
DePaul University (M)
Drexel University (M)
Grantham University (A,B)
Illinois Institute of Technology (GC,M)
National University (M,B)
Nova Southeastern University (D)
Randolph Community College (A)
Shippensburg University of Pennsylvania (M)
Strayer University (GC,M,A,B,UC)
University of Colorado at Denver and Health Sciences Center—Downtown Denver Campus (M)
University of Great Falls (M)
University of Illinois at Urbana–Champaign (GC)
University of North Dakota (B)
University of the Incarnate Word (A)
Vance-Granville Community College (A)

INFORMATION SYSTEMS (3 YEAR)

Athabasca University (B)

INFORMATION SYSTEMS (4 YEAR)

Athabasca University (B)

INFORMATION SYSTEMS AND INFORMATION SECURITY

The University of North Carolina at Charlotte (GC)

INFORMATION SYSTEMS AND TELECOMMUNICATIONS MANAGEMENT

Syracuse University (GC)
Syracuse University (GC)

INFORMATION SYSTEMS CONCENTRATION

American InterContinental University Online (A)

INFORMATION SYSTEMS IMPLEMENTATION

New Jersey Institute of Technology (GC)

INFORMATION SYSTEMS MANAGEMENT

DeVry University Online (M)
University of Maryland University College (B)

INFORMATION SYSTEMS SECURITY

Westwood Online (B)

INFORMATION SYSTEMS SECURITY CONCENTRATION

Colorado Technical University (M)

INFORMATION SYSTEMS SECURITY–CERTIFICATE OF ADVANCED STUDY

University of Denver (UC)

INFORMATION SYSTEMS TECHNOLOGY

Northern Virginia Community College (UC)
Patrick Henry Community College (A)
Southern Illinois University Carbondale (B)
University of Central Florida (B)

INFORMATION SYSTEMS–MASTER OF INFORMATION SYSTEMS

University of Phoenix Online Campus (M)

INFORMATION SYSTEMS/ NETWORK ADMINISTRATION AND SUPPORT

Vance-Granville Community College (A)

INFORMATION TECHNOLOGIES

East Carolina University (B)

INFORMATION TECHNOLOGY

DePaul University (M)
DeVry University Online (B)
Excelsior College (B)
Franklin University (A,B)
Granite State College (B)
Grantham University (M)
Jamestown Community College (GC,A)
Kaplan University (M)
Kettering University (M)
Memorial University of Newfoundland (M)
Myers University (B)
Rochester Institute of Technology (M)
Southern New Hampshire University (A,B)
Southern Polytechnic State University (B)
University of Dallas (GC,M)
University of Maryland University College (M)
University of Massachusetts Lowell (A,B,UC)
University of Phoenix Online Campus (A,B)
Virginia Polytechnic Institute and State University (M)
Kaplan University (B)

INFORMATION TECHNOLOGY AND MANAGEMENT

Illinois Institute of Technology (M)

INFORMATION TECHNOLOGY BASICS

Lansing Community College (UC)

INFORMATION TECHNOLOGY CONCENTRATION

Colorado Technical University (B)

INFORMATION TECHNOLOGY COORDINATOR

New Mexico State University (UC)

INFORMATION TECHNOLOGY HELP DESK TECHNICIAN

Peirce College (UC)

INFORMATION TECHNOLOGY MANAGEMENT

American Military University (B)
American Public University (B)
Capella University (M)
Franklin Pierce College (M)
Granite State College (UC)
Illinois Institute of Technology (M)
Mount Saint Vincent University (UC)
National University (B)
Saint Joseph's College of Maine (A,UC)
Touro University International (M,B)
University of Management and Technology (B)

INFORMATION TECHNOLOGY MANAGEMENT CONCENTRATION

Colorado Technical University (M)

INFORMATION TECHNOLOGY ONLINE

Bryant and Stratton Online (A)
Oregon Institute of Technology (B)

INFORMATION TECHNOLOGY PATHWAY CERTIFICATE

Kaplan University (UC)

INFORMATION TECHNOLOGY WITH .NET TECHNOLOGY

Peirce College (UC)

INFORMATION TECHNOLOGY WITH BUSINESS MINOR

University of Massachusetts Lowell (B)

INFORMATION TECHNOLOGY WITH DESKTOP APPLICATIONS FOR BUSINESS

Peirce College (A,B)

INFORMATION TECHNOLOGY WITH NETWORK SECURITY

Peirce College (A)

INFORMATION TECHNOLOGY WITH PROGRAMMING

Peirce College (UC)

INFORMATION TECHNOLOGY WITH PROGRAMMING AND APPLICATION DEVELOPMENT

Peirce College (B)

INFORMATION TECHNOLOGY WITH PROGRAMMING APPLICATION DEVELOPMENT

Peirce College (A)

INFORMATION TECHNOLOGY WITH WINDOWS NETWORK OPERATING SYSTEM

Peirce College (UC)

INFORMATION TECHNOLOGY–BACHELOR OF INFORMATION TECHNOLOGY (BIT)–COMPUTER SYSTEMS CONCENTRATION (COMPLETION PROGRAM)

American InterContinental University Online (B)

INFORMATION TECHNOLOGY–BACHELOR OF INFORMATION TECHNOLOGY (BIT)–NETWORK ADMINISTRATION CONCENTRATION (COMPLETION PROGRAM)

American InterContinental University Online (B)

INFORMATION TECHNOLOGY–BACHELOR OF INFORMATION TECHNOLOGY (BIT)–PROGRAMMING CONCENTRATION (COMPLETION PROGRAM)

American InterContinental University Online (B)

INFORMATION TECHNOLOGY–BACHELOR OF SCIENCE IN INFORMATION TECHNOLOGY (BSIT)

New Jersey Institute of Technology (B)

INFORMATION TECHNOLOGY–FUNDAMENTALS OF INFORMATION TECHNOLOGY

University of Massachusetts Boston (UC)

INFORMATION TECHNOLOGY–INFORMATION SECURITY CONCENTRATION

Peirce College (A,B)

INFORMATION TECHNOLOGY–INFORMATION SERVICES LIBRARY PARAPROFESSIONAL

Belmont Technical College (A)

INFORMATION TECHNOLOGY–IT MANAGEMENT

University of Management and Technology (M)

INFORMATION TECHNOLOGY–IT PROJECT MANAGEMENT

University of Management and Technology (M)

INFORMATION TECHNOLOGY–MANAGEMENT INFORMATION SYSTEMS

University of Management and Technology (M)

INFORMATION TECHNOLOGY–NETWORK SECURITY CONCENTRATION

Peirce College (B)

INFORMATION TECHNOLOGY–NETWORKING CONCENTRATION

Peirce College (A,B)

INFORMATION TECHNOLOGY–TECHNOLOGY MANAGEMENT CONCENTRATION

Peirce College (A,B)

INFORMATION TECHNOLOGY–WEB ANALYST/PROGRAMMER

Wisconsin Indianhead Technical College (A)

INFORMATION TECHNOLOGY, GENERAL

The Community College of Baltimore County (A)

INFORMATION TECHNOLOGY/GENERAL

Capella University (B)

INFORMATION TECHNOLOGY/GENERAL INFORMATION TECHNOLOGY

Capella University (M)

INFORMATION TECHNOLOGY/GRAPHICS AND MULTIMEDIA

Capella University (B)

INFORMATION TECHNOLOGY/INFORMATION ASSURANCE AND SECURITY

Capella University (B)

INFORMATION TECHNOLOGY/INFORMATION SECURITY

Capella University (M)

INFORMATION TECHNOLOGY/NETWORK ARCHITECTURE AND DESIGN

Capella University (M)

INFORMATION TECHNOLOGY/NETWORK TECHNOLOGY

Capella University (B)

INFORMATION TECHNOLOGY/PROJECT MANAGEMENT

Capella University (M,B)

INFORMATION TECHNOLOGY/SYSTEM DESIGN AND PROGRAMMING

Capella University (M)

INFORMATION TECHNOLOGY/VISUAL COMMUNICATION

University of Phoenix Online Campus (B)

INFORMATION TECHNOLOGY/WEB APPLICATION DEVELOPMENT

Capella University (B)

INFRASTRUCTURE CONSTRUCTION

University of Washington (UC)

INITIAL TEACHER PROFESSIONAL PREPARATION

University of Central Florida (GC)

INSTITUTIONAL ADMINISTRATION (NUTRITION)

Texas Woman's University (M)

INSTITUTIONAL RESEARCH

The Pennsylvania State University University Park Campus (GC)

INSTRUCTION AND CURRICULUM

University of Florida (GC)

INSTRUCTIONAL AND PERFORMANCE TECHNOLOGY

Boise State University (M)
Boise State University (M)

INSTRUCTIONAL DESIGN

Roosevelt University (GC)
Southern Polytechnic State University (GC)
University of Massachusetts Boston (M)

INSTRUCTIONAL DESIGN AND DEVELOPMENT

University of South Alabama (M)

INSTRUCTIONAL DESIGN FOR ONLINE LEARNING

Capella University (M)

INSTRUCTIONAL DESIGN FOR SIMULATIONS

University of Central Florida (GC)

INSTRUCTIONAL MATH

Drury University (M)

INSTRUCTIONAL SYSTEMS

Florida State University (M)

INSTRUCTIONAL SYSTEMS EDUCATIONAL TECHNOLOGY

The Pennsylvania State University University Park Campus (M)

INSTRUCTIONAL TECHNOLOGY

Boston University (GC)
Boston University (GC)
Drury University (M)
Duquesne University (D)
East Carolina University (M)
Fort Hays State University (M)
San Diego State University (UC)
University of Houston–Clear Lake (M)
University of Nebraska at Kearney (M)
University of Nevada, Las Vegas (GC)
University of the Incarnate Word (M)
University of West Florida (M)
West Texas A&M University (M)

INSTRUCTIONAL TECHNOLOGY (DISTANCE EDUCATION EMPHASIS)

Texas Tech University (M)

INSTRUCTIONAL TECHNOLOGY CONCENTRATION (10-MONTH PROGRAM)

American InterContinental University Online (M)

INSTRUCTIONAL TECHNOLOGY DESIGN

University of Massachusetts Boston (GC)

INSTRUCTIONAL TECHNOLOGY EDUCATION SPECIALIST

Bloomsburg University of Pennsylvania (M)

INSTRUCTIONAL TECHNOLOGY FOR EDUCATORS

University of Massachusetts Boston (GC)

INSTRUCTIONAL TECHNOLOGY SPECIALIST

Drexel University (UC)
Missouri State University (GC)

INSTRUCTIONAL TECHNOLOGY SYSTEMS

DePaul University (M)

INSTRUCTIONAL TECHNOLOGY–CURRICULUM AND INSTRUCTION EMPHASIS

Virginia Polytechnic Institute and State University (M)

INSTRUCTIONAL TECHNOLOGY–DISTANCE EDUCATION

University of South Florida (GC)

INSTRUCTIONAL TECHNOLOGY–EDUCATIONAL TECHNOLOGY EMPHASIS

Utah State University (M)

INSTRUCTIONAL TECHNOLOGY–FLORIDA DIGITAL EDUCATOR

University of South Florida (GC)

INSTRUCTIONAL TECHNOLOGY–WEB DESIGN

University of South Florida (GC)

INSTRUCTIONAL TECHNOLOGY/MEDIA–E-LEARNING PROFESSIONAL TRACK

University of Central Florida (M)

INSTRUCTIONAL TECHNOLOGY/MEDIA–EDUCATIONAL MEDIA TRACK

University of Central Florida (M)

INSTRUCTIONAL TECHNOLOGY/MEDIA–EDUCATIONAL TECHNOLOGY TRACK

University of Central Florida (M)

INSTRUCTIONAL TECHNOLOGY/MEDIA–INSTRUCTIONAL SYSTEMS TRACK

University of Central Florida (M)

INSTRUCTIONAL/EDUCATIONAL TECHNOLOGY

University of Central Florida (GC)

INSURANCE

Thomas Edison State College (A,B)

INSURANCE AND RISK MANAGEMENT

Indiana State University (B)

INSURANCE MANAGEMENT–MASTER OF SCIENCE IN INSURANCE MANAGEMENT

Boston University (M)

INTEGRATED DIRECT MARKETING

University of Maryland University College (GC)

INTEGRATED MARKETING COMMUNICATIONS

Eastern Michigan University (M)
West Virginia University (M,UC)

INTEGRATED MICROSYSTEMS

University of Michigan (M)

INTEGRATED STUDIES

Athabasca University (M)

INTEGRATIVE PROFESSIONAL STUDIES

Davenport University Online (B)

INTEGRATIVE SUPPLY CHAIN MANAGEMENT

University of Maryland University College (GC)

INTELLIGENT SYSTEMS

Columbia University (UC)

INTERACTIVE DESIGN

Savannah College of Art and Design (GC)

INTERCULTURAL CONFLICT MANAGEMENT

Antioch University McGregor (M)

INTERCULTURAL MINISTRIES DEGREE COMPLETION

Northwestern College (B)

INTERCULTURAL STUDIES

Crown College (M)

INTERDISCIPLINARY (CUSTOM CURRICULUM)

University of Dallas (GC,M)

INTERDISCIPLINARY EARLY CHILDHOOD EDUCATION

Western Kentucky University (A)

INTERDISCIPLINARY PROGRAM IN TECHNICAL STUDIES

The University of Toledo (A)

INTERDISCIPLINARY SOCIAL SCIENCE

Florida State University (B)

INTERDISCIPLINARY SOCIAL SCIENCES

Kansas State University (B)

INTERDISCIPLINARY STUDIES

Adams State College (B)
American Military University (B)
American Public University (B)
Arizona State University
Columbia College (B)
Eastern Wyoming College (A)
Grantham University (A,B)
Kaplan University (A)
Marylhurst University (B)
Mississippi State University (B)
New York Institute of Technology (B)
Regent University (B)
State University of New York Empire State College (A,B)
Stephen F. Austin State University (B)
The University of Alabama (B)
Upper Iowa University (B)

INTERDISCIPLINARY STUDIES–ACTION FOR A VIABLE FUTURE

Sonoma State University (M)

INTERDISCIPLINARY STUDIES, COMMUNITY DEVELOPMENT SPECIALIZATION

Iowa State University of Science and Technology (M)

INTERDISCIPLINARY STUDIES/ EDUCATIONAL PARAPROFESSIONAL (TEACHER'S AIDE)

Kaplan University (A)

INTERIOR ARCHITECTURE AND DESIGN

Academy of Art University (M,A,B)

INTERIOR DESIGN

Northern Arizona University (B)

INTERNATIONAL

University of the Incarnate Word (M)

INTERNATIONAL AFFAIRS

Skidmore College (B)

INTERNATIONAL BUSINESS

Berkeley College (A)
Caldwell College (B)
Colorado Technical University (B)
Dallas Baptist University (M)
Lansing Community College (A)
Park University (M)
Regent University (GC)
Schiller International University (B)
Southern New Hampshire University (GC,B)
Strayer University (B)
Thomas Edison State College (A,B)
University of Wisconsin–Platteville (UC)
University of Wisconsin–Platteville (UC)
Schiller International University (M)

INTERNATIONAL BUSINESS CONCENTRATION (10-MONTH PROGRAM)

American InterContinental University Online (M)

INTERNATIONAL BUSINESS CONCENTRATION (COMPLETION PROGRAM)

American InterContinental University Online (B)

INTERNATIONAL BUSINESS DEVELOPMENT

Champlain College (UC)

INTERNATIONAL CONSTRUCTION MANAGEMENT

University of Florida (M)

INTERNATIONAL DEVELOPMENT

Hope International University (M)

INTERNATIONAL HOTEL AND TOURISM MANAGEMENT

Schiller International University (M,B)

INTERNATIONAL LOGISTICS AND TRANSPORTATION MANAGEMENT

Rochester Institute of Technology (UC)

INTERNATIONAL MANAGEMENT

University of Management and Technology (B)

INTERNATIONAL MARKETING

University of Maryland University College (GC)

INTERNATIONAL MASTERS IN MANAGEMENT PROGRAM (IMM)

Purdue University (M)

INTERNATIONAL NONGOVERNMENTAL ORGANIZATIONS (NGOS)

Walden University (M)

INTERNATIONAL PEACE AND CONFLICT RESOLUTION

American Military University (M)
American Public University (M)

INTERNATIONAL RELATIONS

American Military University (B)
American Public University (B)
St. Mary's University of San Antonio (M)
Salve Regina University (M)
Troy University (M)

INTERNATIONAL SCIENTIFIC AND TECHNICAL COMMUNICATION

Bowling Green State University (GC)

INTERNATIONAL SECURITY

Stanford University (GC)

INTERNATIONAL SPORT DIPLOMA

United States Sports Academy (UC)

INTERNATIONAL TOURISM MANAGEMENT

Northern Arizona University (UC)

INTERNATIONAL TRADE

University of Maryland University College (GC)

INTERNET AND WEBSITE DEVELOPMENT

Kaplan University (UC)

INTERNET BUSINESS SYSTEMS

Mercy College (M)

INTERNET ENGINEERING

Capitol College (M)

INTERNET PROGRAMMING

University of Washington (UC)

INTERNET SECURITY CONCENTRATION (10-MONTH PROGRAM)

American InterContinental University Online (M)

INTERNET SYSTEMS AND SOFTWARE TECHNOLOGY

Bellevue University (B)

INTERNET SYSTEMS ENGINEERING

New Jersey Institute of Technology (GC)

INTERNET TECHNOLOGIES

Pace University (GC)

INTERNET TECHNOLOGY

Pace University (GC)

INTERNET TECHNOLOGY FOR E-COMMERCE

Pace University (M)

INTERNET TECHNOLOGY MULTIMEDIA AND DESIGN AST

Penn Foster Career School (A)

INTERNET TECHNOLOGY WEB PROGRAMMING

Penn Foster Career School (A)

INTERNET TECHNOLOGY–E-COMMERCE ADMINISTRATION AST

Penn Foster Career School (A)

INTERNETWORKING TECHNOLOGY

Strayer University (A,B,UC)

INTERPERSONAL COMMUNICATIONS

Seminole Community College (A)

INTERPRETER TRAINING (GENERAL TECHNOLOGY–AD IN OCCUPATIONAL TECHNOLOGY)

Spartanburg Technical College (A)

INTRODUCTION TO COMPUTER PROGRAMMING LANGUAGE

Kaplan University (UC)

INTRODUCTION TO HOME AUTOMATION INSTALLATION

Cleveland Institute of Electronics (UC)

INTRODUCTION TO PROGRAMMING–NTID

Rochester Institute of Technology (UC)

INTRODUCTORY C++ PROGRAMMING

Bellevue Community College (UC)

IOWA TEACHER INTERN CERTIFICATE

Kaplan University (UC)

IT BUSINESS INFORMATION SYSTEMS

Virginia Polytechnic Institute and State University (GC)

IT COMMUNICATION

Virginia Polytechnic Institute and State University (GC)

IT DECISION SUPPORT SYSTEMS

Virginia Polytechnic Institute and State University (GC)

IT NETWORKING

Virginia Polytechnic Institute and State University (GC)

IT/DATABASE

Kaplan University (B)

IT/MULTIMEDIA AND ANIMATION

Kaplan University (B)

IT/NETWORKING

Kaplan University (B)

IT/PROGRAMMING

Kaplan University (B)

IT/WEB DEVELOPMENT

Kaplan University (B)

JAVA DEVELOPMENT

Champlain College (UC)

JEWISH EARLY CHILDHOOD EDUCATION

Gratz College (GC)

JEWISH EDUCATION

Gratz College (GC)

JEWISH EDUCATION–MASTER OF SCIENCE IN JEWISH EDUCATION (MSJE)

Spertus Institute of Jewish Studies (M)

JEWISH NON-PROFIT MANAGEMENT

Gratz College (GC)

JEWISH STUDIES

Gratz College (GC,M)
Hebrew College (M)
Laura and Alvin Siegal College of Judaic Studies (M)
Spertus Institute of Jewish Studies (D,M)

JOURNALISM

Prescott College (B)
Regent University (M)
Saint Mary-of-the-Woods College (B)
Seminole Community College (A)
Thomas Edison State College (B)

JOURNALISM (MEDIA MANAGEMENT)

University of Missouri–Columbia (M)

JOURNALISM (STRATEGIC COMMUNICATIONS)

University of Missouri–Columbia (M)

JOURNALISM AND MASS COMMUNICATION

Darton College (A)

JOURNALISM AND MASS COMMUNICATIONS

University of Nebraska–Lincoln (M)

JOURNALISM EDUCATION

University of Missouri–Columbia (M)

JOURNALISM–ONLINE JOURNALISM

University of Massachusetts Amherst (UC)

JURISPRUDENCE

College of the Humanities and Sciences, Harrison Middleton University (M)

JUSTICE ADMINISTRATION—MINISTRY CONCENTRATION

Taylor University (A)

JUSTICE ADMINISTRATION—PUBLIC POLICY CONCENTRATION

Taylor University (A)

JUSTICE AND MINISTRY

Taylor University (UC)

JUSTICE STUDIES

Fort Hays State University (B)

JUSTICE STUDIES–CRIMINAL JUSTICE

Berkeley College (A)

JUSTICE SYSTEMS AND POLICY PLANNING (BAS)

Northern Arizona University (B)

K-12 STUDIES IN EDUCATION (FOR LICENSED K-12 TEACHERS)

Capella University (M)

K-12 TECHNOLOGY INTEGRATION

University of Florida (GC)

KINESIOLOGY

The University of Texas at Tyler (M)
The University of Texas of the Permian Basin (M)
The University of Texas System (M)

KINESIOLOGY AND HEALTH

University of Wyoming (M)

KNOWLEDGE AND INFORMATION TECHNOLOGIES–MASTER OF APPLIED SCIENCE IN KNOWLEDGE AND INFORMATION TECHNOLOGIES

University of Denver (M)

KNOWLEDGE AND LEARNING MANAGEMENT

Walden University (M)

KNOWLEDGE MANAGEMENT
Walden University (M)

LABOR STUDIES
State University of New York Empire State College (A,B)
Thomas Edison State College (B)

LABOR STUDIES AND INDUSTRIAL RELATIONS
The Pennsylvania State University University Park Campus (UC)

LABORATORY ANIMAL SCIENCE
Thomas Edison State College (A,B)

LABOUR STUDIES
Athabasca University (UC)

LABOUR STUDIES (3 YEAR)
Athabasca University (B)

LABOUR STUDIES (4 YEAR)
Athabasca University (B)

LAND SURVEYING
University of Wyoming (UC)

LAND USE PLANNING
Prescott College (M)

LANDSCAPE PEST MANAGEMENT
University of Florida (GC)

LANDSCAPE TECHNICIAN
Minot State University–Bottineau Campus (UC)

LANGUAGE LITERACY EDUCATION
Texas Tech University (M)

LASER AND FIBER OPTIC TECHNOLOGY
Three Rivers Community College (GC)

LATIN
University of Florida (M)

LATIN AND ROMAN STUDIES
University of Florida (D)

LAW AND JUSTICE
Laurentian University (UC)

LAW AND JUSTICE (IN DEVELOPMENT)
Laurentian University (B)

LAW AND SOCIETY
The Pennsylvania State University University Park Campus (B)

LAW ENFORCEMENT
Indiana State University (UC)

LAW ENFORCEMENT ADMINISTRATION
Austin Peay State University (A)

LAW ENFORCEMENT STUDIES
Vincennes University (A)

LAW–PRE-LAW
Darton College (A)

LAW–SCHOOL LAW
Park University (M)

LEADERSHIP
Bellevue University (M,B)
Fort Hays State University (M,UC)
Franklin Pierce College (M)
Luther Rice University (M)
Southwestern College (M)

LEADERSHIP AND BUSINESS ETHICS
Duquesne University (M)

LEADERSHIP AND HUMAN PERFORMANCE
University of Wisconsin–Platteville (UC)
University of Wisconsin–Platteville (UC)

LEADERSHIP AND INFORMATION TECHNOLOGY–MASTERS OF LEADERSHIP AND INFORMATION TECHNOLOGY
Duquesne University (M)

LEADERSHIP AND LIBERAL STUDIES
Duquesne University (M)

LEADERSHIP AND MANAGEMENT
Drexel University (M)
Regions University (M)
University of Maryland University College (GC)

LEADERSHIP AND MINISTRY
Williamson Christian College (B)

LEADERSHIP AND RENEWAL
Regent University (D)

LEADERSHIP DEVELOPMENT
Brenau University (M)
Taylor University (UC)

LEADERSHIP IN EDUCATIONAL ADMINISTRATION (FOR LICENSED K-12 TEACHERS)
Capella University (M)

LEADERSHIP IN HIGHER EDUCATION
Capella University (M)

LEADERSHIP IN NURSING AND HEALTHCARE SYSTEMS
University of Missouri–Columbia (M)

LEADERSHIP OF EDUCATIONAL ORGANIZATIONS CONCENTRATION (10-MONTH PROGRAM)
American InterContinental University Online (M)

LEADERSHIP OF LEARNING
Abilene Christian University (M)

LEADERSHIP STUDIES
Temple Baptist Seminary (UC)

LEADERSHIP VERSATILITY IN FINANCIAL SERVICES
New England College of Finance (GC)

LEADERSHIP VERSATILITY IN RETAIL BANKING
New England College of Finance (GC)

LEADERSHIP–CERTIFICATE OF ADVANCED STUDY
University of Denver (UC)

LEADERSHIP–CERTIFICATE OF GRADUATE STUDIES
Regent University (GC)

LEADING ORGANIZATIONAL TRANSFORMATION
Saybrook Graduate School and Research Center (GC)

LEARNING AND KNOWLEDGE MANAGEMENT SYSTEMS
Rochester Institute of Technology (GC,M)

LEARNING SYSTEMS DESIGN AND DEVELOPMENT

University of Missouri–Columbia (M)

LEARNING SYSTEMS DESIGN AND DEVELOPMENT (EDUCATIONAL SPECIALIST)

University of Missouri–Columbia

LEGAL ADMINISTRATIVE ASSISTANT

South Central College (A)

LEGAL ADMINSTRATIVE ASSISTANT

South Central College (UC)

LEGAL NURSE CONSULTING

Kaplan University (UC)

LEGAL SERVICES

Thomas Edison State College (A,B)

LEGAL STUDIES

American Military University (B)
American Public University (B)
Florida Gulf Coast University (B)
Strayer University (B)
University of Maryland University College (B)
West Virginia University (M)

LEGAL STUDIES (MLS)

West Virginia University

LEGAL STUDIES–HOMELAND SECURITY

California University of Pennsylvania (M)

LEGAL STUDIES–LAW AND PUBLIC POLICY

California University of Pennsylvania (M)

LETTERS, ARTS, AND SCIENCES

The Pennsylvania State University University Park Campus (A,B)

LIBERAL ARTS

Citrus College (A)
Excelsior College (A,B)
Lehigh Carbon Community College (A)
Lock Haven University of Pennsylvania (M)
Minot State University–Bottineau Campus (A)
Monroe Community College (A)
Mountain Empire Community College (A)
The New School (B)
Northern Virginia Community College (A)
Peninsula College (A)
Piedmont Technical College (A)
St. Cloud State University (A)
Saint Leo University (A)
San Bernardino Valley College (A)
Schoolcraft College (A)
Seattle Central Community College (A)
Southern New Hampshire University (A)
Southwestern Community College (A)
Syracuse University (A)
Taft College (A)
The University of Maine at Augusta (A)
University of Wisconsin Colleges (A)
Upper Iowa University (A)
Virginia Polytechnic Institute and State University (GC)
Colorado State University (B)
Austin Peay State University (A)

LIBERAL ARTS (BLA)

University of Massachusetts Lowell (B)

LIBERAL ARTS (MILITARY HISTORY)

Louisiana State University and Agricultural and Mechanical College (M)

LIBERAL ARTS—HISTORY CONCENTRATION

Taylor University (A)

LIBERAL ARTS—INTERDISCIPLINARY CONCENTRATION

Taylor University (A)

LIBERAL ARTS—SOCIAL SCIENCE CONCENTRATION

Taylor University (A)

LIBERAL ARTS AND GENERAL STUDIES

Dallas County Community College District (A)
Mount Saint Vincent University (B)

LIBERAL ARTS AND HUMANITIES

Cayuga County Community College (A)

LIBERAL ARTS AND SCIENCE

San Joaquin Delta College (GC)

LIBERAL ARTS AND SCIENCE/ HUMANITIES AND SOCIAL SCIENCE

Erie Community College (A)

LIBERAL ARTS AND SCIENCES

Burlington County College (A)
Mercy College (A)
Middlesex Community College (A)
Sinclair Community College (A)

LIBERAL ARTS AND SCIENCES/ MATHEMATICS AND SCIENCES

Cayuga County Community College (A)

LIBERAL ARTS AND STUDIES

Iowa Western Community College (A)

LIBERAL ARTS–ASSOCIATE OF ARTS IN LIBERAL ARTS

Arkansas State University–Beebe (A)

LIBERAL ARTS–HUMANITIES AND SOCIAL SCIENCE

Jefferson Community College (A)

LIBERAL ARTS–MASTER OF LIBERAL ARTS

Texas Christian University (GC)

LIBERAL ARTS/GENERAL STUDIES

Thomas Edison State College (A)

LIBERAL ARTS/HUMANITIES AND SOCIAL SCIENCE

Clinton Community College (A)

LIBERAL ARTS/SOCIAL SCIENCE

Westchester Community College (A)

LIBERAL EDUCATION

Lake Superior College (A)

LIBERAL SCIENCE

Laurentian University (B)

LIBERAL STUDIES

California State University, Chico (B)
Eastern Oregon University (B)
East Tennessee State University (M)
Excelsior College (M,B)
Fort Hays State University (M)
Jacksonville State University (M,B)
Limestone College (A,B)
Middlesex Community College (A)
Middle Tennessee State University (B)
Neumann College (A)
Oral Roberts University (B)
Oregon State University (B)
Regions University (A,B)
St. John's University (A,B)
Sonoma State University (B)
State University of New York Empire State College (M)
Stony Brook University, State University of New York (M)
Syracuse University (B)
Thomas Edison State College (B)
University of Central Florida (B)
University of Illinois at Springfield (B)
The University of Iowa (B)
The University of Maine at Augusta (A)

The University of North Carolina at Greensboro (M)
University of Northern Iowa (B)
University of Oklahoma (M,B)
University of Pittsburgh at Bradford (A)
University of the Incarnate Word (A)
The University of Toledo (M)

LIBERAL STUDIES (HUMANITIES CONCENTRATION)

The University of North Carolina at Greensboro (B)

LIBERAL STUDIES–BACHELOR OF LIBERAL STUDIES ONLINE DEGREE PROGRAM

Bowling Green State University (B)

LIBERAL STUDIES–MANAGEMENT AND COMMUNICATION CONCENTRATION

Montana State University–Billings (B)

LIBERAL STUDIES–MASTER OF LIBERAL STUDIES

University of Denver (M)

LIBRARY AND INFORMATION SCIENCE

Drexel University (M)
Syracuse University (M)
Syracuse University (M)
University of Illinois at Urbana–Champaign (GC,M)
University of South Florida (M)
University of Washington (M)

LIBRARY AND INFORMATION SCIENCE IN SCHOOL MEDIA

Syracuse University (M)

LIBRARY AND INFORMATION SCIENCES

Louisiana State University and Agricultural and Mechanical College (M)
University of North Texas (GC)

LIBRARY AND INFORMATION SERVICES

The University of Maine at Augusta (A,B)

LIBRARY AND INFORMATION STUDIES

The University of North Carolina at Greensboro (M)

LIBRARY AND INFORMATION STUDIES–MASTER OF LIBRARY AND INFORMATION STUDIES

The University of Alabama (M)

LIBRARY AND INFORMATION TECHNOLOGIES–SCHOOL LIBRARY AND INFORMATION TECHNOLOGIES

Mansfield University of Pennsylvania (M)

LIBRARY ASSISTANT

Ivy Tech Community College–Bloomington (A)
Ivy Tech Community College–Central Indiana (A)
Ivy Tech Community College–Columbus (A)
Ivy Tech Community College–Southeast (A)
Ivy Tech Community College–Southern Indiana (A)
Ivy Tech Community College–Southwest (A)
Ivy Tech Community College–Wabash Valley (A)
Ivy Tech Community College–Whitewater (A)

LIBRARY INFORMATION MANAGEMENT

Chadron State College (B)

LIBRARY INFORMATION SCIENCE

University of Southern Mississippi (M)

LIBRARY MEDIA

The University of Montana (UC)

LIBRARY MEDIA CERTIFICATION

Montana State University (UC)

LIBRARY MEDIA EDUCATION

Western Kentucky University (M)

LIBRARY MEDIA SERVICES

Indiana State University (GC)

LIBRARY MEDIA TEACHING

Azusa Pacific University (UC)

LIBRARY SCIENCE

Clarion University of Pennsylvania (M)
Connecticut State University System (M)
East Carolina University (M)
Texas Woman's University (M)
University of Missouri–Columbia (M)
University of North Texas (M)

LIBRARY SCIENCE–SCHOOL LIBRARIANSHIP

Azusa Pacific University (M)

LIBRARY STUDIES

Memorial University of Newfoundland (UC)

LIBRARY TECHNICAL ASSISTANT

Ivy Tech Community College–East Central (A)
Ivy Tech Community College–Kokomo (A)
Ivy Tech Community College–Lafayette (A)
Ivy Tech Community College–North Central (A)
Ivy Tech Community College–Northeast (A)
Ivy Tech Community College–Northwest (A)

LIBRARY TECHNICIAN

Pueblo Community College (A,UC)

LIFE CARE PLANNING

Kaplan University (UC)

LIFE ISSUES

Fort Hays State University (UC)

LIFE SCIENCES

University of Maryland, College Park (M)

LINGUISTICS–APPLIED LINGUISTICS, ESL CONCENTRATION

University of Massachusetts Boston (M)

LITERACY

University of Missouri–Columbia (M)

LITERACY (WYOMING READING ENDORSEMENT)

University of Wyoming (UC)

LOCAL CHURCH MINISTRY

Grace College (M)

LOGISTICS

Thomas Edison State College (B)

LOGISTICS MANAGEMENT

Florida Institute of Technology (M)

LONG-TERM CARE ADMINISTRATION

Saint Joseph's College of Maine (B,UC)

LONG-TERM CARE ADMINISTRATION, ADVANCED

Saint Joseph's College of Maine (UC)

MAED

Northern Kentucky University (M)

MAINE STUDIES

University of Maine (UC)

MAINTENANCE AND RELIABILITY ENGINEERING

The University of Tennessee (GC)

MANAGEMENT

Amberton University (M,B)
American Military University (M,B)
American Public University (M,B)
Ashworth College (A)
Athabasca University (GC)
Bellevue University (M,B)
Berkeley College (B)
Brenau University (B)
Caldwell College (B)
Dallas Baptist University (M,B)
Darton College (A)
Davenport University Online (A)
Des Moines Area Community College (UC)
Embry-Riddle Aeronautical University, Extended Campus (M)
Florida Atlantic University (M)
Florida Institute of Technology (M)
Fort Hays State University (B,UC)
Franklin Pierce College (A,B,UC)
Franklin University (B)
Granite State College (B)
Hope International University (M)
Indiana Tech (B)
Indiana Wesleyan University (M)
International Institute of the Americas (B)
International Institute of the Americas (B)
Jackson Community College (UC)
Kaplan University (B)
Liberty University (M)
Metropolitan State University (B)
National University (M)
Old Dominion University (B)
Park University (B)
Prescott College (B)
Regent University (M)
Saint Joseph's College of Maine (A)
Salve Regina University (M,UC)
Spartanburg Technical College (A)
Strayer University (B)
Thomas Edison State College (M)
Troy University (M)
University of Alaska Southeast (B)
University of Houston–Victoria (B)
The University of Maine at Augusta (B)
University of Management and Technology (M,B)
University of Maryland University College (D,M)
University of North Texas (M)
University of Phoenix Online Campus (M)
University of St. Francis (M)
University of Wisconsin–Stout (B)
Upper Iowa University (B)
Worcester Polytechnic Institute (GC)

MANAGEMENT (BACHELOR COMPLETION)

Indiana Wesleyan University (B)

MANAGEMENT (BSBA)

Northern Arizona University (B)

MANAGEMENT ADVISORY SERVICES

Southern New Hampshire University (B)

MANAGEMENT AND FORENSICS

Stevens Institute of Technology (M)

MANAGEMENT AND LEADERSHIP

Judson College (B)

MANAGEMENT COMMUNICATION

Regions University (B)

MANAGEMENT CONCENTRATION

Andrew Jackson University (M)

MANAGEMENT CONCENTRATION

Colorado Technical University (B)

MANAGEMENT CONCENTRATION (10-MONTH PROGRAM)

American InterContinental University Online (M)

MANAGEMENT CONCENTRATION (COMPLETION PROGRAM)

American InterContinental University Online (B)

MANAGEMENT DEVELOPMENT

College of Southern Maryland (A,UC)

MANAGEMENT DEVELOPMENT–MARKETING

College of Southern Maryland (UC)

MANAGEMENT EMPHASIS, GENERAL MANAGEMENT

Community College of Denver (A)

MANAGEMENT INFORMATION SCIENCES

Franklin University (B)

MANAGEMENT INFORMATION SYSTEMS

Auburn University (M)
Bellevue University (B)
Dallas Baptist University (M,B)
Excelsior College (B)
Florida State University (M)
Liberty University (A,B)
Myers University (B)
Northwest Missouri State University (B)
Nova Southeastern University (M)
Raritan Valley Community College (A)
Seminole Community College (A)
Stevens Institute of Technology (GC)
Strayer University (M)
University of Illinois at Springfield (M)

MANAGEMENT OF HUMAN RESOURCES

Bellevue University (B)
Excelsior College (B)

MANAGEMENT OF INFORMATION SYSTEMS

Keiser College (B)

MANAGEMENT OF INFORMATION TECHNOLOGY

Schiller International University (M)

MANAGEMENT OF TECHNOLOGY

New Jersey Institute of Technology (GC)
Walden University (M)

MANAGEMENT POST-DIPLOMA (3 YEAR)

Athabasca University (B)

MANAGEMENT POST-DIPLOMA (4 YEAR)

Athabasca University (B)

MANAGEMENT SCIENCE

Neumann College (M)

MANAGEMENT SCIENCE AND ENGINEERING

Stanford University (GC,M)

MANAGEMENT SCIENCES–MASTER OF MANAGEMENT SCIENCES ONLINE (MMSC)

University of Waterloo (M)

MANAGEMENT STUDIES

University of Maryland University College (B)

MANAGEMENT STUDIES, ADVANCED

Brenau University (M)

MANAGEMENT–FINANCIAL MANAGEMENT SPECIALTY

Davenport University Online (B)

MANAGEMENT–GENERAL MANAGEMENT EMPHASIS

City University (M)

MANAGEMENT–GOVERNANCE AND LEADERSHIP SPECIALTY

Davenport University Online (B)

MANAGEMENT–MANUFACTURING SPECIALTY

Davenport University Online (B)

MANAGEMENT–MASTER OF MANAGEMENT

Oral Roberts University (M)

MANAGEMENT, COMMUNICATION AND QUALITY

Kaplan University (M)

MANAGEMENT, GENERAL

Dallas Baptist University (M)
Thomas Edison State College (A)
University of Calgary (UC)
The University of Texas at Arlington (M)

MANAGEMENT/COMPUTER INFORMATION SYSTEMS

Park University (B)

MANAGEMENT/E-BUSINESS

Kaplan University (B)

MANAGEMENT/HEALTH CARE MANAGEMENT

Kaplan University (B)

MANAGEMENT/HUMAN RESOURCES

Park University (B)

MANAGEMENT/HUMAN RESOURCES MANAGEMENT

Kaplan University (B)

MANAGEMENT/MARKETING

Park University (B)

MANAGEMENT/SALES AND MARKETING

Kaplan University (B)

MANAGERIAL ACCOUNTING

Champlain College (UC)

MANAGING APPLIED RESEARCH IN TECHNOLOGY

University of Colorado at Boulder (GC)

MANAGING INNOVATION AND INFORMATION TECHNOLOGY

Champlain College (M)

MANAGING THROUGH INFORMATION TECHNOLOGY

Champlain College (UC)

MANAGMENT ESSENTIALS

New Jersey Institute of Technology (GC)

MANUFACTURING

Cape Breton University (B)

MANUFACTURING ENGINEERING

Boston University (M)
Columbia University (UC)
Illinois Institute of Technology (M)
University of Michigan (M)
University of Washington (M)
University of Wisconsin–Stout (M)

MANUFACTURING ENGINEERING TECHNOLOGY

Thomas Edison State College (A,B)

MANUFACTURING MANAGEMENT

Kettering University (M)
Missouri State University (UC)

MANUFACTURING MANAGEMENT–BACHELOR OF MANUFACTURING MANAGEMENT ONLINE

University of Minnesota, Crookston (B)

MANUFACTURING OPERATIONS

Kettering University (M)

MANUFACTURING SYSTEMS ENGINEERING

Lehigh University (M)

MANUFACTURING SYSTEMS MANAGEMENT

Southern Methodist University (M)

MANUFACTURING TECHNOLOGY

Illinois Institute of Technology (M)

MANUFACTURING TECHNOLOGY DEGREE COMPLETION

Illinois Institute of Technology (B)

MARINE ENGINEERING TECHNOLOGY

Thomas Edison State College (A,B)

MARITIME STUDIES

University of West Florida (B)

MARITIME STUDIES–BACHELOR OF MARITIME STUDIES (BMS)

Memorial University of Newfoundland (B)

MARKETING

Adirondack Community College (A)
American Military University (B)
American Public University (B)
Brenau University (B)
Caldwell College (B)
Capella University (M)
City University (GC,UC)
Colorado Technical University (M)
Columbus State Community College (A)
Dallas Baptist University (M)
Davenport University Online (A)
Excelsior College (B)
Franklin Pierce College (A,B,UC)
Indiana Tech (B)
Kaplan University (M)
Metropolitan State University (B)
Mount Saint Vincent University (B)
Myers University (B)
Regent University (GC)
Saint Mary-of-the-Woods College (B)
Southern New Hampshire University (A,B)
Strayer University (A,B)
Thomas Edison State College (A,B)
University of Alaska Southeast (B)
University of Houston–Victoria (B)
University of Maryland University College (B)
Upper Iowa University (B,UC)
Walden University (M)

MARKETING AND RETAILING

Blue Ridge Community College (A)

MARKETING AND SALES TECHNOLOGY

The University of Toledo (A,UC)

MARKETING COMMUNICATIONS SPECIALIST

Dakota County Technical College (UC)

MARKETING CONCENTRATION

Andrew Jackson University (M)
Colorado Technical University (B)

MARKETING CONCENTRATION (10-MONTH PROGRAM)

American InterContinental University Online (M)

MARKETING CONCENTRATION (COMPLETION PROGRAM)

American InterContinental University Online (B)

MARKETING EMPHASIS

Community College of Denver (A)

MARKETING MANAGEMENT

Bellevue University (B)
Concordia University, St. Paul (B)
University of Dallas (GC,M)
University of Management and Technology (B)

MARKETING STRATEGY IN THE DIGITAL AGE

University of Illinois at Chicago (UC)

MARKETING–ADVERTISING/ PROMOTION SPECIALTY

Davenport University Online (B)

MARKETING–BUSINESS TO BUSINESS SPECIALTY

Davenport University Online (B)

MARKETING–MARKETING MANAGEMENT SPECIALTY

Davenport University Online (B)

MARRIAGE AND FAMILY THERAPY

Liberty University (M)
Regions University (M)
Saybrook Graduate School and Research Center (M)

MARRIAGE EDUCATION (FOR CREDIT)

University of Bridgeport (UC)

MARRIAGE EDUCATION (NON-CREDIT)

University of Bridgeport (UC)

MASSAGE THERAPY–DISTANCE EDUCATION

Ohio College of Massotherapy (A)

MASTER TEACHER PROGRAM

Regent University (M)

MATERIAL ACQUISITION MANAGEMENT

Florida Institute of Technology (M)

MATERIAL AND CHEMICAL SYNTHESIS

Illinois Institute of Technology (M)

MATERIALS ENGINEERING

Auburn University (M)
University of Illinois at Urbana–Champaign (GC)

MATERIALS FAILURE ANALYSIS

University of Illinois at Urbana–Champaign (GC)

MATERIALS SCIENCE AND ENGINEERING

Columbia University (M,UC)
University of Florida (GC,M)
University of Florida (M)
University of Washington (M)
Arizona State University (M)

MATH

Chadron State College (M,B)

MATHEMATICAL SCIENCES

University of Illinois at Springfield (B)

MATHEMATICS

Mercy College (B)
Middle Tennessee State University (M)
Montana State University (M)
Northern Arizona University (M)
Saint Mary-of-the-Woods College (B)
Skidmore College (B)
Thomas Edison State College (A,B)

MATHEMATICS EDUCATION

Florida State University (M)
University of Alaska Southeast (UC)

MATHEMATICS–APPLIED MATHEMATICS

Columbia University (M,UC)

MBA ENERGY ELECTIVE

Athabasca University (M)

MBA ONLINE

University of Tulsa (M)

MBA–POLICING ELECTIVE

Athabasca University (M)

MECHANICAL AND AEROSPACE ENGINEERING

University of Florida (M)

MECHANICAL AND AEROSPACE ENGINEERING–FUNDAMENTALS OF THERMAL FLUIDS TRANSPORT TRACK

University of Florida (M)

MECHANICAL AND AEROSPACE ENGINEERING–SOLID MECHANICS AND DESIGN TRACK

University of Florida (M)

MECHANICAL ENGINEERING

Auburn University (M)
Columbia University (GC,M)
Georgia Institute of Technology (M)
Iowa State University of Science and Technology (M)
Kansas State University (M)
North Carolina State University (M)
Southern Methodist University (M)
Stanford University (M)
The University of Alabama (B)
University of Delaware (M)
University of Illinois at Urbana–Champaign (M)
University of Maryland, College Park (M)
University of North Dakota (B)
The University of Texas at Arlington (M)
University of Washington (M)
University of Wisconsin–Madison (M)

MECHANICAL ENGINEERING (ENGINEERING MANAGEMENT PROGRAM)

Colorado State University (M)

MECHANICAL ENGINEERING (IND ENGG AND OPERATIONS RES PROGRAM)

Colorado State University (D,M)

MECHANICAL ENGINEERING (MATERIALS ENGINEERING)

Colorado State University (M)

MECHANICAL ENGINEERING (MS OR MENG)

Lehigh University (M)

MECHANICAL ENGINEERING TECHNOLOGY

Indiana State University (B)
Old Dominion University (B)
Thomas Edison State College (A,B)

MECHANICAL ENGINEERING TECHNOLOGY AST

Penn Foster Career School (A)

MECHANICS AND MAINTENANCE

Thomas Edison State College (A)

MED MASTERS OF EDUCATION

Eastern New Mexico University (M)

MEDIA

Southwestern Assemblies of God University (A)

MEDIA COMMUNICATION, COMMUNICATION MANAGEMENT EMPHASIS
Webster University (M)

MEDIA MANAGEMENT PROGRAM
The New School (GC)

MEDIA PSYCHOLOGY
Fielding Graduate University (D)

MEDIA STUDIES
The New School (M)

MEDICAL ASSISTANT
Minot State University–Bottineau Campus (A,UC)

MEDICAL ASSISTING
Keiser College (A)

MEDICAL BILLING
Davenport University Online (UC)

MEDICAL CODING
Darton College (UC)
Davenport University Online (UC)
Minot State University–Bottineau Campus (UC)

MEDICAL CODING SPECIALIST
Southwest Wisconsin Technical College (UC)

MEDICAL IMAGING
Clarkson College (B)
Thomas Edison State College (A,B)

MEDICAL LABORATORY TECHNICIAN
South Central College (A)

MEDICAL LABORATORY TECHNICIAN FAST TRACK
South Central College (A)

MEDICAL LABORATORY TECHNOLOGY
Central Virginia Community College (A)
Clark State Community College (A)
Darton College (A)
St. Petersburg College (A)

MEDICAL OFFICE ADMINISTRATION
Presentation College (A)

MEDICAL OFFICE ASSISTANT
Edison State Community College (A)

MEDICAL OFFICE CODING SPECIALIST
Sinclair Community College (UC)

MEDICAL OFFICE SPECIALIST
University of Alaska Southeast (UC)

MEDICAL PHYSICS
Georgia Institute of Technology (M)

MEDICAL SECRETARY
Minot State University–Bottineau Campus (A)

MEDICAL TECHNOLOGY
Darton College (A)

MEDICAL TRANSCRIPTION
Indiana Business College (UC)
Minot State University–Bottineau Campus (UC)
North Dakota State College of Science (UC)
Presentation College (UC)
Southwest Wisconsin Technical College (UC)

MEDICAL–GRADUATE MEDICAL EDUCATION CORE CURRICULUM
University of Illinois at Chicago (UC)

MEETING AND EVENT MANAGEMENT
Dakota County Technical College (UC)

MENTAL HEALTH AND HUMAN SERVICES
The University of Maine at Augusta (B)

MENTAL HEALTH AND REHABILITATION SERVICES
Thomas Edison State College (B)

MENTAL HEALTH COUNSELING
Prescott College (M)
Walden University (M)

MENTAL HEALTH NURSE PRACTITIONER
University of Missouri–Columbia (M)

MENTAL HEALTH PRACTICES IN SCHOOLS
University of Missouri–Columbia (M)

MENTAL HEALTH PRACTICES IN SCHOOLS (EDUCATIONAL SPECIALIST)
University of Missouri–Columbia

MERCHANDISING
Kansas State University (M)
North Dakota State University (GC,M)
San Joaquin Delta College (UC)
University of North Texas (GC,M)

METEOROLOGY–BROADCAST METEOROLOGY PROGRAM
Mississippi State University

METEOROLOGY–OPERATIONAL METEOROLOGY PROGRAM
Mississippi State University

MICROBIOLOGY
Illinois Institute of Technology (M)

MICROCOMPUTER OFFICE SPECIALIST
Lake Superior College (UC)

MICROELECTRONICS AND PHOTONICS
Stevens Institute of Technology (M)

MICROELECTRONICS MANUFACTURING ENGINEERING
Rochester Institute of Technology (M)

MICROELECTRONICS PACKAGING
Arizona State University (M)

MICROSOFT OFFICE SPECIALIST CERTIFICATION PREPARATION
Lansing Community College (UC)

MIDDLE EASTERN STUDIES
American Military University (B)
American Public University (B)

MIDDLE GRADES EDUCATION
Brenau University (M)

MIDDLE SCHOOL EDUCATION
Northern Arizona University (UC)

MIDWIFERY
Philadelphia University (M)

MILITARY HISTORY, MILITARY MANAGEMENT, INTELLIGENCE STUDIES

American Military University (B)
American Public University (B)

MILITARY SPECIALTIES

Fort Hays State University (B)

MILITARY STUDIES

American Military University (M)
American Public University (M)

MINISTERIAL LEADERSHIP

Regions University (M)

MINISTRY

Liberty University (D)
Oral Roberts University (D)
Regions University (M)

MINISTRY (MINISTERIAL LEADERSHIP AND YOUTH MINISTRY CONCENTRATIONS)

Indiana Wesleyan University (M)

MINISTRY AND LEADERSHIP DEGREE COMPLETION PROGRAM

Life Pacific College (B)

MINISTRY LEADERSHIP

Crown College (M)

MINISTRY STUDIES

Judson College (B)

MINISTRY STUDIES–6 DISTINCT CONCENTRATIONS AVAILABLE

Temple Baptist Seminary (D)

MINISTRY–MASTER OF MINISTRY–VARIOUS CONCENTRATIONS AVAILABLE

Temple Baptist Seminary (M)

MINISTRY–MINISTERIAL DIPLOMA

Master's College and Seminary (UC)

MINISTRY/BIBLE

Regions University (B)

MISSIONS STUDIES

Taylor University (UC)

MISSIONS/MISSIOLOGICAL STUDIES

Temple Baptist Seminary (UC)

MODELING AND SIMULATION

Arizona State University (M)

MODERN LANGUAGES–CERTIFICATE OF ADVANCED STUDY

University of Denver (UC)

MOLECULAR BIOLOGY

Lehigh University (M)

MOTION PICTURES AND TELEVISION

Academy of Art University (M,A,B)

MULTI-CULTURAL EDUCATION

Park University (M)

MULTI-MEDIA WRITING AND TECHNICAL COMMUNICATION

Arizona State University (UC)
Arizona State University at the Polytechnic Campus (UC)

MULTI-MEDIA WRITING AND TECHNICAL COMMUNICATION POST-BACCALAUREATE CERTIFICATE

Arizona State University

MULTICULTURAL LITERATURE

East Carolina University (GC)

MULTIDISCIPLINARY STUDIES

Liberty University (B)
West Virginia University (B)

MULTIDISCIPLINARY STUDIES–EDUCATION CONCENTRATION

Liberty University (B)

MULTIDISCIPLINARY STUDIES/ HUMANITIES

Caldwell College (B)

MULTIDISCIPLINARY STUDIES/ SOCIAL SCIENCE/FIRE SCIENCE

Caldwell College (B)

MULTIDISCIPLINARY STUDIES/ SOCIAL SCIENCE/PHARMACY MANAGEMENT

Caldwell College (B)

MULTIDISCIPLINARY STUDIES/ SOCIAL SCIENCES

Caldwell College (B)

MULTIDISCIPLINARY STUDY

Johnson County Community College (A)

MULTIMEDIA APPLICATIONS

University of Massachusetts Lowell (UC)

MULTIMEDIA NETWORKING

Columbia University (UC)

MULTIMEDIA TECHNOLOGY

Stevens Institute of Technology (GC)
University of Management and Technology (M)

MUSEUM STUDIES

Prescott College (M)

MUSIC

Auburn University (M)
Darton College (A)
Judson College (B)
Prescott College (B)
Skidmore College (B)
Thomas Edison State College (B)

MUSIC EDUCATION

East Carolina University (M)
Stephen F. Austin State University (M)
University of South Florida (M)

MUSIC EDUCATION–MASTER OF MUSIC EDUCATION

Boston University
University of Southern Mississippi (M)

MUSIC EDUCATION–MASTER'S OR DOCTORATE

Boston University

MUSIC EDUCATION–MASTERS IN MUSIC EDUCATION

Duquesne University (M)

MUSIC THERAPY

Saint Mary-of-the-Woods College (M)

MUTUAL FUNDS AND INVESTMENTS

New England College of Finance (GC)

NANOSCALE MATERIALS SCIENCE

Stanford University (GC)

NANOTECHNOLOGY
Columbia University (UC)

NATIONAL SECURITY STUDIES
American Military University (M)
American Public University (M)

NATIVE STUDIES
Laurentian University (B)

NATIVE STUDIES (HONOURS)
Laurentian University (B)

NATURAL RESOURCE MANAGEMENT–CERTIFICATE OF ADVANCED STUDY
University of Denver (UC)

NATURAL RESOURCES
Oregon State University (B)
Virginia Polytechnic Institute and State University (GC)

NATURAL RESOURCES AND CONSERVATION
Prescott College (M,B)

NATURAL RESOURCES AND THE ENVIRONMENT
Colorado State University (UC)

NATURAL SCIENCE
College of the Humanities and Sciences, Harrison Middleton University (M)

NATURAL SCIENCES/ MATHEMATICS
Thomas Edison State College (B)

NCA CASI SCHOOL IMPROVEMENT SPECIALIST
University of Nebraska–Lincoln (GC)

NECF-UC BERKELEY ACCELERATED PROGRAM IN FINANCIAL SERVICES
New England College of Finance (GC)

NEGOTIATION, CONFLICT RESOLUTION AND PEACEBUILDING
California State University, Dominguez Hills (M)

NETWORK AND COMMUNICATIONS MANAGEMENT
DeVry University Online (M,B)

NETWORK AND INTERNET ADMINISTRATION
Southwest Virginia Community College (UC)

NETWORK ENGINEERING
Illinois Institute of Technology (M)

NETWORK SECURITY
Capitol College (M)
Strayer University (UC)

NETWORK SECURITY AND INFORMATION ASSURANCE
New Jersey Institute of Technology (GC)

NETWORK SYSTEMS ADMINISTRATION
DeVry University Online (A)

NETWORK+ CERTIFICATION AND COMPUTER TECHNOLOGY
Cleveland Institute of Electronics (UC)

NETWORKED INFORMATION SYSTEMS
Stevens Institute of Technology (GC,M)

NETWORKING (ELECTRICAL ENGINEERING)
Stanford University (GC)

NETWORKING AND SYSTEMS
Columbia University (UC)

NETWORKING AND TELECOMMUNICATIONS
Illinois Institute of Technology (GC,M)

NETWORKING/ TELECOMMUNICATIONS
City University (UC)

NETWORKS AND DISTRIBUTED SYSTEMS
University of Illinois at Urbana–Champaign (GC)

NEUROPSYCHOLOGY
Fielding Graduate University (UC)

NEW MEDIA ENGINEERING
Columbia University (UC)

NEW TESTAMENT
Johnson Bible College (M)

NEWFOUNDLAND STUDIES
Memorial University of Newfoundland (UC)

NON-DEGREE GIFTED ENDORSEMENT COURSE WORK
University of South Florida (UC)

NON-PROFIT ORGANIZATION MANAGEMENT
Green Mountain College (M)

NONDESTRUCTIVE TESTING TECHNOLOGY
Thomas Edison State College (A,B)

NONPROFIT AND ASSOCIATION FINANCIAL MANAGEMENT
University of Maryland University College (GC)

NONPROFIT AND COMMUNITY SERVICES MANAGEMENT
Park University (M)

NONPROFIT MANAGEMENT
George Mason University (GC)
Hope International University (M)
Oral Roberts University (M)
University of Central Florida (GC,M)
University of Colorado at Denver and Health Sciences Center—Downtown Denver Campus (UC)
University of Illinois at Chicago (UC)
Walden University (M)

NONPROFIT MANAGEMENT (POST-BACCALAUREATE)
The University of North Carolina at Greensboro (UC)

NONPROFIT MANAGEMENT AND LEADERSHIP
Walden University (M)

NONTRADITIONAL PHARMD
The Ohio State University (D)

NOT-FOR-PROFIT
University of Dallas (GC,M)

NOT-FOR-PROFIT CHILD CARE ADMINISTRATION

Saint Mary-of-the-Woods College (B)

NOT-FOR-PROFIT FINANCIAL ADMINISTRATION

Saint Mary-of-the-Woods College (B)

NOT-FOR-PROFIT HUMAN SERVICES

Saint Mary-of-the-Woods College (B)

NOT-FOR-PROFIT MANAGEMENT

Regent University (GC)

NOT-FOR-PROFIT PUBLIC RELATIONS

Saint Mary-of-the-Woods College (B)

NUCLEAR CRITICALITY SAFETY

The University of Tennessee (GC)

NUCLEAR ENGINEERING

The University of Tennessee (M)

NUCLEAR ENGINEERING TECHNOLOGY

Excelsior College (B)
Thomas Edison State College (A,B)

NUCLEAR MEDICINE TECHNOLOGY

Darton College (A)
Thomas Edison State College (A,B)

NUCLEAR POWER TECHNOLOGY

Bismarck State College (A)

NUCLEAR TECHNOLOGY

Excelsior College (A)

NURSE EDUCATOR

Florida State University (M)
Missouri State University (GC)

NURSE MIDWIFERY

East Carolina University (M,)
University of Cincinnati (M)
University of Minnesota, Twin Cities Campus (M)

NURSE PRACTITIONER

University of St. Francis (M)

NURSE PRACTITIONER AND CLINICAL SPECIALIST

University of Colorado at Colorado Springs (M)

NURSE-MIDWIFERY

Philadelphia University (UC)

NURSING

Alcorn State University (M)
Athabasca University (M)
Ball State University (M,B)
California College for Health Sciences (M)
California State University, Chico (B)
California State University, Dominguez Hills (M)
Central Missouri State University (B)
Clarion University of Pennsylvania (B)
Clemson University (M,B)
Concordia University Wisconsin (M)
Darton College (A)
Duquesne University (D,M)
Eastern New Mexico University (B)
Excelsior College (M,A,B)
Indiana State University (B)
Jacksonville State University (M)
Liberty University (M)
Lock Haven University of Pennsylvania (A)
Memorial University of Newfoundland (M)
Mercy College (B)
Metropolitan State University (M)
Middle Tennessee State University (M,B)
Missouri State University (B)
Montana State University (M)
National University (B)
New Mexico State University (B)
Northern Arizona University (M,B)
Northern Kentucky University (M)
Northwestern Michigan College (A)
Old Dominion University (B)
Rush University (B)
Sacred Heart University (B)
Saint Francis Medical Center College of Nursing (M)
Saint Joseph's College of Maine (M,B)
Samuel Merritt College (M)
Seton Hall University (M)
Southern Illinois University Edwardsville (B)
State University of New York at Plattsburgh (B)
Texas Christian University (M)
Texas Woman's University (D)
Thomas Edison State College (M,B)
The University of Alabama (B)
University of Calgary (B)
University of Central Florida (B)
University of Delaware (B)
University of Maryland (M)
University of Michigan–Flint (B)
University of Nebraska Medical Center (B)
The University of North Carolina at Greensboro (M,B)
University of North Dakota (B)
University of Phoenix Online Campus (M,B)
University of South Alabama (M,B)
University of Southern Indiana (M,B)
University of South Florida (M)
The University of Texas at Tyler (B)
University of Wisconsin–Madison (B)
Washburn University (B)
Western University of Health Sciences (M)
West Virginia University (M)
Pennsylvania College of Technology (B)

NURSING (RN TO BS COMPLETION)

Indiana Wesleyan University (B)

NURSING (RN TO BS)

University of Northern Colorado (B)

NURSING (STEP NURSING PROGRAM)

Jacksonville State University (B)

NURSING ADMINISTRATION

California College for Health Sciences (M)
Fort Hays State University (M)
Mercy College (M)

NURSING ADMINISTRATION AND LEADERSHIP

Saint Joseph's College of Maine (GC)

NURSING AND HEALTH PROFESSIONAL EDUCATION

University of Central Florida (GC)

NURSING AND HEALTHCARE EDUCATION

Saint Joseph's College of Maine (GC)

NURSING CARE HEALTH CARE LEADERSHIP

Clarkson College

NURSING CASE MANAGEMENT

The University of Alabama (M)

NURSING COMMUNITY HEALTH

California College for Health Sciences (M)

NURSING COMPLETION PROGRAM

California State University, Dominguez Hills (B)

NURSING EDUCATION

Clarkson College (M,)
Drexel University (M,UC)
East Carolina University (M,)
Fort Hays State University (M)
Mansfield University of Pennsylvania (M)
Mercy College (M)
University of Missouri–Columbia (M)
The University of North Carolina at Charlotte (GC)
University of Northern Colorado (GC,D)
The University of Texas System (GC)

NURSING EDUCATION AND HOSPITALITY ADMINISTRATION–PH.D. NURSING EDUCATION, MASTER'S IN HOSPITALITY ADMINISTRATION

University of Nevada, Las Vegas

NURSING EDUCATION AND NURSING ADMINISTRATION MAJORS

Indiana Wesleyan University (M)

NURSING FAST TRACK

University of St. Francis (B)

NURSING GERONTOLOGY

California College for Health Sciences (M)

NURSING HEALTH CARE LEADERSHIP

Clarkson College (M)

NURSING HOME ADMINISTRATION

Southeast Community College, Beatrice Campus (UC)
Southeast Community College, Lincoln Campus (UC)
Southeast Community College, Milford Campus (UC)

NURSING LEADERSHIP

East Carolina University (M)

NURSING WELLNESS

California College for Health Sciences (M)

NURSING–ACCELERATED OPTION

Northern Arizona University (B)

NURSING–ACCELERATED RN-BSN

Holy Names University (B)

NURSING–ACUTE CARE NURSE PRACTITIONER

Drexel University (M)

NURSING–AD-LPN TO BSN NURSING COMPLETION

Presentation College (B)

NURSING–ADULT HEALTH SPECIALIZATION

Indiana State University (M)

NURSING–ADULT PSYCHIATRIC MENTAL HEALTH NURSE PRACTITIONER

Drexel University (M)

NURSING–BACCALAUREATE PROGRAM FOR REGISTERED NURSES

University of Manitoba (B)

NURSING–BSN COMPLETION PROGRAM

New Mexico State University–Carlsbad (B)

NURSING–BSN FOR REGISTERED NURSES

Laurentian University (B)

NURSING–BSN TRACK, EDUCATION

Walden University (M)

NURSING–BSN TRACK, LEADERSHIP AND MANAGEMENT

Walden University (M)

NURSING–COMMUNITY HEALTH

The University of North Carolina at Charlotte (M)

NURSING–COMMUNITY HEALTH SPECIALIZATION

Indiana State University (M)

NURSING–COMPLETION PROGRAM FOR NURSE PRACTITIONERS

Drexel University (M)

NURSING–CONTINENCE CARE NURSE

Metropolitan State University (UC)

NURSING–EDUCATION SPECIALIZATION

University of North Dakota (M)

NURSING–FAMILY NURSE PRACTITIONER

Clarion University of Pennsylvania (M)
East Carolina University (M,)
Indiana State University (GC)
Western University of Health Sciences (UC)

NURSING–FAMILY NURSE PRACTITIONER SPECIALIZATION

Indiana State University (M)

NURSING–FAMILY NURSE PRACTITIONER--FIRST MASTER'S

Wright State University (M)

NURSING–FAMILY NURSE PRACTITIONER--SECOND MASTER'S

Wright State University (M)

NURSING–FORENSIC NURSING

Duquesne University
Kaplan University (UC)

NURSING–GERONTOLOGICAL/ ADULT AND FAMILY NURSE PRACTITIONER

University of Massachusetts Boston (GC)

NURSING–HEALTH SERVICES ADMINISTRATION

University of Delaware (M)

NURSING–INTEGRATIVE HEALTH CARE

University of Phoenix Online Campus (M)

NURSING–LEADERSHIP AND MANAGEMENT

Drexel University (UC)

NURSING–LEADERSHIP AND MANAGEMENT TRACK

University of Central Florida (M)

NURSING–LPN CERTIFICATE TO BSN NURSING COMPLETION

Presentation College (B)

NURSING–MASTER OF BUSINESS ADMINISTRATION, HEALTH CARE MANAGEMENT

University of Phoenix Online Campus (M)

NURSING–NEONATAL NURSE PRACTIONER

East Carolina University

NURSING–NURSE EDUCATOR OPTION

University of Wyoming (M)

NURSING–NURSE EDUCATOR TRACK

University of Central Florida (M)

NURSING–NURSE LEADER AND NURSE EDUCATOR OPTIONS

Old Dominion University (M)

NURSING–NURSING ADMINISTRATION SPECIALIZATION

Indiana State University (M)

NURSING–NURSING PRACTICE, ADVANCED

Athabasca University (GC)

NURSING–NURSING/HEALTH CARE EDUCATION

University of Phoenix Online Campus (M)

NURSING–ONLINE ADN NURSING PROGRAM

John Tyler Community College (A)

NURSING–ONLINE RN TO BSN PROGRAM

California State University, San Bernardino (B)

NURSING–OSTOMY CARE NURSE

Metropolitan State University (UC)

NURSING–PATIENT CARE SERVICES ADMINISTRATION–FAMILY NURSE PRACTITIONER

Sacred Heart University (M)

NURSING–PERIOPERATIVE NURSING

St. Petersburg College (UC)

NURSING–POST-BSN

Duquesne University (UC)

NURSING–POST-LPN

Athabasca University (B)

NURSING–POST-MASTER'S

Duquesne University (GC)

NURSING–POST-RN

Athabasca University (B)
Memorial University of Newfoundland (B)

NURSING–PRACTICAL NURSING

North Dakota State College of Science (A)

NURSING–PUBLIC HEALTH NURSING

University of Minnesota, Twin Cities Campus (M)

NURSING–REGISTERED NURSING

Clark State Community College (A)

NURSING–RN COMPLETION PROGRAM FOR ASSOCIATE DEGREE HOLDING NURSES

University of South Florida (B)

NURSING–RN TO BA COMPLETION

The College of St. Scholastica (B)

NURSING–RN TO BS

The Pennsylvania State University University Park Campus (B)
Southern Illinois University Edwardsville (B)
University of Massachusetts Boston (B)
Washington State University (B)

NURSING–RN TO BS MOBILITY ONLINE TRACK

University of Massachusetts Amherst (B)

NURSING–RN TO BSN

Brenau University (B)
Clarkson College (B)
Drexel University (B)
East Carolina University (B)
Florida State University (B)
Fort Hays State University (B)
Mansfield University of Pennsylvania (B)
Northern Arizona University (B)
Northwestern State University of Louisiana (B)
Seton Hall University (B)
Southwestern College (B)
University of Maine at Fort Kent (B)
University of Maryland (B)
University of North Alabama (B)
The University of Texas System (B)
University of Wyoming (B)
Liberty University (B)
West Virginia University (B)

NURSING–RN TO BSN (LATERAL ENTRY)

Winston-Salem State University (B)

NURSING–RN TO BSN BACHELOR'S COMPLETION PROGRAM

Connecticut State University System (B)

NURSING–RN TO BSN COMPLETION

Kaplan University (B)

NURSING–RN TO BSN COMPLETION

The University of North Carolina at Charlotte (B)

NURSING–RN TO BSN DEGREE COMPLETION PROGRAM

West Texas A&M University (B)

NURSING–RN TO BSN NURSING COMPLETION

Presentation College (B)

NURSING–RN TO BSN ONLINE OPTION (BACHELOR'S COMPLETION PROGRAM)

University of Missouri–Columbia (B)

NURSING–RN TO BSN/MSN

Duquesne University (B)

NURSING–RN TO MSN

University of Delaware (M)

NURSING–RN TRACK, EDUCATION

Walden University (M)

NURSING–RN TRACK, LEADERSHIP AND MANAGEMENT

Walden University (M)

NURSING–RN-BSN

Northern Kentucky University (B)

NURSING–RN-BSN COMPLETION PROGRAM

Wright State University (B)

NURSING–RN-BSN--RN TO BACHELOR OF SCIENCE IN NURSING

Chatham College (B)

NURSING–RN-TO-BSN COMPLETION

Bowling Green State University (B)

NURSING–RURAL FAMILY NURSING

Central Missouri State University (M)

NURSING–WOMEN'S HEALTH CARE NURSE PRACTITIONER

University of Minnesota, Twin Cities Campus (M)

NURSING–WOUND CARE NURSE

Metropolitan State University (UC)

NURSING–WOUND OSTOMY CONTINENCE NURSE

Metropolitan State University (UC)

NURSING/PUBLIC HEALTH–MS IN NURSING AND MS IN PUBLIC HEALTH

University of Massachusetts Amherst (M)

NUTRITION AND DIETETICS

Central Michigan University (M)
East Carolina University (M)

NUTRITION SCIENCE–MASTER OF NUTRITION SCIENCE

American Health Sciences University (UC)

OBJECT-ORIENTED ANALYSIS AND DESIGN USING UML

University of Washington (UC)

OBJECT-ORIENTED DESIGN

New Jersey Institute of Technology (GC)

OCCUPATIONAL AND TECHNICAL STUDIES

Old Dominion University (M,B)

OCCUPATIONAL HEALTH PSYCHOLOGY

Kansas State University (UC)

OCCUPATIONAL MEDICINE

Medical College of Wisconsin (M)

OCCUPATIONAL SAFETY

East Carolina University (M)

OCCUPATIONAL SAFETY AND HEALTH

Montana Tech of The University of Montana (B)
University of Connecticut (UC)

OCCUPATIONAL SAFETY AND HEALTH MANAGEMENT

University of Connecticut (M)

OCCUPATIONAL SAFETY AND HEALTH TECHNOLOGY

Odessa College (A)

OCCUPATIONAL STUDIES

Thomas Edison State College (A)

OCCUPATIONAL STUDIES IN AVIATION STUDIES

Excelsior College (A)

OCCUPATIONAL THERAPY

Darton College (A)
Texas Woman's University (M)
University of Florida (M)
University of St. Augustine for Health Sciences (D)
University of Southern Indiana (M)
West Virginia University (M)

OCCUPATIONAL THERAPY–POST-PROFESSIONAL OCCUPATIONAL THERAPY PROGRAM

Creighton University (D)

OCEAN ENGINEERING

Virginia Polytechnic Institute and State University (M)

OCEANOGRAPHY

University of West Florida (B)

OFFICE ADMINISTRATION

Central New Mexico Community College (A)
Ivy Tech Community College–Bloomington (A)
Ivy Tech Community College–Central Indiana (A)
Ivy Tech Community College–Columbus (A)
Ivy Tech Community College–East Central (A)
Ivy Tech Community College–Kokomo (A)
Ivy Tech Community College–Lafayette (A)
Ivy Tech Community College–North Central (A)
Ivy Tech Community College–Northeast (A)
Ivy Tech Community College–Northwest (A)
Ivy Tech Community College–Southeast (A)
Ivy Tech Community College–Southern Indiana (A)
Ivy Tech Community College–Southwest (A)
Ivy Tech Community College–Wabash Valley (A)
Ivy Tech Community College–Whitewater (A)

OFFICE ADMINISTRATION (ADMINISTRATIVE SUPPORT)

Darton College (A)

OFFICE ADMINISTRATION (SECRETARIAL SCIENCE)

Darton College (A)

OFFICE EDUCATION TEACHER

The University of Texas System (UC)

OFFICE INFORMATION SYSTEMS

Northwest Missouri State University (B)
Western Wyoming Community College (A)

OFFICE SOFTWARE APPLICATIONS

Seminole Community College (UC)

OFFICE SUPPORT

Seminole Community College (UC)

OFFICE SUPPORT SYSTEMS

Utah State University (A)

OFFICE SYSTEMS TECHNOLOGY

Randolph Community College (A)
Western Oklahoma State College (A)

OHIO READING ENDORSEMENT PROGRAM

Bowling Green State University (GC)

OIL AND GAS ENGINEERING MANAGEMENT

The Pennsylvania State University University Park Campus (M)

ONLINE PRINCIPAL LICENSURE PROGRAM AND MASTERS DEGREE IN CURRICULUM AND INSTRUCTION

University of Colorado at Colorado Springs (M)

ONLINE PROGRAM IN BASICS IN EXERCISE AND NUTRITION FOR HEALTH AND HUMAN PERFORMANCE

University of Massachusetts Amherst (UC)

OPERATIONS MANAGEMENT

Bellingham Technical College (A)
Excelsior College (B)
Kettering University (M)
Southwestern College (B)
Thomas Edison State College (A,B)
The University of Alabama (M)

OPERATIONS MANAGEMENT CONCENTRATION (10-MONTH PROGRAM)

American InterContinental University Online (M)

OPERATIONS MANAGEMENT CONCENTRATION (COMPLETION PROGRAM)

American InterContinental University Online (B)

OPERATIONS RESEARCH

Columbia University (UC)
Florida Institute of Technology (M)
Georgia Institute of Technology (M)
Southern Methodist University (M)

OPTICIANRY

Arkansas State University–Mountain Home (A)
Hillsborough Community College (A)

OPTICS, IMAGING, AND COMMUNICATIONS

Stanford University (GC)

OPTOMETRIC TECHNICIAN

Madison Area Technical College (UC)

OPTOMETRY–PRE-OPTOMETRY

Darton College (A)

ORGANIZATION AND MANAGEMENT/GENERAL

Capella University (M)

ORGANIZATION AND MANAGEMENT/GENERAL BUSINESS

Capella University (D)

ORGANIZATION AND MANAGEMENT/HUMAN RESOURCE MANAGEMENT

Capella University (D,M)

ORGANIZATION AND MANAGEMENT/INFORMATION TECHNOLOGY MANAGEMENT

Capella University (D,M)

ORGANIZATION AND MANAGEMENT/LEADERSHIP

Capella University (D,M)

ORGANIZATION DEVELOPMENT AND ORGANIZATIONAL MANAGEMENT

Fielding Graduate University (UC)

ORGANIZATIONAL ADMINISTRATION

Metropolitan State University (B)

ORGANIZATIONAL BEHAVIOR

National University (B)

ORGANIZATIONAL CHANGE AND DEVELOPMENT

Regent University (GC)

ORGANIZATIONAL CHANGE AND LEADERSHIP

Pfeiffer University (M)

ORGANIZATIONAL COMMUNICATION

The Pennsylvania State University University Park Campus (UC)
Seminole Community College (A)

ORGANIZATIONAL COMMUNICATIONS

Upper Iowa University (UC)

ORGANIZATIONAL CONSULTING

Saybrook Graduate School and Research Center (GC)

ORGANIZATIONAL DEVELOPMENT

University of the Incarnate Word (M,B)

ORGANIZATIONAL LEADERSHIP

Crown College (M)
Fort Hays State University (B)
Mercy College (M)
National University (M)
Northern Kentucky University (B)
The Pennsylvania State University University Park Campus (B)
Regent University (D,M)
Roosevelt University (B,UC)
Southern New Hampshire University (M)
Syracuse University (B,UC)
University of St. Francis (B)
Upper Iowa University (UC)

ORGANIZATIONAL LEADERSHIP AND MANAGEMENT

Regent University (B)

ORGANIZATIONAL LEADERSHIP IN ANIMAL ADVOCACY

Duquesne University (GC)

ORGANIZATIONAL LEADERSHIP–MASTER OF PROFESSIONAL STUDIES IN ORGANIZATIONAL LEADERSHIP

University of Denver (M)

ORGANIZATIONAL LEADERSHIP, INFORMATION SYSTEMS AND TECHNOLOGY SPECIALIZATION

University of Phoenix Online Campus (D)

ORGANIZATIONAL MANAGEMENT

Ashford University (B)
Concordia University, St. Paul (M)
Indiana Business College (A)
Mercy College (B)
St. Joseph's College, New York (B)
Thomas Edison State College (B)
University of La Verne (B)
University of Phoenix Online Campus (D)

ORGANIZATIONAL MANAGEMENT IN CHRISTIAN LEADERSHIP

Colorado Christian University (B)

ORGANIZATIONAL MANAGEMENT IN HUMAN RESOURCES

Colorado Christian University (B)

ORGANIZATIONAL MANAGEMENT–APPLIED ORGANIZATIONAL MANAGEMENT

University of St. Francis (B)

ORGANIZATIONAL MANAGEMENT–HUMAN RESOURCES

Concordia University, St. Paul (M,B)

ORGANIZATIONAL MANAGEMENT/ ORGANIZATIONAL DEVELOPMENT

Fielding Graduate University (M)

ORGANIZATIONAL MANAGMENT AND COMMUNICATIONS

Concordia University, St. Paul (B)

ORGANIZATIONAL PSYCHOLOGY AND DEVELOPMENT CONCENTRATION (10-MONTH PROGRAM)

American InterContinental University Online (M)

ORGANIZATIONAL PSYCHOLOGY AND DEVELOPMENT CONCENTRATION (COMPLETION PROGRAM)

American InterContinental University Online (B)

ORGANIZATIONAL SECURITY AND MANAGEMENT

University of Phoenix Online Campus (B)

ORGANIZATIONAL SECURITY–CERTIFICATE OF ADVANCED STUDY

University of Denver (UC)

ORGANIZATIONAL STUDIES

Saybrook Graduate School and Research Center (D)

ORGANIZATIONAL SYSTEMS

Saybrook Graduate School and Research Center (M)

ORIENTATION AND MOBILITY

Texas Tech University (UC)

ORNAMENTAL HORTICULTURE

Utah State University (A)

PACKAGING OF ELECTRONIC AND OPTICAL DEVICES

Southern Methodist University (M)

PACS ADMINISTRATOR

Clarkson College (UC)

PACS MANAGER

Clarkson College (UC)

PAPER SCIENCE AND ENGINEERING

University of Minnesota, Twin Cities Campus (M,UC)

PARAEDUCATION

Minot State University–Bottineau Campus (A)

PARALEGAL

Ashworth College (A)
Franklin Pierce College (UC)
Ivy Tech Community College–Bloomington (A)
Ivy Tech Community College–Central Indiana (A)
Ivy Tech Community College–Columbus (A)
Ivy Tech Community College–Kokomo (A)
Ivy Tech Community College–Southeast (A)
Ivy Tech Community College–Southern Indiana (A)
Ivy Tech Community College–Southwest (A)
Ivy Tech Community College–Wabash Valley (A)
Ivy Tech Community College–Whitewater (A)
The University of Texas System (UC)
University of Washington (GC)

PARALEGAL STUDIES

Colorado State University-Pueblo (UC)
Ivy Tech Community College–East Central (A)
Ivy Tech Community College–Kokomo (A)
Ivy Tech Community College–Lafayette (A)
Ivy Tech Community College–North Central (A)
Ivy Tech Community College–Northeast (A)
Ivy Tech Community College–Northwest (A)
Kaplan University (B)
Keiser College (A)
Lake Superior College (A)
Mount Wachusett Community College (A)
Peirce College (A,B,UC)
Penn Foster Career School (A)
Saint Mary-of-the-Woods College (A,B,UC)
Tompkins Cortland Community College (A)
University of Great Falls (B)
University of Massachusetts Lowell (UC)
Western Piedmont Community College (A)

PARALEGAL STUDIES/ ALTERNATIVE DISPUTE RESOLUTION

Kaplan University (B)

PARALEGAL STUDIES/OFFICE MANAGEMENT

Kaplan University (B)

PARALEGAL STUDIES/PERSONAL INJURY

Kaplan University (B)

PARAMEDICINE COMPLETION

Western Kentucky University (A)

PARKS AND RECREATION MANAGEMENT

Northern Arizona University (B,UC)

PARTICLE PROCESSING

Illinois Institute of Technology (GC)

PASTORAL COUNSELING

Liberty University (M)
Regions University (M)

PASTORAL MINISTRY

Newman University (B)

PASTORAL STUDIES

Southwestern College (B)
Temple Baptist Seminary (UC)

PASTORAL THEOLOGY

Saint Mary-of-the-Woods College (M)

PAYROLL CLERK

Shoreline Community College (UC)

PEACE AND CONFLICT RESOLUTION (INTERNATIONAL FOCUS)

Saybrook Graduate School and Research Center (GC)

PEACE STUDIES

Prescott College (M)

PEDIATRIC NURSE PRACTITIONER

University of Missouri–Columbia (M)

PERFORMANCE EXCELLENCE IN TECHNOLOGY MANAGEMENT

University of Colorado at Boulder (GC)

PERFORMANCE IMPROVEMENT

East Carolina University (GC)

PERFUSION TECHNOLOGY

Thomas Edison State College (B)

PERSONAL FINANCIAL PLANNING

City University (GC,M)
Kansas State University (M,UC)

PERSONAL FINANCIAL PLANNING AND COUNSELING

The University of Alabama (UC)

PEST CONTROL TECHNOLOGY

University of Florida (GC)

PEST MANAGEMENT

University of Florida (M)

PHARMACEUTICAL BUSINESS

University of the Sciences in Philadelphia (M)

PHARMACEUTICAL ENGINEERING

University of Michigan (M)

PHARMACEUTICAL MANAGEMENT

Drexel University (M)

PHARMACEUTICAL MANAGMENT

New Jersey Institute of Technology (GC)

PHARMACEUTICAL MANUFACTURING PRACTICES

Stevens Institute of Technology (GC)

PHARMACEUTICAL MARKETING
Saint Joseph's University (M)

PHARMACEUTICAL PROCESSING
Illinois Institute of Technology (GC)

PHARMACEUTICAL SCIENCE–FORENSIC DNA AND SEROLOGY
University of Florida (M)

PHARMACEUTICAL SCIENCE–FORENSIC DRUG CHEMISTRY
University of Florida (M)

PHARMACY
Auburn University (D)
Creighton University (D)
University of Cincinnati (D)
University of Wisconsin–Madison (D)

PHARMACY REGULATION AND POLICY
University of Florida (M)

PHARMACY TECHNICIAN
North Dakota State College of Science (A)
Vincennes University (UC)

PHARMACY–PRE-PHARMACY
Darton College (A)

PHARMACY, FIRST PROFESSIONAL DEGREE
University of Florida (D)

PHARMACY, WORKING PROFESSIONAL
University of Florida (D)

PHILOSOPHY
American Military University (B)
American Public University (B)
Darton College (A)
Holy Apostles College and Seminary (M)
Prescott College (M)
Skidmore College (B)
Thomas Edison State College (B)
University of Illinois at Springfield (B)
University of Waterloo (B)

PHILOSOPHY AND RELIGION
College of the Humanities and Sciences, Harrison Middleton University (M)

PHILOSOPHY, POLITICS, AND ECONOMICS
Eastern Oregon University (B)

PHLEBOTOMY
South Central College (UC)

PHOTOGRAPHY
Academy of Art University (M,A,B)
Prescott College (M)
Thomas Edison State College (B)

PHYSICAL ACTIVITY AND HEALTH
Eastern Oregon University (B)

PHYSICAL EDUCATION
Florida State University (M)
Jacksonville State University (M)

PHYSICAL EDUCATION STUDIES
Monroe Community College (A)

PHYSICAL EDUCATION TEACHER EDUCATION
West Virginia University (M)

PHYSICAL EDUCATION–COACHING SPECIALIZATION
Ball State University (M)

PHYSICAL EDUCATION, HEALTH, AND LEISURE STUDIES
Central Washington University (M)

PHYSICAL EDUCATION, TEACHING OPTION (LATERAL ENTRY)
Winston-Salem State University (B)

PHYSICAL THERAPIST ASSISTANT
Clark State Community College (A)

PHYSICAL THERAPY
Boston University (D)
Creighton University (D)
Darton College (A)

PHYSICAL THERAPY (IMPRINTS)
The University of Texas System (UC)

PHYSICAL THERAPY ASSISTANT
Darton College (A)

PHYSICAL THERAPY–POST-PROFESSIONAL DOCTOR OF PHYSICAL THERAPY
Rosalind Franklin University of Medicine and Science (D)

PHYSICAL THERAPY–TRANSITIONAL DOCTOR OF PHYSICAL THERAPY
MGH Institute of Health Professions (D)
University of St. Augustine for Health Sciences (D)

PHYSICAL THERAPY–TRANSITIONAL DOCTORATE OF PHYSICAL THERAPY
Utica College (D)

PHYSICIAN ASSISTANCE–MASTER OF PHYSICIAN ASSISTANCE (MPA)
Chatham College

PHYSICIAN ASSISTANT
Lock Haven University of Pennsylvania (M)

PHYSICIAN EXECUTIVE
The University of Tennessee (M)

PHYSICIANS ASSISTANT STUDIES
Drexel University (M)

PHYSICIANS EXECUTIVE MBA
Auburn University (M)

PHYSICS
Skidmore College (B)

PLASTICS ENGINEERING FUNDAMENTALS
University of Massachusetts Lowell (GC)

PLAYWRITING AND SCREENWRITING
Prescott College (M)

POLICE AND PUBLIC SAFETY PSYCHOLOGY (COPDOC)
Saybrook Graduate School and Research Center (D)

POLICY STUDIES
State University of New York Empire State College (M)

POLITICAL ECONOMY (3 YEAR)
Athabasca University (B)

POLITICAL ECONOMY (4 YEAR)
Athabasca University (B)

POLITICAL SCIENCE
American Military University (M,B)
American Public University (B)

Austin Peay State University (B)
Caldwell College (B)
Darton College (A)
Jacksonville State University (M)
Prescott College (B)
Regent University (B)
Thomas Edison State College (B)
Virginia Polytechnic Institute and State University (M)
American Public University (M)

POLYMER SCIENCE AND ENGINEERING

Lehigh University (M)

POLYMER SYNTHESIS AND CHARACTERIZATION/ PROCESSING

Illinois Institute of Technology (GC)

POST MASTER'S NURSING ADMINISTRATION

Fort Hays State University (UC)

POST MASTER'S NURSING EDUCATION

Fort Hays State University (UC)

POSTSECONDARY AND ADULT EDUCATION

Capella University (M)

POSTSECONDARY EDUCATION

Troy University (M)

POSTSECONDARY STUDIES

Memorial University of Newfoundland (M)

POSTSECONDARY TEACHING

Colorado State University (UC)

POWER ELECTRONICS

University of Colorado at Boulder (GC)

POWER ENGINEERING

Illinois Institute of Technology (GC)

POWER PLANT TECHNOLOGY

Bismarck State College (A,UC)

POWER SYSTEMS ENGINEERING

Iowa State University of Science and Technology (UC)

PRACTICAL THEOLOGY

Oral Roberts University (M)
Regent University (M)
Regions University (M)

PRACTICE OF TECHNICAL COMMUNICATIONS

New Jersey Institute of Technology (GC)

PRE-BACHELOR OF ARTS

Miami Dade College (A)

PRE-KINDERGARTEN HANDICAPPED ENDORSEMENT

University of Central Florida (GC)

PRE-MEDICINE

Darton College (A)

PRE-PHYSICIAN'S ASSISTANT

Darton College (A)

PREVENTIVE MEDICINE, GENERAL

Medical College of Wisconsin (M)

PRINCIPAL'S CERTIFICATION

Drexel University (UC)

PRINCIPALSHIP

Northern Arizona University (UC)

PRINT MEDIA

Rochester Institute of Technology (M)

PRIVATE SECURITY

Kaplan University (UC)

PRIVATE SECURITY AND LOSS PREVENTION

Indiana State University (UC)

PROCESS ENGINEERING

University of South Florida (GC)

PROCESS OPERATIONS MANAGEMENT

Illinois Institute of Technology (GC)

PROCESS PLANT TECHNOLOGY

Bismarck State College (A,UC)

PROCUREMENT

Thomas Edison State College (A,B)

PROCUREMENT AND ACQUISITIONS MANAGEMENT

Webster University (M)

PROCUREMENT AND CONTRACT MANAGEMENT

University of Maryland University College (GC)

PRODUCT CREATION AND INNOVATIVE MANUFACTURING

Stanford University (GC)

PRODUCTION AND INVENTORY CONTROL

California State University, Dominguez Hills (UC)

PROFESSIONAL (WEEKEND) PROGRAM

The University of Tennessee (M)

PROFESSIONAL ACCOUNTING

Strayer University (M,)

PROFESSIONAL AERONAUTICS

Embry-Riddle Aeronautical University, Extended Campus (A,B)

PROFESSIONAL AND TECHNICAL COMMUNICATIONS

New Jersey Institute of Technology (M)

PROFESSIONAL ARTS

Saint Joseph's College of Maine (B)

PROFESSIONAL COMMUNICATIONS

Stevens Institute of Technology (GC)

PROFESSIONAL COUNSELING

Regions University (M)
Liberty University (M)

PROFESSIONAL DEVELOPMENT

Amberton University (M,B)

PROFESSIONAL DEVELOPMENT FOR TEACHERS

Kaplan University (UC)

PROFESSIONAL DIPLOMA IN EDUCATIONAL ADMINISTRATION AND SUPERVISION

St. John's University (GC)

PROFESSIONAL DOCTOR OF OCCUPATIONAL THERAPY

Chatham College (D)

PROFESSIONAL MASTER OF BUSINESS ADMINISTRATION

Florida Institute of Technology (M)

PROFESSIONAL MASTER OF ENGINEERING IN FIRE PROTECTION

University of Maryland, College Park (M)

PROFESSIONAL MASTERS

University of Maryland, College Park (M)

PROFESSIONAL PRACTICE

University of Wisconsin–Madison (M)

PROFESSIONAL STUDIES

Austin Peay State University (B)
Champlain College (B)
Saint Joseph's College of Maine (UC)
Southwestern Assemblies of God University (B)
Thomas Edison State College (M)

PROFESSIONAL STUDIES IN EDUCATION

Capella University (M)

PROFESSIONAL STUDIES, INFORMATION TECHNOLOGY CONCENTRATION

Middle Tennessee State University (B)

PROFESSIONAL STUDIES, ORGANIZATIONAL LEADERSHIP CONCENTRATION

Middle Tennessee State University (B)

PROFESSIONAL STUDIES, STRATEGIC LEADERSHIP CONCENTRATION

Middle Tennessee State University (M)

PROFESSIONAL TECHNOLOGY STUDIES

Pace University (B)

PROFESSIONAL WRITING

Northern Arizona University (UC)
Saint Mary-of-the-Woods College (B)
Taylor University (UC)
University of Central Florida (GC)
Washington State University (UC)

PROFESSIONAL WRITING–MASTER OF PROFESSIONAL WRITING (MPW)

Chatham College

PROGRAMMER ANALYST–FAST TRACK--PROGRAMMER ANALYST SHORT-TERM CERTIFICATE

Sinclair Community College (UC)

PROGRAMMING AND ANALYSIS (WWW PROGRAMMING SPECIALIZATION)

Seminole Community College (A)

PROGRAMMING AND SOFTWARE DEVELOPMENT

The University of Toledo (A)

PROGRAMMING AND SOFWARE DEVELOPMENT

The University of Toledo (UC)

PROGRAMMING ENVIRONMENT TOOLS

New Jersey Institute of Technology (GC)

PROGRAMMING IN C++

City University (UC)

PROJECT ENGINEERING AND MANAGEMENT

Montana Tech of The University of Montana (M)

PROJECT MANAGEMENT

Athabasca University (GC,M)
Boston University
Capella University (M)
City University (GC,M,UC)
DeVry University Online (M)
Florida Institute of Technology (M)
Grantham University (M)
Kaplan University (UC)
Lehigh University (UC)
Missouri State University (GC)
New Jersey Institute of Technology (GC)
The Pennsylvania State University University Park Campus (GC,M)
Stevens Institute of Technology (GC,M)
University of Colorado at Boulder (GC)
University of Dallas (GC,M)
University of Illinois at Chicago (UC)
University of Management and Technology (GC,M,UC)
University of Washington (UC)
University of Wisconsin–Platteville (M)
University of Wisconsin–Platteville (M)
University of Wisconsin–Platteville (UC)
University of Wisconsin–Platteville (UC)
Colorado Christian University (UC)
University of Maryland University College (GC)

PROJECT MANAGEMENT CONCENTRATION

Colorado Technical University (M,B)

PROJECT MANAGEMENT CONCENTRATION (10-MONTH PROGRAM)

American InterContinental University Online (M)

PROJECT MANAGEMENT CONCENTRATION (COMPLETION PROGRAM)

American InterContinental University Online (B)

PROJECT MANAGEMENT–CERTIFICATE OF ADVANCED STUDY

University of Denver (UC)

PROJECT MANAGEMENT–MASTER OF PROJECT MANAGEMENT

American Graduate University (M)

PROJECT MANAGEMENT, ADVANCED

The Pennsylvania State University University Park Campus (GC)

PSYCH MENTAL HEALTH

University of Minnesota, Twin Cities Campus (M)

PSYCHIATRIC REHABILITATION

University of Medicine and Dentistry of New Jersey (M)

PSYCHIATRIC-MENTAL HEALTH

New Mexico State University (M)

PSYCHOLOGIE

Laurentian University (B)

PSYCHOLOGY

American Military University (B)
American Public University (B)
Ashford University (B)
Ashworth College (A)
Bethany University (B)
Caldwell College (B)
Chadron State College (B)
Columbia College (B)
Dallas Baptist University (B)
Darton College (A)
Drexel University (B)
Drury University (A)
Eastern Oregon University (B)
Judson College (B)
Kentucky State University (B)
Laurentian University (B)
Liberty University (A,B)
Limestone College (B)
Mercy College (B)
National University (B)

New York Institute of Technology (B)
Northern Arizona University (B)
Northwestern State University of Louisiana (B)
Pacific Graduate School of Psychology (M)
Regent University (B)
Saint Joseph's College of Maine (A)
Saint Mary-of-the-Woods College (B)
Saybrook Graduate School and Research Center (D,M)
Seminole Community College (A)
Skidmore College (B)
Southern New Hampshire University (B)
Southwestern Assemblies of God University (A)
Thomas Edison State College (B)
University of Great Falls (B)
University of Maryland University College (B)
University of Waterloo (B)
University of Wyoming (B)
Upper Iowa University (B)
Utah State University (B)
Wilfrid Laurier University (B)
Eastern Oregon University (B)

PSYCHOLOGY (3 YEAR)

Athabasca University (B)

PSYCHOLOGY (4 YEAR)

Athabasca University (B)

PSYCHOLOGY EMPHASIS

Community College of Denver (A)
Community College of Southern Nevada (A)

PSYCHOLOGY OF THE WORKPLACE

Jamestown Community College (GC)

PSYCHOLOGY–APPLIED PSYCHOLOGY

City University (B)

PSYCHOLOGY–CLINICAL PSYCHOLOGY (LICENSURE)

Walden University (D)

PSYCHOLOGY–COUNSELING PSYCHOLOGY (LICENSURE)

Walden University (D)

PSYCHOLOGY–GENERAL

Walden University (M)

PSYCHOLOGY–GENERAL PROGRAM, EDUCATIONAL PSYCHOLOGY TRACK

Walden University (D)

PSYCHOLOGY–GENERAL PROGRAM, RESEARCH AND EVALUATION TRACK

Walden University (D)

PSYCHOLOGY–HEALTH PSYCHOLOGY

Walden University (D)

PSYCHOLOGY–INDUSTRIAL/ ORGANIZATIONAL PSYCHOLOGY

Walden University (M)

PSYCHOLOGY–ORGANIZATIONAL

Walden University (D)

PSYCHOLOGY–SCHOOL COUNSELING SPECIALIZATION

Utah State University (M)

PSYCHOLOGY–SCHOOL PSYCHOLOGY (LICENSURE)

Walden University (D)

PSYCHOLOGY, GENERAL

East Carolina University (M)

PSYCHOLOGY-SOCIOLOGY

Skidmore College (B)

PSYCHOLOGY/CLINICAL PSYCHOLOGY

Capella University (M)

PSYCHOLOGY/COUNSELING PSYCHOLOGY

Capella University (M)

PSYCHOLOGY/EDUCATIONAL PSYCHOLOGY

Capella University (D,M)

PSYCHOLOGY/FAMILY STUDIES

Corban College (B)

PSYCHOLOGY/GENERAL PSYCHOLOGY

Capella University (M,D)

PSYCHOLOGY/INDUSTRIAL-ORGANIZATIONAL PSYCHOLOGY

Capella University (D,M)

PSYCHOLOGY/SCHOOL PSYCHOLOGY

Capella University (M)

PSYCHOLOGY/SPORT PSYCHOLOGY

Capella University (M)

PUBLIC ADMINISTRATION

American Military University (M)
American Public University (M)
Andrew Jackson University (M)
Athabasca University (UC)
Cape Breton University (UC)
DeVry University Online (M)
Fisher College (B)
Florida Gulf Coast University (M)
Florida Institute of Technology (M)
Georgia Southern University (M)
Indiana State University (GC)
Kentucky State University (B)
Marist College (M)
Memorial University of Newfoundland (UC)
Strayer University (M)
Thomas Edison State College (A,B)
Troy University (M)
University of Alaska Southeast (M)
University of Colorado at Denver and Health Sciences Center—Downtown Denver Campus (M)
University of Illinois at Springfield (M)
University of La Verne (B)
University of Management and Technology (M)
The University of Montana (M)
University of Nebraska at Omaha (M)
University of North Dakota (M)
University of Phoenix Online Campus (M)
The University of Texas at Arlington (M)
The University of Texas System (M)
University of Wyoming (M)
Upper Iowa University (B)

PUBLIC ADMINISTRATION (MSA)

University of West Florida (M)

PUBLIC ADMINISTRATION–FIRE SCIENCE EMPHASIS

Upper Iowa University (B)

PUBLIC ADMINISTRATION–LAW ENFORCEMENT EMPHASIS

Upper Iowa University (B)

PUBLIC ADMINISTRATION–MASTER OF PUBLIC ADMINISTRATION

National University (M)

PUBLIC ADMINISTRATION/PUBLIC HEALTH–MPH MASTER OF PUBLIC ADMINISTRATION AND MASTER OF PUBLIC HEALTH DUAL DEGREE

Walden University (M)

PUBLIC AGENCY SERVICES (BAS)

Northern Arizona University (B)

PUBLIC AND NON-PROFIT MANAGEMENT–MASTER OF PUBLIC AND NON-PROFIT MANAGEMENT

Metropolitan State University (M)

PUBLIC HEALTH

American Military University (M,B)
American Public University (M,B)
California College for Health Sciences (M)
University of Florida (GC)
University of West Florida (M)

PUBLIC HEALTH GENERALIST

University of South Florida (GC)

PUBLIC HEALTH INFORMATICS

University of Illinois at Chicago (M)

PUBLIC HEALTH INFORMATICS CAMPUS CERTIFICATE

University of Illinois at Chicago (UC)

PUBLIC HEALTH OR SCHOOL HEALTH NURSING

University of Missouri–Columbia (M)

PUBLIC HEALTH POLICY AND PROGRAMS

University of South Florida (GC)

PUBLIC HEALTH PRACTICE

University of South Florida (M)

PUBLIC HEALTH PREPAREDNESS

University of Illinois at Chicago (UC)

PUBLIC HEALTH–BACHELOR OF TECHNOLOGY IN PUBLIC HEALTH

Cape Breton University (B)

PUBLIC HEALTH–CAREER MASTER OF PUBLIC HEALTH PROGRAM

Emory University (M)

PUBLIC HEALTH–COMMUNITY HEALTH PROMOTION AND EDUCATION

Walden University (D)

PUBLIC HEALTH–EPIDEMIOLOGY

Walden University (D)

PUBLIC JUSTICE

State University of New York at Oswego (B)

PUBLIC LIBRARY TECHNOLOGY (PLT)

Marshall University (UC)

PUBLIC MANAGEMENT

Northern Arizona University (GC)
Park University (M)

PUBLIC MANAGEMENT AND LEADERSHIP

Walden University (M)

PUBLIC PERSONNEL ADMINISTRATION

Indiana State University (GC)

PUBLIC POLICY

Walden University (M)

PUBLIC POLICY ADMINISTRATION

Mississippi State University (M)

PUBLIC POLICY AND ADMINISTRATION–HEALTH SERVICES

Walden University (D)

PUBLIC POLICY AND ADMINISTRATION–HOMELAND SECURITY, POLICY, AND COORDINATION

Walden University (D)

PUBLIC POLICY AND ADMINISTRATION–INTERNATIONAL NONGOVERNMENTAL ORGANIZATIONS (NGOS)

Walden University (D)

PUBLIC POLICY AND ADMINISTRATION–KNOWLEDGE MANAGEMENT

Walden University (D)

PUBLIC POLICY AND ADMINISTRATION–NONPROFIT MANAGEMENT AND LEADERSHIP

Walden University (D)

PUBLIC POLICY AND ADMINISTRATION–PUBLIC MANAGEMENT AND LEADERSHIP

Walden University (D)

PUBLIC POLICY AND ADMINISTRATION–PUBLIC POLICY

Walden University (D)

PUBLIC POLICY AND ADMINISTRATION–PUBLIC SAFETY MANAGEMENT

Walden University (D)

PUBLIC POLICY AND ADMINISTRATION, GENERAL

Walden University (D)

PUBLIC RELATIONS

Montana State University–Billings (M,B)
University of Maryland University College (GC)

PUBLIC RELATIONS AND MARKETING COMMUNICATIONS–CERTIFICATE OF ADVANCED STUDY

University of Denver (UC)

PUBLIC RELATIONS AND ORGANIZATIONAL COMMUNICATION

Seminole Community College (A)

PUBLIC RELATIONS COMMUNICATIONS–PROFESSIONAL WRITING

Rochester Institute of Technology (UC)

PUBLIC SAFETY AND CRIMINAL JUSTICE

Regions University (B)

PUBLIC SAFETY AND SECURITY MANAGEMENT

Davenport University Online (B)

PUBLIC SAFETY MANAGEMENT

Franklin University (B)
Walden University (M)

PUBLIC SAFETY/CRIMINAL JUSTICE

University of Connecticut (B)

PUBLIC SCHOOL ADMINISTRATION

Oral Roberts University (D,M)

PUBLIC WORKS OPTION

The University of Tennessee (M)

PUBLISHING

Pace University (M)

PURCHASING

California State University, Dominguez Hills (UC)

PURCHASING AND MATERIALS MANAGEMENT

Thomas Edison State College (A,B)

PURCHASING MANAGEMENT

Shoreline Community College (UC)

QUALITY

Eastern Michigan University (M)

QUALITY AND RELIABILITY

Arizona State University (M)

QUALITY ASSURANCE

California State University, Dominguez Hills (M,B,UC)
Southern Polytechnic State University (M)

QUALITY ASSURANCE AND SOFTWARE TESTING

St. Petersburg College (UC)

QUALITY ASSURANCE SCIENCE

California National University for Advanced Studies (B)

QUALITY ENGINEERING

Lehigh University (M)

QUALITY IMPLEMENTATION

Rochester Institute of Technology (UC)

QUALITY IMPROVEMENT

Dakota County Technical College (UC)

QUALITY IMPROVEMENT AND OUTCOMES MANAGEMENT

George Mason University (GC)

QUALITY LEADERSHIP

Saint Joseph's College of Maine (M)

QUALITY MANAGEMENT

Madison Area Technical College (UC)

QUALITY MANAGEMENT, BASIC

Rochester Institute of Technology (UC)

QUALITY SYSTEMS

Bowling Green State University (GC)

QUALITY SYSTEMS FOR PRODUCT AND PROCESS ENGINEERING

University of Colorado at Boulder (GC)

QUANTITATIVE CONSTRUCTION MANAGEMENT

University of Washington (UC)

QUANTITATIVE METHODS IN FINANCE AND RISK MANAGEMENT (STATISTICS)

Stanford University (GC)

QUANTITATIVE SOFTWARE ENGINEERING

Stevens Institute of Technology (GC,M)

RADIATION HEALTH PHYSICS

Oregon State University (D,M)

RADIATION PROTECTION

Thomas Edison State College (A,B)

RADIATION THERAPY

Thomas Edison State College (A,B)

RADIOLOGIC AND IMAGING SCIENCES

University of Southern Indiana (B)

RADIOLOGIC PHYSICS

Illinois Institute of Technology (GC)

RADIOLOGIC SCIENCES

University of Central Florida (B)

RADIOLOGIC SCIENCES BACHELOR'S COMPLETION PROGRAM (RADIOGRAPHY)

University of Missouri–Columbia (B)

RADIOLOGIC TECHNOLOGY COMPLETION PROGRAM

Presentation College (B)

RADIOLOGIC TECHNOLOGY CONTINUING EDUCATION UNITS (CEUS)

Sinclair Community College (UC)

RADIOLOGIC TECHNOLOGY PROGRAM

Southeast Community College, Beatrice Campus (A)
Southeast Community College, Milford Campus (A)

RADIOLOGICAL SCIENCE–DEGREE COMPLETION IN RADIOLOGICAL SCIENCE

Oregon Institute of Technology (B)

RADIOLOGICAL SCIENCES

Saint Joseph's College of Maine (B)
Weber State University (B,UC)

RADIOLOGICAL TECHNOLOGY

Southeast Community College, Lincoln Campus (A)

RADIOLOGIST ASSISTANT

Bloomsburg University of Pennsylvania (M)

RANGELAND ECOSYSTEM SCIENCE

Colorado State University (M)

READING

Concordia University Wisconsin (M)
New Mexico State University (UC)
University of Alaska Southeast (M,UC)
The University of North Carolina at Charlotte (M)
Northern Arizona University (UC)

READING AND LANGUAGE

University of Massachusetts Lowell (M)

READING AND LITERACY (FOR LICENSED K-12 TEACHERS)

Capella University (M)

READING INSTRUCTION FOR SPECIAL EDUCATION–RISE

The Pennsylvania State University University Park Campus (UC)

READING SPECIALIST

The University of Texas System (UC)

READING TEACHER CERTIFICATION

University of Wisconsin–Stout (UC)

REAL ESTATE

Marylhurst University (B)
Thomas Edison State College (A,B)
University of Wyoming (UC)

RECEPTION SERVICES

Minot State University–Bottineau Campus (UC)

RECREATION MANAGEMENT

Minot State University–Bottineau Campus (A,UC)

RECREATION MANAGEMENT–THERAPEUTIC OPTION

Vincennes University (A)

RECREATION SERVICES

Thomas Edison State College (A,B)

REGENTS BACHELOR OF ARTS

West Virginia University (B)

REGENTS BACHELOR OF ARTS DEGREE

Marshall University (B)

REGENTS ONLINE DEGREE PROGRAM

Austin Peay State University (B)

REGULATORY AFFAIRS

Lehigh University (GC)
San Diego State University (M)

REGULATORY AFFAIRS–MEDICAL DEVICES

University of South Florida (GC)

REHABILITATION COUNSELING

Auburn University (M)
Salve Regina University (M)
San Diego State University (M)
The University of Alabama (M)
Wright State University (M)
West Virginia University (M)

REHABILITATION SCIENCES

The University of British Columbia (GC)

REHABILITATIVE SCIENCE

Clarion University of Pennsylvania (M)

RELIABILITY ENGINEERING

University of Maryland, College Park (M)

RELIABILITY MAINTENANCE

Rochester Institute of Technology (UC)

RELIGION

American Military University (B)
American Public University (B)
Liberty University (M,A,B)
Luther Rice University (B)
Thomas Edison State College (B)

RELIGIOUS EDUCATION

Defiance College (A,B)
Newman Theological College (GC)

RELIGIOUS EDUCATION—WITH 3 DISTINCT CONCENTRATIONS AVAILABLE

Temple Baptist Seminary (M)

RELIGIOUS EDUCATION–BACHELOR OF RELIGIOUS EDUCATION--PASTORAL MINISTRY

Master's College and Seminary (A)

RELIGIOUS STUDIES

Indiana Wesleyan University (UC)
Judson College (B)
Laurentian University (B)
Prescott College (M)
Regent University (B)
Skidmore College (B)
University of Waterloo (B)

RENEWAL STUDIES

Regent University (D)

RESEARCH ADMINISTRATION

Cleveland State University (GC)

RESEARCH AND DEVELOPMENT

University of Colorado at Boulder (GC)

RESOURCE INTERPRETATION

Stephen F. Austin State University (M)

RESPIRATORY CARE

California College for Health Sciences (B)
Oregon Institute of Technology (B)
Southeast Community College, Beatrice Campus (A)
Southeast Community College, Lincoln Campus (A)
Southeast Community College, Milford Campus (A)
Thomas Edison State College (A,B)

RESPIRATORY THERAPY

California College for Health Sciences (A)
Darton College (A)
J. Sargeant Reynolds Community College (A)

RESPIRATORY THERAPY BACHELOR'S COMPLETION PROGRAM

University of Missouri–Columbia (B)

RESTAURANT MANAGEMENT

Northern Arizona University (UC)

RESTAURANT, HOTEL, AND INSTITUTIONAL MANAGEMENT

Texas Tech University (M)

RETAIL MANAGEMENT

Strayer University (B)

RETAILING MANAGEMENT

Thomas Edison State College (A,B)

RETAILING–FIVE COURSE SEQUENCE IN RETAILING

University of North Texas (UC)

RISK ANALYSIS (MANAGEMENT SCIENCE AND ENGINEERING)

Stanford University (GC)

RISK MANAGEMENT

Kaplan University (UC)

RISK MANAGEMENT AND INSURANCE

Excelsior College (B)

RISK MANAGEMENT/INSURANCE

Florida State University (M)
Walden University (M)

RT TO BSRT

Northwestern State University of Louisiana (B)

SAFETY AND HEALTH TECHNOLOGY

Rochester Institute of Technology (UC)

SAFETY TECHNOLOGY

Rochester Institute of Technology (B)

SALES MANAGEMENT CONCENTRATION

Andrew Jackson University (M)

SALES SPECIALIST

Dakota County Technical College (UC)

SCHOOL ADMINISTRATION

Indiana State University (UC)

SCHOOL BUILDING LEADER IN EDUCATIONAL ADMINISTRATION AND SUPERVISION

St. John's University (M)

SCHOOL BUSINESS LEADERSHIP

Wilkes University (M)

SCHOOL COUNCELING LICENSURE

New Mexico State University–Carlsbad (UC)

SCHOOL COUNSELING LICENSURE

New Mexico State University (UC)

SCHOOL DISTRICT LEADER PROFESSIONAL DIPLOMA

St. John's University (GC)

SCHOOL FACILITIES MANAGEMENT

Mohawk Valley Community College (UC)

SCHOOL FOOD SERVICE MANAGEMENT

The Pennsylvania State University University Park Campus (UC)

SCHOOL LIBRARY MEDIA SPECIALIST

University of Washington (UC)

SCHOOL MEDIA

Syracuse University (GC)
Syracuse University (GC)

SCHOOL MEDIA SPECIALIST

Northwestern State University of Louisiana (UC)

SCHOOL NURSE CAMPUS CERTIFICATE

University of Illinois at Chicago (UC)

SCHOOL SYSTEMS, SUPERINTENDENCY AND LEADERSHIP

Webster University

SCHOOL TECHNOLOGY COORDINATION

Boise State University (GC)

SCHOOL TRANSPORTATION MANAGEMENT

Mohawk Valley Community College (UC)

SCIENCE

Excelsior College (A,B)

SCIENCE AND TECHNOLOGY LEGAL STUDIES OPTION

California University of Pennsylvania (B)

SCIENCE EDUCATION

Florida State University (M)
Montana State University (M)
The University of Texas System (M)

SCIENCE IN EDUCATION

Lesley University (M)

SCIENCE OF INSTRUCTION

Drexel University (M)

SCIENCE TEACHER EDUCATION

East Carolina University (M)

SCIENCE TEACHERS

University of Massachusetts Amherst (M)

SCIENCE, GENERAL NON-MAJOR

University of Waterloo (B)

SCIENCE, MATH, AND TECHNOLOGY

State University of New York Empire State College (A,B)

SCIENCES RELIGIEUSES

Laurentian University (B)

SECONDARY EDUCATION

Kaplan University (M)
Northern Arizona University (M)

SECONDARY EDUCATION (BS ED.)

Northern Arizona University (B)

SECONDARY EDUCATION EMPHASIS

Community College of Southern Nevada (A)

SECONDARY EDUCATION POSTDEGREE

Northern Arizona University (UC)

SECONDARY EDUCATION WITH CERTIFICATION EMPHASIS

Northern Arizona University (M)

SECONDARY EDUCATION–ENGLISH

Saint Mary-of-the-Woods College (B)

SECONDARY EDUCATION–MATHEMATICS

Saint Mary-of-the-Woods College (B)

SECONDARY EDUCATION–SOCIAL STUDIES

Saint Mary-of-the-Woods College (B)

SECONDARY EDUCATION, ADVANCED STUDIES

California University of Pennsylvania (M)

SECONDARY TEACHING

University of Great Falls (M)

SECURE NETWORK SYSTEMS DESIGN

Stevens Institute of Technology (GC)

SECURITY ADMINISTRATION

Southwestern College (M)

SECURITY ENGINEERING

Southern Methodist University (M)

SECURITY MANAGEMENT

American Military University (M,B)
American Public University (M,B)
Southwestern College (B)

SECURITY MANAGEMENT AND HOMELAND SECURITY

University of Massachusetts Lowell (UC)

SECURITY MANAGEMENT–MASTER OF APPLIED SCIENCE IN SECURITY MANAGEMENT

University of Denver (M)

SECURITY STUDIES

University of Massachusetts Lowell (GC)
East Carolina University (GC)

SEED ANALYSIS TRAINING

Colorado State University (UC)

SEED TECHNOLOGY AND BUSINESS

Iowa State University of Science and Technology (M)

SELF DESIGNED CONCENTRATION

Green Mountain College (M)

SELF-DESIGN

Granite State College (B)

SELF-DESIGNED

St. Cloud State University (B)

SEMICONDUCTOR PROCESSING AND MANUFACTURING

Arizona State University (M)

SENIOR EXECUTIVE

The University of Tennessee (M)

SENIOR LIVING MANAGEMENT

Rochester Institute of Technology (GC)

SERVICE MANAGEMENT AND MARKETING

Davenport University Online (B)

SERVICE SOCIAL (EN FRANÇAIS)

Laurentian University (B)

SIGNAL PROCESSING

Illinois Institute of Technology (GC)
Stanford University (GC)

SITE PLANNING

University of Washington (UC)

SIX SIGMA EBLACK BELT (20 WEEKS)

Colorado State University (UC)

SIX SIGMA EGREEN BELT (12 WEEKS)

Colorado State University (UC)

SMALL BUSINESS ADMINISTRATION

Middlesex Community College (A)

SMALL BUSINESS ENTREPRENEURSHIP

Myers University (B)

SMALL BUSINESS MANAGEMENT

Middlesex Community College (UC)
University of Alaska Southeast (UC)

SMALL BUSINESS MANAGEMENT/ ENTREPRENEURSHIP

Thomas Edison State College (A,B)

SNA LEVEL 3 CERTIFICATION MODULE

The Pennsylvania State University University Park Campus (UC)

SOCIAL DEVELOPMENT STUDIES

University of Waterloo (B)

SOCIAL PSYCHOLOGY

Park University (B)

SOCIAL SCIENCE

California State University, Chico (B)
College of the Humanities and Sciences, Harrison Middleton University (M)
Southern New Hampshire University (B)
University of Maryland University College (B)
University of North Dakota (B)

SOCIAL SCIENCE EMPHASIS

Community College of Southern Nevada (A)

SOCIAL SCIENCE STUDIES

University of Nevada, Las Vegas (B)

SOCIAL SCIENCE/HISTORY

Saint Mary-of-the-Woods College (B)

SOCIAL SCIENCES

Colorado State University-Pueblo (B)
Edmonds Community College (A)
Syracuse University (M)
University of Hawaii–West Oahu (B)
University of Pittsburgh (B)
University of Waterloo (B)
University of Wyoming (B)
Upper Iowa University (B)
Washington State University (B)

SOCIAL SCIENCES–APPLIED TRACK

University of Hawaii–West Oahu (B)

SOCIAL SCIENCES/HISTORY

Thomas Edison State College (B)

SOCIAL SERVICES

Thomas Edison State College (A,B)
The University of Maine at Augusta (A)

SOCIAL SERVICES ADMINISTRATION

Thomas Edison State College (B)

SOCIAL SERVICES FOR SPECIAL POPULATIONS

Thomas Edison State College (A,B)

SOCIAL STUDIES

Southwestern Assemblies of God University (A)
University of Missouri–Columbia (M)

SOCIAL THEORY, SOCIAL STRUCTURE, AND CHANGE

State University of New York Empire State College (A,B)

SOCIAL WORK

Central Texas College (A)
Cleveland State University (M)
Colorado State University (M)
Darton College (A)
Florida State University (M)
Louisiana State University and Agricultural and Mechanical College (M)
Memorial University of Newfoundland (M)
Missouri State University (M)
New Mexico State University (M)
Northern Arizona University (B)
Seminole Community College (A)
University of Manitoba (B)
University of North Dakota (M)
University of Wyoming (M)

SOCIAL WORK COMPLETION

Presentation College (B)

SOCIAL WORK PARAPROFESSIONAL

Winston-Salem State University (UC)

SOCIAL WORK–MASTER OF SOCIAL WORK

Newman University (M)

SOCIAL WORK–NATIVE HUMAN SERVICES

Laurentian University (B)

SOCIALLY ENGAGED SPIRITUALITY

Saybrook Graduate School and Research Center (GC)

SOCIOLOGY

Adams State College (B)
American Military University (B)
American Public University (B)
Caldwell College (B)
Colorado State University-Pueblo (B)
Columbia College (B)
Dallas Baptist University (B)
Darton College (A)
Fort Hays State University (B)
New Mexico State University (B)

New Mexico State University–Carlsbad (B)
New York Institute of Technology (B)
Seminole Community College (A)
Skidmore College (B)
Thomas Edison State College (B)
University of Colorado at Denver and Health Sciences Center—Downtown Denver Campus (B)
Wilfrid Laurier University (B)

SOCIOLOGY (3 YEAR)

Athabasca University (B)

SOCIOLOGY (4 YEAR)

Athabasca University (B)

SOCIOLOGY (IN DEVELOPMENT)

Laurentian University (B)

SOCIOLOGY EMPHASIS

Community College of Denver (A)

SOCIOLOGY–APPLIED SOCIOLOGY

Fort Hays State University (UC)

SOCIOLOGY-ANTHROPOLOGY

Skidmore College (B)

SOCIOLOGY/CRIMINOLOGY

Colorado State University-Pueblo (B)

SOFTWARE APPLICATIONS FOR THE PROFESSIONAL

Sinclair Community College (UC)

SOFTWARE DEVELOPMENT

Champlain College (A,UC)
Virginia Polytechnic Institute and State University (GC)
Southern New Hampshire University (UC)

SOFTWARE DEVELOPMENT AND MANAGEMENT

Rochester Institute of Technology (M)

SOFTWARE DEVELOPMENT MANAGEMENT

University of Maryland University College (GC)

SOFTWARE ENGINEERING

Arizona State University (M)
Champlain College (B)
DePaul University (M)
Drexel University (M)
Florida State University (B)
Illinois Institute of Technology (GC,M)
Kansas State University (M)
North Dakota State University (GC)
Southern Methodist University (M)
Texas Tech University (M)
University of Colorado at Boulder (GC)
University of Houston–Clear Lake (M)
University of Illinois at Urbana–Champaign (GC)
University of Management and Technology (M)
University of Maryland University College (M)
University of Michigan–Dearborn (M)
Walden University (M)
West Virginia University (M)
Westwood Online (A)

SOFTWARE ENGINEERING TECHNOLOGY

Grantham University (A,B)

SOFTWARE SYSTEMS

Stanford University (GC)

SOFTWARE SYSTEMS, ADVANCED

Stanford University (GC)

SOIL AND WATER SCIENCE–ENVIRONMENTAL SCIENCE

University of Florida (M)

SPACE STUDIES

American Military University (M)
American Public University (M)
University of Colorado at Colorado Springs (M)
University of North Dakota (M)

SPACECRAFT DESIGN AND OPERATION PROFICIENCY

Stanford University (GC)

SPANISH

Mercy College (B)
Northern Arizona University (B)
Skidmore College (B)

SPATIAL ANALYSIS AND EMERGENCY MANAGEMENT

Jacksonville State University (UC)

SPATIAL ANALYSIS AND MANAGEMENT CONCENTRATION

Jacksonville State University (M)

SPECIAL AND ELEMENTARY EDUCATION (BS ED.)

Northern Arizona University (B)

SPECIAL EDUCATION

Campbellsville University (M)
East Carolina University (M)
Eastern New Mexico University (M)
Florida State University (M)
Fort Hays State University (M)
Northern Arizona University (M)
Northwest Missouri State University (M)
Old Dominion University (M)
Prescott College (B)
Southern Oregon University (M)
Texas Tech University (M)
University of Alaska Southeast (UC)
University of Arkansas (M)
University of Central Florida (GC)
University of Nebraska–Lincoln (M,UC)
University of North Dakota (M)
University of West Florida (M)
Utah State University (M,B)
West Virginia University (M)

SPECIAL EDUCATION (CROSS-CATEGORICAL EMPHASIS)

The University of North Carolina at Greensboro (M)

SPECIAL EDUCATION (GIFTED)

University of South Alabama (M)

SPECIAL EDUCATION ALTERNATIVE LICENSURE

New Mexico State University (UC)

SPECIAL EDUCATION AND LEVEL I SPECIALIST CREDENTIAL MILD/MODERATE

National University (M)

SPECIAL EDUCATION EMPHASIS

Community College of Southern Nevada (A)

SPECIAL EDUCATION POSTDEGREE

Northern Arizona University (UC)

SPECIAL EDUCATION–ADAPTED CURRICULUM

The University of North Carolina at Charlotte (UC)

SPECIAL EDUCATION–DEAF AND HARD OF HEARING EMPHASIS

University of Northern Colorado (M)

SPECIAL EDUCATION–GENERAL CURRICULUM (TEACHER LICENSURE)

The University of North Carolina at Charlotte (UC)

SPECIAL EDUCATION–GIFTED EDUCATION

University of Nebraska at Kearney (M)

SPECIAL EDUCATION–VISUAL IMPAIRMENT EMPHASIS
University of Northern Colorado (M)

SPECIAL EDUCATION, GENERIC
Texas Tech University (UC)

SPECIALIZED MINISTRIES–YOUTH AND YOUNG ADULT MINISTRY
Southwestern College (M)

SPECIALTY CONSTRUCTION
Southern Polytechnic State University (UC)

SPEECH
Darton College (A)

SPEECH LANGUAGE AND AUDITORY PATHOLOGY
East Carolina University (M)

SPEECH LANGUAGE PATHOLOGY ASSISTANT
Shoreline Community College (UC)

SPEECH-LANGUAGE PATHOLOGY
Texas Woman's University (M)
University of Northern Colorado (M)
University of Wyoming (M)

SPEECH-LANGUAGE PATHOLOGY–MASTER'S PREPARATION ("LEVELING")
University of Northern Colorado (UC)

SPORT COACHING EDUCATION
University of Southern Mississippi (M)

SPORT MANAGEMENT
University of Southern Mississippi (M)

SPORT MANAGEMENT STUDIES
California University of Pennsylvania (M)

SPORT MANAGEMENT STUDIES–WELLNESS AND FITNESS TRACK
California University of Pennsylvania (B)

SPORTS AND ENTERTAINMENT MANAGEMENT
University of Dallas (GC,M)

SPORTS AND HEALTH SCIENCES
American Military University (B)
American Public University (B)

SPORTS COACHING
United States Sports Academy (M,B,UC)

SPORTS COACHING (INTERNATIONAL CERTIFICATION)
United States Sports Academy (UC)

SPORTS LEADERSHIP
Duquesne University (M)

SPORTS MANAGEMENT
American Military University (M)
American Public University (M)
Missouri State University (GC)
United States Sports Academy (D,M,B,UC)
West Virginia University (M)

SPORTS MANAGEMENT (INTERNATIONAL CERTIFICATION)
United States Sports Academy (UC)

SPORTS MANAGEMENT–SPORTS MEDICINE EMPHASIS
United States Sports Academy (D)

SPORTS MEDICINE
United States Sports Academy (M,UC)

SPORTS NUTRITION
Simmons College (GC)

SPORTS STUDIES
United States Sports Academy (M)

STATISTICAL METHODS FOR PRODUCT AND PROCESS IMPROVEMENT
Rochester Institute of Technology (GC)

STATISTICAL QUALITY
Rochester Institute of Technology (GC)

STATISTICAL THEORY AND METHOD
Colorado State University (UC)

STATISTICS
Colorado State University (M)
Iowa State University of Science and Technology (M)

STATISTICS–GRADUATE CERTIFICATE IN STATISTICS, SIX SIGMA BLACK BELT PROGRAM
Arizona State University (GC)

STRATEGIC COMMUNICATION AND LEADERSHIP
Seton Hall University (M)

STRATEGIC FORESIGHT
Regent University (M)

STRATEGIC INTELLIGENCE
American Military University (M)
American Public University (M)

STRATEGIC LEADERSHIP
Regent University (D)

STRATEGIC LEADERSHIP CONCENTRATION
Andrew Jackson University (M)

STRATEGIC MANAGEMENT SPECIALTY
Davenport University Online (M)

STRATEGIC PLANNING FOR CRITICAL INFRASTRUCTURE
University of Washington (M)

STRATEGIC TECHNOLOGY MANAGEMENT
University of Illinois at Urbana–Champaign (GC)

STRUCTURAL DESIGN
Rochester Institute of Technology (UC)

STUDENT AFFAIRS
Regent University (M)

STUDENT AFFAIRS AND HIGHER EDUCATION
Indiana State University (M)

SUBSTANCE ABUSE AND ADDICTIONS STUDIES
University of Hawaii–West Oahu (UC)

SUPERINTENDENCY
Northern Arizona University (UC)

SUPERINTENDENT CERTIFICATE
The University of Texas System

SUPERINTENDENT'S LETTER OF ELIGIBILITY
California University of Pennsylvania (UC)

SUPERVISION AND MANAGEMENT
San Joaquin Delta College (UC)

SUPERVISORY
Northern Arizona University (UC)

SUPERVISORY LEADERSHIP
Dakota County Technical College (UC)

SUPERVISORY MANAGEMENT
Mid-State Technical College (A)

SUPERVISORY MANAGEMENT/ LEADERSHIP DEVELOPMENT
Madison Area Technical College (A)

SUPPLY CHAIN AND INFORMATION SYSTEMS
The Pennsylvania State University University Park Campus (GC)

SUPPLY CHAIN MANAGEMENT
Lehigh University (UC)

SUPPLY CHAIN MANAGEMENT/ MARKET LOGISTICS
University of Dallas (GC,M)

SURGICAL TECHNOLOGY
Lock Haven University of Pennsylvania (A)
Southeast Community College, Beatrice Campus (A)
Southeast Community College, Lincoln Campus (A)
Southeast Community College, Milford Campus (A)
The University of Montana (A)

SURGICAL TECHNOLOGY ACCELERATED OPTION, CERTIFICATE OF GRADUATION
Vincennes University (GC)

SURVEYING
Thomas Edison State College (A,B)

SUSTAINABILITY EDUCATION
Prescott College (M)

SUSTAINABLE BUSINESS PRACTICES
Green Mountain College (M)

SUSTAINABLE COMMUNITY DEVELOPMENT
Prescott College (M,B)

SUSTAINABLE CONSTRUCTION
University of Florida (GC)

SUSTAINABLE NATURAL RESOURCES
Oregon State University (GC)

SYNTHESIS AND CHARACTERIZATION OF INORGANIC MATERIAL
Illinois Institute of Technology (GC)

SYNTHESIS AND CHARACTERIZATION OF ORGANIC MATERIALS
Illinois Institute of Technology (GC)

SYSTEM SOFTWARE
University of Illinois at Urbana–Champaign (GC)

SYSTEMS ANALYSIS
University of Maryland University College (GC)

SYSTEMS AND ENGINEERING MANAGEMENT
Texas Tech University (M)

SYSTEMS ENGINEERING
Arizona State University (M)
Iowa State University of Science and Technology (GC,M)
Southern Methodist University (M)
Southern Polytechnic State University (M)
Stevens Institute of Technology (M)
The University of Alabama in Huntsville (M)
University of Colorado at Colorado Springs (M)
University of Illinois at Urbana–Champaign (GC)
University of Maryland, College Park (M)
Virginia Polytechnic Institute and State University (M)
Walden University (M)

SYSTEMS MANAGEMENT
Florida Institute of Technology (M)

SYSTEMS SECURITY CERTIFIED PRACTITIONER (SSCP)
Peirce College (UC)

TAXATION
University of Tulsa (M)

TAXATION–EXECUTIVE MASTER OF TAXATION
Florida Atlantic University (M)

TEACH AND LEARNING WITH TECHNOLOGY
Ashford University (M)

TEACHER ASSISTANT
University of Calgary (UC)

TEACHER ASSOCIATE
Haywood Community College (A)

TEACHER CERTIFICATION
Prescott College (UC)

TEACHER EDUCATION
Marygrove College (M)
Newman University (B)

TEACHER EDUCATION (EARLY CHILDHOOD)
Darton College (A)

TEACHER EDUCATION (MIDDLE GRADES)
Darton College (A)

TEACHER EDUCATION (SECONDARY EDUCATION)
Darton College (A)

TEACHER EDUCATION (SPECIAL EDUCATION)
Darton College (A)

TEACHER EDUCATION (TRADE AND INDUSTRIAL EDUCATION)
Darton College (A)

TEACHER EDUCATION, PARAEDUCATOR
Community College of Denver (UC)

TEACHER LEADERSHIP
University of Illinois at Springfield (M)
Walden University (D)

TEACHING
Ashford University (M)
National University (M)
Texas Woman's University (M)

TEACHING AND LEARNING
Lock Haven University of Pennsylvania (M)
Kaplan University (M)

TEACHING AND LEARNING WITH TECHNOLOGY

University of Florida (GC)
University of North Texas (M)

TEACHING AND LEARNING–ONLINE TEACHING AND LEARNING

California State University, East Bay (UC)
New Mexico State University (UC)
University of Florida (GC)

TEACHING AND LEARNING–OPTION IN ONLINE TEACHING AND LEARNING

California State University, East Bay (M)

TEACHING AND LEARNING, ADVANCED STUDIES

Middle Tennessee State University (M)

TEACHING AT-RISK STUDENTS

Park University (M)

TEACHING ENGLISH AS A SECOND LANGUAGE

Northern Arizona University (M)
Oregon State University (GC)
St. Cloud State University (M)

TEACHING ENGLISH AS A SECOND LANGUAGE (TESL)

Drexel University (UC)
Oral Roberts University (M)

TEACHING ENGLISH AS A SECOND/FOREIGN LANGUAGE

Indiana State University (GC)

TEACHING LITERACY AND LANGUAGE–GRADES 6-12

Kaplan University (M)

TEACHING LITERACY AND LANGUAGE–GRADES K-6

Kaplan University (M)

TEACHING MATHEMATICS–GRADES 6-8

Kaplan University (M)

TEACHING MATHEMATICS–GRADES 9-12

Kaplan University (M)

TEACHING MATHEMATICS–GRADES K-5

Kaplan University (M)

TEACHING OF LANGUAGES (MATL)

University of Southern Mississippi (M)

TEACHING SCIENCE–GRADES 6-12

Kaplan University (M)

TEACHING STUDENTS WITH SPECIAL NEEDS

Kaplan University (M)

TEACHING WITH CERTIFICATION

Oral Roberts University (M)

TEACHING WITH TECHNOLOGY

Kaplan University (M)

TEACHING–INSTRUCTIONAL TECHNOLOGY

Northwest Missouri State University (M)

TEACHING–MASTER OF ARTS IN TEACHING

New Mexico State University (M)

TEACHING–ONLINE TEACHING

Boise State University (GC)

TEACHING, LEARNING, AND TEACHER EDUCATION

University of Nebraska–Lincoln (M,UC)

TECHNICAL COMMUNICATION

Southern Polytechnic State University (GC)
Texas Tech University (M)

TECHNICAL COMMUNICATION AND RHETORIC

Texas Tech University (D)

TECHNICAL COMMUNICATION, BASIC

Rochester Institute of Technology (UC)

TECHNICAL COMMUNICATIONS, ADVANCED

Rochester Institute of Technology (UC)

TECHNICAL EDUCATION AND INDUSTRY TRAINING

University of Central Florida (B)

TECHNICAL INFORMATION DESIGN

Rochester Institute of Technology (GC)

TECHNICAL JAPANESE

University of Wisconsin–Madison (M)

TECHNICAL MANAGEMENT

DeVry University Online (B)
Embry-Riddle Aeronautical University, Extended Campus (A,B)
Southern New Hampshire University (B)

TECHNICAL STUDIES

Excelsior College (A)

TECHNOLOGICAL EDUCATION, ADVANCED

Bowling Green State University (B)

TECHNOLOGY

Excelsior College (A,B)

TECHNOLOGY ADMINISTRATION

Washburn University (B)

TECHNOLOGY AND INFORMATION MANAGEMENT

Upper Iowa University (B)

TECHNOLOGY APPRENTICESHIP

Vincennes University (A)

TECHNOLOGY APPRENTICESHIP–GENERAL STUDIES OPTION

Vincennes University (A)

TECHNOLOGY EDUCATION

Ball State University (M)

TECHNOLOGY IN EDUCATION

Lesley University (M)

TECHNOLOGY IN SCHOOLS

University of Missouri–Columbia (M)

TECHNOLOGY IN SCHOOLS (EDUCATIONAL SPECIALIST)

University of Missouri–Columbia

TECHNOLOGY INTEGRATION

Boise State University (GC)

TECHNOLOGY LEADERSHIP

Fort Hays State University (B)

TECHNOLOGY MANAGEMENT

Bowling Green State University (D)
Central Missouri State University (D)
City University (GC)
Indiana State University (D)
Kansas State University (B)
National University (M)
Pennsylvania College of Technology (B)
St. Petersburg College (B)
Stevens Institute of Technology (GC)
University of Maryland University College (M)
University of Phoenix Online Campus (M)
University of South Florida (GC)
University of Wisconsin–Stout (M)
Worcester Polytechnic Institute (M)

TECHNOLOGY MANAGEMENT (DEGREE COMPLETION)

Eastern Michigan University (B)

TECHNOLOGY MANAGEMENT–CERTIFICATE OF ADVANCED STUDY

University of Denver (UC)

TECHNOLOGY MANAGEMENT–MASTER OF APPLIED SCIENCE IN TECHNOLOGY MANAGEMENT

University of Denver (M)

TECHNOLOGY SYSTEMS MANAGEMENT

University of Maryland University College (GC)

TECHNOLOGY SYSTEMS–COMPUTER NETWORKING MANAGEMENT

East Carolina University (M)

TECHNOLOGY SYSTEMS–DIGITAL COMMUNICATIONS

East Carolina University (M)

TECHNOLOGY SYSTEMS–DISTRIBUTION AND LOGISTICS

East Carolina University (M)

TECHNOLOGY SYSTEMS–INFORMATION SECURITY

East Carolina University (M)

TECHNOLOGY SYSTEMS–MANUFACTURING

East Carolina University (M)

TECHNOLOGY SYSTEMS–PERFORMANCE IMPROVEMENT

East Carolina University (M)

TECHNOLOGY–BACHELOR TECHNOLOGY (BTECH)

Memorial University of Newfoundland (B)

TECHNOLOGY–HUMAN RESOURCE DEVELOPMENT

The University of Texas at Tyler (M)

TECHNOLOGY-BASED DISTRIBUTED LEARNING

The University of British Columbia (GC)

TECHNOLOGY-BASED LEARNING FOR SCHOOLS

The University of British Columbia (GC)

TELECOMMUNICATION MANAGEMENT

Stevens Institute of Technology (M)

TELECOMMUNICATION SYSTEMS

DePaul University (M)

TELECOMMUNICATIONS

Columbia University (UC)
Pace University (GC,B)
Southern Methodist University (M)
Stanford University (GC)
University of Colorado at Boulder (M)

TELECOMMUNICATIONS AND NETWORK MANAGEMENT

Syracuse University (M)
Syracuse University (M)

TELECOMMUNICATIONS AND SOFTWARE ENGINEERING

Illinois Institute of Technology (M)

TELECOMMUNICATIONS ENGINEERING TECHNOLOGY

Rochester Institute of Technology (M)

TELECOMMUNICATIONS MANAGEMENT

Stevens Institute of Technology (GC)
University of Dallas (GC,M)
University of Management and Technology (M)
University of Maryland University College (GC,M)

TELECOMMUNICATIONS MANAGEMENT AND POLICY–CERTIFICATE OF ADVANCED STUDY

University of Denver (UC)

TELECOMMUNICATIONS NETWORKING

New Jersey Institute of Technology (GC)

TELECOMMUNICATIONS NETWORKS–CERTIFICATE OF ADVANCED STUDY

University of Denver (UC)

TELECOMMUNICATIONS SYSTEMS MANAGEMENT

Murray State University (B)

TELECOMMUNICATIONS TECHNOLOGY

Rochester Institute of Technology (B)

TELECOMMUNICATIONS TECHNOLOGY–CERTIFICATE OF ADVANCED STUDY

University of Denver (UC)

TELECOMMUNICATIONS TECHNOLOGY–VERIZON

Erie Community College (A)

TELECOMMUNICATIONS–DATA COMMUNICATIONS

Rochester Institute of Technology (UC)

TELECOMMUNICATIONS–MASTER OF APPLIED SCIENCE IN TELECOMMUNICATIONS

University of Denver (M)

TELECOMMUNICATIONS–NETWORK MANAGEMENT

Rochester Institute of Technology (UC)

TELECOMMUNICATIONS–VOICE COMMUNICATIONS

Rochester Institute of Technology (UC)

TELEVISION ARTS

Regent University (M)

TESOL

Regent University (M,UC)

TESOL CERTIFICATE THROUGH DISTANCE LEARNING

University of North Texas (UC)

TEXAS TEACHER CERTIFICATION–SECONDARY EDUCATION

University of North Texas (UC)

TEXTILE AND APPAREL MARKETING

Philadelphia University (M)

TEXTILES OFF-CAMPUS PROGRAMS (TOP)

North Carolina State University (M)

TEXTILES, CLOTHING, AND DESIGN

University of Nebraska–Lincoln (M)

THE ARTS

Briar Cliff University (B)
Community College of Southern Nevada (A)
Lenoir Community College (A)
Stanly Community College (A)
State University of New York Empire State College (A,B)
Triton College (A)

THEATER

Darton College (A)
Prescott College (B)
Skidmore College (B)
Thomas Edison State College (B)

THEATER ARTS

Regent University (M)

THEOLOGICAL STUDIES

Newman Theological College (UC)
Southwestern Assemblies of God University (M)

THEOLOGY

Caldwell College (B)
The Catholic Distance University (M)
Covenant Theological Seminary (GC,M)
Franciscan University of Steubenville (M)
Holy Apostles College and Seminary (M)
Master's College and Seminary
Newman Theological College
Saint Mary-of-the-Woods College (B,UC)
St. Mary's University of San Antonio (M)

THEOLOGY—DEGREE COMPLETION PROGRAM

The Catholic Distance University (B)

TOTAL QUALITY MANAGEMENT

University of South Florida (GC)

TOTAL QUALITY MANAGEMENT ENGINEERING

University of South Florida (GC)

TOURISM AND HOSPITALITY MANAGEMENT

Mount Saint Vincent University (B)

TOURISM PLANNING AND DEVELOPMENT

California University of Pennsylvania (M)

TOXICOLOGY AND INDUSTRIAL HYGIENE

Drexel University (UC)

TRADE & INDUSTRIAL (T&I)

The University of Texas System (UC)

TRADE AND INDUSTRIAL EDUCATION

Darton College (A)

TRAINING AND DEVELOPMENT

North Carolina State University (M)
Roosevelt University (GC,M)
University of St. Francis (M)
University of Wisconsin–Stout (M)

TRAINING AND DEVELOPMENT–CERTIFICATE OF ADVANCED STUDY

University of Denver (UC)

TRAINING AND PERFORMANCE IMPROVEMENT

Capella University (M)

TRANSFER DEGREE

Bellevue Community College (A)

TRANSFER DEGREE FOR BUSINESS STUDENTS

Bellevue Community College (A)

TRANSFER STUDIES, GENERAL

St. Louis Community College System (A)

TRANSFORMATIVE LEADERSHIP

California Institute of Integral Studies (M)

TRANSFORMATIVE STUDIES

California Institute of Integral Studies (D)

TRANSPERSONAL PSYCHOLOGY

Naropa University (M)

TRANSPERSONAL PSYCHOLOGY WITH ECOPSYCHOLOGY CONCENTRATION

Naropa University (M)

TRANSPERSONAL STUDIES

Atlantic University (M)

TRANSPORTATION AND LOGISTICS MANAGEMENT

American Military University (B)
American Public University (B)

TRANSPORTATION MANAGEMENT

American Military University (M)
American Public University (M)

TRANSPORTATION POLICY, OPERATIONS, AND LOGISTICS

George Mason University (M)

TRANSPORTATION SYSTEMS ANALYSIS

University of South Florida (GC)

TRANSPORTATION/DISTRIBUTION MANAGEMENT

Thomas Edison State College (A,B)

TURFGRASS MANAGEMENT

The Pennsylvania State University University Park Campus (UC)

TURFGRASS MANAGEMENT, ADVANCED

The Pennsylvania State University University Park Campus (UC)

TURFGRASS SCIENCE

The Pennsylvania State University University Park Campus (B)

ULTRASOUND–DEGREE COMPLETION IN ULTRASOUND WITH OPTION IN ECHOCARDIOGRAPHY

Oregon Institute of Technology (B)

ULTRASOUND–DEGREE COMPLETION IN ULTRASOUND WITH OPTION IN VASCULAR TECHNOLOGY

Oregon Institute of Technology (B)

UNIVERSITY STUDIES

Eastern New Mexico University (B)
University of Maine (B)
University of Maine at Fort Kent (B)
The University of Tennessee at Martin (B)

UNIX

University of Massachusetts Lowell (UC)

URBAN FORESTRY TECHNOLOGY

Minot State University–Bottineau Campus (UC)

URBAN PEST MANAGEMENT

University of Florida (GC)

USER CENTERED DESIGN

New Jersey Institute of Technology (GC)

VASCULAR SONOGRAPHY

Jackson Community College (A)

VASCULAR TECHNOLOGY

Jackson Community College (UC)

VETERINARY HOSPITAL MANAGEMENT

St. Petersburg College (UC)

VETERINARY HOSPITAL MANAGER

St. Petersburg College (UC)

VETERINARY MEDICAL SCIENCES–FORENSIC TOXICOLOGY

University of Florida (M)

VETERINARY MEDICINE ONLINE

Colorado State University (UC)

VETERINARY SCIENCE–PRE-VETERINARY SCIENCE

Darton College (A)

VETERINARY TECHNICIAN

Penn Foster Career School (A)

VETERINARY TECHNOLOGY

St. Petersburg College (A)

VIOLENCE PREVENTION AND RESPONSE

Saybrook Graduate School and Research Center (GC)

VIRTUAL FINE ARTS

Florida Atlantic University (M)

VIRTUAL REALITY IN EDUCATION AND TRAINING

East Carolina University (GC)

VISUAL COMMUNICATION AND GRAPHICS

Southern Polytechnic State University (GC)

VISUAL COMMUNICATION CONCENTRATION

American InterContinental University Online (A)

VISUAL COMMUNICATION–DIGITAL DESIGN CONCENTRATION (COMPLETION PROGRAM)

American InterContinental University Online (B)

VISUAL COMMUNICATION–WEB DESIGN CONCENTRATION (COMPLETION PROGRAM)

American InterContinental University Online (B)

VISUAL COMMUNICATIONS

Westwood Online (B)

VISUAL IMPAIRMENT

Indiana State University (UC)
Texas Tech University (UC)

VOCATIONAL BUSINESS EDUCATION

Indiana State University (UC)

VOCATIONAL DIVERSIFIED OCCUPATIONS ENDORSEMENT

University of Nebraska at Kearney (UC)

VOCATIONAL EDUCATION

University of Central Florida (M)

VOCATIONAL EDUCATION–INFORMATION TECHNOLOGIES

East Carolina University (M)

VOCATIONAL TEACHER PREPARATION

State University of New York at Oswego (B)

VOLUNTEER AND COMMUNITY RESOURCE MANAGEMENT

University of North Texas (GC)

WATER AND WASTEWATER TREATMENT

Illinois Institute of Technology (GC)

WATER RESOURCES PLANNING AND MANAGEMENT

University of Florida (M)

WATER, WASTEWATER, AND STORMWATER ENGINEERING

University of Florida (M)

WATER/WASTEWATER SPECIALIZATION

Mountain Empire Community College (A)

WEATHER FORECASTING

The Pennsylvania State University University Park Campus (UC)

WEB ADMINISTRATION

University of Washington (UC)

WEB AUTHORING

University of Alaska Southeast (UC)

WEB CONSULTANT FOR SMALL BUSINESS

University of Washington (UC)

WEB DESIGN

City University (UC)

WEB DESIGN AND DEVELOPMENT TECHNOLOGIES–CERTIFICATE OF ADVANCED STUDY

University of Denver (UC)

WEB DESIGN AND MULTIMEDIA

Westwood Online (B)

WEB DESIGNER

Texas State Technical College Waco (A)

WEB DEVELOPER

College of Southern Maryland (UC)
Texas State Technical College Waco (A)

WEB DEVELOPMENT

City University (GC)
Fort Hays State University (UC)
Strayer University (UC)

WEB FOUNDATIONS
University of Alaska Southeast (UC)

WEB LANGUAGES
City University (UC)

WEB MBA
Georgia College & State University (M)

WEB PAGE DEVELOPMENT AND DESIGN
Bismarck State College (A)

WEB PRODUCTION
Champlain College (UC)

WEB PROGRAMMER
South Central College (UC)

WEB PROGRAMMING
Champlain College (UC)

WEB PROGRAMMING IN E-COMMERCE
City University (GC)

WEB PROGRAMMING–VISUAL BASIC OR JAVA TRACK SHORT-TERM CERTIFICATE
Sinclair Community College (UC)

WEB PUBLISHING
Middlesex Community College (UC)

WEB SERVICES
Webster University (GC)

WEB SITE DESIGN
Webster University (UC)

WEB SITE DEVELOPMENT
Webster University (UC)

WEB SITE DEVELOPMENT AND MANAGEMENT
Champlain College (A,B,UC)

WEB SITE DEVELOPMENT CERTIFICATE
Western Wyoming Community College (UC)

WEB TECHNOLOGIES
Wake Technical Community College (A)

WEB TECHNOLOGY ESSENTIALS
University of Washington (UC)

WEB TECHNOLOGY FOCUS
University of Connecticut (B)

WEBSITE DESIGN AND DEVELOPMENT
University of Massachusetts Lowell (UC)

WEBSITE DEVELOPER
East Carolina University (GC)

WELLNESS–MASTER OF ARTS IN WELLNESS (MAW)
Chatham College

WETLANDS MANAGEMENT
Prescott College (M)

WILDLIFE MANAGEMENT
Prescott College (M)

WIRELESS AND ELECTRONIC COMMUNICATIONS
Cleveland Institute of Electronics (UC)

WIRELESS AND MOBILE COMMUNICATIONS
Columbia University (UC)

WIRELESS COMMUNICATION TECHNOLOGY CAMPUS CERTIFICATE
University of Illinois at Chicago (UC)

WIRELESS COMMUNICATIONS
Illinois Institute of Technology (GC)
Stevens Institute of Technology (GC)

WIRELESS ENGINEERING
University of South Florida (GC)
University of South Florida (GC)

WIRELESS PERSONAL COMMUNICATION
Stanford University (GC)

WOMEN'S HEALTH
Rosalind Franklin University of Medicine and Science (GC)

WOMEN'S HEALTH NURSE PRACTITIONER
University of Cincinnati (M)

WOMEN'S STUDIES
Laurentian University (B,UC)
Skidmore College (B)
Western Kentucky University (GC)

WOMEN'S STUDIES (3 YEAR)
Athabasca University (B)

WOMEN'S STUDIES (4 YEAR)
Athabasca University (B)

WOMEN'S HEALTH
Rosalind Franklin University of Medicine and Science (M)

WOOD AND PAPER SCIENCE
North Carolina State University (M)

WORKFORCE DEVELOPMENT EDUCATION
University of Arkansas (M)

WORKFORCE EDUCATION LEADERSHIP
Mississippi State University (M)

WORLD HISTORY FOR EDUCATORS
University of Colorado at Denver and Health Sciences Center—Downtown Denver Campus (UC)

WORSHIP STUDIES
Liberty University (M)

WRITING AND COMMUNICTIONS CONCENTRATION
Green Mountain College (M)

WRITING SOCIAL COMMENTARY
The Pennsylvania State University University Park Campus (UC)

YOUTH DEVELOPMENT
Clemson University (M)
Kansas State University (M)
University of Nebraska–Lincoln (GC)

YOUTH MINISTRY LEADERSHIP MODULE
Defiance College

NON-DEGREE-RELATED COURSE SUBJECT AREAS

Index of individual courses offered by institutions, arranged by subject. U=Undergraduate; G=Graduate; N=Noncredit

ACCOUNTING AND COMPUTER SCIENCE

Athens Technical College (N)
Belmont Technical College (U)
Bismarck State College (U)
Black Hills State University (U)
Blue Ridge Community College (N)
Bramson ORT College (N,U)
California State University, San Bernardino (U)
California State University, San Marcos (N,U)
Cape Fear Community College (U)
Carlow University (U)
Central Michigan University (U,G)
Central Piedmont Community College (N,U)
Chadron State College (U,G)
Chattanooga State Technical Community College (U)
Chesapeake College (U)
Clackamas Community College (U)
Clark College (U)
Clark State Community College (U)
Cleveland Community College (U)
Cleveland Institute of Electronics (N)
Cleveland State University (U)
Colorado State University (N,U)
Colorado Technical University (U)
Community College of Beaver County (N,U)
Community College of Southern Nevada (U)
Darton College (U)
Daymar College (U)
Delta College (U)
Des Moines Area Community College (U)
Drake University (G)
Duquesne University (U,G)
East Central Community College (U)
Eastern Michigan University (G)
Eastern West Virginia Community and Technical College (U)
Elizabethtown College (U)
Finger Lakes Community College (U)
Fort Hays State University (U)
Fort Valley State University (U)
Gadsden State Community College (U)
Galveston College (N,U)
Golden West College (U)
Harvard University (G)
Immaculata University (U)
Independence Community College (U)
Indiana Business College (N)
Indiana State University (U)
Iowa Western Community College (U)
Itawamba Community College (U)
Jacksonville State University (U)
James Sprunt Community College (U)
Kansas State University (U)
Lewis-Clark State College (U)
Macon State College (U)
Madonna University (U,G)
Mesa State College (U)
Middlesex Community College (U)
Mississippi State University (U)
Mitchell Technical Institute (U)
Mount Saint Vincent University (U)
New Mexico Junior College (U)
New Mexico State University–Carlsbad (U)
Niagara University (N,G)
North Idaho College (N)
Northwestern Oklahoma State University (U)
Ozarks Technical Community College (U)
Pueblo Community College (U)
Pulaski Technical College (U)
Quinebaug Valley Community College (N)
Rasmussen College Eden Prarie (U)
Saddleback College (U)
St. Louis Community College System (U)
Seminole Community College (U)
Sinclair Community College (U)
Snow College (U)
South Piedmont Community College (U)
Southwest Georgia Technical College (U)
State University of New York at Buffalo (N)
Texas A&M University–Commerce (U)
Texas A&M University–Kingsville (U)
Three Rivers Community College (U)
Tri-County Community College (N,U)
University of Alaska Anchorage, Kodiak College (U)
University of Cincinnati (N)
University of Massachusetts Lowell (U,G)
University of New Orleans (U,G)
The University of North Carolina at Charlotte (N)
University of Southern Indiana (N)
University of South Florida (G)
University of Wisconsin–Parkside (G)
University of Wisconsin–River Falls (U)
University of Wisconsin–Superior (U)
University of Wisconsin–Whitewater (U)
Upper Iowa University (N)
Viterbo University (U)
Western Piedmont Community College (U)
West Los Angeles College (U)
West Texas A&M University (G)
West Virginia University at Parkersburg (N)
Wharton County Junior College (U)
Yuba College (U)

ACCOUNTING AND RELATED SERVICES

Adams State College (N)
Adirondack Community College (U)
Alcorn State University (G)
Amberton University (U)
American Graduate University (G)
Anne Arundel Community College (U)
Arizona State University (U)
Arizona Western College (U)
Arkansas State University–Beebe (U)
Asheville-Buncombe Technical Community College (U)
Ashworth College (N)
Athabasca University (N,U,G)
Athens Technical College (U)
Auburn University (G)
Bainbridge College (U)
Bellevue Community College (U)
Bellingham Technical College (N,U)
Bergen Community College (U)
Berkeley College (U)
Berkeley College-New York City Campus (U)
Berkeley College-Westchester Campus (U)
Big Sandy Community and Technical College (U)
Bismarck State College (U)
Blackhawk Technical College (U)
Blinn College (U)
Boise State University (U)
Brazosport College (U)
Brenau University (U,G)
Bridgewater State College (N)
Brigham Young University (U)
Broome Community College (N,U)
Bryant and Stratton Online (U)
Buena Vista University (U)
Butler Community College (U)
Butler County Community College (U)
Caldwell College (U)
Caldwell Community College and Technical Institute (N,U)
California National University for Advanced Studies (U,G)
California State University, Dominguez Hills (N)
California State University, San Bernardino (U)
Campbell University (U)
Cape Breton University (U)
Cape Fear Community College (U)
Carl Albert State College (U)
Carl Sandburg College (U)
Casper College (U)
Cayuga County Community College (U)
Central Carolina Community College (U)
Central Missouri State University (N)
Central New Mexico Community College (U)
Central Piedmont Community College (U)
Central Texas College (U)
Central Virginia Community College (U)
Central Washington University (U,G)
Central Wyoming College (U)
Chadron State College (U,G)
Champlain College (U)
Charter Oak State College (U)
Chattanooga State Technical Community College (U)
Cincinnati State Technical and Community College (U)
Clackamas Community College (U)
Clark College (U)
Clatsop Community College (U)
Clemson University (N)
Cleveland State Community College (U)
Cleveland State University (N,U,G)
Clinton Community College (U)
Coleman College (U)
College of DuPage (U)

College of San Mateo (U)
College of Southern Maryland (U)
College of Staten Island of the City University of New York (N)
College of The Albemarle (N,U)
College of the Siskiyous (U)
College of the Southwest (U)
Colorado Christian University (U)
Colorado Mountain College District System (U)
Colorado Technical University (U)
Columbia Basin College (U)
Columbia College (U)
Columbus State Community College (U)
The Community College of Baltimore County (U)
Community College of Denver (U)
Concordia University Wisconsin (U)
Connecticut State University System (U,G)
Contra Costa College (U)
Corning Community College (U)
Cosumnes River College (U)
Dakota State University (U)
Dallas Baptist University (U,G)
Dallas County Community College District (U)
Danville Community College (U)
Darton College (U)
Daymar College (U)
De Anza College (U)
Des Moines Area Community College (U)
DeVry University Online (U,G)
Drake University (U)
Drexel University (U,G)
Drury University (U)
East Carolina University (G)
Eastern Michigan University (N,G)
Eastern New Mexico University (U,G)
Eastern Oregon University (U)
Eastern Wyoming College (U)
East Los Angeles College (U)
East Tennessee State University (U)
Edgecombe Community College (N,U)
Edison State Community College (N,U)
Edmonds Community College (U)
Elgin Community College (U)
Elizabethtown College (U)
Erie Community College (U)
Everett Community College (U)
Florida Atlantic University (U,G)
Florida Gulf Coast University (U)
Florida Institute of Technology (G)
Forrest Junior College (U)
Fort Valley State University (U)
Franklin Pierce College (U)
Franklin University (U)
Frostburg State University (U)
Fulton-Montgomery Community College (N)
Galveston College (N,U)
Georgia Southern University (U,G)
Gogebic Community College (U)
Golden West College (U)
Governors State University (U)
Grantham University (U,G)
Hagerstown Community College (N)
Halifax Community College (U)
Harvard University (G)
Haywood Community College (U)
Heartland Community College (U)
Hillsborough Community College (N)
Houston Community College System (U)
Howard College (U)
Illinois Eastern Community Colleges, Olney Central College (U)
Illinois Eastern Community Colleges, Wabash Valley College (U)
Immaculata University (U)
Indiana Business College (N,U)
Indiana State University (U)
Indiana Tech (U)
Indiana University of Pennsylvania (U)
Indiana University–Purdue University Fort Wayne (U)
Indiana University System (N)
International Institute of the Americas (U)
Iowa Western Community College (U)
Itawamba Community College (U)
Ivy Tech Community College–Northwest (U)
Jacksonville State University (U,G)
James Madison University (U)
Jamestown Community College (N)
Jefferson Davis Community College (U)
John A. Logan College (U)
Johnson County Community College (U)
John Tyler Community College (U)
Jones College (U)
J. Sargeant Reynolds Community College (U)
Kansas State University (U)
Kean University (N)
Keiser College (U)
Kentucky State University (U)
Lake Superior College (U)
Lansing Community College (U)
Lehigh Carbon Community College (U)
Lewis and Clark Community College (U)
Liberty University (U)
Limestone College (U)
Los Angeles Harbor College (U)
Louisiana State University and Agricultural and Mechanical College (N,U)
Madonna University (G)
Mansfield University of Pennsylvania (U)
Marist College (U,G)
Marshall University (U,G)
Maryville University of Saint Louis (N)
Massasoit Community College (U)
Mayville State University (U)
Mercer County Community College (U)
Mercy College (U)
Mesalands Community College (U)
Metropolitan State University (U)
Miami Dade College (U)
Middlesex Community College (U)
Middle Tennessee State University (U)
Midland College (U)
Mid Michigan Community College (U)
Midstate College (U)
Midway College (U)
Minnesota School of Business–Richfield (U)
Mississippi State University (U)
Missouri State University (U,G)
Moberly Area Community College (U)
Mohawk Valley Community College (N,U)
Monroe Community College (U)
Montana State University–Billings (U)
Mountain Empire Community College (U)
Mount Saint Vincent University (U)
Mt. San Antonio College (U)
Myers University (U)
Nassau Community College (U)
National University (U,G)
Naugatuck Valley Community College (N,U)
New England College of Finance (N,U,G)
New Jersey City University (U,G)
New Mexico State University–Carlsbad (N)
New York Institute of Technology (U,G)
Nipissing University (U)
North Arkansas College (U)
North Carolina State University (U)
North Dakota State College of Science (U)
Northeast State Technical Community College (U)
Northern Virginia Community College (U)
North Idaho College (N,U)
North Seattle Community College (U)
Northwestern Michigan College (U)
Northwestern Oklahoma State University (U)
Northwestern State University of Louisiana (U)
Odessa College (U)
Oklahoma State University (U)
Old Dominion University (U,G)
Orange Coast College (U)
Oregon Institute of Technology (U)
Oxnard College (U)
Pace University (U)
Palm Beach Community College (U)
Palomar College (U)
Parkland College (U)
Park University (U)
Patrick Henry Community College (U)
Peirce College (U)
Peninsula College (U)
Penn Foster Career School (N)
Pennsylvania College of Technology (U)
The Pennsylvania State University University Park Campus (U)
Philadelphia University (U,G)
Pine Technical College (U)
Portland Community College (U)
Prescott College (U)
Pueblo Community College (U)
Radford University (N)
Randolph Community College (N,U)
Rappahannock Community College (U)
Rasmussen College Eden Prarie (U)
Reading Area Community College (U)
Red Rocks Community College (U)
Regent University (N,G)
Rend Lake College (N)
Rio Hondo College (U)
Roosevelt University (U)
Ryerson University (U)
Sacramento City College (U)
Sacred Heart University (G)
Saddleback College (U)
St. Clair County Community College (U)
St. Edward's University (U,G)
Saint Joseph's College of Maine (U,G)
Saint Leo University (U)
Saint Mary-of-the-Woods College (U)
St. Petersburg College (U)
Sam Houston State University (U)
San Bernardino Valley College (U)
San Joaquin Delta College (U)
Schenectady County Community College (U)
Schiller International University (U,G)
Schoolcraft College (U)
Seattle Central Community College (U)
Seminole Community College (U)
Shawnee Community College (U)
Shippensburg University of Pennsylvania (U,G)
Shoreline Community College (U)
Simpson College (U)
Solano Community College (U)
South Central College (U)

Southeast Community College, Beatrice Campus (U)
Southeast Community College, Lincoln Campus (U)
Southeast Community College, Milford Campus (U)
Southern Arkansas University Tech (U)
Southern University at Shreveport (U)
South Piedmont Community College (U)
South Plains College (U)
Southwestern Assemblies of God University (U)
Southwestern Community College (U)
Southwest Wisconsin Technical College (U)
Spartanburg Technical College (U)
Stanly Community College (U)
State University of New York at Oswego (G)
State University of New York College at Potsdam (N)
State University of New York College of Agriculture and Technology at Morrisville (U)
State University of New York Empire State College (U)
Stephen F. Austin State University (U)
Stephens College (U,G)
Strayer University (U,G)
Syracuse University (G)
Tacoma Community College (U)
Taft College (U)
Taylor University (N)
Texas A&M University–Commerce (G)
Texas A&M University–Texarkana (U,G)
Texas Tech University (U)
Three Rivers Community College (U)
Thunderbird, The Garvin School of International Management (G)
Tompkins Cortland Community College (U)
Touro University International (U,G)
Tri-County Community College (N,U)
Tri-State University (U)
Triton College (U)
Tyler Junior College (N,U)
The University of Akron (U,G)
The University of Alabama (U)
University of Alaska Fairbanks (U)
University of Arkansas at Pine Bluff (U)
University of California, Berkeley (U,G)
University of Central Arkansas (U)
University of Cincinnati (N,U)
University of Colorado at Denver and Health Sciences Center—Downtown Denver Campus (U,G)
University of Dallas (G)
University of Delaware (U)
The University of Findlay (U,G)
University of Hawaii–West Oahu (U)
University of Houston–Downtown (U)
University of Houston–Victoria (U,G)
University of Illinois at Chicago (G)
University of Illinois at Springfield (U)
University of Maine (U)
The University of Maine at Augusta (U)
University of Maryland University College (U,G)
University of Massachusetts Amherst (U,G)
University of Michigan–Flint (N,U,G)
University of Minnesota, Crookston (U)
University of Minnesota, Twin Cities Campus (U)
University of Missouri–Columbia (U)
The University of Montana (U)
University of Nebraska–Lincoln (U,G)
University of Nevada, Reno (U)
University of New Brunswick Fredericton (U)
University of North Alabama (U,G)
The University of North Carolina at Chapel Hill (U)
The University of North Carolina at Charlotte (N)
The University of North Carolina at Greensboro (N)
University of North Dakota (U)
University of Northern Iowa (U)
University of South Alabama (G)
University of Southern Mississippi (U)
The University of Tennessee (U)
The University of Tennessee at Martin (N,U,G)
The University of Texas at Dallas (G)
The University of Texas at Tyler (U)
The University of Texas of the Permian Basin (U)
The University of Texas System (U)
University of Toronto (N,U)
University of Tulsa (G)
University of Virginia (U)
The University of Virginia's College at Wise (U)
University of Washington (U)
University of Waterloo (U)
University of Wisconsin–La Crosse (G)
University of Wisconsin–Parkside (G)
University of Wisconsin–Platteville (U,G)
University of Wisconsin–Whitewater (G)
Upper Iowa University (N,U)
Utah State University (U)
Utah Valley State College (U)
Vance-Granville Community College (N,U)
Vincennes University (U)
Virginia Polytechnic Institute and State University (G)
Wake Technical Community College (N,U)
Waukesha County Technical College (U)
Wayland Baptist University (U,G)
Wayne State College (U,G)
Weber State University (U)
Westchester Community College (U)
Western Nevada Community College (U)
Western Piedmont Community College (U)
Western Wyoming Community College (U)
West Virginia Northern Community College (U)
West Virginia University at Parkersburg (U)
Westwood Online (U)
Whatcom Community College (U)
Wichita State University (U)
Wilfrid Laurier University (U)
Wilkes Community College (U)
William Rainey Harper College (U)
Wisconsin Indianhead Technical College (N,U)
York County Community College (U)
York Technical College (U)
York University (N,U)

AEROSPACE, AERONAUTICAL AND ASTRONAUTICAL ENGINEERING

Arizona State University (G)
Auburn University (G)
Embry-Riddle Aeronautical University (U)
Georgia Institute of Technology (N,G)
Illinois Institute of Technology (G)
Indiana State University (U)
Middle Tennessee State University (U,G)
North Dakota State University (N)
Old Dominion University (G)
Portland Community College (U)
St. Cloud State University (U)
The University of Alabama (G)
University of Colorado at Boulder (N,G)
University of Colorado at Colorado Springs (G)
University of Michigan (N)
The University of Texas at Arlington (G)
Utah Valley State College (U,G)
Virginia Polytechnic Institute and State University (G)

AGRICULTURAL AND DOMESTIC ANIMAL SERVICES

Coffeyville Community College (U)
Cowley County Community College and Area Vocational–Technical School (U)
Kansas State University (U)
North Carolina State University (U)
University of Florida (U)
University of Maryland Eastern Shore (U)

AGRICULTURAL AND FOOD PRODUCTS PROCESSING

Fort Valley State University (U)
Kansas State University (N,U,G)
North Carolina State University (U,G)
University of Arkansas (G)
University of California, Davis (G)
University of Florida (U)
University of Minnesota, Crookston (U)
University of Missouri–Columbia (U,G)
University of Wisconsin–River Falls (U)
Wisconsin Indianhead Technical College (N,U)

AGRICULTURAL BUSINESS AND MANAGEMENT

Arkansas State University–Beebe (U)
Arkansas Tech University (U)
Athabasca University (G)
Clark State Community College (U)
Dawson Community College (U)
Eastern Oregon University (U)
Fort Valley State University (U)
Iowa State University of Science and Technology (G)
Iowa Western Community College (U)
James Sprunt Community College (U)
Kansas State University (U,G)
Mesalands Community College (U)
Middle Tennessee State University (U)
Missouri State University (U)
Murray State University (U)
North Arkansas College (U)
Nova Scotia Agricultural College (U)
Oregon State University (U)
Parkland College (U)
Sam Houston State University (U)
Southern Illinois University Carbondale (U)
South Plains College (U)
State University of New York College of Agriculture and Technology at Morrisville (U)
Texas Tech University (U)
University of Arkansas at Pine Bluff (U)
The University of British Columbia (U)

University of Florida (U,G)
University of Missouri–Columbia (N,U,G)
University of Nebraska–Lincoln (U,G)
University of Saskatchewan (N)
The University of Tennessee (U)
University of Wisconsin–River Falls (U,G)
Wisconsin Indianhead Technical College (N,U)
Yuba College (U)

AGRICULTURAL MECHANIZATION

Southern Illinois University Carbondale (U)
University of Florida (G)

AGRICULTURAL PRODUCTION

Colorado State University (U)
Kansas State University (U)
North Arkansas College (U)
North Carolina State University (U)
Nova Scotia Agricultural College (U)
Texas A&M University–Commerce (U)
University of Florida (U)

AGRICULTURAL PUBLIC SERVICES

Kansas State University (G)
University of Florida (U,G)

AGRICULTURAL/BIOLOGICAL ENGINEERING AND BIOENGINEERING

Fort Valley State University (U)
University of Missouri–Columbia (U)

AGRICULTURE

Auburn University (U)
California State University, Chico (U)
Central Carolina Community College (U)
Clemson University (G)
Colorado State University (U,G)
Dawson Community College (U)
Iowa State University of Science and Technology (U)
Itawamba Community College (U)
Kansas State University (N,U,G)
Mississippi State University (G)
Murray State University (U)
North Carolina State University (U,G)
Nova Scotia Agricultural College (N,U)
Oregon State University (U)
Rend Lake College (U)
Saybrook Graduate School and Research Center (G)
Southern Illinois University Carbondale (U)
State University of New York College of Agriculture and Technology at Morrisville (U)
Stephen F. Austin State University (U)
Texas A&M University–Commerce (G)
Texas A&M University–Kingsville (U,G)
Texas Tech University (U,G)
Three Rivers Community College (U)
University of Arkansas at Pine Bluff (U)
The University of British Columbia (U)
University of Florida (U,G)
University of Minnesota, Twin Cities Campus (U)
University of Saskatchewan (U)
University of Wisconsin–River Falls (U)
University of Wyoming (U)
Virginia Polytechnic Institute and State University (U)
Wisconsin Indianhead Technical College (N,U)

AGRICULTURE AND AGRICULTURE OPERATIONS RELATED

James Sprunt Community College (U)
Kansas State University (U,G)
Louisiana State University and Agricultural and Mechanical College (G)
Murray State University (U)
North Carolina State University (G)
Oregon State University (U)
South Plains College (U)
University of California, Davis (N,U)
University of California, Riverside (N)
University of Florida (U)
University of Maryland Eastern Shore (U)
University of Massachusetts Boston (N)
University of Saskatchewan (N,U)
Utah State University (G)
Virginia Polytechnic Institute and State University (U,G)
Yuba College (U)

AIR FORCE J.R.O.T.C/R.O.T.C

California State University, San Bernardino (U)
Southwestern Assemblies of God University (U)
University of Arkansas at Pine Bluff (N)

AIR TRANSPORTATION

Community College of Beaver County (U)
Embry-Riddle Aeronautical University (N)
Embry-Riddle Aeronautical University, Extended Campus (N,G)
Iowa Western Community College (U)
University of Nebraska at Omaha (G)
University of New Brunswick Fredericton (U)
Utah Valley State College (U)
Western Michigan University (U)
West Los Angeles College (U)
York University (N)

ALLIED HEALTH AND MEDICAL ASSISTING SERVICES

Anne Arundel Community College (U)
Ashworth College (N)
Athens Technical College (N)
Bainbridge College (N)
Blackhawk Technical College (U)
Brenau University (U)
Bridgewater State College (N)
Butler Community College (U)
Butler County Community College (U)
California State University, San Bernardino (U)
California State University, San Marcos (U)
Central Michigan University (U)
Central Wyoming College (N)
Chattanooga State Technical Community College (U)
Chesapeake College (U)
Cincinnati State Technical and Community College (U)
Clackamas Community College (U)
Clark State Community College (U)
Clemson University (N)
Cleveland Community College (U)
Columbus State Community College (U)
Community College of Southern Nevada (U)
Cosumnes River College (U)
Cowley County Community College and Area Vocational–Technical School (U)
Dakota County Technical College (U)
Danville Community College (U)
Darton College (U)
De Anza College (U)
East Central Community College (U)
East Tennessee State University (N)
Elgin Community College (U)
Everett Community College (U)
Feather River College (U)
Forrest Junior College (U)
Galveston College (U)
Gogebic Community College (U)
Hagerstown Community College (N)
Independence Community College (U)
Iowa Western Community College (U)
Itawamba Community College (U)
James Sprunt Community College (U)
Jones College (U)
Keiser College (U)
Lamar State College–Port Arthur (N)
Lock Haven University of Pennsylvania (N)
Middle Tennessee State University (N)
Mid Michigan Community College (U)
Midstate College (U)
Minot State University–Bottineau Campus (U)
Montgomery Community College (N)
National University (U)
New Mexico Junior College (U)
North Dakota State College of Science (U)
North Dakota State University (N)
North Idaho College (N,U)
Northwestern Connecticut Community College (U)
Orange Coast College (U)
Ozarka College (U)
Ozarks Technical Community College (U)
Peninsula College (U)
Penn Foster Career School (N)
Portland Community College (U)
Quinebaug Valley Community College (N)
Randolph Community College (N,U)
Rappahannock Community College (U)
Raritan Valley Community College (N)
Rasmussen College Eden Prarie (U)
The Richard Stockton College of New Jersey (U,G)
Schoolcraft College (U)
Seminole Community College (U)
Southern University at Shreveport (U)
Southwestern Oregon Community College (U)
Southwest Wisconsin Technical College (U)
Tacoma Community College (U)
Texas State University-San Marcos (U)
Three Rivers Community College (N,U)
The University of Akron (N,U)
University of Illinois at Chicago (G)
The University of Texas System (N,G)
The University of Toledo (U)
Vincennes University (U)

Wake Technical Community College (U)
Waukesha County Technical College (U)
Western Nevada Community College (U)
West Los Angeles College (U)
Wharton County Junior College (U)
William Rainey Harper College (U)

ALLIED HEALTH DIAGNOSTIC, INTERVENTION, AND TREATMENT PROFESSIONS

Brenau University (G)
California State University, San Bernardino (G)
Central Wyoming College (N)
Columbus State Community College (U)
Community College of Southern Nevada (U)
Danville Community College (U)
Darton College (U)
Jackson Community College (U)
James Madison University (N)
Jefferson College of Health Sciences (N,U)
John A. Logan College (U)
Lamar State College–Port Arthur (N)
North Idaho College (N)
Oregon Institute of Technology (U)
Radford University (G)
Randolph Community College (N)
Rasmussen College Eden Prarie (U)
Saybrook Graduate School and Research Center (G)
Stanly Community College (U)
Tacoma Community College (U)
University of Michigan–Flint (U)
University of Minnesota, Twin Cities Campus (U)
University of Missouri–Columbia (N)
Washburn University (U)
William Rainey Harper College (U)

ALTERNATIVE AND COMPLEMENTARY MEDICAL SUPPORT SERVICES

Atlantic University (N,G)
East Tennessee State University (N)
Lamar State College–Port Arthur (N)
Rasmussen College Eden Prarie (U)
Saybrook Graduate School and Research Center (G)

ALTERNATIVE AND COMPLEMENTARY MEDICINE AND MEDICAL SYSTEMS

Atlantic University (N,G)
Lamar State College–Port Arthur (N)
North Idaho College (N)
Saybrook Graduate School and Research Center (G)

AMERICAN LITERATURE (UNITED STATES AND CANADIAN)

Alvin Community College (U)
Arizona State University (U)
Bellevue Community College (U)
Bellevue University (U)
Bergen Community College (U)
Berkeley College (U)
Berkeley College-New York City Campus (U)
Berkeley College-Westchester Campus (U)
Bowling Green State University (U,G)
Brenau University (U)
Brigham Young University (U)
California State University, San Bernardino (U)
Campbell University (U)
Cape Fear Community College (U)
Central Carolina Community College (U)
Chattanooga State Technical Community College (U)
Chesapeake College (U)
College of the Humanities and Sciences, Harrison Middleton University (U)
Columbia College (U)
Columbus State Community College (U)
Community College of Beaver County (U)
Community College of Southern Nevada (U)
Cosumnes River College (U)
Cowley County Community College and Area Vocational–Technical School (U)
Dallas Baptist University (U)
Darton College (U)
Dawson Community College (U)
Delta College (U)
Des Moines Area Community College (U)
D'Youville College (U)
East Central Community College (U)
Elizabethtown College (U)
Everett Community College (U)
Galveston College (U)
Heartland Community College (U)
Hillsborough Community College (U)
Housatonic Community College (U)
Houston Community College System (U)
Immaculata University (U)
Iowa Western Community College (U)
Itawamba Community College (U)
Jackson Community College (U)
Jacksonville State University (U)
James Madison University (N)
John Jay College of Criminal Justice of the City University of New York (U)
John Tyler Community College (U)
J. Sargeant Reynolds Community College (U)
Lamar State College–Port Arthur (N)
Lehigh Carbon Community College (U)
Limestone College (U)
Linn-Benton Community College (U)
Louisiana State University and Agricultural and Mechanical College (U)
Louisiana State University at Eunice (U)
Maranatha Baptist Bible College (U)
Marylhurst University (U)
Mercy College (G)
Miami Dade College (U)
Middle Tennessee State University (U)
Mohawk Valley Community College (U)
Monroe Community College (U)
Montgomery Community College (U)
Mount Allison University (U)
Myers University (U)
Naropa University (U)
New England College of Finance (U)
New Mexico Junior College (U)
North Carolina State University (U)
North Idaho College (N,U)
Oklahoma State University (U)
Oregon State University (U)
Oxnard College (U)
Park University (U)
Peninsula College (U)
Piedmont Technical College (U)
Pueblo Community College (U)
Pulaski Technical College (U)
Rappahannock Community College (U)
Raritan Valley Community College (U)
Rasmussen College Eden Prarie (U)
Rio Hondo College (U)
St. Cloud State University (U)
St. Louis Community College System (U)
St. Petersburg College (U)
San Joaquin Delta College (U)
Schoolcraft College (U)
Southern Illinois University Carbondale (U)
South Plains College (U)
State University of New York at New Paltz (U)
Taylor University (U)
Texas State University-San Marcos (U)
Texas Tech University (U)
Three Rivers Community College (U)
Tyler Junior College (U)
The University of Alabama (U)
University of Alaska Fairbanks (U)
University of Arkansas at Pine Bluff (U)
University of California, Berkeley (U)
University of Central Arkansas (U)
University of Colorado at Colorado Springs (U)
University of Colorado at Denver and Health Sciences Center—Downtown Denver Campus (U)
University of Florida (U)
University of Great Falls (U)
The University of Maine at Augusta (U)
University of Missouri–Columbia (U)
University of Nevada, Reno (U)
University of New Orleans (U,G)
University of South Carolina Sumter (U)
The University of Tennessee (U)
The University of Texas of the Permian Basin (U)
University of Washington (U)
University of Waterloo (U)
University of Wisconsin–Superior (U)
University of Wyoming (U)
Utah Valley State College (U)
Vance-Granville Community College (U)
Wake Technical Community College (U)
Washburn University (U)
Westchester Community College (U)
Western Washington University (U)
West Los Angeles College (U)
West Shore Community College (U)
Wharton County Junior College (U)
Wilkes Community College (U)
York County Community College (U)

AMERICAN SIGN LANGUAGE (ASL)

Blue Ridge Community College (U)
Central Lakes College (U)
Central Piedmont Community College (U)
Chattanooga State Technical Community College (U)
Cleveland Community College (U)
John A. Logan College (U)
Palomar College (U)
Pine Technical College (U)
Presentation College (U)
Snow College (U)
University of New Orleans (U,G)

ANIMAL SCIENCES

Ashworth College (N)
Auburn University (U)
Clemson University (G)
Colorado State University (N,U)
Community College of Southern Nevada (U)
Cowley County Community College and Area Vocational–Technical School (U)
Duquesne University (N)
Fort Valley State University (U,G)
James Sprunt Community College (U)
Kansas State University (U,G)
Mesalands Community College (U)
Minnesota School of Business–Richfield (U)
Murray State University (U)
North Carolina State University (U)
Nova Scotia Agricultural College (N,U)
Oklahoma State University (U)
The Pennsylvania State University University Park Campus (U)
Texas A&M University–Commerce (U)
Texas Tech University (G)
University of Arkansas at Pine Bluff (U)
The University of British Columbia (U)
University of Delaware (U)
University of Maine (G)
University of Missouri–Columbia (U,G)
Yuba College (U)

ANTHROPOLOGY

Alvin Community College (U)
Athabasca University (N,U)
Bellevue Community College (U)
Bergen Community College (U)
Bethany University (U)
Blinn College (U)
Boise State University (U)
Brenau University (U)
Bridgewater State College (U)
Brigham Young University (U)
Burlington County College (U)
Casper College (U)
Cayuga County Community College (U)
Cedarville University (U)
Central Piedmont Community College (U)
Central Texas College (U)
Central Wyoming College (U)
Citrus College (U)
City College of San Francisco (U)
Clatsop Community College (U)
College of DuPage (U)
College of San Mateo (U)
Colorado Mountain College District System (U)
Colorado State University (U)
Colorado State University-Pueblo (U)
Columbia Basin College (U)
Columbia College (U)
Columbia International University (N,G)
Columbus State Community College (U)
Community College of Denver (U)
Community College of Southern Nevada (U)
Connecticut State University System (U,G)
Contra Costa College (U)
Cosumnes River College (U)
Crafton Hills College (U)
Cumberland County College (U)
Dallas County Community College District (U)
Dawson Community College (U)
De Anza College (U)
Des Moines Area Community College (U)
Eastern Oregon University (U)
Edison State Community College (U)
Elgin Community College (U)
Erie Community College (U)
Everett Community College (U)
Evergreen Valley College (U)
Feather River College (U)
Golden West College (U)
Governors State University (U,G)
Greenfield Community College (U)
Haywood Community College (U)
Honolulu Community College (U)
Houston Community College System (U)
Indiana Wesleyan University (U)
Iowa Western Community College (U)
Jackson Community College (U)
Jacksonville State University (U)
John Jay College of Criminal Justice of the City University of New York (U)
Johnson County Community College (U)
Lake Superior College (U)
Louisiana State University and Agricultural and Mechanical College (U)
Massasoit Community College (U)
Memorial University of Newfoundland (U)
Mercer County Community College (U)
Metropolitan State University (U)
Missouri State University (U)
Mt. San Antonio College (U)
Murray State University (U)
Myers University (U)
Naropa University (U,G)
Nassau Community College (U)
New York Institute of Technology (U)
North Arkansas College (U)
North Carolina State University (U)
North Idaho College (U)
North Seattle Community College (U)
Northwestern Michigan College (U)
Oklahoma State University (U)
Orange Coast College (U)
Oregon Institute of Technology (U)
Oregon State University (U)
Oxnard College (U)
Ozarks Technical Community College (U)
Pace University (U)
Palm Beach Community College (U)
Palomar College (U)
Parkland College (U)
Peninsula College (U)
The Pennsylvania State University University Park Campus (U)
Portland Community College (U)
Pueblo Community College (U)
Purdue University Calumet (U)
Raritan Valley Community College (U)
Reading Area Community College (U)
Rend Lake College (U)
The Richard Stockton College of New Jersey (U)
Rio Hondo College (U)
Rochester Institute of Technology (U)
Saddleback College (U)
St. Cloud State University (U)
St. Edward's University (U)
St. Petersburg College (U)
Sam Houston State University (U)
San Bernardino Valley College (U)
San Joaquin Delta College (U)
Schoolcraft College (U)
Seattle Central Community College (U)
Seminole Community College (U)
Shawnee Community College (U)
Snow College (U)
Southeast Arkansas College (U)
South Plains College (U)
State University of New York at New Paltz (U)
State University of New York at Oswego (U,G)
Syracuse University (G)
Tacoma Community College (U)
Texas Tech University (U)
Triton College (U)
Tunxis Community College (U)
The University of Akron (U)
University of Alaska Fairbanks (U)
University of California, Berkeley (U)
University of Colorado at Denver and Health Sciences Center—Downtown Denver Campus (U)
University of Florida (U)
University of Hawaii–West Oahu (U)
University of Houston–Victoria (U,G)
University of Illinois at Springfield (U)
University of La Verne (U)
University of Maine (G)
The University of Maine at Augusta (U)
University of Maine at Fort Kent (U)
University of Maryland University College (U)
University of Massachusetts Amherst (U)
University of Massachusetts Boston (U)
University of Missouri–Columbia (U)
University of Missouri–St. Louis (U)
The University of Montana (U)
University of Nevada, Reno (U)
University of New Orleans (U,G)
The University of North Carolina at Chapel Hill (U)
The University of North Carolina at Greensboro (U)
University of North Dakota (U)
University of North Texas (U,G)
University of Oklahoma (U)
University of Saskatchewan (U)
University of Southern Mississippi (U)
University of South Florida (U)
The University of Tennessee (U)
The University of Texas at Tyler (U)
University of Utah (U)
University of Washington (U)
University of Waterloo (U)
University of West Florida (U)
University of Wisconsin Colleges (U)
University of Wisconsin–Whitewater (U)
Utah State University (U)
Utah Valley State College (U)
Weber State University (U)
Westchester Community College (U)
Western Michigan University (U)
Western Washington University (U)
Western Wyoming Community College (U)
Whatcom Community College (U)
Wichita State University (U)
Wilfrid Laurier University (U)
Yuba College (U)

APPAREL AND TEXTILES

Academy of Art University (U,G)
Blackhawk Technical College (N)
Immaculata University (U)
Kansas State University (G)
Missouri State University (U)
Nassau Community College (U)

The New School (U)
North Carolina State University (U)
Orange Coast College (U)
Philadelphia University (G)
University of Arkansas at Pine Bluff (U)
University of North Texas (U,G)
Virginia Polytechnic Institute and State University (U)
Western Michigan University (U)

APPLIED HORTICULTURE/ HORTICULTURAL BUSINESS SERVICES

Cincinnati State Technical and Community College (U)
Clark State Community College (U)
County College of Morris (U)
Haywood Community College (U)
Kansas State University (U)
Minot State University–Bottineau Campus (U)
New Mexico State University–Carlsbad (N)
Oklahoma State University (U)
Texas Tech University (U)
University of California, Riverside (N)
University of Florida (U)
University of Minnesota, Twin Cities Campus (U)
University of Saskatchewan (N)
Virginia Polytechnic Institute and State University (N,U,G)

APPLIED MATHEMATICS

Alvin Community College (U)
Anne Arundel Community College (U)
Asheville-Buncombe Technical Community College (U)
Bainbridge College (U)
Bethany University (U)
Bowling Green State University (U)
Butler Community College (U)
Butler County Community College (U)
California State University, San Marcos (U)
California University of Pennsylvania (U)
Central Texas College (U)
Central Virginia Community College (U)
Chadron State College (U)
Clinton Community College (U)
College of Staten Island of the City University of New York (N)
Columbia University (N,G)
The Community College of Baltimore County (U)
Corning Community College (U)
County College of Morris (U)
Darton College (U)
Des Moines Area Community College (U)
Eastern Michigan University (U)
Embry-Riddle Aeronautical University, Extended Campus (U)
Eugene Bible College (U)
Everett Community College (U)
Heart of Georgia Technical College (U)
Hillsborough Community College (U)
Illinois Institute of Technology (U)
Iowa Western Community College (U)
Itawamba Community College (U)
Jacksonville State University (U)
James Madison University (N)
Linn-Benton Community College (U)
Lock Haven University of Pennsylvania (U)
Midstate College (U)
Myers University (U)
New Mexico State University–Alamogordo (U)
North Dakota State College of Science (U)
North Dakota State University (U)
North Idaho College (N)
Oxnard College (U)
Raritan Valley Community College (U)
Rasmussen College Eden Prarie (U)
Red Rocks Community College (U)
The Richard Stockton College of New Jersey (U)
Seminole Community College (U)
Snow College (U)
Southeast Arkansas College (U)
South Plains College (U)
Southwest Georgia Technical College (U)
Southwest Wisconsin Technical College (U)
Spartanburg Technical College (U)
Stanly Community College (U)
Tacoma Community College (U)
Taft College (U)
Taylor University (N)
The University of Akron (G)
University of Alaska Fairbanks (U)
University of Florida (U)
The University of Maine at Augusta (U)
University of New Orleans (U,G)
The University of Tennessee (U)
University of Washington (U)
University of Waterloo (U)
Utah State University (U)
Vincennes University (U)
Western Wyoming Community College (U)
West Los Angeles College (U)
Wisconsin Indianhead Technical College (N,U)
York County Community College (U)
Yuba College (U)

ARCHEOLOGY

Bellevue Community College (U)
Bethany University (U)
Everett Community College (U)
Golden West College (U)
James Madison University (N)
Northwestern College (U)
Rio Hondo College (U)
St. Petersburg College (U)
State University of New York at Oswego (U)
The University of Akron (U)
University of California, Los Angeles (G)
University of Massachusetts Boston (U)
University of Saskatchewan (U)
University of South Florida (U)
The University of Texas at Tyler (U)
University of Washington (U)
University of West Florida (U)

ARCHITECTURAL ENGINEERING

Boston Architectural College (N,U,G)
Georgia Institute of Technology (G)
Sinclair Community College (U)
Southern Methodist University (G)
University of Arkansas at Pine Bluff (U)
University of New Orleans (U,G)

ARCHITECTURAL ENGINEERING TECHNOLOGY

Boston Architectural College (N,U,G)
Honolulu Community College (U)
University of New Orleans (U,G)

ARCHITECTURAL TECHNOLOGY

Boston Architectural College (N,U,G)
Central Piedmont Community College (U)
Dakota County Technical College (U)

ARCHITECTURE

Boston Architectural College (N,U,G)
Dakota County Technical College (U)
James Madison University (N)
Lansing Community College (U)
Louisiana Tech University (U)
Orange Coast College (U)
Pennsylvania College of Technology (U)
Texas Tech University (G)
Triton College (U)
University of Colorado at Denver and Health Sciences Center—Downtown Denver Campus (G)
The University of North Carolina at Charlotte (N)
Virginia Polytechnic Institute and State University (N)

ARCHITECTURE RELATED

Boston Architectural College (N,U,G)
Central Michigan University (U)
Georgia Institute of Technology (G)

AREA STUDIES

American Military University (U)
California Institute of Integral Studies (N,G)
Connecticut State University System (U,G)
De Anza College (U)
Naropa University (N)
Oxnard College (U)
Rasmussen College Eden Prarie (U)
St. Petersburg College (U)
South Plains College (U)
Southwestern Community College (U)
Taylor University (U)
Triton College (U)
The University of British Columbia (U)
The University of Iowa (U)
University of Maine (U)
University of Maryland University College (U)
University of Nebraska–Lincoln (U)
University of Nevada, Reno (U)
University of North Alabama (U,G)
The University of North Carolina at Chapel Hill (U)
University of Northern Iowa (U)
University of South Florida (U)
University of Waterloo (U)
Western Washington University (U)

AREA, ETHNIC, CULTURAL, AND GENDER STUDIES RELATED

Berkeley College (U)
Berkeley College-New York City Campus (U)
Berkeley College-Westchester Campus (U)
Bethany University (U)
Bismarck State College (U)
California State University, Chico (U)
California State University, San Bernardino (U)

Central Texas College (U)
Central Wyoming College (U)
Cleveland State University (U,G)
Columbia College (U)
Dakota County Technical College (U)
DeVry University Online (U)
Edgecombe Community College (N)
Elizabethtown College (U)
Frostburg State University (U)
Kansas State University (U)
Louisiana State University and Agricultural and Mechanical College (U)
Mercy College (U)
Middlesex Community College (U)
Middle Tennessee State University (N,U)
Naropa University (N,U,G)
North Idaho College (U)
Oregon State University (U)
Oxnard College (U)
Ozarks Technical Community College (U)
Palomar College (U)
Park University (U)
Prescott College (G)
Providence College and Theological Seminary (N,G)
Raritan Valley Community College (U)
Rasmussen College Eden Prarie (U)
Seminole Community College (U)
Shoreline Community College (U)
South Plains College (U)
State University of New York at Plattsburgh (U)
Strayer University (U)
Taylor University (U)
Tunxis Community College (U)
The University of Akron (N)
University of Bridgeport (U)
University of Colorado at Colorado Springs (U)
University of Connecticut (U)
University of Missouri–Columbia (U)
University of Nevada, Reno (U)
University of New Orleans (U,G)
The University of North Carolina at Chapel Hill (N)
University of South Florida (U)
The University of Toledo (U)
University of Utah (U)
University of Waterloo (U)
University of Wisconsin–Whitewater (U,G)
West Los Angeles College (U)

ARMY J.R.O.T.C/R.O.T.C

Eastern Michigan University (U)
Southern Illinois University Carbondale (U)

ASTRONOMY AND ASTROPHYSICS

Athabasca University (N,U)
Austin Peay State University (U)
Bellevue Community College (U)
Brenau University (U)
Brigham Young University (U)
Broome Community College (U)
Butler Community College (U)
California State University, San Bernardino (U)
Casper College (U)
Cecil Community College (U)
Central Virginia Community College (U)
Clackamas Community College (U)
Clemson University (U)
College of San Mateo (U)
College of Southern Maryland (U)
Colorado Mountain College District System (U)
Columbia College (U)
The Community College of Baltimore County (U)
Community College of Denver (U)
Community College of Southern Nevada (U)
Cowley County Community College and Area Vocational–Technical School (U)
Crafton Hills College (U)
Culver-Stockton College (U)
Dallas County Community College District (U)
Evergreen Valley College (U)
Hillsborough Community College (U)
Honolulu Community College (U)
Houston Community College System (U)
Illinois Eastern Community Colleges, Lincoln Trail College (U)
Independence Community College (U)
Iowa Western Community College (U)
James Madison University (N)
Judson College (U)
Lake Superior College (U)
Lamar State College–Port Arthur (U)
Lansing Community College (U)
Lehigh Carbon Community College (U)
Lewis and Clark Community College (U)
Limestone College (U)
Mesalands Community College (U)
Middle Tennessee State University (U)
Missouri State University (U)
Montana State University (G)
Mountain Empire Community College (U)
Nassau Community College (U)
Northeast State Technical Community College (U)
North Seattle Community College (U)
Northwestern College (U)
Oxnard College (U)
Palm Beach Community College (U)
Parkland College (U)
Peninsula College (U)
Pueblo Community College (U)
Raritan Valley Community College (U)
Rend Lake College (U)
St. Clair County Community College (U)
St. Cloud State University (U)
St. Petersburg College (U)
San Bernardino Valley College (U)
San Joaquin Delta College (U)
Schenectady County Community College (U)
Schoolcraft College (U)
Seattle Pacific University (G)
Seminole Community College (U)
Stephen F. Austin State University (U)
Triton College (U)
Tyler Junior College (U)
The University of Akron (U)
The University of Alabama (U)
University of Florida (U)
University of Maine at Fort Kent (U)
University of Missouri–Columbia (U)
University of Nebraska at Omaha (U)
The University of North Carolina at Chapel Hill (U)
University of Oklahoma (U)
University of Oregon (U)
University of Pittsburgh (U)
The University of Tennessee (U)
University of Washington (U)
University of Waterloo (U)
University of Wisconsin–River Falls (U)
University of Wyoming (U)
Upper Iowa University (U)
Utah Valley State College (U)
Whatcom Community College (U)
Wichita State University (U)
Wilfrid Laurier University (U)
William Rainey Harper College (U)
Yuba College (U)

ATMOSPHERIC SCIENCES AND METEOROLOGY

Bellevue Community College (U)
Clarion University of Pennsylvania (U)
Community College of Southern Nevada (U)
Dallas Baptist University (U)
Iowa State University of Science and Technology (U,G)
Iowa Western Community College (U)
Jacksonville State University (U)
Miami Dade College (U)
Millersville University of Pennsylvania (U)
Mountain Empire Community College (U)
Nassau Community College (U)
Oregon State University (U)
Seminole Community College (U)
University of California, Riverside (N)
University of Michigan (N)
University of Missouri–Columbia (U)
University of Washington (U)
Utah Valley State College (U)

AUDIOVISUAL COMMUNICATIONS TECHNOLOGIES

The University of Akron (U)
University of Florida (G)
University of Southern Indiana (N)

BEHAVIORAL SCIENCES

Anne Arundel Community College (U)
Boise State University (U)
Butler Community College (U)
California State University, Chico (U)
Central Michigan University (U,G)
Chattanooga State Technical Community College (U)
Chesapeake College (U)
Clark College (U)
Clark State Community College (U)
Columbia Basin College (U)
Columbia College (U)
Community College of Beaver County (U)
Community College of Southern Nevada (U)
Contra Costa College (U)
Cowley County Community College and Area Vocational–Technical School (U)
Danville Community College (U)
Des Moines Area Community College (U)
Drury University (U)
East Tennessee State University (N)
Fort Valley State University (U)
Galveston College (U)
Granite State College (U)
Housatonic Community College (U)
Jacksonville State University (U)
Judson College (U)
Kansas State University (U)
Mount Saint Vincent University (U)
North Idaho College (N)

Ouachita Technical College (U)
Ozarks Technical Community College (U)
Palomar College (U)
Purdue University Calumet (U)
Rasmussen College Eden Prarie (U)
St. Cloud State University (G)
Seminole Community College (U)
Sinclair Community College (U)
Snow College (U)
South Piedmont Community College (U)
South Plains College (U)
State University of New York College at Potsdam (U)
Taylor University (U)
Texas State University-San Marcos (U)
The University of Akron (U)
University of California, Berkeley (U,G)
University of Connecticut (U)
The University of Iowa (U)
University of Maine at Fort Kent (U)
University of Massachusetts Lowell (G)
University of Missouri–Columbia (U)
University of New Orleans (U,G)
University of North Texas (N,U,G)
Utah Valley State College (U)
Westchester Community College (U)
West Los Angeles College (U)
Wharton County Junior College (U)
Yuba College (U)

BIBLICAL AND OTHER THEOLOGICAL LANGUAGES AND LITERATURES

Assemblies of God Theological Seminary (G)
Bethany University (U)
Black Hills State University (U)
Briercrest Distance Learning (G)
College of Emmanuel and St. Chad (G)
Colorado Christian University (U)
Columbia International University (G)
Denver Seminary (G)
Des Moines Area Community College (U)
Earlham School of Religion (G)
Eugene Bible College (U)
God's Bible School and College (U)
Gordon-Conwell Theological Seminary (N,G)
Hebrew College (N,U,G)
Immaculata University (U)
Indiana Business College (N)
Indiana Wesleyan University (U)
Lamar State College–Port Arthur (U)
Life Pacific College (N)
Lutheran Theological Seminary at Gettysburg (G)
Master's College and Seminary (U)
Moody Bible Institute (U)
New Mexico Junior College (U)
Ozark Christian College (U)
Peninsula College (U)
Providence College and Theological Seminary (N,U,G)
San Joaquin Delta College (U)
Southwestern Baptist Theological Seminary (G)
Taylor University (N,U)
Tennessee Temple University (U)
Trinity Episcopal School for Ministry (G)
University of Missouri–Columbia (U)
University of Waterloo (U)
Western Seminary (N,G)
Western Washington University (U)

BIBLICAL STUDIES

Abilene Christian University (U,G)
Arlington Baptist College (N,U)
Assemblies of God Theological Seminary (G)
Atlantic School of Theology (N,G)
Atlantic University (N,G)
Bakke Graduate University of Ministry (G)
Baptist Bible College of Pennsylvania (G)
The Baptist College of Florida (U)
Barclay College (U)
Bethany University (U)
Briercrest Distance Learning (N,U,G)
Campbell University (U)
Central Carolina Community College (U)
Central Texas College (U)
Chattanooga State Technical Community College (U)
Clear Creek Baptist Bible College (U)
Clovis Community College (U)
College of Emmanuel and St. Chad (G)
Columbia International University (N,U,G)
Concordia College (U)
Corban College (U)
Covenant Theological Seminary (N,G)
Crown College (G)
Dallas Baptist University (U)
Davis College (U)
Defiance College (U)
Denver Seminary (G)
Earlham School of Religion (G)
East Central Community College (U)
Eastern Mennonite University (G)
Eastern New Mexico University (U)
Eugene Bible College (U)
God's Bible School and College (U)
Gordon-Conwell Theological Seminary (N,G)
Hebrew College (N,U,G)
Hope International University (N,U,G)
Indiana Business College (N)
Indiana Wesleyan University (U)
John A. Logan College (U)
Johnson Bible College (U,G)
Judson College (U)
LeTourneau University (U)
Liberty University (U,G)
Life Pacific College (N,U)
Limestone College (U)
Lipscomb University (U,G)
Lutheran Theological Seminary at Gettysburg (G)
Malone College (U,G)
Maranatha Baptist Bible College (U,G)
Master's College and Seminary (U)
McMurry University (U)
Miami Dade College (U)
Montgomery Community College (N)
Moody Bible Institute (N,U,G)
Northwest Christian College (U)
Northwestern College (U)
Oral Roberts University (N,U)
Ozark Christian College (U)
Park University (U)
Patrick Henry College (U)
Providence College and Theological Seminary (N,U,G)
Regent University (G)
Saint Joseph's College of Maine (N,U)
St. Petersburg College (U)
Shasta Bible College (N)
Southwestern Assemblies of God University (U,G)
Southwestern Baptist Theological Seminary (U,G)
Taylor University (N,U)
Temple Baptist Seminary (N,G)
Tennessee Temple University (U)
Trinity Episcopal School for Ministry (N,G)
The University of Findlay (U)
University of Florida (U)
University of Southern Mississippi (U)
University of Waterloo (U)
Viterbo University (U)
Western Seminary (N,G)
Williamson Christian College (U)

BILINGUAL, MULTILINGUAL, AND MULTICULTURAL EDUCATION

Bethany University (U)
California State University, San Bernardino (U)
Dakota County Technical College (U)
East Carolina University (U)
Golden West College (U)
Hamline University (G)
Indiana State University (G)
Middle Tennessee State University (N)
Murray State University (G)
New Mexico State University–Carlsbad (N)
Northwestern Oklahoma State University (G)
Oxnard College (U)
Pace University (G)
Palomar College (U)
Prescott College (U)
Seattle Pacific University (G)
Texas A&M University–Kingsville (U,G)
Texas Woman's University (G)
The University of Akron (U,G)
University of Alaska Fairbanks (U)
University of Arkansas at Pine Bluff (N,U)

BIOCHEMISTRY, BIOPHYSICS AND MOLECULAR BIOLOGY

Drake University (U)
Florida Atlantic University (U)
Illinois Institute of Technology (U,G)
Iowa State University of Science and Technology (U,G)
Kansas State University (U)
Ozarks Technical Community College (U)
Peninsula College (U)
State University of New York at Plattsburgh (U)
The University of Akron (U)
University of Bridgeport (G)
University of California, Berkeley (U,G)
University of Colorado at Denver and Health Sciences Center—Downtown Denver Campus (U)
University of Florida (U)
University of Minnesota, Twin Cities Campus (U)
University of Southern Mississippi (G)
University of Waterloo (U)

BIOETHICS/MEDICAL ETHICS

Clark College (U)
Cleveland State University (U,G)
Judson College (U)
Lock Haven University of Pennsylvania (U)
Sullivan University (G)
University of New Orleans (U)

BIOLOGICAL AND BIOMEDICAL SCIENCES RELATED

Athabasca University (U)
Bethany University (U)
Brigham Young University (U)
Caldwell Community College and Technical Institute (U)
Casper College (U)
Clark State Community College (U)
Cleveland State University (U)
Columbia College (U)
Columbus State Community College (U)
County College of Morris (U)
Dakota County Technical College (U)
Danville Community College (U)
Darton College (U)
DeVry University Online (U)
D'Youville College (G)
Feather River College (U)
George Mason University (G)
Glenville State College (U)
Humboldt State University (U)
Illinois Institute of Technology (G)
Immaculata University (U)
Iowa Western Community College (U)
Jacksonville State University (U)
James Madison University (N)
Lewis and Clark Community College (U)
Louisiana Tech University (U)
Miami Dade College (U)
Middlesex Community College (U)
Minot State University–Bottineau Campus (U)
Oxnard College (U)
Pennsylvania College of Technology (U)
Reading Area Community College (U)
Saint Leo University (U)
Schoolcraft College (U)
Seminole Community College (U)
Shoreline Community College (U)
Southeast Community College, Beatrice Campus (U)
Southeast Community College, Lincoln Campus (U)
Southeast Community College, Milford Campus (U)
Southern Illinois University Carbondale (U)
Stanly Community College (U)
State University of New York, Fredonia (U)
University of Colorado at Colorado Springs (U)
University of Florida (G)
University of New Orleans (U,G)
University of Waterloo (U)
University of West Florida (U)
University of Wisconsin–River Falls (G)
University of Wyoming (U)
Wright State University (U)

BIOLOGICAL AND PHYSICAL SCIENCES

Anne Arundel Community College (U)
Arkansas State University–Beebe (U)
Athabasca University (U)
Bellevue University (U)
Bethany University (U)
Big Sandy Community and Technical College (U)
Boise State University (U)
Caldwell Community College and Technical Institute (U)
Carl Albert State College (U)
Casper College (U)
Cayuga County Community College (U)
Central Carolina Community College (U)
Central Oregon Community College (U)
Chadron State College (U)
Chesapeake College (U)
Citrus College (U)
Clark State Community College (U)
Cleveland State Community College (U)
Clinton Community College (U)
Coffeyville Community College (U)
Cowley County Community College and Area Vocational–Technical School (U)
Dakota County Technical College (U)
Dallas Baptist University (U)
Davis College (U)
Des Moines Area Community College (U)
D'Youville College (U,G)
East Central Community College (U)
Eastern Michigan University (U)
Eugene Bible College (U)
Fontbonne University (U)
Fort Hays State University (U)
Gogebic Community College (U)
Golden West College (U)
Greenfield Community College (U)
Gulf Coast Community College (U)
Illinois Institute of Technology (U,G)
Immaculata University (U)
Independence Community College (U)
Indiana State University (U)
Jacksonville State University (U)
James Madison University (N)
The Johns Hopkins University (U)
Judson College (U)
Kansas State University (U)
Kentucky State University (U,G)
Lake Superior College (U)
Lehigh University (G)
Louisiana State University and Agricultural and Mechanical College (U)
Massasoit Community College (U)
Miami Dade College (U)
Mid Michigan Community College (U)
Mississippi State University (U)
Montana State University (G)
Myers University (U)
National University (U)
North Arkansas College (U)
North Carolina State University (U,G)
Northeast State Technical Community College (U)
North Seattle Community College (U)
Northwestern Connecticut Community College (U)
Northwestern State University of Louisiana (U)
Ouachita Technical College (U)
Ozarks Technical Community College (U)
Palm Beach Community College (U)
Patrick Henry Community College (U)
Peninsula College (U)
The Pennsylvania State University University Park Campus (U)
Pueblo Community College (U)
Quinebaug Valley Community College (U)
Sacred Heart University (U)
St. Louis Community College System (U)
St. Petersburg College (U)
Schoolcraft College (U)
Seminole Community College (U)
Solano Community College (U)
Southern Arkansas University Tech (U)
Southern Illinois University Carbondale (U)
Syracuse University (U)
Taft College (U)
Taylor University (U)
Texas State University-San Marcos (U)
The University of Akron (U)
The University of Alabama (U)
University of Arkansas at Pine Bluff (U)
University of California, Berkeley (U)
University of Great Falls (U)
University of Houston–Downtown (U)
University of La Verne (N)
University of Massachusetts Boston (G)
University of New Orleans (U,G)
University of Waterloo (U)
University of Wisconsin Colleges (U)
University of Wisconsin–River Falls (G)
Upper Iowa University (N)
Utah Valley State College (U)
Westchester Community College (U)
Western Wyoming Community College (U)
West Virginia University at Parkersburg (U)
York Technical College (U)

BIOLOGY

Acadia University (U)
Adams State College (G)
Alvin Community College (U)
Arkansas State University–Beebe (U)
Arkansas State University–Mountain Home (U)
Arkansas Tech University (U)
Asheville-Buncombe Technical Community College (U)
Athabasca University (N,U)
Bellevue Community College (U)
Bethany University (U)
Bismarck State College (U)
Blinn College (U)
Brigham Young University (U)
Burlington County College (U)
Butler County Community College (U)
Caldwell College (U)
Caldwell Community College and Technical Institute (U)
Casper College (U)
Cayuga County Community College (U)
Cedarville University (U)
Central Lakes College (U)
Central New Mexico Community College (U)
Central Piedmont Community College (U)
Central Virginia Community College (U)
Central Wyoming College (U)
Chattanooga State Technical Community College (U)
Clackamas Community College (U)
Clarion University of Pennsylvania (U)
Clark State Community College (U)
Cleveland Community College (U)
Cleveland State University (U)
Clovis Community College (U)
College of DuPage (U)
The College of St. Scholastica (U,G)
College of Southern Maryland (U)
College of The Albemarle (U)
College of the Humanities and Sciences, Harrison Middleton University (U)
College of the Southwest (U)
Colorado Mountain College District System (U)
Colorado State University (U)
Colorado State University-Pueblo (U)

The Community College of Baltimore County (U)
Community College of Denver (U)
Community College of Southern Nevada (U)
Copiah-Lincoln Community College (U)
County College of Morris (U)
Cowley County Community College and Area Vocational–Technical School (U)
Crafton Hills College (U)
Culver-Stockton College (U)
Dakota County Technical College (U)
Dallas Baptist University (U)
Dallas County Community College District (U)
Danville Community College (U)
Dawson Community College (U)
De Anza College (U)
Delta College (U)
Des Moines Area Community College (U)
Dodge City Community College (U)
Drury University (U)
East Carolina University (U)
Eastern Michigan University (U)
Eastern Oregon University (U)
Eastern Wyoming College (U)
Edison State Community College (U)
Erie Community College (U)
Eugene Bible College (U)
Finger Lakes Community College (U)
Fort Valley State University (U)
Gadsden State Community College (U)
Galveston College (U)
Golden West College (U)
Harvard University (N,U,G)
Housatonic Community College (U)
Houston Community College System (U)
Illinois Institute of Technology (U)
Immaculata University (U)
Indiana State University (U)
Indiana University–Purdue University Fort Wayne (U)
Iowa State University of Science and Technology (U)
Iowa Western Community College (U)
Ivy Tech Community College–North Central (U)
Ivy Tech Community College–Wabash Valley (U)
Jacksonville State University (U,G)
Jefferson Davis Community College (U)
John A. Logan College (U)
The Johns Hopkins University (U)
Johnson County Community College (U)
John Tyler Community College (U)
J. Sargeant Reynolds Community College (U)
Kean University (U)
Lansing Community College (U)
Lehigh Carbon Community College (U)
Lenoir Community College (U)
LeTourneau University (U)
Lewis and Clark Community College (U)
Liberty University (U)
Limestone College (U)
Louisiana State University and Agricultural and Mechanical College (N,U)
Malone College (U)
Mayville State University (U)
Memorial University of Newfoundland (U)
Mercy College (U)
Mesa State College (U)
Miami Dade College (U)
Middlesex Community College (U)
Mid Michigan Community College (U)
Minnesota School of Business–Richfield (U)
Mississippi State University (U)
Moberly Area Community College (U)
Monroe Community College (U)
Montana State University (G)
Montana State University–Billings (U)
Mountain Empire Community College (U)
Mt. San Antonio College (U)
Mount Wachusett Community College (U)
Nassau Community College (U)
New York Institute of Technology (U)
North Central Texas College (U)
North Dakota State College of Science (U)
Northern Virginia Community College (U)
North Idaho College (U)
North Lake College (U)
Northwestern Michigan College (U)
Odessa College (U)
Oral Roberts University (U)
Orange Coast College (U)
Ouachita Technical College (U)
Oxnard College (U)
Pace University (U)
Palomar College (U)
Parkland College (U)
Park University (U)
Pasco-Hernando Community College (U)
Patrick Henry College (U)
Pennsylvania College of Technology (U)
The Pennsylvania State University University Park Campus (U)
Piedmont Technical College (U)
Portland Community College (U)
Pueblo Community College (U)
Pulaski Technical College (U)
Queen's University at Kingston (U)
Rend Lake College (U)
Sacramento City College (U)
St. Cloud State University (U)
St. Petersburg College (U)
San Bernardino Valley College (U)
Schenectady County Community College (U)
Schoolcraft College (U)
Seminole Community College (U)
Shawnee Community College (U)
Southern Illinois University Carbondale (U)
Southern University at Shreveport (U)
South Piedmont Community College (U)
South Plains College (U)
Southwestern Assemblies of God University (U)
Southwestern Community College (U)
Stanly Community College (U)
State University of New York at Oswego (U)
State University of New York at Plattsburgh (U)
State University of New York College at Potsdam (U)
State University of New York Empire State College (U)
Tacoma Community College (U)
Taylor University (U)
Texas A&M University–Commerce (U)
Texas Christian University (U)
Texas State University-San Marcos (U)
Three Rivers Community College (U)
Treasure Valley Community College (U)
Triton College (U)
Tyler Junior College (U)
The University of Akron (U)
The University of Alabama (U)
University of Alaska Fairbanks (U)
University of Arkansas at Pine Bluff (U)
University of California, Berkeley (U,G)
University of Colorado at Denver and Health Sciences Center—Downtown Denver Campus (U)
University of Delaware (U)
University of Florida (U)
University of Houston–Victoria (U)
University of La Verne (U)
University of Maine (U)
University of Maryland University College (U)
University of Massachusetts Amherst (U,G)
University of Massachusetts Boston (U)
University of Minnesota, Crookston (U)
University of Minnesota, Twin Cities Campus (U)
University of Missouri–Columbia (U)
University of Missouri–St. Louis (U)
The University of Montana (U)
University of Nebraska–Lincoln (U)
University of New Brunswick Fredericton (U)
University of New Orleans (U,G)
The University of North Carolina at Chapel Hill (U)
University of Northern Colorado (U)
University of North Texas (U)
University of Pittsburgh at Bradford (U)
University of Southern Indiana (U)
University of Southern Mississippi (U,G)
University of South Florida (U)
The University of Texas at Arlington (U)
The University of Texas at Tyler (U)
The University of Texas System (U)
University of Utah (U)
University of Waterloo (U)
University of West Florida (U)
University of Wisconsin Colleges (U)
University of Wisconsin–Superior (U)
Upper Iowa University (N,U)
Utah State University (U)
Utah Valley State College (U)
Utica College (U)
Vance-Granville Community College (U)
Wake Technical Community College (U)
Washburn University (U)
Westchester Community College (U)
Western Nevada Community College (U)
West Shore Community College (U)
West Virginia Northern Community College (U)
West Virginia University at Parkersburg (U)
Wharton County Junior College (U)
Whatcom Community College (U)
Wilfrid Laurier University (U)
Wilkes Community College (U)
Wright State University (U)
Yuba College (U)

BIOLOGY/BIOTECHNOLOGY LABORATORY TECHNICIAN

Charter Oak State College (U)
Clark State Community College (U)
Cleveland Community College (U)
Delta College (U)
Immaculata University (U)
James Madison University (U)
Seminole Community College (U)
University of Florida (G)
University of Houston–Downtown (U)
University of Minnesota, Twin Cities Campus (U)

BIOMATHEMATICS AND BIOINFORMATICS

California State University, East Bay (G)
Eastern Michigan University (G)

BIOMEDICAL/MEDICAL ENGINEERING

California State University, East Bay (U)
Central Carolina Community College (U)
Columbia University (G)
Georgia Institute of Technology (G)
Illinois Institute of Technology (G)
Louisiana Tech University (G)
New Mexico State University–Alamogordo (U)
Stanford University (N)
University of Colorado at Boulder (N,G)
University of South Florida (G)

BIOPSYCHOLOGY

Golden West College (U)
State University of New York at Plattsburgh (U)
University of Minnesota, Twin Cities Campus (U)

BIOTECHNOLOGY

Central Carolina Community College (U)
Eastern Michigan University (U)
Humboldt State University (U)
Stanford University (N)

BOTANY/PLANT BIOLOGY

Arizona State University (U)
Bellevue Community College (U)
Brigham Young University (U)
Central Piedmont Community College (U)
Eastern Oregon University (U)
Indiana State University (U)
Oregon State University (U)
Oxnard College (U)
Palomar College (U)
St. Cloud State University (U)
South Plains College (U)
Tacoma Community College (U)
Texas A&M University–Commerce (U)
The University of Akron (U)
University of Bridgeport (G)
University of Florida (U)
University of Saskatchewan (N)
University of Wyoming (U)
West Shore Community College (U)

BUILDING/CONSTRUCTION FINISHING, MANAGEMENT, AND INSPECTION

Asheville-Buncombe Technical Community College (N)
Athabasca University (N)
Bowling Green State University (G)
Central Michigan University (U)
Central New Mexico Community College (U)
Chattanooga State Technical Community College (U)
Clackamas Community College (U)
Clemson University (N)
Cleveland Institute of Electronics (N)
East Carolina University (G)
Georgia Institute of Technology (G)
James Madison University (N)
National University (U)
Pennsylvania College of Technology (U)
Quinebaug Valley Community College (N)
Red Rocks Community College (U)
San Diego State University (U)
Southern Polytechnic State University (U)
University of Florida (G)
The University of North Carolina at Charlotte (N)
University of Washington (U,G)
Vance-Granville Community College (N)
Washtenaw Community College (U)
Weber State University (U)

BUSINESS ADMINISTRATION, MANAGEMENT AND OPERATIONS

Acadia University (U)
Adirondack Community College (U)
Alvin Community College (U)
Amberton University (U,G)
American Graduate University (G)
American Military University (U)
American Public University (U)
Andrew Jackson University (U,G)
Anne Arundel Community College (U)
Antioch University McGregor (U)
Arkansas State University–Beebe (U)
Arkansas Tech University (U)
Asheville-Buncombe Technical Community College (N,U)
Ashworth College (N)
Athabasca University (N,U,G)
Auburn University (G)
Auburn University Montgomery (N,U,G)
Bainbridge College (N)
Baker College of Flint (U)
Bellevue Community College (U)
Bellevue University (U,G)
Bellingham Technical College (U)
Bergen Community College (U)
Berkeley College (U)
Berkeley College-New York City Campus (U)
Berkeley College-Westchester Campus (U)
Blackhawk Technical College (U)
Black Hills State University (U)
Blinn College (U)
Bloomfield College (U)
Blue Ridge Community College (U)
Bramson ORT College (U)
Brenau University (U,G)
Bridgewater State College (N)
Briercrest Distance Learning (U)
Brigham Young University (U)
Broome Community College (N)
Bryant and Stratton Online (U)
Buena Vista University (U)
Butler County Community College (U)
Caldwell College (U)
Caldwell Community College and Technical Institute (N,U)
California College for Health Sciences (N)
California National University for Advanced Studies (U,G)
California State University, San Bernardino (U)
California State University, San Marcos (U)
California University of Pennsylvania (U)
Campbell University (U)
Cape Cod Community College (U)
Cape Fear Community College (U)
Capella University (U,G)
Cardinal Stritch University (N)
Carl Albert State College (U)
Casper College (U)
Cayuga County Community College (U)
Central Michigan University (U,G)
Central New Mexico Community College (U)
Central Oregon Community College (U)
Central Texas College (U)
Central Washington University (G)
Chadron State College (U,G)
Champlain College (U)
Chattanooga State Technical Community College (U)
Cincinnati State Technical and Community College (U)
Clackamas Community College (U)
Clarion University of Pennsylvania (G)
Clark College (U)
Clark State Community College (U)
Clatsop Community College (U)
Clemson University (G)
Cleveland Community College (U)
Cleveland Institute of Electronics (N)
Cleveland State University (N)
Clinton Community College (U)
Clovis Community College (U)
Coleman College (U,G)
College of DuPage (U)
College of The Albemarle (N,U)
College of the Southwest (U)
Colorado Christian University (G)
Colorado State University (G)
Colorado State University-Pueblo (N)
Colorado Technical University (U,G)
Columbia Basin College (U)
Columbia College (U,G)
Columbia-Greene Community College (U)
Columbus State Community College (U)
The Community College of Baltimore County (U)
Community College of Beaver County (N,U)
Community College of Denver (U)
Concordia University Wisconsin (G)
Corban College (U)
Corning Community College (U)
Crafton Hills College (U)
Crown College (G)
Culver-Stockton College (U)
Cumberland County College (U)
Dakota County Technical College (N,U)
Dallas Baptist University (U,G)
Danville Community College (U)
Darton College (N,U)
Dawson Community College (U)
Daymar College (U)
De Anza College (U)
Des Moines Area Community College (U)
Drake University (U,G)
Drexel University (U,G)
Duquesne University (U,G)
D'Youville College (U)
East Carolina University (U,G)
East Central Community College (U)
Eastern Michigan University (U,G)
Eastern Oklahoma State College (U)
Eastern Wyoming College (U)
East Tennessee State University (N)
Edgecombe Community College (N,U)
Edison State Community College (N,U)
Edmonds Community College (U)
Elizabethtown College (U)

Embry-Riddle Aeronautical University (U,G)
Embry-Riddle Aeronautical University, Extended Campus (G)
Erie Community College (U)
Fayetteville State University (G)
Fisher College (N)
Florida Atlantic University (G)
Florida Institute of Technology (G)
Forrest Junior College (U)
Fort Hays State University (U)
Franklin Pierce College (U)
Franklin University (U,G)
Fresno City College (U)
Frostburg State University (G)
Fulton-Montgomery Community College (N)
Gadsden State Community College (U)
Galveston College (U)
Georgia Southern University (U)
Granite State College (U)
Grantham University (U)
Halifax Community College (N)
Haywood Community College (U)
Heart of Georgia Technical College (U)
Housatonic Community College (U)
Houston Community College System (U)
Immaculata University (U)
Indiana Business College (N,U)
Indiana State University (U)
Indiana Tech (U)
Indiana University–Purdue University Fort Wayne (G)
International Institute of the Americas (U)
Iona College (U,G)
Iowa Western Community College (U)
Ivy Tech Community College–Bloomington (U)
Ivy Tech Community College–Columbus (U)
Ivy Tech Community College–East Central (U)
Ivy Tech Community College–Northwest (U)
Ivy Tech Community College–Southeast (U)
Ivy Tech Community College–Southern Indiana (U)
Ivy Tech Community College–Southwest (U)
Ivy Tech Community College–Wabash Valley (U)
Ivy Tech Community College–Whitewater (U)
Jackson Community College (N)
Jacksonville State University (U,G)
James Sprunt Community College (U)
Jamestown Community College (N)
Jefferson College of Health Sciences (U)
Jefferson Community College (U)
John Tyler Community College (U)
Jones College (U)
J. Sargeant Reynolds Community College (U)
Judson College (U)
Kansas State University (U)
Kaplan University (N)
Kean University (N,U)
Keiser College (U)
Kentucky State University (U)
Kettering University (N)
Lackawanna College (U)
Lamar State College–Port Arthur (N,U)
Lawrence Technological University (U,G)
Lehigh Carbon Community College (U)
Lehigh University (N,G)
Lewis and Clark Community College (U)
Lewis-Clark State College (U)
Liberty University (G)
Limestone College (U)
Linn-Benton Community College (U)
Lipscomb University (G)
Louisiana State University and Agricultural and Mechanical College (U)
Louisiana State University at Eunice (U)
Madison Area Technical College (U)
Madonna University (G)
Manhattanville College (U)
Mansfield University of Pennsylvania (U)
Marist College (G)
Marshall University (U)
Maryville University of Saint Louis (N)
Massasoit Community College (U)
Mayville State University (U)
McMurry University (U)
Memorial University of Newfoundland (U)
Mercy College (U,G)
Metropolitan State University (U,G)
Miami Dade College (U)
Middlesex Community College (U,N,U)
Middle Tennessee State University (N,U)
Mid-State Technical College (U)
Millersville University of Pennsylvania (U,G)
Milwaukee School of Engineering (G)
Minnesota School of Business–Richfield (U,G)
Mississippi State University (G)
Moberly Area Community College (U)
Mohawk Valley Community College (N)
Montana State University–Billings (U)
Montgomery Community College (N,U)
Mt. San Antonio College (U)
Mount Wachusett Community College (U)
Murray State University (U)
Myers University (U,G)
Nassau Community College (U)
National University (U,G)
Naugatuck Valley Community College (U)
New England College of Finance (N,U,G)
New Jersey City University (G)
New Jersey Institute of Technology (G)
New Mexico Junior College (U)
New Mexico State University (U)
New Mexico State University–Carlsbad (N,U)
The New School (U)
New York Institute of Technology (U,G)
Niagara University (N)
Nipissing University (U)
North Dakota State College of Science (U)
Northeast State Technical Community College (U)
North Idaho College (N)
Northwestern Michigan College (U)
Northwestern Oklahoma State University (U,G)
Northwestern State University of Louisiana (U)
Odessa College (N)
The Ohio State University (G)
Oklahoma State University (U)
Oregon Institute of Technology (U)
Ouachita Technical College (U)
Oxnard College (U)
Ozarka College (U)
Ozarks Technical Community College (U)
Pace University (U,G)
Palomar College (U)
Park University (U,G)
Pasco-Hernando Community College (U)
Patrick Henry Community College (U)
Peirce College (U)
Peninsula College (U)
The Pennsylvania State University University Park Campus (N,U,G)
Philadelphia University (U)
Piedmont Technical College (U)
Plymouth State University (U)
Portland Community College (U)
Prescott College (U)
Pueblo Community College (U)
Radford University (N,G)
Rappahannock Community College (U)
Raritan Valley Community College (U)
Rasmussen College Eden Prarie (U)
Reading Area Community College (U)
Regent University (N,U,G)
Rend Lake College (N)
The Richard Stockton College of New Jersey (U)
Rochester Institute of Technology (U)
Roosevelt University (U)
Ryerson University (U)
Sacred Heart University (U,G)
St. Clair County Community College (U)
St. Edward's University (N,U,G)
St. John's University (U)
Saint Joseph's College of Maine (U,G)
Saint Joseph's University (U)
Saint Leo University (U)
St. Louis Community College System (N)
Saint Mary-of-the-Woods College (U)
St. Petersburg College (U)
Salem Community College (U)
Salve Regina University (G)
San Bernardino Valley College (U)
Saybrook Graduate School and Research Center (N,G)
Schenectady County Community College (U)
Schiller International University (U,G)
Seminole Community College (U)
Shippensburg University of Pennsylvania (G)
Shoreline Community College (U)
Sinclair Community College (U)
Snow College (U)
Solano Community College (U)
Sonoma State University (N)
Southeast Arkansas College (U)
Southeast Community College, Beatrice Campus (U)
Southeast Community College, Lincoln Campus (U)
Southeast Community College, Milford Campus (U)
Southern Arkansas University Tech (U)
Southern Methodist University (G)
South Piedmont Community College (U)
South Plains College (U)
Southwestern Assemblies of God University (U)
Southwestern College (G)
Spartanburg Technical College (U)
Stanford University (N)
Stanly Community College (U)
State University of New York at Oswego (U,G)
State University of New York at Plattsburgh (U,G)
State University of New York College at Potsdam (N,U)
Stephen F. Austin State University (U)
Sullivan University (G)
Syracuse University (U,G)
Tacoma Community College (N)
Taft College (U)
Taylor University (N,U)
Texas A&M University–Commerce (U)
Texas A&M University–Kingsville (G)

Texas A&M University–Texarkana (U,G)
Texas Tech University (N,U)
Texas Woman's University (U,G)
Three Rivers Community College (U)
Thunderbird, The Garvin School of International Management (N,G)
Touro University International (U,G)
Tri-County Community College (N,U)
Tri-State University (U)
Tunxis Community College (U)
Tyler Junior College (N,U)
United States Sports Academy (G)
The University of Akron (U,G)
University of Alaska Fairbanks (U)
University of Arkansas at Pine Bluff (U)
University of California, Berkeley (U,G)
University of California, Los Angeles (G)
University of Central Arkansas (N)
University of Cincinnati Raymond Walters College (U)
University of Colorado at Denver and Health Sciences Center—Downtown Denver Campus (G)
University of Dallas (G)
University of Denver (G)
The University of Findlay (U,G)
University of Florida (U)
University of Hawaii–West Oahu (U)
University of Houston–Clear Lake (G)
University of Houston–Downtown (U)
University of Illinois at Chicago (G)
University of Illinois at Springfield (U)
University of La Verne (U,G)
The University of Maine at Augusta (U)
University of Maryland University College (U,G)
University of Massachusetts Amherst (U)
University of Massachusetts Boston (U)
University of Michigan–Flint (N,G)
University of Minnesota, Crookston (U)
University of Minnesota, Twin Cities Campus (U)
University of Missouri–Columbia (U)
The University of Montana (G)
University of New Brunswick Fredericton (U)
University of New Orleans (U,G)
University of North Alabama (G)
The University of North Carolina at Chapel Hill (U)
The University of North Carolina at Charlotte (N)
The University of North Carolina at Greensboro (N)
University of North Dakota (U,G)
University of North Texas (N,U,G)
University of Oklahoma (U)
University of St. Francis (U,G)
University of South Alabama (G)
University of South Carolina Sumter (G)
University of South Florida (G)
The University of Tennessee (U)
The University of Tennessee at Martin (N,U,G)
The University of Texas at Dallas (G)
The University of Texas at Tyler (G)
University of Toronto (N,U)
University of Tulsa (G)
University of Virginia (N)
The University of Virginia's College at Wise (U)
University of Washington (N)
University of Wisconsin–La Crosse (G)
University of Wisconsin–Parkside (G)
University of Wisconsin–Platteville (U,G)
University of Wisconsin–River Falls (U)
University of Wisconsin–Superior (U)
University of Wisconsin–Whitewater (U,G)
University of Wyoming (G)
Upper Iowa University (U)
Utah State University (U,G)
Utah Valley State College (U)
Vance-Granville Community College (U)
Viterbo University (G)
Wake Technical Community College (N)
Washtenaw Community College (U)
Wayland Baptist University (U,G)
Wayne State College (U,G)
Weber State University (U)
Western Piedmont Community College (U)
Western Wyoming Community College (U)
West Los Angeles College (U)
West Shore Community College (U)
West Virginia University at Parkersburg (U)
Westwood Online (U)
Wharton County Junior College (U)
Wilkes Community College (U)
Winston-Salem State University (U)
Wisconsin Indianhead Technical College (N,U)
Worcester Polytechnic Institute (G)
York County Community College (U)
York Technical College (U)
York University (N,U)

BUSINESS OPERATIONS SUPPORT AND ASSISTANT SERVICES

Alvin Community College (N,U)
Athabasca University (N)
Auburn University Montgomery (N)
Bainbridge College (U)
Bellevue Community College (U)
Big Sandy Community and Technical College (U)
Blackhawk Technical College (N,U)
Blue Ridge Community College (U)
Bridgewater State College (N)
Caldwell Community College and Technical Institute (N,U)
California State University, San Marcos (U)
Central Carolina Community College (U)
Central Lakes College (U)
Central Michigan University (U)
Central New Mexico Community College (U)
Central Texas College (U)
Central Virginia Community College (U)
Cincinnati State Technical and Community College (U)
Clemson University (N)
College of Staten Island of the City University of New York (N)
College of The Albemarle (N)
Colorado State University-Pueblo (N)
Columbia Basin College (U)
The Community College of Baltimore County (U)
Community College of Beaver County (N)
Corning Community College (U)
Crown College (G)
Dallas County Community College District (U)
Danville Community College (U)
Daymar College (U)
Des Moines Area Community College (U)
East Carolina University (U)
Eastern West Virginia Community and Technical College (U)
East Los Angeles College (U)
Edgecombe Community College (N)
Edison State Community College (N,U)
Erie Community College (U)
Feather River College (U)
Forrest Junior College (U)
Indiana Business College (N)
Indiana State University (U)
Indiana University–Purdue University Fort Wayne (N)
Iona College (U)
Ivy Tech Community College–Bloomington (U)
Ivy Tech Community College–Central Indiana (U)
Ivy Tech Community College–Columbus (U)
Ivy Tech Community College–East Central (U)
Ivy Tech Community College–Northwest (U)
Ivy Tech Community College–Southeast (U)
Ivy Tech Community College–Southern Indiana (U)
Ivy Tech Community College–Southwest (U)
Ivy Tech Community College–Wabash Valley (U)
Ivy Tech Community College–Whitewater (U)
James Sprunt Community College (U)
Jamestown Community College (N)
J. Sargeant Reynolds Community College (U)
Lake Superior College (U)
Lamar State College–Port Arthur (N)
Lehigh Carbon Community College (U)
Lewis and Clark Community College (U)
Lewis-Clark State College (U)
Louisiana State University at Eunice (U)
Madison Area Technical College (U)
Marion Technical College (U)
Midland College (U)
Mid Michigan Community College (U)
Minot State University–Bottineau Campus (U)
Mitchell Technical Institute (N)
Montgomery Community College (U)
Mount Wachusett Community College (N)
Naugatuck Valley Community College (U)
New England College of Finance (N,U)
New Mexico State University–Carlsbad (N)
North Central Texas College (U)
North Dakota State University (N)
Odessa College (U)
Orange Coast College (U)
Oxnard College (U)
Ozarka College (U)
Palomar College (U)
Penn Foster Career School (N)
Portland Community College (U)
Providence College and Theological Seminary (G)
Pulaski Technical College (U)
Randolph Community College (N)
Rasmussen College Eden Prarie (U)
Rend Lake College (N)
Schoolcraft College (U)
Seminole Community College (U)
Sinclair Community College (U)
Taylor University (N)
Tompkins Cortland Community College (N)
Tyler Junior College (U)
The University of Akron (U)
University of Arkansas at Pine Bluff (N)
University of Cincinnati (N)
University of Minnesota, Twin Cities Campus (U)

The University of North Carolina at Charlotte (N)
University of Phoenix Online Campus (U)
Utah State University (U)
Vance-Granville Community College (U)
Vincennes University (U)
Wake Technical Community College (U)
Washtenaw Community College (U)
Western Piedmont Community College (U)
Western Wyoming Community College (U)
West Virginia University at Parkersburg (N,U)
William Rainey Harper College (U)
Wisconsin Indianhead Technical College (N,U)
York County Community College (U)

BUSINESS, MANAGEMENT, AND MARKETING RELATED

Acadia University (U)
Adams State College (U)
Anne Arundel Community College (U)
Arkansas State University–Beebe (U)
Athabasca University (N,U,G)
Athens Technical College (N)
Bellevue Community College (U)
Bellevue University (U,G)
Berkeley College (U)
Berkeley College-New York City Campus (U)
Berkeley College-Westchester Campus (U)
Big Sandy Community and Technical College (U)
Blackhawk Technical College (U)
Black Hills State University (U)
Bloomsburg University of Pennsylvania (U,G)
Blue Ridge Community College (N,U)
Boise State University (U)
Bowling Green State University (U)
Bradley University (U)
Brenau University (U,G)
Bridgewater State College (N)
Brigham Young University (U)
Buena Vista University (U)
Butler Community College (U)
Butler County Community College (U)
California State University, Dominguez Hills (N)
California State University, San Bernardino (U)
Cape Breton University (N)
Capella University (U,G)
Carlow University (U,G)
Carroll College (U)
Casper College (U)
Central Michigan University (U,G)
Central New Mexico Community College (U)
Central Texas College (U)
Chadron State College (U,G)
Champlain College (G)
Charter Oak State College (U)
Chattanooga State Technical Community College (U)
Chesapeake College (U)
Clackamas Community College (U)
Clark College (U)
Clark State Community College (U)
Clemson University (N)
Coffeyville Community College (U)
College of The Albemarle (N)
Colorado State University (N)
Colorado Technical University (U,G)
Columbia College (U,G)
Community College of Beaver County (N,U)
Community College of Denver (U)
Community College of Southern Nevada (U)
Concordia University Wisconsin (U)
Contra Costa College (U)
Dakota County Technical College (U)
Danville Community College (U)
Darton College (N)
Davis College (U)
Des Moines Area Community College (U)
Drexel University (U,G)
Drury University (U)
Duquesne University (U)
D'Youville College (U)
East Carolina University (U,G)
Eastern Michigan University (U,G)
Eastern West Virginia Community and Technical College (U)
East Tennessee State University (N)
Edgecombe Community College (N,U)
Elgin Community College (U)
Erie Community College (U)
Forrest Junior College (U)
Fort Valley State University (U)
Fulton-Montgomery Community College (N)
Galveston College (N)
George Mason University (G)
Georgia Southern University (G)
Gogebic Community College (U)
Golden West College (U)
Grand View College (U)
Grantham University (U)
Hagerstown Community College (N)
Indiana Business College (N,U)
Indiana State University (U)
Indiana University of Pennsylvania (U)
Indiana University–Purdue University Fort Wayne (N)
Iona College (U,G)
Iowa Western Community College (U)
Jacksonville State University (U,G)
James Madison University (N)
Jamestown Community College (N)
Jefferson Community College (U)
Jefferson Davis Community College (U)
John A. Logan College (U)
J. Sargeant Reynolds Community College (U)
Kansas State University (U)
Kean University (N)
Kettering University (N)
Lamar State College–Port Arthur (N)
Lehigh Carbon Community College (U)
LeTourneau University (G)
Louisiana State University and Agricultural and Mechanical College (U)
Madonna University (U,G)
Marist College (U,G)
Mercy College (G)
Middle Tennessee State University (N)
Midstate College (U)
Milwaukee School of Engineering (U)
Minot State University–Bottineau Campus (U)
Mitchell Technical Institute (N,U)
Mohawk Valley Community College (N)
Mount Saint Vincent University (U)
Myers University (U)
New England College of Finance (N,U,G)
New Jersey Institute of Technology (G)
New Mexico State University–Carlsbad (U)
New York Institute of Technology (U)
Niagara University (G)
Nipissing University (U)
North Carolina State University (U)
North Central Texas College (U)
North Dakota State College of Science (U)
North Lake College (U)
Northwestern Michigan College (U)
Northwestern State University of Louisiana (U)
Northwood University (U)
Odessa College (N)
Orange Coast College (U)
Oregon State University (N)
Oxnard College (U)
Ozarks Technical Community College (U)
Palomar College (U)
Park University (U,G)
Peirce College (U)
Peninsula College (U)
Pine Technical College (U)
Portland Community College (U)
Pueblo Community College (U)
Quinebaug Valley Community College (U)
Radford University (N)
Raritan Valley Community College (U)
Rasmussen College Eden Prarie (U)
Regent University (N,U,G)
The Richard Stockton College of New Jersey (G)
Rio Hondo College (U)
Saddleback College (U)
St. Edward's University (U)
St. John's University (G)
Saint Joseph's College of Maine (G)
St. Louis Community College System (N)
Sam Houston State University (U)
Schoolcraft College (U)
Seminole Community College (U)
Sinclair Community College (U)
Sonoma State University (N)
South Central College (U)
Southeast Arkansas College (U)
Southern Illinois University Carbondale (U)
Southern Oregon University (U)
Southern University at Shreveport (U)
South Piedmont Community College (U)
Southwest Georgia Technical College (U)
State University of New York at Buffalo (N)
State University of New York College at Potsdam (U)
State University of New York, Fredonia (U)
Syracuse University (U)
Taylor University (N,U)
Texas A&M University–Commerce (U,G)
Thunderbird, The Garvin School of International Management (N,G)
Tompkins Cortland Community College (N)
Touro University International (U)
Tri-County Community College (U)
United States Sports Academy (N,U)
The University of Akron (U)
The University of Alabama (U)
University of Alaska Fairbanks (U)
University of Bridgeport (U)
University of California, Berkeley (U,G)
University of Central Arkansas (G)
University of Colorado at Denver and Health Sciences Center—Downtown Denver Campus (G)
University of Delaware (N)
The University of Findlay (N)
University of Florida (U,G)
University of Hawaii–West Oahu (U)
University of Illinois at Chicago (G)
The University of Maine at Augusta (U)
University of Maryland University College (G)

University of Massachusetts Amherst (N)
University of Michigan–Flint (N)
University of Minnesota, Twin Cities Campus (U)
University of Missouri–Columbia (N,U)
The University of Montana–Western (U)
University of New Brunswick Fredericton (G)
University of New Orleans (U,G)
University of North Alabama (U)
The University of North Carolina at Chapel Hill (N)
The University of North Carolina at Charlotte (N)
University of North Texas (U,G)
University of Pittsburgh at Bradford (U)
University of South Florida (G)
The University of Texas at Arlington (U)
University of Tulsa (G)
University of West Florida (N)
University of Wisconsin–Parkside (G)
University of Wisconsin–Platteville (U)
University of Wisconsin–River Falls (U)
University of Wisconsin–Stout (U)
University of Wisconsin–Whitewater (U,G)
Utah Valley State College (U)
Viterbo University (U)
Washburn University (U)
Waukesha County Technical College (U)
Webster University (G)
West Shore Community College (U)
West Virginia University at Parkersburg (U)
Wharton County Junior College (U)
Wilkes Community College (U)
William Rainey Harper College (U)
York County Community College (U)

BUSINESS/COMMERCE

Acadia University (U)
Adams State College (N,U)
Adirondack Community College (U)
Alvin Community College (U)
American Military University (G)
American Public University (G)
Arizona Western College (U)
Athabasca University (N,U)
Athens Technical College (U)
Bainbridge College (U)
Bellevue Community College (U)
Bellevue University (U,G)
Bellingham Technical College (U)
Berkeley College (U)
Berkeley College-New York City Campus (U)
Berkeley College-Westchester Campus (U)
Berklee College of Music (N,U)
Big Sandy Community and Technical College (U)
Bismarck State College (U)
Black Hills State University (U)
Blue Ridge Community College (N)
Bowling Green State University (N,U)
Brenau University (U,G)
Bridgewater State College (N)
Broome Community College (U)
Bryant and Stratton Online (U)
Buena Vista University (U)
Caldwell Community College and Technical Institute (U)
California State University, Dominguez Hills (G)
California State University, San Marcos (N)
Cape Fear Community College (N,U)
Capella University (U)
Casper College (U)
Cayuga County Community College (U)
Cecil Community College (U)
Central Carolina Community College (U)
Central Lakes College (U)
Central Michigan University (U,G)
Central New Mexico Community College (U)
Central Washington University (U)
Central Wyoming College (N)
Chadron State College (U,G)
Champlain College (U,G)
Chattanooga State Technical Community College (U)
Cincinnati State Technical and Community College (U)
Citrus College (U)
Clark State Community College (U)
Clatsop Community College (U)
Clemson University (N,U)
Cleveland Institute of Electronics (N)
Cleveland State Community College (U)
Cleveland State University (N)
Coconino Community College (U)
Coleman College (G)
College of San Mateo (U)
College of Southern Maryland (U)
College of Staten Island of the City University of New York (N)
College of The Albemarle (N,U)
College of the Siskiyous (U)
Colorado Mountain College District System (U)
Colorado State University (U)
Colorado State University-Pueblo (U)
Colorado Technical University (U,G)
Columbia Basin College (U)
Columbia College (U)
Columbia University (N)
The Community College of Baltimore County (U)
Community College of Beaver County (N)
Concordia University, St. Paul (N,U,G)
Copiah-Lincoln Community College (U)
Cosumnes River College (U)
County College of Morris (U)
Cowley County Community College and Area Vocational–Technical School (U)
Daemen College (U)
Dakota County Technical College (U)
Danville Community College (U)
Darton College (U)
Des Moines Area Community College (U)
DeVry University Online (U,G)
Drake University (U,G)
Drexel University (U,G)
D'Youville College (G)
East Carolina University (U,G)
Eastern Michigan University (U,G)
Eastern New Mexico University (U,G)
Eastern Oregon University (U)
Eastern Wyoming College (U)
Edgecombe Community College (N,U)
Edison State Community College (N,U)
Elizabethtown College (U)
Embry-Riddle Aeronautical University, Extended Campus (U,G)
Endicott College (N,U,G)
Everett Community College (U)
Evergreen Valley College (U)
Fayetteville State University (U)
Finger Lakes Community College (U)
Florida Atlantic University (U)
Florida Institute of Technology (G)
Forrest Junior College (U)
Franklin Pierce College (G)
Fulton-Montgomery Community College (N)
Gateway Community College (U)
Gogebic Community College (U)
Golden West College (U)
Grantham University (U)
Halifax Community College (U)
Haywood Community College (U)
Heartland Community College (U)
Hillsborough Community College (U)
Howard College (U)
Illinois Eastern Community Colleges, Frontier Community College (U)
Illinois Eastern Community Colleges, Lincoln Trail College (U)
Illinois Eastern Community Colleges, Olney Central College (U)
Illinois Eastern Community Colleges, Wabash Valley College (U)
Immaculata University (U)
Indiana Business College (N)
Indiana State University (U)
Indiana Tech (U)
Indiana University of Pennsylvania (U)
Indiana University–Purdue University Fort Wayne (U)
International Institute of the Americas (U)
Iona College (G)
Iowa Western Community College (U)
Jackson Community College (N,U)
Jacksonville State University (U,G)
James Madison University (N,U)
Jamestown Community College (N)
John A. Logan College (U)
Jones College (U)
Kansas State University (U)
Lake Superior College (U)
Lamar State College–Port Arthur (N)
Liberty University (U)
Limestone College (U)
Linn-Benton Community College (U)
Lock Haven University of Pennsylvania (N)
Los Angeles Harbor College (U)
Macon State College (U)
Madonna University (G)
Malone College (U)
Massasoit Community College (N,U)
Mercer County Community College (U)
Mercy College (U,G)
Mesalands Community College (U)
Middlesex Community College (N,U)
Middle Tennessee State University (N)
Midland College (U)
Mid Michigan Community College (U)
Mississippi State University (G)
Mohawk Valley Community College (N,U)
Monroe Community College (U)
Montana State University–Billings (U)
Montana Tech of The University of Montana (U)
Montgomery Community College (U)
Mountain Empire Community College (U)
Murray State University (U)
Myers University (U,G)
Nassau Community College (U)
National University (U,G)
New England College of Finance (N,G)
New Jersey City University (U)
New Mexico State University (U)
Nipissing University (U)
North Carolina State University (U)
North Dakota State University (N)

North Idaho College (N,U)
North Seattle Community College (U)
Northwestern Oklahoma State University (U)
Odessa College (U)
The Ohio State University (U)
Oregon Institute of Technology (U)
Oregon State University (U)
Oxnard College (U)
Ozarka College (N)
Ozarks Technical Community College (U)
Pace University (N,U,G)
Palm Beach Community College (U)
Palomar College (U)
Park University (U)
Pasco-Hernando Community College (U)
Passaic County Community College (U)
Peirce College (U)
Pennsylvania College of Technology (U)
The Pennsylvania State University University Park Campus (U)
Piedmont Technical College (U)
Pulaski Technical College (U)
Radford University (G)
Rasmussen College Eden Prarie (U)
Reading Area Community College (U)
Regent University (N,U,G)
Rend Lake College (U)
Roosevelt University (U)
Ryerson University (U)
St. Louis Community College System (N)
Saint Mary-of-the-Woods College (U)
St. Petersburg College (U)
Salve Regina University (N,G)
San Diego State University (N,U)
San Joaquin Delta College (U)
Schiller International University (U)
Schoolcraft College (U)
Seminole Community College (U)
Shoreline Community College (U)
Solano Community College (U)
Southeast Arkansas College (U)
Southeast Community College, Beatrice Campus (U)
Southeast Community College, Lincoln Campus (U)
Southeast Community College, Milford Campus (U)
Southern Illinois University Carbondale (U)
Southern Illinois University Edwardsville (G)
South Piedmont Community College (U)
Southwestern Assemblies of God University (U)
Southwestern College (U)
Southwestern Oregon Community College (U)
Southwest Georgia Technical College (U)
Spartanburg Technical College (U)
State University of New York College at Potsdam (N)
State University of New York College of Agriculture and Technology at Morrisville (U)
State University of New York Empire State College (G)
Stephens College (U)
Strayer University (U,G)
Syracuse University (G)
Tacoma Community College (U)
Taft College (U)
Taylor University (N,U)
Texas A&M University–Commerce (U)
Texas State University-San Marcos (U)
Texas Woman's University (G)
Thunderbird, The Garvin School of International Management (N)
Tompkins Cortland Community College (U)
Touro University International (G)
Treasure Valley Community College (U)
Tri-State University (U)
Tunxis Community College (N)
Tyler Junior College (N,U)
The University of Akron (U)
The University of Alabama (U)
University of Alaska Fairbanks (U)
University of Bridgeport (U)
University of California, Berkeley (U)
University of California, Los Angeles (G)
University of Cincinnati (N,U)
University of Cincinnati Raymond Walters College (U)
University of Colorado at Colorado Springs (G)
University of Colorado at Denver and Health Sciences Center—Downtown Denver Campus (G)
The University of Findlay (U)
University of Florida (U)
University of Illinois at Chicago (N,G)
University of La Verne (G)
University of Maine (G)
The University of Maine at Augusta (U)
University of Maine at Fort Kent (U)
University of Massachusetts Lowell (U)
University of Michigan–Flint (N,U)
University of Missouri–Columbia (U,G)
The University of Montana (U)
University of Nebraska–Lincoln (N)
University of Nevada, Reno (U)
University of New Brunswick Fredericton (U)
University of North Alabama (G)
The University of North Carolina at Charlotte (N)
University of North Texas (U)
The University of Tennessee at Martin (G)
The University of Texas at Dallas (G)
The University of Texas at Tyler (U)
University of Toronto (U)
University of Tulsa (G)
University of Wisconsin Colleges (U)
University of Wisconsin–Platteville (U,G)
University of Wisconsin–River Falls (U)
University of Wyoming (U)
Vance-Granville Community College (N)
Vincennes University (U)
Virginia Polytechnic Institute and State University (N)
Wake Technical Community College (U)
Westchester Community College (U)
Western Nevada Community College (U)
Western Piedmont Community College (U)
Western Wyoming Community College (U)
West Los Angeles College (U)
West Virginia University at Parkersburg (U)
Wharton County Junior College (U)
Whatcom Community College (U)
Wilfrid Laurier University (U)
Wilkes Community College (U)
William Rainey Harper College (U)
Winston-Salem State University (U)
Wisconsin Indianhead Technical College (N,U)
York County Community College (U)
York Technical College (U)

BUSINESS/CORPORATE COMMUNICATIONS

Abilene Christian University (U)
Acadia University (U)
Adams State College (U)
Adirondack Community College (U)
Alvin Community College (U)
American Graduate University (G)
Arkansas State University–Beebe (U)
Asheville-Buncombe Technical Community College (N)
Athabasca University (N,U,G)
Bellevue Community College (U)
Bellevue University (G)
Bellingham Technical College (U)
Brenau University (U,G)
Bridgewater State College (U)
Brigham Young University (U)
Bryant and Stratton Online (U)
Buena Vista University (U)
Caldwell Community College and Technical Institute (N,U)
California National University for Advanced Studies (U)
California State University, Dominguez Hills (N)
Campbell University (U)
Capella University (U,G)
Cedarville University (U)
Central Michigan University (U,G)
Central Texas College (U)
Chadron State College (U)
Champlain College (U)
Cleveland Institute of Electronics (N)
Cleveland State University (N)
Clinton Community College (U)
Coleman College (G)
College of San Mateo (U)
College of Southern Maryland (U)
College of The Albemarle (N,U)
College of the Siskiyous (U)
Colorado Mountain College District System (U)
Columbus State Community College (U)
The Community College of Baltimore County (U)
Community College of Beaver County (N)
Community College of Denver (U)
Copiah-Lincoln Community College (U)
Cowley County Community College and Area Vocational–Technical School (U)
Dakota County Technical College (U)
Darton College (N)
Delta College (U)
Des Moines Area Community College (U)
Drexel University (U,G)
East Carolina University (U)
Eastern Michigan University (U,G)
Edgecombe Community College (N,U)
Edison State Community College (U)
Elizabethtown College (U)
Erie Community College (U)
Finger Lakes Community College (U)
Forrest Junior College (U)
Immaculata University (U)
Indiana Business College (N)
Indiana University–Purdue University Fort Wayne (N)
International Institute of the Americas (U)
Iona College (U,G)
Iowa Western Community College (U)
Jacksonville State University (G)

James Madison University (N)
James Sprunt Community College (U)
Jamestown Community College (N)
Jones College (U)
Kaplan University (N)
Lake Superior College (U)
Lehigh University (N)
Limestone College (U)
Macon State College (N,U)
Massasoit Community College (U)
Mercy College (G)
Middlesex Community College (U)
Middle Tennessee State University (N,U)
Midland College (U)
Mohawk Valley Community College (N)
Montana State University–Billings (U)
Montgomery Community College (N)
Myers University (U)
North Arkansas College (U)
Northwestern Michigan College (U)
Northwestern Oklahoma State University (U)
Oklahoma State University (U)
Old Dominion University (U)
Oregon State University (U)
Oxnard College (U)
Ozarks Technical Community College (U)
Park University (U)
Pasco-Hernando Community College (N)
Pennsylvania College of Technology (U)
The Pennsylvania State University University Park Campus (N,U)
Radford University (G)
Rappahannock Community College (U)
Rend Lake College (U)
Roosevelt University (U,G)
Ryerson University (U)
St. Clair County Community College (U)
St. Edward's University (U,G)
Saint Joseph's College of Maine (G)
Saint Leo University (U)
St. Petersburg College (U)
Salem Community College (N)
San Joaquin Delta College (U)
Schiller International University (U,G)
Seminole Community College (U)
Shoreline Community College (U)
Sonoma State University (N)
South Central College (U)
Southeast Arkansas College (U)
Southeast Community College, Beatrice Campus (U)
Southeast Community College, Lincoln Campus (U)
Southeast Community College, Milford Campus (U)
South Plains College (U)
Southwest Wisconsin Technical College (U)
Stephen F. Austin State University (U)
Sullivan University (G)
Taylor University (N)
Texas A&M University–Kingsville (U)
Thunderbird, The Garvin School of International Management (N,G)
Tompkins Cortland Community College (U)
Touro University International (U)
Tyler Junior College (U)
The University of Akron (U)
University of Alberta (G)
University of Arkansas at Pine Bluff (U)
University of Colorado at Denver and Health Sciences Center—Downtown Denver Campus (G)
University of Denver (U)
The University of Findlay (G)
University of Houston–Downtown (U)
University of Illinois at Chicago (G)
The University of Maine at Augusta (U)
University of Massachusetts Lowell (U)
University of Michigan–Flint (N)
University of Minnesota, Twin Cities Campus (U)
University of New Orleans (U,G)
The University of North Carolina at Chapel Hill (N,U)
The University of North Carolina at Charlotte (N)
University of Oklahoma (U)
The University of Texas at Tyler (U)
University of Toronto (N,U)
University of Washington (U)
University of West Florida (U)
University of Wisconsin–Platteville (U,G)
Utah Valley State College (U)
Vance-Granville Community College (N)
West Virginia University at Parkersburg (N,U)
William Rainey Harper College (U)
York County Community College (U)
York University (U)

BUSINESS/MANAGERIAL ECONOMICS

Adams State College (U)
American Graduate University (G)
Anne Arundel Community College (U)
Athabasca University (N,U,G)
Bellevue University (U,G)
Berkeley College (U)
Berkeley College-New York City Campus (U)
Berkeley College-Westchester Campus (U)
Brenau University (U,G)
Bridgewater State College (N,U)
Buena Vista University (U)
Caldwell Community College and Technical Institute (N)
California National University for Advanced Studies (U)
Central Michigan University (U,G)
Central New Mexico Community College (U)
Chadron State College (U,G)
Champlain College (G)
Clark College (U)
Cleveland Community College (U)
Columbia College (G)
Community College of Beaver County (N,U)
Corning Community College (U)
Crown College (G)
Des Moines Area Community College (U)
Drake University (U)
Drexel University (U,G)
D'Youville College (G)
East Arkansas Community College (U)
Edgecombe Community College (N)
Embry-Riddle Aeronautical University (U)
Erie Community College (U)
Florida Atlantic University (G)
Florida Institute of Technology (G)
Forrest Junior College (U)
Fort Valley State University (U)
Franklin Pierce College (U)
Gadsden State Community College (U)
Grand View College (U)
Grantham University (U,G)
Housatonic Community College (U)
Immaculata University (U)
Indiana Business College (N)
International Institute of the Americas (U)
Jacksonville State University (U,G)
Jones College (U)
Kaplan University (N)
Lamar State College–Port Arthur (N)
Lewis and Clark Community College (U)
Linn-Benton Community College (U)
Marist College (G)
Marshall University (U)
Mercy College (G)
Middlesex Community College (U)
Middle Tennessee State University (N)
Midland College (U)
Mississippi State University (G)
Mohawk Valley Community College (N,U)
Myers University (U)
New England College of Finance (N,G)
Old Dominion University (U)
The Pennsylvania State University University Park Campus (G)
Radford University (G)
Rasmussen College Eden Prarie (U)
Ryerson University (U)
Saddleback College (U)
St. Edward's University (U,G)
Saint Joseph's College of Maine (G)
Schiller International University (U,G)
Schoolcraft College (U)
Solano Community College (U)
Southeast Arkansas College (U)
Stanford University (N)
State University of New York at Oswego (U)
State University of New York College at Potsdam (U)
Syracuse University (G)
Taylor University (U)
Texas A&M University–Commerce (U,G)
Thunderbird, The Garvin School of International Management (N)
The University of Akron (U)
University of California, Berkeley (U,G)
University of Colorado at Denver and Health Sciences Center—Downtown Denver Campus (G)
The University of Findlay (N,U,G)
University of Houston–Downtown (U)
University of Illinois at Chicago (G)
University of Minnesota, Twin Cities Campus (U)
University of Missouri–Columbia (U)
University of Nevada, Reno (U)
University of New Orleans (U,G)
University of South Florida (G)
The University of Texas at Dallas (G)
University of Toronto (N,U)
University of Tulsa (G)
University of Waterloo (U)
University of Wisconsin–Parkside (G)
Western Piedmont Community College (U)
West Virginia University at Parkersburg (U)
Wilkes Community College (U)
York University (U)

CARPENTRY

Ashworth College (N)
Central Piedmont Community College (U)
Cleveland Community College (U)
Cleveland Institute of Electronics (N)
Penn Foster Career School (N)
University of Arkansas at Pine Bluff (N)
Western Nevada Community College (U)

CELL BIOLOGY AND ANATOMICAL SCIENCES

Carl Sandburg College (U)
Clark State Community College (U)
The Community College of Baltimore County (U)
Darton College (U)
Eastern Michigan University (U)
Edison State Community College (U)
Georgia Highlands College (U)
Illinois Institute of Technology (U,G)
Lehigh University (G)
Louisiana State University and Agricultural and Mechanical College (U)
Ozarks Technical Community College (U)
Palomar College (U)
Parkland College (U)
Piedmont Technical College (U)
Southwestern Community College (U)
Texas State University-San Marcos (U)
Tyler Junior College (U)
University of California, Berkeley (U,G)
University of Colorado at Denver and Health Sciences Center—Downtown Denver Campus (U)
University of Minnesota, Twin Cities Campus (U)
University of Waterloo (U)

CHEMICAL ENGINEERING

Arizona State University (U,G)
Brigham Young University (U)
Cleveland State University (G)
Columbia University (N,G)
Illinois Institute of Technology (U,G)
Kansas State University (G)
Lehigh University (N,G)
Mississippi State University (G)
North Carolina State University (G)
Texas Tech University (G)
University of Delaware (U,G)
University of Illinois at Chicago (G)
University of Massachusetts Amherst (G)
University of North Dakota (U)
University of South Florida (G)

CHEMISTRY

Acadia University (U)
Anne Arundel Community College (U)
Arkansas State University–Beebe (U)
Athabasca University (N,U)
Bellevue Community College (U)
Boise State University (U)
Brazosport College (U)
Brigham Young University (U)
Broome Community College (U)
Butler Community College (U)
Butler County Community College (U)
Caldwell College (U)
Cape Fear Community College (U)
Carlow University (U)
Casper College (U)
Cecil Community College (U)
Central Lakes College (U)
Central Oregon Community College (U)
Central Piedmont Community College (U)
Central Virginia Community College (U)
Central Wyoming College (U)
Champlain College (U)
Chattanooga State Technical Community College (U)
Clackamas Community College (U)
Clarion University of Pennsylvania (U)
Clark College (U)
Clark State Community College (U)
Cleveland Community College (U)
Cleveland State University (U)
Coffeyville Community College (U)
College of DuPage (U)
College of San Mateo (U)
Colorado Mountain College District System (U)
Colorado State University-Pueblo (U)
Columbia College (U)
Columbus State Community College (U)
Community College of Denver (U)
Contra Costa College (U)
Corning Community College (U)
Cowley County Community College and Area Vocational–Technical School (U)
Des Moines Area Community College (U)
Drury University (U)
East Carolina University (U)
East Central Community College (U)
Eastern Michigan University (U)
Eastern Oregon University (U)
Edison State Community College (U)
Erie Community College (U)
Florida Atlantic University (U)
Fort Valley State University (U)
Gadsden State Community College (U)
Galveston College (U)
Georgia Highlands College (U)
Grantham University (U)
Gulf Coast Community College (U)
Honolulu Community College (U)
Housatonic Community College (U)
Houston Community College System (U)
Illinois Eastern Community Colleges, Wabash Valley College (U)
Illinois Institute of Technology (G)
Indiana State University (U)
Iowa Western Community College (U)
Jacksonville State University (U,G)
Johnson County Community College (U)
John Tyler Community College (U)
J. Sargeant Reynolds Community College (U)
Kansas State University (U)
Lansing Community College (U)
Lehigh University (N,G)
Marshall University (U)
Massasoit Community College (U)
Mayville State University (U)
Millersville University of Pennsylvania (U)
Missouri State University (U)
Mt. San Antonio College (U)
New Mexico State University–Alamogordo (U)
North Carolina State University (U)
North Dakota State College of Science (U)
Northeast State Technical Community College (U)
Northwestern College (U)
Northwestern Michigan College (U)
Northwestern State University of Louisiana (U)
Oregon State University (U)
Oxnard College (U)
Pacific Union College (U)
Palm Beach Community College (U)
Palomar College (U)
Parkland College (U)
Peninsula College (U)
Pennsylvania College of Technology (U)
The Pennsylvania State University University Park Campus (U)
Piedmont Technical College (U)
Portland State University (U)
Pueblo Community College (U)
Rochester Institute of Technology (U)
Sacred Heart University (U)
St. Clair County Community College (U)
St. Cloud State University (U)
Saint Joseph's University (U)
St. Petersburg College (U)
Sam Houston State University (U)
San Bernardino Valley College (U)
San Joaquin Delta College (U)
Sinclair Community College (U)
South Dakota School of Mines and Technology (U)
Southern University at Shreveport (U)
Southwestern Oregon Community College (U)
State University of New York at Oswego (U)
Tacoma Community College (U)
Treasure Valley Community College (U)
Triton College (U)
The University of Akron (U)
University of Arkansas at Pine Bluff (U)
University of California, Berkeley (U,G)
University of Central Florida (G)
University of Colorado at Colorado Springs (U)
University of Delaware (U)
The University of Findlay (U)
University of Florida (U)
University of Illinois at Springfield (U)
University of La Verne (U)
University of Maryland University College (U)
University of New Orleans (U,G)
The University of North Carolina at Chapel Hill (U)
University of North Dakota (U)
University of Northern Colorado (U,G)
University of North Texas (U,G)
University of Oklahoma (U)
University of Pittsburgh at Bradford (U)
University of Southern Mississippi (U)
University of South Florida (U,G)
The University of Tennessee (U)
University of Utah (U)
University of Washington (U)
University of Waterloo (N,U)
University of Wisconsin Colleges (U)
University of Wisconsin–Stout (U)
University of Wyoming (U)
Utah State University (U)
Vincennes University (U)
Washburn University (U)
Wayne State College (U)
Weber State University (U)
Westchester Community College (U)
Whatcom Community College (U)
William Rainey Harper College (U)
Yuba College (U)

CITY/URBAN, COMMUNITY AND REGIONAL PLANNING

Arizona State University (U)
Athabasca University (N)
Cleveland State University (U,G)
Middle Tennessee State University (N)
The Pennsylvania State University University Park Campus (G)
Prescott College (G)

University of Massachusetts Boston (N)
University of Missouri–Columbia (N)
University of New Orleans (U,G)
University of Southern Mississippi (G)
University of Washington (N,G)
University of Wisconsin–River Falls (G)

CIVIL ENGINEERING

Auburn University (G)
Brigham Young University (U)
Cleveland State University (U,G)
Colorado State University (G)
Columbia University (N,G)
Gadsden State Community College (U)
Georgia Institute of Technology (N,G)
Iowa State University of Science and Technology (G)
Kansas State University (G)
Louisiana State University and Agricultural and Mechanical College (G)
Mississippi State University (G)
North Carolina State University (G)
Southern Methodist University (G)
Stanford University (N)
Texas Tech University (G)
The University of British Columbia (U)
University of Colorado at Boulder (N,G)
University of Colorado at Denver and Health Sciences Center—Downtown Denver Campus (U)
University of Delaware (U,G)
University of Florida (G)
University of Illinois at Urbana–Champaign (G)
University of Maine (G)
University of Maryland, College Park (G)
University of New Orleans (U,G)
The University of North Carolina at Charlotte (N)
University of North Dakota (U)
University of Washington (G)
University of Wisconsin–Madison (G)
University of Wisconsin–Platteville (G)
Virginia Polytechnic Institute and State University (U)

CIVIL ENGINEERING TECHNOLOGY

Auburn University (G)
Cincinnati State Technical and Community College (U)
Sinclair Community College (U)
Southern Polytechnic State University (U)
University of Maine (U)
University of South Florida (G)

CLASSICAL AND ANCIENT STUDIES

University of Florida (G)
University of Massachusetts Boston (U)
University of Missouri–Columbia (U)
University of New Orleans (U,G)
The University of North Carolina at Greensboro (U)

CLINICAL CHILD PSYCHOLOGY

California State University, San Bernardino (U)
Cumberland County College (U)
Rend Lake College (U)
Saybrook Graduate School and Research Center (G)

CLINICAL PSYCHOLOGY

Athabasca University (N)
Bethany University (U)
Capella University (G)
Erie Community College (U)
Jacksonville State University (U,G)
Naropa University (U)
North Dakota State University (N,U,G)
Oxnard College (U)
Prescott College (G)
Saybrook Graduate School and Research Center (G)
University of Hawaii–West Oahu (U)
Washtenaw Community College (U)

CLINICAL/MEDICAL LABORATORY SCIENCE AND ALLIED PROFESSIONS

Central Carolina Community College (N)
Central New Mexico Community College (U)
Clinton Community College (U)
Darton College (U)
Drexel University (G)
D'Youville College (U)
Marion Technical College (U)
Randolph Community College (N)
South Central College (U)
Triton College (U)
University of Illinois at Chicago (G)
University of Massachusetts Lowell (G)
The University of Texas System (N,U)
University of Wisconsin–Madison (U,G)

COGNITIVE PSYCHOLOGY AND PSYCHOLINGUISTICS

California State University, San Bernardino (U)
Charter Oak State College (U)
Community College of Beaver County (U)
Contra Costa College (U)
Immaculata University (U)
University of New Brunswick Fredericton (U)
University of Southern Mississippi (G)
University of Washington (U)

COGNITIVE SCIENCE

DePaul University (G)
D'Youville College (G)
Rasmussen College Eden Prarie (U)
Saybrook Graduate School and Research Center (G)

COMMUNICATION AND JOURNALISM RELATED

Athabasca University (U)
Austin Peay State University (G)
Bismarck State College (U)
Buena Vista University (U)
Caldwell College (U)
California State University, San Bernardino (U)
California State University, San Marcos (N)
Central Michigan University (G)
Champlain College (U)
Charter Oak State College (U)
Cleveland State University (U)
Columbus State Community College (U)
Community College of Southern Nevada (U)
Drake University (U)
East Carolina University (U)
Eastern Michigan University (U)
East Tennessee State University (N)
Elizabethtown College (U)
Fort Hays State University (U)
Housatonic Community College (U)
Indiana Business College (N)
Iona College (U)
James Madison University (N)
James Sprunt Community College (U)
Kean University (N)
Louisiana State University and Agricultural and Mechanical College (U)
Marshall University (U)
Metropolitan State University (U)
Mississippi State University (U)
Missouri State University (U)
Mount Wachusett Community College (U)
New Jersey Institute of Technology (G)
The New School (U)
North Idaho College (N)
Northwestern State University of Louisiana (U)
Palomar College (U)
Park University (U)
Peninsula College (U)
The Pennsylvania State University University Park Campus (G)
Rasmussen College Eden Prarie (U)
Regent University (N,U,G)
Saddleback College (U)
St. Clair County Community College (U)
St. John's University (U)
St. Louis Community College System (U)
San Bernardino Valley College (U)
Schoolcraft College (U)
Seminole Community College (U)
Southern Polytechnic State University (U,G)
Southwest Wisconsin Technical College (U)
State University of New York at Oswego (U)
State University of New York College at Potsdam (U)
Taylor University (N,U)
Triton College (N)
The University of Akron (U)
University of Alaska Fairbanks (U)
University of Alberta (G)
University of California, Berkeley (U,G)
The University of Findlay (U)
University of Florida (U)
University of Minnesota, Twin Cities Campus (U)
The University of North Carolina at Chapel Hill (G)
University of Southern Indiana (N)
The University of Texas at Arlington (U)
University of Wisconsin Colleges (U)
University of Wisconsin–Whitewater (U,G)
Utah Valley State College (U)
Valley City State University (U)
Washtenaw Community College (U)
Webster University (G)
Western Washington University (U)
West Virginia University at Parkersburg (U)

COMMUNICATION AND MEDIA

Abilene Christian University (U)
Andrew Jackson University (U)
Anne Arundel Community College (U)
Arizona State University at the Polytechnic Campus (U,G)
Arkansas State University–Beebe (U)
Athabasca University (N,U)
Auburn University (U)
Bainbridge College (N)
Bellevue Community College (U)
Bellevue University (U)
Berkeley College (U)
Berkeley College-New York City Campus (U)
Berkeley College-Westchester Campus (U)
Bethany University (U)
Blue Ridge Community College (N)
Bowling Green State University (U)
Bradley University (U)
Brenau University (U)
Bridgewater State College (N,U,G)
Brigham Young University (U)
Buena Vista University (U)
Butler County Community College (U)
Caldwell Community College and Technical Institute (U)
California State University, San Bernardino (U,G)
Cape Fear Community College (U)
Central New Mexico Community College (U)
Central Oregon Community College (U)
Central Texas College (U)
Central Wyoming College (N,U)
Champlain College (U)
Chattanooga State Technical Community College (U)
Chesapeake College (U)
Citrus College (U)
Clarion University of Pennsylvania (U)
Clark State Community College (U)
Clemson University (N,U,G)
Cleveland Institute of Electronics (U)
Cleveland State University (U)
Clovis Community College (U)
Coconino Community College (U)
College of DuPage (U)
College of Southern Maryland (U)
College of Staten Island of the City University of New York (N)
College of The Albemarle (N)
Columbia Basin College (U)
The Community College of Baltimore County (U)
Concordia University, St. Paul (N)
Connecticut State University System (U)
Dallas Baptist University (U)
Danville Community College (U)
Darton College (U)
Dawson Community College (U)
Des Moines Area Community College (U)
DeVry University Online (U,G)
Drake University (U)
Drury University (U,G)
Duquesne University (U,G)
East Carolina University (U)
Eastern Michigan University (U)
Edgecombe Community College (N)
Elizabethtown College (U)
Erie Community College (U)
Fontbonne University (U)
Fort Valley State University (U)
Franklin University (U)
Governors State University (U)
Granite State College (U)
Halifax Community College (U)
Heartland Community College (U)
Illinois Eastern Community Colleges, Olney Central College (U)
Immaculata University (U)
Indiana Business College (N)
Indiana University–Purdue University Fort Wayne (U)
Indiana Wesleyan University (U)
International Institute of the Americas (U)
Iowa Western Community College (U)
Itawamba Community College (U)
Jackson Community College (U)
James Madison University (U)
Jamestown Community College (N)
Jones College (U)
Judson College (U)
Lake Superior College (U)
LeTourneau University (U)
Lewis and Clark Community College (U)
Lewis-Clark State College (U)
Louisiana State University and Agricultural and Mechanical College (U)
Malone College (U)
Marshall University (U)
Marylhurst University (N)
Massasoit Community College (N)
Middlesex Community College (U)
Middle Tennessee State University (U)
Millersville University of Pennsylvania (U)
Minnesota School of Business–Richfield (U)
Mississippi State University (U)
Missouri State University (G)
Monroe Community College (U)
Montana State University–Billings (U,G)
Mountain Empire Community College (U)
Mount Saint Vincent University (U)
Myers University (U)
New Mexico Junior College (U)
New Mexico State University–Carlsbad (U)
The New School (N,U,G)
New York Institute of Technology (U)
North Dakota State University (U,G)
North Idaho College (N,U)
North Seattle Community College (U)
Northwestern College (U)
Northwest Missouri State University (U)
Old Dominion University (U)
Oregon State University (N,U)
Oxnard College (U)
Ozarks Technical Community College (U)
Pace University (U)
Palm Beach Community College (U)
Palomar College (U)
Parkland College (U)
Park University (U)
Passaic County Community College (U)
Patrick Henry Community College (U)
The Pennsylvania State University University Park Campus (U)
Piedmont Technical College (U)
Plymouth State University (U)
Prescott College (U,G)
Providence College and Theological Seminary (U)
Purdue University Calumet (U)
Radford University (G)
Rasmussen College Eden Prarie (U)
Regent University (U,G)
Ryerson University (U)
Sacred Heart University (U)
St. Cloud State University (U)
St. Edward's University (U)
Saint Joseph's College of Maine (U)
St. Petersburg College (U)
Schoolcraft College (U)
Seminole Community College (U)
Shippensburg University of Pennsylvania (U,G)
Simpson College (U)
Sinclair Community College (U)
Snow College (U)
Southwestern Oregon Community College (U)
Southwest Wisconsin Technical College (U)
State University of New York at New Paltz (U)
State University of New York at Oswego (U)
State University of New York College at Potsdam (N)
Syracuse University (G)
Taylor University (N)
Texas A&M University–Commerce (U)
Tompkins Cortland Community College (U)
Tunxis Community College (U)
The University of Akron (U)
The University of Alabama (U)
University of Alberta (G)
University of Arkansas at Pine Bluff (U)
University of California, Berkeley (U)
University of Colorado at Colorado Springs (U)
University of Colorado at Denver and Health Sciences Center—Downtown Denver Campus (U)
University of Delaware (U)
University of Denver (G)
University of Florida (U,G)
University of Houston–Victoria (G)
University of Illinois at Springfield (U,G)
University of La Verne (U)
The University of Maine at Augusta (U)
University of Maine at Fort Kent (U)
University of Maryland University College (U)
University of Massachusetts Boston (U)
University of Massachusetts Lowell (U)
University of Minnesota, Twin Cities Campus (U,G)
The University of Montana (U)
University of Nevada, Reno (U)
University of North Alabama (U)
The University of North Carolina at Chapel Hill (U,G)
University of North Dakota (U)
University of Northern Iowa (U)
University of Oklahoma (U)
University of Southern Indiana (U)
University of Southern Mississippi (G)
The University of Toledo (U)
University of Toronto (N,U)
University of Washington (U)
University of West Florida (U)
University of Wisconsin–Platteville (U,G)
University of Wisconsin–River Falls (U)
University of Wisconsin–Superior (U)
University of Wisconsin–Whitewater (U)
University of Wyoming (U)
Upper Iowa University (N,U)
Utah Valley State College (U)
Valparaiso University (U,G)
Virginia Polytechnic Institute and State University (U)
Washtenaw Community College (U)
Weber State University (U)

Westchester Community College (U)
West Virginia University at Parkersburg (N)
Wichita State University (U)
Wilfrid Laurier University (U)
Wilkes Community College (U)
Wisconsin Indianhead Technical College (N,U)
Wright State University (U,G)
York University (U)
Yuba College (U)

COMMUNICATION DISORDERS SCIENCES AND SERVICES

Athabasca University (N,U)
Auburn University (U)
Bridgewater State College (U)
Brigham Young University (U)
California State University, Northridge (N)
East Carolina University (G)
Fontbonne University (G)
Fort Hays State University (U)
James Madison University (N)
MGH Institute of Health Professions (G)
Murray State University (U,G)
Oklahoma State University (U)
Texas A&M University–Kingsville (U,G)
Texas Woman's University (U,G)
University of Cincinnati (U,G)
University of Maine (U)
University of Northern Colorado (G)
Utah State University (U)

COMMUNICATIONS TECHNOLOGIES AND SUPPORT SERVICES RELATED

Drexel University (U)
North Idaho College (N)
Rasmussen College Eden Prarie (U)
West Virginia University at Parkersburg (N)

COMMUNICATIONS TECHNOLOGY

Athabasca University (N,U)
Bethany University (U)
California State University, San Bernardino (U,G)
Central Michigan University (G)
Community College of Southern Nevada (U)
Dakota State University (U)
DePaul University (G)
DeVry University Online (G)
East Tennessee State University (U)
Grantham University (G)
Indiana University of Pennsylvania (U)
Itawamba Community College (U)
James Madison University (U)
Lawrence Technological University (U)
Maryville University of Saint Louis (N)
Mercy College (U)
Middlesex Community College (U)
Montana State University–Billings (U)
National University (U)
North Georgia College & State University (N)
North Lake College (U)
Rasmussen College Eden Prarie (U)
Regent University (U,G)
Roosevelt University (G)
Syracuse University (U,G)
The University of Akron (N)
University of California, Berkeley (U)
University of Florida (G)
University of Illinois at Urbana–Champaign (G)
University of North Texas (G)
University of West Florida (N,U)
Wilkes Community College (U)

COMMUNITY HEALTH SERVICES

Athabasca University (N,U,G)
Blue Ridge Community College (N)
Brenau University (U)
California College for Health Sciences (N)
California State University, Chico (U)
California State University, San Bernardino (U)
California State University, San Marcos (N)
Central Michigan University (U)
Central Piedmont Community College (U)
Colorado State University (N)
Danville Community College (U)
Duquesne University (G)
Edgecombe Community College (N)
Houston Community College System (U)
Indiana State University (U)
Jacksonville State University (U)
Jefferson College of Health Sciences (U)
Kansas State University (G)
Louisiana State University and Agricultural and Mechanical College (U)
Mercy College (G)
New Mexico State University (U)
Old Dominion University (U)
Radford University (G)
Rappahannock Community College (U)
Ryerson University (U)
Saybrook Graduate School and Research Center (G)
Schoolcraft College (N)
Seminole Community College (U)
State University of New York College at Potsdam (U)
The University of Akron (U)
University of Bridgeport (U)
The University of Maine at Augusta (U)
University of Massachusetts Amherst (U)
University of Northern Colorado (U)
University of South Carolina Sumter (U)
University of Southern Mississippi (U,G)
The University of Texas at Tyler (U)
Vincennes University (U)
Western Washington University (U)
West Virginia University at Parkersburg (U)

COMMUNITY ORGANIZATION AND ADVOCACY

Athabasca University (N,U,G)
Central Michigan University (U)
Colorado State University (N)
Duquesne University (G)
Kansas State University (G)
Mercy College (U)
Prescott College (U,G)
Saybrook Graduate School and Research Center (G)
South Central College (U)
Sullivan University (G)
The University of Akron (U)
University of Massachusetts Boston (U)
University of New Orleans (U)
University of North Texas (G)
University of Southern Mississippi (U)
University of Waterloo (U)
University of Wisconsin–River Falls (G)

COMMUNITY PSYCHOLOGY

Athabasca University (N,U,G)
Bethany University (U)
Central Texas College (U)
Colorado State University (N)
Jones College (U)
Kansas State University (G)
Middlesex Community College (U)
Naropa University (U)
Rasmussen College Eden Prarie (U)
St. Cloud State University (G)
Saybrook Graduate School and Research Center (G)
Sullivan University (G)
Texas State University-San Marcos (U)

COMPARATIVE LITERATURE

Athabasca University (U)
Bellevue Community College (U)
Bellevue University (U)
California State University, San Marcos (N)
Columbus State Community College (U)
Community College of Denver (U)
Dakota County Technical College (U)
Des Moines Area Community College (U)
D'Youville College (U)
East Tennessee State University (U)
Indiana University–Purdue University Fort Wayne (U)
Limestone College (U)
Lock Haven University of Pennsylvania (U)
Louisiana State University and Agricultural and Mechanical College (U)
Mercy College (U,G)
Naropa University (U)
The Pennsylvania State University University Park Campus (U)
Rasmussen College Eden Prarie (U)
Rio Hondo College (U)
Southwestern Oregon Community College (U)
State University of New York at New Paltz (U)
Texas State University-San Marcos (U)
University of California, Berkeley (U,G)
The University of Maine at Augusta (U)
University of Massachusetts Amherst (U)
University of Minnesota, Twin Cities Campus (U)
University of New Orleans (U,G)
University of Southern Mississippi (U)
Wichita State University (U)

COMPUTER AND INFORMATION SCIENCES

Alvin Community College (N,U)
Anne Arundel Community College (U)
Arizona Western College (U)
Arkansas State University–Beebe (U)
Arkansas Tech University (U)
Asheville-Buncombe Technical Community College (U)
Ashworth College (N)
Athabasca University (N,U,G)
Athens Technical College (U)
Bainbridge College (U)
Bellevue Community College (U)

Bellevue University (U)
Bellingham Technical College (N)
Big Sandy Community and Technical College (U)
Blinn College (U)
Blue Ridge Community College (N,U)
Bowling Green State University (U)
Bradley University (U)
Brazosport College (U)
Brenau University (U,G)
Brigham Young University (N)
Broome Community College (N)
Caldwell Community College and Technical Institute (U)
California National University for Advanced Studies (U,G)
California State University, Dominguez Hills (N)
California State University, San Marcos (N)
Capitol College (G)
Carl Albert State College (U)
Casper College (U)
Central Carolina Community College (N)
Central Lakes College (U)
Central Michigan University (G)
Central New Mexico Community College (U)
Central Oregon Community College (U)
Central Texas College (U)
Central Virginia Community College (U)
Central Wyoming College (N,U)
Chadron State College (U)
Champlain College (U)
Charter Oak State College (U)
Chattanooga State Technical Community College (U)
Cincinnati State Technical and Community College (U)
Citrus College (U)
Clatsop Community College (U)
Clemson University (N)
Cleveland State Community College (U)
Cleveland State University (U)
Clinton Community College (U)
Clovis Community College (U)
Coconino Community College (U)
Coleman College (U)
The College of St. Scholastica (U)
College of The Albemarle (N,U)
Colorado Christian University (U)
Colorado Technical University (U)
Columbia College (U)
Columbus State Community College (U)
The Community College of Baltimore County (N,U)
Community College of Beaver County (N,U)
Contra Costa College (U)
Cosumnes River College (U)
Cowley County Community College and Area Vocational–Technical School (N)
Culver-Stockton College (U)
Dakota State University (U,G)
Dallas Baptist University (U)
Dallas County Community College District (U)
Delta College (U)
DePaul University (U,G)
Des Moines Area Community College (U)
DeVry University Online (U,G)
Drake University (U)
Drexel University (U,G)
Drury University (U)
Duquesne University (N,U)
D'Youville College (U)
East Carolina University (U,G)
East Central Community College (U)
Eastern New Mexico University (U)
Eastern West Virginia Community and Technical College (U)
Eastern Wyoming College (U)
East Los Angeles College (U)
East Tennessee State University (N)
Edgecombe Community College (N,U)
Edison State Community College (N,U)
Elgin Community College (U)
Erie Community College (U)
Eugene Bible College (U)
Everett Community College (N,U)
Evergreen Valley College (U)
Finger Lakes Community College (U)
Forrest Junior College (U)
Fort Hays State University (U)
Fort Valley State University (U)
Franklin Pierce College (U)
Fresno City College (U)
Frostburg State University (U)
Galveston College (U)
Gogebic Community College (U)
Grantham University (U)
Harford Community College (N,U)
Haywood Community College (U)
Hillsborough Community College (U)
Illinois Eastern Community Colleges, Olney Central College (U)
Illinois Institute of Technology (U)
Immaculata University (U)
Independence Community College (U)
Indiana Business College (N,U)
Indiana Tech (U)
Indiana Wesleyan University (U)
International Institute of the Americas (U)
Iowa Western Community College (U)
Jacksonville State University (U,G)
Jamestown Community College (N)
John A. Logan College (U)
John Tyler Community College (U)
Jones College (U)
Kansas State University (U)
Kauai Community College (U)
Kean University (N)
Kentucky State University (U)
Lake Superior College (U)
Lamar State College–Port Arthur (N,U)
Lansing Community College (U)
Lehigh Carbon Community College (U)
Lewis and Clark Community College (U)
Lewis-Clark State College (U)
Limestone College (U)
Los Angeles Harbor College (U)
Louisiana State University and Agricultural and Mechanical College (U)
Macon State College (U)
Madison Area Technical College (U)
Madonna University (U)
Mansfield University of Pennsylvania (U)
Marshall University (U,G)
Maryville University of Saint Louis (N)
Massasoit Community College (N,U)
Mercer County Community College (U)
Mercy College (U,G)
Mesalands Community College (U)
Miami Dade College (U)
Middlesex Community College (U)
Middle Tennessee State University (N)
Midland College (N,U)
Mid Michigan Community College (U)
Midstate College (U)
Mid-State Technical College (U)
Milwaukee School of Engineering (U)
Mississippi State University (U)
Missouri State University (U,G)
Mitchell Technical Institute (N,U)
Mohawk Valley Community College (N,U)
Montgomery Community College (N,U)
Motlow State Community College (U)
Mountain Empire Community College (U)
Mount Saint Vincent University (U)
Mt. San Antonio College (U)
Murray State University (U)
Myers University (U)
Nassau Community College (U)
National University (G)
Naugatuck Valley Community College (U)
New England College of Finance (U)
New Jersey Institute of Technology (U)
New Mexico State University–Alamogordo (U)
New Mexico State University–Carlsbad (N,U)
New York Institute of Technology (N)
North Dakota State College of Science (U)
North Dakota State University (N,U)
Northeast State Technical Community College (U)
North Georgia College & State University (N,U)
North Idaho College (N)
Northwestern Connecticut Community College (N,U)
Northwestern Michigan College (U)
Northwestern State University of Louisiana (U)
Northwest Missouri State University (U,G)
Nova Southeastern University (G)
Odessa College (U)
Old Dominion University (U)
Orange Coast College (U)
Oregon Institute of Technology (U)
Ouachita Technical College (U)
Oxnard College (U)
Ozarka College (N,U)
Ozarks Technical Community College (U)
Pace University (N,G)
Pacific Union College (U)
Palm Beach Community College (U)
Palomar College (U)
Parkland College (U)
Park University (U,G)
Pasco-Hernando Community College (N)
Passaic County Community College (U)
Peninsula College (U)
Pennsylvania College of Technology (U)
Plymouth State University (G)
Portland Community College (U)
Pueblo Community College (U)
Pulaski Technical College (U)
Purdue University Calumet (U)
Radford University (N)
Randolph Community College (U)
Raritan Valley Community College (U)
Rasmussen College Eden Prarie (U)
Reading Area Community College (U)
Red Rocks Community College (U)
Rio Hondo College (U)
Sacramento City College (U)
Sacred Heart University (U)
St. Clair County Community College (U)
Saint Leo University (U)
St. Louis Community College System (U)
Saint Mary-of-the-Woods College (U)
Schoolcraft College (U)

Seminole Community College (U)
Shenandoah University (N,U)
Shoreline Community College (U)
Sinclair Community College (U)
Solano Community College (U)
South Central College (U)
Southern Illinois University Carbondale (U)
Southern Methodist University (G)
Southern Polytechnic State University (G)
South Piedmont Community College (U)
South Plains College (U)
Southwest Georgia Technical College (U)
Southwest Wisconsin Technical College (U)
Stanly Community College (U)
State University of New York at Buffalo (N)
State University of New York at Oswego (U)
State University of New York at Plattsburgh (U)
State University of New York College at Potsdam (N)
Stephens College (U)
Syracuse University (U,G)
Tacoma Community College (N,U)
Taylor University (N,U)
Texas A&M University–Commerce (U,G)
Texas A&M University–Kingsville (U)
Texas Woman's University (U,G)
Three Rivers Community College (U)
Tompkins Cortland Community College (U)
Tri-County Community College (N,U)
Triton College (N)
Tunxis Community College (N,U)
Tyler Junior College (N,U)
The University of Akron (N,U,G)
The University of Alabama (U)
University of Alaska Fairbanks (U,G)
University of Arkansas at Pine Bluff (U)
The University of British Columbia (U)
University of California, Davis (N)
University of Central Arkansas (N)
University of Central Oklahoma (N)
University of Cincinnati (N)
University of Dallas (G)
University of Denver (G)
University of Florida (G)
University of Great Falls (U,G)
University of Houston–Clear Lake (G)
University of Houston–Victoria (U,G)
University of Illinois at Urbana–Champaign (G)
The University of Maine at Augusta (U)
University of Maryland University College (U)
University of Massachusetts Boston (U)
University of Massachusetts Lowell (U)
University of Michigan–Dearborn (U,G)
University of Nevada, Reno (U)
University of New Orleans (U,G)
University of North Alabama (U)
The University of North Carolina at Chapel Hill (U)
University of North Florida (U)
University of North Texas (U,G)
University of Pittsburgh at Bradford (U)
University of Southern Indiana (N)
University of South Florida (G)
The University of Tennessee at Martin (N)
The University of Texas of the Permian Basin (U)
The University of Texas System (U,G)
The University of Toledo (U)
University of Tulsa (G)
University of Washington (N)
University of Waterloo (U)
University of Wisconsin–River Falls (U)
Utah Valley State College (N,U)
Vance-Granville Community College (N)
Vermont Technical College (U)
Vincennes University (U)
Washtenaw Community College (U)
Wayne State College (U)
Weber State University (U)
Webster University (U)
Westchester Community College (U)
Western Nevada Community College (U)
Western Oklahoma State College (U)
Western Piedmont Community College (U)
West Shore Community College (U)
West Virginia University at Parkersburg (N,U)
Wharton County Junior College (U)
Wilkes Community College (U)
William Rainey Harper College (U)
Wisconsin Indianhead Technical College (N,U)
York County Community College (U)

COMPUTER AND INFORMATION SCIENCES AND SUPPORT SERVICES RELATED

Alvin Community College (N,U)
Athabasca University (U,G)
Bellevue Community College (U)
Bellevue University (U)
Bellingham Technical College (U)
Blackhawk Technical College (U)
Bowling Green State University (N)
Caldwell College (U)
Caldwell Community College and Technical Institute (N)
California State University, San Marcos (U)
Capitol College (G)
Central Michigan University (G)
Central Texas College (U)
Champlain College (U)
Chesapeake College (U)
Clark State Community College (U)
Columbia Basin College (U)
The Community College of Baltimore County (N)
Dakota State University (U,G)
Dallas County Community College District (U)
DePaul University (G)
Des Moines Area Community College (U)
Drexel University (G)
Duquesne University (G)
East Carolina University (U)
East Tennessee State University (N)
Edgecombe Community College (N,U)
Forrest Junior College (U)
Glenville State College (U)
Halifax Community College (U)
Heart of Georgia Technical College (U)
Immaculata University (U)
International Institute of the Americas (U)
Iona College (U)
Jackson Community College (U)
Jacksonville State University (U,G)
Jamestown Community College (N)
Jones College (U)
Limestone College (U)
Lock Haven University of Pennsylvania (N)
Marshall University (U)
Mercy College (G)
Middlesex Community College (U)
Midland College (N)
Mid-State Technical College (U)
Mohawk Valley Community College (N)
Myers University (U)
New York Institute of Technology (N)
North Arkansas College (N)
North Dakota State College of Science (U)
North Idaho College (N)
Northwestern Michigan College (U)
Northwest Missouri State University (G)
Nova Southeastern University (G)
Pace University (U,G)
Palomar College (U)
Peirce College (U)
Portland Community College (U)
Radford University (N)
Raritan Valley Community College (U)
Rasmussen College Eden Prarie (U)
Sacramento City College (U)
Saint Leo University (U)
St. Louis Community College System (U)
Seminole Community College (U)
Solano Community College (U)
Southern Methodist University (G)
South Piedmont Community College (U)
Southwest Virginia Community College (N)
Stanly Community College (U)
State University of New York, Fredonia (U)
Taylor University (N)
Texas Tech University (G)
Treasure Valley Community College (U)
Tri-County Community College (N)
Tyler Junior College (U)
The University of Akron (N)
The University of Alabama (G)
University of California, Berkeley (U)
University of Central Arkansas (G)
University of Central Florida (U)
University of Connecticut (U)
University of Dallas (G)
University of Denver (G)
University of Maine (U)
The University of North Carolina at Greensboro (N)
The University of Texas System (U)
University of Washington (N)
Wake Technical Community College (U)
Webster University (G)
Westchester Community College (U)
Wilkes Community College (U)
William Rainey Harper College (U)
York Technical College (N)
Yuba College (U)

COMPUTER ENGINEERING

Bellingham Technical College (N)
California National University for Advanced Studies (G)
Cleveland Institute of Electronics (U)
Cleveland State University (U,G)
College of The Albemarle (N)
Dallas County Community College District (U)
Drexel University (G)
Edison State Community College (U)
Georgia Institute of Technology (N,G)
Grantham University (U)
Illinois Institute of Technology (U,G)
Jacksonville State University (G)
Kansas State University (G)
Marshall University (U)
Mississippi State University (G)

Mohawk Valley Community College (N)
Myers University (U)
North Carolina State University (G)
North Dakota State University (G)
Oxnard College (U)
Seminole Community College (U)
Shenandoah University (U)
Southern Methodist University (G)
Southern Polytechnic State University (G)
Southwestern Oregon Community College (U)
University of Colorado at Boulder (N,G)
University of Florida (G)
University of Michigan–Dearborn (G)
University of South Florida (G)
University of Washington (U)
University of West Florida (N)
University of Wisconsin–Platteville (G)
Virginia Polytechnic Institute and State University (U,G)
Western Michigan University (G)

COMPUTER ENGINEERING TECHNOLOGIES

Capitol College (G)
Drexel University (G)
Grantham University (U)
Macon State College (N)
Seminole Community College (U)
Shenandoah University (N)
Southern Methodist University (G)

COMPUTER PROGRAMMING

Acadia University (U)
Alvin Community College (U)
Arkansas State University–Beebe (U)
Asheville-Buncombe Technical Community College (N,U)
Ashworth College (N)
Athabasca University (N,U)
Athens Technical College (N)
Bellevue Community College (U)
Bellevue University (U)
Bergen Community College (U)
Blackhawk Technical College (U)
Blinn College (U)
Blue Ridge Community College (N,U)
Broome Community College (N)
Bryant and Stratton Online (U)
Butler Community College (U)
Butler County Community College (U)
California State University, San Marcos (U)
Cape Breton University (N)
Casper College (U)
Central Carolina Community College (U)
Central Missouri State University (N)
Central New Mexico Community College (U)
Central Piedmont Community College (U)
Central Texas College (U)
Champlain College (U)
Clemson University (N)
Cleveland Community College (U)
Cleveland Institute of Electronics (N)
Cleveland State University (U)
Clinton Community College (U)
Coleman College (U)
College of DuPage (U)
College of San Mateo (U)
College of Staten Island of the City University of New York (N)
College of The Albemarle (N)
Columbia Basin College (U)
Columbia-Greene Community College (U)
Columbus State Community College (U)
Columbus State University (G)
The Community College of Baltimore County (N,U)
Community College of Beaver County (U)
Community College of Southern Nevada (U)
Corning Community College (U)
Dakota County Technical College (U)
Dakota State University (U)
Dallas County Community College District (U)
Danville Community College (U)
De Anza College (U)
Delta College (U)
DePaul University (U,G)
Des Moines Area Community College (U)
East Tennessee State University (N)
Edgecombe Community College (N,U)
Edison State Community College (U)
Edmonds Community College (U)
Erie Community College (U)
Fisher College (N)
Galveston College (N)
Granite State College (U)
Grantham University (U)
Hagerstown Community College (N)
Harford Community College (N,U)
Haywood Community College (U)
Hillsborough Community College (U)
Illinois Institute of Technology (U)
Indiana Business College (N)
Indiana State University (U)
Iowa Western Community College (U)
Itawamba Community College (U)
Jacksonville State University (U,G)
James Madison University (N)
Jones College (U)
Kean University (N)
Kentucky State University (U)
Lamar State College–Port Arthur (N,U)
Lansing Community College (U)
Limestone College (U)
Lock Haven University of Pennsylvania (U)
Los Angeles Harbor College (U)
Macon State College (U)
Madison Area Technical College (U)
Middlesex Community College (U)
Middle Tennessee State University (N)
Mid Michigan Community College (U)
Mohawk Valley Community College (N)
Mount Wachusett Community College (U)
Murray State University (U)
Myers University (U)
New Mexico State University–Carlsbad (N)
North Carolina State University (U)
North Dakota State College of Science (U)
North Dakota State University (N)
North Idaho College (N)
North Seattle Community College (U)
Northwestern Michigan College (U)
Nova Southeastern University (G)
Orange Coast College (U)
Oxnard College (U)
Ozarka College (N)
Pace University (U,G)
Palomar College (U)
Parkland College (U)
Park University (U)
Pasco-Hernando Community College (N,U)
Peirce College (U)
Penn Foster Career School (N)
Portland Community College (N)
Raritan Valley Community College (U)
Red Rocks Community College (U)
Rio Hondo College (U)
Sacramento City College (U)
Saint Leo University (U)
San Diego State University (N)
Schoolcraft College (N,U)
Seminole Community College (U)
Shenandoah University (N)
Sinclair Community College (U)
Solano Community College (U)
Southeast Arkansas College (U)
Southern Polytechnic State University (N,G)
South Piedmont Community College (U)
South Plains College (U)
Southwest Georgia Technical College (U)
Southwest Wisconsin Technical College (U)
State University of New York College at Potsdam (N)
Tacoma Community College (U)
Taylor University (N)
Texas A&M University–Kingsville (N)
Texas State Technical College Waco (N,U)
Tompkins Cortland Community College (U)
Treasure Valley Community College (U)
Tri-County Community College (N)
Tyler Junior College (N,U)
The University of Akron (N)
University of California, Berkeley (U)
University of California, Davis (U)
University of Cincinnati (N)
University of Colorado at Denver and Health Sciences Center—Downtown Denver Campus (U)
University of Connecticut (U)
University of Houston–Clear Lake (G)
University of Houston–Downtown (U)
University of Massachusetts Lowell (U)
University of Missouri–Columbia (U)
University of New Orleans (U,G)
University of North Dakota (N)
University of South Florida (G)
University of Washington (N,U)
University of West Florida (U)
Utah State University (G)
Vance-Granville Community College (N,U)
Washtenaw Community College (U)
Westchester Community College (U)
Western Piedmont Community College (U)
Westwood Online (U)
Wilkes Community College (U)
William Rainey Harper College (U)
Winston-Salem State University (U)
Wisconsin Indianhead Technical College (N,U)
York County Community College (U)
Yuba College (U)

COMPUTER SCIENCE

Acadia University (U)
Alvin Community College (U)
Anne Arundel Community College (U)
Arizona State University (U)
Arkansas State University–Mountain Home (U)
Athabasca University (N,U,G)
Auburn University (U,G)
Azusa Pacific University (U,G)
Bellevue Community College (U)
Bellingham Technical College (U)
Bergen Community College (U)
Bismarck State College (U)

Bowling Green State University (U)
Broome Community College (U)
Buffalo State College, State University of New York (U)
Butler County Community College (U)
California State University, Chico (G)
Cape Fear Community College (U)
Capitol College (G)
Carlow University (U)
Carroll College (U,G)
Casper College (U)
Cayuga County Community College (U)
Central Carolina Community College (U)
Central Missouri State University (U)
Central Piedmont Community College (U)
Central Texas College (U)
Central Wyoming College (U)
Chattanooga State Technical Community College (U)
Clackamas Community College (U)
Clarion University of Pennsylvania (U)
Cleveland Institute of Electronics (N)
Cleveland State University (U)
College of The Albemarle (N,U)
College of the Siskiyous (U)
College of the Southwest (U)
Colorado Mountain College District System (U)
Colorado State University (U,G)
Colorado Technical University (U)
Columbia Basin College (U)
Columbia University (N,U,G)
Columbus State University (U)
The Community College of Baltimore County (U)
Community College of Beaver County (N,U)
Concordia University Wisconsin (U)
Connecticut State University System (U)
Copiah-Lincoln Community College (U)
County College of Morris (U)
Dakota State University (U)
Dallas County Community College District (U)
Danville Community College (U)
DePaul University (U,G)
Des Moines Area Community College (U)
Drexel University (U,G)
East Carolina University (G)
Eastern Oregon University (U)
Edgecombe Community College (N)
Edison State Community College (U)
Embry-Riddle Aeronautical University, Extended Campus (U)
Erie Community College (U)
Florida Atlantic University (U,G)
Florida Gulf Coast University (U)
Fort Valley State University (U)
Franklin University (U)
Gadsden State Community College (U)
George Mason University (U,G)
Golden West College (U)
Grantham University (U)
Halifax Community College (U)
Harvard University (N,G)
Hillsborough Community College (U)
Houston Community College System (U)
Illinois Institute of Technology (U,G)
Immaculata University (U)
Indiana State University (U)
Indiana University–Purdue University Fort Wayne (U)
International Institute of the Americas (U)
Iowa Western Community College (U)
Itawamba Community College (U)
Jacksonville State University (U,G)
James Madison University (N)
J. Sargeant Reynolds Community College (U)
Kansas State University (G)
Lamar State College–Port Arthur (N,U)
Lamar University (U)
LeTourneau University (U)
Limestone College (U)
Memorial University of Newfoundland (U)
Mercy College (U,G)
Mesalands Community College (U)
Middlesex Community College (U)
Middle Tennessee State University (N)
Mid Michigan Community College (U)
Midway College (U)
Minnesota School of Business–Richfield (U)
Mississippi State University (U,G)
Moberly Area Community College (U)
Mohawk Valley Community College (N)
Murray State University (U)
Myers University (U)
New Jersey Institute of Technology (U,G)
New Mexico Institute of Mining and Technology (G)
North Dakota State University (N)
Nova Southeastern University (G)
Old Dominion University (U)
Oxnard College (U)
Pace University (U)
Palomar College (U)
Piedmont Technical College (U)
Portland Community College (U)
Purdue University Calumet (G)
Rasmussen College Eden Prarie (U)
Red Rocks Community College (U)
Rend Lake College (U)
Sacred Heart University (U,G)
Saddleback College (U)
St. John's University (U)
St. Petersburg College (U)
San Joaquin Delta College (U)
Schoolcraft College (U)
Seminole Community College (U)
Shippensburg University of Pennsylvania (U)
Simpson College (U)
Solano Community College (U)
Southeast Arkansas College (U)
Southern Arkansas University Tech (U)
Southern Methodist University (G)
Southern Polytechnic State University (U,G)
Southern University at Shreveport (U)
Southwestern Oregon Community College (U)
Stanford University (N)
State University of New York at New Paltz (U,G)
State University of New York at Oswego (U)
State University of New York College at Cortland (G)
Tacoma Community College (U)
Taft College (U)
Taylor University (U)
Texas A&M University–Commerce (U)
Texas A&M University–Kingsville (U)
Texas State Technical College Waco (U)
Texas Tech University (G)
Touro University International (U)
Tri-County Community College (N,U)
Tyler Junior College (U)
The University of Akron (N,U)
The University of Alabama (U)
University of Alaska Fairbanks (U)
University of Arkansas at Pine Bluff (U)
University of California, Davis (U)
University of Colorado at Boulder (N,G)
The University of Findlay (U)
University of Florida (G)
University of Great Falls (U)
University of Houston–Clear Lake (G)
University of Houston–Downtown (U)
University of Illinois at Springfield (U,G)
University of Illinois at Urbana–Champaign (G)
University of Massachusetts Boston (U)
University of Michigan–Dearborn (U,G)
University of Michigan–Flint (U)
University of Missouri–Columbia (U)
The University of Montana (U)
University of New Hampshire (G)
University of New Orleans (U,G)
University of Pittsburgh at Bradford (U)
University of Saskatchewan (U)
The University of Tennessee at Martin (U)
The University of Texas at Tyler (U,G)
University of Washington (U,G)
University of Waterloo (U)
University of West Florida (U)
University of Wisconsin–Madison (U,G)
Utah State University (G)
Virginia Polytechnic Institute and State University (U,G)
Waukesha County Technical College (U)
Westchester Community College (U)
Western Michigan University (G)
Western Wyoming Community College (U)
West Los Angeles College (U)
Wharton County Junior College (U)
Wilkes Community College (U)
William Rainey Harper College (U)
York Technical College (U)

COMPUTER SOFTWARE AND MEDIA APPLICATIONS

Adams State College (N)
Adirondack Community College (U)
Alvin Community College (U)
Athabasca University (N,U)
Athens Technical College (N)
Auburn University Montgomery (N)
Bainbridge College (N)
Bellevue Community College (U)
Bellevue University (U)
Bellingham Technical College (N)
Belmont Technical College (U)
Berkeley College (U)
Berkeley College-New York City Campus (U)
Berkeley College-Westchester Campus (U)
Bismarck State College (U)
Blackhawk Technical College (N)
Blue Ridge Community College (N,U)
Boise State University (G)
Bowling Green State University (N,U,G)
Brigham Young University (N)
Broome Community College (N,U)
Bryant and Stratton Online (U)
Caldwell Community College and Technical Institute (N)
California State University, East Bay (U)
Cape Breton University (N)
Cape Cod Community College (U)
Cape Fear Community College (U)
Capella University (U)
Capitol College (G)
Cardinal Stritch University (N)
Carl Sandburg College (U)

Carroll College (G)
Casper College (U)
Central Lakes College (U)
Central Missouri State University (N)
Central Texas College (U)
Central Wyoming College (N)
Champlain College (U)
Cincinnati State Technical and Community College (U)
Clark College (U)
Clark State Community College (U)
Clemson University (N)
Cleveland Community College (U)
Cleveland Institute of Electronics (N)
Cleveland State University (N,U)
Coconino Community College (N)
Coffeyville Community College (U)
College of DuPage (U)
College of The Albemarle (N)
Colorado Christian University (U)
Colorado Mountain College District System (U)
Colorado State University-Pueblo (N)
Columbia Basin College (U)
Columbus State Community College (U)
The Community College of Baltimore County (N)
Community College of Beaver County (N,U)
Community College of Denver (U)
Community College of Southern Nevada (U)
Cowley County Community College and Area Vocational–Technical School (U)
Dakota County Technical College (U)
Dallas County Community College District (U)
Danville Community College (U)
Darton College (N,U)
Dawson Community College (U)
Daymar College (U)
De Anza College (U)
Delta College (U)
DePaul University (G)
Des Moines Area Community College (N)
Duquesne University (G)
East Carolina University (G)
Eastern Michigan University (G)
Eastern New Mexico University (U)
Eastern Oklahoma State College (U)
Eastern Wyoming College (U)
East Tennessee State University (N)
Edgecombe Community College (N,U)
Edison State Community College (N,U)
Everett Community College (N)
Finger Lakes Community College (N)
Florida State University (N)
Fontbonne University (U,G)
Forrest Junior College (U)
Fulton-Montgomery Community College (N)
Gateway Community College (N)
Glenville State College (U)
Golden West College (U)
Grantham University (U)
Hagerstown Community College (N)
Halifax Community College (N)
Haywood Community College (N)
Hillsborough Community College (U)
Illinois Eastern Community Colleges, Lincoln Trail College (U)
Immaculata University (U)
Indiana Business College (N)
Indiana University–Purdue University Fort Wayne (N)
Indiana Wesleyan University (U)
Iowa Western Community College (U)
Jackson Community College (N,U)
Jacksonville State University (U,G)
James Sprunt Community College (U)
Jamestown Community College (N)
Jefferson College of Health Sciences (U)
Jefferson Davis Community College (U)
Johnson County Community College (N,U)
Jones College (U)
J. Sargeant Reynolds Community College (U)
Judson College (U)
Kansas State University (G)
Kean University (N)
Lake Superior College (U)
Lamar State College–Port Arthur (N,U)
Lewis and Clark Community College (N)
Limestone College (U)
Linn-Benton Community College (U)
Louisiana State University at Eunice (N,U)
Macon State College (N,U)
Madison Area Technical College (U)
Marion Technical College (U)
Maryville University of Saint Louis (N)
Massasoit Community College (N,U)
Mercer County Community College (U)
Mercy College (G)
Middlesex Community College (N,U)
Middle Tennessee State University (N)
Midland College (U)
Mid Michigan Community College (U)
Midstate College (U)
Mitchell Technical Institute (N,U)
Mohawk Valley Community College (N,U)
Montana Tech of The University of Montana (U)
Montgomery Community College (N,U)
Mt. San Antonio College (N)
Mount Wachusett Community College (N,U)
Myers University (U)
National University (U)
New Mexico Junior College (U)
New York Institute of Technology (N)
Niagara University (N)
North Arkansas College (N)
North Dakota State University (N)
North Georgia College & State University (N)
North Idaho College (N)
North Seattle Community College (U)
Northwestern College (U)
Northwestern Connecticut Community College (N)
Northwestern Michigan College (U)
Northwestern State University of Louisiana (U)
Nova Southeastern University (G)
Odessa College (N)
Orange Coast College (U)
Oregon State University (N)
Ouachita Technical College (U)
Oxnard College (U)
Pace University (U,G)
Palomar College (U)
Parkland College (U)
Pasco-Hernando Community College (N,U)
Peirce College (U)
Portland Community College (N,U)
Quinebaug Valley Community College (N)
Radford University (N)
Randolph Community College (N,U)
Raritan Valley Community College (U)
Rasmussen College Eden Prarie (U)
Red Rocks Community College (U)
Rend Lake College (N)
Sacramento City College (U)
Saint Leo University (U)
St. Louis Community College System (U)
San Diego State University (N)
San Francisco State University (N)
San Joaquin Delta College (U)
Schenectady County Community College (U)
Schoolcraft College (N,U)
Seattle Pacific University (G)
Seminole Community College (U)
Shenandoah University (U)
Sinclair Community College (U)
Snow College (U)
Solano Community College (U)
Sonoma State University (N)
South Central College (U)
Southeast Arkansas College (U)
Southern Methodist University (G)
South Piedmont Community College (U)
Southwestern Oregon Community College (U)
Southwest Georgia Technical College (U)
Southwest Wisconsin Technical College (U)
Spartanburg Technical College (U)
State University of New York College at Potsdam (N)
State University of New York College of Agriculture and Technology at Morrisville (U)
Syracuse University (G)
Taylor University (N)
Texas A&M University–Kingsville (N)
Texas State Technical College Waco (N,U)
Three Rivers Community College (N)
Tompkins Cortland Community College (N,U)
Tyler Junior College (N,U)
The University of Akron (N,U,G)
University of Alaska Fairbanks (U)
University of Alberta (G)
University of California, Berkeley (U)
University of California, Davis (U)
University of California, Riverside (N)
University of Cincinnati (U)
University of Cincinnati Raymond Walters College (U)
University of Connecticut (U)
University of Florida (G)
University of Great Falls (U)
University of Houston–Clear Lake (G)
University of Houston–Downtown (U)
University of Illinois at Urbana–Champaign (G)
University of Lethbridge (U)
The University of Maine at Augusta (U)
University of Michigan–Flint (N)
University of Minnesota, Twin Cities Campus (U)
The University of Montana–Western (U)
The University of North Carolina at Charlotte (N)
The University of North Carolina at Greensboro (N)
University of North Dakota (N)
University of North Texas (U,G)
University of Southern Indiana (N)
University of South Florida (G)
The University of Texas at Dallas (G)
University of Tulsa (G)
University of Washington (N)
University of West Florida (U)
Utah State University (G)
Utah Valley State College (N)
Vance-Granville Community College (N)

Virginia Polytechnic Institute and State University (N)
Wake Technical Community College (N,U)
Washtenaw Community College (U)
Western Michigan University (U)
Western Piedmont Community College (U)
Western Wyoming Community College (U)
West Virginia University (N)
Westwood Online (U)
Wharton County Junior College (U)
William Rainey Harper College (U)
York County Community College (U)
York University (N)

COMPUTER SYSTEMS ANALYSIS

Athabasca University (N,U,G)
Bellevue University (U)
Bridgewater State College (N)
Central Michigan University (G)
Central Texas College (U)
College of Southern Maryland (U)
The Community College of Baltimore County (U)
Dakota State University (U)
Dallas County Community College District (U)
DePaul University (G)
East Tennessee State University (N)
Edgecombe Community College (U)
Edison State Community College (U)
Granite State College (U)
Grantham University (U)
Heart of Georgia Technical College (U)
Immaculata University (U)
Jacksonville State University (U,G)
Jones College (U)
Lamar State College–Port Arthur (N)
Limestone College (U)
Macon State College (U)
Maryville University of Saint Louis (N)
Mercy College (G)
Middlesex Community College (N)
Midland College (N)
Mohawk Valley Community College (N)
Myers University (U)
Nova Southeastern University (G)
Oxnard College (U)
Ozarka College (N)
Pace University (G)
Pueblo Community College (U)
Red Rocks Community College (U)
St. Edward's University (N,U,G)
Saint Leo University (U)
Seminole Community College (U)
Shenandoah University (N)
Southeast Arkansas College (U)
Southern Polytechnic State University (G)
South Piedmont Community College (U)
Syracuse University (G)
Texas State Technical College Waco (U)
Tri-County Community College (U)
Tyler Junior College (U)
The University of Akron (N)
University of California, Davis (U)
University of Dallas (G)
University of Houston–Downtown (U)
University of Illinois at Urbana–Champaign (G)
University of New Orleans (U,G)
The University of North Carolina at Greensboro (N)
University of Washington (N)
Utah State University (G)

COMPUTER SYSTEMS NETWORKING AND TELECOMMUNICATIONS

Alpena Community College (U)
Arizona State University (U)
Arkansas State University–Beebe (U)
Asheville-Buncombe Technical Community College (N)
Athabasca University (U)
Bainbridge College (N)
Bellevue University (U)
Bellingham Technical College (U)
Blackhawk Technical College (U)
Bloomfield College (N)
Blue Ridge Community College (N,U)
Bowling Green State University (U)
Bryant and Stratton Online (U)
Capella University (U,G)
Capitol College (G)
Carl Albert State College (U)
Cayuga County Community College (U)
Central Missouri State University (N)
Central Texas College (U)
Champlain College (U)
Cincinnati State Technical and Community College (U)
Clark College (U)
Clemson University (N)
Cleveland State University (N)
Coffeyville Community College (U)
College of DuPage (U)
College of Southern Maryland (U)
College of The Albemarle (N)
The Community College of Baltimore County (U)
Connecticut State University System (G)
Corning Community College (U)
Dakota County Technical College (U)
Dallas County Community College District (U)
Darton College (U)
De Anza College (U)
DePaul University (U,G)
DeVry University Online (G)
East Carolina University (G)
Eastern Michigan University (U)
East Tennessee State University (N)
Edgecombe Community College (U)
Edison State Community College (U)
Forrest Junior College (U)
Fresno City College (U)
Fulton-Montgomery Community College (N)
George Mason University (G)
Grantham University (U)
Hagerstown Community College (N)
Halifax Community College (N)
Harford Community College (N,U)
Heart of Georgia Technical College (U)
Illinois Eastern Community Colleges, Lincoln Trail College (U)
Illinois Institute of Technology (G)
Independence Community College (U)
Indiana University–Purdue University Fort Wayne (N)
Jacksonville State University (U,G)
James Madison University (N)
Jamestown Community College (N)
Johnson County Community College (U)
Keiser College (U)
Lamar State College–Port Arthur (N,U)
Limestone College (U)
Macon State College (N,U)
Madison Area Technical College (U)
Maryville University of Saint Louis (N)
Mercer County Community College (N)
Middle Tennessee State University (N)
Midland College (N)
Mohawk Valley Community College (N)
Murray State University (U,G)
Myers University (U)
New Jersey Institute of Technology (U,G)
North Central Texas College (U)
North Idaho College (N)
North Seattle Community College (U)
Northwestern Michigan College (U)
Nova Southeastern University (G)
Old Dominion University (U)
Ouachita Technical College (U)
Oxnard College (U)
Ozarka College (N)
Pace University (U,G)
Pasco-Hernando Community College (U)
Patrick Henry Community College (U)
Peirce College (U)
Portland Community College (N)
Pueblo Community College (U)
Pulaski Technical College (U)
Raritan Valley Community College (U)
Rasmussen College Eden Prarie (U)
Red Rocks Community College (U)
Saint Leo University (U)
Salem Community College (U)
San Joaquin Delta College (U)
Seminole Community College (U)
Shenandoah University (U)
Sinclair Community College (U)
Solano Community College (U)
Sonoma State University (N)
Southeast Arkansas College (U)
Southern Arkansas University Tech (U)
Southern Methodist University (G)
Southern Polytechnic State University (G)
South Piedmont Community College (U)
Southwest Georgia Technical College (U)
Southwest Wisconsin Technical College (U)
Stanford University (N)
Stanly Community College (U)
State University of New York at Buffalo (U)
State University of New York at Oswego (U)
Syracuse University (U,G)
Taylor University (N)
Texas State Technical College Waco (U)
Tompkins Cortland Community College (N)
Tunxis Community College (U)
Tyler Junior College (U)
The University of Akron (N,U)
The University of Alabama (U)
University of California, Davis (U)
University of Colorado at Boulder (N,G)
University of Dallas (G)
University of Denver (G)
University of Houston–Downtown (U)
University of Illinois at Urbana–Champaign (G)
University of Maryland University College (G)
University of Massachusetts Lowell (U)
University of Minnesota, Twin Cities Campus (U)
The University of Texas System (U)
University of Tulsa (G)
University of West Florida (U)
University of Wisconsin–Stout (N)

Utah State University (G)
Vance-Granville Community College (N,U)
Wake Technical Community College (U)
Waukesha County Technical College (U)
Westchester Community College (U)
Western Piedmont Community College (U)
Westwood Online (U)
Wharton County Junior College (U)
William Rainey Harper College (U)
Worcester Polytechnic Institute (G)
Yuba College (U)

COMPUTER/INFORMATION TECHNOLOGY ADMINISTRATION AND MANAGEMENT

Alpena Community College (U)
Alvin Community College (U)
American Military University (U)
American Public University (U)
Athabasca University (N,U,G)
Baker College of Flint (U)
Bellevue University (U)
Bellingham Technical College (N)
Big Sandy Community and Technical College (U)
Bloomfield College (U)
Blue Ridge Community College (N,U)
Bridgewater State College (U)
Broome Community College (U)
Bryant and Stratton Online (U)
Caldwell Community College and Technical Institute (N)
California State University, Dominguez Hills (N)
Cape Breton University (N)
Capella University (U,G)
Capitol College (G)
Central Washington University (U)
Champlain College (U)
Cincinnati State Technical and Community College (U)
Cleveland Community College (U)
Cleveland Institute of Electronics (N)
Coleman College (U)
College of Southern Maryland (N)
College of Staten Island of the City University of New York (N)
College of The Albemarle (N)
Colorado Technical University (U,G)
The Community College of Baltimore County (U)
Community College of Denver (U)
Copiah-Lincoln Community College (U)
Dakota County Technical College (U)
Dallas Baptist University (G)
Dallas County Community College District (U)
DePaul University (G)
Drexel University (G)
Duquesne University (G)
D'Youville College (U)
East Carolina University (U,G)
Edgecombe Community College (N,U)
Edison State Community College (N,U)
Elgin Community College (U)
Forrest Junior College (U)
Franklin Pierce College (U,G)
Galveston College (N)
Gogebic Community College (U)
Granite State College (U)
Grantham University (U)
Greenfield Community College (U)
Hillsborough Community College (U)
Houston Community College System (U)
Immaculata University (U)
Jacksonville State University (U,G)
John Jay College of Criminal Justice of the City University of New York (U)
Keiser College (U)
Kettering University (N)
Lamar State College–Port Arthur (N)
Limestone College (U)
Madison Area Technical College (U)
Mercy College (G)
Middle Tennessee State University (N)
Mohawk Valley Community College (N)
Myers University (U)
New Jersey Institute of Technology (G)
New York Institute of Technology (N)
North Arkansas College (N,U)
North Central Texas College (U)
North Dakota State College of Science (U)
North Idaho College (N)
Northwest Missouri State University (G)
Nova Southeastern University (G)
Orange Coast College (U)
Oregon Institute of Technology (U)
Oxnard College (U)
Ozarka College (N)
Pace University (G)
Patrick Henry Community College (U)
Peirce College (U)
Portland Community College (N)
Raritan Valley Community College (U)
Rasmussen College Eden Prarie (U)
Ryerson University (U)
St. Edward's University (N,G)
Saint Joseph's College of Maine (U)
Salem Community College (U)
Schiller International University (G)
Seminole Community College (U)
Sonoma State University (N)
Southeast Arkansas College (U)
Southern Illinois University Carbondale (U)
Southern Methodist University (G)
South Piedmont Community College (U)
Southwestern College (U)
Southwest Georgia Technical College (U)
State University of New York at Buffalo (U)
State University of New York College of Agriculture and Technology at Morrisville (U)
Syracuse University (G)
Taylor University (N,U)
Touro University International (U,G)
Tyler Junior College (U)
The University of Akron (N)
University of Alberta (G)
University of Arkansas at Pine Bluff (N)
University of California, Davis (U)
University of Cincinnati Raymond Walters College (U)
University of Connecticut (U)
University of Denver (G)
University of Houston–Downtown (U)
University of Illinois at Urbana–Champaign (G)
University of Maryland University College (G)
University of Massachusetts Boston (U)
University of North Texas (U)
University of Southern Indiana (U)
The University of Tennessee (N)
The University of Toledo (U)
University of Toronto (N,U)
University of Tulsa (G)
University of Virginia (N,U)
University of Washington (N)
Vance-Granville Community College (U)
West Los Angeles College (U)
West Virginia University at Parkersburg (N,U)
William Rainey Harper College (U)
York County Community College (U)

CONSTRUCTION ENGINEERING

Cleveland Institute of Electronics (N)
Seminole Community College (U)
University of South Florida (G)

CONSTRUCTION ENGINEERING TECHNOLOGY

Bowling Green State University (G)
Clemson University (N)
College of Staten Island of the City University of New York (N)
Indiana State University (U)
Ivy Tech Community College–Northeast (U)
James Madison University (N)
National University (U)
Orange Coast College (U)
Pennsylvania College of Technology (U)
Seminole Community College (U)
Stanford University (N)
University of Southern Mississippi (G)
University of Washington (U,G)

CONSTRUCTION MANAGEMENT

Auburn University (N)
Central Michigan University (U)
Clemson University (U,G)
Colorado State University (U)
Columbus State Community College (U)
East Carolina University (G)
Indiana State University (U)
Sullivan University (G)
Texas A&M University–Commerce (G)
University of California, Berkeley (U)
University of Florida (G)
Washtenaw Community College (U)

CONSTRUCTION TRADES

Central Michigan University (U)
Cleveland Institute of Electronics (N)
Lock Haven University of Pennsylvania (N)

CONSTRUCTION TRADES RELATED

Bowling Green State University (N)
James Madison University (N)
Sullivan University (G)
West Virginia University at Parkersburg (N)

COSMETOLOGY AND RELATED PERSONAL GROOMING SERVICES

James Madison University (N)
Southwest Wisconsin Technical College (U)

COUNSELING PSYCHOLOGY

Amberton University (G)
Athabasca University (N,U,G)
Atlantic University (N,G)

Baptist Bible College of Pennsylvania (G)
The Baptist College of Florida (U)
Bethany University (U)
Briercrest Distance Learning (U)
Capella University (G)
Carlow University (G)
Central Texas College (U)
Chadron State College (G)
Cleveland Institute of Electronics (N)
College of the Southwest (G)
Columbia Basin College (U)
Columbus State Community College (U)
Corban College (U)
Housatonic Community College (U)
Immaculata University (U)
Indiana State University (G)
James Madison University (N)
Liberty University (G)
Master's College and Seminary (U)
Mercy College (G)
Mississippi State University (U,G)
Montana State University–Billings (G)
Moody Bible Institute (U)
Naropa University (U)
National University (U)
Oklahoma State University (U)
Palomar College (U)
Prescott College (U)
Providence College and Theological Seminary (N,G)
Regent University (G)
St. Cloud State University (U)
St. Edward's University (G)
Saybrook Graduate School and Research Center (G)
Southwestern Assemblies of God University (G)
State University of New York at Oswego (U,G)
Taylor University (U)
The University of Akron (G)
University of Alaska Fairbanks (G)
University of Bridgeport (U)
University of California, Berkeley (U)
University of Great Falls (U)
University of Hawaii–West Oahu (U)
University of Houston–Victoria (G)
The University of Maine at Augusta (U)
University of Maryland Eastern Shore (G)
University of Massachusetts Boston (G)
University of Missouri–Columbia (G)
University of Nevada, Reno (U,G)
The University of North Carolina at Charlotte (N)
The University of Toledo (G)
University of Wisconsin–River Falls (G)
Wayland Baptist University (G)
Wayne State College (G)
Western Michigan University (G)

CRAFTS, FOLK ART AND ARTISANRY

Blackhawk Technical College (N)
Cleveland Institute of Electronics (N)
Cleveland State University (G)
Hillsborough Community College (N)
James Madison University (N)
Maryville University of Saint Louis (N)
Middle Tennessee State University (N)
Naugatuck Valley Community College (N)
The University of Tennessee at Martin (N)
Western Oklahoma State College (U)

West Virginia University at Parkersburg (N)

CREATIVE WRITING

Adams State College (N)
Alvin Community College (U)
Arkansas State University–Beebe (U)
Athabasca University (U)
Athens Technical College (N)
Atlantic University (N,G)
Bellevue Community College (U)
Blackhawk Technical College (N)
Blue Ridge Community College (N)
Bowling Green State University (U,G)
Bridgewater State College (N)
Brigham Young University (N)
Butler County Community College (U)
Caldwell Community College and Technical Institute (N)
Cape Breton University (U)
Cape Fear Community College (U)
Cardinal Stritch University (N)
Casper College (U)
Central New Mexico Community College (U)
Champlain College (U)
Clark State Community College (U)
Clatsop Community College (U)
Clemson University (N)
Cleveland Institute of Electronics (N)
Coconino Community College (N)
Coleman College (U)
College of Southern Maryland (U)
College of the Siskiyous (N)
College of the Southwest (U)
Columbus State Community College (U)
Community College of Denver (U)
County College of Morris (U)
Cowley County Community College and Area Vocational–Technical School (U)
Dakota County Technical College (U)
Dallas County Community College District (U)
Darton College (N)
Dawson Community College (U)
Des Moines Area Community College (U)
DeVry University Online (U)
Drake University (U)
D'Youville College (G)
Earlham School of Religion (G)
East Tennessee State University (N)
Erie Community College (U)
Feather River College (U)
Hillsborough Community College (U)
Immaculata University (U)
Indiana Business College (N)
Iowa Western Community College (U)
James Madison University (N)
Jamestown Community College (N)
John A. Logan College (U)
John Tyler Community College (U)
Judson College (U)
Kean University (N)
Lamar State College–Port Arthur (N)
Lansing Community College (U)
Limestone College (U)
Linn-Benton Community College (U)
Marylhurst University (U)
Maryville University of Saint Louis (N)
Massasoit Community College (N)
Mercy College (U)
Middlesex Community College (N)
Missouri State University (U)
Mount Allison University (N)
Mount Saint Vincent University (N)
Mt. San Antonio College (U)
Naropa University (N,U)
National University (G)
New Mexico State University–Carlsbad (N)
The New School (N,U)
New York Institute of Technology (U)
Northern Virginia Community College (U)
North Idaho College (N)
Northwestern Michigan College (U)
Northwestern State University of Louisiana (U)
Odessa College (N)
Oklahoma State University (U)
Oregon State University (U)
Oxnard College (U)
Ozarka College (N)
Ozarks Technical Community College (U)
Park University (U)
The Pennsylvania State University University Park Campus (U)
Portland Community College (N)
Prescott College (U,G)
Pueblo Community College (U)
Queen's University at Kingston (U)
Raritan Valley Community College (U)
Sacramento City College (U)
St. Clair County Community College (U)
St. Cloud State University (U)
Saint Mary-of-the-Woods College (U)
Sam Houston State University (U)
San Joaquin Delta College (U)
Shoreline Community College (U)
Sinclair Community College (U)
Solano Community College (U)
Southwestern Assemblies of God University (U)
Southwest Virginia Community College (U)
State University of New York College at Potsdam (N)
State University of New York College of Agriculture and Technology at Morrisville (U)
Stephens College (U)
Taft College (U)
Taylor University (N,U)
Texas A&M University–Commerce (U)
Texas State University-San Marcos (U)
Three Rivers Community College (U)
Treasure Valley Community College (U)
Tyler Junior College (U)
The University of Akron (U)
The University of Alabama (U)
University of California, Berkeley (U,G)
University of Central Arkansas (U)
University of Colorado at Denver and Health Sciences Center—Downtown Denver Campus (U)
University of Denver (G)
University of Illinois at Springfield (U)
The University of Iowa (U,G)
University of La Verne (U)
University of Maine (U)
The University of Maine at Augusta (U)
University of Maine at Fort Kent (U)
University of Minnesota, Twin Cities Campus (U)
University of Missouri–Columbia (U)
University of Nevada, Reno (U)
University of New Brunswick Fredericton (N)
University of New Orleans (U,G)
The University of North Carolina at Chapel Hill (N,U)

University of Northern Colorado (U)
University of Southern Mississippi (U)
The University of Tennessee (N,U)
The University of Texas System (U)
University of Utah (U)
University of Washington (N,U)
University of Wisconsin–Whitewater (U,G)
Utah Valley State College (U)
Vincennes University (U)
Western Washington University (U)
West Los Angeles College (U)
Wharton County Junior College (U)
Wilkes Community College (U)
William Rainey Harper College (U)

CRIMINAL JUSTICE AND CORRECTIONS

Adams State College (U)
Adirondack Community College (U)
Alpena Community College (U)
American Military University (U,G)
American Public University (U,G)
Andrew Jackson University (U,G)
Anne Arundel Community College (U)
Arizona Western College (U)
Arkansas State University–Beebe (U)
Athabasca University (N,U)
Auburn University Montgomery (U,G)
Bergen Community College (U)
Berkeley College (U)
Big Sandy Community and Technical College (U)
Bismarck State College (U)
Blackhawk Technical College (N,U)
Blinn College (U)
Blue Ridge Community College (N,U)
Boise State University (U)
Brenau University (U)
Buena Vista University (U)
Butler Community College (U)
Caldwell College (U)
Caldwell Community College and Technical Institute (N)
California State University, San Bernardino (U,G)
California University of Pennsylvania (U,G)
Capella University (G)
Central Carolina Community College (N,U)
Central Lakes College (U)
Central Missouri State University (U,G)
Central New Mexico Community College (U)
Central Oregon Community College (U)
Central Piedmont Community College (U)
Central Texas College (U)
Central Washington University (U)
Central Wyoming College (U)
Chesapeake College (U)
Clackamas Community College (U)
Clinton Community College (U)
Clovis Community College (U)
Coconino Community College (U)
College of DuPage (U)
College of Southern Maryland (U)
College of the Southwest (U)
Colorado Technical University (U)
Columbia College (U)
The Community College of Baltimore County (U)
Community College of Beaver County (U)
Community College of Southern Nevada (U)
Connecticut State University System (U)
Contra Costa College (U)
Dallas Baptist University (U,G)
Danville Community College (U)
Darton College (U)
Dawson Community College (U)
Delta College (U)
Des Moines Area Community College (U)
Drury University (N)
East Carolina University (G)
Eastern Oklahoma State College (U)
Eastern Wyoming College (U)
East Tennessee State University (U)
Erie Community College (U)
Fayetteville State University (U,G)
Florida Atlantic University (U)
Florida Gulf Coast University (U)
Fort Hays State University (U)
Fort Valley State University (U)
Franklin Pierce College (U)
Frostburg State University (U)
Glenville State College (U)
Golden West College (U)
Grand View College (U)
Granite State College (U)
Grantham University (U)
Indiana State University (U,G)
Indiana Wesleyan University (U)
Iowa State University of Science and Technology (U)
Iowa Western Community College (U)
Ivy Tech Community College–Bloomington (U)
Ivy Tech Community College–Central Indiana (U)
Ivy Tech Community College–East Central (U)
Ivy Tech Community College–Kokomo (U)
Ivy Tech Community College–Southeast (U)
Ivy Tech Community College–Southern Indiana (U)
Ivy Tech Community College–Southwest (U)
Ivy Tech Community College–Whitewater (U)
Jacksonville State University (U,G)
James Madison University (N)
James Sprunt Community College (U)
John Jay College of Criminal Justice of the City University of New York (U)
John Tyler Community College (U)
J. Sargeant Reynolds Community College (U)
Judson College (U)
Kean University (U)
Keiser College (U)
Lehigh Carbon Community College (U)
Lewis and Clark Community College (U)
Limestone College (U)
Linn-Benton Community College (U)
Los Angeles Harbor College (U)
Madison Area Technical College (U)
Madonna University (N,U)
Mansfield University of Pennsylvania (U)
Mercy College (U)
Metropolitan State University (U,G)
Middlesex Community College (U)
Middle Tennessee State University (U)
Missouri State University (G)
Mohawk Valley Community College (U)
Monmouth University (G)
Monroe Community College (U)
Montgomery Community College (U)
Mountain Empire Community College (U)
Mount Wachusett Community College (U)
Myers University (U)
National University (U)
Naugatuck Valley Community College (U)
New Jersey City University (U)
New Mexico Junior College (U)
New Mexico State University (G)
New Mexico State University–Carlsbad (N,U)
New York Institute of Technology (U)
Northwestern Michigan College (U)
Northwestern Oklahoma State University (U)
Northwestern State University of Louisiana (U)
Old Dominion University (U)
Ouachita Technical College (U)
Oxnard College (U)
Ozarka College (U)
Ozarks Technical Community College (U)
Pace University (U)
Palomar College (U)
Park University (U)
Passaic County Community College (U)
Peninsula College (U)
The Pennsylvania State University University Park Campus (U)
Portland State University (U)
Pueblo Community College (U)
Randolph Community College (U)
Rappahannock Community College (U)
Raritan Valley Community College (U)
Rasmussen College Eden Prarie (U)
Roger Williams University (U)
Roosevelt University (U)
Ryerson University (U)
St. Cloud State University (U,G)
St. Edward's University (U)
St. John's University (U)
Saint Leo University (U)
San Joaquin Delta College (U)
Saybrook Graduate School and Research Center (G)
Schenectady County Community College (U)
Schoolcraft College (U)
Seminole Community College (U)
Shippensburg University of Pennsylvania (U,G)
Shoreline Community College (U)
Simpson College (U)
Snow College (U)
Solano Community College (U)
Southeast Arkansas College (U)
Southern Illinois University Carbondale (U)
Southern Oregon University (U)
South Piedmont Community College (U)
Southwestern Oregon Community College (U)
Southwest Georgia Technical College (U)
Stanly Community College (U)
State University of New York at Oswego (U)
Tacoma Community College (U)
Taft College (U)
Taylor University (U)
Texas A&M University–Commerce (U)
Texas A&M University–Kingsville (U)
Texas A&M University–Texarkana (U)
Touro University International (U,G)
Tunxis Community College (N,U)
Tyler Junior College (U)
The University of Akron (U)
The University of Alabama (U)
University of Alaska Fairbanks (U)
University of Cincinnati (U)
University of Colorado at Colorado Springs (G)
University of Connecticut (U)
University of Delaware (U)
The University of Findlay (U)
University of Florida (U)

University of Great Falls (U,G)
University of Hawaii–West Oahu (U)
University of Houston–Downtown (U,G)
The University of Maine at Augusta (U)
University of Maine at Fort Kent (U)
University of Maryland University College (U)
University of Massachusetts Amherst (U)
University of Massachusetts Boston (U,G)
University of Massachusetts Lowell (G)
University of Nevada, Reno (U)
University of North Alabama (U)
The University of North Carolina at Chapel Hill (U)
The University of North Carolina Wilmington (U)
University of Pittsburgh at Bradford (U)
University of Southern Mississippi (U,G)
University of South Florida (U,G)
The University of Tennessee at Martin (N)
The University of Texas at Tyler (U)
The University of Texas of the Permian Basin (G)
University of Wisconsin–Platteville (G)
University of Wyoming (U)
Upper Iowa University (U)
Vance-Granville Community College (U)
Vincennes University (U)
Wake Technical Community College (U)
Washburn University (G)
Wayland Baptist University (U)
Westchester Community College (U)
Western Piedmont Community College (U)
West Los Angeles College (U)
West Shore Community College (U)
West Virginia Northern Community College (U)
West Virginia University at Parkersburg (U)
Westwood Online (U)
Wharton County Junior College (U)
William Rainey Harper College (U)

CRIMINOLOGY

Adams State College (U)
Adirondack Community College (U)
American Military University (U)
American Public University (U)
Athabasca University (N,U)
Bellevue Community College (U)
Berkeley College (U)
Berkeley College-New York City Campus (U)
Berkeley College-Westchester Campus (U)
Bismarck State College (U)
Blinn College (U)
Brenau University (U)
Bridgewater State College (U)
Butler Community College (U)
Butler County Community College (U)
Cape Fear Community College (U)
Central Texas College (U)
Chadron State College (U)
Charter Oak State College (U)
Clatsop Community College (U)
Colorado Technical University (U)
The Community College of Baltimore County (U)
Dallas Baptist University (U)
Danville Community College (U)
Des Moines Area Community College (U)
Drury University (U,G)
East Carolina University (G)
Eastern Oregon University (U)
Everett Community College (U)
Florida Atlantic University (G)
Golden West College (U)
Granite State College (U)
Houston Community College System (U)
Indiana State University (U,G)
Indiana University of Pennsylvania (U)
Indiana Wesleyan University (U)
Iowa Western Community College (U)
Itawamba Community College (U)
Jacksonville State University (U,G)
Lehigh Carbon Community College (U)
Lewis and Clark Community College (U)
Lock Haven University of Pennsylvania (U)
Los Angeles Harbor College (U)
Louisiana State University and Agricultural and Mechanical College (U)
Memorial University of Newfoundland (G)
Mohawk Valley Community College (U)
Mountain Empire Community College (U)
Mount Wachusett Community College (U)
Myers University (U)
National University (G)
Neumann College (U)
New Jersey City University (G)
North Central Texas College (U)
Ozarks Technical Community College (U)
Pace University (U)
Park University (U)
Radford University (G)
Raritan Valley Community College (U)
Rasmussen College Eden Prarie (U)
Roger Williams University (U)
Saint Joseph's College of Maine (U)
Saint Leo University (U)
Seminole Community College (U)
Solano Community College (U)
Southeast Arkansas College (U)
Southern Illinois University Carbondale (U)
Southern Oregon University (U)
Southwest Georgia Technical College (U)
Texas State University-San Marcos (U)
Tunxis Community College (U)
The University of Akron (U)
University of Connecticut (G)
The University of Findlay (U)
University of Florida (U)
University of Hawaii–West Oahu (U)
University of La Verne (U)
University of Massachusetts Lowell (G)
University of Northern Iowa (U,G)
University of Southern Mississippi (U)
University of South Florida (G)
The University of Texas at Arlington (U)
The University of Texas at Tyler (U)
The University of Texas of the Permian Basin (U,G)
The University of Toledo (U)
University of Washington (U)
University of Waterloo (U)
University of Wisconsin–Platteville (G)
Vance-Granville Community College (U)

CULINARY ARTS AND RELATED SERVICES

Ashworth College (N)
Blackhawk Technical College (U)
Central New Mexico Community College (U)
Central Piedmont Community College (N)
Central Texas College (U)
Columbus State Community College (U)
Contra Costa College (U)
East Tennessee State University (N)
Hagerstown Community College (N)
James Madison University (N)
Middle Tennessee State University (N)
Mitchell Technical Institute (U)
Mohawk Valley Community College (U)
Naugatuck Valley Community College (U)
New York Institute of Technology (N)
Oxnard College (U)
Ozarka College (U)
Ozarks Technical Community College (U)
Schenectady County Community College (U)
Schoolcraft College (U)
Southwest Wisconsin Technical College (U)
State University of New York College at Potsdam (N)
Western Nevada Community College (U)
York County Community College (U)

CURRICULUM AND INSTRUCTION

Alcorn State University (U)
Alvin Community College (U)
Arizona State University (U,G)
Athabasca University (G)
Bloomsburg University of Pennsylvania (G)
Boise State University (U,G)
Boston University (G)
Brenau University (U)
Bridgewater State College (U)
Brigham Young University (U)
Buena Vista University (U,G)
California State University, Chico (U)
Central Michigan University (G)
Central Missouri State University (U,G)
Chadron State College (G)
Cleveland State University (G)
The College of St. Scholastica (G)
College of the Southwest (G)
Columbia College (U)
Columbia International University (G)
Concordia University Wisconsin (G)
Connecticut State University System (U,G)
Dallas Baptist University (G)
Drexel University (G)
Duquesne University (G)
East Carolina University (U)
East Tennessee State University (U)
Fort Valley State University (U)
Frostburg State University (G)
Georgia Southern University (G)
Indiana State University (U,G)
Jacksonville State University (U,G)
Lehigh Carbon Community College (U)
Lesley University (G)
Lewis and Clark Community College (N)
Liberty University (G)
Louisiana State University and Agricultural and Mechanical College (U)
McMurry University (U)
Mississippi State University (U,G)
Missouri State University (G)
Mitchell Technical Institute (U)
Montana State University–Billings (U,G)
North Carolina State University (G)
North Dakota State University (G)
Northwestern Oklahoma State University (U)
The Pennsylvania State University University Park Campus (G)
Radford University (G)
Saint Joseph's College of Maine (G)
Seattle Pacific University (G)
Shoreline Community College (N)

Southern Arkansas University Tech (U)
Southwestern Assemblies of God University (U)
Southwestern Oregon Community College (U)
Southwest Wisconsin Technical College (U)
State University of New York at New Paltz (U)
State University of New York at Oswego (G)
Stephen F. Austin State University (U)
Texas A&M University–Commerce (G)
Texas Tech University (G)
The University of Akron (N,U,G)
University of Alaska Fairbanks (G)
University of Arkansas (U)
University of Central Arkansas (G)
University of Florida (G)
University of Houston–Victoria (G)
University of La Verne (N)
University of Massachusetts Lowell (G)
University of Missouri–Columbia (U,G)
The University of Montana (U,G)
University of Nebraska–Lincoln (U,G)
University of Nevada, Reno (U,G)
University of New Orleans (U,G)
The University of North Carolina at Greensboro (G)
University of North Florida (U,G)
University of North Texas (U,G)
University of Saskatchewan (U)
University of Southern Mississippi (G)
University of South Florida (U,G)
The University of Tennessee (U)
The University of Texas at Arlington (G)
The University of Texas at Tyler (U)
The University of Texas of the Permian Basin (U,G)
The University of Texas System (U,G)
The University of Toledo (U,G)
University of Washington (U)
University of Wisconsin–River Falls (G)
University of Wisconsin–Whitewater (U)
Utah State University (G)
Vanguard University of Southern California (U)
Virginia Polytechnic Institute and State University (G)
Western Washington University (U)
Winston-Salem State University (U)

DANCE

Arizona State University at the Polytechnic Campus (U)
Brigham Young University (U)
California State University, Chico (U)
Central Wyoming College (N)
Middle Tennessee State University (N)
Naugatuck Valley Community College (N)
Orange Coast College (U)
Texas State University-San Marcos (U)
The University of North Carolina at Greensboro (G)
University of Waterloo (U)
West Virginia University at Parkersburg (N)

DATA ENTRY/MICROCOMPUTER APPLICATIONS

Arkansas State University–Beebe (U)
Asheville-Buncombe Technical Community College (N,U)
Athabasca University (N)
Athens Technical College (N)
Berkeley College (U)
Berkeley College-New York City Campus (U)
Berkeley College-Westchester Campus (U)
Broome Community College (N)
Butler Community College (U)
Butler County Community College (U)
Carl Albert State College (U)
Central Wyoming College (N)
Clemson University (N)
Cleveland Institute of Electronics (N)
Cleveland State Community College (U)
Cleveland State University (N)
College of The Albemarle (N)
Colorado State University-Pueblo (N)
Dallas County Community College District (U)
De Anza College (U)
Des Moines Area Community College (U)
East Carolina University (U)
Edgecombe Community College (N,U)
Grantham University (U)
Halifax Community College (N)
Iowa Western Community College (U)
James Madison University (N)
Lamar State College–Port Arthur (N,U)
Lewis and Clark Community College (U)
Limestone College (U)
Maryville University of Saint Louis (N)
Middlesex Community College (U)
Mitchell Technical Institute (N)
Mount Saint Vincent University (U)
Myers University (U)
Naugatuck Valley Community College (N)
North Dakota State University (N,U)
Oxnard College (U)
Ozarka College (U)
Palomar College (U)
St. Louis Community College System (U)
Seminole Community College (U)
Solano Community College (U)
South Central College (U)
Southeast Arkansas College (U)
Spartanburg Technical College (U)
State University of New York at Buffalo (U)
State University of New York College at Potsdam (N)
Tacoma Community College (U)
Taylor University (N)
Texas State Technical College Waco (U)
Tri-County Community College (U)
The University of Akron (N)
University of California, Berkeley (U)
University of Minnesota, Crookston (U)
The University of North Carolina at Greensboro (N)
University of North Texas (U)
University of West Florida (U)
Utah State University (U)
Vance-Granville Community College (N)
West Los Angeles College (U)

DATA PROCESSING

Adams State College (N)
Athabasca University (N,U)
Central New Mexico Community College (U)
Cincinnati State Technical and Community College (U)
Clemson University (N)
College of The Albemarle (N)
The Community College of Baltimore County (U)
Dallas County Community College District (U)
Des Moines Area Community College (U)
East Carolina University (U,G)
Erie Community College (U)
Feather River College (U)
Jacksonville State University (U)
John A. Logan College (U)
Jones College (U)
Lamar State College–Port Arthur (N)
Lewis and Clark Community College (U)
Limestone College (U)
Maryville University of Saint Louis (N,U)
Naugatuck Valley Community College (N)
Ozarks Technical Community College (U)
Rasmussen College Eden Prarie (U)
Red Rocks Community College (U)
Seminole Community College (U)
Southwest Georgia Technical College (U)
State University of New York College at Potsdam (U)
Syracuse University (G)
Taylor University (N)
Tompkins Cortland Community College (N)
The University of Akron (N)
University of California, Berkeley (U)
University of Illinois at Urbana–Champaign (G)
University of Minnesota, Crookston (U)
Utah State University (U)
Westchester Community College (U)
Wilkes Community College (U)

DEMOGRAPHY AND POPULATION

Athabasca University (U)
Bethany University (U)
University of Southern Mississippi (G)

DENTAL SUPPORT SERVICES AND ALLIED PROFESSIONS

Blackhawk Technical College (U)
Cape Cod Community College (N)
Chattanooga State Technical Community College (U)
Community College of Southern Nevada (U)
Danville Community College (U)
Gulf Coast Community College (U)
John A. Logan College (U)
Middlesex Community College (U)
Monroe Community College (U)
Oregon Institute of Technology (U)
Oxnard College (U)
Peninsula College (U)
Pennsylvania College of Technology (U)
Portland Community College (U)
Southern University at Shreveport (U)
Tunxis Community College (U)
University of Bridgeport (U)
The University of British Columbia (U)
University of Southern Indiana (U)
Washtenaw Community College (U)
Waukesha County Technical College (U)

DENTISTRY AND ORAL SCIENCES (ADVANCED/GRADUATE)

Danville Community College (U)
West Los Angeles College (U)

DESIGN AND APPLIED ARTS

Academy of Art University (U,G)
Brenau University (U)

Central Wyoming College (N)
Colorado State University (U)
Dakota County Technical College (U)
Danville Community College (U)
Edison State Community College (U)
John A. Logan College (U)
Lansing Community College (U)
Minneapolis College of Art and Design (N,U,G)
Mohawk Valley Community College (U)
New Mexico Junior College (U)
The New School (U)
New York Institute of Technology (U)
San Joaquin Delta College (U)
South Piedmont Community College (U)
Tacoma Community College (U)
The University of Akron (U)
University of California, Los Angeles (G)
West Los Angeles College (U)
Westwood Online (U)

DEVELOPMENTAL AND CHILD PSYCHOLOGY

Adirondack Community College (U)
Anne Arundel Community College (U)
Arkansas State University–Beebe (U)
Athabasca University (N,U,G)
Bellevue Community College (U)
Bergen Community College (U)
Bethany University (U)
Black Hills State University (U,G)
Brenau University (U)
Brigham Young University (U)
Burlington County College (U)
Butler Community College (U)
Cape Breton University (U)
Cape Cod Community College (U)
Central Oregon Community College (U)
Central Piedmont Community College (U)
Central Texas College (U)
Chadron State College (U)
Chattanooga State Technical Community College (U)
Clatsop Community College (U)
Clovis Community College (U)
College of DuPage (U)
College of the Southwest (U)
Colorado Mountain College District System (U)
Colorado State University (U)
Columbia-Greene Community College (U)
Columbus State Community College (U)
Community College of Beaver County (U)
Community College of Southern Nevada (U)
Concordia University, St. Paul (U,G)
Cowley County Community College and Area Vocational–Technical School (U)
Crafton Hills College (U)
Dakota County Technical College (U)
Dallas County Community College District (U)
Danville Community College (U)
Dawson Community College (U)
De Anza College (U)
Delta College (U)
Des Moines Area Community College (U)
East Central Community College (U)
East Tennessee State University (U)
Edmonds Community College (U)
Erie Community College (U)
Georgia Highlands College (U)
Golden West College (U)
Gordon-Conwell Theological Seminary (N,G)
Governors State University (U,G)
Gulf Coast Community College (U)
Halifax Community College (U)
Hillsborough Community College (U)
Housatonic Community College (U)
Houston Community College System (U)
Indiana State University (G)
Itawamba Community College (U)
Jacksonville State University (U,G)
J. Sargeant Reynolds Community College (U)
Judson College (U)
Kansas State University (U)
Lehigh Carbon Community College (U)
Lewis and Clark Community College (U)
Liberty University (U)
Louisiana State University and Agricultural and Mechanical College (U)
Malone College (U)
Marshall University (U)
Mercy College (U)
Middlesex Community College (U)
Midland College (U)
Mississippi State University (U)
Missouri State University (U)
Mohawk Valley Community College (U)
Mountain Empire Community College (U)
Naropa University (U)
Nassau Community College (U)
National University (U)
North Dakota State College of Science (U)
North Dakota State University (U)
Northern Virginia Community College (U)
Odessa College (U)
Oxnard College (U)
Ozarks Technical Community College (U)
Palm Beach Community College (U)
Palomar College (U)
Parkland College (U)
Patrick Henry Community College (U)
Peninsula College (U)
Portland Community College (U)
Pueblo Community College (U)
Rasmussen College Eden Prarie (U)
Reading Area Community College (U)
Red Rocks Community College (U)
Saddleback College (U)
St. Johns River Community College (U)
Saint Joseph's College of Maine (U)
Saybrook Graduate School and Research Center (G)
Schoolcraft College (U)
Seattle Central Community College (U)
Seminole Community College (U)
Shawnee Community College (U)
Simmons College (N)
Sinclair Community College (U)
Solano Community College (U)
Southwestern Assemblies of God University (U)
Southwestern Oregon Community College (U)
Southwest Virginia Community College (U)
Stanly Community College (U)
State University of New York at New Paltz (U)
State University of New York at Oswego (U)
Stephens College (U)
Taylor University (U)
Texas A&M University–Commerce (U)
Texas State University-San Marcos (U)
Texas Tech University (U)
Three Rivers Community College (U)
Tompkins Cortland Community College (U)
Triton College (U)
Tunxis Community College (U)
University of Arkansas (U)
University of Bridgeport (U)
University of California, Berkeley (U)
University of Florida (U)
University of Great Falls (U)
University of Hawaii–West Oahu (U)
University of Houston–Downtown (U)
University of Houston–Victoria (G)
University of La Verne (U)
University of Maine (U)
The University of Maine at Augusta (U)
University of Maine at Fort Kent (U)
University of Maryland Eastern Shore (U)
University of Minnesota, Morris (U)
University of Minnesota, Twin Cities Campus (U)
University of Missouri–Columbia (U)
University of Missouri–St. Louis (U)
University of Nebraska–Lincoln (U)
University of Nevada, Reno (U)
University of New Orleans (U,G)
University of North Texas (U,G)
The University of Texas System (U)
The University of Toledo (U)
University of Utah (U)
University of Washington (U)
University of Waterloo (U)
University of Wisconsin–Stout (U,G)
Vincennes University (U)
Western Michigan University (G)
Western Oklahoma State College (U)
Western Washington University (U)
Wilfrid Laurier University (U)
William Rainey Harper College (U)
Winston-Salem State University (U)
York Technical College (U)

DIETETICS AND CLINICAL NUTRITION SERVICES

Auburn University (N)
Central Michigan University (G)
Central Piedmont Community College (N)
Eastern Michigan University (U,G)
Indiana Business College (N)
Kansas State University (U)
Mount Saint Vincent University (U)
South Piedmont Community College (U)

DRAFTING/DESIGN ENGINEERING TECHNOLOGIES

Blackhawk Technical College (N)
Butler Community College (U)
Cleveland Institute of Electronics (N)
Colorado State University (G)
Columbus State Community College (U)
Dallas County Community College District (U)
Danville Community College (U)
Indiana State University (U)
Jackson Community College (U)
Kentucky State University (U)
Madison Area Technical College (U)
North Dakota State College of Science (U)
Orange Coast College (U)
Sinclair Community College (U)
Triton College (U)
University of Alaska Fairbanks (U)

DRAMATIC/THEATER ARTS AND STAGECRAFT

Arizona State University (U)
Arkansas State University–Mountain Home (U)
Bergen Community College (U)
Boise State University (U)
Brigham Young University (U)
California State University, San Marcos (N)
California University of Pennsylvania (U)
City College of San Francisco (U)
Columbus State Community College (U)
Contra Costa College (U)
Eastern Michigan University (U)
Eastern Oregon University (U)
Edison State Community College (U)
Erie Community College (U)
Fort Valley State University (U)
Iowa Western Community College (U)
John A. Logan College (U)
Limestone College (U)
Louisiana State University and Agricultural and Mechanical College (U)
Metropolitan State University (U)
Middle Tennessee State University (N)
Montana State University–Billings (U)
Northern Virginia Community College (U)
Northwest Missouri State University (U)
Oxnard College (U)
Ozarks Technical Community College (U)
Parkland College (U)
Queen's University at Kingston (U)
Snow College (U)
State University of New York at Oswego (U)
Texas Christian University (U)
Triton College (U)
University of Alaska Fairbanks (U)
University of Arkansas (U)
University of Colorado at Denver and Health Sciences Center—Downtown Denver Campus (U)
University of New Orleans (G)
The University of North Carolina at Chapel Hill (U)
University of Oklahoma (U)
The University of Texas at Arlington (U)
University of Wisconsin–River Falls (U)
Utah Valley State College (U)
West Los Angeles College (U)
West Virginia University at Parkersburg (U)
Wilkes Community College (U)

ECOLOGY, EVOLUTION, AND POPULATION BIOLOGY

Bellevue Community College (U)
Boston Architectural College (N,U,G)
Burlington County College (U)
California Institute of Integral Studies (N,G)
City College of San Francisco (U)
Des Moines Area Community College (U)
Edison State Community College (U)
Gogebic Community College (U)
Judson College (U)
Louisiana State University and Agricultural and Mechanical College (U)
Oregon State University (U)
Seminole Community College (U)
University of Florida (U)
University of Minnesota, Twin Cities Campus (U)
University of Nebraska–Lincoln (U)
University of Waterloo (U)
Yuba College (U)

ECONOMICS

Abilene Christian University (U)
Acadia University (U)
Adirondack Community College (U)
Alvin Community College (U)
Anne Arundel Community College (U)
Arkansas State University–Beebe (U)
Arkansas State University–Mountain Home (U)
Asheville-Buncombe Technical Community College (U)
Athabasca University (N,U,G)
Athens Technical College (U)
Bellevue Community College (U)
Berkeley College (U)
Berkeley College-New York City Campus (U)
Berkeley College-Westchester Campus (U)
Big Sandy Community and Technical College (U)
Black Hills State University (U)
Blinn College (U)
Boise State University (U)
Brazosport College (U)
Brenau University (U,G)
Bridgewater State College (G)
Brigham Young University (U)
Butler Community College (U)
Butler County Community College (U)
Caldwell College (U)
California National University for Advanced Studies (U)
California State University, San Bernardino (U)
Cape Cod Community College (U)
Cape Fear Community College (U)
Casper College (U)
Cayuga County Community College (U)
Central Carolina Community College (U)
Central Michigan University (U,G)
Central New Mexico Community College (U)
Central Texas College (U)
Central Virginia Community College (U)
Central Wyoming College (U)
Chadron State College (U,G)
Champlain College (U)
Chattanooga State Technical Community College (U)
Citrus College (U)
Clarion University of Pennsylvania (U)
Clark College (U)
Clemson University (U)
Cleveland Community College (U)
Clinton Community College (U)
Clovis Community College (U)
College of DuPage (U)
The College of St. Scholastica (U)
College of Southern Maryland (U)
College of The Albemarle (U)
College of the Southwest (U)
Colorado Mountain College District System (U)
Colorado State University (U)
Colorado State University-Pueblo (U)
Columbia Basin College (U)
Columbus State Community College (U)
The Community College of Baltimore County (U)
Community College of Beaver County (U)
Community College of Denver (U)
Concordia University Wisconsin (U)
Connecticut State University System (U)
Corning Community College (U)
Cosumnes River College (U)
County College of Morris (U)
Crafton Hills College (U)
Cumberland County College (U)
Dakota County Technical College (U)
Dallas Baptist University (U,G)
Dallas County Community College District (U)
Darton College (U)
De Anza College (U)
Delta College (U)
Des Moines Area Community College (U)
DeVry University Online (U,G)
Dodge City Community College (U)
Drake University (U,G)
D'Youville College (U)
East Central Community College (U)
Eastern Oregon University (U)
Eastern West Virginia Community and Technical College (U)
Eastern Wyoming College (U)
Edison State Community College (U)
Embry-Riddle Aeronautical University, Extended Campus (U)
Erie Community College (U)
Everett Community College (U)
Finger Lakes Community College (U)
Florida Atlantic University (U,G)
Fontbonne University (U)
Fort Hays State University (U)
Franklin Pierce College (U)
Franklin University (U)
Galveston College (U)
Glenville State College (U)
Grantham University (U)
Gulf Coast Community College (U)
Halifax Community College (U)
Haywood Community College (U)
Heartland Community College (U)
Hillsborough Community College (U)
Housatonic Community College (U)
Houston Community College System (U)
Howard College (U)
Illinois Eastern Community Colleges, Olney Central College (U)
Indiana Business College (N)
Indiana State University (U)
Indiana University–Purdue University Fort Wayne (U)
International Institute of the Americas (U)
Iowa State University of Science and Technology (U)
Iowa Western Community College (U)
Itawamba Community College (U)
Ivy Tech Community College–North Central (U)
Ivy Tech Community College–Northwest (U)
Jackson Community College (U)
Jacksonville State University (U,G)
Jefferson Community College (U)
Jefferson Davis Community College (U)
John Jay College of Criminal Justice of the City University of New York (U)
Johnson County Community College (U)
John Tyler Community College (U)
Jones College (U)
J. Sargeant Reynolds Community College (U)
Judson College (U)
Kentucky State University (U)
Lake Superior College (U)

Lamar State College–Port Arthur (U)
Lehigh Carbon Community College (U)
Lewis and Clark Community College (U)
Liberty University (U)
Limestone College (U)
Linn-Benton Community College (U)
Los Angeles Harbor College (U)
Louisiana State University and Agricultural and Mechanical College (U)
Louisiana Tech University (U)
Mansfield University of Pennsylvania (U)
Marist College (U)
Marshall University (U)
Memorial University of Newfoundland (U)
Mercer County Community College (U)
Mesalands Community College (U)
Metropolitan State University (U,G)
Miami Dade College (U)
Middlesex Community College (U)
Middle Tennessee State University (U,G)
Mid Michigan Community College (U)
Millersville University of Pennsylvania (U)
Missouri State University (U,G)
Montana State University–Billings (U)
Mountain Empire Community College (U)
Mount Allison University (U)
Mount Saint Vincent University (U)
Mt. San Antonio College (U)
Mount Wachusett Community College (U)
Myers University (U)
Nassau Community College (U)
New England College of Finance (U)
New Jersey City University (U)
New Mexico Junior College (U)
New Mexico State University–Alamogordo (U)
New Mexico State University–Carlsbad (U)
New York Institute of Technology (U)
Nipissing University (U)
North Arkansas College (U)
North Central Texas College (U)
North Dakota State College of Science (U)
Northeast State Technical Community College (U)
North Seattle Community College (U)
Northwestern Michigan College (U)
Northwestern State University of Louisiana (U)
Oklahoma State University (U)
Oregon Institute of Technology (U)
Oregon State University (U)
Oxnard College (U)
Ozarks Technical Community College (U)
Palm Beach Community College (U)
Palomar College (U)
Parkland College (U)
Park University (U)
Patrick Henry College (U)
Patrick Henry Community College (U)
Peninsula College (U)
The Pennsylvania State University University Park Campus (U)
Philadelphia University (U)
Portland Community College (U)
Portland State University (U)
Pueblo Community College (U)
Purdue University Calumet (U)
Randolph Community College (U)
Raritan Valley Community College (U)
Rasmussen College Eden Prarie (U)
Reading Area Community College (U)
Rio Hondo College (U)
Ryerson University (U)
Sacred Heart University (G)
St. Clair County Community College (U)
St. Cloud State University (U)
St. Edward's University (U)
St. John's University (U,G)
St. Petersburg College (U)
Salem Community College (U)
Sam Houston State University (U)
San Bernardino Valley College (U)
Schoolcraft College (U)
Seminole Community College (U)
Shippensburg University of Pennsylvania (U)
Sinclair Community College (U)
Solano Community College (U)
Southeast Arkansas College (U)
Southeast Community College, Beatrice Campus (U)
Southeast Community College, Lincoln Campus (U)
Southeast Community College, Milford Campus (U)
Southern University at Shreveport (U)
South Piedmont Community College (U)
South Plains College (U)
Southwestern College (U)
Southwest Georgia Technical College (U)
Southwest Wisconsin Technical College (U)
Stanly Community College (U)
State University of New York at New Paltz (U)
State University of New York at Oswego (U,G)
State University of New York College at Potsdam (U)
Stephen F. Austin State University (U)
Stephens College (U)
Strayer University (U,G)
Taft College (U)
Taylor University (U)
Texas A&M University–Commerce (N,U,G)
Texas A&M University–Kingsville (U,G)
Texas A&M University–Texarkana (G)
Texas Tech University (U)
Tri-County Community College (U)
Tri-State University (U)
Triton College (U)
Tyler Junior College (U)
The University of Akron (U,G)
The University of Alabama (U)
University of Alaska Fairbanks (U)
University of Arkansas at Pine Bluff (U)
University of Bridgeport (U)
University of California, Berkeley (U,G)
University of California, Los Angeles (G)
University of Colorado at Colorado Springs (U)
University of Colorado at Denver and Health Sciences Center—Downtown Denver Campus (U)
University of Delaware (U)
The University of Findlay (U)
University of Florida (U)
University of Hawaii–West Oahu (U)
University of Houston–Clear Lake (G)
University of Illinois at Chicago (G)
The University of Iowa (G)
The University of Maine at Augusta (U)
University of Maryland University College (U)
University of Massachusetts Boston (U)
University of Minnesota, Crookston (U)
University of Minnesota, Morris (U)
University of Minnesota, Twin Cities Campus (U)
University of Missouri–Columbia (U,G)
University of Nebraska–Lincoln (U)
University of Nevada, Reno (U)
University of New Brunswick Fredericton (U)
University of New Orleans (U,G)
The University of North Carolina at Chapel Hill (U)
The University of North Carolina at Greensboro (U)
University of North Dakota (U)
University of Northern Colorado (U)
University of North Texas (U)
University of Oklahoma (U)
University of Oregon (U)
University of Pittsburgh (U)
University of Pittsburgh at Bradford (U)
University of Saskatchewan (U)
University of Southern Indiana (U,G)
University of Southern Mississippi (G)
The University of Tennessee (U)
The University of Tennessee at Martin (U)
The University of Texas at Arlington (U)
The University of Texas System (U)
The University of Toledo (U)
University of Toronto (N,U)
University of Tulsa (G)
University of Utah (U)
The University of Virginia's College at Wise (U)
University of Washington (U)
University of Waterloo (U)
University of West Florida (U)
University of Wisconsin–La Crosse (G)
University of Wisconsin–Parkside (G)
University of Wisconsin–Platteville (U)
University of Wisconsin–River Falls (G)
University of Wisconsin–Stout (U)
University of Wisconsin–Whitewater (U,G)
Utah State University (U)
Utica College (U)
Vance-Granville Community College (U)
Vincennes University (U)
Wake Technical Community College (U)
Waukesha County Technical College (U)
Wayland Baptist University (U,G)
Wayne State College (U,G)
Westchester Community College (U)
Western Michigan University (U,G)
Western Piedmont Community College (U)
Western Washington University (U)
Western Wyoming Community College (U)
West Los Angeles College (U)
Whatcom Community College (U)
Wilfrid Laurier University (U)
William Rainey Harper College (U)
Woodbury University (U)
Wright State University (N,U,G)
York Technical College (U)
York University (U)
Yuba College (U)

EDUCATION

Abilene Christian University (U,G)
Acadia University (U)
Adams State College (G)
Antioch University McGregor (U)
Auburn University (G)
Baptist Bible College of Pennsylvania (G)
Bellevue Community College (U)
Bergen Community College (U)

Black Hills State University (G)
Blue Ridge Community College (U)
Boise State University (U)
Bradley University (U,G)
Brenau University (U,G)
Bridgewater State College (U)
Brigham Young University (U,G)
Brock University (U)
Buena Vista University (U,G)
Butler County Community College (U)
Caldwell College (U)
California State University, Chico (U)
California State University, Dominguez Hills (N,U)
California State University, San Bernardino (U,G)
California University of Pennsylvania (U)
Cape Breton University (G)
Cape Fear Community College (U)
Capella University (G)
Cardinal Stritch University (G)
Carlow University (U,G)
Casper College (U)
Central Carolina Community College (U)
Central Washington University (N,G)
Chadron State College (U,G)
Chattanooga State Technical Community College (U)
Chesapeake College (U)
Clackamas Community College (U)
Clarion University of Pennsylvania (G)
Cleveland Community College (U)
Cleveland State Community College (U)
Cleveland State University (U,G)
Coconino Community College (U)
College of Southern Maryland (N)
College of the Southwest (U)
Colorado State University (N,U,G)
Colorado State University-Pueblo (U,G)
Columbia College (U)
Columbia International University (N,G)
Columbus State University (U)
Community College of Beaver County (U)
Community College of Southern Nevada (U)
Concordia College (U)
Concordia University, St. Paul (U,G)
Contra Costa College (U)
Corning Community College (U)
Cowley County Community College and Area Vocational–Technical School (U)
Crown College (G)
Daemen College (U)
Dallas Baptist University (U)
Dallas County Community College District (U)
Darton College (U)
Drake University (U,G)
Drexel University (G)
Drury University (G)
Duquesne University (G)
D'Youville College (U,G)
East Carolina University (U,G)
East Central Community College (U)
Eastern Michigan University (N,U,G)
Eastern New Mexico University (U)
East Tennessee State University (U,G)
Endicott College (U,G)
Eugene Bible College (U)
Fayetteville State University (G)
Finger Lakes Community College (U)
Florida Atlantic University (U)
Fort Valley State University (U)
Galveston College (U)
Georgia College & State University (G)
Goucher College (G)
Greenfield Community College (U)
Hamline University (N,G)
Haywood Community College (U)
Humboldt State University (U,G)
Indiana State University (U,G)
Indiana University–Purdue University Fort Wayne (U)
Iona College (G)
Iowa Western Community College (U)
Jacksonville State University (U,G)
James Madison University (N)
J. Sargeant Reynolds Community College (U)
Judson College (U)
Kansas State University (N)
Kean University (N)
Laura and Alvin Siegal College of Judaic Studies (N,U,G)
Lehigh Carbon Community College (U)
Lesley University (G)
LeTourneau University (U)
Lewis-Clark State College (U)
Liberty University (U)
Lock Haven University of Pennsylvania (N,G)
Louisiana State University and Agricultural and Mechanical College (U)
Louisiana State University at Eunice (U)
Madonna University (U)
Marquette University (N,U,G)
Mayville State University (U)
Memorial University of Newfoundland (U)
Mesalands Community College (U)
Mesa State College (U)
Miami Dade College (U)
Middlesex Community College (U)
Middle Tennessee State University (U)
Millersville University of Pennsylvania (U,G)
Missouri State University (G)
Mohawk Valley Community College (U)
Monmouth University (U,G)
Montana State University–Billings (U,G)
Mount Saint Vincent University (U)
Murray State University (U)
Naropa University (N,G)
National University (U,G)
New Mexico State University–Carlsbad (U)
North Central Texas College (U)
North Dakota State University (U,G)
Northeast State Technical Community College (U)
Northwestern Oklahoma State University (U)
Northwest Missouri State University (G)
Oregon State University (U,G)
Oxnard College (U)
Ozarks Technical Community College (U)
Pace University (N,U,G)
Palm Beach Community College (U)
Park University (G)
Pasco-Hernando Community College (N)
Peninsula College (U)
Plymouth State University (G)
Portland Community College (U)
Prescott College (U,G)
Pueblo Community College (U)
Pulaski Technical College (U)
Quinebaug Valley Community College (U)
Regent University (N,U,G)
Roosevelt University (U,G)
Sacred Heart University (G)
St. Edward's University (U)
St. John's University (U,G)
Saint Joseph's University (U,G)
Saint Mary-of-the-Woods College (U)
St. Petersburg College (U)
San Diego State University (N)
Seattle Pacific University (G)
Seminole Community College (U)
Shenandoah University (N,U,G)
Shippensburg University of Pennsylvania (U)
Shoreline Community College (U)
Snow College (U)
South Central College (U)
Southern Arkansas University Tech (U)
Southern Illinois University Carbondale (G)
Southern Illinois University Edwardsville (G)
South Piedmont Community College (U)
South Plains College (U)
Southwestern Assemblies of God University (U,G)
Southwestern College (G)
State University of New York at New Paltz (G)
State University of New York at Oswego (G)
State University of New York at Plattsburgh (U,G)
State University of New York, Fredonia (G)
Stony Brook University, State University of New York (G)
Taylor University (U)
Tennessee Temple University (G)
Texas A&M University–Commerce (G)
Texas A&M University–Kingsville (U,G)
Texas Tech University (G)
Texas Woman's University (U,G)
Touro University International (G)
Tyler Junior College (U)
The University of Akron (U,G)
University of Alaska Fairbanks (U)
University of Arkansas at Pine Bluff (U,G)
University of Bridgeport (U)
The University of British Columbia (U,G)
University of Calgary (G)
University of California, Berkeley (U)
University of California, Davis (U)
University of Colorado at Denver and Health Sciences Center—Downtown Denver Campus (G)
University of Delaware (U,G)
University of Florida (U,G)
University of Houston–Downtown (U)
University of Houston–Victoria (U,G)
The University of Iowa (U,G)
University of La Verne (N)
University of Lethbridge (G)
University of Maine (G)
University of Massachusetts Boston (G)
University of Massachusetts Lowell (G)
University of Minnesota, Morris (U)
University of Missouri–Columbia (U,G)
The University of Montana (G)
The University of Montana–Western (U)
University of Nevada, Reno (G)
University of New Orleans (U,G)
University of North Alabama (U,G)
The University of North Carolina at Charlotte (U,G)
University of Northern Iowa (U,G)
University of North Texas (N,U,G)
University of Oklahoma (U)
University of Phoenix Online Campus (G)
University of San Diego (U)
University of Sioux Falls (G)
University of South Carolina Sumter (U)
University of Southern Indiana (U,G)
University of Southern Mississippi (G)

University of South Florida (U,G)
The University of Tennessee (U)
The University of Tennessee at Martin (N)
The University of Texas System (U,G)
The University of Toledo (U,G)
University of Virginia (G)
University of Washington (U)
University of Wisconsin–River Falls (G)
University of Wisconsin–Stout (U,G)
University of Wisconsin–Superior (U,G)
University of Wisconsin–Whitewater (U)
University of Wyoming (U,G)
Utah State University (G)
Valley City State University (G)
Valparaiso University (U)
Vanguard University of Southern California (U)
Vincennes University (U)
Virginia Polytechnic Institute and State University (N)
Viterbo University (G)
Washburn University (U,G)
Wayne State College (U,G)
Webster University (G)
West Texas A&M University (U)
West Virginia University (N)
Whatcom Community College (U)
William Rainey Harper College (U)
Wright State University (U)

EDUCATION (SPECIFIC LEVELS AND METHODS)

Arkansas Tech University (U)
Auburn University (G)
Blackhawk Technical College (U)
Blue Ridge Community College (U)
Brenau University (U)
Caldwell College (U)
Central Michigan University (G)
Chadron State College (U,G)
Cleveland State University (G)
Community College of Denver (U)
Connecticut State University System (U,G)
Danville Community College (U)
Darton College (U)
Drexel University (G)
East Arkansas Community College (U)
Eastern Michigan University (G)
Fayetteville State University (U)
Fort Valley State University (U)
Granite State College (U)
Halifax Community College (N)
Hamline University (G)
Indiana State University (G)
Indiana University System (N)
Iona College (G)
Jacksonville State University (U)
James Madison University (N,U)
Judson College (U)
Kansas State University (N)
Kean University (U,G)
Lawrence Technological University (G)
Lehigh Carbon Community College (U)
Limestone College (U)
Louisiana State University and Agricultural and Mechanical College (U)
McMurry University (U)
Midland College (U)
Mississippi State University (U)
Missouri State University (G)
North Dakota State University (G)
North Georgia College & State University (U,G)
Northwest Christian College (U)
Northwestern State University of Louisiana (U)
Oregon State University (G)
Pasco-Hernando Community College (U)
Radford University (G)
St. Clair County Community College (U)
St. John's University (G)
Saint Mary-of-the-Woods College (U)
San Diego State University (U,G)
San Francisco State University (N)
Seattle Pacific University (G)
Seminole Community College (N)
Southeast Community College, Lincoln Campus (U)
South Piedmont Community College (U)
Southwest Georgia Technical College (U)
State University of New York College at Potsdam (G)
Stephen F. Austin State University (G)
Texas A&M University–Texarkana (G)
The University of Akron (N,U,G)
The University of Alabama (U)
University of Alaska Fairbanks (G)
University of Calgary (N)
University of Great Falls (G)
University of Houston–Downtown (G)
University of Houston–Victoria (U,G)
University of Maine at Fort Kent (U)
University of Maryland University College (G)
University of Massachusetts Lowell (U)
The University of Montana–Western (U)
University of New Brunswick Fredericton (U,G)
University of New Orleans (U,G)
University of North Dakota (U)
University of Saskatchewan (U)
University of South Alabama (G)
University of Southern Indiana (U)
University of South Florida (G)
The University of Tennessee at Martin (N)
The University of Texas at Tyler (U)
The University of Texas of the Permian Basin (G)
University of Wisconsin–Platteville (G)
University of Wisconsin–River Falls (G)
Utah State University (G)
Virginia Polytechnic Institute and State University (U)
Western Piedmont Community College (U)
Western Washington University (U)
Western Wyoming Community College (U)
Winston-Salem State University (U)
Wright State University (U)

EDUCATION (SPECIFIC SUBJECT AREAS)

Adams State College (G)
Alcorn State University (U)
Arkansas Tech University (U,G)
Auburn University (G)
Azusa Pacific University (G)
Blue Ridge Community College (U)
Boise State University (G)
Brenau University (U)
California State University, San Bernardino (U,G)
California State University, San Marcos (U,G)
Central Michigan University (G)
Central Missouri State University (U)
Central Wyoming College (U)
Chadron State College (U,G)
Cleveland State University (G)
Colorado Christian University (U)
Columbus State University (G)
Community College of Denver (U)
Darton College (U)
Drexel University (G)
D'Youville College (U)
East Carolina University (U)
Eastern Michigan University (U,G)
Edgecombe Community College (U)
Fontbonne University (G)
Fort Hays State University (G)
Fort Valley State University (U,G)
Glenville State College (U)
Hamline University (N,G)
Indiana State University (G)
Iona College (G)
Jacksonville State University (U,G)
Judson College (U)
Kansas State University (N)
Kean University (U)
Marygrove College (U,G)
Millersville University of Pennsylvania (U,G)
Mississippi State University (U,G)
Missouri State University (G)
Montana State University (G)
Mount Saint Vincent University (U)
National University (G)
New Mexico Institute of Mining and Technology (G)
North American Baptist Seminary (G)
North Carolina State University (U,G)
North Georgia College & State University (U,G)
Oregon State University (G)
Ozarka College (U)
Pace University (U)
Randolph Community College (U)
Roosevelt University (U)
St. John's University (G)
Saint Joseph's College of Maine (U,G)
Saint Mary-of-the-Woods College (U)
Salem Community College (N)
San Diego State University (U)
Seattle Pacific University (G)
Seminole Community College (U)
Simpson College (G)
Southern Illinois University Carbondale (U)
Southern Oregon University (G)
South Piedmont Community College (U)
Southwestern Assemblies of God University (U,G)
State University of New York at Buffalo (G)
State University of New York at Oswego (U,G)
State University of New York College at Potsdam (U)
Texas A&M University–Texarkana (U)
Touro University International (G)
The University of Akron (U,G)
University of Arkansas (G)
University of California, Berkeley (U)
University of California, Davis (U)
University of Florida (U,G)
University of Houston–Victoria (U,G)
University of Illinois at Chicago (G)
University of La Verne (N)
University of Maine (U)
University of Maryland University College (G)
University of Massachusetts Boston (G)
University of Michigan–Flint (N)

University of Minnesota, Morris (U)
University of Missouri–Columbia (G)
University of Nebraska at Omaha (G)
University of New Orleans (U,G)
The University of North Carolina Wilmington (U)
University of North Dakota (U,G)
University of Saskatchewan (N)
University of Sioux Falls (U)
University of Southern Indiana (G)
University of South Florida (G)
The University of Tennessee at Martin (G)
The University of Texas of the Permian Basin (U,G)
The University of Texas System (U,G)
University of Utah (U)
University of West Florida (N)
University of Wisconsin–River Falls (U,G)
Utah State University (G)
Virginia Polytechnic Institute and State University (U,G)
Wayne State College (U,G)
Western Washington University (U)
West Texas A&M University (G)
Yuba College (U)

EDUCATION RELATED

Acadia University (U,G)
Arizona State University West (U,G)
Arkansas Tech University (U,G)
Ashford University (G)
Athabasca University (N,G)
Atlantic University (N,G)
Auburn University (G)
Auburn University Montgomery (U)
Barclay College (U)
Black Hills State University (U,G)
Blue Ridge Community College (N)
Boise State University (G)
Brenau University (U,G)
Brigham Young University (U)
Brock University (U)
Buffalo State College, State University of New York (G)
California State University, Dominguez Hills (U)
California State University, East Bay (G)
California State University, San Bernardino (N,U)
California State University, San Marcos (G)
Casper College (U)
Central Virginia Community College (U)
Chadron State College (U,G)
Clarion University of Pennsylvania (U)
Clark College (U)
Cleveland State University (N,G)
College of Southern Maryland (U)
College of The Albemarle (U)
College of the Humanities and Sciences, Harrison Middleton University (G)
Colorado Mountain College District System (U)
Colorado State University (G)
Columbia International University (G)
Concordia University Wisconsin (G)
Cowley County Community College and Area Vocational–Technical School (U)
Crown College (G)
Dakota County Technical College (U)
Dakota State University (U,G)
Dallas Baptist University (G)
Dallas County Community College District (U)
Darton College (U)
Des Moines Area Community College (U)
Drake University (U)
Drexel University (G)
Eastern Michigan University (N,G)
Eastern New Mexico University (G)
East Tennessee State University (U,G)
Elgin Community College (U)
Florida Atlantic University (G)
Florida Gulf Coast University (U,G)
Fort Hays State University (U,G)
Fulton-Montgomery Community College (N)
Gateway Community College (N)
Hamline University (N,G)
Haywood Community College (U)
Heart of Georgia Technical College (U)
Hebrew College (N,U,G)
Indiana State University (U,G)
Indiana University of Pennsylvania (G)
Indiana University System (G)
Jacksonville State University (U,G)
Kansas State University (N)
Lehigh Carbon Community College (U)
Lenoir Community College (U)
Liberty University (G)
Memorial University of Newfoundland (U,G)
Mississippi State University (U)
Naropa University (N)
New Mexico Junior College (U)
New Mexico State University (G)
North Arkansas College (U)
Northern Kentucky University (G)
Northwestern Oklahoma State University (G)
Northwestern State University of Louisiana (U,G)
Nova Southeastern University (G)
The Ohio State University (G)
Oklahoma State University (U)
Old Dominion University (U,G)
Oregon State University (U,G)
Ozarks Technical Community College (U)
Pace University (G)
Park University (U)
Pasco-Hernando Community College (N)
Portland Community College (N)
Providence College and Theological Seminary (N,G)
Red Rocks Community College (U)
Regent University (N)
Rio Hondo College (U)
Roosevelt University (G)
St. John's University (G)
Saint Mary-of-the-Woods College (U)
San Diego State University (U)
San Joaquin Delta College (U)
Seminole Community College (U)
Shasta Bible College (U)
Shenandoah University (G)
Southern Illinois University Carbondale (U)
Southwestern Assemblies of God University (U,G)
Southwestern Baptist Theological Seminary (G)
State University of New York at Plattsburgh (U,G)
Stephen F. Austin State University (G)
Taylor University (U)
Texas A&M University–Texarkana (G)
Texas Tech University (G)
Texas Woman's University (G)
Tunxis Community College (N)
The University of Akron (N,U,G)
University of Alaska Fairbanks (G)
University of Bridgeport (N)
University of California, Berkeley (U)
University of California, Riverside (N)
University of Central Arkansas (G)
University of Central Florida (U,G)
University of Central Oklahoma (U,G)
University of Colorado at Denver and Health Sciences Center—Downtown Denver Campus (G)
University of Florida (G)
University of Houston–Victoria (U,G)
University of Illinois at Springfield (G)
University of La Verne (N)
University of Lethbridge (U,G)
University of Maryland (G)
University of Massachusetts Amherst (U,G)
University of Massachusetts Lowell (N)
University of Missouri–Columbia (U,G)
University of Nevada, Reno (U,G)
The University of North Carolina at Greensboro (G)
University of Northern Colorado (G)
University of North Texas (G)
University of Saskatchewan (N,G)
University of South Carolina Sumter (G)
University of Southern Mississippi (U)
The University of Texas of the Permian Basin (U)
The University of Texas System (U,G)
The University of Toledo (U,G)
University of West Florida (N)
University of Wisconsin–Whitewater (U)
Vanguard University of Southern California (U)
Virginia Polytechnic Institute and State University (G)
Wayland Baptist University (U,G)
Western Nevada Community College (U)
Whatcom Community College (U)
Wilkes Community College (U)
Wright State University (N,G)
Yuba College (U)

EDUCATIONAL ADMINISTRATION AND SUPERVISION

Arkansas Tech University (G)
Athabasca University (N,G)
Auburn University Montgomery (U,G)
Azusa Pacific University (G)
Bowling Green State University (U)
Brenau University (U,G)
Bridgewater State College (U,G)
Brigham Young University (U)
California State University, Dominguez Hills (U)
California University of Pennsylvania (G)
Campbellsville University (G)
Capella University (G)
Chadron State College (U,G)
Charter Oak State College (U)
College of The Albemarle (N)
College of the Southwest (G)
Columbia International University (G)
Concordia University Wisconsin (G)
Crown College (G)
Dallas Baptist University (G)
Drexel University (G)
Eastern Michigan University (U,G)
Florida Atlantic University (G)
Florida Gulf Coast University (U)
Fort Hays State University (U)
Frostburg State University (G)

Georgia Southern University (U,G)
Hamline University (N)
Heart of Georgia Technical College (U)
Indiana State University (G)
Indiana University–Purdue University Fort Wayne (G)
Iona College (G)
Jacksonville State University (U,G)
Kansas State University (N)
Kean University (G)
LeTourneau University (G)
Liberty University (G)
Louisiana Tech University (U,G)
Mercy College (U)
Mississippi State University (G)
Missouri State University (G)
Murray State University (G)
National University (G)
New Jersey City University (G)
North Carolina State University (G)
North Dakota State University (G)
North Georgia College & State University (G)
Northwestern Oklahoma State University (G)
Northwestern State University of Louisiana (G)
The Ohio State University (G)
Oregon State University (G)
Pace University (G)
Park University (G)
Radford University (G)
Regent University (N)
St. Cloud State University (U)
St. John's University (G)
Saint Joseph's College of Maine (G)
San Diego State University (G)
Saybrook Graduate School and Research Center (N,G)
Shasta Bible College (G)
Shenandoah University (G)
Southern Illinois University Carbondale (U)
South Piedmont Community College (U)
Southwestern Assemblies of God University (U,G)
Southwestern Baptist Theological Seminary (G)
State University of New York at Plattsburgh (G)
Stephen F. Austin State University (G)
Stony Brook University, State University of New York (G)
Sullivan University (G)
Texas A&M University–Commerce (G)
Texas A&M University–Kingsville (G)
Texas A&M University–Texarkana (G)
Texas Tech University (G)
The University of Akron (U,G)
University of Alaska Fairbanks (U,G)
University of Calgary (G)
University of Central Arkansas (G)
University of Central Oklahoma (U,G)
University of Colorado at Colorado Springs (G)
University of Florida (G)
University of Houston–Victoria (G)
University of Massachusetts Amherst (G)
University of Massachusetts Lowell (G)
University of Michigan–Flint (N)
University of Missouri–Columbia (G)
The University of Montana (U,G)
University of New Orleans (U,G)
University of North Texas (N,U,G)
University of Sioux Falls (G)
University of South Alabama (G)
University of South Carolina Sumter (U,G)
University of Southern Mississippi (U,G)
University of South Florida (G)
The University of Tennessee at Martin (G)
The University of Texas of the Permian Basin (G)
University of Wisconsin–Superior (G)
Utah State University (G)
Vanguard University of Southern California (U)
Virginia Polytechnic Institute and State University (G)
Wayne State College (G)
Webster University (G)
Western Michigan University (U)
Western Washington University (U)

EDUCATIONAL ASSESSMENT, EVALUATION, AND RESEARCH

Acadia University (G)
Athabasca University (N,U,G)
Auburn University Montgomery (G)
Azusa Pacific University (G)
Black Hills State University (G)
Boise State University (G)
Bowling Green State University (G)
Brenau University (U,G)
Bridgewater State College (U)
Central Missouri State University (U,G)
Chadron State College (U,G)
Cleveland State University (G)
College of the Southwest (G)
Colorado Christian University (G)
Dallas Baptist University (G)
Drexel University (G)
East Carolina University (U,G)
Eastern Michigan University (U,G)
East Tennessee State University (G)
Florida Atlantic University (G)
Frostburg State University (G)
Indiana State University (G)
Jacksonville State University (U,G)
Kansas State University (N)
Louisiana State University and Agricultural and Mechanical College (U)
Middle Tennessee State University (G)
Mississippi State University (G)
North Georgia College & State University (G)
Northwestern State University of Louisiana (G)
The Pennsylvania State University University Park Campus (U)
Plymouth State University (G)
St. John's University (G)
Saint Joseph's College of Maine (U,G)
St. Petersburg College (U)
Southwestern Baptist Theological Seminary (G)
Texas Tech University (G)
The University of Akron (U,G)
University of Calgary (G)
The University of Findlay (G)
University of Florida (U,G)
University of Houston–Victoria (G)
University of Lethbridge (G)
University of Maryland Eastern Shore (G)
University of Michigan–Flint (N)
University of Missouri–Columbia (G)
University of New Orleans (U,G)
University of North Texas (U,G)
University of St. Francis (G)
University of Sioux Falls (G)
University of South Carolina Sumter (U)
University of Southern Mississippi (U,G)
University of South Florida (G)
The University of Toledo (G)
Utah State University (G)
West Texas A&M University (G)

EDUCATIONAL PSYCHOLOGY

Athabasca University (N,G)
Bergen Community College (U)
Black Hills State University (U)
Brenau University (U,G)
Brigham Young University (U)
Butler County Community College (U)
Caldwell Community College and Technical Institute (U)
Capella University (G)
Casper College (U)
Central Missouri State University (U,G)
Chadron State College (U,G)
Chattanooga State Technical Community College (U)
College of Southern Maryland (U)
Columbia International University (N)
Concordia University Wisconsin (G)
Des Moines Area Community College (U)
East Carolina University (U,G)
Eastern Michigan University (G)
East Tennessee State University (U)
Eugene Bible College (U)
Fort Valley State University (G)
Georgia Southern University (G)
Harford Community College (U)
Indiana State University (G)
Indiana University of Pennsylvania (G)
Indiana Wesleyan University (G)
Jacksonville State University (U,G)
Kansas State University (N)
Lehigh Carbon Community College (U)
Liberty University (U)
Louisiana State University and Agricultural and Mechanical College (U)
Mercy College (U)
Middlesex Community College (U)
Middle Tennessee State University (U)
Mississippi State University (U,G)
Naropa University (N)
North Carolina State University (U)
Northwestern State University of Louisiana (G)
Ozarks Technical Community College (U)
St. Petersburg College (U)
Shenandoah University (G)
Southern Illinois University Carbondale (U)
Southwestern Baptist Theological Seminary (G)
State University of New York at Oswego (U)
Stephen F. Austin State University (U,G)
Taylor University (U)
Texas Tech University (U)
Triton College (U)
The University of Akron (G)
University of Calgary (G)
University of Central Arkansas (U)
University of Florida (U)
University of Houston–Victoria (G)
University of Massachusetts Boston (G)
University of Minnesota, Twin Cities Campus (U)
University of Missouri–Columbia (U,G)
University of Nevada, Reno (U)
University of North Texas (N,U,G)

University of Saskatchewan (G)
University of Southern Indiana (U)
University of South Florida (G)
The University of Texas of the Permian Basin (G)
The University of Texas System (G)
University of Washington (U)
University of Waterloo (U)
University of Wisconsin–La Crosse (G)
University of Wisconsin–Madison (G)
Utah State University (G)

EDUCATIONAL/INSTRUCTIONAL MEDIA DESIGN

Acadia University (U,G)
Adams State College (G)
Arizona State University (U)
Arizona State University West (G)
Arkansas Tech University (U,G)
Athabasca University (N)
Azusa Pacific University (G)
Black Hills State University (G)
Bloomsburg University of Pennsylvania (G)
Boise State University (U,G)
Boston University (G)
Bowling Green State University (U)
Brenau University (U)
California State University, San Bernardino (U,G)
Capella University (G)
Chadron State College (U,G)
Charter Oak State College (U)
Connecticut State University System (G)
Dakota State University (G)
Danville Community College (U)
DePaul University (G)
Drexel University (G)
Duquesne University (G)
East Carolina University (G)
Eastern Michigan University (G)
East Tennessee State University (G)
Florida Atlantic University (U,G)
Florida State University (G)
Georgia Southern University (G)
Hamline University (N,G)
Humboldt State University (G)
Indiana State University (G)
Iona College (G)
Jacksonville State University (U,G)
Maranatha Baptist Bible College (U)
Mississippi State University (U,G)
National University (G)
New Jersey City University (G)
New York Institute of Technology (G)
North Dakota State University (G)
North Georgia College & State University (N)
Northwestern State University of Louisiana (U,G)
Northwest Missouri State University (N,G)
Nova Southeastern University (G)
Ozarks Technical Community College (U)
Pace University (G)
Palomar College (U)
The Pennsylvania State University University Park Campus (G)
St. John's University (G)
St. Petersburg College (U)
San Diego State University (U,G)
Sonoma State University (U)
Southern Polytechnic State University (U)
Southwestern Baptist Theological Seminary (G)
Southwest Wisconsin Technical College (U)
State University of New York at Plattsburgh (G)
Taylor University (U)
Texas A&M University–Commerce (G)
Texas A&M University–Texarkana (G)
Texas Tech University (G)
Tyler Junior College (N,U)
The University of Akron (N,U,G)
University of Alberta (G)
The University of British Columbia (U,G)
University of Calgary (G)
University of California, Berkeley (U,G)
University of Central Florida (G)
The University of Findlay (G)
University of Florida (G)
University of Houston–Clear Lake (G)
University of Houston–Victoria (U,G)
University of Illinois at Urbana–Champaign (G)
University of Maryland Eastern Shore (U)
University of Maryland University College (G)
University of Massachusetts Boston (G)
University of Massachusetts Lowell (N)
University of Michigan–Flint (N)
University of Missouri–Columbia (G)
University of New Orleans (G)
University of Northern Colorado (G)
University of North Texas (U,G)
University of Saskatchewan (N)
University of South Alabama (G)
University of South Florida (G)
The University of Texas System (U,G)
University of West Florida (G)
University of Wyoming (G)
Utah State University (G)
Western Michigan University (U,G)
Wright State University (G)

ELECTRICAL AND ELECTRONIC ENGINEERING TECHNOLOGIES

Alpena Community College (U)
Arizona State University (U)
Bismarck State College (N)
Boise State University (U)
Bradley University (G)
California National University for Advanced Studies (U,G)
Central Carolina Community College (U)
Clark College (U)
Clemson University (U,G)
Cleveland Institute of Electronics (U)
Cleveland State University (U)
College of The Albemarle (U)
Columbia University (U)
Drexel University (G)
Fort Valley State University (U)
Grantham University (U)
Heart of Georgia Technical College (U)
Indiana State University (U,G)
Iowa Western Community College (U)
Moberly Area Community College (U)
Mohawk Valley Community College (U)
Oklahoma State University (U)
Palm Beach Community College (U)
St. Clair County Community College (U)
Seminole Community College (U)
Solano Community College (U)
Southern Methodist University (G)
Southern Polytechnic State University (U)
Texas Tech University (G)
University of Colorado at Boulder (N,G)
University of Illinois at Chicago (G)
University of Massachusetts Lowell (G)
University of New Orleans (U,G)
The University of North Carolina at Charlotte (N)
University of North Texas (U,G)
University of South Florida (G)
University of Washington (G)
Virginia Polytechnic Institute and State University (U)

ELECTRICAL AND POWER TRANSMISSION INSTALLATION

Central Wyoming College (N)
Cleveland Institute of Electronics (N)

ELECTRICAL, ELECTRONICS AND COMMUNICATIONS ENGINEERING

Arkansas Tech University (U)
Boston University (G)
Cleveland State University (G)
Columbia University (G)
Drexel University (G)
Florida Atlantic University (U)
Frostburg State University (U)
Grantham University (U)
Illinois Institute of Technology (G)
Indiana State University (G)
Kansas State University (G)
Kettering University (N)
Mesa State College (U)
Mississippi State University (G)
Southern Methodist University (G)
Stanford University (N)
University of Colorado at Denver and Health Sciences Center—Downtown Denver Campus (U,G)
University of Maryland, College Park (G)
University of New Hampshire (G)
University of South Florida (G)
University of Wisconsin–Platteville (G)

ELECTRICAL/ELECTRONICS MAINTENANCE AND REPAIR TECHNOLOGY

Athens Technical College (U)
Cleveland Institute of Electronics (N)
Orange Coast College (U)
Seminole Community College (U)
Utah Valley State College (U)

ELECTROMECHANICAL AND INSTRUMENTATION AND MAINTENANCE TECHNOLOGIES

Blackhawk Technical College (U)
Indiana State University (G)
Orange Coast College (U)
The Pennsylvania State University University Park Campus (G)

ENGINEERING

Auburn University (N)
California National University for Advanced Studies (U,G)
Capitol College (G)

Casper College (U)
Cleveland Institute of Electronics (U)
Cleveland State University (U,G)
Colorado State University (U)
Columbia University (N)
Drexel University (G)
Eastern Michigan University (G)
Florida Atlantic University (G)
Frostburg State University (U)
Grantham University (U)
Jacksonville State University (U)
Kansas State University (G)
Kettering University (N)
Memorial University of Newfoundland (U)
Mississippi State University (G)
New Jersey Institute of Technology (U)
North Carolina State University (G)
Purdue University Calumet (G)
Schoolcraft College (U)
Tacoma Community College (U)
Texas Tech University (G)
The University of Akron (G)
The University of Alabama (U)
University of Colorado at Denver and Health Sciences Center—Downtown Denver Campus (U,G)
University of Florida (G)
University of Illinois at Chicago (G)
University of Illinois at Urbana–Champaign (G)
University of Maryland, College Park (G)
University of Michigan (N,G)
University of Michigan–Dearborn (G)
University of Missouri–Columbia (U)
University of New Brunswick Fredericton (U)
University of New Orleans (U,G)
The University of North Carolina at Charlotte (N,U)
University of Oklahoma (U)
University of South Carolina Sumter (U)
University of South Florida (N,U,G)
The University of Toledo (G)
University of Wisconsin–Madison (G)
University of Wisconsin–Platteville (G)
Virginia Polytechnic Institute and State University (N,U)

ENGINEERING DESIGN

Boston University (G)
Cleveland Institute of Electronics (N)
Edison State Community College (U)
Georgia Institute of Technology (G)
Kettering University (N)
Pueblo Community College (U)
Southern Methodist University (G)
Southern Polytechnic State University (U)
University of Colorado at Denver and Health Sciences Center—Downtown Denver Campus (G)
University of Michigan (N)
University of South Florida (G)
University of Wisconsin–Platteville (G)

ENGINEERING MECHANICS

Columbus State Community College (U)
Georgia Southern University (U)
Illinois Institute of Technology (U)
New Mexico Institute of Mining and Technology (G)
Rochester Institute of Technology (U)
Southern Methodist University (G)
The University of Alabama (G)
University of Delaware (G)
University of Missouri–Columbia (U)
The University of Texas at Arlington (G)

ENGINEERING PHYSICS

Southern Methodist University (G)
Tacoma Community College (U)

ENGINEERING RELATED

Cleveland State University (G)
Drexel University (G)
Eastern Michigan University (G)
Kansas State University (G)
Kettering University (N)
Lawrence Technological University (U)
North Georgia College & State University (U)
The Ohio State University (U,G)
The Pennsylvania State University University Park Campus (N)
South Dakota School of Mines and Technology (G)
Southern Methodist University (G)
Tacoma Community College (U)
Texas Tech University (G)
The University of Akron (U)
University of Cincinnati (U,G)
University of Colorado at Denver and Health Sciences Center—Downtown Denver Campus (G)
University of Illinois at Chicago (G)
University of Maryland, College Park (G)
University of Michigan (N,G)
The University of Toledo (G)
University of Washington (G)
University of Wisconsin–Platteville (G)
West Virginia University (N)

ENGINEERING SCIENCE

Auburn University (G)
Casper College (U)
Drexel University (G)
Eastern Michigan University (G)
Kansas State University (G)
Southern Methodist University (G)
University of Colorado at Denver and Health Sciences Center—Downtown Denver Campus (U)
University of Delaware (U)
University of Michigan (N,G)
University of Michigan–Dearborn (N,G)

ENGINEERING TECHNOLOGIES RELATED

Cincinnati State Technical and Community College (U)
Colorado State University (U)
Columbus State Community College (U)
Dakota County Technical College (U)
East Carolina University (G)
Eastern Michigan University (G)
Haywood Community College (U)
Heart of Georgia Technical College (U)
Indiana University of Pennsylvania (G)
Mississippi State University (G)
New Jersey Institute of Technology (G)
Northern Kentucky University (G)
Oklahoma State University (U)
Old Dominion University (U)
Southern Methodist University (G)
University of Colorado at Denver and Health Sciences Center—Downtown Denver Campus (G)
University of Michigan (N,G)
University of North Texas (U)
University of Southern Mississippi (U)
The University of Toledo (U)
University of West Florida (U)
Virginia Polytechnic Institute and State University (N)
Western Washington University (U)

ENGINEERING TECHNOLOGY

Cleveland State University (U)
Drexel University (G)
East Carolina University (U)
Glenville State College (U)
Southern Methodist University (G)
University of Illinois at Chicago (G)
University of Michigan (G)
Wake Technical Community College (U)

ENGINEERING-RELATED FIELDS

Auburn University (G)
Cleveland State University (U,G)
Drexel University (G)
Kettering University (N)
Quinebaug Valley Community College (N)
Southern Methodist University (G)
University of New Orleans (U,G)

ENGINEERING-RELATED TECHNOLOGIES

Cleveland State University (G)
Indiana State University (U)
Southern Methodist University (G)
University of Michigan (N)
University of North Texas (U)

ENGINEERING/INDUSTRIAL MANAGEMENT

Cleveland Institute of Electronics (N)
Cleveland State University (G)
Columbia University (N,G)
Delta College (U)
Eastern Michigan University (G)
Edison State Community College (U)
Florida Institute of Technology (G)
Georgia Institute of Technology (G)
Indiana University–Purdue University Fort Wayne (U)
Kansas State University (G)
Lehigh University (N)
Middle Tennessee State University (N)
Montana Tech of The University of Montana (G)
Oregon Institute of Technology (U)
The Pennsylvania State University University Park Campus (G)
Southern Methodist University (G)
Stanford University (N)
Sullivan University (G)
The University of Alabama in Huntsville (G)
University of Colorado at Boulder (N,G)
University of Colorado at Denver and Health Sciences Center—Downtown Denver Campus (G)
University of Massachusetts Amherst (G)

University of Michigan (N,G)
University of Michigan–Dearborn (G)
University of Nebraska–Lincoln (U)
University of South Florida (G)
University of Washington (G)
University of Wisconsin–Platteville (G)
Western Michigan University (G)

ENGLISH

Abilene Christian University (U)
Acadia University (U)
Adirondack Community College (U)
Alvin Community College (U)
American Military University (U)
American Public University (U)
Arizona State University (U)
Arizona Western College (U)
Arkansas State University–Beebe (U)
Athabasca University (N,U)
Barclay College (U)
Bellevue Community College (U)
Bellevue University (U)
Bethany University (U)
Big Sandy Community and Technical College (U)
Bismarck State College (U)
Black Hills State University (U)
Blinn College (U)
Bloomfield College (U)
Blue Ridge Community College (U)
Bowling Green State University (U,G)
Bradley University (U)
Brenau University (U)
Briercrest Distance Learning (U)
Buena Vista University (U)
Caldwell Community College and Technical Institute (U)
California State University, San Bernardino (U)
Carlow University (U)
Carl Sandburg College (U)
Carroll College (U)
Cayuga County Community College (U)
Cedarville University (U)
Central Carolina Community College (U)
Central New Mexico Community College (U)
Central Texas College (U)
Central Virginia Community College (U)
Chadron State College (G)
Champlain College (U)
Chattanooga State Technical Community College (U)
Chesapeake College (U)
Clark College (U)
Clark State Community College (U)
Clatsop Community College (U)
Clemson University (G)
Cleveland State University (U)
Clinton Community College (U)
College of The Albemarle (N)
Colorado State University (U)
Colorado State University-Pueblo (U)
Columbia Basin College (U)
Columbus State Community College (U)
Community College of Beaver County (U)
Community College of Denver (U)
Community College of Southern Nevada (U)
Cowley County Community College and Area Vocational–Technical School (U)
Dakota County Technical College (U)
Dakota State University (U)
Dallas Baptist University (U)
Danville Community College (U)
Darton College (U)
Davis College (U)
Delta College (U)
Des Moines Area Community College (U)
Dodge City Community College (U)
Drake University (U)
Drury University (U)
East Carolina University (G)
East Central Community College (U)
Eastern Michigan University (U)
Eastern Oregon University (U)
Eastern West Virginia Community and Technical College (U)
Eastern Wyoming College (U)
East Tennessee State University (U)
Edgecombe Community College (N)
Edmonds Community College (U)
Elgin Community College (U)
Elizabethtown College (U)
Embry-Riddle Aeronautical University, Extended Campus (U)
Fort Hays State University (U)
Frostburg State University (U)
Gadsden State Community College (U)
Glenville State College (U)
Grand View College (U)
Harford Community College (U)
Haywood Community College (U)
Heart of Georgia Technical College (U)
Hillsborough Community College (U)
Honolulu Community College (U)
Housatonic Community College (U)
Independence Community College (U)
Indiana State University (U)
Iowa Western Community College (U)
Jackson Community College (U)
Jacksonville State University (U)
James Madison University (N)
John A. Logan College (U)
Jones College (N,U)
Judson College (U)
Kansas State University (U)
Kentucky State University (U)
Lenoir Community College (U)
LeTourneau University (U)
Limestone College (U)
Lipscomb University (U)
Los Angeles Harbor College (U)
Louisiana State University and Agricultural and Mechanical College (U)
Louisiana Tech University (G)
Macon State College (N)
Mansfield University of Pennsylvania (U)
Memorial University of Newfoundland (U)
Mercy College (U,G)
Mesalands Community College (U)
Mesa State College (U)
Miami Dade College (U)
Middlesex Community College (U)
Middle Tennessee State University (U)
Midland College (U)
Mid Michigan Community College (U)
Moberly Area Community College (U)
Montgomery Community College (N,U)
Mount Allison University (U)
Mount Saint Vincent University (U)
Naropa University (G)
National University (U)
Neumann College (U)
New England College of Finance (U)
New Mexico State University–Carlsbad (U)
New York Institute of Technology (U)
North Carolina State University (U)
North Central Texas College (U)
North Dakota State College of Science (U)
Northeast State Technical Community College (U)
North Lake College (U)
Northwestern Oklahoma State University (U)
Northwestern State University of Louisiana (U)
Oral Roberts University (U)
Oregon State University (N,U)
Oxnard College (U)
Ozarks Technical Community College (U)
Pace University (U)
Palomar College (U)
Park University (U)
Passaic County Community College (U)
Plymouth State University (U)
Portland State University (U)
Prescott College (U)
Pueblo Community College (U)
Purdue University Calumet (U)
Raritan Valley Community College (U)
Rasmussen College Eden Prarie (U)
Regent University (U)
Rend Lake College (U)
Rio Hondo College (U)
Ryerson University (U)
St. Cloud State University (U)
St. Edward's University (U)
St. John's University (U)
Saint Leo University (U)
Sam Houston State University (U)
San Bernardino Valley College (U)
Schoolcraft College (U)
Seminole Community College (U)
Shippensburg University of Pennsylvania (U,G)
Shoreline Community College (U)
Simpson College (U)
Southeast Arkansas College (U)
Southeast Community College, Beatrice Campus (U)
Southeast Community College, Lincoln Campus (U)
Southeast Community College, Milford Campus (U)
Southern Arkansas University Tech (U)
Southern Illinois University Carbondale (U)
Southern University at Shreveport (U)
South Piedmont Community College (U)
South Plains College (U)
Southwestern College (U)
Southwest Georgia Technical College (U)
Spartanburg Technical College (U)
Stephens College (U)
Strayer University (U)
Taft College (U)
Taylor University (U)
Texas A&M University–Commerce (U)
Texas A&M University–Kingsville (U,G)
Texas A&M University–Texarkana (U)
Texas State University-San Marcos (U)
Texas Tech University (G)
Texas Woman's University (U)
Tompkins Cortland Community College (U)
Tri-County Community College (U)
Tunxis Community College (U)
The University of Alabama (U)
University of Alaska Fairbanks (U)
University of Arkansas at Pine Bluff (U)
The University of British Columbia (U)
University of California, Berkeley (U,G)

University of Central Arkansas (N)
University of Central Oklahoma (U,G)
University of Colorado at Denver and Health Sciences Center—Downtown Denver Campus (U)
University of Delaware (U)
University of Florida (U)
University of Great Falls (U)
The University of Maine at Augusta (U)
University of Maine at Fort Kent (U)
University of Massachusetts Amherst (U)
University of Minnesota, Twin Cities Campus (U)
University of Missouri–Columbia (U,G)
University of Nebraska–Lincoln (U)
University of Nevada, Reno (U)
University of New Brunswick Fredericton (U)
University of New Orleans (U,G)
University of North Alabama (U,G)
University of Northern Iowa (U)
University of Oregon (U)
University of St. Francis (U)
University of Saskatchewan (U)
University of Sioux Falls (U)
University of Southern Indiana (U)
University of Southern Mississippi (U)
University of South Florida (U,G)
The University of Tennessee (U)
The University of Texas System (U)
The University of Toledo (U)
University of Washington (N,U)
University of West Florida (U)
University of Wisconsin Colleges (U)
University of Wisconsin–Superior (U)
University of Wisconsin–Whitewater (U,G)
Upper Iowa University (U)
Utah State University (U,G)
Utah Valley State College (U)
Utica College (U)
Virginia Polytechnic Institute and State University (G)
Washtenaw Community College (U)
Wayne State College (U,G)
Weber State University (U)
Westchester Community College (U)
Western Washington University (U)
West Los Angeles College (U)
Wharton County Junior College (U)
Whatcom Community College (U)
Wilfrid Laurier University (U)
Wilkes Community College (U)
William Rainey Harper College (U)
Wright State University (U)
York Technical College (U)

ENGLISH AS A SECOND LANGUAGE

Ashworth College (N)
Athabasca University (N,U)
Blackhawk Technical College (N)
California State University, San Marcos (N)
Central Carolina Community College (N)
Chesapeake College (U)
College of DuPage (U)
College of the Humanities and Sciences, Harrison Middleton University (U)
College of the Southwest (U)
Dallas County Community College District (U)
Drexel University (G)
Edgecombe Community College (N)
Gateway Community College (U)
Hamline University (N,G)
Indiana State University (G)
James Madison University (N)
Linn-Benton Community College (N,U)
Middle Tennessee State University (N)
Mt. San Antonio College (U)
Murray State University (G)
Naugatuck Valley Community College (N)
Oregon State University (N,G)
Oxnard College (U)
Red Rocks Community College (U)
Regent University (N,G)
St. Cloud State University (U,G)
St. Petersburg College (U)
San Diego State University (N)
Shoreline Community College (U)
Tacoma Community College (U)
Texas A&M University–Kingsville (G)
Tompkins Cortland Community College (U)
University of Central Oklahoma (U,G)
University of Florida (N,U)
University of Maine (U)
University of New Orleans (U,G)
The University of North Carolina at Chapel Hill (U)
University of Saskatchewan (N)
The University of Texas of the Permian Basin (U,G)
The University of Texas System (U)
University of Washington (N,U)
University of Wisconsin–Whitewater (U,G)
Valley City State University (U)
Wake Technical Community College (N)
Westchester Community College (U)
Western Washington University (U)
West Los Angeles College (U)
Wharton County Junior College (N)
William Rainey Harper College (U)

ENGLISH AS A SECOND/FOREIGN LANGUAGE (TEACHING)

Athabasca University (N)
Briercrest Distance Learning (U)
Buena Vista University (G)
Drexel University (G)
Hamline University (N,G)
Indiana State University (G)
Murray State University (G)
The New School (G)
North Carolina State University (U)
Oregon State University (G)
Seattle Pacific University (G)
The University of Akron (U)
University of Florida (U)
University of Maine (U)
University of Massachusetts Boston (G)
University of Nevada, Reno (U)
The University of North Carolina at Greensboro (G)
University of North Dakota (G)
University of Saskatchewan (N,U)
University of South Florida (G)
The University of Texas System (G)
Western Washington University (U)

ENGLISH COMPOSITION

Acadia University (U)
Adams State College (U)
Adirondack Community College (U)
Alpena Community College (U)
Alvin Community College (U)
American Military University (U)
American Public University (U)
Anne Arundel Community College (U)
Arizona State University (U)
Arizona State University at the Polytechnic Campus (U)
Arkansas State University–Beebe (U)
Arkansas State University–Mountain Home (U)
Athabasca University (N,U)
Athens Technical College (U)
Barclay College (U)
Bellevue Community College (U)
Bergen Community College (U)
Berkeley College (U)
Berkeley College-New York City Campus (U)
Berkeley College-Westchester Campus (U)
Bethany University (U)
Bismarck State College (U)
Black Hills State University (U)
Blinn College (U)
Blue Ridge Community College (U)
Boise State University (U)
Bowling Green State University (U)
Brazosport College (U)
Brenau University (U)
Bridgewater State College (U)
Brigham Young University (U)
Broome Community College (U)
Buena Vista University (U)
Burlington County College (U)
Butler Community College (U)
Butler County Community College (U)
Caldwell Community College and Technical Institute (U)
Campbell University (U)
Cape Cod Community College (U)
Cape Fear Community College (U)
Carl Albert State College (U)
Carl Sandburg College (U)
Casper College (U)
Central Lakes College (U)
Central New Mexico Community College (U)
Central Piedmont Community College (U)
Central Texas College (U)
Central Virginia Community College (U)
Central Wyoming College (U)
Chadron State College (U)
Champlain College (U)
Chattanooga State Technical Community College (U)
Citrus College (U)
Clackamas Community College (U)
Clarion University of Pennsylvania (U)
Clark College (U)
Clark State Community College (U)
Clatsop Community College (U)
Clemson University (N,U)
Cleveland State Community College (U)
Clinton Community College (U)
Clovis Community College (U)
Coconino Community College (N,U)
Coffeyville Community College (U)
Coleman College (U)
College of DuPage (U)
College of San Mateo (U)
College of Southern Maryland (U)
College of The Albemarle (N,U)
College of the Humanities and Sciences, Harrison Middleton University (U)
College of the Siskiyous (U)
College of the Southwest (U)

Colorado Mountain College District System (U)
Colorado State University (U)
Colorado State University-Pueblo (U)
Columbia Basin College (U)
Columbia-Greene Community College (U)
Columbus State Community College (U)
The Community College of Baltimore County (U)
Community College of Beaver County (U)
Community College of Denver (U)
Connecticut State University System (U,G)
Copiah-Lincoln Community College (U)
Corning Community College (U)
Cosumnes River College (U)
County College of Morris (U)
Cowley County Community College and Area Vocational–Technical School (U)
Cumberland County College (U)
Daemen College (U)
Dakota County Technical College (U)
Dakota State University (U)
Dallas County Community College District (U)
Danville Community College (U)
Darton College (U)
Dawson Community College (U)
De Anza College (U)
Delta College (U)
Des Moines Area Community College (U)
DeVry University Online (U)
East Arkansas Community College (U)
East Central Community College (U)
Eastern Michigan University (U)
Eastern New Mexico University (U)
Eastern Oklahoma State College (U)
Eastern Wyoming College (U)
East Tennessee State University (U)
Edgecombe Community College (U)
Edison State Community College (U)
Elgin Community College (U)
Embry-Riddle Aeronautical University (U)
Erie Community College (U)
Eugene Bible College (U)
Everett Community College (U)
Evergreen Valley College (U)
Feather River College (U)
Fontbonne University (U)
Frostburg State University (U)
Galveston College (U)
George Mason University (U)
Georgia Highlands College (U)
Georgia Southern University (U)
Gogebic Community College (U)
Golden West College (U)
Governors State University (U)
Grand View College (U)
Grantham University (U)
Greenfield Community College (U)
Gulf Coast Community College (U)
Halifax Community College (U)
Harford Community College (U)
Haywood Community College (U)
Heartland Community College (U)
Hillsborough Community College (U)
Honolulu Community College (U)
Housatonic Community College (U)
Houston Community College System (U)
Howard College (U)
Illinois Eastern Community Colleges, Lincoln Trail College (U)
Illinois Eastern Community Colleges, Olney Central College (U)
Immaculata University (U)
Independence Community College (U)
Indiana State University (U)
Indiana Tech (U)
Indiana University–Purdue University Fort Wayne (U)
Indiana Wesleyan University (U)
Iowa Western Community College (U)
Itawamba Community College (U)
Ivy Tech Community College–Kokomo (U)
Ivy Tech Community College–North Central (U)
Ivy Tech Community College–Northwest (U)
Jackson Community College (U)
Jacksonville State University (U)
James Madison University (N,U)
James Sprunt Community College (U)
Jamestown Community College (N)
Jefferson College of Health Sciences (U)
Jefferson Community College (U)
Jefferson Davis Community College (U)
John A. Logan College (U)
Johnson County Community College (U)
John Tyler Community College (U)
Jones College (U)
J. Sargeant Reynolds Community College (U)
Judson College (U)
Kauai Community College (U)
Kentucky State University (U)
Lake Superior College (U)
Lansing Community College (U)
Lehigh Carbon Community College (U)
LeTourneau University (U)
Lewis-Clark State College (U)
Liberty University (U)
Limestone College (U)
Lock Haven University of Pennsylvania (U)
Los Angeles Harbor College (U)
Louisiana State University and Agricultural and Mechanical College (N,U)
Louisiana State University at Eunice (U)
Macon State College (U)
Madison Area Technical College (U)
Madonna University (U)
Malone College (U)
Marion Technical College (U)
Marshall University (U)
Marylhurst University (U)
Mayville State University (U)
Mercer County Community College (U)
Mercy College (U)
Metropolitan State University (U)
Miami Dade College (U)
Middlesex Community College (U)
Middle Tennessee State University (U)
Midland College (U)
Mid Michigan Community College (U)
Midstate College (U)
Millersville University of Pennsylvania (U,G)
Mohawk Valley Community College (U)
Monroe Community College (U)
Montana State University–Billings (U)
Montana Tech of The University of Montana (U)
Montgomery Community College (N,U)
Moody Bible Institute (U)
Mountain Empire Community College (U)
Mt. San Antonio College (U)
Mount Wachusett Community College (U)
Murray State University (U)
Myers University (U)
Nassau Community College (U)
New England Institute of Technology (U)
New Mexico Junior College (U)
New Mexico State University–Alamogordo (U)
The New School (N,U)
New York Institute of Technology (U)
North Arkansas College (U)
North Carolina State University (U)
North Central Texas College (U)
North Dakota State College of Science (U)
Northeast State Technical Community College (U)
Northern Virginia Community College (U)
North Idaho College (U)
North Seattle Community College (U)
Northwestern Connecticut Community College (U)
Northwestern Michigan College (U)
Northwestern State University of Louisiana (U)
Odessa College (U)
Oklahoma State University (U)
Orange Coast College (U)
Oregon State University (U)
Ouachita Technical College (U)
Oxnard College (U)
Ozarks Technical Community College (U)
Palomar College (U)
Parkland College (U)
Park University (U)
Pasco-Hernando Community College (U)
Patrick Henry College (U)
Patrick Henry Community College (U)
Peninsula College (U)
The Pennsylvania State University University Park Campus (U)
Piedmont Technical College (U)
Portland Community College (U)
Portland State University (U)
Pueblo Community College (U)
Pulaski Technical College (U)
Queen's University at Kingston (U)
Randolph Community College (U)
Rappahannock Community College (U)
Raritan Valley Community College (U)
Rasmussen College Eden Prarie (U)
Reading Area Community College (U)
Red Rocks Community College (U)
Rend Lake College (U)
The Richard Stockton College of New Jersey (U)
Rio Hondo College (U)
Rochester Institute of Technology (U)
Roosevelt University (U)
Sacramento City College (U)
Sacred Heart University (U)
St. Clair County Community College (U)
St. Cloud State University (U)
St. Johns River Community College (U)
Saint Joseph's College of Maine (U)
Saint Leo University (U)
San Diego State University (N)
San Joaquin Delta College (U)
Schenectady County Community College (U)
Schiller International University (U)
Schoolcraft College (U)
Seattle Central Community College (U)
Seminole Community College (U)
Shawnee Community College (U)
Shoreline Community College (U)
Sinclair Community College (U)
Solano Community College (U)
Southeast Arkansas College (U)

Southeast Community College, Beatrice Campus (U)
Southeast Community College, Lincoln Campus (U)
Southeast Community College, Milford Campus (U)
South Piedmont Community College (U)
South Plains College (U)
Southwestern Assemblies of God University (U)
Southwestern College (U)
Southwestern Community College (U)
Southwest Georgia Technical College (U)
Southwest Virginia Community College (U)
Spartanburg Technical College (U)
Stanly Community College (U)
State University of New York at Buffalo (U)
State University of New York at New Paltz (U)
State University of New York College of Agriculture and Technology at Morrisville (U)
State University of New York Empire State College (U)
Strayer University (U)
Tacoma Community College (U)
Taft College (U)
Taylor University (N,U)
Texas A&M University–Commerce (U,G)
Texas State Technical College Waco (U)
Texas State University-San Marcos (U)
Texas Tech University (U,G)
Tompkins Cortland Community College (U)
Touro University International (U)
Triton College (U)
Tunxis Community College (U)
Tyler Junior College (U)
The University of Akron (U)
The University of Alabama (U)
University of Alaska Fairbanks (U)
University of Arkansas (U)
The University of British Columbia (N)
University of California, Davis (N)
University of Central Arkansas (U)
University of Cincinnati Raymond Walters College (U)
University of Colorado at Colorado Springs (U)
University of Colorado at Denver and Health Sciences Center—Downtown Denver Campus (U)
University of Delaware (U)
University of Florida (U)
University of Houston–Victoria (U)
University of Illinois at Springfield (U)
University of La Verne (U)
University of Maine (U)
The University of Maine at Augusta (U)
University of Maine at Presque Isle (U)
University of Massachusetts Lowell (U)
University of Minnesota, Crookston (U)
University of Minnesota, Morris (U)
University of Minnesota, Twin Cities Campus (U)
University of Missouri–Columbia (U)
The University of Montana (U)
The University of Montana–Western (U)
University of Nebraska at Omaha (U)
University of Nebraska–Lincoln (N,U)
University of Nevada, Reno (U)
University of New Orleans (U,G)
University of North Alabama (U)
The University of North Carolina at Chapel Hill (U)
University of North Dakota (U)
University of Oklahoma (U)
University of Pittsburgh (U)
University of Southern Indiana (U)
University of Southern Mississippi (U)
University of South Florida (U)
The University of Tennessee (U)
The University of Tennessee at Martin (U)
The University of Texas of the Permian Basin (U)
The University of Texas System (U)
The University of Toledo (U)
University of Washington (U)
University of Waterloo (N,U)
University of West Florida (U)
University of Wisconsin Colleges (U)
University of Wyoming (U)
Upper Iowa University (N,U)
Utah Valley State College (U)
Valley City State University (U)
Vance-Granville Community College (U)
Vincennes University (U)
Virginia Polytechnic Institute and State University (U)
Wake Technical Community College (U)
Washburn University (U)
Washington State University (U)
Washtenaw Community College (U)
Waukesha County Technical College (U)
Weber State University (U)
Westchester Community College (U)
Western Michigan University (U)
Western Oklahoma State College (U)
Western Piedmont Community College (U)
Western Wyoming Community College (U)
West Los Angeles College (U)
West Shore Community College (U)
West Virginia Northern Community College (U)
West Virginia University at Parkersburg (U)
Wharton County Junior College (U)
Whatcom Community College (U)
Wilfrid Laurier University (N)
Wilkes Community College (U)
William Rainey Harper College (U)
Wright State University (U)
York County Community College (U)
York Technical College (U)
Yuba College (U)

ENGLISH LANGUAGE AND LITERATURE RELATED

Acadia University (U)
Adams State College (U)
Alvin Community College (U)
Arkansas Tech University (U)
Athens Technical College (N)
Bellevue Community College (U)
Berkeley College (U)
Berkeley College-New York City Campus (U)
Berkeley College-Westchester Campus (U)
Brenau University (U)
Brigham Young University (N)
Charter Oak State College (U)
College of the Humanities and Sciences, Harrison Middleton University (G)
College of the Siskiyous (U)
Columbus State Community College (U)
Community College of Southern Nevada (U)
Danville Community College (U)
Davis College (U)
Des Moines Area Community College (U)
Iowa Western Community College (U)
Jacksonville State University (U)
James Sprunt Community College (U)
John A. Logan College (U)
Jones College (U)
Limestone College (U)
Los Angeles Harbor College (U)
Louisiana State University and Agricultural and Mechanical College (U)
Mercy College (G)
Metropolitan State University (U)
Middlesex Community College (U)
Missouri State University (U)
Mount Allison University (U)
Nassau Community College (U)
New York Institute of Technology (U)
Northwestern Michigan College (U)
Pennsylvania College of Technology (U)
Pueblo Community College (U)
Quinebaug Valley Community College (U)
Raritan Valley Community College (U)
Rasmussen College Eden Prarie (U)
Sacred Heart University (U)
Schoolcraft College (U)
South Plains College (U)
State University of New York College at Cortland (G)
Stony Brook University, State University of New York (G)
Syracuse University (U)
Taft College (U)
Texas State University-San Marcos (U)
Three Rivers Community College (U)
The University of Akron (U,G)
The University of Alabama (U)
University of Alaska Fairbanks (U)
University of California, Berkeley (U,G)
University of Delaware (U)
University of Florida (U)
University of Houston–Downtown (U)
University of Houston–Victoria (U,G)
University of Minnesota, Twin Cities Campus (U)
University of Missouri–Columbia (U,G)
University of Nebraska at Omaha (U)
University of New Orleans (U,G)
The University of Tennessee (U)
The University of Texas System (U)
Utah Valley State College (U)
Westchester Community College (U)
West Los Angeles College (U)
West Virginia University at Parkersburg (U)
Wharton County Junior College (U)
Wilkes Community College (U)
William Rainey Harper College (U)

ENGLISH LITERATURE (BRITISH AND COMMONWEALTH)

Bellevue Community College (U)
Bellevue University (U)
Bowling Green State University (U,G)
Chadron State College (U)
Chattanooga State Technical Community College (U)
Clackamas Community College (U)
College of The Albemarle (U)
College of the Humanities and Sciences, Harrison Middleton University (U)
College of the Siskiyous (U)
Columbia College (U)

Columbus State Community College (U)
Community College of Beaver County (U)
Danville Community College (U)
Darton College (U)
Des Moines Area Community College (U)
D'Youville College (U)
East Arkansas Community College (U)
Eugene Bible College (U)
Galveston College (U)
Halifax Community College (U)
Housatonic Community College (U)
Houston Community College System (U)
Howard College (U)
Itawamba Community College (U)
Jacksonville State University (U)
James Sprunt Community College (U)
Johnson County Community College (U)
John Tyler Community College (U)
Judson College (U)
Louisiana State University and Agricultural and Mechanical College (U)
Malone College (U)
Marylhurst University (U)
Mercy College (U,G)
Middlesex Community College (U)
Mohawk Valley Community College (U)
Mount Allison University (U)
Mount Saint Vincent University (U)
Neumann College (U)
North Central Texas College (U)
Northwestern Oklahoma State University (U)
Oklahoma State University (U)
Pasco-Hernando Community College (U)
Patrick Henry Community College (U)
Peninsula College (U)
Piedmont Technical College (U)
Queen's University at Kingston (U)
South Plains College (U)
State University of New York at New Paltz (U)
Taylor University (U)
Texas State University-San Marcos (U)
Texas Tech University (U)
Three Rivers Community College (U)
The University of Akron (U)
The University of Alabama (U)
University of California, Berkeley (U,G)
University of Minnesota, Twin Cities Campus (U)
University of Missouri–Columbia (U)
University of New Orleans (U,G)
University of Saskatchewan (U)
University of Southern Indiana (U)
University of Southern Mississippi (U)
The University of Tennessee (U)
The University of Tennessee at Martin (U)
University of Utah (U)
University of Waterloo (U)
University of Wyoming (U)
Utah State University (U)
Wake Technical Community College (U)
Wharton County Junior College (U)
Wilfrid Laurier University (U)
Wilkes Community College (U)

ENTREPRENEURIAL AND SMALL BUSINESS OPERATIONS

Adams State College (N)
Andrew Jackson University (U,G)
Asheville-Buncombe Technical Community College (N)
Ashworth College (N)
Bellevue Community College (U)
Berkeley College (U)
Berkeley College-New York City Campus (U)
Berkeley College-Westchester Campus (U)
Blue Ridge Community College (U)
Bridgewater State College (U)
Central Michigan University (G)
Central Missouri State University (N)
Central New Mexico Community College (U)
Central Texas College (U)
Champlain College (U)
Clark College (U)
Cleveland State University (N)
Colorado State University-Pueblo (N)
Columbia College (U)
The Community College of Baltimore County (U)
Community College of Beaver County (N)
Community College of Denver (U)
Daemen College (U)
Dakota County Technical College (U)
Dallas Baptist University (G)
Des Moines Area Community College (U)
DeVry University Online (G)
Drexel University (G)
Eastern Michigan University (U)
East Tennessee State University (N)
Erie Community College (U)
Franklin Pierce College (G)
Fulton-Montgomery Community College (N)
Immaculata University (U)
Iona College (U)
Iowa Western Community College (U)
James Madison University (N)
Jamestown Community College (N)
Lamar State College–Port Arthur (N)
Manhattanville College (U)
Maryville University of Saint Louis (N)
Minnesota School of Business–Richfield (U)
Mitchell Technical Institute (N)
Mount Saint Vincent University (U)
Myers University (U)
Nassau Community College (U)
New Mexico State University–Carlsbad (N)
Northern Kentucky University (U)
North Idaho College (N)
Peirce College (U)
Peninsula College (U)
The Pennsylvania State University University Park Campus (U)
Rend Lake College (N)
Ryerson University (U)
St. Edward's University (G)
Saint Joseph's College of Maine (G)
St. Petersburg College (U)
Schenectady County Community College (U)
Schoolcraft College (U)
Shippensburg University of Pennsylvania (G)
Sinclair Community College (U)
Southeast Arkansas College (U)
Stanford University (N)
State University of New York at Buffalo (U)
State University of New York at Plattsburgh (U,G)
State University of New York College at Potsdam (N,U)
Stephens College (G)
Syracuse University (G)
Taylor University (N)
Touro University International (G)
United States Sports Academy (G)
The University of Akron (N)
University of Bridgeport (U)
University of California, Berkeley (U,G)
University of Florida (U)
University of Illinois at Urbana–Champaign (G)
University of Maryland University College (G)
University of Minnesota, Crookston (U)
University of Minnesota, Twin Cities Campus (U)
University of New Orleans (U,G)
University of Tulsa (G)
Vance-Granville Community College (N)
Vincennes University (U)
Wake Technical Community College (N)

ENVIRONMENTAL CONTROL TECHNOLOGIES

Arizona State University at the Polytechnic Campus (U,G)
Athabasca University (N,U)
Bowling Green State University (U)
Columbus State Community College (U)
Cosumnes River College (U)
De Anza College (U)
Immaculata University (U)
Jacksonville State University (U,G)
Judson College (U)
New York Institute of Technology (U)
Odessa College (U)
Oxnard College (U)
The Pennsylvania State University University Park Campus (G)
The University of British Columbia (U)
The University of Findlay (G)
University of Florida (N,G)

ENVIRONMENTAL DESIGN

Boston Architectural College (N,U,G)
The Pennsylvania State University University Park Campus (N,G)
University of New Brunswick Fredericton (N)
University of Wisconsin–River Falls (G)

ENVIRONMENTAL PSYCHOLOGY

Saybrook Graduate School and Research Center (G)
The University of Montana (U)

ENVIRONMENTAL/ ENVIRONMENTAL HEALTH ENGINEERING

Alcorn State University (G)
Arizona State University (G)
Bowling Green State University (U)
California National University for Advanced Studies (U,G)
Cape Breton University (U)
Clackamas Community College (U)
Cleveland State University (G)
Columbia University (N,G)
East Arkansas Community College (U)
Florida Gulf Coast University (U)
Fort Valley State University (G)
Georgia Institute of Technology (N,G)
Harvard University (N,U,G)
Illinois Institute of Technology (G)
Louisiana State University and Agricultural and Mechanical College (G)
Mercy College (U)

New Mexico Institute of Mining and Technology (G)
Odessa College (U)
Old Dominion University (G)
Oregon State University (G)
Pennsylvania College of Technology (U)
St. Cloud State University (U)
Southern Methodist University (G)
Texas A&M University–Kingsville (G)
Texas Tech University (G)
Three Rivers Community College (U)
University of Colorado at Boulder (N,G)
University of Florida (G)
University of Massachusetts Amherst (U)
University of Massachusetts Boston (U)
University of New Brunswick Fredericton (N)
University of South Florida (G)
The University of Texas at Arlington (G)
Worcester Polytechnic Institute (G)
York Technical College (U)

ETHNIC, CULTURAL MINORITY, AND GENDER STUDIES

American Public University (G)
Antioch University McGregor (U)
Arizona State University (U)
Athabasca University (N)
Berkeley College (U)
Berkeley College-New York City Campus (U)
Berkeley College-Westchester Campus (U)
Bethany University (U)
Bowling Green State University (U)
Bridgewater State College (U)
California Institute of Integral Studies (N,G)
California State University, Chico (U)
California State University, San Bernardino (U)
Central Texas College (U)
Central Wyoming College (N)
Colorado Christian University (U)
Colorado State University (U)
Columbia Basin College (U)
Columbus State Community College (U)
De Anza College (U)
Eastern Michigan University (U,G)
Edgecombe Community College (U)
Hebrew College (N,U,G)
Hope International University (N,G)
Jackson Community College (U)
Kansas State University (U)
Laura and Alvin Siegal College of Judaic Studies (N,U,G)
Louisiana State University and Agricultural and Mechanical College (U)
Marylhurst University (N)
Master's College and Seminary (U)
Middlesex Community College (U)
Naropa University (N,U)
Northwestern College (U)
Oregon State University (U)
Palomar College (U)
The Pennsylvania State University University Park Campus (U)
Prescott College (U,G)
Queen's University at Kingston (U)
Randolph Community College (U)
Rasmussen College Eden Prarie (U)
The Richard Stockton College of New Jersey (U)
San Diego State University (U)
Saybrook Graduate School and Research Center (G)
South Plains College (U)
State University of New York at Plattsburgh (U)
Syracuse University (U,G)
University of Alaska Fairbanks (U)
The University of British Columbia (U)
University of Colorado at Denver and Health Sciences Center—Downtown Denver Campus (U)
University of Connecticut (U)
The University of Findlay (U)
University of Illinois at Springfield (U)
The University of Iowa (U,G)
University of Maine (U)
University of Massachusetts Lowell (U)
University of Minnesota, Twin Cities Campus (U)
University of Missouri–Columbia (U)
The University of North Carolina at Chapel Hill (N,U)
University of South Florida (U)
The University of Toledo (U)
University of Washington (U)
University of Waterloo (U)
University of Wisconsin–Whitewater (U)
University of Wyoming (U)
Virginia Polytechnic Institute and State University (U,G)
Western Michigan University (U)
Western Washington University (U)
Western Wyoming Community College (U)
Wilkes Community College (U)

EXPERIMENTAL PSYCHOLOGY

Acadia University (U)
Naropa University (U)

FAMILY AND CONSUMER ECONOMICS

Asheville-Buncombe Technical Community College (N)
Athens Technical College (N)
California State University, San Marcos (N)
Cleveland State University (N)
College of the Siskiyous (U)
Cosumnes River College (U)
Eastern Oklahoma State College (U)
East Los Angeles College (U)
Immaculata University (U)
Iowa State University of Science and Technology (G)
Kansas State University (N)
Louisiana State University and Agricultural and Mechanical College (U)
North Dakota State University (G)
The Ohio State University (U)
Oregon State University (N)
Ozarks Technical Community College (U)
Palomar College (U)
Pasco-Hernando Community College (N)
Sam Houston State University (U)
Stephen F. Austin State University (U)
Taylor University (N)
Texas Tech University (G)
Texas Woman's University (U,G)
The University of Alabama (U,G)
University of Minnesota, Twin Cities Campus (U)
University of Northern Iowa (U)
University of North Texas (U,G)
University of Wyoming (U)
Utah State University (U)
Western Michigan University (U,G)
Wichita State University (U)

FAMILY AND CONSUMER SCIENCES/HUMAN SCIENCES

Bradley University (U)
Central Michigan University (U)
Chadron State College (U)
Feather River College (N)
Immaculata University (U)
Jacksonville State University (U)
James Madison University (N)
Kansas State University (N,U,G)
Kean University (N)
Northwestern State University of Louisiana (U)
Palomar College (U)
Sacramento City College (U)
Saybrook Graduate School and Research Center (G)
Texas A&M University–Kingsville (U,G)
The University of Alabama (U)
University of Maryland Eastern Shore (U)
University of Minnesota, Twin Cities Campus (U)
Utah State University (U,G)
Wayne State College (U,G)

FAMILY AND CONSUMER SCIENCES/HUMAN SCIENCES BUSINESS SERVICES

Cardinal Stritch University (N)
Sullivan University (G)
The University of Alabama (U)

FAMILY AND CONSUMER SCIENCES/HUMAN SCIENCES RELATED

Central Michigan University (U)
Chadron State College (U)
Galveston College (N)
Jacksonville State University (U,G)
Kansas State University (N,U,G)
Mount Saint Vincent University (U)
Palomar College (U)
The University of Alabama (U)
Western Michigan University (U)

FAMILY PSYCHOLOGY

Dakota County Technical College (U)
Kansas State University (N,G)
Peninsula College (U)
Rasmussen College Eden Prarie (U)
Saybrook Graduate School and Research Center (G)
Seminole Community College (U)
Texas State University-San Marcos (U)
University of Alaska Fairbanks (G)
University of Houston–Victoria (G)

FILM/VIDEO AND PHOTOGRAPHIC ARTS

Academy of Art University (U,G)
Asheville-Buncombe Technical Community College (N)
Auburn University (U)

Blackhawk Technical College (N)
Blue Ridge Community College (N)
Brigham Young University (U)
Burlington County College (U)
City College of San Francisco (U)
Cleveland Institute of Electronics (N)
Cleveland State University (N)
College of San Mateo (U)
College of Staten Island of the City University of New York (N)
Delta College (U)
Feather River College (N)
Houston Community College System (U)
Humboldt State University (G)
James Madison University (N)
John A. Logan College (U)
Kean University (N)
Marylhurst University (U)
Massasoit Community College (U)
Minneapolis College of Art and Design (N,U,G)
Missouri State University (U)
Mohawk Valley Community College (U)
Mount Wachusett Community College (U)
Northern Virginia Community College (U)
North Idaho College (N)
North Seattle Community College (U)
Oregon State University (N)
Oxnard College (U)
Rasmussen College Eden Prarie (U)
Regent University (N,U)
The Richard Stockton College of New Jersey (U)
Sam Houston State University (U)
San Diego State University (N)
Seattle Central Community College (U)
Sinclair Community College (U)
University of Alaska Fairbanks (U)
University of Bridgeport (U)
The University of British Columbia (U)
University of California, Berkeley (U)
University of California, Los Angeles (G)
University of Cincinnati Raymond Walters College (U)
University of Missouri–Columbia (U)
The University of North Carolina at Charlotte (N)
The University of North Carolina at Greensboro (U)
University of Southern Indiana (N)
The University of Toledo (U)
Wake Technical Community College (N)
Western Michigan University (G)
William Rainey Harper College (U)

FINANCE AND FINANCIAL MANAGEMENT SERVICES

Adams State College (U)
Andrew Jackson University (G)
Anne Arundel Community College (U)
Ashworth College (N)
Athabasca University (N,U)
Bellevue University (U)
Bergen Community College (U)
Berkeley College (U)
Berkeley College-New York City Campus (U)
Berkeley College-Westchester Campus (U)
Black Hills State University (U)
Boston University (N)
Brenau University (G)
Bridgewater State College (N)
Buena Vista University (U)
Butler County Community College (U)
Caldwell Community College and Technical Institute (N)
California National University for Advanced Studies (U)
California State University, Dominguez Hills (N)
California State University, San Bernardino (U)
Carroll College (U)
Central Michigan University (G)
Central Wyoming College (N)
Champlain College (U)
Charter Oak State College (U)
Chattanooga State Technical Community College (U)
Clark College (U)
Colorado Christian University (G)
Colorado State University (U)
Colorado Technical University (U)
Columbia University (N,G)
Columbus State Community College (U)
Concordia University Wisconsin (U)
Dallas Baptist University (U,G)
Darton College (N,U)
Des Moines Area Community College (U)
DeVry University Online (G)
Drake University (G)
Drexel University (U,G)
Eastern Michigan University (U)
Embry-Riddle Aeronautical University (U)
Erie Community College (U)
Feather River College (N)
Florida Atlantic University (U,G)
Florida Gulf Coast University (U)
Florida Institute of Technology (N)
Florida State University (N)
Franklin Pierce College (U)
Franklin University (U)
Granite State College (U)
Grantham University (U,G)
Hillsborough Community College (U)
Housatonic Community College (N)
Indiana State University (U,G)
Iona College (U,G)
Iowa Western Community College (U)
Jacksonville State University (U,G)
Jamestown Community College (N)
The Johns Hopkins University (U)
Kansas State University (N,U,G)
Kaplan University (N)
Kean University (N)
Lamar State College–Port Arthur (N)
Lehigh Carbon Community College (U)
Limestone College (U)
Louisiana State University and Agricultural and Mechanical College (U)
Marist College (U)
Mercer County Community College (N)
Metropolitan State University (U)
Middlesex Community College (N)
Midway College (U)
Missouri State University (U,G)
Mount Saint Vincent University (U)
Myers University (U)
New England College of Finance (N,U,G)
New York Institute of Technology (U)
Niagara University (G)
Nipissing University (U)
Northern Virginia Community College (U)
Northwestern State University of Louisiana (U)
Oklahoma State University (U)
Old Dominion University (U,G)
Pace University (U)
Palomar College (U)
Park University (U)
Pennsylvania College of Technology (U)
The Pennsylvania State University University Park Campus (U)
Philadelphia University (U,G)
Radford University (G)
Randolph Community College (U)
Rasmussen College Eden Prarie (U)
Roger Williams University (U)
Ryerson University (U)
Sacred Heart University (G)
Saint Joseph's University (U)
St. Petersburg College (U)
Sam Houston State University (U)
San Joaquin Delta College (U)
Schiller International University (G)
Shippensburg University of Pennsylvania (U)
Simpson College (U)
Southern Illinois University Carbondale (U)
South Piedmont Community College (U)
Stanford University (N)
Stanly Community College (U)
State University of New York College at Potsdam (N)
State University of New York Empire State College (U)
Stephen F. Austin State University (U)
Stephens College (G)
Strayer University (U)
Syracuse University (G)
Texas A&M University–Commerce (N,G)
Texas A&M University–Kingsville (U)
The University of Akron (U)
The University of Alabama (U,G)
University of California, Berkeley (U)
University of Dallas (G)
University of Florida (U)
University of Houston–Downtown (U)
University of Illinois at Chicago (G)
The University of Maine at Augusta (U)
University of Massachusetts Amherst (U,G)
University of Massachusetts Lowell (G)
University of Minnesota, Twin Cities Campus (U)
University of Nebraska–Lincoln (U)
University of New Brunswick Fredericton (U)
University of New Orleans (U,G)
The University of North Carolina at Charlotte (N)
University of Oklahoma (U)
University of South Alabama (G)
The University of Texas at Arlington (G)
The University of Texas at Dallas (G)
The University of Texas at Tyler (U)
University of Toronto (N,U)
University of Tulsa (G)
University of Utah (U)
University of Waterloo (U)
University of Wisconsin–La Crosse (G)
University of Wisconsin–Parkside (G)
University of Wisconsin–Platteville (U)
University of Wisconsin–Whitewater (G)
Waukesha County Technical College (U)
Wayland Baptist University (U)
Webster University (G)
West Virginia University (N)
Wilfrid Laurier University (U)
William Rainey Harper College (U)

FINE AND STUDIO ART

Acadia University (U)
Adirondack Community College (U)
Alpena Community College (U)
Arizona State University (U,G)
Athabasca University (N,U)
Atlantic University (N,G)
Bellevue University (U)
Bethany University (U)
Black Hills State University (U)
Blinn College (U)
Brazosport College (U)
Brigham Young University (U)
Burlington County College (U)
Butler Community College (U)
Caldwell College (U)
Caldwell Community College and Technical Institute (U)
California State University, East Bay (U)
California State University, San Marcos (N)
Campbell University (U)
Cape Cod Community College (U)
Cape Fear Community College (U)
Carl Sandburg College (U)
Casper College (U)
Central Texas College (U)
Central Wyoming College (U)
City College of San Francisco (U)
Clovis Community College (U)
College of Southern Maryland (U)
College of The Albemarle (U)
Colorado Mountain College District System (U)
Colorado State University (U)
Columbia Basin College (U)
Community College of Beaver County (U)
Community College of Denver (U)
Concordia University, St. Paul (N)
Cosumnes River College (U)
Dakota State University (U)
Dallas Baptist University (U)
Dawson Community College (U)
Delta College (U)
Drake University (U)
Duquesne University (U)
East Carolina University (G)
Eastern Michigan University (U)
East Los Angeles College (U)
Edison State Community College (U)
Erie Community College (U)
Florida Atlantic University (G)
Governors State University (U,G)
Halifax Community College (U)
Haywood Community College (U)
Houston Community College System (U)
Independence Community College (U)
Indiana Wesleyan University (U)
Iowa Western Community College (U)
James Madison University (N)
John A. Logan College (U)
Judson College (U)
Kean University (N)
Lake Superior College (U)
Lenoir Community College (U)
Lewis and Clark Community College (U)
Lock Haven University of Pennsylvania (U)
Louisiana State University and Agricultural and Mechanical College (U)
Malone College (U)
Mercy College (U)
Middlesex Community College (N,U)
Middle Tennessee State University (N)
Minneapolis College of Art and Design (N,U,G)
Mississippi State University (U)
Moberly Area Community College (U)
Montana State University–Billings (U)
Mountain Empire Community College (U)
Naugatuck Valley Community College (U)
Niagara University (U)
North Arkansas College (U)
North Central Texas College (U)
Northern Virginia Community College (U)
North Idaho College (U)
Northwestern State University of Louisiana (U)
Oregon State University (N)
Oxnard College (U)
Pace University (U)
Palomar College (U)
Parkland College (U)
Patrick Henry Community College (U)
Pennsylvania College of Technology (U)
The Pennsylvania State University University Park Campus (U)
Piedmont Technical College (U)
Rappahannock Community College (U)
Red Rocks Community College (U)
Rio Hondo College (U)
Sacred Heart University (U)
Saint Leo University (U)
St. Petersburg College (U)
San Bernardino Valley College (U)
Schoolcraft College (U)
Shippensburg University of Pennsylvania (U)
Sinclair Community College (U)
Southwestern Community College (U)
Tacoma Community College (U)
Taylor University (U)
Texas Christian University (U)
Texas State University-San Marcos (U)
Tompkins Cortland Community College (U)
Tri-State University (U)
Triton College (U)
Tyler Junior College (U)
University of Alaska Fairbanks (U)
University of Central Oklahoma (U,G)
University of Colorado at Denver and Health Sciences Center—Downtown Denver Campus (U)
The University of Findlay (U)
University of Great Falls (U)
The University of Iowa (U,G)
University of Massachusetts Boston (U)
University of Minnesota, Twin Cities Campus (U)
University of Nebraska–Lincoln (U)
University of Nevada, Reno (U)
The University of North Carolina at Chapel Hill (N,U)
University of North Texas (U)
University of Sioux Falls (U)
University of Southern Indiana (U)
University of South Florida (U)
The University of Tennessee at Martin (U)
The University of Texas at Arlington (U)
The University of Texas of the Permian Basin (U)
The University of Texas System (U)
University of Utah (U)
University of West Florida (U)
University of Wisconsin Colleges (U)
University of Wisconsin–Superior (U)
Utah Valley State College (U)
Western Piedmont Community College (U)
Wilfrid Laurier University (U)
Wilkes Community College (U)

FIRE PROTECTION

Arizona State University at the Polytechnic Campus (U)
Arizona Western College (U)
Bellevue Community College (U)
Blackhawk Technical College (N,U)
Butler County Community College (U)
Caldwell Community College and Technical Institute (U)
Central New Mexico Community College (U)
Central Texas College (U)
Chattanooga State Technical Community College (U)
Cleveland Community College (N,U)
Community College of Southern Nevada (U)
Des Moines Area Community College (U)
Gulf Coast Community College (U)
Honolulu Community College (U)
Houston Community College System (U)
Ivy Tech Community College–Northeast (U)
Ivy Tech Community College–Northwest (U)
Jacksonville State University (G)
James Madison University (N)
John Jay College of Criminal Justice of the City University of New York (U)
Louisiana State University and Agricultural and Mechanical College (U)
Louisiana State University at Eunice (U)
Middlesex Community College (U)
Oklahoma State University (N,U)
Oxnard College (U)
Palomar College (U)
Passaic County Community College (U)
Portland Community College (U)
Red Rocks Community College (U)
Rio Hondo College (U)
Schenectady County Community College (U)
Seminole Community College (U)
Solano Community College (U)
Southeast Arkansas College (U)
State University of New York Empire State College (U)
Tyler Junior College (U)
The University of Akron (U)
University of Florida (U)
University of Maryland University College (U)
University of Missouri–Columbia (N)
The University of Texas at Tyler (U)
Utah Valley State College (U)
Vincennes University (U)
Waukesha County Technical College (U)
Wharton County Junior College (N)
Worcester Polytechnic Institute (G)

FISHING AND FISHERIES SCIENCES AND MANAGEMENT

Colorado State University (U,G)
Oregon State University (U)
University of Arkansas at Pine Bluff (U,G)
University of Maryland Eastern Shore (G)
Virginia Polytechnic Institute and State University (U)
West Virginia University at Parkersburg (N)

FOOD SCIENCE AND TECHNOLOGY

Brigham Young University (U)
Central Michigan University (G)

Eastern Michigan University (U,G)
Illinois Institute of Technology (G)
Iowa State University of Science and Technology (U,G)
Jamestown Community College (N)
J. Sargeant Reynolds Community College (U)
Kansas State University (N,U)
Middle Tennessee State University (U)
Orange Coast College (U)
Saint Joseph's University (G)
Texas Tech University (U)
University of California, Davis (U)
University of Florida (U)
University of Minnesota, Twin Cities Campus (U)
University of Missouri–Columbia (U,G)
University of North Texas (U,G)
University of Wisconsin–River Falls (G)

FOODS, NUTRITION, AND RELATED SERVICES

Acadia University (U)
Adirondack Community College (U)
Athabasca University (N,U)
Auburn University (G)
Bergen Community College (U)
Blackhawk Technical College (N)
Bowling Green State University (U,G)
Butler County Community College (U)
Central Michigan University (G)
Central Missouri State University (U)
Central New Mexico Community College (U)
Central Oregon Community College (U)
Central Texas College (U)
Charter Oak State College (U)
Clark College (U)
Clatsop Community College (U)
Cleveland State University (N)
Colorado State University (U)
Columbus State Community College (U)
Cosumnes River College (U)
Danville Community College (U)
Des Moines Area Community College (U)
East Carolina University (G)
Eastern Michigan University (U,G)
East Los Angeles College (U)
Feather River College (N)
Heartland Community College (U)
Hillsborough Community College (U)
Honolulu Community College (U)
Houston Community College System (U)
Howard College (U)
Illinois Eastern Community Colleges, Frontier Community College (U)
Immaculata University (U)
Indiana University of Pennsylvania (U)
Iowa State University of Science and Technology (G)
Jacksonville State University (U)
James Madison University (N)
Jefferson College of Health Sciences (U)
Kansas State University (N,U)
Lamar State College–Port Arthur (U)
Louisiana Tech University (G)
Middlesex Community College (U)
Mohawk Valley Community College (U)
Montana State University (G)
Mount Saint Vincent University (U)
North Dakota State College of Science (U)
North Dakota State University (U)
Oklahoma State University (U)
Orange Coast College (U)
Oregon State University (G)
Ozarks Technical Community College (U)
Palomar College (U)
Penn Foster Career School (N)
The Pennsylvania State University University Park Campus (U)
Portland Community College (U)
Purdue University Calumet (U)
Ryerson University (U)
Snow College (U)
Southeast Arkansas College (U)
Southeast Community College, Beatrice Campus (U)
Southeast Community College, Lincoln Campus (U)
Southeast Community College, Milford Campus (U)
South Piedmont Community College (U)
Southwest Wisconsin Technical College (U)
Texas Tech University (U)
The University of Alabama (U)
University of Bridgeport (U,G)
The University of British Columbia (U)
University of Cincinnati Raymond Walters College (U)
University of Delaware (N,U,G)
University of Florida (N,U,G)
University of Massachusetts Amherst (U)
University of Minnesota, Crookston (U)
University of Minnesota, Twin Cities Campus (U)
University of Missouri–Columbia (U,G)
University of Nevada, Reno (U)
University of North Alabama (U)
The University of North Carolina at Chapel Hill (U)
University of Northern Colorado (U)
University of Southern Mississippi (U)
University of Utah (U)
University of Wyoming (U)
West Virginia University at Parkersburg (N)
Wisconsin Indianhead Technical College (N,U)
Yuba College (U)

FORENSIC PSYCHOLOGY

Charter Oak State College (U)
University of Massachusetts Lowell (G)
West Virginia University (N)

FOREST ENGINEERING

University of Minnesota, Twin Cities Campus (U,G)
University of New Brunswick Fredericton (U)

FORESTRY

Haywood Community College (U)
Humboldt State University (U)
James Madison University (N)
Louisiana Tech University (U)
Mississippi State University (U)
Mount Wachusett Community College (N)
North Carolina State University (U)
The Ohio State University (U)
Oregon State University (U)
Stephen F. Austin State University (G)
The University of British Columbia (U)
University of Florida (U)
University of New Brunswick Fredericton (U)
Virginia Polytechnic Institute and State University (G)

FUNERAL SERVICE AND MORTUARY SCIENCE

Des Moines Area Community College (U)
John Tyler Community College (U)
St. Louis Community College System (U)
St. Petersburg College (U)
University of Central Oklahoma (U,G)
Vincennes University (U)

GENETICS

Charter Oak State College (U)
Eastern Michigan University (U)
North Carolina State University (U)
University of California, Berkeley (U)
University of Florida (G)
University of Illinois at Urbana–Champaign (N,G)
University of Minnesota, Twin Cities Campus (U)

GEOGRAPHY AND CARTOGRAPHY

Alvin Community College (U)
Anne Arundel Community College (U)
Arizona State University (U)
Arkansas State University–Beebe (U)
Athabasca University (U)
Auburn University (U)
Bellevue Community College (U)
Bethany University (U)
Black Hills State University (U)
Blinn College (U)
Bowling Green State University (U)
Brenau University (U)
Bridgewater State College (U)
Brigham Young University (U)
Campbell University (U)
Carl Sandburg College (U)
Casper College (U)
Central Oregon Community College (U)
Central Piedmont Community College (U)
Central Wyoming College (U)
Chadron State College (U)
Champlain College (U)
Chattanooga State Technical Community College (U)
Cleveland State University (U)
Coconino Community College (U)
College of Southern Maryland (U)
Colorado Mountain College District System (U)
Colorado State University (U)
Colorado State University-Pueblo (U)
Columbia Basin College (U)
Columbus State Community College (U)
The Community College of Baltimore County (U)
Community College of Denver (U)
Connecticut State University System (U)
Crafton Hills College (U)
Danville Community College (U)
Des Moines Area Community College (U)
Drury University (U)
East Arkansas Community College (U)
Eastern Michigan University (U,G)
Eastern Oklahoma State College (U)
Eastern Oregon University (U)

East Tennessee State University (U)
Erie Community College (U)
George Mason University (U)
Governors State University (U)
Houston Community College System (U)
Indiana State University (U)
Iowa Western Community College (U)
Jacksonville State University (U,G)
James Madison University (N)
Kansas State University (U)
Lake Superior College (U)
Lansing Community College (U)
Lehigh Carbon Community College (U)
Limestone College (U)
Louisiana State University and Agricultural and Mechanical College (U)
Marshall University (U)
Massasoit Community College (U)
Mesalands Community College (U)
Middlesex Community College (U)
Moberly Area Community College (U)
Montana State University–Billings (U)
Murray State University (U)
Myers University (U)
Northern Virginia Community College (U)
Northwestern Connecticut Community College (U)
Northwest Missouri State University (N,U,G)
Oklahoma State University (U)
Oregon State University (G)
Ozarks Technical Community College (U)
Park University (U)
The Pennsylvania State University University Park Campus (N)
Plymouth State University (U)
Portland Community College (U)
Pueblo Community College (U)
Queen's University at Kingston (U)
Red Rocks Community College (U)
Ryerson University (U)
Sacramento City College (U)
St. Clair County Community College (U)
St. Edward's University (U)
St. Petersburg College (U)
Schoolcraft College (U)
Seattle Central Community College (U)
Seattle Pacific University (G)
Seminole Community College (U)
Shippensburg University of Pennsylvania (U)
Shoreline Community College (U)
Solano Community College (U)
South Dakota School of Mines and Technology (U)
Southeast Arkansas College (U)
Southern Arkansas University Tech (U)
Southern Illinois University Carbondale (U)
Southwestern Community College (U)
State University of New York at New Paltz (U)
State University of New York College at Potsdam (U)
Tacoma Community College (U)
Taylor University (U)
The University of Akron (U)
The University of Alabama (U)
University of Alaska Fairbanks (U)
University of Arkansas (U)
The University of British Columbia (U)
University of California, Riverside (N)
University of Central Arkansas (G)
University of Cincinnati (U)
University of Colorado at Colorado Springs (U)
University of Colorado at Denver and Health Sciences Center—Downtown Denver Campus (U)
University of Florida (U)
University of Missouri–Columbia (U)
University of Nebraska–Lincoln (U)
University of Nevada, Reno (U)
University of New Orleans (U,G)
University of North Alabama (U,G)
The University of North Carolina at Chapel Hill (U)
The University of North Carolina at Charlotte (N)
University of North Dakota (U)
University of Northern Colorado (U)
University of Northern Iowa (U,G)
University of Oklahoma (U)
University of Oregon (U)
University of Saskatchewan (U)
University of Sioux Falls (U)
University of Southern Mississippi (U,G)
University of South Florida (U)
The University of Tennessee (U)
The University of Texas at Tyler (U)
The University of Toledo (U)
University of Washington (U)
University of Wisconsin Colleges (U)
University of Wyoming (U)
Virginia Polytechnic Institute and State University (U,G)
Weber State University (U)
Westchester Community College (U)
Western Michigan University (U)
Western Nevada Community College (U)
Western Piedmont Community College (U)
Whatcom Community College (U)
Wichita State University (U)
Wilfrid Laurier University (U)
William Rainey Harper College (U)

GEOLOGICAL AND EARTH SCIENCES/GEOSCIENCES

Acadia University (U)
Alvin Community College (U)
Athabasca University (N,U)
Bellevue Community College (U)
Bergen Community College (U)
Blinn College (U)
Boise State University (U)
Bowling Green State University (U)
Bridgewater State College (U)
Brigham Young University (U)
Broome Community College (U)
California University of Pennsylvania (U)
Charter Oak State College (U)
Clark State Community College (U)
Cleveland State University (U)
Colorado State University-Pueblo (U)
Community College of Denver (U)
Cosumnes River College (U)
Crafton Hills College (U)
Dallas Baptist University (U)
Eastern Michigan University (G)
Eastern Wyoming College (U)
Florida Atlantic University (U)
Fort Hays State University (U)
Hillsborough Community College (U)
Honolulu Community College (U)
Indiana University of Pennsylvania (U)
Jacksonville State University (U,G)
James Madison University (N)
Lake Superior College (U)
Lamar University (U)
Louisiana State University and Agricultural and Mechanical College (U)
Mesalands Community College (U)
Middle Tennessee State University (U)
Mid Michigan Community College (U)
Mississippi State University (U)
Mountain Empire Community College (U)
Murray State University (U)
Nassau Community College (U)
New Mexico Junior College (U)
North Seattle Community College (U)
Oklahoma State University (U)
Oregon State University (U,G)
Oxnard College (U)
Palomar College (U)
Park University (U)
Peninsula College (U)
Pennsylvania College of Technology (U)
Portland State University (U)
Pueblo Community College (U)
Rend Lake College (U)
Rio Hondo College (U)
Sam Houston State University (U)
San Diego State University (N,U)
Seminole Community College (U)
Shoreline Community College (U)
Solano Community College (U)
State University of New York at New Paltz (U)
State University of New York at Oswego (U)
State University of New York at Plattsburgh (U)
Tacoma Community College (U)
Taft College (U)
Texas A&M University–Kingsville (U)
Tri-State University (U)
The University of Akron (U)
University of Cincinnati (U)
University of Colorado at Denver and Health Sciences Center—Downtown Denver Campus (U)
University of Florida (U)
University of Houston–Victoria (G)
University of Maine at Fort Kent (U)
University of Minnesota, Twin Cities Campus (U)
University of Missouri–Columbia (U)
University of New Orleans (U,G)
The University of North Carolina at Chapel Hill (U)
University of Northern Colorado (U)
University of North Texas (U)
University of Oklahoma (U)
University of Oregon (U)
University of Saskatchewan (U)
University of South Florida (U)
The University of Tennessee at Martin (U)
The University of Texas System (U)
University of Washington (U)
University of Waterloo (U)
University of Wisconsin–River Falls (U,G)
Wake Technical Community College (U)
Weber State University (U)
West Shore Community College (U)
Wharton County Junior College (U)
Wilfrid Laurier University (U)
Wright State University (G)

GEOLOGICAL/GEOPHYSICAL ENGINEERING

University of New Orleans (U,G)

GERONTOLOGY

Acadia University (U)
Adams State College (N)
Athabasca University (N)
Athens Technical College (N)
Bowling Green State University (G)
Butler Community College (U)
California College for Health Sciences (N)
The College of St. Scholastica (U)
College of The Albemarle (N)
Des Moines Area Community College (U)
Feather River College (N)
Florida Gulf Coast University (U)
Housatonic Community College (U)
Jefferson College of Health Sciences (U)
Kansas State University (G)
Kaplan University (N)
Liberty University (U)
Limestone College (U)
Madonna University (N,U)
Massasoit Community College (N)
Middlesex Community College (N)
Midland College (N,U)
Mount Saint Vincent University (U)
Naropa University (U)
New Mexico State University–Carlsbad (N)
North Georgia College & State University (U,G)
The Ohio State University (N)
The Pennsylvania State University University Park Campus (U)
Randolph Community College (N)
The Richard Stockton College of New Jersey (U)
Ryerson University (U)
Sacramento City College (U)
Sacred Heart University (G)
Saint Mary-of-the-Woods College (U)
Sam Houston State University (U)
Saybrook Graduate School and Research Center (G)
Shippensburg University of Pennsylvania (U,G)
State University of New York at Oswego (G)
Texas Tech University (G)
University of Alaska Fairbanks (U)
University of Colorado at Colorado Springs (U)
University of Florida (N,U,G)
The University of Iowa (U,G)
University of Maryland University College (U)
University of Massachusetts Boston (G)
University of Missouri–Columbia (U,G)
University of New Orleans (U,G)
University of North Alabama (U)
University of Northern Colorado (U,G)
University of North Texas (N,G)
University of Southern Indiana (U)
University of Washington (U,G)
University of Waterloo (U)
University of Wisconsin–Stout (N)
Utica College (U)
Weber State University (U)
Wichita State University (U)

GRAPHIC COMMUNICATIONS

Academy of Art University (U,G)
Columbus State Community College (U)
Community College of Beaver County (N)
Danville Community College (U)
De Anza College (U)
Macon State College (N)
Murray State University (U)
Palomar College (U)
University of North Dakota (N)

HEALTH AIDES/ATTENDANTS/ORDERLIES

College of Staten Island of the City University of New York (N)
Forrest Junior College (U)
James Madison University (N)
Lamar State College–Port Arthur (N)
South Central College (U)
South Piedmont Community College (N)

HEALTH AND MEDICAL ADMINISTRATIVE SERVICES

Alpena Community College (U)
American Military University (U)
American Public University (U)
Arkansas Tech University (U)
Athabasca University (U)
Auburn University Montgomery (N)
Bellevue University (U,G)
Berkeley College (U)
Blackhawk Technical College (U)
Blue Ridge Community College (N)
Boise State University (U,G)
Bowling Green State University (U)
Brenau University (G)
Bridgewater State College (N)
Broome Community College (U)
California State University, Chico (U)
California State University, Dominguez Hills (N)
Central Michigan University (U,G)
Chattanooga State Technical Community College (U)
Cincinnati State Technical and Community College (U)
Cleveland State University (G)
The College of St. Scholastica (U,G)
Colorado State University-Pueblo (N)
Colorado Technical University (U,G)
Columbus State Community College (U)
Creighton University (G)
Daemen College (U)
Dakota County Technical College (U)
Dakota State University (U)
Dallas County Community College District (U)
Darton College (U)
Des Moines Area Community College (U)
D'Youville College (G)
East Georgia College (N)
Edgecombe Community College (N,U)
Feather River College (N)
Florida Gulf Coast University (U)
Forrest Junior College (U)
Franklin University (U)
Gogebic Community College (U)
Granite State College (U)
Housatonic Community College (N)
Jamestown Community College (N)
Jefferson College of Health Sciences (U)
Johnson County Community College (N)
Kean University (U)
Keiser College (U)
Lehigh Carbon Community College (U)
Linn-Benton Community College (U)
Macon State College (U)
Miami Dade College (U)
Midland College (U)
Minnesota School of Business–Richfield (U)
Minot State University–Bottineau Campus (U)
Montana State University–Billings (G)
Niagara University (N)
North Dakota State College of Science (U)
Orange Coast College (U)
Oregon State University (N,U,G)
Park University (U)
Penn Foster Career School (N)
The Pennsylvania State University University Park Campus (U)
Quinebaug Valley Community College (N,U)
Radford University (G)
Rasmussen College Eden Prarie (U)
Rio Hondo College (U)
Roger Williams University (U)
Saint Joseph's College of Maine (U,G)
Saint Joseph's University (G)
Salve Regina University (N,G)
Seminole Community College (N,U)
Southeast Community College, Beatrice Campus (U)
Southeast Community College, Lincoln Campus (U)
Southeast Community College, Milford Campus (U)
Stephens College (U)
Sullivan University (G)
Tacoma Community College (U)
Texas State University-San Marcos (N,U)
The University of Akron (U)
University of Central Florida (U,G)
University of Dallas (G)
University of Houston–Clear Lake (G)
University of Illinois at Chicago (N)
University of Maryland Eastern Shore (G)
University of Maryland University College (G)
University of Minnesota, Crookston (U)
University of Minnesota, Twin Cities Campus (U)
University of Missouri–Columbia (U,G)
The University of North Carolina at Charlotte (N)
The University of North Carolina at Greensboro (N)
University of North Dakota (N)
University of Northern Colorado (U)
University of North Texas (G)
University of St. Francis (G)
University of Southern Indiana (U)
Wayland Baptist University (U,G)
Weber State University (U)

HEALTH AND PHYSICAL EDUCATION/FITNESS

Adirondack Community College (U)
Anne Arundel Community College (U)
Arizona State University at the Polytechnic Campus (U)
Asheville-Buncombe Technical Community College (U)
Auburn University (U)
Austin Peay State University (U,G)
Brigham Young University (U)
Butler Community College (U)
Butler County Community College (U)
California University of Pennsylvania (U,G)
Cape Fear Community College (U)
Carl Albert State College (U)

Cayuga County Community College (U)
Central Carolina Community College (U)
Central Michigan University (U)
Central Texas College (U)
Central Washington University (G)
Central Wyoming College (N,U)
Clarion University of Pennsylvania (U)
Clark College (U)
Clatsop Community College (U)
Cleveland State University (N)
College of San Mateo (U)
College of Southern Maryland (U)
College of The Albemarle (U)
College of the Siskiyous (U)
Colorado State University (N,U)
Columbia Basin College (U)
Columbus State Community College (U)
Contra Costa College (U)
Copiah-Lincoln Community College (U)
Corning Community College (U)
County College of Morris (U)
Cowley County Community College and Area Vocational–Technical School (U)
Crafton Hills College (U)
Dakota County Technical College (U)
Dallas Baptist University (U)
Danville Community College (U)
Darton College (U)
Delta College (U)
East Arkansas Community College (U)
Eastern Oregon University (U)
Eastern Wyoming College (U)
East Los Angeles College (U)
Erie Community College (U)
Feather River College (U)
Fort Hays State University (U,G)
Fort Valley State University (U)
Georgia Highlands College (U)
Haywood Community College (U)
Illinois Eastern Community Colleges, Frontier Community College (U)
Indiana State University (U)
Iowa Western Community College (U)
Jacksonville State University (U,G)
James Madison University (N,U)
Jefferson College of Health Sciences (U)
Jefferson Davis Community College (U)
John Jay College of Criminal Justice of the City University of New York (U)
J. Sargeant Reynolds Community College (U)
Kean University (N)
Lehigh Carbon Community College (U)
Linn-Benton Community College (U)
Louisiana State University and Agricultural and Mechanical College (U)
Malone College (U)
Mercer County Community College (U)
Middle Tennessee State University (U)
Midland College (U)
Millersville University of Pennsylvania (U,G)
Missouri State University (U,G)
Montana State University (G)
Mountain Empire Community College (U)
Nassau Community College (U)
Naugatuck Valley Community College (N)
North Carolina State University (U)
North Dakota State College of Science (U)
Northwestern State University of Louisiana (U)
Oklahoma State University (U)
Palomar College (U)
Parkland College (U)
Pasco-Hernando Community College (U)
Patrick Henry Community College (U)
Peninsula College (U)
The Pennsylvania State University University Park Campus (U)
Portland Community College (U)
Purdue University Calumet (U)
Rappahannock Community College (U)
Rend Lake College (U)
Rio Hondo College (U)
San Joaquin Delta College (U)
Solano Community College (U)
Southeast Arkansas College (U)
Southern Arkansas University Tech (U)
State University of New York at Plattsburgh (U)
Texas Woman's University (U,G)
Treasure Valley Community College (U)
Triton College (U)
United States Sports Academy (N,U,G)
University of California, Los Angeles (G)
University of Great Falls (U)
University of Missouri–Columbia (U)
University of Nebraska–Lincoln (U)
University of Northern Colorado (G)
University of Northern Iowa (U)
University of North Texas (U)
University of Oklahoma (U)
University of Sioux Falls (U)
University of Southern Mississippi (U,G)
The University of Tennessee at Martin (U)
The University of Texas at Tyler (U)
The University of Texas of the Permian Basin (U,G)
Utah Valley State College (U)
Valley City State University (U)
Washburn University (U)
Westchester Community College (U)
West Los Angeles College (U)
West Virginia University at Parkersburg (U)

HEALTH PROFESSIONS RELATED

Arkansas State University–Mountain Home (U)
Athabasca University (N,U,G)
Bellevue Community College (U)
Bowling Green State University (N)
Brenau University (U,G)
Butler Community College (U)
California University of Pennsylvania (G)
Central Michigan University (U,G)
Central Virginia Community College (U)
Chattanooga State Technical Community College (U)
Cincinnati State Technical and Community College (U)
Clark State Community College (U)
Cleveland State University (N,G)
Coconino Community College (U)
College of Southern Maryland (N)
Colorado Mountain College District System (U)
Columbus State Community College (U)
Cowley County Community College and Area Vocational–Technical School (U)
Creighton University (G)
Daemen College (U)
Dakota County Technical College (N,U)
Dallas County Community College District (U)
Danville Community College (U)
Darton College (U)
DeVry University Online (G)
Drake University (U,G)
Drexel University (U,G)
D'Youville College (U)
Florida Atlantic University (U,G)
Fontbonne University (U)
Franklin Pierce College (G)
Fulton-Montgomery Community College (N)
Galveston College (U)
George Mason University (G)
Georgia College & State University (U,G)
Heart of Georgia Technical College (U)
Hillsborough Community College (U)
Illinois Eastern Community Colleges, Lincoln Trail College (U)
Iona College (G)
Jackson Community College (N)
Jacksonville State University (U,G)
James Madison University (U)
Jefferson College of Health Sciences (U)
Kaplan University (N)
Lake Superior College (U)
Lamar State College–Port Arthur (U)
Lehigh Carbon Community College (U)
Lock Haven University of Pennsylvania (G)
Louisiana Tech University (U)
Massasoit Community College (N)
Mercy College (U)
MGH Institute of Health Professions (G)
Miami Dade College (N)
Midland College (U)
Mississippi State University (G)
Mitchell Technical Institute (N)
Monmouth University (U)
Montana Tech of The University of Montana (U,G)
Naugatuck Valley Community College (U)
New Mexico State University–Carlsbad (N)
North Dakota State College of Science (U)
Orange Coast College (U)
Oregon State University (G)
Pasco-Hernando Community College (N)
Passaic County Community College (U)
Peninsula College (U)
Pennsylvania College of Technology (U)
Pine Technical College (U)
Portland Community College (N,U)
Pueblo Community College (U)
Radford University (G)
Rasmussen College Eden Prarie (U)
The Richard Stockton College of New Jersey (U)
Ryerson University (U)
Sacramento City College (U)
Sacred Heart University (U,G)
Sam Houston State University (U)
Schoolcraft College (U)
Seminole Community College (U)
Shoreline Community College (U)
Sinclair Community College (N)
Southeast Arkansas College (U)
Southeast Community College, Beatrice Campus (U)
Southeast Community College, Lincoln Campus (U)
Southeast Community College, Milford Campus (U)
South Piedmont Community College (U)
State University of New York at Buffalo (U)
State University of New York at Plattsburgh (U)
Sullivan University (G)
Tacoma Community College (U)
Texas State University-San Marcos (U)

Touro University International (U,G)
The University of Akron (G)
The University of Alabama (U,G)
University of Alaska Fairbanks (U)
University of Central Arkansas (G)
University of Cincinnati Raymond Walters College (U)
University of Colorado at Colorado Springs (U,G)
University of Connecticut (N,U,G)
University of Delaware (G)
University of Illinois at Chicago (G)
University of Maine at Fort Kent (U)
University of Maryland Eastern Shore (G)
University of Massachusetts Amherst (G)
University of Massachusetts Lowell (G)
University of Medicine and Dentistry of New Jersey (U,G)
University of Minnesota, Twin Cities Campus (U)
University of Missouri–Columbia (N,U)
University of New Brunswick Fredericton (N)
University of New Hampshire (G)
University of New Orleans (U,G)
The University of North Carolina at Greensboro (U)
University of North Dakota (N)
University of Northern Colorado (U)
University of North Florida (U,G)
University of St. Augustine for Health Sciences (N)
University of St. Francis (U)
University of Sioux Falls (U)
University of Southern Indiana (N,G)
University of Southern Mississippi (U)
The University of Texas at Tyler (U,G)
The University of Texas System (U,G)
The University of Toledo (U)
University of Wisconsin–La Crosse (U)
University of Wyoming (G)
Washtenaw Community College (U)
West Virginia University (N)
West Virginia University at Parkersburg (U)
William Rainey Harper College (U)

HEALTH PSYCHOLOGY

Acadia University (U)
California College for Health Sciences (N)
Dakota County Technical College (U)
Saybrook Graduate School and Research Center (G)
University of Alaska Fairbanks (U,G)
University of Maryland Eastern Shore (G)
University of Wisconsin–Superior (G)

HEALTH SERVICES/ALLIED HEALTH/HEALTH SCIENCES

California State University, San Marcos (N)
Carl Sandburg College (U)
Central Michigan University (U)
Charter Oak State College (U)
Cleveland State University (G)
Community College of Southern Nevada (U)
Dakota County Technical College (U)
Darton College (U)
Drake University (G)
Drexel University (U)
East Arkansas Community College (U)
Florida Gulf Coast University (U)
Fulton-Montgomery Community College (N)
Itawamba Community College (U)
John Tyler Community College (U)
Macon State College (U)
Mercy College (U,G)
New Mexico State University–Carlsbad (U)
Oregon State University (U)
Rasmussen College Eden Prarie (U)
Rend Lake College (U)
Roger Williams University (U)
Schoolcraft College (U)
State University of New York at Oswego (U)
Texas Woman's University (U,G)
Touro University International (U)
University of Connecticut (U)
University of Illinois at Chicago (G)
University of Lethbridge (U)
University of Massachusetts Lowell (G)
University of Minnesota, Twin Cities Campus (U)
University of South Florida (G)
University of the Sciences in Philadelphia (G)
West Virginia University (N)

HEALTH/MEDICAL PREPARATORY PROGRAMS

Athabasca University (U,G)
Bellingham Technical College (N)
Brenau University (U)
Caldwell Community College and Technical Institute (N)
California State University, San Marcos (N)
Chattanooga State Technical Community College (U)
Cleveland State University (G)
Community College of Denver (U)
Daemen College (U)
Darton College (U)
Edgecombe Community College (U)
Erie Community College (U)
Fresno City College (U)
Gulf Coast Community College (U)
James Madison University (N)
Jefferson College of Health Sciences (U)
Johnson County Community College (N)
Lake Superior College (U)
Naugatuck Valley Community College (N)
Radford University (G)
Rasmussen College Eden Prarie (U)
Saddleback College (U)
Seminole Community College (U)
Solano Community College (U)
Southern Illinois University Carbondale (U)
Southwest Wisconsin Technical College (U)
University of Florida (G)
University of Minnesota, Twin Cities Campus (U)
Waukesha County Technical College (U)
West Los Angeles College (U)

HEATING, AIR CONDITIONING, VENTILATION AND REFRIGERATION MAINTENANCE TECHNOLOGY

Ashworth College (N)
Blackhawk Technical College (U)
Boston Architectural College (N,U,G)
Cleveland Community College (U)
Mitchell Technical Institute (N)
Orange Coast College (U)
Oxnard College (U)
University of North Dakota (N)
Wake Technical Community College (U)

HEAVY/INDUSTRIAL EQUIPMENT MAINTENANCE TECHNOLOGIES

Bismarck State College (N)

HISTORIC PRESERVATION AND CONSERVATION

Feather River College (N)
The University of North Carolina at Greensboro (G)

HISTORY

Acadia University (U)
Adams State College (U)
Adirondack Community College (U)
Alvin Community College (U)
American Military University (U,G)
American Public University (U,G)
Anne Arundel Community College (U)
Arizona State University (U)
Arizona State University at the Polytechnic Campus (U)
Arkansas State University–Beebe (U)
Arkansas Tech University (U)
Asheville-Buncombe Technical Community College (U)
Assemblies of God Theological Seminary (G)
Athabasca University (N,U,G)
Azusa Pacific University (U)
Bellevue Community College (U)
Bergen Community College (U)
Berkeley College (U)
Berkeley College-New York City Campus (U)
Berkeley College-Westchester Campus (U)
Bethany University (U)
Big Sandy Community and Technical College (U)
Bismarck State College (U)
Blinn College (U)
Boise State University (U)
Bowling Green State University (U)
Brazosport College (U)
Brenau University (U)
Bridgewater State College (U)
Briercrest Distance Learning (N,U,G)
Brigham Young University (N,U)
Broome Community College (U)
Burlington County College (U)
Butler Community College (U)
Butler County Community College (U)
Caldwell Community College and Technical Institute (U)
California State University, Chico (U)
Campbell University (U)
Cape Cod Community College (U)
Cape Fear Community College (U)
Carl Albert State College (U)
Carroll College (U)
Cayuga County Community College (U)
Cedarville University (U)
Central Carolina Community College (U)
Central Lakes College (U)
Central Oregon Community College (U)
Central Texas College (U)
Central Virginia Community College (U)
Central Washington University (U)
Central Wyoming College (N,U)
Chadron State College (U,G)
Champlain College (U)

Chattanooga State Technical Community College (U)
Citrus College (U)
Clark State Community College (U)
Clatsop Community College (U)
Clemson University (G)
Cleveland State Community College (U)
Cleveland State University (U)
Clinton Community College (U)
Clovis Community College (U)
Coconino Community College (U)
Coffeyville Community College (U)
Coleman College (U)
College of DuPage (U)
College of Southern Maryland (U)
College of The Albemarle (U)
College of the Humanities and Sciences, Harrison Middleton University (U)
College of the Siskiyous (U)
College of the Southwest (U)
Colorado Christian University (U)
Colorado Mountain College District System (U)
Colorado State University-Pueblo (U)
Columbia Basin College (U)
Columbia College (U)
Columbia International University (G)
Columbus State Community College (U)
The Community College of Baltimore County (U)
Community College of Beaver County (U)
Community College of Denver (U)
Community College of Southern Nevada (U)
Concordia University Wisconsin (U)
Corban College (U)
Corning Community College (U)
County College of Morris (U)
Cowley County Community College and Area Vocational–Technical School (U)
Crafton Hills College (U)
Cumberland County College (U)
Dakota County Technical College (U)
Dallas Baptist University (U)
Dallas County Community College District (U)
Darton College (U)
De Anza College (U)
Delta College (U)
Denver Seminary (G)
Des Moines Area Community College (U)
Drake University (U,G)
Drury University (U)
D'Youville College (U)
East Arkansas Community College (U)
East Central Community College (U)
Eastern Michigan University (U)
Eastern New Mexico University (U,G)
Eastern Oklahoma State College (U)
Eastern West Virginia Community and Technical College (U)
East Los Angeles College (U)
East Tennessee State University (U)
Edgecombe Community College (U)
Elizabethtown College (U)
Erie Community College (U)
Eugene Bible College (U)
Everett Community College (U)
Evergreen Valley College (U)
Fayetteville State University (U,G)
Feather River College (N,U)
Florida Atlantic University (U)
Florida Gulf Coast University (U)
Fort Hays State University (U)
Fort Valley State University (U)
Frostburg State University (U)
Gadsden State Community College (U)
Galveston College (U)
Georgia Highlands College (U)
Glenville State College (U)
Gogebic Community College (U)
Golden West College (U)
Grand View College (U)
Granite State College (U)
Grantham University (U)
Greenfield Community College (U)
Gulf Coast Community College (U)
Hamline University (U)
Haywood Community College (U)
Heartland Community College (U)
Honolulu Community College (U)
Hope International University (N,U)
Housatonic Community College (U)
Houston Community College System (U)
Illinois Eastern Community Colleges, Wabash Valley College (U)
Immaculata University (U)
Indiana State University (U)
Indiana University–Purdue University Fort Wayne (U)
Indiana Wesleyan University (U)
Iowa Western Community College (U)
Itawamba Community College (U)
Ivy Tech Community College–Kokomo (U)
Ivy Tech Community College–Northwest (U)
Jackson Community College (U)
Jacksonville State University (U)
James Madison University (N)
James Sprunt Community College (U)
Jefferson Community College (U)
John A. Logan College (U)
Johnson County Community College (U)
John Tyler Community College (U)
J. Sargeant Reynolds Community College (U)
Judson College (U)
Kansas State University (U)
Kean University (U)
Lake Superior College (U)
Lamar University (U)
Lansing Community College (U)
Lehigh Carbon Community College (U)
Lenoir Community College (U)
LeTourneau University (U)
Lewis and Clark Community College (U)
Limestone College (U)
Lock Haven University of Pennsylvania (U)
Louisiana State University and Agricultural and Mechanical College (U)
Louisiana Tech University (G)
Madonna University (U)
Malone College (U)
Marshall University (U)
Marylhurst University (U)
Massasoit Community College (U)
Mercer County Community College (U)
Mercy College (U)
Mesalands Community College (U)
Mesa State College (U)
Metropolitan State University (U)
Middlesex Community College (U)
Midland College (U)
Mid Michigan Community College (U)
Missouri State University (U,G)
Moberly Area Community College (U)
Montana State University–Billings (U)
Mountain Empire Community College (U)
Mount Allison University (U)
Mount Wachusett Community College (U)
Murray State University (U)
Myers University (U)
Nassau Community College (U)
National University (U)
New England College of Finance (U)
New Mexico Junior College (U)
New Mexico State University–Carlsbad (U)
North Arkansas College (U)
North Carolina State University (U)
North Central Texas College (U)
North Dakota State College of Science (U)
Northeast State Technical Community College (U)
Northern Virginia Community College (U)
Northwestern College (U)
Northwestern Connecticut Community College (U)
Northwestern Michigan College (U)
Northwestern State University of Louisiana (U)
Northwest Missouri State University (U)
Oklahoma State University (U)
Oral Roberts University (U)
Oregon State University (U)
Ouachita Technical College (U)
Oxnard College (U)
Ozark Christian College (U)
Ozarks Technical Community College (U)
Pace University (U)
Palomar College (U)
Parkland College (U)
Park University (U)
Pasco-Hernando Community College (U)
Passaic County Community College (U)
Patrick Henry College (U)
Patrick Henry Community College (U)
Peninsula College (U)
Pennsylvania College of Technology (U)
The Pennsylvania State University University Park Campus (U)
Piedmont Technical College (U)
Portland Community College (U)
Portland State University (U)
Prescott College (U,G)
Pueblo Community College (U)
Queen's University at Kingston (U)
Quinebaug Valley Community College (U)
Randolph Community College (U)
Rappahannock Community College (U)
Raritan Valley Community College (U)
Red Rocks Community College (U)
Regent University (U)
Rend Lake College (U)
Rio Hondo College (U)
Roger Williams University (U)
Ryerson University (U)
Sacramento City College (U)
Sacred Heart University (U)
Saddleback College (U)
St. Clair County Community College (U)
St. Cloud State University (U)
St. Edward's University (U)
St. John's University (U)
St. Louis Community College System (U)
Saint Mary-of-the-Woods College (U)
St. Petersburg College (U)
Salem Community College (U)
Sam Houston State University (U)
San Diego State University (N,U)
San Joaquin Delta College (U)
Schenectady County Community College (U)
Schiller International University (U)

Schoolcraft College (U)
Seattle Pacific University (G)
Seminole Community College (U)
Shippensburg University of Pennsylvania (U,G)
Shoreline Community College (U)
Sinclair Community College (U)
Snow College (U)
Solano Community College (U)
Southeast Arkansas College (U)
Southeast Community College, Beatrice Campus (U)
Southeast Community College, Lincoln Campus (U)
Southeast Community College, Milford Campus (U)
Southern Arkansas University Tech (U)
Southern Illinois University Carbondale (U)
South Piedmont Community College (U)
South Plains College (U)
Southwestern Assemblies of God University (U)
Southwest Virginia Community College (U)
State University of New York at New Paltz (U)
State University of New York at Oswego (U)
State University of New York Empire State College (U)
Stephens College (U)
Strayer University (U)
Syracuse University (G)
Tacoma Community College (U)
Taft College (U)
Taylor University (U)
Texas A&M University–Commerce (U)
Texas A&M University–Kingsville (U)
Texas A&M University–Texarkana (U)
Texas Christian University (U)
Texas State University-San Marcos (U)
Texas Tech University (U)
Texas Woman's University (U)
Three Rivers Community College (U)
Touro University International (U)
Tri-County Community College (U)
Tri-State University (U)
Triton College (U)
Tunxis Community College (U)
Tyler Junior College (U)
The University of Akron (U)
The University of Alabama (U)
University of Alaska Fairbanks (U)
University of Arkansas (U)
University of Bridgeport (U)
The University of British Columbia (U)
University of California, Berkeley (U,G)
University of Central Arkansas (U)
University of Cincinnati (U)
University of Colorado at Colorado Springs (U)
University of Colorado at Denver and Health Sciences Center—Downtown Denver Campus (U,G)
University of Delaware (U)
The University of Findlay (U)
University of Florida (U)
University of Great Falls (U)
University of Hawaii–West Oahu (U)
University of Houston–Downtown (U)
University of Houston–Victoria (U)
The University of Iowa (U,G)
University of La Verne (N,U)
The University of Maine at Augusta (U)
University of Maine at Fort Kent (U)
University of Massachusetts Boston (U,G)
University of Minnesota, Morris (U)
University of Minnesota, Twin Cities Campus (U)
University of Missouri–Columbia (U)
University of Missouri–St. Louis (U)
University of Nebraska at Omaha (U)
University of Nebraska–Lincoln (U)
University of Nevada, Reno (U)
University of New Orleans (U,G)
University of North Alabama (U)
The University of North Carolina at Chapel Hill (N,U)
The University of North Carolina at Greensboro (U)
The University of North Carolina Wilmington (U)
University of North Dakota (U)
University of Northern Iowa (U,G)
University of North Texas (U)
University of Oklahoma (U)
University of St. Francis (U)
University of Saskatchewan (U)
University of Sioux Falls (U)
University of South Carolina Sumter (U)
University of Southern Indiana (U)
University of South Florida (U)
The University of Tennessee (U)
The University of Tennessee at Martin (U)
The University of Texas at Tyler (U)
The University of Texas of the Permian Basin (U)
The University of Texas System (U)
The University of Toledo (U)
University of Utah (U)
University of Washington (U)
University of Waterloo (U)
University of West Florida (U)
University of Wisconsin Colleges (U)
University of Wisconsin–River Falls (U,G)
University of Wisconsin–Whitewater (U,G)
University of Wyoming (U)
Upper Iowa University (N,U)
Utah State University (U)
Utah Valley State College (U)
Vance-Granville Community College (U)
Vermont Technical College (U)
Vincennes University (U)
Virginia Polytechnic Institute and State University (N,U)
Wake Technical Community College (U)
Washburn University (U)
Wayland Baptist University (U)
Weber State University (U)
Westchester Community College (U)
Western Michigan University (G)
Western Oklahoma State College (U)
Western Piedmont Community College (U)
Western Washington University (U)
West Los Angeles College (U)
West Shore Community College (U)
West Virginia Northern Community College (U)
West Virginia University at Parkersburg (U)
Wharton County Junior College (U)
Whatcom Community College (U)
Wichita State University (U)
Wilfrid Laurier University (U)
Wilkes Community College (U)
William Rainey Harper College (U)
Winston-Salem State University (U)
Wright State University (U)
York Technical College (U)
York University (U)

HOSPITALITY ADMINISTRATION

Anne Arundel Community College (U)
Arkansas Tech University (U)
Ashworth College (N)
Big Sandy Community and Technical College (U)
Black Hills State University (G)
Central Michigan University (G)
Central Texas College (U)
Colorado Mountain College District System (U)
Columbus State Community College (U)
Des Moines Area Community College (U)
East Carolina University (U)
Eastern Michigan University (U)
Erie Community College (U)
Indiana University of Pennsylvania (U)
Ivy Tech Community College–Northwest (U)
Louisiana State University at Eunice (U)
Metropolitan State University (U)
Mohawk Valley Community College (U)
Mount Saint Vincent University (U)
Niagara University (U)
North Dakota State University (U)
Orange Coast College (U)
The Pennsylvania State University University Park Campus (U)
Roosevelt University (U,G)
Ryerson University (U)
Schenectady County Community College (U)
Schiller International University (G)
Southern University at Shreveport (U)
Southwest Wisconsin Technical College (U)
State University of New York College of Agriculture and Technology at Morrisville (U)
Stephen F. Austin State University (U)
Sullivan University (G)
Tompkins Cortland Community College (U)
The University of Akron (U)
The University of Alabama (U)
University of Delaware (N,U)
University of Maryland Eastern Shore (U)
University of Massachusetts Amherst (U)
University of Nevada, Reno (U)
University of New Orleans (U,G)
The University of North Carolina at Chapel Hill (U)
The University of North Carolina at Charlotte (N)
University of North Texas (U,G)
University of Wisconsin–River Falls (G)
Utah Valley State College (U)
Virginia Polytechnic Institute and State University (U)
York County Community College (U)

HOUSING AND HUMAN ENVIRONMENTS

Arizona State University (U)
Chadron State College (U)
Saybrook Graduate School and Research Center (G)

HUMAN DEVELOPMENT, FAMILY STUDIES, AND RELATED SERVICES

Abilene Christian University (G)
American Military University (U)

American Public University (U)
Arizona State University (U)
Asheville-Buncombe Technical Community College (N,U)
Ashworth College (N)
Athabasca University (N,U,G)
Bethany University (U)
Blackhawk Technical College (N)
Blue Ridge Community College (U)
Bowling Green State University (U)
Brenau University (U)
Brigham Young University (N)
Butler Community College (U)
Caldwell Community College and Technical Institute (U)
California State University, Chico (U)
Central Michigan University (U)
Central Wyoming College (N,U)
Chadron State College (U)
Clackamas Community College (U)
Clark College (U)
Clatsop Community College (U)
Cleveland Community College (U)
Cleveland State University (N)
College of Southern Maryland (U)
College of Staten Island of the City University of New York (N)
College of The Albemarle (U)
Community College of Denver (U)
Concordia University, St. Paul (U,G)
Corban College (U)
Crafton Hills College (U)
Dakota County Technical College (U)
Dallas County Community College District (U)
Danville Community College (U)
De Anza College (U)
Des Moines Area Community College (U)
East Carolina University (U)
Edgecombe Community College (U)
Edison State Community College (U)
Everett Community College (U)
Feather River College (N)
Granite State College (U)
Heartland Community College (U)
Hillsborough Community College (U)
Housatonic Community College (U)
Houston Community College System (U)
Iowa State University of Science and Technology (U)
Iowa Western Community College (U)
Jacksonville State University (U,G)
J. Sargeant Reynolds Community College (U)
Kansas State University (U)
Lehigh Carbon Community College (U)
Lewis-Clark State College (U)
Linn-Benton Community College (U)
Louisiana Tech University (G)
Madison Area Technical College (U)
Marylhurst University (U)
Maryville University of Saint Louis (N)
Massasoit Community College (U)
Mayville State University (U)
Miami Dade College (U)
Mississippi State University (U)
Missouri State University (U)
Moberly Area Community College (U)
Mountain Empire Community College (U)
Mount Wachusett Community College (U)
Murray State University (U)
Naropa University (N)
Naugatuck Valley Community College (U)
New Mexico State University–Carlsbad (N)
North Dakota State University (N,U,G)
North Idaho College (U)
North Seattle Community College (U)
Orange Coast College (U)
Oregon Institute of Technology (U)
Oxnard College (U)
Ozarka College (U)
Palomar College (U)
Peninsula College (U)
Penn Foster Career School (N)
The Pennsylvania State University University Park Campus (U)
Portland Community College (U)
Prescott College (U,G)
Randolph Community College (U)
Raritan Valley Community College (U)
Reading Area Community College (U)
Ryerson University (U)
Saddleback College (U)
Salem Community College (U)
San Bernardino Valley College (U)
San Joaquin Delta College (U)
Saybrook Graduate School and Research Center (G)
Schenectady County Community College (U)
Seminole Community College (U)
Snow College (U)
South Central College (U)
South Piedmont Community College (U)
Southwestern Baptist Theological Seminary (G)
Southwestern Oregon Community College (U)
Stanly Community College (U)
Tacoma Community College (U)
Taft College (U)
Taylor University (N)
The University of Alabama (U)
University of Alaska Fairbanks (U,G)
University of Bridgeport (N,U)
University of California, Berkeley (U,G)
University of Delaware (U)
University of Florida (U)
University of Houston–Victoria (U)
The University of Maine at Augusta (U)
University of Missouri–Columbia (U,G)
University of Nebraska–Lincoln (U)
The University of North Carolina at Greensboro (U)
University of North Texas (U,G)
University of Southern Mississippi (U,G)
The University of Tennessee at Martin (N)
The University of Texas of the Permian Basin (U)
University of Waterloo (U)
University of Wisconsin–Madison (U)
University of Wisconsin–Stout (N)
Utah State University (G)
Vance-Granville Community College (U)
Vanguard University of Southern California (U)
Weber State University (U)
Western Washington University (U)
Wilkes Community College (U)
Wisconsin Indianhead Technical College (N,U)
York County Community College (U)

HUMAN RESOURCES MANAGEMENT

Adams State College (U)
American Military University (U)
American Public University (U)
Andrew Jackson University (G)
Antioch University McGregor (U)
Asheville-Buncombe Technical Community College (N)
Athabasca University (N,U,G)
Bellevue University (U)
Bellingham Technical College (U)
Berkeley College (U)
Berkeley College-New York City Campus (U)
Berkeley College-Westchester Campus (U)
Black Hills State University (U)
Boise State University (U,G)
Brenau University (U)
Butler Community College (U)
Butler County Community College (U)
California National University for Advanced Studies (U,G)
California State University, Dominguez Hills (N)
Capella University (U,G)
Central Michigan University (U,G)
Central Texas College (U)
Chadron State College (U,G)
Champlain College (U)
Clemson University (G)
Coleman College (U)
College of Southern Maryland (U)
Colorado State University (G)
Colorado Technical University (U,G)
Columbus State Community College (U)
The Community College of Baltimore County (U)
Dakota County Technical College (U)
Dakota State University (U)
Dallas Baptist University (G)
Dallas County Community College District (U)
Des Moines Area Community College (U)
DeVry University Online (G)
Drake University (U,G)
D'Youville College (U)
Eastern Michigan University (N,U,G)
Edison State Community College (N,U)
Elizabethtown College (U)
Erie Community College (U)
Feather River College (N)
Florida Institute of Technology (G)
Florida State University (G)
Forrest Junior College (U)
Franklin University (U)
Granite State College (U)
Grantham University (U)
Houston Community College System (U)
Illinois Eastern Community Colleges, Wabash Valley College (U)
Immaculata University (U)
Indiana State University (U,G)
Iona College (U,G)
Jacksonville State University (G)
James Madison University (N,U)
Jamestown Community College (N)
Jefferson College of Health Sciences (U)
John Tyler Community College (U)
Kansas State University (G)
Lamar State College–Port Arthur (N)
Lawrence Technological University (G)
Lehigh Carbon Community College (U)
Limestone College (U)
Louisiana State University and Agricultural and Mechanical College (G)
Manhattanville College (U)
Maryville University of Saint Louis (N)
Massasoit Community College (N)

Mesalands Community College (U)
Metropolitan State University (U)
Middlesex Community College (U)
Middle Tennessee State University (N,U)
Montana State University–Billings (U)
Montgomery Community College (U)
Mount Wachusett Community College (U)
Myers University (U)
National University (G)
Neumann College (U)
Nipissing University (U)
North Arkansas College (U)
Oregon State University (N)
Ouachita Technical College (U)
Ozarks Technical Community College (U)
Park University (U)
Peirce College (U)
The Pennsylvania State University University Park Campus (N,U)
Providence College and Theological Seminary (N)
Regent University (N)
Rend Lake College (N)
Ryerson University (U)
St. Edward's University (U,G)
Saint Leo University (U)
Saint Mary-of-the-Woods College (U)
Salve Regina University (N)
Schiller International University (U,G)
Simpson College (U)
Southwestern Assemblies of God University (U)
Southwest Wisconsin Technical College (U)
State University of New York at Buffalo (N,U)
Stony Brook University, State University of New York (G)
Sullivan University (G)
Taylor University (N)
Touro University International (G)
The University of Akron (N,U,G)
University of Alaska Fairbanks (U)
University of California, Berkeley (U,G)
University of Connecticut (G)
The University of Findlay (U,G)
University of Florida (U)
University of Hawaii–West Oahu (U)
University of Houston–Clear Lake (G)
The University of Maine at Augusta (U)
University of Maryland University College (U,G)
University of Massachusetts Amherst (G)
University of Michigan–Flint (G)
University of Minnesota, Twin Cities Campus (U)
University of Missouri–Columbia (N,U,G)
University of New Brunswick Fredericton (U)
University of New Orleans (U,G)
The University of North Carolina at Charlotte (N)
The University of North Carolina at Greensboro (N)
University of North Dakota (N)
University of North Texas (G)
University of Phoenix Online Campus (U)
University of Southern Indiana (N)
The University of Texas at Tyler (U,G)
The University of Toledo (U)
University of Toronto (N,U)
University of Tulsa (G)
University of Virginia (N)
University of West Florida (N)
University of Wisconsin–Madison (U)
University of Wisconsin–Platteville (U)
University of Wisconsin–Stout (N,U,G)
Upper Iowa University (U)
Utah State University (U,G)
Virginia Polytechnic Institute and State University (U)
Washburn University (N)
Wayne State College (U,G)
Western Michigan University (G)
Western Piedmont Community College (U)
West Virginia University at Parkersburg (U)
York University (U)

HUMAN SERVICES

Antioch University McGregor (U)
Athabasca University (N,U,G)
Bellevue University (U)
Big Sandy Community and Technical College (U)
Bismarck State College (U)
Broome Community College (U)
Capella University (G)
Central Michigan University (U)
Central Wyoming College (U)
Chadron State College (U)
College of DuPage (U)
College of The Albemarle (N)
Colorado State University (G)
Corning Community College (U)
Dawson Community College (U)
Des Moines Area Community College (U)
Florida Gulf Coast University (U)
Granite State College (U)
Houston Community College System (U)
Indiana State University (U)
Iowa Western Community College (U)
James Madison University (N)
Jamestown Community College (N)
Limestone College (U)
Louisiana State University and Agricultural and Mechanical College (G)
Mercy College (U,G)
Metropolitan State University (U)
Mount Wachusett Community College (U)
Murray State University (G)
New Mexico State University (U)
Oxnard College (U)
Prescott College (U,G)
Regions University (N,U,G)
St. Edward's University (U,G)
Saint Joseph's College of Maine (U)
Saint Mary-of-the-Woods College (U)
Sinclair Community College (U)
South Central College (U)
Southeast Community College, Beatrice Campus (U)
Southeast Community College, Lincoln Campus (U)
Southeast Community College, Milford Campus (U)
Southwestern Oregon Community College (U)
Stanly Community College (U)
Sullivan University (G)
Tacoma Community College (U)
The University of Akron (G)
University of Bridgeport (U)
University of Connecticut (G)
University of Great Falls (U,G)
The University of Maine at Augusta (U)
University of Massachusetts Boston (N)
University of Northern Colorado (U)
University of North Florida (G)
Upper Iowa University (U)
Vance-Granville Community College (U)
Washburn University (U)
Western Washington University (U)

INDUSTRIAL AND ORGANIZATIONAL PSYCHOLOGY

Athabasca University (N,U,G)
Berkeley College (U)
Berkeley College-New York City Campus (U)
Berkeley College-Westchester Campus (U)
Capella University (G)
Central Michigan University (U)
Chadron State College (U,G)
College of the Southwest (U)
Florida Atlantic University (U)
Illinois Institute of Technology (G)
Indiana State University (G)
Kansas State University (G)
Middle Tennessee State University (N)
Montana State University–Billings (U)
Old Dominion University (U)
The Pennsylvania State University University Park Campus (U)
Saint Joseph's College of Maine (U)
Saybrook Graduate School and Research Center (N,G)
Schiller International University (G)
State University of New York at New Paltz (U)
Sullivan University (G)
Texas State University-San Marcos (U)
Tunxis Community College (U)
University of Arkansas (U)
University of California, Berkeley (U,G)
University of Colorado at Denver and Health Sciences Center—Downtown Denver Campus (U)
University of Florida (U)
University of Houston–Downtown (U)
University of North Dakota (U)
University of North Texas (G)
The University of Texas of the Permian Basin (U)
Upper Iowa University (N,U)

INDUSTRIAL ENGINEERING

Cleveland State University (G)
Kettering University (N)
New Mexico State University (G)
Southern Methodist University (G)
Texas A&M University–Commerce (U,G)
The University of Alabama in Huntsville (G)
University of Michigan (G)
University of South Florida (G)

INDUSTRIAL PRODUCTION TECHNOLOGIES

Bismarck State College (N)
Boston University (G)
California University of Pennsylvania (U)
Delta College (U)
East Carolina University (U,G)
Edison State Community College (U)
Missouri State University (U,G)
Roger Williams University (U)
Southwestern College (U)
University of Minnesota, Crookston (U)
The University of Texas at Tyler (U)
Wayne State College (U,G)

INFORMATION SCIENCE/STUDIES

Athabasca University (G)
Bismarck State College (U)
Bowling Green State University (U)
Brenau University (U)
Bridgewater State College (N)
Brigham Young University (U)
Caldwell College (U)
Capitol College (G)
Carlow University (U)
Central New Mexico Community College (U)
Central Oregon Community College (U)
Central Virginia Community College (U)
Chadron State College (U)
Champlain College (G)
Cincinnati State Technical and Community College (U)
College of Southern Maryland (U)
College of The Albemarle (N)
Colorado State University (N)
Connecticut State University System (U)
Dakota State University (U,G)
Dallas Baptist University (G)
DePaul University (G)
Drake University (U,G)
Drexel University (G)
D'Youville College (G)
East Carolina University (U)
Erie Community College (U)
Florida Atlantic University (G)
Florida Gulf Coast University (U)
Florida Institute of Technology (G)
Franklin University (U)
Galveston College (U)
Grantham University (U)
Haywood Community College (U)
Indiana University of Pennsylvania (U)
Jacksonville State University (U,G)
James Madison University (N)
Jones College (U)
J. Sargeant Reynolds Community College (U)
Kansas State University (U)
Lamar State College–Port Arthur (N)
Lawrence Technological University (G)
Limestone College (U)
Louisiana State University and Agricultural and Mechanical College (U)
Louisiana State University at Eunice (U)
Maryville University of Saint Louis (N,U)
Metropolitan State University (U)
Missouri State University (N)
Myers University (U)
National University (U)
New Jersey Institute of Technology (U,G)
North Carolina State University (G)
Pace University (U,G)
Palomar College (U)
Peirce College (U)
The Pennsylvania State University University Park Campus (U)
The Richard Stockton College of New Jersey (G)
Shippensburg University of Pennsylvania (U,G)
Southern Illinois University Carbondale (U)
Southern Methodist University (G)
Southern Polytechnic State University (U)
State University of New York at Oswego (U,G)
Strayer University (U,G)
Syracuse University (U,G)
Tacoma Community College (U)
Taylor University (N,U)
Tunxis Community College (N)
Tyler Junior College (N)
The University of Akron (N,G)
University of Alberta (G)
University of California, Berkeley (U)
University of Illinois at Chicago (G)
University of Maryland (G)
University of Maryland University College (U)
University of Massachusetts Lowell (U)
University of Minnesota, Crookston (U)
University of Missouri–Columbia (G)
The University of Montana (G)
The University of North Carolina at Charlotte (G)
University of North Texas (G)
University of Oregon (G)
University of South Florida (G)
The University of Texas at Dallas (G)
The University of Texas System (U)
University of the Sciences in Philadelphia (U)
University of Toronto (U)
University of Tulsa (G)
University of Washington (N)
Vance-Granville Community College (U)
Vincennes University (U)
William Rainey Harper College (U)

INSURANCE

Cleveland Community College (U)
Drake University (G)
Feather River College (U)
Indiana State University (U)
Mississippi State University (U)
New England College of Finance (U)
Pasco-Hernando Community College (N)
Southeast Arkansas College (U)
Southern Illinois University Carbondale (U)
Sullivan University (G)
University of Central Arkansas (N)
University of Florida (U)
University of Nebraska–Lincoln (U)
University of Toronto (N)
University of Waterloo (U)

INTERCULTURAL/ MULTICULTURAL AND DIVERSITY STUDIES

Anne Arundel Community College (U)
Berkeley College (U)
Berkeley College-New York City Campus (U)
Berkeley College-Westchester Campus (U)
Dakota County Technical College (U)
Ozark Christian College (U)
Roosevelt University (U)
Saybrook Graduate School and Research Center (G)
South Piedmont Community College (U)
University of Alaska Fairbanks (G)
University of Houston–Victoria (G)
University of Missouri–Columbia (U)
West Virginia University at Parkersburg (U)

INTERIOR ARCHITECTURE

Academy of Art University (U,G)
Boston Architectural College (N,U,G)

INTERNATIONAL AND COMPARATIVE EDUCATION

Drexel University (G)
North Georgia College & State University (U,G)

INTERNATIONAL BUSINESS

American Military University (U)
American Public University (U)
Arizona State University (G)
Athabasca University (N,G)
Berkeley College (U)
Berkeley College-New York City Campus (U)
Berkeley College-Westchester Campus (U)
Black Hills State University (U)
Bradley University (U)
Brenau University (U,G)
Broome Community College (U)
California National University for Advanced Studies (U)
Cape Breton University (U)
Capella University (G)
Central New Mexico Community College (U)
Champlain College (U)
College of Southern Maryland (U)
Dakota County Technical College (U)
Dallas Baptist University (G)
Des Moines Area Community College (U)
D'Youville College (U,G)
Immaculata University (U)
Iona College (G)
James Madison University (N)
Jones College (U)
Lawrence Technological University (G)
Limestone College (U)
Massasoit Community College (U)
Mercy College (U)
Metropolitan State University (U)
Minnesota School of Business–Richfield (U)
Mount Saint Vincent University (U)
Myers University (U)
New England College of Finance (G)
Nipissing University (U)
Oxnard College (U)
Pace University (U)
Palomar College (U)
Park University (G)
Pennsylvania College of Technology (U)
Philadelphia University (G)
Regent University (N,U,G)
Rio Hondo College (U)
Sacred Heart University (U)
Saddleback College (U)
Schiller International University (U,G)
Shippensburg University of Pennsylvania (U,G)
Shoreline Community College (U)
Southeast Arkansas College (U)
State University of New York at Buffalo (U)
State University of New York Empire State College (U)
Strayer University (U)
Sullivan University (G)
Thunderbird, The Garvin School of International Management (N,G)
Tompkins Cortland Community College (U)
Touro University International (U,G)
University of California, Berkeley (U,G)
University of Dallas (G)
The University of Findlay (U)
University of Florida (U)
University of Houston–Downtown (U)
University of Illinois at Chicago (G)
University of Maryland University College (U,G)

University of Massachusetts Amherst (G)
University of Nebraska–Lincoln (U,G)
The University of Texas at Dallas (G)
University of Tulsa (G)
University of Washington (U)
University of Wisconsin–Platteville (U)
Upper Iowa University (N,U)
Waukesha County Technical College (U)
William Rainey Harper College (U)
Worcester Polytechnic Institute (G)

INTERNATIONAL RELATIONS AND AFFAIRS

American Military University (U,G)
American Public University (U,G)
Athabasca University (N,U,G)
Drake University (U)
Fort Valley State University (U)
Jones College (U)
Miami Dade College (U)
New Jersey City University (U)
North Georgia College & State University (U)
Regent University (N)
Salve Regina University (G)
Schiller International University (U)
University of Massachusetts Boston (U,G)
University of Missouri–Columbia (U)
West Los Angeles College (U)

INTERNATIONAL/GLOBAL STUDIES

Bowling Green State University (U)
Des Moines Area Community College (U)
Drexel University (G)
National University (U)
Regent University (N)
Thunderbird, The Garvin School of International Management (N)
The University of North Carolina at Greensboro (G)

JOURNALISM

Arizona State University (U)
Arkansas Tech University (U,G)
Athabasca University (N,U)
Bergen Community College (U)
Brenau University (U)
Central Carolina Community College (U)
Citrus College (U)
Cleveland State University (N)
College of DuPage (U)
Dallas County Community College District (U)
De Anza College (U)
Des Moines Area Community College (U)
Drake University (U,G)
East Carolina University (U)
Everett Community College (U)
Feather River College (N)
Housatonic Community College (U)
Indiana University–Purdue University Fort Wayne (U)
Iowa Western Community College (U)
James Madison University (N)
Jamestown Community College (N)
Kauai Community College (U)
Linn-Benton Community College (U)
Louisiana State University and Agricultural and Mechanical College (U)
Louisiana Tech University (U)
Marshall University (U)
Maryville University of Saint Louis (N)
Massasoit Community College (N)
Middle Tennessee State University (U)
Midland College (U)
Mt. San Antonio College (U)
Mount Wachusett Community College (U)
Murray State University (U)
New York Institute of Technology (U)
Northern Virginia Community College (U)
North Seattle Community College (U)
Northwestern State University of Louisiana (U)
Oklahoma State University (U)
Old Dominion University (U)
Palomar College (U)
Parkland College (U)
Peninsula College (U)
Penn Foster Career School (N)
The Pennsylvania State University University Park Campus (U)
The Richard Stockton College of New Jersey (U)
Sacramento City College (U)
Saint Mary-of-the-Woods College (U)
Schoolcraft College (U)
Seattle Central Community College (U)
Simpson College (U)
Southern Illinois University Carbondale (U)
Southwestern Community College (U)
State University of New York at Oswego (U)
Taylor University (U)
Texas A&M University–Commerce (U)
Texas Tech University (U)
The University of Akron (U)
The University of Alabama (U)
University of Alaska Fairbanks (U)
University of Arkansas (U)
University of California, Berkeley (G)
University of Central Arkansas (N)
University of Florida (U)
The University of Iowa (U,G)
University of Maryland University College (U)
University of Massachusetts Amherst (U)
University of Minnesota, Twin Cities Campus (U)
University of Missouri–Columbia (G)
The University of Montana (U)
University of Nebraska–Lincoln (U,G)
University of New Orleans (U,G)
The University of North Carolina at Chapel Hill (U,G)
University of North Texas (U)
University of Oklahoma (U)
University of Southern Indiana (U)
The University of Toledo (U)
University of Washington (U)
University of Wisconsin Colleges (U)
University of Wisconsin–Whitewater (U,G)

LANDSCAPE ARCHITECTURE

Ashworth College (N)
Colorado State University (U)
James Madison University (N)
Mississippi State University (U)
Southern Illinois University Carbondale (U)
The University of British Columbia (U)
University of Massachusetts Boston (N)
University of Saskatchewan (N)

LANGUAGES (AMERICAN INDIAN/ NATIVE AMERICAN)

Central Wyoming College (U)
Palomar College (U)

LANGUAGES (CLASSICS AND CLASSICAL)

Bethany University (U)
Columbia International University (G)
Louisiana State University and Agricultural and Mechanical College (U)
Moody Bible Institute (U)
North Idaho College (N)
Patrick Henry College (U)
University of Alaska Fairbanks (U)
University of Colorado at Denver and Health Sciences Center—Downtown Denver Campus (U)
University of Florida (U)
The University of Iowa (U)
University of Massachusetts Boston (U)
University of Minnesota, Twin Cities Campus (U)
University of Missouri–Columbia (U)
The University of North Carolina at Chapel Hill (U)
University of Waterloo (U)

LANGUAGES (EAST ASIAN)

Darton College (U)
Feather River College (N)
Naropa University (G)
Southern Illinois University Carbondale (U)
The University of Akron (U)
University of Toronto (N)
University of Wisconsin–Madison (U)
Western Washington University (U)

LANGUAGES (FOREIGN LANGUAGES RELATED)

Acadia University (U)
Blackhawk Technical College (N)
Black Hills State University (U)
Blue Ridge Community College (N)
California State University, San Bernardino (U)
California State University, San Marcos (N)
Central Carolina Community College (U)
Clarion University of Pennsylvania (U)
Cleveland State University (N)
College of the Humanities and Sciences, Harrison Middleton University (U)
Colorado Mountain College District System (U)
Community College of Southern Nevada (U)
Cumberland County College (U)
Darton College (U)
Dodge City Community College (U)
Fisher College (N)
Florida Atlantic University (U)
Fort Hays State University (U)
Fort Valley State University (U)
Fulton-Montgomery Community College (N)
Itawamba Community College (U)
Kean University (N)
Lipscomb University (U)
Louisiana State University and Agricultural and Mechanical College (U)
Mercy College (U)

Middlesex Community College (U)
Mount Allison University (N)
Mount Saint Vincent University (U)
New Mexico State University–Carlsbad (U)
Niagara University (U)
Oxnard College (U)
Portland Community College (N)
Sacred Heart University (U)
Seattle Central Community College (U)
Snow College (U)
Triton College (N)
University of California, Los Angeles (G)
University of Illinois at Springfield (U)
University of Maine (U)
University of Missouri–Columbia (U)
University of New Orleans (U,G)
The University of North Carolina at Chapel Hill (U)
University of Southern Indiana (U)
University of Toronto (N,U)
University of Waterloo (U)
University of Wisconsin–Whitewater (U)
Utah Valley State College (U)
Wayne State College (U)
Webster University (U)

LANGUAGES (GERMANIC)

Brigham Young University (U)
Darton College (U)
Eastern Michigan University (G)
James Madison University (N)
Louisiana State University and Agricultural and Mechanical College (U)
Oklahoma State University (U)
Ozarks Technical Community College (U)
The Pennsylvania State University University Park Campus (U)
Queen's University at Kingston (U)
The University of Akron (U)
University of Arkansas (U)
University of Central Arkansas (U)
University of Florida (U)
University of Minnesota, Twin Cities Campus (U)
University of Missouri–Columbia (U)
University of Nevada, Reno (U)
University of New Orleans (U,G)
University of South Florida (G)
The University of Tennessee (U)
University of Toronto (N)
University of Waterloo (U)
Wilfrid Laurier University (U)

LANGUAGES (MIDDLE/NEAR EASTERN AND SEMITIC)

Brigham Young University (U)
Feather River College (N)
Hebrew College (N,U,G)
Laura and Alvin Siegal College of Judaic Studies (N,U,G)
University of Colorado at Colorado Springs (U)

LANGUAGES (MODERN GREEK)

Bethany University (U)
Eugene Bible College (U)
Harvard University (N,G)
North Carolina State University (U)
Northwestern College (U)
University of Washington (U)
University of Waterloo (U)
Western Washington University (U)

LANGUAGES (ROMANCE LANGUAGES)

Boise State University (U)
Bowling Green State University (G)
Brigham Young University (U)
Burlington County College (U)
Central Lakes College (U)
City College of San Francisco (U)
Clemson University (N)
Clovis Community College (U)
College of DuPage (U)
College of San Mateo (U)
College of Southern Maryland (U)
College of the Humanities and Sciences, Harrison Middleton University (U)
Columbus State Community College (U)
Darton College (U)
Delta College (U)
Erie Community College (U)
Evergreen Valley College (U)
Hillsborough Community College (N)
Houston Community College System (U)
James Madison University (N)
John Jay College of Criminal Justice of the City University of New York (U)
Kauai Community College (U)
Louisiana State University and Agricultural and Mechanical College (U)
Midland College (U)
Mountain Empire Community College (U)
Nassau Community College (U)
North Carolina State University (U)
Northern Virginia Community College (U)
Oklahoma State University (U)
Oregon State University (N)
Palomar College (U)
The Pennsylvania State University University Park Campus (U)
Piedmont Technical College (U)
Reading Area Community College (U)
Rio Hondo College (U)
St. John's University (U)
St. Louis Community College System (U)
Southeast Community College, Lincoln Campus (U)
Southern Illinois University Carbondale (U)
Southwest Virginia Community College (U)
State University of New York College at Potsdam (N)
Texas State University-San Marcos (U)
Texas Tech University (N,U)
Triton College (U)
Tyler Junior College (U)
The University of Alabama (U)
University of Alaska Fairbanks (U)
University of Arkansas (U)
The University of British Columbia (U)
University of Florida (U)
The University of Iowa (U)
University of Massachusetts Boston (U)
University of Minnesota, Twin Cities Campus (U)
University of Missouri–Columbia (N,U)
University of Nevada, Reno (U)
University of New Orleans (U,G)
The University of North Carolina at Chapel Hill (U)
The University of North Carolina at Greensboro (G)
University of South Florida (U)
The University of Tennessee (U)
University of Toronto (N)
University of Waterloo (U)
Virginia Polytechnic Institute and State University (U)
Western Nevada Community College (U)
Western Washington University (U)
Wilfrid Laurier University (U)

LANGUAGES (SLAVIC, BALTIC AND ALBANIAN)

Feather River College (N)
University of Minnesota, Twin Cities Campus (U)
The University of North Carolina at Chapel Hill (U)
University of Washington (U)
University of Waterloo (U)

LANGUAGES (SOUTH ASIAN)

North Carolina State University (U)
University of Toronto (N)

LEATHERWORKING AND UPHOLSTERY

Blackhawk Technical College (N)

LEGAL PROFESSIONS AND STUDIES RELATED

California State University, Chico (U)
Cape Fear Community College (U)
Chadron State College (U)
Clackamas Community College (U)
Clarion University of Pennsylvania (U)
Clemson University (N)
Colorado Technical University (U)
East Arkansas Community College (U)
Eastern Michigan University (U)
Florida Gulf Coast University (G)
Humboldt State University (N,U)
Iona College (U,G)
Itawamba Community College (U)
Kean University (N)
Lock Haven University of Pennsylvania (N)
Michigan State University College of Law (N,G)
Minnesota School of Business–Richfield (U)
Mount Wachusett Community College (U)
Palomar College (U)
Portland Community College (N)
Pulaski Technical College (U)
Quinebaug Valley Community College (N)
Roosevelt University (G)
Saint Joseph's University (U)
Seminole Community College (U)
Shenandoah University (N)
South Piedmont Community College (U)
State University of New York at Buffalo (N,U)
Texas State University-San Marcos (U)
University of Massachusetts Amherst (U)
The University of North Carolina at Greensboro (N)
University of Southern Indiana (N)

LEGAL RESEARCH AND ADVANCED PROFESSIONAL STUDIES

California University of Pennsylvania (G)
Drake University (U)
Eastern Michigan University (U,G)
Michigan State University College of Law (N,G)
Missouri State University (G)
Palomar College (U)
Schiller International University (G)
Seminole Community College (U)
Strayer University (G)
Sullivan University (G)
The University of Akron (G)
University of Northern Colorado (G)
University of Tulsa (G)

LEGAL STUDIES (NON-PROFESSIONAL GENERAL, UNDERGRADUATE)

Adams State College (U)
Anne Arundel Community College (U)
Arizona State University (U)
Athabasca University (U)
Athens Technical College (U)
Berkeley College (U)
Berkeley College-New York City Campus (U)
Berkeley College-Westchester Campus (U)
Blinn College (U)
Brenau University (U)
California State University, Chico (U)
Cape Fear Community College (U)
Central New Mexico Community College (U)
Central Piedmont Community College (U)
Central Texas College (U)
Chadron State College (U)
College of San Mateo (U)
College of Southern Maryland (U)
College of The Albemarle (U)
Columbus State Community College (U)
The Community College of Baltimore County (U)
De Anza College (U)
Delta College (U)
DeVry University Online (U)
Drury University (U)
Eastern Michigan University (U)
Elgin Community College (U)
Embry-Riddle Aeronautical University (U)
Embry-Riddle Aeronautical University, Extended Campus (U)
Finger Lakes Community College (U)
Forrest Junior College (U)
Galveston College (N)
Grantham University (U)
Hillsborough Community College (U)
Iowa Western Community College (U)
John Jay College of Criminal Justice of the City University of New York (U)
Jones College (U)
Keiser College (U)
Lansing Community College (U)
Limestone College (U)
Louisiana State University and Agricultural and Mechanical College (U)
Marion Technical College (U)
Marist College (U)
Mercy College (U)
Metropolitan State University (U)
Michigan State University College of Law (N)
Middlesex Community College (U)
Midland College (U)
Minnesota School of Business–Richfield (U)
Mountain Empire Community College (U)
Mount Saint Vincent University (U)
Mt. San Antonio College (U)
Murray State University (U)
Myers University (U)
Nassau Community College (U)
New Mexico State University–Alamogordo (U)
New York Institute of Technology (U)
Northern Virginia Community College (U)
Northwestern Michigan College (U)
Oklahoma State University (U)
Oxnard College (U)
Pace University (U)
Palomar College (U)
Parkland College (U)
Patrick Henry College (U)
Peirce College (U)
Philadelphia University (U)
Piedmont Technical College (U)
Randolph Community College (U)
Raritan Valley Community College (U)
Roger Williams University (U)
Roosevelt University (U)
Ryerson University (U)
St. John's University (U)
Sam Houston State University (U)
San Joaquin Delta College (U)
Schenectady County Community College (U)
Seminole Community College (U)
Shawnee Community College (U)
Sinclair Community College (U)
Southeast Community College, Lincoln Campus (U)
State University of New York at Buffalo (U)
State University of New York Empire State College (U)
Strayer University (U)
Tacoma Community College (U)
Texas Tech University (U)
Tompkins Cortland Community College (U)
Tri-State University (U)
Triton College (U)
Tyler Junior College (U)
University of Alaska Fairbanks (U)
University of Arkansas (U)
University of Bridgeport (U)
University of California, Berkeley (U)
University of Florida (U)
University of Great Falls (U)
University of Houston–Downtown (U)
University of Minnesota, Morris (U)
The University of Toledo (U)
Upper Iowa University (U)
Utah Valley State College (U)
Washtenaw Community College (U)

LEGAL SUPPORT SERVICES

Adams State College (U)
Anne Arundel Community College (U)
Blackhawk Technical College (U)
Blue Ridge Community College (N)
Cleveland State University (N)
Colorado State University (N)
Columbus State Community College (U)
Duquesne University (N)
Eastern Michigan University (U)
East Tennessee State University (N)
Johnson County Community College (U)
Michigan State University College of Law (N,G)
Palomar College (U)
Seminole Community College (U)
Tyler Junior College (U)
The University of North Carolina at Charlotte (N)
The University of North Carolina at Greensboro (N)
University of North Dakota (N)
The University of Texas System (N)
West Virginia University (N)

LIBERAL ARTS AND SCIENCES, GENERAL STUDIES AND HUMANITIES

Acadia University (U)
Alvin Community College (U)
American Military University (U)
American Public University (U)
Arizona State University (U)
Arizona Western College (U)
Athabasca University (N)
Bainbridge College (U)
Bellevue Community College (U)
Berkeley College (U)
Berkeley College-New York City Campus (U)
Berkeley College-Westchester Campus (U)
Bethany University (U)
Bowling Green State University (U)
Brenau University (U)
Brigham Young University (U)
Caldwell Community College and Technical Institute (U)
California State University, Chico (U)
California State University, Dominguez Hills (G)
California State University, San Bernardino (U)
Central Oregon Community College (U)
Chadron State College (U)
Champlain College (U)
Chattanooga State Technical Community College (U)
Chesapeake College (U)
Citrus College (U)
Clark College (U)
Clinton Community College (U)
College of DuPage (U)
College of the Siskiyous (U)
Colorado State University-Pueblo (U)
Community College of Beaver County (U)
Community College of Denver (U)
Community College of Southern Nevada (U)
Dakota County Technical College (U)
Dallas Baptist University (U)
Dallas County Community College District (U)
Darton College (U)
DePaul University (U)
DeVry University Online (U)
Drake University (U)
Drury University (U)
Eastern Michigan University (U)
East Los Angeles College (U)
East Tennessee State University (N)
Elgin Community College (U)
Erie Community College (U)
Everett Community College (U)
Fort Hays State University (U,G)
Fort Valley State University (U)
Franklin Pierce College (U)

Gogebic Community College (U)
Granite State College (U)
Haywood Community College (U)
Honolulu Community College (U)
Illinois Eastern Community Colleges, Olney Central College (U)
Illinois Eastern Community Colleges, Wabash Valley College (U)
Indiana University of Pennsylvania (U)
Indiana University System (U)
Indiana Wesleyan University (U)
Iona College (U)
Iowa Western Community College (U)
Jacksonville State University (U,G)
James Madison University (N)
Jamestown Community College (N)
John A. Logan College (U)
Jones College (U)
Judson College (U)
Lake Superior College (U)
Lehigh Carbon Community College (U)
Lewis-Clark State College (U)
Linn-Benton Community College (U)
Lock Haven University of Pennsylvania (G)
Madison Area Technical College (U)
Madonna University (N,U)
Marylhurst University (U)
Mercy College (U)
Miami Dade College (U)
Middlesex Community College (U)
Middle Tennessee State University (U)
Minnesota School of Business–Richfield (U)
Minot State University–Bottineau Campus (U)
Monmouth University (G)
Monroe Community College (U)
Montana State University–Billings (U)
Montgomery Community College (U)
Naropa University (U,G)
Naugatuck Valley Community College (U)
New Mexico State University–Alamogordo (U)
New Mexico State University–Carlsbad (U)
The New School (N,U)
Northern Kentucky University (U)
Northwestern College (U)
Oral Roberts University (U)
Oregon State University (U)
Ouachita Technical College (U)
Ozarks Technical Community College (U)
Pace University (N)
Palomar College (U)
Patrick Henry College (U)
Peninsula College (U)
Prescott College (U)
Pueblo Community College (U)
Quinebaug Valley Community College (U)
Rasmussen College Eden Prarie (U)
Regions University (N,U)
Rend Lake College (U)
The Richard Stockton College of New Jersey (U)
Roosevelt University (U)
Ryerson University (U)
Sacred Heart University (U)
St. Edward's University (G)
Saint Leo University (U)
Saint Mary-of-the-Woods College (U)
St. Petersburg College (U)
San Bernardino Valley College (U)
Seminole Community College (U)
Simpson College (U)
Sinclair Community College (U)
Skidmore College (U,G)
South Central College (U)
South Dakota School of Mines and Technology (U)
Southeast Community College, Beatrice Campus (U)
Southeast Community College, Lincoln Campus (U)
Southeast Community College, Milford Campus (U)
Southwestern College (U)
Stony Brook University, State University of New York (G)
Syracuse University (U)
Taylor University (U)
Tennessee Temple University (U)
Texas State University-San Marcos (U)
Texas Tech University (U)
Tri-State University (U)
Triton College (U)
Tyler Junior College (U)
The University of Akron (U)
The University of Alabama (U)
University of Alaska Fairbanks (U)
University of Bridgeport (U)
University of California, Berkeley (U)
University of California, Los Angeles (G)
University of Colorado at Denver and Health Sciences Center—Downtown Denver Campus (U)
University of Connecticut (U)
University of Denver (G)
University of Florida (U)
University of Great Falls (U)
University of Houston–Downtown (U)
University of Illinois at Springfield (U)
The University of Iowa (U)
University of La Verne (U)
University of Maine (G)
The University of Maine at Augusta (U)
University of Maine at Fort Kent (U)
University of Massachusetts Boston (U)
University of Massachusetts Lowell (U)
University of Minnesota, Twin Cities Campus (U,G)
University of Missouri–Columbia (U)
The University of Montana–Western (U)
University of New Orleans (U,G)
The University of North Carolina at Greensboro (U,G)
The University of North Carolina Wilmington (G)
University of Southern Mississippi (U)
University of South Florida (U)
The University of Tennessee (U)
The University of Texas System (U)
The University of Toledo (U,G)
University of Waterloo (U)
University of West Florida (U)
University of Wisconsin–River Falls (U)
University of Wyoming (U)
Upper Iowa University (U)
Utah State University (U)
Utica College (U)
Vance-Granville Community College (U)
Viterbo University (U)
Washburn University (G)
West Shore Community College (U)
Wharton County Junior College (U)
William Rainey Harper College (U)
Winston-Salem State University (U)
Wright State University (U)
York University (U)
Yuba College (U)

LIBRARY ASSISTANT

College of DuPage (U)
James Madison University (N)
Palomar College (U)
Pueblo Community College (U)
Syracuse University (G)

LIBRARY SCIENCE

Central Missouri State University (U,G)
Central Wyoming College (U)
Chadron State College (U)
Clarion University of Pennsylvania (U,G)
College of DuPage (U)
Drexel University (G)
East Carolina University (G)
Louisiana State University and Agricultural and Mechanical College (U)
Mayville State University (U)
Memorial University of Newfoundland (U,G)
Palomar College (U)
St. John's University (G)
Seattle Pacific University (G)
Seminole Community College (U)
Syracuse University (G)
Tacoma Community College (U)
Texas Woman's University (G)
The University of Alabama (G)
University of Alaska Fairbanks (U)
University of Central Oklahoma (U,G)
University of Cincinnati Raymond Walters College (U)
University of Illinois at Urbana–Champaign (G)
University of Missouri–Columbia (G)
University of Nevada, Reno (U,G)
The University of North Carolina at Greensboro (G)
University of North Texas (N,U,G)
University of South Florida (U,G)
University of Washington (U,G)
University of Wisconsin–Whitewater (U)
Valley City State University (U)
West Los Angeles College (U)

LIBRARY SCIENCE RELATED

Black Hills State University (U)
Bowling Green State University (U)
Central Carolina Community College (U)
Central Virginia Community College (U)
Chadron State College (U)
The College of St. Scholastica (G)
Colorado Mountain College District System (U)
Contra Costa College (U)
Des Moines Area Community College (U)
Drexel University (G)
Everett Community College (U)
Evergreen Valley College (U)
Indiana State University (U,G)
Louisiana State University and Agricultural and Mechanical College (U)
Miami Dade College (U)
Montana State University (G)
North Seattle Community College (U)
Northwestern State University of Louisiana (U)
Oxnard College (U)
Palomar College (U)
Rio Hondo College (U)
Sacramento City College (U)

Saddleback College (U)
Seminole Community College (U)
Shoreline Community College (U)
State University of New York at Plattsburgh (U)
Syracuse University (G)
Tacoma Community College (U)
Texas A&M University–Commerce (G)
The University of British Columbia (U)
University of Central Arkansas (G)
The University of Maine at Augusta (U)
University of Missouri–Columbia (G)
The University of Montana (U,G)
The University of Montana–Western (U)
The University of North Carolina at Greensboro (G)
University of North Texas (N,U,G)
University of Oklahoma (U)
University of Southern Mississippi (U)
University of Washington (G)
Utah State University (G)
Western Washington University (U)

LINGUISTIC, COMPARATIVE, AND RELATED LANGUAGE STUDIES

Acadia University (U)
Adams State College (N)
Arizona State University (U)
Asheville-Buncombe Technical Community College (N,U)
Athabasca University (N,U)
Bainbridge College (N)
Bethany University (U)
Brenau University (U)
Bridgewater State College (G)
Caldwell Community College and Technical Institute (N)
Central Wyoming College (N)
Cleveland State University (U,G)
Coconino Community College (N)
College of Staten Island of the City University of New York (N)
Columbia International University (G)
Daemen College (U)
Darton College (U)
Feather River College (N)
Florida Atlantic University (G)
Golden West College (U)
Harford Community College (U)
Hebrew College (N,U,G)
James Madison University (N,U)
James Sprunt Community College (U)
Jamestown Community College (N)
J. Sargeant Reynolds Community College (U)
Kauai Community College (U)
Kentucky State University (U)
Lansing Community College (U)
Lenoir Community College (U)
Louisiana State University and Agricultural and Mechanical College (U)
Middlesex Community College (U)
Middle Tennessee State University (N)
Millersville University of Pennsylvania (U,G)
Mountain Empire Community College (U)
North Georgia College & State University (U)
Northwest Missouri State University (U)
Odessa College (N)
The Ohio State University (U)
Oregon State University (N)
Pace University (U)
The Pennsylvania State University University Park Campus (U)
Plymouth State University (U)
Sacred Heart University (U)
St. Petersburg College (U)
Seattle Pacific University (U)
Southwestern Baptist Theological Seminary (G)
State University of New York College at Potsdam (N)
Strayer University (U)
Tacoma Community College (U)
Triton College (U)
Tunxis Community College (U)
The University of Akron (U)
The University of Alabama (U)
University of Alaska Fairbanks (U)
University of California, Davis (N,U)
University of Colorado at Denver and Health Sciences Center—Downtown Denver Campus (U)
University of Denver (G)
University of Florida (U)
University of Massachusetts Boston (U)
University of Minnesota, Twin Cities Campus (U)
University of Missouri–Columbia (U)
University of Nevada, Reno (U)
University of New Orleans (U,G)
University of North Dakota (U)
University of North Texas (U,G)
University of Southern Indiana (U)
University of Southern Mississippi (U,G)
The University of Tennessee (U)
The University of Tennessee at Martin (U)
The University of Texas System (U)
University of Waterloo (U)
University of Wisconsin–La Crosse (U)
Virginia Polytechnic Institute and State University (U)
Weber State University (U)
William Rainey Harper College (U)
Wright State University (U)

MANAGEMENT INFORMATION SYSTEMS

American Military University (U)
American Public University (U)
Athabasca University (N,U,G)
Bellevue Community College (U)
Bellevue University (U,G)
Blinn College (U)
Boston University (G)
Brenau University (U,G)
California National University for Advanced Studies (U,G)
Capitol College (G)
Central Carolina Community College (N)
Central Michigan University (G)
Central Piedmont Community College (N)
Central Texas College (U)
Central Wyoming College (N)
Chadron State College (U,G)
Charter Oak State College (U)
Cincinnati State Technical and Community College (U)
Cleveland State University (N)
College of The Albemarle (N)
Colorado State University-Pueblo (N)
Connecticut State University System (U,G)
Culver-Stockton College (U)
Dallas Baptist University (U)
Des Moines Area Community College (U)
Drake University (U)
Drexel University (G)
Drury University (U)
Duquesne University (G)
East Carolina University (U)
East Los Angeles College (U)
Edgecombe Community College (N,U)
Edison State Community College (U)
Embry-Riddle Aeronautical University (G)
Erie Community College (U)
Everett Community College (N)
Feather River College (N)
Florida Atlantic University (U)
Forrest Junior College (U)
Franklin Pierce College (G)
Fresno City College (U)
Georgia College & State University (G)
Granite State College (U)
Grantham University (U,G)
Haywood Community College (U)
Heart of Georgia Technical College (U)
Houston Community College System (U)
Immaculata University (U)
Indiana State University (U)
Iona College (U,G)
Itawamba Community College (U)
Jacksonville State University (U,G)
Jones College (U)
Kansas State University (U)
Kentucky State University (U)
Kettering University (N)
Lamar State College–Port Arthur (N)
Lewis-Clark State College (U)
Limestone College (U)
Louisiana State University and Agricultural and Mechanical College (U)
Madison Area Technical College (U)
Marion Technical College (U)
Marshall University (U)
Maryville University of Saint Louis (N)
Mercy College (U,G)
Metropolitan State University (U,G)
Middle Tennessee State University (N)
Milwaukee School of Engineering (U)
Missouri State University (N)
Mohawk Valley Community College (N,U)
Motlow State Community College (U)
Mount Wachusett Community College (U)
Myers University (U)
New Jersey Institute of Technology (U)
New Mexico State University–Carlsbad (N)
New York Institute of Technology (G)
North Arkansas College (U)
Northern Virginia Community College (U)
Nova Southeastern University (G)
Oklahoma State University (U)
Old Dominion University (U,G)
Oregon Institute of Technology (U)
Ozarka College (U)
Park University (U)
Patrick Henry Community College (U)
Peirce College (U)
The Pennsylvania State University University Park Campus (U)
Philadelphia University (U,G)
Piedmont Technical College (U)
Ryerson University (U)
Saddleback College (U)
St. Cloud State University (U)
St. Louis Community College System (N)
Seminole Community College (U)
Shippensburg University of Pennsylvania (U,G)
Southwest Wisconsin Technical College (U)

Stanly Community College (U)
State University of New York College at Potsdam (U)
State University of New York Empire State College (U)
Syracuse University (U,G)
Tacoma Community College (N)
Taylor University (N,U)
Texas A&M University–Commerce (U)
Texas A&M University–Texarkana (G)
Thunderbird, The Garvin School of International Management (G)
Touro University International (G)
Tunxis Community College (U)
Tyler Junior College (N)
University of Colorado at Denver and Health Sciences Center—Downtown Denver Campus (G)
University of Dallas (G)
The University of Findlay (N)
University of Houston–Downtown (U)
University of Illinois at Springfield (G)
University of Massachusetts Amherst (G)
University of Massachusetts Boston (U)
University of Massachusetts Lowell (G)
University of Michigan–Flint (N)
University of Minnesota, Crookston (U)
University of New Orleans (U,G)
University of Oregon (G)
University of Pittsburgh at Bradford (U)
University of Southern Mississippi (U)
University of Tulsa (G)
University of Waterloo (G)
University of Wisconsin–Parkside (G)
University of Wisconsin–Whitewater (U,G)
Upper Iowa University (N,U)
Utah Valley State College (U)
Virginia Polytechnic Institute and State University (G)
Wayland Baptist University (U,G)
Webster University (G)
Westchester Community College (U)
Western Piedmont Community College (U)
West Virginia Northern Community College (U)
West Virginia University (N)
West Virginia University at Parkersburg (U)
Wilkes Community College (U)
York County Community College (U)

MANAGEMENT SCIENCES AND QUANTITATIVE METHODS

Athabasca University (N,G)
Bellevue University (U,G)
Berkeley College (U)
Berkeley College-New York City Campus (U)
Berkeley College-Westchester Campus (U)
Brenau University (U,G)
Capitol College (G)
Central Michigan University (G)
Chadron State College (U,G)
Colorado State University (N)
Colorado Technical University (U,G)
Concordia University Wisconsin (U)
Dallas Baptist University (G)
Des Moines Area Community College (U)
Drake University (U)
Drexel University (U,G)
Embry-Riddle Aeronautical University (U,G)
Florida Gulf Coast University (U)
Florida Institute of Technology (G)
Georgia Southern University (U)
Immaculata University (U)
Jacksonville State University (U,G)
James Madison University (N)
Kettering University (N)
Limestone College (U)
Louisiana State University and Agricultural and Mechanical College (U)
Marist College (G)
Mercy College (U,G)
Mesa State College (U)
Miami Dade College (U)
Mohawk Valley Community College (N)
Myers University (U)
National University (U)
New Mexico Institute of Mining and Technology (G)
Nipissing University (U)
Old Dominion University (U)
The Pennsylvania State University University Park Campus (G)
Philadelphia University (U,G)
Ryerson University (U)
Saint Joseph's College of Maine (G)
Saint Leo University (U)
Shippensburg University of Pennsylvania (U)
South Dakota School of Mines and Technology (G)
Southeast Community College, Beatrice Campus (N)
Southeast Community College, Lincoln Campus (N)
Southeast Community College, Milford Campus (N)
Southern Illinois University Carbondale (U)
Stanford University (N)
State University of New York College of Agriculture and Technology at Morrisville (U)
Syracuse University (G)
Texas A&M University–Kingsville (U)
Tompkins Cortland Community College (U)
University of California, Berkeley (U,G)
University of California, Davis (N)
University of Colorado at Denver and Health Sciences Center—Downtown Denver Campus (G)
The University of Findlay (N)
University of Florida (U)
University of Illinois at Urbana–Champaign (N,G)
University of Massachusetts Amherst (N,U)
University of Michigan (N)
University of Michigan–Flint (U,G)
University of New Orleans (U,G)
The University of Texas at Dallas (G)
The University of Texas at Tyler (G)
University of Toronto (N,U)
University of Tulsa (G)
University of Wisconsin–Parkside (G)
University of Wisconsin–Platteville (G)
University of Wisconsin–Stout (G)
Upper Iowa University (U)
Western Nevada Community College (U)
Western Washington University (U)
York University (U)

MANUFACTURING ENGINEERING

Bellingham Technical College (N)
Boston University (G)
Cleveland State University (G)
Dakota County Technical College (N,U)
East Carolina University (U)
Housatonic Community College (U)
Kettering University (N)
New Mexico State University (G)
University of Michigan (G)

MARKETING

Acadia University (U)
Adirondack Community College (U)
Anne Arundel Community College (U)
Arizona State University (U)
Arkansas Tech University (U)
Asheville-Buncombe Technical Community College (N)
Ashworth College (N)
Athabasca University (N,U,G)
Bellevue Community College (U)
Bellevue University (U)
Berkeley College (U)
Berkeley College-New York City Campus (U)
Berkeley College-Westchester Campus (U)
Blackhawk Technical College (U)
Black Hills State University (U)
Blue Ridge Community College (N,U)
Brenau University (U,G)
Brigham Young University (U)
Buena Vista University (U)
Burlington County College (U)
Butler Community College (U)
Butler County Community College (U)
Caldwell Community College and Technical Institute (U)
California National University for Advanced Studies (U,G)
Cape Breton University (U)
Cape Cod Community College (U)
Cape Fear Community College (U)
Capella University (U,G)
Central Carolina Community College (U)
Central Lakes College (U)
Central Michigan University (U,G)
Central Texas College (U)
Central Virginia Community College (U)
Chadron State College (U,G)
Charter Oak State College (U)
Chattanooga State Technical Community College (U)
Clemson University (U)
Cleveland Institute of Electronics (N)
Coleman College (U,G)
College of San Mateo (U)
College of Southern Maryland (U)
College of The Albemarle (U)
College of the Southwest (U)
Colorado Christian University (U,G)
Colorado State University (U)
Colorado State University-Pueblo (U)
Colorado Technical University (U)
Columbus State Community College (U)
The Community College of Baltimore County (U)
Concordia University Wisconsin (U)
Connecticut State University System (U,G)
Corban College (U)
Cosumnes River College (U)
Dakota County Technical College (U)
Dallas Baptist University (U,G)
Dallas County Community College District (U)
Danville Community College (U)
De Anza College (U)
Delta College (U)
Des Moines Area Community College (U)

DeVry University Online (U,G)
Drake University (U)
Drexel University (U,G)
Drury University (U)
Eastern Michigan University (U,G)
East Tennessee State University (N,G)
Edison State Community College (U)
Elgin Community College (U)
Embry-Riddle Aeronautical University (U)
Erie Community College (U)
Finger Lakes Community College (U)
Florida Atlantic University (U,G)
Florida Gulf Coast University (U)
Florida Institute of Technology (G)
Fort Hays State University (U)
Fort Valley State University (U)
Franklin University (U)
Frostburg State University (G)
Georgia Southern University (U)
Governors State University (U)
Grantham University (U,G)
Hillsborough Community College (U)
Housatonic Community College (U)
Houston Community College System (U)
Illinois Eastern Community Colleges, Frontier Community College (U)
Indiana State University (U)
Indiana University of Pennsylvania (U)
Iona College (U,G)
Iowa Western Community College (U)
Itawamba Community College (U)
Ivy Tech Community College–Northwest (U)
Jackson Community College (U)
Jacksonville State University (U,G)
James Madison University (N)
James Sprunt Community College (U)
Jamestown Community College (N)
John A. Logan College (U)
Johnson County Community College (U)
J. Sargeant Reynolds Community College (U)
Kansas State University (U)
Kean University (U)
Lamar State College–Port Arthur (N)
Lawrence Technological University (U,G)
Lehigh Carbon Community College (U)
Lewis and Clark Community College (U)
Liberty University (U)
Limestone College (U)
Louisiana State University and Agricultural and Mechanical College (U)
Louisiana State University at Eunice (U)
Madison Area Technical College (U)
Marshall University (U,G)
Mercy College (U,G)
Mesalands Community College (U)
Metropolitan State University (U,G)
Miami Dade College (U)
Middlesex Community College (U)
Middle Tennessee State University (G)
Missouri State University (U,G)
Mohawk Valley Community College (N)
Montana State University–Billings (U)
Mountain Empire Community College (U)
Mount Saint Vincent University (U)
Mount Wachusett Community College (U)
Murray State University (G)
Myers University (U)
Nassau Community College (U)
New Mexico State University–Carlsbad (N)
The New School (G)
New York Institute of Technology (U,G)
Nipissing University (U)
North Dakota State College of Science (U)
Northern Virginia Community College (U)
Northwestern State University of Louisiana (U)
Oklahoma State University (U)
Old Dominion University (U,G)
Oxnard College (U)
Pace University (U,G)
Palomar College (U)
Parkland College (U)
Park University (U)
Peirce College (U)
Pennsylvania College of Technology (U)
The Pennsylvania State University University Park Campus (U)
Philadelphia University (U,G)
Portland Community College (U)
Pueblo Community College (U)
Randolph Community College (U)
Raritan Valley Community College (U)
Rasmussen College Eden Prarie (U)
The Richard Stockton College of New Jersey (U)
Ryerson University (U)
Sacred Heart University (U,G)
Saddleback College (U)
St. Edward's University (G)
St. John's University (U)
Saint Joseph's College of Maine (U,G)
Saint Joseph's University (U,G)
Saint Leo University (U)
St. Louis Community College System (U)
Saint Mary-of-the-Woods College (U)
Sam Houston State University (U)
Schiller International University (U,G)
Schoolcraft College (U)
Seminole Community College (U)
Shippensburg University of Pennsylvania (U)
Shoreline Community College (U)
Simpson College (U)
Sinclair Community College (U)
Southeast Arkansas College (U)
Southern Illinois University Carbondale (N,U)
Southwestern Oregon Community College (U)
Stanly Community College (U)
State University of New York at Plattsburgh (U)
Stephens College (G)
Syracuse University (G)
Taylor University (N,U)
Texas A&M University–Commerce (U,G)
Texas A&M University–Kingsville (U)
Texas A&M University–Texarkana (U,G)
Texas Tech University (U)
Thunderbird, The Garvin School of International Management (N)
Tompkins Cortland Community College (U)
Tri-County Community College (U)
Tri-State University (U)
Triton College (U)
United States Sports Academy (G)
University of Alaska Fairbanks (U)
University of California, Berkeley (U,G)
University of Colorado at Denver and Health Sciences Center—Downtown Denver Campus (G)
University of Dallas (G)
University of Delaware (U)
The University of Findlay (U,G)
University of Florida (U)
University of Houston–Downtown (U)
University of Illinois at Chicago (N,G)
University of Maryland University College (G)
University of Massachusetts Amherst (U,G)
University of Massachusetts Boston (U)
University of Massachusetts Lowell (G)
University of Michigan–Flint (U,G)
University of Minnesota, Crookston (U)
University of Minnesota, Twin Cities Campus (U)
University of Missouri–Columbia (U)
University of Nebraska–Lincoln (U,G)
University of Nevada, Reno (U)
University of New Orleans (U,G)
University of North Alabama (U)
The University of North Carolina at Charlotte (N)
University of Northern Colorado (G)
University of Northern Iowa (U)
University of North Texas (N,U,G)
University of Oklahoma (U)
University of Pittsburgh at Bradford (U)
University of St. Francis (G)
University of Southern Indiana (G)
University of Southern Mississippi (U,G)
University of South Florida (G)
The University of Texas at Dallas (G)
The University of Texas at Tyler (U)
University of Toronto (N,U)
University of Tulsa (G)
University of Washington (U)
University of Wisconsin–Platteville (U)
University of Wisconsin–Whitewater (U,G)
Upper Iowa University (N,U)
Vance-Granville Community College (U)
Virginia Polytechnic Institute and State University (U,G)
Wake Technical Community College (U)
Waukesha County Technical College (U)
Wayland Baptist University (U)
Webster University (G)
Western Piedmont Community College (U)
West Shore Community College (U)
West Virginia University at Parkersburg (U)
Wharton County Junior College (U)
Wilkes Community College (U)
Worcester Polytechnic Institute (G)
York University (U)

MATERIALS ENGINEERING

Boston University (G)
Delta College (U)
New Mexico Institute of Mining and Technology (G)
University of Florida (G)
University of Illinois at Urbana–Champaign (G)
University of Michigan (N)
University of South Florida (G)
University of Washington (U,G)

MATERIALS SCIENCE

Columbia University (U,G)
University of Florida (G)
University of Illinois at Urbana–Champaign (G)
University of Michigan (N)
University of Minnesota, Twin Cities Campus (U)

MATHEMATICS

Adirondack Community College (U)
Alvin Community College (U)

Arizona State University (U)
Arkansas State University–Beebe (U)
Arkansas State University–Mountain Home (U)
Arkansas Tech University (U)
Asheville-Buncombe Technical Community College (U)
Athabasca University (N,U)
Athens Technical College (U)
Barclay College (U)
Bellevue Community College (U)
Big Sandy Community and Technical College (U)
Bismarck State College (U)
Black Hills State University (U)
Boise State University (U)
Bowling Green State University (U,G)
Brazosport College (U)
Brenau University (U)
Broome Community College (U)
Butler Community College (U)
Butler County Community College (U)
Caldwell Community College and Technical Institute (U)
California State University, San Bernardino (U)
California State University, San Marcos (N,U)
Cape Cod Community College (U)
Cape Fear Community College (U)
Carl Albert State College (U)
Carlow University (U)
Casper College (U)
Cayuga County Community College (U)
Cecil Community College (U)
Cedarville University (U)
Central Carolina Community College (U)
Central Lakes College (U)
Central New Mexico Community College (U)
Central Oregon Community College (U)
Central Texas College (U)
Central Wyoming College (U)
Chadron State College (U,G)
Champlain College (U)
Chattanooga State Technical Community College (U)
Citrus College (U)
Clackamas Community College (U)
Clark College (U)
Clatsop Community College (U)
Clemson University (N,U)
Cleveland Institute of Electronics (N)
Cleveland State Community College (U)
Clovis Community College (U)
Coconino Community College (U)
Coffeyville Community College (U)
Coleman College (U)
College of DuPage (U)
College of San Mateo (U)
College of Southern Maryland (U)
College of the Humanities and Sciences, Harrison Middleton University (U,G)
College of the Siskiyous (U)
Colorado State University (U,G)
Colorado State University-Pueblo (U)
Columbia Basin College (U)
Columbia College (U)
Columbus State Community College (U)
The Community College of Baltimore County (U)
Community College of Beaver County (U)
Community College of Denver (U)
Community College of Southern Nevada (U)
Corning Community College (U)
Cosumnes River College (U)
County College of Morris (U)
Cowley County Community College and Area Vocational–Technical School (U)
Dakota County Technical College (U)
Dakota State University (U)
Dallas Baptist University (U)
Dallas County Community College District (U)
Danville Community College (U)
Darton College (U)
Davis College (U)
Delta College (U)
Des Moines Area Community College (U)
DeVry University Online (U,G)
Dodge City Community College (U)
Drury University (U)
East Arkansas Community College (U)
East Central Community College (U)
Eastern Michigan University (U,G)
East Los Angeles College (U)
Edison State Community College (U)
Edmonds Community College (U)
Elgin Community College (U)
Erie Community College (U)
Eugene Bible College (U)
Everett Community College (U)
Feather River College (U)
Florida Gulf Coast University (U)
Fontbonne University (U)
Fort Valley State University (U)
Frostburg State University (U)
Gadsden State Community College (U)
Georgia Institute of Technology (N,G)
Georgia Southern University (U)
Golden West College (U)
Granite State College (U)
Grantham University (U)
Greenfield Community College (U)
Gulf Coast Community College (U)
Halifax Community College (U)
Hamline University (G)
Harford Community College (U)
Haywood Community College (U)
Heart of Georgia Technical College (U)
Houston Community College System (U)
Howard College (U)
Illinois Eastern Community Colleges, Lincoln Trail College (U)
Illinois Eastern Community Colleges, Olney Central College (U)
Illinois Eastern Community Colleges, Wabash Valley College (U)
Indiana State University (U)
Indiana University of Pennsylvania (U)
Indiana University–Purdue University Fort Wayne (U)
Indiana Wesleyan University (U)
Iowa Western Community College (U)
Itawamba Community College (U)
Ivy Tech Community College–Bloomington (U)
Ivy Tech Community College–Central Indiana (U)
Ivy Tech Community College–Columbus (U)
Ivy Tech Community College–East Central (U)
Ivy Tech Community College–Northwest (U)
Ivy Tech Community College–Southern Indiana (U)
Ivy Tech Community College–Southwest (U)
Ivy Tech Community College–Wabash Valley (U)
Ivy Tech Community College–Whitewater (U)
Jackson Community College (U)
Jacksonville State University (U)
James Sprunt Community College (U)
John A. Logan College (U)
Johnson County Community College (U)
John Tyler Community College (U)
Jones College (N,U)
J. Sargeant Reynolds Community College (U)
Judson College (U)
Kean University (N,U)
Lake Superior College (U)
Lamar State College–Port Arthur (U)
Lamar University (U)
Lansing Community College (U)
Lawrence Technological University (U)
Lehigh Carbon Community College (U)
Lewis and Clark Community College (U)
Limestone College (U)
Linn-Benton Community College (N,U)
Louisiana State University and Agricultural and Mechanical College (N,U)
Louisiana Tech University (U)
Macon State College (U)
Mansfield University of Pennsylvania (U)
Marion Technical College (U)
Marshall University (U)
Marylhurst University (N)
Massasoit Community College (U)
Memorial University of Newfoundland (U)
Mercer County Community College (U)
Mesalands Community College (U)
Mesa State College (U)
Metropolitan State University (U)
Miami Dade College (U)
Middlesex Community College (U)
Middle Tennessee State University (U,G)
Midway College (U)
Minnesota School of Business–Richfield (U)
Mississippi State University (U)
Moberly Area Community College (U)
Mohawk Valley Community College (U)
Monroe Community College (U)
Montana State University (G)
Montana State University–Billings (U)
Montana Tech of The University of Montana (U)
Motlow State Community College (U)
Mountain Empire Community College (U)
Mount Saint Vincent University (N,U)
Mount Wachusett Community College (U)
Myers University (U)
Nassau Community College (N,U)
New England Institute of Technology (U)
New Jersey City University (U)
New Mexico Institute of Mining and Technology (G)
New Mexico Junior College (U)
New Mexico State University–Carlsbad (U)
North Arkansas College (U)
North Carolina State University (U)
North Central Texas College (U)
North Dakota State College of Science (U)
North Dakota State University (U)
Northeast State Technical Community College (U)
North Idaho College (U)
North Lake College (U)
North Seattle Community College (U)
Northwestern College (U)
Northwestern State University of Louisiana (U)
Northwest Missouri State University (U)

Odessa College (U)
Oral Roberts University (U)
Oregon Institute of Technology (U)
Ouachita Technical College (U)
Oxnard College (U)
Ozarks Technical Community College (U)
Pace University (U)
Pacific Union College (U)
Park University (U)
Patrick Henry Community College (U)
Peninsula College (U)
Pennsylvania College of Technology (U)
The Pennsylvania State University University Park Campus (U)
Portland Community College (U)
Pueblo Community College (U)
Pulaski Technical College (U)
Purdue University Calumet (G)
Rappahannock Community College (U)
Raritan Valley Community College (U)
Rasmussen College Eden Prarie (U)
Reading Area Community College (U)
Red Rocks Community College (U)
Regent University (U)
Rend Lake College (U)
Rio Hondo College (U)
Sacramento City College (U)
Sacred Heart University (G)
St. Clair County Community College (U)
St. Cloud State University (U)
St. John's University (U)
Saint Joseph's University (U)
Saint Leo University (U)
St. Louis Community College System (U)
Saint Mary-of-the-Woods College (U)
St. Petersburg College (U)
Schenectady County Community College (U)
Schiller International University (U)
Schoolcraft College (U)
Seattle Pacific University (G)
Seminole Community College (U)
Shippensburg University of Pennsylvania (U)
Shoreline Community College (U)
Sinclair Community College (U)
Snow College (U)
Southeast Arkansas College (U)
Southeast Community College, Beatrice Campus (N,U)
Southeast Community College, Lincoln Campus (N,U)
Southeast Community College, Milford Campus (N,U)
Southern Arkansas University Tech (U)
Southern Illinois University Carbondale (U)
Southern University at Shreveport (U)
South Plains College (U)
Southwest Georgia Technical College (U)
Southwest Wisconsin Technical College (U)
Spartanburg Technical College (U)
Stanly Community College (U)
State University of New York College of Agriculture and Technology at Morrisville (U)
Stephens College (U)
Strayer University (U,G)
Tacoma Community College (U)
Taft College (U)
Taylor University (N,U)
Texas A&M University–Commerce (U)
Texas A&M University–Texarkana (U)
Texas State Technical College Waco (U)
Texas State University-San Marcos (U,G)
Texas Tech University (G)
Three Rivers Community College (U)
Tompkins Cortland Community College (U)
The University of Akron (U,G)
The University of Alabama (U)
University of Alaska Fairbanks (U)
University of California, Berkeley (U)
University of California, Los Angeles (G)
University of Central Arkansas (U)
University of Colorado at Colorado Springs (U)
The University of Findlay (U)
University of Florida (U)
University of Great Falls (U)
University of Houston–Victoria (U,G)
University of Illinois at Springfield (U)
University of Illinois at Urbana–Champaign (G)
The University of Iowa (U,G)
The University of Maine at Augusta (U)
University of Maryland University College (U)
University of Massachusetts Boston (U)
University of Michigan–Flint (U)
University of Minnesota, Crookston (U)
University of Minnesota, Morris (U)
University of Minnesota, Twin Cities Campus (U)
University of Missouri–Columbia (U)
The University of Montana (U,G)
University of Nebraska–Lincoln (U)
University of Nevada, Reno (U)
University of New Orleans (U,G)
University of North Dakota (N,U)
University of Northern Colorado (U)
University of Northern Iowa (U)
University of North Texas (U)
University of Oklahoma (U)
University of Pittsburgh (U)
University of Saskatchewan (U)
University of South Florida (U)
The University of Tennessee (N,U)
The University of Texas at Tyler (U)
The University of Texas of the Permian Basin (U)
The University of Texas System (U)
The University of Toledo (U)
University of Utah (U)
University of Washington (U)
University of Waterloo (U)
University of West Florida (U)
University of Wisconsin Colleges (U)
University of Wisconsin–Platteville (U,G)
University of Wyoming (U)
Upper Iowa University (U)
Utah State University (U)
Utah Valley State College (U)
Utica College (U)
Vincennes University (U)
Virginia Polytechnic Institute and State University (U,G)
Wake Technical Community College (U)
Washtenaw Community College (U)
Waukesha County Technical College (U)
Wayne State College (U,G)
Weber State University (U)
Westchester Community College (U)
Western Washington University (U)
West Los Angeles College (U)
West Shore Community College (U)
West Virginia University at Parkersburg (U)
Whatcom Community College (U)
Wilkes Community College (U)
Wright State University (U)
York County Community College (U)
York Technical College (U)
York University (U)

MATHEMATICS AND COMPUTER SCIENCE

Alvin Community College (U)
Athabasca University (N,U,G)
Austin Peay State University (U)
Caldwell College (U)
Campbell University (U)
Chadron State College (U,G)
Champlain College (U)
Chesapeake College (U)
Cleveland Institute of Electronics (N)
Columbia College (U)
Concordia University, St. Paul (N)
Cowley County Community College and Area Vocational–Technical School (U)
Dallas County Community College District (U)
Danville Community College (U)
Darton College (U)
Drake University (U)
Edison State Community College (U)
Fort Hays State University (U)
Franklin University (U)
Grantham University (U)
Haywood Community College (U)
Indiana State University (U)
Iowa State University of Science and Technology (U)
Itawamba Community College (U)
Jacksonville State University (U,G)
James Madison University (N)
Marshall University (U)
Middlesex Community College (U)
Peninsula College (U)
Seminole Community College (U)
Southeast Arkansas College (U)
Taylor University (N)
Texas State University-San Marcos (U)
Touro University International (U)
The University of Akron (U,G)
University of Alaska Fairbanks (U)
University of Massachusetts Lowell (U)
University of New Orleans (U,G)
University of South Florida (U)
University of Wisconsin Colleges (U)
University of Wisconsin–Superior (U)
Westchester Community College (U)
Yuba College (U)

MATHEMATICS AND STATISTICS RELATED

Alvin Community College (U)
Anne Arundel Community College (U)
Bellevue Community College (U)
Berkeley College (U)
Berkeley College-New York City Campus (U)
Berkeley College-Westchester Campus (U)
Blinn College (U)
Blue Ridge Community College (U)
Brenau University (U)
Brigham Young University (U)
Butler Community College (U)
Cape Fear Community College (U)
Central Piedmont Community College (U)
Central Texas College (U)
Chadron State College (U,G)
Charter Oak State College (U)

Chattanooga State Technical Community College (U)
Clark College (U)
Clovis Community College (U)
College of Southern Maryland (U)
College of The Albemarle (U)
Colorado Mountain College District System (U)
Columbia Basin College (U)
Copiah-Lincoln Community College (U)
Cowley County Community College and Area Vocational–Technical School (U)
Dakota County Technical College (U)
Dallas Baptist University (U)
Dallas County Community College District (U)
Darton College (U)
De Anza College (U)
Delta College (U)
Des Moines Area Community College (U)
East Arkansas Community College (U)
Eastern Michigan University (G)
Eastern Oklahoma State College (U)
Embry-Riddle Aeronautical University (U)
Georgia Highlands College (U)
Grantham University (U)
Housatonic Community College (U)
Houston Community College System (U)
Illinois Eastern Community Colleges, Wabash Valley College (U)
Indiana State University (U)
Iowa Western Community College (U)
Itawamba Community College (U)
Jacksonville State University (U)
Jefferson Community College (U)
Jones College (U)
Kettering University (N)
Lansing Community College (U)
Lenoir Community College (U)
Louisiana State University and Agricultural and Mechanical College (U)
Madison Area Technical College (U)
Marshall University (U)
Marylhurst University (U)
Mercy College (U)
Middlesex Community College (U)
Midland College (U)
Mid Michigan Community College (U)
Missouri State University (U)
Montana State University (G)
Mount Allison University (U)
Mount Wachusett Community College (U)
Murray State University (U)
Nassau Community College (U)
Neumann College (U)
New England College of Finance (U)
New Mexico Junior College (U)
Northern Virginia Community College (U)
Northwestern Michigan College (U)
Oklahoma State University (U)
Oregon State University (U)
Pace University (U)
Parkland College (U)
Passaic County Community College (U)
The Pennsylvania State University University Park Campus (U)
Piedmont Technical College (U)
Portland Community College (U)
Portland State University (U)
Raritan Valley Community College (U)
Rasmussen College Eden Prarie (U)
Sam Houston State University (U)
San Bernardino Valley College (U)
San Joaquin Delta College (U)
Seattle Central Community College (U)
Seminole Community College (U)
Southeast Arkansas College (U)
Southern Illinois University Carbondale (U)
South Piedmont Community College (U)
Southwestern Community College (U)
Southwest Virginia Community College (U)
State University of New York Empire State College (U)
Taft College (U)
Texas Tech University (U)
Treasure Valley Community College (U)
Tyler Junior College (U)
The University of Akron (G)
University of Alaska Fairbanks (U)
University of Arkansas (U)
University of Bridgeport (U)
University of California, Berkeley (U,G)
University of Colorado at Denver and Health Sciences Center—Downtown Denver Campus (U)
University of Delaware (U)
University of Florida (U)
University of Great Falls (U)
University of Houston–Victoria (G)
University of Missouri–Columbia (U)
University of Nebraska–Lincoln (N,U)
University of New Orleans (U,G)
The University of North Carolina at Chapel Hill (U)
The University of North Carolina at Greensboro (U)
University of Southern Mississippi (U)
The University of Texas System (U)
University of Utah (U)
University of Washington (U)
University of Waterloo (N,U)
University of West Florida (U)
Utah State University (U)
West Shore Community College (U)
West Virginia Northern Community College (U)
York University (N)

MECHANIC AND REPAIR TECHNOLOGIES RELATED

Arkansas Tech University (U)
Cleveland Institute of Electronics (N)
Oxnard College (U)

MECHANICAL ENGINEERING

Arizona State University (G)
Arizona State University at the Polytechnic Campus (G)
California National University for Advanced Studies (U,G)
Cleveland State University (G)
Colorado State University (G)
Columbia University (N,G)
Connecticut State University System (U,G)
Florida Atlantic University (U,G)
Frostburg State University (U)
Georgia Institute of Technology (N,G)
Illinois Institute of Technology (U,G)
Kansas State University (G)
Kettering University (N)
Louisiana State University and Agricultural and Mechanical College (U)
New Mexico Institute of Mining and Technology (G)
New Mexico State University (G)
New York Institute of Technology (U)
Northern Virginia Community College (U)
The Ohio State University (G)
Old Dominion University (G)
Rochester Institute of Technology (U)
Southern Methodist University (G)
Texas Tech University (G)
University of Colorado at Boulder (N,G)
University of Colorado at Colorado Springs (U,G)
University of Colorado at Denver and Health Sciences Center—Downtown Denver Campus (U)
University of Delaware (N,U,G)
University of Illinois at Urbana–Champaign (N,G)
University of Maine (U,G)
University of Maryland, College Park (G)
University of Massachusetts Amherst (G)
University of Michigan (N)
University of Michigan–Dearborn (G)
University of New Hampshire (G)
University of New Orleans (U,G)
The University of North Carolina at Charlotte (N)
University of North Dakota (U)
University of South Florida (G)
The University of Texas at Arlington (G)
University of Washington (U,G)
University of Wisconsin–Madison (U,G)
University of Wisconsin–Platteville (G)
Virginia Polytechnic Institute and State University (G)
Western Nevada Community College (U)

MECHANICAL ENGINEERING RELATED TECHNOLOGIES

Blackhawk Technical College (U)
Boston University (G)
Cincinnati State Technical and Community College (U)
Cleveland Institute of Electronics (N)
Cleveland State University (G)
Columbus State Community College (U)
Indiana State University (U)
Kansas State University (G)
Southern Methodist University (G)
University of Michigan (N)

MECHANICS AND REPAIR

Cleveland Institute of Electronics (N)

MEDICAL BASIC SCIENCES

Athabasca University (N)
Bellingham Technical College (U)
Daymar College (U)
Indiana Business College (N,U)
Jacksonville State University (U,G)
Minot State University–Bottineau Campus (U)
Montgomery Community College (U)
Randolph Community College (N)
Triton College (N)
The University of Akron (U)
University of Florida (N)
Waukesha County Technical College (U)

MEDICAL CLINICAL SCIENCES/ GRADUATE MEDICAL STUDIES

Daemen College (G)
D'Youville College (G)

University of Illinois at Chicago (N)

MEDICAL ILLUSTRATION AND INFORMATICS

Nova Southeastern University (G)

MEDIEVAL AND RENAISSANCE STUDIES

Adams State College (U)
Arizona State University (U,G)
Bellevue Community College (U)
Elizabethtown College (U)
Seattle Central Community College (U)
Taylor University (U)
The University of British Columbia (U)
University of Nebraska–Lincoln (U)
University of New Orleans (U,G)
University of Waterloo (U)
Western Michigan University (U)
Western Washington University (U)

MENTAL AND SOCIAL HEALTH SERVICES AND ALLIED PROFESSIONS

Athabasca University (N,U,G)
Central Texas College (U)
Central Wyoming College (N)
College of The Albemarle (N)
Columbus State Community College (U)
Fort Valley State University (G)
Madonna University (U)
Missouri State University (N)
Mount Wachusett Community College (U)
The Ohio State University (N)
The Pennsylvania State University University Park Campus (G)
Sullivan University (G)
Tompkins Cortland Community College (U)
The University of Maine at Augusta (U)
University of Missouri–Columbia (U,G)

METALLURGICAL ENGINEERING

Delta College (U)
The University of British Columbia (U)

MICROBIOLOGICAL SCIENCES AND IMMUNOLOGY

Acadia University (U)
Arkansas State University–Beebe (U)
Brigham Young University (U)
Central New Mexico Community College (U)
Community College of Denver (U)
Delta College (U)
Gateway Community College (U)
Honolulu Community College (U)
Illinois Institute of Technology (G)
Immaculata University (U)
The Johns Hopkins University (U)
Montana State University (G)
North Dakota State College of Science (U)
Oxnard College (U)
Rend Lake College (U)
St. Petersburg College (U)
The University of Akron (U)
University of Arkansas (U)
University of Minnesota, Crookston (U)
University of New Brunswick Fredericton (U)
University of Southern Mississippi (U)
University of Waterloo (U)
University of Wisconsin–La Crosse (G)
Weber State University (U)
West Virginia Northern Community College (U)
Winston-Salem State University (U)

MILITARY STUDIES

American Military University (U,G)
American Public University (U,G)
Central Texas College (U)
Eastern Michigan University (U)
Louisiana State University and Agricultural and Mechanical College (U)
Myers University (U)
North Georgia College & State University (N,U)
University of Colorado at Colorado Springs (U)
Washburn University (U)

MILITARY TECHNOLOGIES

American Military University (U,G)
American Public University (U,G)
Fort Valley State University (U)

MISSIONARY STUDIES AND MISSIOLOGY

Assemblies of God Theological Seminary (G)
Baptist Bible College of Pennsylvania (G)
Barclay College (U)
Bethany University (U)
Briercrest Distance Learning (U)
Columbia International University (N,U,G)
Covenant Theological Seminary (N,G)
Crown College (U,G)
Dallas Baptist University (U)
Eugene Bible College (U)
Master's College and Seminary (U)
Northwestern College (U)
Providence College and Theological Seminary (N,G)
Regions University (N,U,G)
Southwestern Assemblies of God University (U,G)
Taylor University (U)
Temple Baptist Seminary (N,G)
Trinity Episcopal School for Ministry (N,G)

MOVEMENT AND MIND-BODY THERAPIES

Atlantic University (N,G)
Prescott College (G)

MULTI-/INTERDISCIPLINARY STUDIES RELATED

Acadia University (U)
Berkeley College (U)
Berkeley College-New York City Campus (U)
Berkeley College-Westchester Campus (U)
California State University, San Bernardino (U)
Central Michigan University (U,G)
Central Texas College (U)
Columbia College (U)
Davis College (U)
Fort Hays State University (U,G)
Glenville State College (U)
Granite State College (U)
Marylhurst University (G)
Metropolitan State University (U)
Mississippi State University (U)
Naropa University (U,G)
North Carolina State University (U)
Roosevelt University (U)
Saint Joseph's College of Maine (U)
Southwestern Assemblies of God University (U)
Taylor University (U)
University of Connecticut (U)
University of Florida (U)
University of Houston–Victoria (G)
University of Minnesota, Morris (U)
University of Oregon (U)
University of Waterloo (U)
Wayne State College (U,G)

MUSEUM STUDIES

Brenau University (U)
Feather River College (N)
Florida State University (G)
Harvard University (N,U,G)
James Madison University (N)
University of La Verne (N)

MUSIC

Arkansas State University–Beebe (U)
Arkansas Tech University (U)
Athabasca University (N,U)
Bellevue Community College (U)
Berklee College of Music (N,U)
Boise State University (U)
Bowling Green State University (U)
Brenau University (U)
Bridgewater State College (U)
Brigham Young University (U)
Butler Community College (U)
Butler County Community College (U)
Caldwell College (U)
Caldwell Community College and Technical Institute (U)
California State University, Dominguez Hills (N)
California University of Pennsylvania (U)
Cape Fear Community College (U)
Carl Sandburg College (U)
Casper College (U)
Central Lakes College (U)
Central Virginia Community College (U)
Central Wyoming College (N,U)
Chattanooga State Technical Community College (U)
Clackamas Community College (U)
Clarion University of Pennsylvania (U)
Clark College (U)
Clemson University (U)
Cleveland Institute of Music (N,U,G)
Cleveland State Community College (U)
Clinton Community College (U)
Coconino Community College (N)
Coffeyville Community College (U)
College of DuPage (U)
The College of St. Scholastica (U,G)
Colorado State University (U)
Dakota State University (U)
Dallas County Community College District (U)
Danville Community College (U)

Darton College (U)
De Anza College (U)
Des Moines Area Community College (U)
Dodge City Community College (U)
Drake University (G)
Drury University (U)
Duquesne University (G)
East Central Community College (U)
Eastern Oregon University (U)
Eastern West Virginia Community and Technical College (U)
Elgin Community College (U)
Erie Community College (U)
Eugene Bible College (U)
Everett Community College (U)
Evergreen Valley College (U)
Feather River College (N)
Fort Hays State University (U)
Frostburg State University (U)
Gadsden State Community College (U)
Gulf Coast Community College (U)
Indiana State University (U)
Indiana Wesleyan University (U)
Itawamba Community College (U)
Jacksonville State University (U)
James Madison University (N)
Judson College (U)
Kansas State University (U)
Lansing Community College (U)
Lehigh Carbon Community College (U)
Lewis and Clark Community College (U)
Limestone College (U)
Lock Haven University of Pennsylvania (U)
Louisiana State University and Agricultural and Mechanical College (U)
Marylhurst University (U)
Massasoit Community College (U)
Mesalands Community College (U)
Metropolitan State University (U)
Midland College (U)
Millersville University of Pennsylvania (U)
Missouri State University (U)
Mountain Empire Community College (U)
Murray State University (U)
Nassau Community College (U)
Naugatuck Valley Community College (U)
North Carolina State University (U)
Northeast State Technical Community College (U)
North Seattle Community College (U)
Northwestern Michigan College (U)
Northwest Missouri State University (U)
Oklahoma State University (U)
Orange Coast College (U)
Oxnard College (U)
Ozarks Technical Community College (U)
Pacific Union College (U)
Palomar College (U)
Parkland College (U)
Patrick Henry College (U)
Peninsula College (U)
The Pennsylvania State University University Park Campus (U)
Piedmont Technical College (U)
Plymouth State University (U)
Portland Community College (U)
Pueblo Community College (U)
Randolph Community College (U)
Red Rocks Community College (U)
Rend Lake College (U)
Sacred Heart University (U)
Saddleback College (U)
Saint Mary-of-the-Woods College (G)
St. Petersburg College (U)
Schenectady County Community College (U)
Schoolcraft College (U)
Seminole Community College (U)
Shippensburg University of Pennsylvania (U)
Shoreline Community College (U)
Solano Community College (U)
Southern Illinois University Carbondale (U)
Southwestern Assemblies of God University (U)
Southwestern Community College (U)
State University of New York College at Potsdam (U)
Stephen F. Austin State University (U,G)
Tacoma Community College (U)
Taylor University (U)
Texas State University-San Marcos (U)
Texas Tech University (U,G)
Treasure Valley Community College (U)
Triton College (U)
Tunxis Community College (U)
Tyler Junior College (U)
The University of Akron (U)
University of Alaska Fairbanks (U)
University of Bridgeport (U)
The University of British Columbia (U)
University of Colorado at Denver and Health Sciences Center—Downtown Denver Campus (U)
University of Delaware (U)
University of La Verne (N,U)
University of Maine (U)
The University of Maine at Augusta (U)
University of Maine at Fort Kent (U)
University of Massachusetts Boston (U)
University of Minnesota, Twin Cities Campus (U)
University of Nevada, Reno (U)
University of New Orleans (U,G)
The University of North Carolina at Chapel Hill (N,U)
The University of North Carolina at Greensboro (G)
University of Northern Iowa (U)
University of North Texas (U)
University of Pittsburgh (U)
University of Saskatchewan (U)
University of Southern Mississippi (U,G)
University of South Florida (U,G)
The University of Texas System (U)
The University of Toledo (U)
University of Utah (U)
University of Wisconsin Colleges (U)
University of Wisconsin–Platteville (U)
University of Wyoming (U)
Virginia Polytechnic Institute and State University (N,U)
Washburn University (U)
Wayland Baptist University (U)
Weber State University (U)
Western Michigan University (U)
Western Washington University (U)
Whatcom Community College (U)
Wichita State University (U)
Winston-Salem State University (U)
Wright State University (U)
Yuba College (U)

NATURAL RESOURCES AND CONSERVATION RELATED

Drury University (U)
James Madison University (N)
Kansas State University (U)
Oregon State University (U)
Prescott College (G)
Saint Mary-of-the-Woods College (G)
University of Florida (U,G)
University of La Verne (N)
University of Massachusetts Amherst (U)
University of Massachusetts Boston (N,U)
University of New Orleans (U,G)
University of Wisconsin–River Falls (G)

NATURAL RESOURCES CONSERVATION AND RESEARCH

Ashworth College (N)
Athabasca University (U)
Colorado State University (U)
Erie Community College (U)
Kansas State University (U)
Lansing Community College (U)
Oregon State University (U,G)
Prescott College (U)
University of La Verne (N)
University of Massachusetts Amherst (U)
Virginia Polytechnic Institute and State University (N)

NATURAL RESOURCES MANAGEMENT AND POLICY

Athabasca University (U)
Colorado State University (G)
Humboldt State University (N,U)
Kansas State University (U)
Oregon State University (U,G)
Prescott College (G)
Sullivan University (G)
University of Denver (G)
University of Florida (U,G)
University of Wisconsin–River Falls (G)
Virginia Polytechnic Institute and State University (G)

NATURAL SCIENCES

Bellevue Community College (U)
Cape Cod Community College (U)
Cape Fear Community College (U)
Columbus State Community College (U)
Cowley County Community College and Area Vocational–Technical School (U)
Dakota County Technical College (U)
Dallas Baptist University (U)
Danville Community College (U)
Des Moines Area Community College (U)
D'Youville College (U)
Itawamba Community College (U)
Kansas State University (U)
Marylhurst University (U)
New Mexico State University–Carlsbad (U)
Palomar College (U)
Peninsula College (U)
Regent University (U)
University of Great Falls (U)
University of Houston–Victoria (U,G)
University of South Florida (U)
Wayne State College (U)

NAVAL ARCHITECTURE AND MARINE ENGINEERING

University of New Orleans (U,G)

NUCLEAR AND INDUSTRIAL RADIOLOGIC TECHNOLOGIES

Bismarck State College (N,U)
Galveston College (U)
Oregon State University (G)

NUCLEAR ENGINEERING

Bismarck State College (N)
The Ohio State University (G)
University of Missouri–Columbia (U,G)

NURSING

Alcorn State University (U)
Arkansas Tech University (U)
Athabasca University (N,U,G)
Auburn University Montgomery (U)
Azusa Pacific University (G)
Blackhawk Technical College (U)
Blinn College (U)
Bloomfield College (U)
Bloomsburg University of Pennsylvania (U)
Boise State University (U)
Bowling Green State University (U)
Bradley University (U,G)
Brenau University (U,G)
Brigham Young University (U)
Butler Community College (U)
California State University, Chico (U)
California State University, Dominguez Hills (U,G)
California State University, San Bernardino (U)
California State University, San Marcos (N)
Cape Cod Community College (U)
Carlow University (U,G)
Central Lakes College (U)
Central Missouri State University (G)
Central New Mexico Community College (U)
Central Texas College (U)
Central Wyoming College (U)
Charter Oak State College (N)
Chesapeake College (U)
Clarion University of Pennsylvania (U,G)
Clark State Community College (U)
Cleveland State University (U,G)
The College of St. Scholastica (U,G)
College of Southern Maryland (N)
College of the Siskiyous (U)
Colorado State University-Pueblo (U)
Columbus State Community College (U)
Community College of Beaver County (U)
Community College of Denver (U)
Community College of Southern Nevada (U)
Concordia University Wisconsin (U,G)
Connecticut State University System (U)
Contra Costa College (U)
Culver-Stockton College (U)
Daemen College (U,G)
Danville Community College (U)
Des Moines Area Community College (U)
Drexel University (U,G)
Duquesne University (G)
D'Youville College (G)
East Carolina University (U,G)
East Central Community College (U)
Eastern Michigan University (U,G)
Eastern Oklahoma State College (U)
Edison State Community College (U)
Erie Community College (U)
Fayetteville State University (U)
Finger Lakes Community College (U)
Florida Atlantic University (U)
Florida Gulf Coast University (U)
Fort Hays State University (U,G)
Gadsden State Community College (U)
George Mason University (G)
Georgia College & State University (G)
Georgia Southern University (U,G)
Glenville State College (U)
Gulf Coast Community College (U)
Howard College (U)
Indiana State University (U,G)
Indiana University–Purdue University Fort Wayne (U,G)
Itawamba Community College (U)
Ivy Tech Community College–Northwest (U)
Jackson Community College (U)
Jacksonville State University (U,G)
James Madison University (N)
Jefferson College of Health Sciences (N,U,G)
John Tyler Community College (U)
J. Sargeant Reynolds Community College (U)
Los Angeles Harbor College (U)
Madonna University (U,G)
Mansfield University of Pennsylvania (U)
Marshall University (U)
Memorial University of Newfoundland (U,G)
Mercy College (U)
Mesa State College (U)
Metropolitan State University (U,G)
MGH Institute of Health Professions (G)
Miami Dade College (U)
Middle Tennessee State University (N,U,G)
Millersville University of Pennsylvania (U,G)
Missouri State University (U,G)
Mohawk Valley Community College (U)
Monmouth University (U,G)
Montana Tech of The University of Montana (U)
Mount Wachusett Community College (U)
Murray State University (U,G)
National University (U)
Naugatuck Valley Community College (U)
New Mexico State University–Carlsbad (U)
North Arkansas College (U)
North Georgia College & State University (U,G)
Northwestern Michigan College (U)
Northwestern State University of Louisiana (U)
The Ohio State University (G)
Old Dominion University (U,G)
Ozarka College (U)
Pace University (N,U,G)
Pacific Union College (U)
Peninsula College (U)
Pennsylvania College of Technology (U)
Portland Community College (U)
Pueblo Community College (U)
Purdue University Calumet (U,G)
Radford University (N,G)
Raritan Valley Community College (U)
Rend Lake College (U)
The Richard Stockton College of New Jersey (U,G)
Ryerson University (U)
Sacred Heart University (G)
Saddleback College (U)
St. Clair County Community College (U)
Saint Francis Medical Center College of Nursing (U,G)
Saint Joseph's College of Maine (U,G)
San Joaquin Delta College (U)
Shawnee State University (U)
Snow College (U)
Solano Community College (U)
South Central College (U)
Southeast Arkansas College (U)
Southern Illinois University Edwardsville (U,G)
Southwestern College (U)
Southwest Wisconsin Technical College (U)
Stanly Community College (U)
State University of New York at Plattsburgh (U)
Sullivan University (G)
Tacoma Community College (U)
Texas Woman's University (U,G)
Tompkins Cortland Community College (U)
Triton College (U)
The University of Akron (N,U,G)
The University of Alabama (G)
The University of British Columbia (U)
University of Calgary (U)
University of California, Riverside (N)
University of Central Arkansas (G)
University of Central Florida (U,G)
University of Colorado at Colorado Springs (U,G)
University of Delaware (N,U,G)
University of Illinois at Chicago (N,G)
The University of Iowa (U,G)
University of Maine (U)
The University of Maine at Augusta (U)
University of Maine at Fort Kent (U)
University of Maryland (U,G)
University of Massachusetts Amherst (G)
University of Massachusetts Boston (U,G)
University of Michigan–Flint (U)
University of Minnesota, Twin Cities Campus (U)
University of Missouri–Columbia (U,G)
The University of Montana (U)
University of Nebraska–Lincoln (U)
University of Nebraska Medical Center (N,U,G)
University of New Brunswick Fredericton (U)
University of North Alabama (U)
The University of North Carolina at Chapel Hill (N)
The University of North Carolina at Charlotte (N,U,G)
University of North Dakota (U)
University of Northern Colorado (U)
University of North Florida (U)
University of Phoenix Online Campus (G)
University of Pittsburgh at Bradford (U)
University of Pittsburgh at Johnstown (G)
University of St. Francis (U,G)
University of Saskatchewan (U)
University of South Alabama (G)
University of South Carolina Sumter (G)
University of Southern Indiana (N,U,G)
University of Southern Mississippi (U,G)
University of South Florida (U,G)
The University of Texas at Tyler (U,G)
The University of Texas System (G)
University of Wisconsin–Madison (U)
University of Wyoming (U,G)
Valparaiso University (U)
Viterbo University (U,G)
Washburn University (U)
Washtenaw Community College (U)
Waukesha County Technical College (U)
Western Nevada Community College (U)
Western Piedmont Community College (U)

Western University of Health Sciences (N,G)
West Virginia University (N)
West Virginia University at Parkersburg (U)
William Rainey Harper College (U)
Wisconsin Indianhead Technical College (N,U)
Wright State University (U,G)
York Technical College (U)
York University (U)

NUTRITION SCIENCES

Acadia University (U)
American Health Sciences University (N,U)
Arizona State University at the Polytechnic Campus (U)
Bellevue Community College (U)
Brazosport College (U)
Butler Community College (U)
Central Michigan University (G)
Clemson University (U,G)
Columbus State Community College (U)
Community College of Beaver County (U)
Corning Community College (U)
Cowley County Community College and Area Vocational–Technical School (U)
Danville Community College (U)
D'Youville College (G)
East Carolina University (G)
Eastern Michigan University (U)
Erie Community College (U)
Everett Community College (U)
Illinois Eastern Community Colleges, Frontier Community College (U)
Itawamba Community College (U)
Jacksonville State University (U)
Kansas State University (U)
Lamar University (U)
Marylhurst University (U)
Mount Saint Vincent University (U)
North Carolina State University (U)
North Central Texas College (U)
Palomar College (U)
Peninsula College (U)
Pueblo Community College (U)
Queen's University at Kingston (U)
Rend Lake College (U)
Sam Houston State University (U)
Schenectady County Community College (U)
Seminole Community College (U)
Shoreline Community College (U)
State University of New York at Buffalo (U)
Texas Woman's University (U,G)
Treasure Valley Community College (U)
University of Alaska Fairbanks (U)
University of California, Berkeley (U)
University of Florida (N,U)
University of Massachusetts Amherst (N)
University of Massachusetts Boston (U)
University of Medicine and Dentistry of New Jersey (U,G)
University of North Texas (U)
University of South Florida (U)
The University of Toledo (U)
University of Wisconsin–Madison (U)

OCEAN ENGINEERING

Florida Atlantic University (U,G)
Utah Valley State College (U)

OPERATIONS RESEARCH

Boston University (G)
Philadelphia University (U)
Saybrook Graduate School and Research Center (G)
The University of Alabama in Huntsville (G)
University of Minnesota, Twin Cities Campus (U)

OPHTHALMIC AND OPTOMETRIC SUPPORT SERVICES AND ALLIED PROFESSIONS

Community College of Southern Nevada (U)
Ferris State University (G)
Hillsborough Community College (U)
Madison Area Technical College (U)

PARKS, RECREATION AND LEISURE

Clemson University (U)
The Community College of Baltimore County (U)
Kean University (N)
Madison Area Technical College (U)
Mesa State College (U)
Prescott College (U)
Seattle Pacific University (G)
United States Sports Academy (N)
University of Florida (U)
University of Missouri–Columbia (U)
The University of North Carolina at Chapel Hill (U)

PARKS, RECREATION AND LEISURE FACILITIES MANAGEMENT

Kean University (U)
North Carolina State University (U)
Prescott College (G)
United States Sports Academy (N)
University of Florida (U)
University of Wisconsin–La Crosse (G)
University of Wisconsin–River Falls (G)
Vincennes University (U)

PARKS, RECREATION, AND LEISURE RELATED

The Community College of Baltimore County (U)
James Madison University (N)
San Diego State University (U)
United States Sports Academy (N)
University of Florida (U)
University of La Verne (N)
University of Massachusetts Boston (N)
University of Southern Mississippi (G)
Western Washington University (U)

PASTORAL COUNSELING AND SPECIALIZED MINISTRIES

Assemblies of God Theological Seminary (G)
Bethany University (U)
Crown College (U)
Duquesne University (G)
Earlham School of Religion (G)
Eastern Mennonite University (G)
Gordon-Conwell Theological Seminary (N,G)
Hartford Seminary (G)
Maranatha Baptist Bible College (G)
Master's College and Seminary (U)
Moravian Theological Seminary (N,G)
Providence College and Theological Seminary (N,G)
Regent University (N,G)
Regions University (N,U,G)
Saint Joseph's College of Maine (N,U)
Southwestern Assemblies of God University (U)
Southwestern Baptist Theological Seminary (G)
Sullivan University (G)
Taylor University (U)
Temple Baptist Seminary (N,G)
Tennessee Temple University (U)

PEACE STUDIES AND CONFLICT RESOLUTION

Arizona State University (U)
Atlantic University (N,G)
Brenau University (U)
Caldwell Community College and Technical Institute (N)
California State University, Dominguez Hills (G)
Drake University (U,G)
Earlham School of Religion (G)
Eastern Mennonite University (G)
Massasoit Community College (N)
Mercy College (G)
Mount Saint Vincent University (U)
Naropa University (N,U)
Prescott College (G)
St. Edward's University (G)
Saybrook Graduate School and Research Center (G)
Sullivan University (G)
Taylor University (U)
University of Bridgeport (U)
University of Massachusetts Boston (G)
The University of North Carolina at Greensboro (G)
University of Waterloo (U)

PERSONAL AND CULINARY SERVICES RELATED

Gateway Community College (N)
Jackson Community College (N)
Kean University (N)
Linn-Benton Community College (N)
Pace University (N)
Pasco-Hernando Community College (N)
Texas State Technical College Waco (N)
University of Missouri–Columbia (N)
Vance-Granville Community College (N)

PERSONALITY PSYCHOLOGY

Des Moines Area Community College (U)
Indiana State University (U)
New England College of Finance (U)
Roosevelt University (U)
University of Alaska Fairbanks (U)
University of Minnesota, Twin Cities Campus (U)
University of New Orleans (U,G)
Yuba College (U)

PETROLEUM ENGINEERING

Texas Tech University (G)

PHARMACOLOGY AND TOXICOLOGY

Brenau University (U)
Cleveland State Community College (U)
Cowley County Community College and Area Vocational–Technical School (U)
Northwestern Michigan College (U)
Peninsula College (U)
Queen's University at Kingston (U)
University of Maryland Eastern Shore (G)

PHARMACY, PHARMACEUTICAL SCIENCES, AND ADMINISTRATION

Auburn University (G)
Broome Community College (U)
Charter Oak State College (N)
Cleveland State University (U)
Creighton University (G)
Drake University (U,G)
Oregon State University (N)
Portland Community College (N)
Randolph Community College (N)
St. John's University (U)
Shoreline Community College (U)
The University of Akron (U)
University of Illinois at Chicago (N,G)
The University of North Carolina at Greensboro (N)
University of Washington (U)
University of Wisconsin–Madison (G)
Vincennes University (U)
Waukesha County Technical College (U)

PHILOSOPHY

Acadia University (U)
Adirondack Community College (U)
Alpena Community College (U)
American Military University (U)
American Public University (U)
Anne Arundel Community College (U)
Arkansas State University–Beebe (U)
Athabasca University (N,U,G)
Bellevue Community College (U)
Bergen Community College (U)
Berkeley College (U)
Berkeley College-New York City Campus (U)
Berkeley College-Westchester Campus (U)
Bismarck State College (U)
Blinn College (U)
Boise State University (U)
Bowling Green State University (U)
Brenau University (U)
Brigham Young University (U)
Butler Community College (U)
Butler County Community College (U)
California State University, San Marcos (N)
California University of Pennsylvania (U)
Cape Fear Community College (U)
Carlow University (U)
Central Lakes College (U)
Central New Mexico Community College (U)
Central Texas College (U)
Central Virginia Community College (U)
Chadron State College (U)
Chattanooga State Technical Community College (U)
Citrus College (U)
Clarion University of Pennsylvania (U)
Cleveland State University (U,G)
Coconino Community College (U)
Coleman College (U)
College of San Mateo (U)
College of Southern Maryland (U)
College of the Humanities and Sciences, Harrison Middleton University (U)
Colorado Mountain College District System (U)
Columbus State Community College (U)
Community College of Beaver County (U)
Community College of Denver (U)
Community College of Southern Nevada (U)
Connecticut State University System (U)
Contra Costa College (U)
Corning Community College (U)
Cowley County Community College and Area Vocational–Technical School (U)
Dallas Baptist University (U)
Dallas County Community College District (U)
Darton College (U)
Delta College (U)
Des Moines Area Community College (U)
Duquesne University (U)
East Carolina University (U)
Eastern Mennonite University (G)
Eastern Michigan University (U)
Eastern Oregon University (U)
East Los Angeles College (U)
Edison State Community College (U)
Erie Community College (U)
Everett Community College (U)
Feather River College (N)
Finger Lakes Community College (U)
Florida Atlantic University (U)
Fontbonne University (U)
Fort Hays State University (U)
Franciscan University of Steubenville (N,U)
Gadsden State Community College (U)
Gateway Community College (U)
Golden West College (U)
Granite State College (U)
Harvard University (N,U,G)
Honolulu Community College (U)
Houston Community College System (U)
Indiana University–Purdue University Fort Wayne (U)
Iowa Western Community College (U)
Itawamba Community College (U)
Ivy Tech Community College–North Central (U)
James Madison University (U)
Jefferson College of Health Sciences (U,G)
John Tyler Community College (U)
J. Sargeant Reynolds Community College (U)
Kean University (N)
Lamar State College–Port Arthur (U)
Lehigh Carbon Community College (U)
Liberty University (U)
Limestone College (U)
Louisiana State University and Agricultural and Mechanical College (U)
Malone College (U)
Marshall University (U)
Massasoit Community College (U)
Memorial University of Newfoundland (U)
Mercer County Community College (U)
Metropolitan State University (U)
Middlesex Community College (U)
Mid Michigan Community College (U)
Montana Tech of The University of Montana (U)
Moody Bible Institute (U)
Mt. San Antonio College (U)
Murray State University (U)
Naropa University (N)
New Mexico State University–Alamogordo (U)
New York Institute of Technology (U)
North Carolina State University (U)
North Idaho College (U)
North Seattle Community College (U)
Northwestern Connecticut Community College (U)
Northwestern Michigan College (U)
Northwest Missouri State University (U)
Old Dominion University (U)
Oregon State University (U)
Ouachita Technical College (U)
Oxnard College (U)
Ozarks Technical Community College (U)
Palomar College (U)
Parkland College (U)
Patrick Henry College (U)
Peninsula College (U)
The Pennsylvania State University University Park Campus (U)
Pueblo Community College (U)
Pulaski Technical College (U)
Queen's University at Kingston (U)
Ryerson University (U)
Sacred Heart University (U)
St. Cloud State University (U)
St. Edward's University (U)
Saint Joseph's University (U)
Saint Leo University (U)
St. Petersburg College (U)
Sam Houston State University (U)
Schoolcraft College (U)
Shippensburg University of Pennsylvania (U)
Shoreline Community College (U)
Snow College (U)
Southeast Community College, Beatrice Campus (U)
Southeast Community College, Lincoln Campus (U)
Southeast Community College, Milford Campus (U)
Southern Arkansas University Tech (U)
Southern Illinois University Carbondale (U)
Southwestern College (U)
State University of New York at New Paltz (U)
Stephens College (U)
Taylor University (U)
Tennessee Temple University (U)
Texas State University-San Marcos (U)
Touro University International (U)
Triton College (U)
Tunxis Community College (U)
The University of Akron (U)
The University of Alabama (U)
University of Bridgeport (U)
The University of British Columbia (U)
University of California, Berkeley (U,G)
University of Cincinnati (U)
University of Florida (U)
University of Hawaii–West Oahu (U)
University of Illinois at Springfield (U,G)
University of La Verne (U)
The University of Maine at Augusta (U)
University of Maine at Fort Kent (U)
University of Massachusetts Amherst (U)
University of Massachusetts Lowell (U)
University of Minnesota, Crookston (U)
University of Minnesota, Twin Cities Campus (U)

University of Missouri–Columbia (U,G)
University of Missouri–St. Louis (U)
The University of Montana (U,G)
The University of Montana–Western (U)
University of Nebraska–Lincoln (U)
University of New Orleans (U,G)
University of North Alabama (U)
The University of North Carolina at Chapel Hill (N,U)
The University of North Carolina at Greensboro (U)
University of Oklahoma (U)
University of Saskatchewan (U)
University of South Florida (U)
The University of Toledo (U,G)
University of Washington (U)
University of Waterloo (U)
University of West Florida (U)
University of Wisconsin Colleges (U)
Utah State University (U)
Utah Valley State College (U)
Virginia Polytechnic Institute and State University (U)
Wake Technical Community College (U)
Washtenaw Community College (U)
Wayne State College (U)
Weber State University (U)
Webster University (U)
Westchester Community College (U)
Western Wyoming Community College (U)
West Virginia University at Parkersburg (U)
Whatcom Community College (U)
Wilfrid Laurier University (U)
York Technical College (U)
York University (U)

PHILOSOPHY AND RELIGIOUS STUDIES RELATED

American Military University (U)
American Public University (U)
Asheville-Buncombe Technical Community College (U)
Assemblies of God Theological Seminary (G)
Athabasca University (N,U)
Atlantic University (N,G)
The Baptist College of Florida (U)
Bergen Community College (U)
Berkeley College (U)
Berkeley College-New York City Campus (U)
Berkeley College-Westchester Campus (U)
Bethany University (U)
Bismarck State College (U)
Bowling Green State University (U)
Brigham Young University (U)
Butler Community College (U)
Butler County Community College (U)
California Institute of Integral Studies (N,G)
California University of Pennsylvania (U)
Central Texas College (U)
Central Washington University (U)
Chadron State College (U)
Charter Oak State College (U)
Chattanooga State Technical Community College (U)
Cleveland State University (G)
College of DuPage (U)
College of Southern Maryland (U)
Colorado Christian University (U)
Columbia College (U)
Columbus State Community College (U)
Community College of Denver (U)
Covenant Theological Seminary (N,G)
Crafton Hills College (U)
Crown College (U,G)
Dallas County Community College District (U)
Darton College (U)
Davis College (U)
De Anza College (U)
Denver Seminary (G)
Des Moines Area Community College (U)
Drury University (U)
Duquesne University (U,G)
East Carolina University (U)
Eastern Mennonite University (G)
Eastern Michigan University (U)
Edison State Community College (U)
Feather River College (N)
Galveston College (U)
Gordon-Conwell Theological Seminary (N,G)
Hebrew College (N,U,G)
Holy Apostles College and Seminary (G)
Honolulu Community College (U)
Indiana Wesleyan University (U)
Iona College (U)
Iowa Western Community College (U)
Judson College (U)
Lake Superior College (U)
Lamar State College–Port Arthur (U)
Life Pacific College (U)
Louisiana State University and Agricultural and Mechanical College (U)
Marylhurst University (N,U,G)
Master's College and Seminary (U)
Miami Dade College (U)
Middlesex Community College (U)
Midland College (U)
Mohawk Valley Community College (U)
Moody Bible Institute (U)
Murray State University (U)
Naropa University (N,U)
New York Institute of Technology (U)
Northern Virginia Community College (U)
Northwestern College (U)
Oregon State University (U)
Ozark Christian College (U)
Ozarks Technical Community College (U)
Palomar College (U)
Park University (U)
Patrick Henry College (U)
Pennsylvania College of Technology (U)
Piedmont Technical College (U)
Prescott College (U,G)
Randolph Community College (U)
Regions University (N,U,G)
Rend Lake College (U)
Sacramento City College (U)
Sacred Heart University (U)
St. Edward's University (U)
Saint Joseph's College of Maine (U)
Saint Leo University (U)
San Bernardino Valley College (U)
San Joaquin Delta College (U)
Schoolcraft College (U)
Seattle Central Community College (U)
Southeast Community College, Lincoln Campus (U)
Southern Illinois University Carbondale (U)
Southwestern Baptist Theological Seminary (G)
Southwestern Community College (U)
Stanly Community College (U)
State University of New York at Oswego (U)
Taylor University (U)
Temple Baptist Seminary (N,G)
Triton College (U)
The University of Akron (U)
The University of Alabama (U)
University of Arkansas (U)
University of Bridgeport (U)
University of California, Berkeley (U,G)
University of California, Los Angeles (G)
University of Cincinnati (U)
University of Colorado at Denver and Health Sciences Center—Downtown Denver Campus (U)
University of Delaware (U)
The University of Findlay (U)
University of Florida (U)
University of Great Falls (U)
The University of Montana (U)
University of New Orleans (U,G)
The University of North Carolina at Greensboro (U)
University of Pittsburgh (U)
University of St. Francis (U)
University of Southern Mississippi (U)
University of South Florida (U)
The University of Texas of the Permian Basin (U)
The University of Toledo (U)
University of Waterloo (U)
Upper Iowa University (U)
Wilkes Community College (U)

PHYSICAL SCIENCES

Arkansas State University–Beebe (U)
Arkansas Tech University (U)
Athabasca University (N,U)
Barclay College (U)
Bellevue Community College (U)
Bethany University (U)
Brigham Young University (U)
Broome Community College (U)
Butler Community College (U)
Caldwell Community College and Technical Institute (U)
Chadron State College (U)
Champlain College (U)
Coleman College (U)
The Community College of Baltimore County (U)
Community College of Southern Nevada (U)
Contra Costa College (U)
Corban College (U)
Dallas County Community College District (U)
Darton College (U)
Des Moines Area Community College (U)
Drury University (U)
East Central Community College (U)
Everett Community College (U)
Frostburg State University (U)
Gulf Coast Community College (U)
Houston Community College System (U)
Iowa Western Community College (U)
Itawamba Community College (U)
Ivy Tech Community College–Northwest (U)
Jacksonville State University (U,G)
James Madison University (N)
Kansas State University (U)
Lake Superior College (U)
Louisiana State University and Agricultural and Mechanical College (U)
Massasoit Community College (U)
Mesalands Community College (U)
Middlesex Community College (U)

Moody Bible Institute (U)
New Mexico State University–Carlsbad (U)
Northwestern State University of Louisiana (U)
Oxnard College (U)
Pace University (U)
Pasco-Hernando Community College (U)
Passaic County Community College (U)
Peninsula College (U)
Pueblo Community College (U)
Regent University (U)
Roosevelt University (U)
Sacred Heart University (U)
Saint Leo University (U)
Schiller International University (U)
Schoolcraft College (U)
Seminole Community College (U)
State University of New York College at Potsdam (U)
Taylor University (U)
Treasure Valley Community College (U)
The University of Akron (U)
University of California, Berkeley (U,G)
University of Houston–Victoria (U,G)
University of La Verne (N,U)
The University of Maine at Augusta (U)
The University of Montana (U)
University of New Orleans (U,G)
University of North Dakota (U)
The University of Texas System (U)
University of Waterloo (U)
University of West Florida (U)
University of Wisconsin–Superior (U)
Utah State University (U)
Utah Valley State College (U)
Wayne State College (U)
Wilkes Community College (U)

PHYSICAL SCIENCES RELATED

Bellevue Community College (U)
Bismarck State College (U)
Butler Community College (U)
Chadron State College (U)
Dallas County Community College District (U)
Iowa Western Community College (U)
James Madison University (N)
Kansas State University (U)
Miami Dade College (U)
Mississippi State University (U)
Nassau Community College (U)
Portland Community College (U)
Roger Williams University (U)
Seminole Community College (U)
Taylor University (U)
The University of Akron (U)
University of Houston–Victoria (U,G)
University of Maryland Eastern Shore (U)
The University of Texas System (U)
University of West Florida (U)

PHYSICS

Acadia University (U)
Boise State University (U)
Brigham Young University (U)
Broome Community College (U)
Butler Community College (U)
Cecil Community College (U)
Chattanooga State Technical Community College (U)
Clackamas Community College (U)
Clemson University (U)
College of DuPage (U)
College of Southern Maryland (U)
Colorado Mountain College District System (U)
Community College of Denver (U)
Cosumnes River College (U)
D'Youville College (U)
Eastern Oregon University (U)
Edison State Community College (U)
Fort Hays State University (U)
Grantham University (U)
Indiana University of Pennsylvania (U,G)
Itawamba Community College (U)
Jacksonville State University (U)
James Madison University (N)
Lehigh Carbon Community College (U)
Louisiana State University and Agricultural and Mechanical College (U)
Metropolitan State University (U)
Mississippi State University (U)
Missouri State University (U)
Montana State University (G)
Montana State University–Billings (U)
New England Institute of Technology (U)
New Jersey City University (U)
North Carolina State University (U)
Northwestern Michigan College (U)
Oxnard College (U)
Parkland College (U)
The Pennsylvania State University University Park Campus (U)
Pueblo Community College (U)
St. Cloud State University (U)
St. John's University (U)
Schoolcraft College (U)
Shippensburg University of Pennsylvania (U)
Tacoma Community College (U)
Texas A&M University–Kingsville (U)
University of California, Berkeley (U,G)
University of Cincinnati Raymond Walters College (U)
University of Colorado at Denver and Health Sciences Center—Downtown Denver Campus (U)
University of Houston–Victoria (U,G)
University of Minnesota, Crookston (U)
University of Minnesota, Twin Cities Campus (U)
University of Missouri–Columbia (U)
University of Nebraska–Lincoln (U)
University of New Orleans (U,G)
The University of North Carolina at Chapel Hill (U)
University of North Dakota (U)
University of Oregon (U)
The University of Tennessee (U)
University of Utah (U)
University of Waterloo (N,U)
University of Wyoming (U)
Utah State University (U)
Virginia Polytechnic Institute and State University (U)
Wayne State College (U)
Weber State University (U)

PHYSIOLOGICAL PSYCHOLOGY/ PSYCHOBIOLOGY

Athabasca University (U)
Chadron State College (U)
Colorado Christian University (U)
Eastern Wyoming College (U)
Mount Saint Vincent University (U)

PHYSIOLOGY, PATHOLOGY AND RELATED SCIENCES

Darton College (U)
Georgia Highlands College (U)
Louisiana State University and Agricultural and Mechanical College (U)
The Pennsylvania State University University Park Campus (U)
Pueblo Community College (U)
Rasmussen College Eden Prarie (U)
Sacramento City College (U)
San Diego State University (U)
Saybrook Graduate School and Research Center (G)
University of California, Berkeley (U)
University of Minnesota, Twin Cities Campus (U)
University of Waterloo (U)

PLANT SCIENCES

Arizona State University (U)
Athabasca University (U)
Bellevue Community College (U)
Bismarck State College (N)
Colorado State University (U)
James Madison University (N)
Kansas State University (G)
Nova Scotia Agricultural College (N,U)
The Ohio State University (U,G)
Oregon State University (U)
The Pennsylvania State University University Park Campus (U)
Piedmont Technical College (U)
Rend Lake College (U)
Southern Illinois University Carbondale (U)
Texas Tech University (G)
University of California, Riverside (N)
University of Maine (U)
University of Missouri–Columbia (U)
University of Nebraska–Lincoln (U)
Yuba College (U)

POLITICAL SCIENCE AND GOVERNMENT

Acadia University (U)
Alpena Community College (U)
American Military University (U)
American Public University (U)
Anne Arundel Community College (U)
Arizona State University at the Polytechnic Campus (U)
Arkansas State University–Beebe (U)
Arkansas Tech University (U)
Athabasca University (N,U,G)
Auburn University (U)
Bellevue Community College (U)
Bergen Community College (U)
Berkeley College (U)
Berkeley College-New York City Campus (U)
Berkeley College-Westchester Campus (U)
Bethany University (U)
Big Sandy Community and Technical College (U)
Blinn College (U)
Bloomfield College (U)
Bowling Green State University (U)
Bradley University (G)
Brazosport College (U)

Brenau University (U)
Bridgewater State College (U)
Brigham Young University (U)
Broome Community College (U)
Buena Vista University (U)
Butler Community College (U)
Butler County Community College (U)
Caldwell College (U)
California State University, San Bernardino (U)
Campbell University (U)
Carl Albert State College (U)
Carlow University (U)
Cayuga County Community College (U)
Central Lakes College (U)
Central Michigan University (U,G)
Central Texas College (U)
Central Virginia Community College (U)
Central Wyoming College (U)
Chattanooga State Technical Community College (U)
Clatsop Community College (U)
Coffeyville Community College (U)
College of San Mateo (U)
College of Southern Maryland (U)
College of the Siskiyous (U)
Colorado State University-Pueblo (U)
Columbia Basin College (U)
Columbia College (U)
Columbus State Community College (U)
The Community College of Baltimore County (U)
Community College of Denver (U)
Community College of Southern Nevada (U)
Contra Costa College (U)
Cowley County Community College and Area Vocational–Technical School (U)
Crafton Hills College (U)
Dallas Baptist University (U)
Darton College (U)
De Anza College (U)
Delta College (U)
Drake University (U,G)
Drury University (U)
D'Youville College (U)
Eastern Michigan University (U)
Eastern Oklahoma State College (U)
Eastern Oregon University (U)
Eastern West Virginia Community and Technical College (U)
Eastern Wyoming College (U)
Erie Community College (U)
Evergreen Valley College (U)
Florida Atlantic University (U)
Fort Hays State University (U)
Fort Valley State University (U)
Frostburg State University (U)
Gadsden State Community College (U)
Galveston College (U)
Gateway Community College (U)
Georgia Southern University (U)
Glenville State College (U)
Golden West College (U)
Hamline University (N)
Haywood Community College (U)
Honolulu Community College (U)
Houston Community College System (U)
Independence Community College (U)
Indiana University of Pennsylvania (U)
Indiana University–Purdue University Fort Wayne (U)
Iowa Western Community College (U)
Ivy Tech Community College–North Central (U)
Jacksonville State University (U,G)
James Madison University (N)
John A. Logan College (U)
John Jay College of Criminal Justice of the City University of New York (U)
J. Sargeant Reynolds Community College (U)
Judson College (U)
Kansas State University (U)
Kean University (U)
Lake Superior College (U)
Lamar University (U)
Lehigh Carbon Community College (U)
Limestone College (U)
Los Angeles Harbor College (U)
Louisiana State University and Agricultural and Mechanical College (U)
Louisiana Tech University (U)
Malone College (U)
Marylhurst University (U)
Memorial University of Newfoundland (U)
Mesa State College (U)
Metropolitan State University (U)
Miami Dade College (U)
Middlesex Community College (U)
Middle Tennessee State University (U)
Mid Michigan Community College (U)
Missouri State University (U,G)
Mount Allison University (U)
Mount Wachusett Community College (U)
Myers University (U)
New Jersey City University (U)
New York Institute of Technology (U)
North Carolina State University (U)
North Central Texas College (U)
Northeast State Technical Community College (U)
North Idaho College (U)
Northwest Missouri State University (U)
The Ohio State University (U)
Oklahoma State University (U)
Oral Roberts University (U)
Oregon State University (U)
Ouachita Technical College (U)
Oxnard College (U)
Ozarks Technical Community College (U)
Pace University (U)
Parkland College (U)
Park University (U)
Pasco-Hernando Community College (U)
Patrick Henry College (U)
Peninsula College (U)
The Pennsylvania State University University Park Campus (U)
Piedmont Technical College (U)
Queen's University at Kingston (U)
Quinebaug Valley Community College (U)
Regent University (U,G)
Rend Lake College (U)
Rio Hondo College (U)
Rochester Institute of Technology (U)
Ryerson University (U)
Sacramento City College (U)
Sacred Heart University (U)
Saddleback College (U)
St. Clair County Community College (U)
St. John's University (U)
Saint Joseph's University (U)
Saint Mary-of-the-Woods College (U)
St. Petersburg College (U)
Sam Houston State University (U)
San Bernardino Valley College (U)
San Joaquin Delta College (U)
Seminole Community College (U)
Shippensburg University of Pennsylvania (U,G)
Solano Community College (U)
Southern Arkansas University Tech (U)
Southern Illinois University Carbondale (U)
Southern University at Shreveport (U)
Stanly Community College (U)
State University of New York at Plattsburgh (U)
State University of New York Empire State College (G)
State University of New York, Fredonia (U)
Strayer University (U)
Tacoma Community College (U)
Taylor University (U)
Tennessee Temple University (U)
Texas A&M University–Texarkana (U)
Texas State University-San Marcos (U)
Touro University International (U)
Tyler Junior College (U)
The University of Akron (U,G)
The University of Alabama (U)
University of Alaska Fairbanks (U)
University of Bridgeport (U)
The University of British Columbia (U)
University of California, Berkeley (U)
University of Central Arkansas (U)
University of Colorado at Denver and Health Sciences Center—Downtown Denver Campus (U,G)
University of Delaware (U,G)
University of Florida (U)
University of Hawaii–West Oahu (U)
University of Houston–Downtown (U)
University of Illinois at Springfield (G)
The University of Maine at Augusta (U)
University of Maine at Fort Kent (U)
University of Massachusetts Boston (U)
University of Minnesota, Morris (U)
University of Missouri–Columbia (U)
The University of Montana (G)
University of Nebraska at Omaha (U)
University of Nebraska–Lincoln (U,G)
University of New Brunswick Fredericton (U)
University of New Orleans (U,G)
University of North Alabama (U)
The University of North Carolina at Chapel Hill (N,U)
University of Northern Colorado (U)
University of Oklahoma (U)
University of Oregon (U)
University of Pittsburgh (U)
University of Southern Indiana (U)
The University of Tennessee (U)
The University of Texas at Arlington (U,G)
The University of Texas at Tyler (U)
The University of Texas System (N,U,G)
The University of Toledo (U,G)
University of Utah (U)
University of Washington (U,G)
University of West Florida (U)
University of Wisconsin Colleges (U)
University of Wisconsin–Platteville (G)
University of Wisconsin–River Falls (U,G)
University of Wisconsin–Whitewater (U,G)
Upper Iowa University (N,U)
Utah Valley State College (U)
Vance-Granville Community College (U)
Virginia Polytechnic Institute and State University (U,G)
Washburn University (U)

Washtenaw Community College (U)
Wayland Baptist University (U)
Weber State University (U)
West Los Angeles College (U)
York University (U)

POLYMER/PLASTICS ENGINEERING

Lehigh University (N,G)
The University of Akron (U)
University of Massachusetts Lowell (G)

PRECISION METAL WORKING

Central Wyoming College (N)

PRECISION SYSTEMS MAINTENANCE AND REPAIR TECHNOLOGIES

James Madison University (N)
Massasoit Community College (N)

PSYCHOLOGY

Acadia University (U)
Adirondack Community College (U)
Alpena Community College (U)
Alvin Community College (U)
American Military University (U)
American Public University (U)
Arkansas State University–Beebe (U)
Arkansas Tech University (U)
Asheville-Buncombe Technical Community College (U)
Athabasca University (N,U,G)
Athens Technical College (U)
Austin Peay State University (U)
Barclay College (U)
Bellevue Community College (U)
Bergen Community College (U)
Berkeley College (U)
Berkeley College-New York City Campus (U)
Berkeley College-Westchester Campus (U)
Bethany University (U)
Big Sandy Community and Technical College (U)
Bismarck State College (U)
Black Hills State University (U)
Blinn College (U)
Bloomfield College (U)
Boise State University (U)
Bowling Green State University (U,G)
Bradley University (U)
Brazosport College (U)
Brenau University (U)
Bridgewater State College (U,G)
Brigham Young University (U)
Broome Community College (U)
Buena Vista University (U)
Butler Community College (U)
Butler County Community College (U)
Caldwell College (U)
Caldwell Community College and Technical Institute (U)
California State University, Chico (U)
California State University, San Bernardino (U)
California University of Pennsylvania (U)
Campbell University (U)
Cape Cod Community College (U)
Cape Fear Community College (U)
Capella University (G)
Carl Albert State College (U)
Carlow University (U)
Carl Sandburg College (U)
Casper College (U)
Cayuga County Community College (U)
Cecil Community College (U)
Central Lakes College (U)
Central Michigan University (U)
Central New Mexico Community College (U)
Central Oregon Community College (U)
Central Texas College (U)
Central Virginia Community College (U)
Central Washington University (U)
Central Wyoming College (N,U)
Chadron State College (U,G)
Champlain College (U)
Charter Oak State College (U)
Chattanooga State Technical Community College (U)
Citrus College (U)
Clarion University of Pennsylvania (U)
Clark College (U)
Clark State Community College (U)
Clatsop Community College (U)
Cleveland Community College (U)
Cleveland State Community College (U)
Clinton Community College (U)
Coconino Community College (U)
Coffeyville Community College (U)
Coleman College (U)
College of DuPage (U)
The College of St. Scholastica (U)
College of San Mateo (U)
College of Southern Maryland (U)
College of The Albemarle (U)
College of the Siskiyous (U)
College of the Southwest (U)
Colorado Mountain College District System (U)
Colorado State University (U)
Colorado State University-Pueblo (U)
Columbia Basin College (U)
Columbia College (U)
Columbia-Greene Community College (U)
Columbus State Community College (U)
Columbus State University (G)
The Community College of Baltimore County (U)
Community College of Beaver County (U)
Community College of Denver (U)
Corning Community College (U)
County College of Morris (U)
Cowley County Community College and Area Vocational–Technical School (U)
Cumberland County College (U)
Dakota County Technical College (U)
Dakota State University (U)
Dallas Baptist University (U)
Dallas County Community College District (U)
Danville Community College (U)
Darton College (U)
Dawson Community College (U)
De Anza College (U)
Delta College (U)
Des Moines Area Community College (U)
Dodge City Community College (U)
Drake University (U,G)
Drexel University (U)
Drury University (U)
East Carolina University (G)
East Central Community College (U)
Eastern Michigan University (U)
Eastern New Mexico University (U)
Eastern Oklahoma State College (U)
Eastern Oregon University (U)
Eastern West Virginia Community and Technical College (U)
East Los Angeles College (U)
East Tennessee State University (U)
Edgecombe Community College (U)
Elgin Community College (U)
Embry-Riddle Aeronautical University, Extended Campus (G)
Erie Community College (U)
Everett Community College (U)
Evergreen Valley College (U)
Fayetteville State University (U)
Feather River College (N,U)
Finger Lakes Community College (U)
Florida Gulf Coast University (U)
Fontbonne University (U)
Fort Hays State University (U)
Fort Valley State University (U)
Frostburg State University (U,G)
Gadsden State Community College (U)
Galveston College (U)
Glenville State College (U)
Gogebic Community College (U)
Golden West College (U)
Governors State University (U)
Grand View College (U)
Grantham University (U)
Greenfield Community College (U)
Gulf Coast Community College (U)
Harford Community College (U)
Harvard University (G)
Haywood Community College (U)
Heartland Community College (U)
Heart of Georgia Technical College (U)
Hillsborough Community College (U)
Honolulu Community College (U)
Hope International University (N,U,G)
Houston Community College System (U)
Howard College (U)
Illinois Eastern Community Colleges, Lincoln Trail College (U)
Illinois Eastern Community Colleges, Olney Central College (U)
Illinois Eastern Community Colleges, Wabash Valley College (U)
Immaculata University (U)
Indiana State University (U)
Indiana Tech (U)
Indiana University of Pennsylvania (U)
Indiana University–Purdue University Fort Wayne (U)
Indiana Wesleyan University (U)
Iona College (U,G)
Iowa Western Community College (U)
Itawamba Community College (U)
Ivy Tech Community College–East Central (U)
Ivy Tech Community College–North Central (U)
Ivy Tech Community College–Northwest (U)
Ivy Tech Community College–Wabash Valley (U)
Ivy Tech Community College–Whitewater (U)
Jacksonville State University (U)
James Madison University (U)
James Sprunt Community College (U)
Jefferson College of Health Sciences (U)
Jefferson Community College (U)
John A. Logan College (U)

John Jay College of Criminal Justice of the City University of New York (U)
Johnson County Community College (U)
John Tyler Community College (U)
J. Sargeant Reynolds Community College (U)
Judson College (U)
Kansas State University (U,G)
Kean University (U)
Kentucky State University (U)
Lake Superior College (U)
Lamar State College–Port Arthur (U)
Lamar University (U)
Lansing Community College (U)
Lehigh Carbon Community College (U)
Lenoir Community College (U)
LeTourneau University (U)
Lewis and Clark Community College (U)
Lewis-Clark State College (U)
Liberty University (U,G)
Limestone College (U)
Los Angeles Harbor College (U)
Louisiana State University and Agricultural and Mechanical College (U)
Louisiana State University at Eunice (U)
Macon State College (U)
Madonna University (U)
Malone College (U)
Marshall University (U)
Massasoit Community College (U)
Memorial University of Newfoundland (U)
Mercy College (G)
Mesa State College (U)
Metropolitan State University (U)
Miami Dade College (U)
Middlesex Community College (U)
Mid Michigan Community College (U)
Midstate College (U)
Millersville University of Pennsylvania (U)
Missouri State University (G)
Moberly Area Community College (U)
Mohawk Valley Community College (U)
Monroe Community College (U)
Montana State University–Billings (U)
Montana Tech of The University of Montana (U)
Montgomery Community College (U)
Moody Bible Institute (U)
Mountain Empire Community College (U)
Mount Allison University (U)
Mt. San Antonio College (U)
Mount Wachusett Community College (U)
Myers University (U)
Naropa University (N,U)
Nassau Community College (U)
National University (U)
Neumann College (U)
New England Institute of Technology (U)
New Mexico State University–Alamogordo (U)
North Arkansas College (U)
North Carolina State University (U)
North Central Texas College (U)
North Dakota State College of Science (U)
North Dakota State University (G)
Northeast State Technical Community College (U)
North Georgia College & State University (U,G)
North Idaho College (U)
North Lake College (U)
North Seattle Community College (U)
Northwestern College (U)
Northwestern Connecticut Community College (U)
Northwestern Michigan College (U)
Northwestern State University of Louisiana (U,G)
Northwest Missouri State University (U)
Oklahoma State University (U)
Oregon Institute of Technology (U)
Oregon State University (N,U)
Ouachita Technical College (U)
Oxnard College (U)
Ozarks Technical Community College (U)
Pace University (U)
Pacific Graduate School of Psychology (G)
Palomar College (U)
Parkland College (U)
Park University (U)
Pasco-Hernando Community College (U)
Passaic County Community College (U)
Patrick Henry Community College (U)
Peninsula College (U)
The Pennsylvania State University University Park Campus (U)
Piedmont Technical College (U)
Portland Community College (U)
Portland State University (U)
Prescott College (U,G)
Presentation College (U)
Pueblo Community College (U)
Pulaski Technical College (U)
Purdue University Calumet (U)
Queen's University at Kingston (U)
Randolph Community College (U)
Rappahannock Community College (U)
Raritan Valley Community College (U)
Rasmussen College Eden Prarie (U)
Reading Area Community College (U)
Regent University (U,G)
Rend Lake College (U)
The Richard Stockton College of New Jersey (U)
Rio Hondo College (U)
Rochester Institute of Technology (U)
Roosevelt University (U)
Ryerson University (U)
Sacramento City College (U)
St. Clair County Community College (U)
St. Cloud State University (U)
Saint Joseph's University (U,G)
Saint Leo University (U)
Saint Mary-of-the-Woods College (U)
St. Petersburg College (U)
Salem Community College (U)
Sam Houston State University (U)
San Joaquin Delta College (U)
Saybrook Graduate School and Research Center (N,G)
Schenectady County Community College (U)
Schiller International University (U)
Schoolcraft College (U)
Seminole Community College (U)
Shippensburg University of Pennsylvania (U,G)
Shoreline Community College (U)
Sinclair Community College (U)
Solano Community College (U)
Southeast Arkansas College (U)
Southeast Community College, Beatrice Campus (U)
Southeast Community College, Lincoln Campus (U)
Southeast Community College, Milford Campus (U)
Southern Arkansas University Tech (U)
Southern University at Shreveport (U)
South Piedmont Community College (U)
South Plains College (U)
Southwestern Assemblies of God University (U)
Southwestern Baptist Theological Seminary (G)
Southwestern Oregon Community College (U)
Southwest Georgia Technical College (U)
Southwest Wisconsin Technical College (U)
Spartanburg Technical College (U)
Stanly Community College (U)
State University of New York at Buffalo (U)
State University of New York at New Paltz (U)
State University of New York at Oswego (U,G)
State University of New York College at Cortland (G)
State University of New York College at Potsdam (U)
Stephen F. Austin State University (U,G)
Stephens College (U)
Strayer University (U)
Syracuse University (G)
Tacoma Community College (U)
Taft College (U)
Taylor University (U)
Tennessee Temple University (U)
Texas A&M University–Commerce (U,G)
Texas A&M University–Kingsville (U)
Texas A&M University–Texarkana (U)
Texas State University-San Marcos (U)
Texas Tech University (U)
Texas Woman's University (U)
Three Rivers Community College (U)
Tompkins Cortland Community College (U)
Touro University International (U)
Treasure Valley Community College (U)
Triton College (U)
Tunxis Community College (U)
Tyler Junior College (U)
The University of Akron (U,G)
The University of Alabama (U)
University of Alaska Fairbanks (U,G)
University of Bridgeport (U)
The University of British Columbia (U)
University of California, Berkeley (U,G)
University of California, Los Angeles (G)
University of Central Arkansas (U)
University of Cincinnati (U)
University of Cincinnati Raymond Walters College (U)
University of Colorado at Colorado Springs (U)
University of Colorado at Denver and Health Sciences Center—Downtown Denver Campus (U)
University of Florida (U)
University of Great Falls (U)
University of Hawaii–West Oahu (U)
University of Houston–Victoria (U,G)
University of Illinois at Springfield (U)
The University of Iowa (U,G)
University of La Verne (U)
University of Maine (U)
The University of Maine at Augusta (U)
University of Maine at Fort Kent (U)
University of Maryland University College (U)
University of Massachusetts Amherst (U)
University of Massachusetts Boston (U)

University of Minnesota, Crookston (U)
University of Minnesota, Morris (U)
University of Minnesota, Twin Cities Campus (U)
University of Missouri–Columbia (U)
The University of Montana (U)
The University of Montana–Western (U)
University of Nebraska at Omaha (U)
University of Nebraska–Lincoln (U)
University of Nevada, Reno (U)
University of New Orleans (U,G)
The University of North Carolina at Chapel Hill (U)
The University of North Carolina at Greensboro (U)
The University of North Carolina Wilmington (U)
University of North Dakota (U)
University of Northern Colorado (U)
University of Northern Iowa (U)
University of Pittsburgh (U)
University of Saskatchewan (U)
University of Southern Indiana (U)
University of South Florida (G)
The University of Tennessee (U)
The University of Texas at Tyler (U)
The University of Texas of the Permian Basin (U)
The University of Texas System (U)
The University of Toledo (U)
University of Utah (U)
University of Washington (U)
University of Waterloo (U)
University of Wisconsin Colleges (U)
University of Wisconsin–Platteville (G)
University of Wisconsin–River Falls (U)
Upper Iowa University (N,U)
Utah State University (U,G)
Utah Valley State College (U)
Utica College (U)
Valley City State University (U)
Vance-Granville Community College (U)
Vincennes University (U)
Wake Technical Community College (U)
Washburn University (U)
Washtenaw Community College (U)
Waukesha County Technical College (U)
Wayland Baptist University (U)
Weber State University (U)
Westchester Community College (U)
Western Piedmont Community College (U)
Western Washington University (U)
Western Wyoming Community College (U)
West Los Angeles College (U)
West Virginia Northern Community College (U)
West Virginia University at Parkersburg (U)
Wharton County Junior College (U)
Whatcom Community College (U)
Wichita State University (U)
Wilfrid Laurier University (U)
Wilkes Community College (U)
William Rainey Harper College (U)
York County Community College (U)
York Technical College (U)
Yuba College (U)

PSYCHOLOGY RELATED

Alvin Community College (U)
Athabasca University (U)
Athens Technical College (U)
Atlantic University (N,G)
Bellevue Community College (U)
Black Hills State University (U)
Brenau University (U)
California State University, San Marcos (N)
Cape Cod Community College (U)
Central Michigan University (U)
Central Texas College (U)
Chadron State College (U,G)
Charter Oak State College (U)
Clark College (U)
Clark State Community College (U)
Coconino Community College (U)
Community College of Beaver County (U)
Corban College (U)
Cosumnes River College (U)
Des Moines Area Community College (U)
Drake University (U)
East Carolina University (G)
Eastern Michigan University (G)
Everett Community College (U)
Feather River College (U)
Granite State College (U)
Grantham University (U)
Illinois Eastern Community Colleges, Lincoln Trail College (U)
Jacksonville State University (U)
Jamestown Community College (N)
Lehigh Carbon Community College (U)
Limestone College (U)
Louisiana State University and Agricultural and Mechanical College (U)
Marylhurst University (N)
Massasoit Community College (U)
Master's College and Seminary (U)
Mercer County Community College (U)
Mercy College (G)
Mount Saint Vincent University (U)
Naropa University (N,G)
Nassau Community College (U)
North Dakota State College of Science (U)
Northwestern Michigan College (U)
Palomar College (U)
Portland Community College (N)
Raritan Valley Community College (U)
Rasmussen College Eden Prarie (U)
St. Cloud State University (G)
San Bernardino Valley College (U)
Saybrook Graduate School and Research Center (N,G)
Seminole Community College (U)
Southwestern Baptist Theological Seminary (G)
Southwestern Oregon Community College (U)
State University of New York at Plattsburgh (U)
Sullivan University (G)
Taft College (U)
Taylor University (U)
Texas State University-San Marcos (U)
Tompkins Cortland Community College (U)
Treasure Valley Community College (U)
The University of Akron (G)
University of Alaska Fairbanks (G)
University of California, Berkeley (U)
University of Florida (U)
University of Hawaii–West Oahu (U)
University of Maryland Eastern Shore (G)
University of Missouri–Columbia (U)
University of Nevada, Reno (G)
University of North Texas (U)
University of Waterloo (U)
University of Wisconsin–Whitewater (G)
Upper Iowa University (U)
Wilfrid Laurier University (U)
Wilkes Community College (U)
York University (U)
Yuba College (U)

PSYCHOMETRICS AND QUANTITATIVE PSYCHOLOGY

University of Alaska Fairbanks (U)
University of New Orleans (U,G)

PSYCHOPHARMACOLOGY

Jacksonville State University (U,G)
Rasmussen College Eden Prarie (U)

PUBLIC ADMINISTRATION

American Military University (U)
American Public University (U)
Andrew Jackson University (G)
Athabasca University (N,U,G)
Austin Peay State University (U)
Brenau University (U)
California State University, Dominguez Hills (G)
California State University, San Bernardino (G)
California University of Pennsylvania (G)
Central Michigan University (U,G)
Cleveland State University (U,G)
College of The Albemarle (N)
DeVry University Online (G)
Drake University (G)
Duquesne University (G)
Feather River College (N)
Florida Atlantic University (G)
Florida Gulf Coast University (U,G)
Hamline University (N)
Indiana State University (G)
Jacksonville State University (U,G)
James Madison University (N)
John Jay College of Criminal Justice of the City University of New York (U,G)
Metropolitan State University (U,G)
Mississippi State University (G)
Myers University (U)
National University (U,G)
North Georgia College & State University (G)
Pace University (G)
Park University (G)
Regent University (G)
Roger Williams University (U)
Ryerson University (U)
St. Edward's University (U)
Saint Joseph's College of Maine (G)
Saint Leo University (U)
Sullivan University (G)
The University of Akron (U,G)
University of Colorado at Colorado Springs (G)
University of Colorado at Denver and Health Sciences Center—Downtown Denver Campus (G)
University of Delaware (G)
The University of Findlay (G)
University of Florida (U)
University of Hawaii–West Oahu (U)
University of Illinois at Springfield (U,G)
University of La Verne (U)
University of Maine (U)
University of Maine at Fort Kent (U)

University of Maryland University College (G)
The University of Montana (U,G)
University of Nebraska at Omaha (G)
University of New Orleans (U,G)
University of North Dakota (G)
University of North Texas (U)
University of South Carolina Sumter (U)
University of South Florida (G)
The University of Texas at Tyler (G)
University of Wyoming (G)
Upper Iowa University (N,U)
Virginia Polytechnic Institute and State University (G)
Washburn University (U)

PUBLIC ADMINISTRATION AND SOCIAL SERVICE PROFESSIONS RELATED

American Military University (G)
American Public University (G)
Athabasca University (N,G)
Brenau University (U)
Central Michigan University (U,G)
Charter Oak State College (U)
Cleveland State University (U,G)
College of The Albemarle (N)
Drake University (G)
Florida Atlantic University (U)
George Mason University (G)
Georgia Southern University (G)
Hamline University (N,G)
Indiana State University (G)
Jacksonville State University (U,G)
John Jay College of Criminal Justice of the City University of New York (U)
Kentucky State University (U,G)
Mercy College (U)
North Georgia College & State University (G)
Park University (G)
Pine Technical College (U)
Roger Williams University (U)
Ryerson University (U)
Saybrook Graduate School and Research Center (N,G)
Sullivan University (G)
The University of Akron (U)
University of Central Florida (G)
University of Colorado at Denver and Health Sciences Center—Downtown Denver Campus (G)
University of Hawaii–West Oahu (U)
University of Illinois at Chicago (N)
University of La Verne (U)
University of New Orleans (U,G)
The University of North Carolina at Charlotte (N)
The University of Toledo (U)
Upper Iowa University (U)
York University (U)

PUBLIC HEALTH

Athabasca University (N,U,G)
Bowling Green State University (U)
Cleveland State University (N)
Drake University (G)
Drexel University (G)
Emory University (G)
James Madison University (N)
Jefferson College of Health Sciences (U)
Medical College of Wisconsin (G)
Mercy College (U)
Montana Tech of The University of Montana (G)
New Jersey City University (U,G)
Oregon State University (G)
Oxnard College (U)
Radford University (N)
Seminole Community College (U)
Touro University International (G)
The University of Akron (G)
University of Bridgeport (U)
University of Illinois at Chicago (N,G)
University of Massachusetts Amherst (G)
University of Minnesota, Twin Cities Campus (U,G)
The University of Montana (U)
The University of North Carolina at Greensboro (U)
University of South Carolina Sumter (U)
University of Southern Mississippi (G)
University of South Florida (G)
Virginia Polytechnic Institute and State University (N)

PUBLIC POLICY ANALYSIS

American Military University (U)
American Public University (U)
Athabasca University (N,U,G)
Central Michigan University (U,G)
Duquesne University (G)
Patrick Henry College (U)
Regent University (N,G)
University of Colorado at Denver and Health Sciences Center—Downtown Denver Campus (G)
University of Denver (U)
University of Illinois at Springfield (U)
University of South Florida (G)

PUBLIC RELATIONS, ADVERTISING, AND APPLIED COMMUNICATION RELATED

Arizona State University (U)
Athabasca University (N,U,G)
Berkeley College (U)
Berkeley College-New York City Campus (U)
Berkeley College-Westchester Campus (U)
Brenau University (U)
Central Michigan University (G)
Champlain College (U)
Columbus State Community College (U)
Dakota County Technical College (U)
Drake University (U,G)
Edison State Community College (U)
Erie Community College (U)
Indiana Business College (U)
Iona College (G)
Iowa Western Community College (U)
James Madison University (N)
Judson College (U)
Lamar State College–Port Arthur (N)
Linn-Benton Community College (U)
Madonna University (U)
Maryville University of Saint Louis (N)
Middlesex Community College (U)
Monroe Community College (U)
Montana State University–Billings (U,G)
Mount Saint Vincent University (U)
Murray State University (U)
Myers University (U)
Northwestern Oklahoma State University (U)
Oxnard College (U)
Ryerson University (U)
St. Edward's University (G)
Schoolcraft College (U)
State University of New York at Buffalo (U)
State University of New York at New Paltz (U)
State University of New York at Oswego (U)
Sullivan University (G)
Taylor University (N)
The University of Alabama (U)
University of Alaska Fairbanks (U)
University of Alberta (G)
University of California, Berkeley (U)
University of Florida (U)
University of Minnesota, Twin Cities Campus (U)
University of Missouri–Columbia (G)
University of Southern Indiana (U)
University of Wisconsin–Platteville (U)
Upper Iowa University (U)
Utah Valley State College (U)
Webster University (U)
West Shore Community College (U)
Wilkes Community College (U)
Wisconsin Indianhead Technical College (N,U)

PUBLISHING

Clemson University (N)
Hagerstown Community College (N)
North Idaho College (N)
Pace University (G)
Ryerson University (U)
University of Cincinnati (N)
University of Minnesota, Twin Cities Campus (U)

QUALITY CONTROL AND SAFETY TECHNOLOGIES

Asheville-Buncombe Technical Community College (N)
California National University for Advanced Studies (U)
California State University, Dominguez Hills (U,G)
Columbus State Community College (U)
East Carolina University (G)
Eastern Michigan University (G)
Ivy Tech Community College–Kokomo (U)
Jacksonville State University (U,G)
James Madison University (N)
Kansas State University (G)
Kettering University (N)
Mitchell Technical Institute (N)
Murray State University (G)
Southern Illinois University Carbondale (U)
The University of Alabama in Huntsville (G)
University of California, Berkeley (U,G)
University of Michigan (N)
University of South Florida (G)
The University of Texas at Tyler (G)
University of Wisconsin–Platteville (N)
West Virginia University at Parkersburg (N)

RADIO, TELEVISION, AND DIGITAL COMMUNICATION

Athabasca University (N)
Feather River College (N)
James Madison University (N)

Middle Tennessee State University (U)
Murray State University (U)
Oxnard College (U)
San Bernardino Valley College (U)
Texas A&M University–Commerce (G)
University of Alaska Fairbanks (U)
University of Missouri–Columbia (G)
University of Missouri–St. Louis (U)
University of Nebraska–Lincoln (U)
The University of North Carolina at Chapel Hill (G)
University of Southern Indiana (U)

REAL ESTATE

Athens Technical College (N)
Bainbridge College (N)
Blackhawk Technical College (N)
Central New Mexico Community College (U)
Central Texas College (U)
Chadron State College (U)
Clarion University of Pennsylvania (N,U)
Crafton Hills College (U)
Dallas County Community College District (U)
Darton College (N)
De Anza College (U)
Feather River College (N)
Galveston College (N)
Golden West College (U)
Houston Community College System (U)
James Madison University (N)
Jamestown Community College (N)
Johnson County Community College (N)
Madison Area Technical College (U)
Middle Tennessee State University (N)
Mt. San Antonio College (U)
Naugatuck Valley Community College (N)
Orange Coast College (U)
Palomar College (U)
Peirce College (U)
Portland Community College (U)
Rappahannock Community College (N)
Rend Lake College (U)
Sacramento City College (U)
Saddleback College (U)
Southeast Arkansas College (U)
Southern Illinois University Carbondale (U)
Southwest Georgia Technical College (N)
Sullivan University (G)
Treasure Valley Community College (N)
Triton College (U)
The University of Akron (U)
University of Alaska Fairbanks (U)
University of California, Berkeley (U)
University of Florida (U)
University of Missouri–Columbia (N,U,G)
University of Nebraska–Lincoln (U)
University of New Orleans (U,G)
University of North Dakota (N)
University of Utah (N)
University of Wyoming (U)
Waukesha County Technical College (U)
William Rainey Harper College (U)

REHABILITATION AND THERAPEUTIC PROFESSIONS

Arkansas Tech University (U)
Brenau University (G)
Clarion University of Pennsylvania (G)
Drake University (G)
East Carolina University (G)
Jefferson College of Health Sciences (U)
Montana State University–Billings (G)
Salve Regina University (G)
Saybrook Graduate School and Research Center (G)
Southern Illinois University Carbondale (G)
Texas Woman's University (G)
The University of British Columbia (U,G)
University of Central Arkansas (G)
University of Maryland Eastern Shore (U,G)
University of Minnesota, Twin Cities Campus (U)
University of Northern Colorado (U)
University of North Texas (N,U,G)
University of St. Augustine for Health Sciences (G)
Vincennes University (U)
Western Michigan University (U)

RELIGIOUS EDUCATION

Atlantic School of Theology (N,G)
Bethany University (U)
Briercrest Distance Learning (U,G)
Brigham Young University (U)
The Catholic Distance University (N,U,G)
Crown College (U)
Dallas Baptist University (G)
Defiance College (U)
Denver Seminary (G)
Des Moines Area Community College (U)
Eugene Bible College (U)
Gordon-Conwell Theological Seminary (N,G)
Laura and Alvin Siegal College of Judaic Studies (N,U,G)
Lutheran Theological Seminary at Gettysburg (G)
Marylhurst University (U)
Master's College and Seminary (U)
Montgomery Community College (U)
Moody Bible Institute (U)
Mount Allison University (U)
Mount Saint Vincent University (U)
Naropa University (N,G)
Newman Theological College (G)
Ozark Christian College (U)
Regent University (N)
Sacred Heart University (U)
Saint Joseph's College of Maine (U)
Southwestern Assemblies of God University (U,G)
Southwestern Baptist Theological Seminary (U,G)
Taylor University (U)
Temple Baptist Seminary (G)
Tennessee Temple University (U)
Union Theological Seminary and Presbyterian School of Christian Education (N,G)
Wayland Baptist University (U,G)
Webster University (U)
Western Seminary (N,G)

RELIGIOUS STUDIES

Assemblies of God Theological Seminary (G)
Atlantic School of Theology (N,G)
Atlantic University (N,G)
Azusa Pacific University (U)
Bakke Graduate University of Ministry (G)
Baptist Bible College of Pennsylvania (G)
Bergen Community College (U)
Bethany University (U)
Briercrest Distance Learning (N,U,G)
Brigham Young University (N,U)
Caldwell College (U)
California Institute of Integral Studies (N,G)
Campbellsville University (U,G)
Cape Fear Community College (U)
The Catholic Distance University (N,U,G)
Central Texas College (U)
Central Virginia Community College (U)
Central Wyoming College (U)
Chattanooga State Technical Community College (U)
Cleveland State Community College (U)
College of DuPage (U)
College of the Southwest (U)
Columbia International University (N,U,G)
Community College of Denver (U)
Concordia College (U)
Corban College (U)
Covenant Theological Seminary (N,G)
Cowley County Community College and Area Vocational–Technical School (U)
Crafton Hills College (U)
Crown College (U)
Dallas Baptist University (U,G)
Denver Seminary (G)
Des Moines Area Community College (U)
Drury University (U)
Earlham School of Religion (G)
Eastern Mennonite University (G)
Eugene Bible College (U)
Fontbonne University (U)
Gordon-Conwell Theological Seminary (N,G)
Halifax Community College (U)
Hartford Seminary (N,G)
Harvard University (G)
Haywood Community College (U)
Hebrew College (N,U,G)
Hope International University (N,U,G)
Immaculata University (U)
Itawamba Community College (U)
James Sprunt Community College (U)
John Tyler Community College (U)
Laura and Alvin Siegal College of Judaic Studies (N,U,G)
Liberty University (G)
Life Pacific College (N)
Limestone College (U)
Lutheran Theological Seminary at Gettysburg (G)
Madonna University (U)
Maranatha Baptist Bible College (G)
Master's College and Seminary (U)
McMurry University (U)
Memorial University of Newfoundland (U)
Miami Dade College (U)
Missouri State University (U,G)
Moody Bible Institute (N,U,G)
Mountain Empire Community College (U)
Mount Allison University (U)
Mt. San Antonio College (U)
Naropa University (N,U)
Neumann College (U)
Northwestern College (U)
Ozark Christian College (U)
Ozarks Technical Community College (U)
Pacific Union College (U)
Pasco-Hernando Community College (U)
Patrick Henry Community College (U)
The Pennsylvania State University University Park Campus (U)
Providence College and Theological Seminary (G)
Queen's University at Kingston (U)

Rappahannock Community College (U)
Regent University (N)
Regions University (N,U,G)
Rend Lake College (U)
Sacred Heart University (U)
Saint Joseph's College of Maine (N)
Shasta Bible College (U)
Southern Illinois University Carbondale (U)
Southwestern Assemblies of God University (U,G)
Southwestern Baptist Theological Seminary (U,G)
Stanly Community College (U)
Stephens College (U)
Taylor University (N,U)
Temple Baptist Seminary (N)
Tennessee Temple University (U)
Trinity Episcopal School for Ministry (N,G)
Union Theological Seminary and Presbyterian School of Christian Education (N)
The University of Alabama (U)
University of Bridgeport (U)
The University of Findlay (U)
University of Florida (U)
The University of Iowa (U,G)
The University of North Carolina at Chapel Hill (U)
University of North Dakota (U)
University of Northern Iowa (U,G)
University of Saskatchewan (U)
The University of Tennessee (U)
The University of Toledo (U)
University of Washington (U)
University of Waterloo (U)
University of West Florida (U)
Virginia Polytechnic Institute and State University (U)
Wayland Baptist University (U,G)
Western Michigan University (U)
Western Seminary (N,G)
Wilfrid Laurier University (U)
Wilkes Community College (U)
Williamson Christian College (U)
York University (U)

RELIGIOUS/SACRED MUSIC

Atlantic School of Theology (G)
Barclay College (U)
Eugene Bible College (U)
Lutheran Theological Seminary at Gettysburg (G)
Naropa University (N)
North American Baptist Seminary (G)
Northwestern College (U)
Providence College and Theological Seminary (N)
Southwestern Assemblies of God University (U)
Southwestern Baptist Theological Seminary (G)
Taylor University (U)

SALES, MERCHANDISING, AND RELATED MARKETING OPERATIONS (GENERAL)

Adams State College (N)
Athabasca University (N,U,G)
Berkeley College (U)
Berkeley College-New York City Campus (U)
Berkeley College-Westchester Campus (U)
Bismarck State College (U)
Blue Ridge Community College (U)
Brenau University (G)
Broome Community College (U)
California State University, Dominguez Hills (N)
Cape Fear Community College (U)
Capella University (U,G)
Central Michigan University (G)
Central New Mexico Community College (U)
Chadron State College (U,G)
College of DuPage (U)
Colorado Technical University (U)
Columbia College (U)
Columbus State Community College (U)
Community College of Denver (U)
Dakota County Technical College (U)
Dallas Baptist University (G)
Drexel University (U,G)
Eastern Michigan University (U,G)
East Tennessee State University (N,U,G)
Feather River College (N)
Grantham University (U)
Indiana Business College (U)
Iowa Western Community College (U)
Ivy Tech Community College–North Central (U)
Jacksonville State University (U,G)
James Madison University (N)
Jones College (U)
Kentucky State University (U)
Lamar State College–Port Arthur (N)
Lansing Community College (U)
Limestone College (U)
Madison Area Technical College (U)
Massasoit Community College (N)
Middle Tennessee State University (U)
Mohawk Valley Community College (N,U)
Oklahoma State University (U)
Oregon State University (U)
Palomar College (U)
Park University (U)
Peirce College (U)
The Pennsylvania State University University Park Campus (U,G)
Quinebaug Valley Community College (N)
Raritan Valley Community College (U)
Rasmussen College Eden Prarie (U)
Rend Lake College (N)
Ryerson University (U)
Saddleback College (U)
St. Edward's University (U,G)
San Joaquin Delta College (U)
South Central College (U)
Southern Illinois University Carbondale (U)
South Piedmont Community College (U)
Spartanburg Technical College (U)
Strayer University (U)
Syracuse University (G)
Taylor University (N)
Texas A&M University–Texarkana (U)
The University of Akron (U)
University of Bridgeport (U)
University of California, Berkeley (U,G)
University of Colorado at Denver and Health Sciences Center—Downtown Denver Campus (G)
University of Dallas (G)
The University of Findlay (G)
University of Florida (U)
University of Houston–Downtown (U)
University of Maryland University College (U,G)
University of Southern Indiana (N)
University of Tulsa (G)
University of Wisconsin–La Crosse (G)
University of Wisconsin–Parkside (G)
William Rainey Harper College (U)
Worcester Polytechnic Institute (G)

SALES, MERCHANDISING, AND RELATED MARKETING OPERATIONS (SPECIALIZED)

Adams State College (N)
Andrew Jackson University (G)
Arizona State University (U)
Asheville-Buncombe Technical Community College (N)
Ashworth College (N)
Athabasca University (N,G)
Bellevue University (U,G)
Berkeley College (U)
Berkeley College-New York City Campus (U)
Berkeley College-Westchester Campus (U)
Blackhawk Technical College (N)
Blue Ridge Community College (N)
Brenau University (U,G)
Bridgewater State College (N)
Caldwell Community College and Technical Institute (N)
California State University, Dominguez Hills (N)
California State University, East Bay (U)
Central Texas College (U)
Chadron State College (U,G)
Cleveland State University (N)
College of The Albemarle (N)
Colorado State University-Pueblo (N)
Dakota County Technical College (U)
Darton College (N)
Des Moines Area Community College (U)
Drexel University (G)
East Carolina University (U)
Eastern Michigan University (U)
Edgecombe Community College (N)
Feather River College (N)
Finger Lakes Community College (U)
Forrest Junior College (U)
Immaculata University (U)
Indiana Business College (U)
Jacksonville State University (U,G)
James Madison University (N)
Lamar State College–Port Arthur (N)
Madison Area Technical College (U)
Marist College (G)
Massasoit Community College (N,U)
Mercy College (G)
Middle Tennessee State University (N)
Missouri State University (G)
Mohawk Valley Community College (N,U)
Mt. San Antonio College (U)
Myers University (U)
Naugatuck Valley Community College (U)
Odessa College (N)
Orange Coast College (U)
Oregon State University (N)
Oxnard College (U)
Pasco-Hernando Community College (N)
Radford University (N)
Rasmussen College Eden Prarie (U)
St. Edward's University (G)
Saint Joseph's College of Maine (G)
Schiller International University (G)
Southeast Community College, Beatrice Campus (U)

Southeast Community College, Lincoln Campus (U)
Southeast Community College, Milford Campus (U)
State University of New York at Plattsburgh (U)
State University of New York College at Potsdam (N)
Stephen F. Austin State University (U)
Taylor University (N)
Texas Tech University (U)
Thunderbird, The Garvin School of International Management (G)
The University of Akron (U)
The University of Alabama (U)
University of Colorado at Denver and Health Sciences Center—Downtown Denver Campus (G)
University of Dallas (G)
University of Michigan–Flint (N)
University of Missouri–Columbia (N)
The University of North Carolina at Charlotte (N)
University of North Texas (U,G)
The University of Texas at Tyler (U)
University of Wisconsin–Platteville (U)
University of Wisconsin–River Falls (G)
Vance-Granville Community College (N)
Vincennes University (U)
Westchester Community College (U)
Western Michigan University (U)
West Los Angeles College (U)
Wilkes Community College (U)
William Rainey Harper College (U)
Wisconsin Indianhead Technical College (N,U)

SCHOOL PSYCHOLOGY

Athabasca University (N)
Capella University (G)
Chadron State College (G)
Eastern Michigan University (G)
Eugene Bible College (U)
Indiana State University (G)
Jacksonville State University (U,G)
Liberty University (G)
Louisiana State University and Agricultural and Mechanical College (U)
Ozarks Technical Community College (U)
Texas Woman's University (G)
The University of Akron (G)
University of Houston–Victoria (G)
University of Massachusetts Boston (G)
University of Missouri–Columbia (G)
University of North Texas (N)
Utah State University (G)

SCIENCE TECHNOLOGIES RELATED

Athabasca University (N)
Columbus State Community College (U)
Drexel University (G)
Everett Community College (U)
St. John's University (U)
Virginia Polytechnic Institute and State University (U,G)

SCIENCE, TECHNOLOGY AND SOCIETY

Athabasca University (N)
Everett Community College (U)
Oregon State University (U)
Pace University (U)
The Pennsylvania State University University Park Campus (U)
Syracuse University (U)
University of Alberta (G)
University of Denver (U)
University of Illinois at Urbana–Champaign (G)
The University of Montana (U)
Western Michigan University (U)

SECURITY AND PROTECTIVE SERVICES RELATED

Arkansas Tech University (U)
Ashworth College (N)
Jacksonville State University (U,G)
John Jay College of Criminal Justice of the City University of New York (U,G)
Peirce College (U)
Schoolcraft College (U)
Seminole Community College (N)
The University of Akron (U)
University of Connecticut (G)
University of Massachusetts Lowell (U,G)
Webster University (G)

SOCIAL AND PHILOSOPHICAL FOUNDATIONS OF EDUCATION

Athabasca University (N)
Brenau University (U)
D'Youville College (G)
Marylhurst University (N)
State University of New York at New Paltz (U)
The University of Akron (U,G)
University of Florida (U)
University of North Texas (G)
University of South Carolina Sumter (U)
University of Southern Mississippi (G)
University of South Florida (G)
The University of Texas System (U,G)
Winston-Salem State University (U)

SOCIAL PSYCHOLOGY

Anne Arundel Community College (U)
Athabasca University (N)
Bellevue Community College (U)
Bergen Community College (U)
Bethany University (U)
Cape Breton University (U)
Carlow University (U)
Cayuga County Community College (U)
City College of San Francisco (U)
College of DuPage (U)
College of the Southwest (U)
Colorado Mountain College District System (U)
Community College of Beaver County (U)
Corning Community College (U)
Crafton Hills College (U)
Dakota County Technical College (U)
Dallas Baptist University (U)
Danville Community College (U)
De Anza College (U)
Des Moines Area Community College (U)
Eastern Oklahoma State College (U)
Grand View College (U)
Houston Community College System (U)
Jackson Community College (U)
Kansas State University (U)
Lansing Community College (U)
Liberty University (U)
Limestone College (U)
Mercy College (U)
Middlesex Community College (U)
Midland College (U)
New York Institute of Technology (U)
Northwestern Oklahoma State University (U)
Odessa College (U)
Old Dominion University (U)
Oxnard College (U)
Ozarks Technical Community College (U)
Palomar College (U)
Parkland College (U)
Park University (U)
Queen's University at Kingston (U)
Red Rocks Community College (U)
Saint Joseph's College of Maine (U)
St. Petersburg College (U)
Saybrook Graduate School and Research Center (G)
Seminole Community College (U)
Sinclair Community College (U)
Southeast Community College, Beatrice Campus (U)
Southeast Community College, Lincoln Campus (U)
Southeast Community College, Milford Campus (U)
Southwestern Assemblies of God University (U)
Southwestern Oregon Community College (U)
State University of New York Empire State College (U)
Taylor University (U)
Texas State University-San Marcos (U)
Texas Tech University (U)
Tompkins Cortland Community College (U)
Tri-County Community College (U)
Triton College (U)
The University of Akron (G)
University of Alaska Fairbanks (U)
University of Bridgeport (U)
University of California, Berkeley (U)
University of Central Arkansas (U)
University of Colorado at Denver and Health Sciences Center—Downtown Denver Campus (U)
University of Florida (U)
University of Maine (U)
University of Nebraska at Omaha (U)
University of New Brunswick Fredericton (U)
University of South Carolina Sumter (U)
University of Utah (U)
University of Washington (U)
University of Waterloo (U)
University of Wyoming (U)
Upper Iowa University (U)
Utah State University (U)
Western Nevada Community College (U)
William Rainey Harper College (U)

SOCIAL SCIENCES

Acadia University (U)
Athabasca University (N,U,G)
Bellevue Community College (U)
Bergen Community College (U)
Bethany University (U)
Bismarck State College (U)
Black Hills State University (U)
Brenau University (U)

Butler Community College (U)
Caldwell Community College and Technical Institute (U)
California State University, Chico (U)
Cape Cod Community College (U)
Cape Fear Community College (U)
Cayuga County Community College (U)
Cedarville University (U)
Central Texas College (U)
Central Wyoming College (U)
Chadron State College (U)
Coconino Community College (U)
College of DuPage (U)
College of the Humanities and Sciences, Harrison Middleton University (U)
College of the Siskiyous (U)
Colorado State University (U)
Community College of Beaver County (U)
Community College of Southern Nevada (U)
Concordia University, St. Paul (N)
Cowley County Community College and Area Vocational–Technical School (U)
Dakota County Technical College (U)
Dallas County Community College District (U)
Des Moines Area Community College (U)
Drury University (U)
D'Youville College (U)
Eastern Michigan University (U)
Embry-Riddle Aeronautical University, Extended Campus (U)
Erie Community College (U)
Everett Community College (U)
Galveston College (U)
Gateway Community College (U)
Granite State College (U)
Gulf Coast Community College (U)
Illinois Eastern Community Colleges, Olney Central College (U)
Indiana Tech (U)
Iowa Western Community College (U)
Itawamba Community College (U)
Jacksonville State University (U,G)
James Madison University (N)
Jones College (U)
Judson College (U)
Kansas State University (U)
Lehigh Carbon Community College (U)
Lewis-Clark State College (U)
Louisiana State University and Agricultural and Mechanical College (U)
Massasoit Community College (N)
Miami Dade College (U)
Middlesex Community College (U)
Middle Tennessee State University (U)
Mid Michigan Community College (U)
Mohawk Valley Community College (U)
Monroe Community College (U)
Mount Wachusett Community College (U)
Murray State University (U)
New Mexico State University–Carlsbad (U)
North Dakota State College of Science (U)
Northeast State Technical Community College (U)
Oregon Institute of Technology (U)
Ouachita Technical College (U)
Ozarks Technical Community College (U)
Palomar College (U)
Peninsula College (U)
Portland Community College (U)
Pueblo Community College (U)
Pulaski Technical College (U)
Raritan Valley Community College (U)
Rasmussen College Eden Prarie (U)
Regent University (U)
Rend Lake College (U)
Roosevelt University (U)
Ryerson University (U)
St. Clair County Community College (U)
Schoolcraft College (U)
Seminole Community College (U)
Southern Illinois University Carbondale (U)
South Plains College (U)
Southwestern Assemblies of God University (U)
Southwestern College (U)
Southwest Wisconsin Technical College (U)
State University of New York at Plattsburgh (U)
State University of New York Empire State College (G)
Stephens College (U)
Syracuse University (U)
Taft College (U)
Taylor University (U)
Texas State University-San Marcos (U)
Tri-County Community College (U)
Tri-State University (U)
Triton College (U)
The University of Alabama (U)
University of Alaska Fairbanks (U)
University of Bridgeport (U)
University of California, Berkeley (U)
University of California, Los Angeles (G)
The University of Findlay (U)
University of Great Falls (U)
University of Hawaii–West Oahu (U)
The University of Maine at Augusta (U)
University of Maryland Eastern Shore (U)
University of Maryland University College (U)
University of Massachusetts Boston (U)
University of New Orleans (U,G)
University of North Texas (U,G)
University of St. Francis (U)
University of South Carolina Sumter (U)
University of South Florida (U)
The University of Texas System (U)
The University of Toledo (U)
University of Utah (U)
University of Waterloo (U)
University of Wisconsin–Superior (U)
Utah State University (U)
Utah Valley State College (U)
Vincennes University (U)
Viterbo University (U)
Westchester Community College (U)
West Virginia University at Parkersburg (U)
York University (U)

SOCIAL SCIENCES RELATED

Anne Arundel Community College (U)
Athabasca University (N,G)
Bellevue Community College (U)
Berkeley College (U)
Berkeley College-New York City Campus (U)
Berkeley College-Westchester Campus (U)
Bethany University (U)
Big Sandy Community and Technical College (U)
Butler Community College (U)
Cayuga County Community College (U)
Central Texas College (U)
Chadron State College (U)
Charter Oak State College (U)
Cleveland Institute of Electronics (U)
College of DuPage (U)
College of the Humanities and Sciences, Harrison Middleton University (G)
Columbia College (U)
Columbus State Community College (U)
Community College of Beaver County (U)
Copiah-Lincoln Community College (U)
Dakota County Technical College (U)
Dallas County Community College District (U)
Des Moines Area Community College (U)
Drake University (U)
Florida Atlantic University (U)
Gogebic Community College (U)
Harford Community College (U)
Honolulu Community College (U)
Itawamba Community College (U)
Jones College (U)
J. Sargeant Reynolds Community College (U)
Kansas State University (N,U)
Lehigh Carbon Community College (U)
Louisiana State University and Agricultural and Mechanical College (U)
Malone College (U)
Mercy College (G)
Middlesex Community College (U)
Moberly Area Community College (U)
Murray State University (U)
North Arkansas College (U)
Oregon State University (U)
Parkland College (U)
Pasco-Hernando Community College (U)
Sacred Heart University (U)
Saddleback College (U)
St. Cloud State University (U)
St. Edward's University (U)
Saint Leo University (U)
Saint Mary-of-the-Woods College (U)
San Bernardino Valley College (U)
Saybrook Graduate School and Research Center (G)
Schoolcraft College (U)
Seminole Community College (U)
Solano Community College (U)
Southwestern Assemblies of God University (U)
Taft College (U)
Taylor University (U)
Texas State University-San Marcos (U)
The University of Alabama (U)
University of Alaska Fairbanks (U)
University of California, Berkeley (U)
University of Denver (U)
University of Florida (U)
University of Hawaii–West Oahu (U)
University of Massachusetts Lowell (U)
The University of Texas System (U)
University of Waterloo (U)
Utah State University (G)
Utah Valley State College (U)
Vermont Technical College (U)
Washburn University (N)

SOCIAL WORK

Athabasca University (N,G)
Boise State University (U)
Bowling Green State University (U)
Brigham Young University (U)
Broome Community College (U)
California State University, San Bernardino (U)

California State University, San Marcos (U)
Campbellsville University (U,G)
Carlow University (U)
Chadron State College (U)
Cleveland State University (U,G)
Colorado State University (G)
Columbia College (U)
Connecticut State University System (G)
Darton College (U)
Fayetteville State University (G)
Florida Atlantic University (G)
Fort Hays State University (U)
Fort Valley State University (U)
Governors State University (U,G)
Jacksonville State University (U,G)
Kentucky State University (U)
Limestone College (U)
Louisiana State University and Agricultural and Mechanical College (U)
Marshall University (U,G)
Memorial University of Newfoundland (U,G)
Middle Tennessee State University (U)
Missouri State University (U,G)
Mohawk Valley Community College (U)
Monmouth University (G)
Murray State University (U)
Naugatuck Valley Community College (U)
New York Institute of Technology (U)
Niagara University (U)
Northwestern State University of Louisiana (U)
The Ohio State University (U,G)
Raritan Valley Community College (U)
Shippensburg University of Pennsylvania (U,G)
Southwestern Oregon Community College (U)
Stephen F. Austin State University (U)
Sullivan University (G)
Tacoma Community College (U)
Taylor University (U)
Texas A&M University–Commerce (U,G)
Three Rivers Community College (U)
The University of Akron (U,G)
University of Alaska Fairbanks (U)
University of Arkansas (U)
The University of British Columbia (U)
University of Calgary (U,G)
The University of Iowa (U,G)
University of Maine (G)
University of Michigan–Flint (U)
University of Minnesota, Twin Cities Campus (U)
University of Missouri–Columbia (U)
The University of Montana (U)
University of Nevada, Reno (U)
University of North Alabama (U)
University of North Dakota (U,G)
University of Northern Iowa (U,G)
University of North Texas (U)
University of South Carolina Sumter (G)
University of Southern Indiana (G)
University of Southern Mississippi (U,G)
The University of Texas at Arlington (U,G)
The University of Toledo (U)
University of Waterloo (U)
University of Wisconsin–Madison (U,G)
University of Wyoming (G)
Utah State University (U)
Vincennes University (U)
Wake Technical Community College (U)
Washburn University (U)
Western Michigan University (U)
Western Washington University (U)
Wilfrid Laurier University (U)
Winston-Salem State University (U)
York University (N,U)

SOCIOLOGY

Abilene Christian University (U)
Acadia University (U)
Adams State College (U)
Adirondack Community College (U)
Alpena Community College (U)
Anne Arundel Community College (U)
Arizona State University (U)
Arizona State University at the Polytechnic Campus (U)
Asheville-Buncombe Technical Community College (U)
Athabasca University (N,U,G)
Austin Peay State University (U)
Barclay College (U)
Bellevue Community College (U)
Bergen Community College (U)
Berkeley College (U)
Berkeley College-New York City Campus (U)
Berkeley College-Westchester Campus (U)
Bethany University (U)
Big Sandy Community and Technical College (U)
Bismarck State College (U)
Black Hills State University (U)
Blinn College (U)
Boise State University (U)
Bowling Green State University (U)
Bradley University (U)
Brenau University (U)
Bridgewater State College (U)
Brigham Young University (U)
Burlington County College (U)
Butler Community College (U)
Butler County Community College (U)
Caldwell College (U)
Caldwell Community College and Technical Institute (U)
California Institute of Integral Studies (N,G)
California State University, Chico (U)
California University of Pennsylvania (U)
Campbell University (U)
Cape Cod Community College (U)
Cape Fear Community College (U)
Carlow University (U)
Carl Sandburg College (U)
Casper College (U)
Cecil Community College (U)
Cedarville University (U)
Central Carolina Community College (U)
Central New Mexico Community College (U)
Central Piedmont Community College (U)
Central Texas College (U)
Central Virginia Community College (U)
Central Wyoming College (U)
Chadron State College (U)
Champlain College (U)
Chattanooga State Technical Community College (U)
Citrus College (U)
Clark State Community College (U)
Clatsop Community College (U)
Clemson University (U)
Cleveland State Community College (U)
Clinton Community College (U)
Clovis Community College (U)
Coconino Community College (U)
Coffeyville Community College (U)
College of DuPage (U)
College of San Mateo (U)
College of Southern Maryland (U)
College of The Albemarle (U)
College of the Southwest (U)
Colorado Mountain College District System (U)
Colorado State University (U)
Colorado State University-Pueblo (U)
Columbia Basin College (U)
Columbia College (U)
Columbia-Greene Community College (U)
Columbus State Community College (U)
The Community College of Baltimore County (U)
Community College of Beaver County (U)
Community College of Denver (U)
Concordia University, St. Paul (U,G)
Connecticut State University System (U,G)
Contra Costa College (U)
Corning Community College (U)
County College of Morris (U)
Cowley County Community College and Area Vocational–Technical School (U)
Crafton Hills College (U)
Cumberland County College (U)
Dakota County Technical College (U)
Dakota State University (U)
Dallas Baptist University (U)
Dallas County Community College District (U)
Danville Community College (U)
Darton College (U)
Dawson Community College (U)
De Anza College (U)
Delta College (U)
Des Moines Area Community College (U)
Dodge City Community College (U)
Drury University (U)
East Central Community College (U)
Eastern Michigan University (U)
Eastern New Mexico University (U,G)
Eastern West Virginia Community and Technical College (U)
Eastern Wyoming College (U)
Edgecombe Community College (U)
Edison State Community College (U)
Erie Community College (U)
Eugene Bible College (U)
Everett Community College (U)
Evergreen Valley College (U)
Fayetteville State University (U)
Feather River College (U)
Finger Lakes Community College (U)
Florida Atlantic University (U)
Fort Hays State University (U)
Fort Valley State University (U)
Frostburg State University (U)
Gadsden State Community College (U)
Georgia Highlands College (U)
Georgia Southern University (U)
Gogebic Community College (U)
Golden West College (U)
Governors State University (U,G)
Grand View College (U)
Grantham University (U)
Greenfield Community College (U)
Gulf Coast Community College (U)
Hartford Seminary (G)
Haywood Community College (U)
Hillsborough Community College (U)
Houston Community College System (U)
Howard College (U)

Immaculata University (U)
Independence Community College (U)
Indiana State University (U)
Indiana University–Purdue University Fort Wayne (U)
Iowa State University of Science and Technology (U)
Iowa Western Community College (U)
Itawamba Community College (U)
Ivy Tech Community College–North Central (U)
Ivy Tech Community College–Northwest (U)
Ivy Tech Community College–Southern Indiana (U)
Jackson Community College (U)
Jacksonville State University (U,G)
James Sprunt Community College (U)
Jamestown Community College (N)
Jefferson College of Health Sciences (U)
Jefferson Community College (U)
Johnson County Community College (U)
John Tyler Community College (U)
Jones College (U)
J. Sargeant Reynolds Community College (U)
Judson College (U)
Kansas State University (U)
Kean University (U)
Kentucky State University (U)
Lake Superior College (U)
Lansing Community College (U)
Lehigh Carbon Community College (U)
Limestone College (U)
Lock Haven University of Pennsylvania (U)
Los Angeles Harbor College (U)
Louisiana State University and Agricultural and Mechanical College (U)
Malone College (U)
Mansfield University of Pennsylvania (U)
Marshall University (U,G)
Massasoit Community College (U)
Memorial University of Newfoundland (U)
Mercer County Community College (U)
Mercy College (U)
Mesalands Community College (U)
Middlesex Community College (U)
Middle Tennessee State University (U)
Midland College (U)
Mid-State Technical College (U)
Millersville University of Pennsylvania (U)
Missouri State University (U)
Moberly Area Community College (U)
Mohawk Valley Community College (U)
Montana Tech of The University of Montana (U)
Montgomery Community College (U)
Mountain Empire Community College (U)
Mt. San Antonio College (U)
Mount Wachusett Community College (U)
Murray State University (U)
Myers University (U)
Nassau Community College (U)
New Mexico State University (U)
New York Institute of Technology (U)
North Central Texas College (U)
North Dakota State College of Science (U)
Northern Virginia Community College (U)
North Georgia College & State University (U,G)
North Idaho College (U)
Northwestern Connecticut Community College (U)
Northwestern Michigan College (U)
Northwestern Oklahoma State University (U)
Odessa College (U)
Oklahoma State University (U)
Old Dominion University (U)
Oregon State University (U)
Ouachita Technical College (U)
Oxnard College (U)
Ozarks Technical Community College (U)
Pace University (U)
Palomar College (U)
Parkland College (U)
Pasco-Hernando Community College (U)
Passaic County Community College (U)
Patrick Henry Community College (U)
Peninsula College (U)
The Pennsylvania State University University Park Campus (U)
Piedmont Technical College (U)
Portland Community College (U)
Portland State University (U)
Pueblo Community College (U)
Purdue University Calumet (U)
Queen's University at Kingston (U)
Quinebaug Valley Community College (U)
Randolph Community College (U)
Rappahannock Community College (U)
Raritan Valley Community College (U)
Reading Area Community College (U)
Red Rocks Community College (U)
Rend Lake College (U)
The Richard Stockton College of New Jersey (U)
Rio Hondo College (U)
Rochester Institute of Technology (U)
Roger Williams University (U)
Roosevelt University (U)
Ryerson University (U)
Sacramento City College (U)
Saddleback College (U)
St. Clair County Community College (U)
St. Cloud State University (U)
St. Johns River Community College (U)
St. John's University (U)
Saint Joseph's College of Maine (U)
Saint Joseph's University (U)
St. Louis Community College System (U)
Salem Community College (U)
Sam Houston State University (U)
San Bernardino Valley College (U)
San Joaquin Delta College (U)
Schenectady County Community College (U)
Schoolcraft College (U)
Seattle Central Community College (U)
Seminole Community College (U)
Shawnee Community College (U)
Shippensburg University of Pennsylvania (U,G)
Shoreline Community College (U)
Sinclair Community College (U)
Snow College (U)
Solano Community College (U)
Southeast Arkansas College (U)
Southeast Community College, Lincoln Campus (U)
Southern Illinois University Carbondale (U)
South Piedmont Community College (U)
Southwestern Assemblies of God University (U)
Southwestern Community College (U)
Southwestern Oregon Community College (U)
Southwest Georgia Technical College (U)
Southwest Virginia Community College (U)
Southwest Wisconsin Technical College (U)
Spartanburg Technical College (U)
Stanly Community College (U)
State University of New York at New Paltz (U)
State University of New York at Oswego (U)
State University of New York at Plattsburgh (U)
State University of New York College at Potsdam (U)
State University of New York Empire State College (U)
Strayer University (U)
Syracuse University (G)
Tacoma Community College (U)
Taft College (U)
Taylor University (U)
Tennessee Temple University (U)
Texas A&M University–Commerce (U)
Texas A&M University–Kingsville (U,G)
Texas A&M University–Texarkana (U)
Texas State University-San Marcos (U)
Texas Tech University (U)
Texas Woman's University (U,G)
Three Rivers Community College (U)
Tompkins Cortland Community College (U)
Touro University International (U)
Treasure Valley Community College (U)
Tri-County Community College (U)
Triton College (U)
Tunxis Community College (U)
Tyler Junior College (U)
The University of Akron (U)
University of Alaska Fairbanks (U)
University of Arkansas (U)
University of Bridgeport (U)
University of California, Berkeley (U,G)
University of Central Arkansas (U)
University of Central Florida (U)
University of Central Oklahoma (U,G)
University of Cincinnati Raymond Walters College (U)
University of Colorado at Colorado Springs (U)
University of Colorado at Denver and Health Sciences Center—Downtown Denver Campus (U)
University of Connecticut (U)
University of Delaware (U)
The University of Findlay (U)
University of Florida (U)
University of Great Falls (U)
University of Hawaii–West Oahu (U)
University of Houston–Downtown (U)
University of Illinois at Springfield (U)
The University of Iowa (U,G)
University of Maine (U)
The University of Maine at Augusta (U)
University of Maine at Fort Kent (U)
University of Maryland Eastern Shore (U)
University of Maryland University College (U)
University of Massachusetts Amherst (U)
University of Massachusetts Boston (U,G)
University of Massachusetts Lowell (U)
University of Minnesota, Crookston (U)
University of Minnesota, Morris (U)
University of Missouri–Columbia (U,G)
University of Missouri–St. Louis (U)
The University of Montana (U)
University of Nebraska at Omaha (U)
University of Nebraska–Lincoln (U)
University of Nevada, Reno (U)
University of New Brunswick Fredericton (U)
University of New Orleans (U,G)

University of North Alabama (U)
The University of North Carolina at Chapel Hill (U)
The University of North Carolina at Greensboro (U)
University of North Dakota (U)
University of Northern Iowa (U,G)
University of North Florida (U)
University of North Texas (U)
University of Oklahoma (U)
University of Saskatchewan (U)
University of Sioux Falls (U)
University of South Carolina Sumter (G)
University of Southern Mississippi (U)
University of South Florida (U)
The University of Tennessee (U)
The University of Tennessee at Martin (U)
The University of Texas at Arlington (U)
The University of Texas at Tyler (U)
The University of Texas of the Permian Basin (U)
The University of Texas System (U)
The University of Toledo (U)
University of Washington (U)
University of Waterloo (U)
University of Wisconsin Colleges (U)
University of Wisconsin–Platteville (G)
University of Wisconsin–River Falls (U)
Upper Iowa University (N,U)
Utah State University (U)
Utah Valley State College (U)
Vance-Granville Community College (U)
Vincennes University (U)
Virginia Polytechnic Institute and State University (U)
Wake Technical Community College (U)
Washburn University (U)
Washtenaw Community College (U)
Waukesha County Technical College (U)
Wayland Baptist University (U)
Westchester Community College (U)
Western Michigan University (U)
Western Nevada Community College (U)
Western Oklahoma State College (U)
Western Piedmont Community College (U)
Western Washington University (U)
West Shore Community College (U)
West Virginia Northern Community College (U)
West Virginia University at Parkersburg (U)
Wharton County Junior College (U)
Whatcom Community College (U)
Wichita State University (U)
Wilfrid Laurier University (U)
Wilkes Community College (U)
William Rainey Harper College (U)
Winston-Salem State University (U)
York County Community College (U)
York Technical College (U)
York University (U)
Yuba College (U)

SOIL SCIENCES

Cedarville University (U)
Montana State University (G)
North Carolina State University (U)
Oregon State University (U)
The University of British Columbia (U)
University of Florida (U,G)
University of Saskatchewan (N)

SOMATIC BODYWORK AND RELATED THERAPEUTIC SERVICES

Saybrook Graduate School and Research Center (G)

SPECIAL EDUCATION

Acadia University (U)
Arizona State University (U)
Arizona State University West (U,G)
Athabasca University (G)
Auburn University (G)
Blue Ridge Community College (U)
Bowling Green State University (G)
Brenau University (U)
Bridgewater State College (U,G)
Brigham Young University (U)
Carlow University (U,G)
Casper College (U)
Cedarville University (U)
Central Missouri State University (G)
Chadron State College (U,G)
Cleveland State University (U,G)
Drake University (U)
D'Youville College (U,G)
East Carolina University (G)
Eastern Michigan University (U)
East Tennessee State University (U)
Fayetteville State University (U,G)
Florida State University (G)
Fort Hays State University (U,G)
Granite State College (U,G)
Hamline University (G)
Indiana State University (G)
Jacksonville State University (U,G)
James Madison University (N,G)
Kean University (G)
Liberty University (G)
Millersville University of Pennsylvania (U,G)
Mississippi State University (U)
Missouri State University (U)
Mohawk Valley Community College (U)
Montana State University–Billings (U)
Murray State University (G)
National University (G)
New Jersey City University (G)
North Dakota State University (G)
Northwestern State University of Louisiana (G)
Northwest Missouri State University (G)
The Ohio State University (N)
Oxnard College (U)
St. Cloud State University (U)
Saint Mary-of-the-Woods College (U)
Seattle Pacific University (G)
State University of New York at Plattsburgh (G)
Stephen F. Austin State University (U,G)
Sullivan University (G)
Texas A&M University–Commerce (G)
Texas Tech University (G)
The University of Akron (U,G)
University of California, Berkeley (U)
University of Houston–Victoria (U,G)
University of Maine (U)
University of Maine at Presque Isle (U)
University of Massachusetts Boston (G)
University of Massachusetts Lowell (G)
University of Nebraska at Omaha (G)
University of New Orleans (U,G)
The University of North Carolina at Greensboro (G)
University of Northern Colorado (U,G)
University of North Florida (U,G)
University of North Texas (N,U,G)
University of South Alabama (G)
University of Southern Mississippi (U,G)
University of South Florida (G)
The University of Tennessee at Martin (U,G)
The University of Texas at Tyler (U,G)
The University of Texas of the Permian Basin (U)
The University of Toledo (G)
University of Utah (U)
University of Wisconsin–River Falls (G)
Utah State University (U,G)
Wayne State College (G)
Western Washington University (U)

SPEECH AND RHETORIC

Asheville-Buncombe Technical Community College (U)
Auburn University (U)
Austin Peay State University (U)
Bainbridge College (U)
Bellevue Community College (U)
Bergen Community College (U)
Blinn College (U)
Bowling Green State University (G)
Brigham Young University (U)
Butler Community College (U)
Central Lakes College (U)
Central New Mexico Community College (U)
Central Virginia Community College (U)
Chattanooga State Technical Community College (U)
Clackamas Community College (U)
Cleveland State Community College (U)
Coffeyville Community College (U)
Colorado State University (U)
Columbus State Community College (U)
Community College of Denver (U)
Contra Costa College (U)
Cowley County Community College and Area Vocational–Technical School (U)
Cumberland County College (U)
Dakota State University (U)
Dallas Baptist University (U)
Dallas County Community College District (U)
Darton College (U)
Delta College (U)
Dodge City Community College (U)
East Los Angeles College (U)
Eugene Bible College (U)
Gadsden State Community College (U)
Galveston College (U)
Grand View College (U)
Honolulu Community College (U)
Indiana Business College (N)
Iowa Western Community College (U)
James Madison University (N)
Johnson County Community College (U)
J. Sargeant Reynolds Community College (U)
Kentucky State University (U)
Lansing Community College (U)
Lehigh Carbon Community College (U)
Lewis and Clark Community College (U)
Louisiana State University and Agricultural and Mechanical College (U)
Massasoit Community College (U)
Miami Dade College (U)
Midland College (U)
Moberly Area Community College (U)

Mountain Empire Community College (U)
New York Institute of Technology (U)
North Central Texas College (U)
Northeast State Technical Community College (U)
Northwestern College (U)
Oxnard College (U)
Ozarks Technical Community College (U)
Parkland College (U)
Pasco-Hernando Community College (U)
The Pennsylvania State University University Park Campus (U)
Piedmont Technical College (U)
Pueblo Community College (U)
Rend Lake College (U)
St. Clair County Community College (U)
St. Cloud State University (U)
Salem Community College (U)
San Bernardino Valley College (U)
Schoolcraft College (U)
Seminole Community College (U)
Shippensburg University of Pennsylvania (U)
Sinclair Community College (U)
Southeast Community College, Beatrice Campus (U)
Southeast Community College, Lincoln Campus (U)
Southeast Community College, Milford Campus (U)
Southern Polytechnic State University (U)
Syracuse University (U)
Tacoma Community College (U)
Taylor University (U)
Three Rivers Community College (U)
Triton College (U)
The University of Akron (U,G)
University of La Verne (U)
University of Minnesota, Crookston (U)
University of Minnesota, Twin Cities Campus (U,G)
The University of Montana (U)
University of New Orleans (U,G)
University of Southern Indiana (U)
University of Washington (U)
University of Wisconsin–Platteville (U)
University of Wisconsin–River Falls (U)
Valley City State University (U)
Vincennes University (U)
West Los Angeles College (U)
Wharton County Junior College (U)
Wichita State University (U)

STATISTICS

Anne Arundel Community College (U)
Asheville-Buncombe Technical Community College (U)
Athabasca University (N,U)
Berkeley College (U)
Berkeley College-New York City Campus (U)
Berkeley College-Westchester Campus (U)
Bethany University (U)
Big Sandy Community and Technical College (U)
Brenau University (U)
Brigham Young University (U)
Broome Community College (U)
Burlington County College (U)
Campbell University (U)
Cape Breton University (U)
Cape Fear Community College (U)
Casper College (U)
Cayuga County Community College (U)
Central Piedmont Community College (U)
Central Texas College (U)
Chadron State College (U,G)
Charter Oak State College (U)
Chattanooga State Technical Community College (U)
Clark College (U)
Clatsop Community College (U)
Clemson University (G)
Clinton Community College (U)
Coleman College (U)
College of Southern Maryland (U)
Colorado Mountain College District System (U)
Colorado State University (U,G)
The Community College of Baltimore County (U)
Community College of Beaver County (U)
Connecticut State University System (N,U,G)
Cowley County Community College and Area Vocational–Technical School (U)
Dallas Baptist University (U)
Darton College (U)
De Anza College (U)
Delta College (U)
Des Moines Area Community College (U)
D'Youville College (U,G)
Eastern Michigan University (G)
East Tennessee State University (U)
Edison State Community College (U)
Embry-Riddle Aeronautical University (U)
Embry-Riddle Aeronautical University, Extended Campus (U)
Erie Community College (U)
Franklin University (U)
Galveston College (U)
Gulf Coast Community College (U)
Housatonic Community College (U)
Illinois Eastern Community Colleges, Wabash Valley College (U)
Iowa Western Community College (U)
Itawamba Community College (U)
Jacksonville State University (U,G)
James Madison University (U)
Jefferson College of Health Sciences (U)
The Johns Hopkins University (U)
Kansas State University (U)
Limestone College (U)
Louisiana State University and Agricultural and Mechanical College (U)
Macon State College (U)
Madison Area Technical College (U)
Marist College (U)
Marshall University (U)
Massasoit Community College (U)
Memorial University of Newfoundland (U)
Mercy College (U)
Metropolitan State University (U)
Miami Dade College (U)
Middlesex Community College (U)
Midland College (U)
Mississippi State University (U)
Montana State University (G)
Montana State University–Billings (U)
Motlow State Community College (U)
Mount Allison University (U)
Mount Wachusett Community College (U)
Nassau Community College (U)
New England College of Finance (U)
New York Institute of Technology (U)
Northern Virginia Community College (U)
North Lake College (U)
Northwestern Michigan College (U)
Oklahoma State University (U)
Oregon State University (U)
Pace University (U)
Palomar College (U)
Parkland College (U)
Park University (U)
Passaic County Community College (U)
Pennsylvania College of Technology (U)
The Pennsylvania State University University Park Campus (U,G)
Philadelphia University (U,G)
Piedmont Technical College (U)
Portland Community College (U)
Portland State University (U)
Presentation College (U)
Pueblo Community College (U)
Purdue University Calumet (G)
Queen's University at Kingston (U)
Raritan Valley Community College (U)
St. Clair County Community College (U)
St. Cloud State University (U,G)
San Joaquin Delta College (U)
Schiller International University (U,G)
Seattle Central Community College (U)
Seminole Community College (U)
Simmons College (N)
Southeast Arkansas College (U)
Southern Polytechnic State University (U)
Southwest Virginia Community College (U)
Southwest Wisconsin Technical College (U)
Spartanburg Technical College (U)
State University of New York at Plattsburgh (U)
State University of New York Empire State College (U)
Stephens College (G)
Syracuse University (U)
Taft College (U)
Texas Tech University (G)
Touro University International (U,G)
Triton College (U)
The University of Akron (U,G)
The University of Alabama in Huntsville (G)
University of Alaska Fairbanks (U)
University of California, Berkeley (U,G)
University of Central Florida (U)
University of Colorado at Denver and Health Sciences Center—Downtown Denver Campus (U)
The University of Findlay (U)
University of Florida (U,G)
University of Hawaii–West Oahu (U)
University of Houston–Downtown (U)
University of Illinois at Chicago (G)
The University of Maine at Augusta (U)
University of Maryland Eastern Shore (U)
University of Massachusetts Amherst (G)
University of Massachusetts Boston (U,G)
University of Minnesota, Crookston (U)
University of Minnesota, Morris (U)
University of Missouri–Columbia (U)
University of Nebraska–Lincoln (U,G)
University of Nevada, Reno (U)
University of New Brunswick Fredericton (U)
University of New Hampshire (G)
University of New Orleans (U,G)
The University of North Carolina at Chapel Hill (U)
University of Southern Mississippi (G)
The University of Texas at Tyler (U)
The University of Texas of the Permian Basin (G)
The University of Texas System (U)

The University of Toledo (U)
University of Utah (U)
University of Washington (U)
University of Waterloo (U)
University of West Florida (U)
University of Wisconsin Colleges (U)
University of Wisconsin–Parkside (G)
University of Wisconsin–Platteville (G)
University of Wisconsin–River Falls (G)
University of Wyoming (U)
Upper Iowa University (N,U)
Utah State University (U)
Vance-Granville Community College (U)

STUDENT COUNSELING AND PERSONNEL SERVICES

Cleveland State University (G)
College of the Siskiyous (U)
Indiana State University (G)
Jacksonville State University (U)
James Madison University (N)
Solano Community College (U)
University of Houston–Victoria (G)
University of Massachusetts Boston (G)
The University of North Carolina at Greensboro (G)

SYSTEMS ENGINEERING

Boston University (G)
Capitol College (G)
Colorado Technical University (U,G)
DePaul University (G)
Florida Institute of Technology (G)
Grantham University (G)
James Madison University (N)
Mid-State Technical College (U)
Southern Methodist University (G)
Stanford University (N)
The University of Alabama in Huntsville (G)
University of Illinois at Urbana–Champaign (G)
University of Michigan (N)
University of New Orleans (U,G)
University of South Florida (G)

SYSTEMS SCIENCE AND THEORY

Capitol College (G)
Florida Institute of Technology (G)
Nova Southeastern University (G)
Syracuse University (U,G)
Worcester Polytechnic Institute (G)

TAXATION

Ashworth College (N)
Athabasca University (N,G)
Brenau University (U,G)
DeVry University Online (U,G)
Drexel University (U)
Housatonic Community College (N,U)
Indiana University System (N)
James Madison University (N)
Jones College (U)
Liberty University (U)
Massasoit Community College (N)
Miami Dade College (U)
Middlesex Community College (U)
Minnesota School of Business–Richfield (U)
Missouri State University (G)
Oxnard College (U)
Saint Leo University (U)
The University of Akron (U)
The University of Maine at Augusta (U)
The University of North Carolina at Charlotte (N)
The University of Texas at Dallas (G)
University of Tulsa (G)
Western Piedmont Community College (U)

TEACHING ASSISTANTS/AIDES

Ashworth College (N)
Athens Technical College (N)
Blue Ridge Community College (U)
Casper College (U)
Clemson University (N)
Cleveland Community College (U)
College of the Siskiyous (U)
Community College of Denver (U)
Drexel University (G)
Halifax Community College (U)
Haywood Community College (U)
Heart of Georgia Technical College (U)
Lewis and Clark Community College (U)
Mesalands Community College (U)
Minot State University–Bottineau Campus (U)
Penn Foster Career School (N)
South Piedmont Community College (U)
Southwestern Oregon Community College (U)
University of Houston–Victoria (G)
University of Michigan–Flint (N)
The University of Texas System (G)
Vance-Granville Community College (U)
Waukesha County Technical College (U)

TECHNICAL AND BUSINESS WRITING

Adirondack Community College (U)
Arizona State University (U)
Athens Technical College (N,U)
Bismarck State College (U)
Black Hills State University (U)
Blue Ridge Community College (N)
Boise State University (U)
Bowling Green State University (U,G)
Brenau University (U)
Bridgewater State College (U)
Butler County Community College (U)
Caldwell Community College and Technical Institute (N,U)
Cape Fear Community College (U)
Central Texas College (U)
Central Virginia Community College (U)
Chadron State College (U)
Chattanooga State Technical Community College (U)
Clackamas Community College (U)
Clark State Community College (U)
Clemson University (N)
Coleman College (U)
College of Southern Maryland (U)
College of Staten Island of the City University of New York (N)
College of The Albemarle (N)
Columbia Basin College (U)
Columbus State Community College (U)
The Community College of Baltimore County (U)
Community College of Beaver County (U)
Community College of Denver (U)
Community College of Southern Nevada (U)
Dakota County Technical College (U)
Darton College (N)
Delta College (U)
Des Moines Area Community College (U)
DeVry University Online (U)
East Carolina University (G)
East Tennessee State University (U)
Edgecombe Community College (U)
Embry-Riddle Aeronautical University, Extended Campus (U)
Erie Community College (U)
Feather River College (N)
Fresno City College (U)
George Mason University (U)
Grantham University (U)
Haywood Community College (U)
Heart of Georgia Technical College (U)
Indiana State University (U)
Indiana University of Pennsylvania (U)
James Madison University (U)
Jefferson College of Health Sciences (U)
Jefferson Community College (U)
John Jay College of Criminal Justice of the City University of New York (U)
Johnson County Community College (U)
Jones College (U)
Judson College (U)
Kean University (N)
Lake Superior College (U)
Lamar State College–Port Arthur (N)
Lehigh Carbon Community College (U)
Limestone College (U)
Linn-Benton Community College (U)
Louisiana State University and Agricultural and Mechanical College (U)
Louisiana Tech University (U)
Mercer County Community College (N)
Middlesex Community College (N,U)
Minnesota School of Business–Richfield (U)
Montana Tech of The University of Montana (U)
Montgomery Community College (U)
Neumann College (U)
New Jersey Institute of Technology (U,G)
North Arkansas College (U)
North Carolina State University (U)
North Dakota State College of Science (U)
North Idaho College (N)
Northwestern Connecticut Community College (N)
Northwestern Michigan College (U)
Northwestern State University of Louisiana (U)
Oklahoma State University (U)
Oregon Institute of Technology (U)
Oregon State University (U)
Oxnard College (U)
Ozarks Technical Community College (U)
Pasco-Hernando Community College (N)
The Pennsylvania State University University Park Campus (U)
Portland Community College (U)
Saint Mary-of-the-Woods College (U)
Schenectady County Community College (U)
Schoolcraft College (U)
Seminole Community College (U)
Sinclair Community College (U)
Southeast Community College, Beatrice Campus (U)
Southeast Community College, Lincoln Campus (U)
Southeast Community College, Milford Campus (U)
Southwestern Oregon Community College (U)

State University of New York College of Agriculture and Technology at Morrisville (U)
Stephen F. Austin State University (U)
Syracuse University (U)
Taylor University (N)
Texas Tech University (U,G)
The University of Akron (U)
University of Alaska Fairbanks (U)
University of California, Berkeley (U)
University of California, Los Angeles (G)
University of Central Florida (G)
University of Cincinnati (N)
University of Colorado at Denver and Health Sciences Center—Downtown Denver Campus (U)
University of Delaware (U)
University of Florida (U)
University of Great Falls (U)
University of Illinois at Chicago (N)
University of Maine (U)
The University of Maine at Augusta (U)
University of Massachusetts Amherst (G)
University of Minnesota, Twin Cities Campus (U)
University of Missouri–Columbia (U)
University of New Orleans (U,G)
University of North Texas (U)
University of Southern Mississippi (U)
The University of Tennessee (U)
University of the Sciences in Philadelphia (G)
The University of Toledo (U)
University of Washington (U)
University of West Florida (U)
Vance-Granville Community College (N)
Wake Technical Community College (N)
Weber State University (U)
Westchester Community College (U)
West Los Angeles College (U)
West Virginia University at Parkersburg (N)
Wilkes Community College (U)
William Rainey Harper College (U)
Wright State University (U,G)
York County Community College (U)

TECHNOLOGY EDUCATION/ INDUSTRIAL ARTS

Adams State College (G)
Bowling Green State University (U,G)
Brigham Young University (U)
California University of Pennsylvania (U)
Central Missouri State University (U,G)
Chadron State College (G)
Cleveland State University (N,G)
Colorado Christian University (U)
Duquesne University (G)
East Carolina University (U,G)
Eastern Michigan University (U,G)
Fort Hays State University (U)
Heart of Georgia Technical College (U)
Indiana State University (U)
Itawamba Community College (U)
Jacksonville State University (U)
John A. Logan College (U)
Marshall University (G)
Millersville University of Pennsylvania (G)
Mississippi State University (U)
National University (G)
Nova Southeastern University (G)
Ozarks Technical Community College (U)
Quinebaug Valley Community College (N)
Rasmussen College Eden Prarie (U)
The University of Akron (U,G)
University of Alaska Fairbanks (U)
University of Massachusetts Boston (U,G)
University of Missouri–Columbia (G)
The University of Texas at Tyler (U)
University of West Florida (N)
Valley City State University (U,G)
Washburn University (U)
West Virginia University (N)
West Virginia University at Parkersburg (U)

TEXTILE SCIENCES AND ENGINEERING

North Carolina State University (U,G)
Southern Polytechnic State University (U)
Texas Tech University (G)
University of Florida (U)

THEOLOGICAL AND MINISTERIAL STUDIES

Arlington Baptist College (N,U)
Assemblies of God Theological Seminary (G)
Atlantic School of Theology (N,G)
Azusa Pacific University (G)
Bakke Graduate University of Ministry (G)
Baptist Bible College of Pennsylvania (G)
Barclay College (U)
Bethany University (U)
Bradley University (U)
Briercrest Distance Learning (U,G)
The Catholic Distance University (N)
Clear Creek Baptist Bible College (U)
College of Emmanuel and St. Chad (G)
Columbia International University (N,U,G)
Corban College (U)
Covenant Theological Seminary (N,G)
Crown College (G)
Dallas Baptist University (U)
Danville Community College (U)
Denver Seminary (G)
Drew University (N,G)
Duquesne University (U)
Earlham School of Religion (G)
Eastern Mennonite University (G)
Franciscan University of Steubenville (N,U,G)
God's Bible School and College (U)
Gordon-Conwell Theological Seminary (N,G)
Liberty University (G)
Life Pacific College (U)
Lutheran Theological Seminary at Gettysburg (N,G)
Marylhurst University (G)
Master's College and Seminary (U)
Moody Bible Institute (N,U,G)
Moravian Theological Seminary (N,G)
Naropa University (N)
Newman Theological College (U)
North American Baptist Seminary (G)
Northwestern College (U)
Oral Roberts University (N)
Ozark Christian College (U)
Providence College and Theological Seminary (N,U,G)
Regent University (U,G)
Regions University (N,U,G)
Saint Mary-of-the-Woods College (G)
Saybrook Graduate School and Research Center (G)
Southwestern Assemblies of God University (U,G)
Southwestern Baptist Theological Seminary (U,G)
Taylor University (N,U)
Trinity Episcopal School for Ministry (N,G)
University of Great Falls (U)
Viterbo University (G)
Western Seminary (N,G)
Williamson Christian College (U)

THEOLOGY AND RELIGIOUS VOCATIONS RELATED

Assemblies of God Theological Seminary (G)
Atlantic School of Theology (N,G)
Bakke Graduate University of Ministry (G)
Baptist Bible College of Pennsylvania (G)
Briercrest Distance Learning (U,G)
The Catholic Distance University (N,U,G)
Clear Creek Baptist Bible College (U)
College of Emmanuel and St. Chad (G)
Columbia International University (N,U,G)
Covenant Theological Seminary (N,G)
Duquesne University (U)
Earlham School of Religion (G)
God's Bible School and College (U)
Gordon-Conwell Theological Seminary (N,G)
Immaculata University (U)
Itawamba Community College (U)
Liberty University (U,G)
Lutheran Theological Seminary at Gettysburg (N,G)
Master's College and Seminary (U)
Moody Bible Institute (U,G)
Moravian Theological Seminary (N)
Naropa University (N)
North American Baptist Seminary (G)
Northwestern College (U)
Ozark Christian College (U)
Ozarks Technical Community College (U)
Providence College and Theological Seminary (N,U,G)
Regent University (N,U,G)
St. John's University (U)
Saint Joseph's University (U)
Saint Mary-of-the-Woods College (U)
Saybrook Graduate School and Research Center (N)
Southwestern Assemblies of God University (U,G)
Southwestern Baptist Theological Seminary (G)
Taylor University (U)
Trinity Episcopal School for Ministry (N,G)
Union Theological Seminary and Presbyterian School of Christian Education (N,G)
University of St. Michael's College (U,G)
Valparaiso University (U,G)
Western Seminary (N,G)

TRANSPORTATION AND MATERIALS MOVING RELATED

James Madison University (N)
Mohawk Valley Community College (U)
The Pennsylvania State University University Park Campus (G)

URBAN STUDIES/AFFAIRS

Bakke Graduate University of Ministry (G)
Cleveland State University (U,G)
Florida Atlantic University (G)
James Madison University (N)

Ozarks Technical Community College (U)
Saybrook Graduate School and Research Center (G)
The University of Akron (U)
University of Delaware (U)
University of Massachusetts Boston (N)
University of New Orleans (U,G)
University of Washington (U)
Virginia Polytechnic Institute and State University (G)

VEHICLE MAINTENANCE AND REPAIR TECHNOLOGIES

Columbus State Community College (U)
Naugatuck Valley Community College (U)

VETERINARY BIOMEDICAL AND CLINICAL SCIENCES

Auburn University (N)
Colorado State University (N)
Community College of Southern Nevada (U)
Minnesota School of Business–Richfield (U)
Shenandoah University (N)
Virginia Polytechnic Institute and State University (G)
Yuba College (U)

VISUAL AND PERFORMING ARTS

Academy of Art University (U,G)
Arkansas State University–Beebe (U)
Atlantic University (N,G)
Bergen Community College (U)
Berklee College of Music (N,U)
Brigham Young University (U)
California State University, San Bernardino (U)
Central Lakes College (U)
Coffeyville Community College (U)
Community College of Southern Nevada (U)
De Anza College (U)
Delta College (U)
East Los Angeles College (U)
Everett Community College (U)
Glenville State College (U)
Itawamba Community College (U)
James Madison University (N)
John A. Logan College (U)
Marshall University (U,G)
Mesa State College (U)
Minneapolis College of Art and Design (N,U,G)
Pace University (U)
The Pennsylvania State University University Park Campus (U)
Prescott College (U,G)
Regent University (N,U,G)
Texas Tech University (G)
Texas Woman's University (U,G)
Tompkins Cortland Community College (U)
University of Bridgeport (U)
University of California, Los Angeles (G)
The University of Findlay (U)
University of Maine (U)
University of Southern Indiana (U)
University of South Florida (G)
The University of Tennessee at Martin (U)
The University of Texas of the Permian Basin (U)
West Los Angeles College (U)
Wilfrid Laurier University (U)

VISUAL AND PERFORMING ARTS RELATED

Brenau University (U)
Central Virginia Community College (U)
Clarion University of Pennsylvania (U)
Columbus State Community College (U)
Drake University (U)
Ivy Tech Community College–North Central (U)
Minneapolis College of Art and Design (N,U,G)
Naugatuck Valley Community College (U)
The Ohio State University (U)
Ozarks Technical Community College (U)
Red Rocks Community College (U)
Syracuse University (U,G)
University of Oregon (U)
The University of Toledo (U)

WILDLIFE AND WILDLANDS SCIENCE AND MANAGEMENT

Clark College (U)
Colorado State University (U,G)
Middle Tennessee State University (N)
Oregon State University (U)
The Pennsylvania State University University Park Campus (N,U)
Prescott College (U,G)
University of Massachusetts Amherst (U)
University of Wisconsin–River Falls (G)

WOODWORKING

Blackhawk Technical College (N)
Cleveland Institute of Electronics (N)

WORK AND FAMILY STUDIES

California State University, San Marcos (N)
Central Michigan University (U)
Davis College (U)
Indiana Business College (N)
Kansas State University (N)
Kean University (N)
Ozarks Technical Community College (U)
Rend Lake College (U)
University of Minnesota, Twin Cities Campus (U)
University of Missouri–Columbia (N)

ZOOLOGY/ANIMAL BIOLOGY

Brigham Young University (U)
Casper College (U)
Central Wyoming College (U)
Eastern Wyoming College (U)
Mississippi State University (U)
North Carolina State University (U)
Northwestern State University of Louisiana (U)
The University of Akron (U)
Utah Valley State College (U)
Weber State University

GEOGRAPHICAL LISTING OF DISTANCE LEARNING PROGRAMS

In this index, the page locations of the profiles are printed in regular type and **In-Depth Descriptions** in **bold type.**

U.S. and U.S. Territories

ALABAMA

ALASKA

ARIZONA

ARKANSAS

CALIFORNIA

COLORADO

CONNECTICUT

DELAWARE

DISTRICT OF COLUMBIA

FLORIDA

GEORGIA

HAWAII

IDAHO

ILLINOIS

INDIANA

IOWA

KANSAS

KENTUCKY

LOUISIANA

MAINE

MARYLAND

MASSACHUSETTS

MICHIGAN

MINNESOTA

MISSISSIPPI

MISSOURI

MONTANA

NEBRASKA

NEVADA

NEW HAMPSHIRE

NEW JERSEY

NEW MEXICO

NEW YORK

NORTH CAROLINA

NORTH DAKOTA

OHIO

OKLAHOMA

OREGON

PENNSYLVANIA

RHODE ISLAND

SOUTH CAROLINA

SOUTH DAKOTA

TENNESSEE

TEXAS

UTAH

VERMONT

VIRGINIA

WASHINGTON

WEST VIRGINIA

WISCONSIN

WYOMING

CANADA

ALBERTA

BRITISH COLUMBIA

MANITOBA

NEW BRUNSWICK

NEWFOUNDLAND AND LABRADOR

NOVA SCOTIA

ONTARIO

SASKATCHEWAN